International Conference

"UNIFORM BUILDING CODE STANDARDS™"

1991 Edition

INTERNATIONAL CONFERENCE OF BUILDING OFFICIALS · UNIFORM BUILDING CODE · 1922 ®

First Printing

Publication Date: May 1, 1991

ISSN 0896-9663

5360 SOUTH WORKMAN MILL ROAD • WHITTIER, CALIFORNIA 90601

PRINTED IN THE U.S.A.

Preface

The author organizations assume no responsibility for the rewriting and excerpting of these standards, which is the work of the technical staff of the International Conference of Building Officials.

The Conference has been asked why it is necessary to follow this plan in the publication of reference standards. Possibly the following explanations will help clarify this point:

1. Frequently only a very small section of the reference standard is required for the enforcement of a specific section of the code in which the standard is referenced. Therefore, those portions of the source standard that are irrelevant insofar as the requirements in the Building Code are concerned are deleted.

2. Many standards are developed by cooperating manufacturing interests who are interested in establishing standardized products for marketing purposes, and the market for which a product is manufactured may be very broad. For example, paper products may be manufactured under a general standard that provides a satisfactory product for manufacturing boxes as well as products for use in building construction. Since the building official is interested only in that portion of the standard pertaining to the quality of the material used in building construction, other provisions are deleted. Also, the provisions of some standards are optional rather than mandatory. Optional provisions are not enforceable and are therefore deleted as being redundant or are changed to mandatory requirements if they are essential to building safety.

3. Some omitted material deals with subjects extraneous to the Uniform Building Code™. For example, particularly in American Society for Testing and Materials (ASTM) documents, data such as purchaser's rights, appearance of the product, shipment and handling are omitted. References to sampling and testing are confined to a brief statement that sampling and testing shall be in accordance with standard practice. Other material, such as grading rules for nonstructural lumber and test reports, is omitted because it has no application to the Uniform Building Code.

4. Other changes are made in the standards where a conflict with the Uniform Building Code would be introduced by inclusion of certain sections from a standard, so it becomes necessary either to eliminate the standard completely or to edit it to eliminate the conflict.

5. Finally, it is necessary to provide members of the International Conference of Building Officials with an inexpensive and complete building code. Without the reference standards, this is impossible.

It will be necessary for users to refer to the complete unabridged specifications for those requirements of materials and processes not delineated in this publication. For this purpose, the source material is clearly designated in both the table of contents and the heading of each standard.

It should be noted that the 1991 edition of the Uniform Building Code Standards™ incorporates as number of standards by reference. The statutory requirements on adoption by reference should be consulted when adopting the 1991 Uniform Building Code Standards.

Where other codes, standards or specifications are referred to in these standards, they are to be considered as only an indication of an acceptable method or material that can be used with approval by the building official. Other methods or materials providing equivalent performance may be used when approved by the building official under the provisions of Section 105 of the Uniform Building Code. See also Chapter 60 of the Uniform Building Code for guideline standards.

▒▒▒▒▒▒ vertically in the margin of the table of contents indicates that the standard has been updated from the 1988 edition or that the standard is an addition to the 1988 edition. Deletion indicators (➧) are provided in the margin where a standard has been deleted.

—F—F— vertically in the margin in the table of contents indicates that the standard is maintained under the code change procedures of the Western Fire Chiefs Association.

RELATED PUBLICATIONS

Known widely for its Uniform Building Code™, the International Conference of Building Officials (ICBO) publishes other related codes as well as textbooks to improve the user's knowledge of code enforcement and the administration of a building inspection program. Publications are continually being added, so inquiries should be directed to Conference headquarters for a list of those available. At the time of this publication, the following publications were available:

Uniform Building Code. Covers the fire, life and structural safety aspects of all buildings and related structures.

Handbook to the Uniform Building Code—An illustrative commentary. A new publication containing a description of the purpose and intent of individual code sections appearing in the 1991 edition of the Uniform Building Code. Where appropriate, provides historical background and references other documents for additional information. Also included are numerous drawings and figures clarifying the application and intent of the 1991 code provisions.

Uniform Mechanical Code™. Contains requirements for the installation and maintenance of heating, ventilating, cooling and refrigeration systems. This publication is sponsored jointly by ICBO and the International Association of Plumbing and Mechanical Officials (IAPMO).

Uniform Plumbing Code. Published by IAPMO, the Uniform Plumbing Code covers all aspects of plumbing, including requirements for plumbing materials, and IAPMO installation standards. It is endorsed by the Conference as a companion document to ICBO's model codes and is available from either organization.

Uniform Housing Code™. Provides complete requirements affecting conservation and rehabilitation of housing. Its regulations are compatible with the Uniform Building Code.

Uniform Code for the Abatement of Dangerous Buildings. Sets forth orderly procedures for remedying dangerous buildings. Follows due process provisions which reflect the latest court decisions in such matters. This code covers all structures and may be used to supplement the Uniform Housing Code and the Uniform Building Code.

Uniform Sign Code™. Dedicated to the development of better sign regulation. Its requirements pertain to all signs and sign construction attached to buildings.

Uniform Administrative Code™. This code covers administration areas in connection with adoption of the Uniform Building Code, Uniform Mechanical Code and related codes by a jurisdiction. It contains provisions which relate to site preparation, construction, alteration, moving, repair and occupancies of buildings or structures. It also contains administrative provisions for implementing plumbing, electrical and mechanical regulations. The code is compatible with the administrative provisions of all codes published by the Conference.

Uniform Building Security Code™. This code establishes minimum standards to make dwelling units resistant to unlawful entry. It regulates swinging doors, sliding doors, windows and hardware in connection with dwelling units of apartment houses or one- and two-family dwellings. The code gives consideration to the concerns of police, fire and building officials in establishing requirements for resistance to burglary which are compatible with fire and life safety.

Uniform Code for Building Conservation. A building conservation guideline presented in code format which will provide a community with the means to preserve its existing buildings while achieving appropriate levels of safety. It is formatted in the same manner as the Uniform Building Code, compatible with other Uniform Codes, and may be adopted as a code or used as a guideline.

Dwelling Construction under the Uniform Building Code™. Designed to acquaint the home builder with basic Uniform Building Code requirements relating to dwelling construction. A useful text for apprentice training programs.

Dwelling Construction under the Uniform Mechanical Code™. This is a new publication for the convenience of the homeowner or contractor interested in installing mechanical equipment in a one- and two-family dwelling in conformance with the Uniform Mechanical Code. The material conforms with the 1991 edition of the Uniform Mechanical Code, which is dedicated to the development of better equipment and installations and greater safety to the public.

Uniform Fire Code™. Sets out provisions necessary for fire prevention while achieving uniformity in terms and requirements with other codes published by the Conference. This code is sponsored jointly by the Western Fire Chiefs Association and ICBO.

Uniform Fire Code Standards™. This publication is a companion to the Uniform Fire Code. It contains standards of the American Society for Testing and Materials and of the National Fire Protection Association (NFPA) referenced by the Uniform Fire Code.

U.B.C. Supplements. Between new editions of the codes, changes approved each year are incorporated in the supplements.

Analysis of Revisions to the Uniform Codes. Discusses the changes included in the latest codes published by the Conference as compared to the prior editions.

Uniform Building Code—1927 Edition. A special 60th anniversary printing of the first published Uniform Building Code.

CABO One and Two Family Dwelling Code. This code is jointly sponsored by the three model code organizations of the Council of American Building Officials (CABO): ICBO, Building Officials and Code Administrators International, Inc. (BOCA), and Southern Building Code Congress International, Inc. (SBCCI). It eliminates conflicts and duplications among the model codes to achieve national uniformity. Covers mechanical and plumbing requirements as well as construction and occupancy.

Application and Commentary: CABO One and Two Family Dwelling Code. An interpretive commentary on the CABO One and Two Family Dwelling Code intended to enhance uniformity of interpretation and application of the code nationwide. Developed by the three model code organizations under contract with HUD and in cooperation with the National Association of Home Builders.

CABO Model Energy Code. This code sets forth minimum requirements for effective use of energy in the design of new buildings and structures and additions to existing buildings. It is based on ASHRAE Standard 90A-1980 and was originally developed jointly by ICBO, BOCA, SBCCI and the National Conference of States on Building Codes and Standards under a contract funded by the United States Department of Energy. The code is now maintained by CABO and is adopted by reference in the Uniform Building Code.

Uniform Disaster Mitigation Plan. A plan developed to aid building departments in coping with major disasters such as fires, floods and earthquakes. Defines standard operating procedures for initiating disaster assessment and mitigation and includes samples of records, reports, entry signs, etc.

National Electrical Code ®. The National Electrical Code is the electrical code for the majority of states, counties and cities in the United States. Researched and published every three years by NFPA, it is an indispensable aid to every electrician, electrical inspector, electrical equipment manufacturer, architect, builder, consulting engineer, contractor, fire marshal, fire chief, building inspector and anyone who must specify or certify electrical installations.

Building Department Administration. An excellent guide for improvement of skills in departmental management and in the enforcement and application of the Uniform Building Code and other regulations administered by a building inspection department. Recommended for both undergraduate and advanced study.

Uniform Building Code Application/Interpretation Manual. A manual discussing sections of the Uniform Building Code with a question and answer format providing a comprehensive analysis of the intent of the code section. Most sections include illustrative examples. The manual is in loose-leaf form so that code interpretations published in *Building Standards* magazine may be inserted.

Plan Review Manual. Provides an understanding of the extent of Uniform Building Code provisions and illustrates application to given situations. Covers nonstructural aspects and provides an insight into the basic engineering considerations a plans examiner or checker must utilize.

Field Inspection Manual. Designed to improve inspection skills and techniques. A fundamental and important text for courses of study at the community college and trade or technical school level.

Building Official Management Manual. This manual addresses the unique nature of code administration and the managerial duties of the building official. A supplementary insert addresses the budgetary and financial aspects of a building department. It is also an ideal resource for those preparing for the management module of the CABO Building Official Certification Examination.

Legal Aspects of Code Administration. A manual developed by the three model code organizations to inform the building official on the legal aspects of the profession. The text is written in a logical sequence with explanation of legal terminology and is designed to serve as a refresher to those preparing to take the legal module of the CABO Building Official Certification Examination.

Illustrated Mechanical Manual. Contains a series of illustrations with explanatory text covering requirements in the Uniform Mechanical Code which respond to graphic treatment. It is highly useful for code application and for training purposes.

Concrete Manual. A publication for individuals seeking an understanding of the fundamentals of concrete field technology and inspection practices. Of particular interest to concrete construction inspectors, it will also benefit employees of concrete producers, concrete contractors, testing and inspection laboratories, and material suppliers.

You Can Build It! Published by ICBO in cooperation with CABO, this booklet contains information and advice to aid "do-it-yourselfers" with building projects. Provides guidance in necessary procedures such as permit requirements, codes, plans, cost estimation, etc.

Guidelines for Manufactured Housing Installations. A guideline in code form implementing the Uniform Building Code and its companion code documents to regulate the permanent installation of a manufactured home on a privately owned nonrental site. A commentary is included to explain specific provisions, and codes applying to each component part are defined.

Tabulated Fire-Resistive Requirements by Occupancy. Related code requirements are assembled for quick access. The tabulations assemble the limitations in Tables Nos. 5-A, 5-B, 5-C, and 17-A and the provisions of the 01 through 03 sections of the occupancy and type of construction chapters in the Uniform Building Code.

Introduction to the Uniform Building Code Workbook. A student workbook containing a series of exercises designed to complement the course "Introduction to the Uniform Building Code, BIT-100." Assignments are arranged to provide an overview of the basics of the Uniform Building Code.

Plan Reading and Nonstructural Plan Review Workbook. A series of exercises intended to be a useful tool in understanding the concepts developed in "Plan Reading and Nonstructural Plan Review, BIT-101." The student exercises include assignments on code requirements and plan reading.

CONTENTS

*ASTM refers to the American Society for Testing and Materials.

U.B.C. STD. AND SEC. NO.	TITLE AND SOURCE	PAGE
24-30; 2402 (b) 8		
	Standard Test Method for Flexural Bond Strength of Mortar Cement. Test Standard of the International Conference of Building Officials.	111
CHAPTER 25		
25-1; 2501 (a), 2502 (a)		
	Classification, Definition and Methods of Grading for All Species of Lumber. Standard Methods D 245-70 and D 2555-70 of the ASTM, Handbook No. 72 of the United States Department of Agriculture, American Softwood Lumber Standard PS20-70 and National Grading Rule for Dimension Lumber of the National Grading Rule Committee.	117
25-9; 2501 (a), 2501 (e), 2502 (a), 2513 (a), 2513 (c), 4702, Tables Nos. 25-B, 25-J-1, 25-K-1, 25-S-2, 25-T-1 and 47-J		
	Construction and Industrial Plywood. Products Standard PS 1-83 of the United States Department of Commerce, and National Bureau of Standards Calculation Diaphragm Action, an Engineering Standard of the International Conference of Building Officials.	155
25-15; 2501 (a), 2507 (a) 2, 2507 (b)		
	Spaced Wood Column Design. National Design Specification for Wood Construction (1982), including the 1982 Supplement, National Forest Products Association.	203
25-17; 2501 (a), 2504 (c), 2510 (a), 2510 (b), 2510 (d), 2510 (f), 2513 (b), 2516 (j) 1, 4702, Tables Nos. 25-F, 25-G, 25-H, 25-J-1, 25-J-2, 25-K-1, 25-K-2, 25-O, 32-B-1, 32-B-2, 32-D-1, 32-D-2, 43-B, 43-C, 47-G, 47-H, 47-I, Appendix Table No. A-24-4		
	Timber Connector Joints, Bolted Joints, Drift Bolts and Wood Screws, and Lag Screws; Metal Plate Connected Wood Truss Design; and Nails and Staples. National Design Specification for Wood Construction (1986), including the 1986 Supplement, National Forest Products Association; Design Specifications for Metal Plate Connected Wood Truss TPI-85, and Design Specification for Metal Plate Connected Parallel Chord Wood Trusses, PCT-80 of the Truss Plate Institute; and Federal Specification No. FF-N-105B, March 17, 1971.	207
25-18; 2501 (a), 2512		
	Structural Glued Built-up Members—Plywood Components. Design and Fabrication Specifications of the American Plywood Association.	297
25-21; 2501 (a), Tables Nos. 25-U-J-1, 25-U-J-6, 25-U-R-1, 25-U-R-2, 25-U-R-7, 25-U-R-8, 25-U-R-10, 25-U-R-11, 25-U-R-13 and 25-U-R-14		
	Span Tables for Joists and Rafters. Specification Standard of the International Conference of Building Officials.	325
25-22; 2501 (a)		
	Plank-and-Beam Framing. Wood Construction Data No. 4 (1970) of the National Forest Products Association.	363
25-25; 2501 (a), 2502 (a), 2516 (g) 5, 2517 (f)		
	Wood Particleboard. American National Standard for Wood Particleboard, ANSI** A208.1-1989.	369

**ANSI refers to the American National Standards Institute

U.B.C. STD. AND SEC. NO.	TITLE AND SOURCE	PAGE

CHAPTER 28

U.B.C. STD. AND SEC. NO.	TITLE AND SOURCE	PAGE

U.B.C. STD. AND SEC. NO.	TITLE AND SOURCE	PAGE

UNIFORM BUILDING CODE STANDARD NO. 4-1

NONCOMBUSTIBLE MATERIAL—TESTS

Based on Standard Method of Test E 136-79 of the American Society for Testing and Materials. Extracted, with permission, from the Annual Book of ASTM Standards, copyright American Society for Testing and Materials, 1916 Race Street, Philadelphia, PA 19103.

See Sections 401 (b) and 415, Uniform Building Code; Section 416, Uniform Mechanical Code; and Section 211, Uniform Sign Code

Scope

Sec. 4.101. This standard describes a procedure for the determination of noncombustibility of elementary materials of which building materials are composed, to indicate those materials which do not act to aid combustion or add appreciable heat to an ambient fire. It is not intended to apply to laminated or coated materials.

Apparatus

Sec. 4.102. The apparatus shall consist primarily of the following:

Refractory tubes. Two 10-inch-long, concentric refractory tubes, 3 inches and 4 inches in inside diameter, with axes vertical and with heat applied by electric heating coils outside of the larger tube. A controlled flow of air is admitted tangentially near the top of the annular space between the tubes and passes to the bottom of the inner tube. The outer tube rests on a refractory bottom and the inner tube rests on three spacer blocks so as to afford a total opening under the inner tube equal to or greater than that of the annular space. The refractory bottom plate has a removable plug for cleaning.

Transparent cover. A transparent cover of heat-resisting glass or other transparent material shall be provided over the top of the inner tube with a 1-inch square opening over the axis of the tubes. This cover may be in two movable parts.

Thermocouples or other temperature-measuring devices, preferably automatically recording, shall be provided, one for the air in the lower part of the inner tube, another on the specimen in the appoximate center of the space, and a third within the interior of the specimen. A thermocouple may be provided in the region of the heating coils for better regulation of the temperature of the air in the furnace space. The two specimen thermocouples shall have a time constant (time to reach 63.2 percent of the furnace air temperature of 1382°F.) of 5 to 10 seconds.

Test Specimens

Sec. 4.103. All test specimens shall be 1½ inches wide by 1½ inches thick in cross section perpendicular to the air flow in the furnace and 2 inches long with tolerances on the dimensions of plus or minus 1/10 inch. The specimens shall be dried at 140°F. plus or minus 5°F. for not less than 24 hours nor more than 48 hours before being tested.

Specimens in granular or powder form may be contained in thin-wall, open-top vessels of inert materials whose outside dimensions conform to the specimen shape and maximum size specified in this section. These vessels may have solid walls or be of mesh.

Not less than four identical specimens shall be tested.

Procedure

Sec. 4.104. Prepare the furnace by bringing the temperature (at the approximate position to be occupied by the center of the specimen) of the air in the furnace tube to 1382° plus or minus 10°F., maintaining the furnace setting long enough to ascertain that it will remain at constant temperature in the unloaded furnace for at least 15 minutes while air passes at a velocity of 10 feet per minute plus or minus 20 percent past a loaded specimen in the tube, computed on the basis of air supply and velocity at room temperature and pressure.

As rapidly as possible, insert the test specimen into the furnace, with a thermocouple attached to the side surface of the specimen and a thermocouple inserted from the top of the specimen to its approximate volumetric center. Close the top cover to the 1-square-inch opening immediately after insertion of the specimen. Readings for the specimen thermocouples shall be made at intervals not to exceed 10 seconds during the first 5 minutes, and as often afterwards as necessary to produce a smooth curve. Do not change the regulation of the current through the heating coils and the air flow during the test.

Continue the test until the temperatures at the specimen thermocouples have reached maxima or until it is clearly evident that the specimen does not pass this test.

Throughout the test make and record visual observations on the specimens, noting quality, quantity or intensity and duration of flaming or smoking, or both, and change of state.

Weigh each specimen before and after testing and record the weight loss to the nearest 1 percent.

Interpretation of Results

Sec. 4.105. Materials subjected to the test described in this method shall be reported as noncombustible if, for three or more of the four specimens tested, (1) the recorded temperatures of the surface and interior thermocouples do not at any time during the test rise to more than 54°F. above the furnace air temperature at the beginning of the test, (2) if there is no flaming from the specimen after the first 30 seconds and (3) when the weight loss of the specimen during testing exceeds 50 percent, the recorded temperature of the surface and interior themocouples do not at any time during the test rise above the furnace air temperature at the beginning of the test and there is no flaming of the specimen.

UNIFORM BUILDING CODE STANDARD NO. 6-1

PROSCENIUM FIRE-SAFETY CURTAINS

Installation Standard of the International Conference of Building Officials

See Sections 608 and 3903 (d), Uniform Building Code

General Requirements

Sec. 6.101. Proscenium curtains, when required, shall be made of approved materials constructed and mounted so as to intercept hot gases, flames and smoke, and to prevent a glow from a severe fire on the stage from showing on the auditorium side within a period of 30 minutes. The closing of the curtain from the full-open position shall be effected in less than 30 seconds, but the last 8 feet of travel shall not require less than five seconds.

Sec. 6.102. Curtain styles regulated by this standard are defined as follows:

BRAILLE PROSCENIUM FIRE-SAFETY CURTAIN is a curtain that folds up and stores in a very limited space above the proscenium opening. (See Figure No. 1.)

FRAME PROSCENIUM FIRE-SAFETY CURTAIN is a curtain that has a rigid frame, and stores over the proscenium opening in one flat panel.

MODIFIED FRAME PROSCENIUM FIRE-SAFETY CURTAIN is a curtain made of various components of both the frame and straight-lift-style curtains, and stores over the proscenium opening in one flat panel.

STRAIGHT LIFT PROSCENIUM FIRE-SAFETY CURTAIN is a curtain which stores over the proscenium opening in one flat panel.

Curtain Fabrics

Sec. 6.103. (a) **General.** A proscenium curtain shall be constructed and installed as specified in this standard.

(b) **Fabrics.** 1. **Asbestos.** When not prohibited by federal, state or local law, an existing installed curtain may be made of one or more thicknesses of not less than $2^3/_4$-pound-per-square-yard AAA grade wire-inserted asbestos fabric, or of another wire-inserted asbestos fabric obviously of greater fire resistance than this $2^3/_4$-pound AAA grade wire-inserted fabric. Nonasbestos portions of these fabrics, if any, shall be flame-resistant treated so as not to support combustion.

2. **Other fabrics.** Curtains not meeting the above criteria shall be made of one or more thicknesses of a noncombustible fabric, or a fabric with a noncombustible base material which may be given a coating provided the modified fabric meets the criteria detailed in this section.

Curtain fabrics shall not weigh less than $2^3/_8$ pounds per square yard unless it can be substantiated by approved tests that the fabric is equivalent in strength and durability.

(c) **Tensile Strength.** Curtain fabric shall have tensile strength of not less than 400 pounds per inch in both the warp and fill directions.

(d) **Wire-insertion Reinforcement.** Curtain fabric shall be reinforced with noncorrosive wire intertwined with the base fiber at a minimum rate of one wire per yarn. Wire may be omitted if it can be substantiated by approved tests that it is equivalent in strength and durability.

(e) **Fire Test.** A sample curtain with a minimum of two vertical seams shall be subjected to the standard fire test specified in U.B.C. Standard No. 43-1 as applicable to nonbearing walls and partitions for a period of 30 minutes. Surface temperature measurements need not be taken and the hose stream exposure need not be made. The curtain shall overlap the furnace edges an appropriate amount to seal the top and sides. It shall have a bottom pocket containing a minimum 4 pounds per linear foot of batten. The unexposed surface of the curtain shall not glow, and neither flame nor smoke shall penetrate the curtain during the test period.

(f) **Smoke Test.** Curtain fabrics shall have a smoke density of no greater than 25 when tested in accordance with U.B.C. Standard No. 42-1. The curtain fabric shall be tested in the condition in which it is intended to be used.

Design and Construction

Sec. 6.104. (a) **General.** The various style curtains detailed below shall all be acceptable for use, except when the fly space above the stage is sufficient to allow the straight-lift, frame or modified frame styles to be used.

When the fly space is sufficient for these above-mentioned full-lift-style curtains, the straight-lift, frame or modified frame styles shall be used for proscenium openings 50 feet wide or less and 30 feet high or less; and the frame or modified frame styles shall be used for openings over 50 feet in width or 30 feet in height.

Curtain installations in new facilities with openings over 50 feet in width or 30 feet in height shall be the frame or modified frame construction.

Regardless of curtain style, the curtain shall be made of continuous strips of fabric as specified above, sewn together vertically using minimum 1-inch-wide double-needled overlap seams. These vertical seams and all other functional stitching on the curtain shall consist of two rows of lockstitch stitching using flame-resistant thread, conforming to the test requirements of Section 6.103.

The curtain shall overlap the sides of the opening at least 18 inches and the top of the opening at least 24 inches.

All style curtains, except the frame style and the modified frame style (unless it has batten pockets and vertical side edge hems), shall have minimum 6-inch flat (12-inch circumference) single-thickness pockets at the top and bottom of the curtain to hold the pipe battens, and double-thick vertical side edge hems each a minimum of $^1/_2$ inch wider than length of side edge guide brackets being used and width of the metal hem reinforcing pieces being used, if any, except that hems shall not be less than 4 inches in width. Should the curtain fabric being used be an acceptable nonwire-inserted (nonwire reinforced) fabric, batten pockets shall be double thick and vertical side edge hems shall be triple thick or faced with wire-inserted (wire reinforced) webbing or fabric (raw edges turned under). Pockets and vertical side edge hems shall be sewn as specified above. Minimum $1^1/_2$-inch inside diameter metal battens shall be placed in the top and bottom curtain pockets when the proscenium opening height is 18 feet or less and width is 34 feet or less. For openings 50 feet or less in width (but more than 34 feet), and 30 feet or less in height (but more than 18 feet), the top and bottom metal battens shall not be less than 2 inches inside diameter. Metal battens shall be Schedule 40 steel pipe, Schedule 80 steel pipe or other metallic tubing meeting or exceeding the tensile strength and performance standards of Schedule 40 steel pipe. All batten joints shall be reinforced with minimum 18-inch sections of said pipes or tubing internally and shall be riveted.

A minimum 3-inch-thick yield pad made with an outer covering of the curtain fabric, filled with fiberglass or other noncombustible materials, in such a manner so as to achieve a minimum 3-pound-per-cubic-foot density, shall be sewn beneath the bottom batten pocket with four rows of flame-resistant thread (two on each side of the pocket) in such a manner so as to force the bottom batten to compress the yield pad firmly against the stage floor, producing the best possible seal when the curtain is lowered.

(b) **Straight-lift Style.** The straight-lift-style curtain shall meet the general requirements detailed above with vertical side edge hems reinforced with one piece of 0.064-inch-thick (16 gauge) plated or painted sheet metal on each side of the hem on each side of the curtain for its full vertical height so that both faces are covered $5^1/_2$ inches deep, or with minimum 2-inch-wide by $1^1/_2$-inch projection by $^1/_8$-inch-thick steel angle/2-inch-wide by $^1/_8$-inch-thick steel flat piece set (plated or painted) clamped on both edges for the curtain's full height. Either edge-reinforcement system shall be fastened to the side edge hems with pairs of minimum $^3/_{16}$-inch plated tubular or solid steel rivets, or bolts spaced not more than 6 inches on center vertically.

Curtains for proscenium openings, 50 feet or less in width and 30 feet or less in height, shall use a roller guide/metal track side edge guide system, using guides with at least two roller or ball bearing steel wheels each, and 0.079-inch-thick (14 gauge) galvanized steel tracks (installed rigidly in place so that roller guides will operate smoothly with a wind load of 2 pounds per square foot over entire area of curtain). Each guide shall be attached to the curtain's metal stiffened edges by way of three or more minimum $^3/_{16}$-inch plated tubular or solid steel rivets, or bolts through a plated steel strap assembly (0.064-inch-thick sheet metal stiffening system), a minimum $^3/_8$-inch machine screw assembly (attached to the projecting flange of the angle iron/flat steel edge stiffening system), or an equivalent attachment system. Guides shall be on maximum 18-inch vertical centers.

Curtains for proscenium openings 42 feet or less in width and 22 feet or less in height may have a bronze-alloy, oil-impregnated wood, or other spool-type guide wire side edge system, where the guide wires are at least $^1/_4$-inch diameter 7 by 19 galvanized aircraft cable installed securely using at least $^3/_8$-inch locked turnbuckles, thimbles and three forged wire rope clips (or one swaged fitting) at the end of each guide wire; or the roller guide system with either hem reinforcing/stiffening system as detailed above. Guides shall not be more than 18 inches on vertical centers.

Curtains for proscenium openings less than 34 feet in width and less than 18 feet in height may have a spool-type guide wire side guide system, as detailed in the paragraph above, except neither edge reinforcing/stiffening systems is required. Guides shall be on maximum 18-inch vertical centers.

An approximate 3-inch-diameter smoke seal made of the curtain fabric and filled with fiberglass insulation or other noncombustible materials, to a density of not less than 3 pounds per cubic foot, shall be attached to the upstage side of the proscenium wall, above the proscenium opening. The seal shall contact with the curtain's top batten pocket, and compress against it when the curtain is in its deployed position to make as smoketight a seal as practical.

(c) **Braille Style.** The dead hung braille-style curtain shall meet the requirements detailed above in Section 6.104 (a) and (b), except for the following:

1. Curtain shall have minimum 5 percent fullness in the height only.

2. Side edge guide system shall be bronze spool guides on a maximum 18-inch vertical centers on both of the curtain vertical edges, without any type of edge reinforcing/stiffening system.

3. Galvanized minimum $^1/_4$-inch diameter 7 by 19 aircraft cable vertical life lines shall be located on maximum 10-foot horizontal centers with the outermost two cables a maximum of 3 feet from either of the curtain's vertical edges. Each life line shall operate on a path reinforced with a layer of the curtain's fabric (raw edges turned under) or equivalent webbing, with plated steel D (dee) rings on maximum 18-inch vertical centers.

4. Seven by 19 aircraft cable for $^3/_8$-diameter or smaller sized and 6 by 19 or other flexible independent wire rope core, wire rope for larger sizes, sized using a minimum 8 to 1 safety factor, shall be used for the drive lines which connect the winch to the cable clew.

5. In lieu of the approximate 3-inch-diameter smoke seal detailed in Subsection (b) above, an attached fill piece smoke seal made of the curtain fabric, spanning the gap from the curtain to the upstage portion of the proscenium opening's wall above the opening, shall be installed.

The lift lines detailed above in conjunction with the D (dee) rings create an accordion-fold-type storage arrangement.

(d) **Frame and Modified Frame Style.** 1. **Frame-style curtain.** The frame-style curtain shall consist of a rigid steel or metallic alloy frame, with a frame thickness not less than $^1/_{120}$ of the width, and $^1/_{96}$ of the height of the proscenium opening, but in no case less than 4 inches in thickness, complete with interior steel or metallic alloy members, such that when the required single thickness is battened to the downstage side (audience side) of the frame, the assembly will operate smoothly, and perform as required, when subjected to a lateral load of 2 pounds per square foot over the entire area of the curtain.

The side edge guide system shall consist of vertical steel flat edges parallel to the face of the curtain with bronze bushings on this vertical steel edge on both upstage and downstage surfaces, or in the grooves traveled by these vertical steel edges located in the vertical steel smoke pockets on each side of the proscenium opening.

A separate yield pad, the cross section of which shall be square with each edge measuring approximately the same as the thickness of the frame, shall be made of the curtain fabric and filled with fiberglass or other noncombustible materials to a density of not less than 3 pounds per cubic foot. The yield pad shall be attached beneath the bottom frame member so that it will compress and seal when the curtain is lowered.

A separate upper smoke seal the same as detailed in Subsection (b) above, except that the seal shall be approximately 5 inches in diameter, shall be attached to the top of the frame on the downstage edge (edge facing the audience), and rigged so that the smoke seal is forced to compress against a steel or metallic alloy angle or other solid noncombustible material protruding from the proscenium wall above the opening (optionally, seal may be mounted above the proscenium opening on the upstage side and rigged to force the smoke seal to compress against a steel or metallic alloy member protruding downstage from the top member of the curtain's frame).

This curtain style is rigged like and operates like a straight-lift curtain except that the lift lines, blocks and all other involved operating equipment shall be sized to accommodate the size and weight of the assembly with a minimum 8 to 1 safety margin.

2. **Modified frame-style curtain.** The modified frame-style curtain shall be any variation or combination of the frame style immediately above, and the straight-lift-style curtain that minimizes the horizontal movement or bowing of a curtain to a point where the curtain assembly will operate smoothly and perform as required when subjected to a lateral load of 2 pounds per square foot over the entire area of the curtain.

This curtain style, like the frame style, is rigged like and operates like a straight-lift curtain, except that the lift lines, blocks and all other involved operating equipment shall be sized to accommodate the size and weight of the assembly with a minimum 8 to 1 safety margin.

Operating Equipment

Sec. 6.105. Vertical smoke pockets which contain the curtain's vertical edges and guide system shall be fabricated of minimum $^1/_4$-inch-thick structural steel shapes and plates (plated or painted), with a bolted construction using minimum $^3/_8$-inch diameter Grade 5 bolts spaced not more than 4 feet on center to attach plates to the steel shapes for the entire height of the smoke pockets, or at least for removable sections at the bottom of each smoke pocket (plate portions only), at least the height of the opening plus 4 feet for frame and modified frame styles of semirigid construction, or at least 6 feet for all other styles. These smoke pockets shall extend vertically from the stage floor to a point 1 to 3 feet above the top of the raised curtain and shall be securely fastened to the upstage side (side away from audience) of the proscenium wall, with minimum $^1/_2$-inch-diameter Grade 5 anchors or bolts in concrete spaced not more than 4 feet on center, with minimum $^3/_8$-inch-diameter Grade 5 anchors or bolts in concrete spaced not more than 2 feet on center, or an anchoring system equivalent in strength on concrete or other surfaces. The smoke pockets may vary in depth and width, depending on the style of curtain and the distance the smoke pockets are set back from the vertical edges. Straight-lift curtains shall not have less than 6-inch-deep pockets, braille curtains shall not have less than 8-inch-deep pockets, and frame and modified frame curtains shall have pockets at least 4 inches deeper than the thickest batten or frame member; the pockets shall be at least 11 inches wide set back a minimum of 6 inches from the vertical edges (stage left/stage right) of the proscenium opening, and contain at least 8 inches of the curtain's vertical edges.

The curtain's side edge guide system shall be as specified in Section 6.104 above.

Straight-lift and braille curtains for proscenium openings 50 feet or less in width and 30 feet or less in height shall not have less than $^1/_4$-inch-diameter 7 by 19 galvanized aircraft cable life lines 10 feet or less on center, with the end overhang not more than 3 feet. Attachment to battens shall be accomplished through the use of two-piece pipe clamps made of minimum 0.105-inch-thick (12 gauge) steel, or equivalent material (plated or painted) with corners rounded and the entire assembly deburred.

The clamps shall attach to the battens using two minimum $^3/_8$-inch Grade 5 bolts, one under the batten and one over the batten, with the lift cable securely attached using a thimble and three forged wire rope clips (or one swaged-type fitting). Other methods of attachment that can be shown to be equivalent shall be acceptable as long as the lift lines are not tied in a clove hitch, and they do not require cutting the curtain fabric and leaving exposed cut edges. Frame and modified frame curtains may require larger diameter lift lines to meet the requirements in Section 6.104 (d); galvanized cable or wire rope, 7 by 19 aircraft cable for $^3/_8$-inch diameter or smaller sizes, and 6 by 19 or other flexible independent wire rope core rope for larger sizes shall be used.

Straight-lift-style curtains for openings 34 feet or less in width and 18 feet or less in height, and braille-style curtains of all sizes, may be designed to operate using properly sized manual and electric winches of various styles, all with adjustable hydraulic-assisted speed-governing devices; any model with handles shall be so designed that the handle is removable, with an appropriate sign in English and other languages prevalent to the facility's area, stating DANGER! REMOVE HANDLE AFTER USE! prominently displayed near the location of the winch.

Curtain lift lines shall pass through sheaves in or under the gridiron, over to the counterweight guides or winch clew. Cables shall fasten to the curtain's top batten as detailed above. Connections to the braille curtain's bottom batten shall be accomplished by a loop at the end of each lift line secured with three forged wire rope clips, or minimum $^3/_{16}$-inch-thick clam-shell-type steel pipe clamps, and to the counterweight guides or winch drive line clew, using $^3/_8$-inch locked turnbuckles, thimbles and three forged wire rope clips (each lift line cable). Swaged-type fittings (one per connection) may be used in lieu of three forged wire rope clips. Clove hitches shall not be used and the batten pocket shall not be cut to facilitate the installation of the lift lines.

Straight-lift- and braille-style curtains shall have safety stay chains of a straight-welded link minimum $^1/_4$-inch proof coil chain fastened securely to the curtain's top batten. Frame and modified frame-style curtains shall also have the same type safety stay chains, except they shall be sized to support safely the weight of the curtain. There shall be one more stay chain than the number of supporting cables and, except for the stay chains at the ends of the curtain, all stay chains shall be centered between the supporting cables. One end of each stay chain shall be securely attached to the curtain's top batten (or top of a frame), with the other to the gridiron, if of steel construction; otherwise, the upper stay chain ends shall be fastened to $^3/_4$-inch bolts bolted through the proscenium wall. Safety chains shall be so adjusted that they support the curtain when it is lowered and the bottom batten is resting on the yield pad and supported by the floor. In the case of the braille-style curtain, the safety chains will also be the method of holding the curtain's top batten in its stationary position.

All cables shall be carried overhead using head and loft blocks fitted with precision ball or tapered roller bearings of ample capacity to accommodate the weight at the speeds required. Grooves in the blocks shall be machined properly to cradle and protect the cable. All blocks supporting the proscenium fire-safety curtain shall be supported on the proscenium wall by means of steel brackets of suitable size to safely carry the weight, or shall be mounted on structural steel beams and other steel shapes that may be added.

Head and loft blocks shall be installed so as to prevent cable fouling.

For all style curtains using $^1/_4$-inch-diameter 7 by 19 galvanized aircraft cable lift lines, the minimum diameter of loft blocks shall be 8 inches when the height of the proscenium is 20 feet or less, and 12 inches for all others. Curtains using larger diameter lift lines shall use loft blocks with a minimum diameter 38 times the diameter of the cable. Head blocks shall be at least 4 inches greater in diameter than the loft blocks.

The mechanism and devices for controlling the curtain shall be of simple design and positive in operation. Normal day-to-day operation of straight-lift, braille curtains installed on proscenium openings of 1,500 square feet or less may be by manual means as long as operation can be accomplished with relative ease by a single person. Curtains meeting the size criteria in the previous sentence that are difficult for a single person to operate and other curtains not meeting the size criteria shall be operated by electric devices.

Automatic emergency release shall be by gravity obtained by overbalancing the curtain. The emergency control line shall be of minimum $^3/_8$-inch-diameter manila rope, or $^3/_{32}$-inch-diameter 7 by 19 galvanized aircraft cable, fitted with not less than four 165°F. or less nonelectric fusible links. One of these fusible links shall be located on each side of the stage and two overhead. When any link in the series separates, or the emergency control line is burned, the curtain shall automatically lower properly to its deployed position (see Section 6.101 above). This emergency control line shall extend up both sides and above the proscenium opening. As is the case with the manual emergency tripping mechanism detailed below, any attachment to the hand line on any operation machine or device that must be disconnected from the hand line or device for proper curtain deployment shall be a mechanical quick-release device that is easily resettable. The fire curtain emergency-release system shall not be interconnected mechanically, electromechanically, electrically or electronically with the emergency ventilator release system, unless a time delay is incorporated to assure that, in the event of a fire, the fire curtain will be fully deployed before the vents open. The building's fire alarm system shall not be interconnected with the fire curtain emergency-release system.

Manual emergency deployment of the fire curtain shall be accomplished by the activation of one of two mechanical quick-release assemblies (one on each side of the proscenium opening). Activation of either assembly shall be by pulling a minimum $1^1/_2$-inch-diameter red (color) ring, attached to a quick-release pin that is normally pinned through two steel plates housing a minimum 1-inch-diameter ring that is securely attached to the emergency-release line; these quick-release mechanisms shall be such that they can quickly (within a few minutes) and easily be reset in the event of erroneous activations. Other similar activation assemblies that are positive in nature and meet the basic criteria of the quick-release system detailed above may be used. Knife, axe and other emergency-release systems shall be allowable only until a new fire curtain is installed.

Appropriate signs in English and other languages prevalent to the facility's area, shall be prominently displayed near the location of the emergency control line quick-release mechanisms. For the release assembly detailed above, the sign would read IN CASE OF FIRE, PULL RED RING TO LOWER FIRE CURTAIN AUTOMATICALLY! with an arrow pointing to the location of the ring. There shall also be a less prominent sign or instruction pamphlet located on the main control side of the opening only, detailing the procedure required to properly and quickly reset the fire curtain in its raised position (this would include the mechanical quick-release mechanisms mentioned in this paragraph and the paragraph above).

Electric operation shall be from a single station located on either side of the proscenium opening and shall consist of two hold-to-operate-style push buttons, one labeled "Up" and one labeled "Down." Alternately, three push buttons that function from a single push of a button; one button shall be labeled "Up" for raising the curtain, one labeled "Down" for lowering the curtain, and one labeled "Stop" for stopping the curtain at the point it is located when the button is pushed; a sign stating NONEMERGENCY FIRE CURTAIN OPERATION shall be adjacent to the push-button station. Buttons and sign shall be labeled in English only.

All manually rigged counterweight curtains shall have their minimum $^3/_4$-inch manila endless operation hand line securely fastened to both the top and bottom of the counterweight arbor and shall pass under a minimum 12-inch-diameter floor block which is adjustable for tension.

The top and bottom counterweight sections of the arbor shall be of steel, sufficiently heavy to safely accommodate the loads. The top and bottom sections shall be connected with rods not less than $^3/_4$ inch in diameter, with one tie plate for every 4 feet of rod. Counterweights may be cast iron or flame cut steel with edges deburred. There shall be smooth grooves on the ends of the top and bottom weights which engage the steel guides. The arbor top and bottom shall be provided with an oilless-type bushing.

Counterweight guide tracks shall be structural tees or angles properly tied together and securely anchored to the proscenium wall. All joints where the counterweight travels shall be ground smooth. These guide tracks shall be caged their entire length.

All proscenium fire-safety curtains shall have an approved adjustable checking device or system, whether it be a counterweight arrangement, a hydraulic speed-governing system, a hydraulic dash pot shock-absorbing unit, or some other equivalent device or system that will enable the installation to meet the automatic-closing requirements detailed in Section 6.101.

Tests

Sec. 6.106. The complete installation of every proscenium fire-safety curtain shall be subjected to a minimum of two successful emergency-type operating tests triggered by release of the end of the emergency control line away from the hand line, winch or motor, and an on-site review of specifications by the building official prior to a new facility being issued an occupancy permit, and an existing facility being allowed the use of the newly renovated facilities.

New Designs

Sec. 6.107. A water curtain or deluge system complying with U.B.C. Standard No. 38-1 may be used in conjunction with an automatically closing opaque noncombustible curtain in lieu of the proscenium fire-safety curtain described in U.B.C. Standard No. 6-1. Both the deluge system and curtain closure shall be actuated by combination rate-of-temperature-rise and temperature devices located on the stage. The water system shall be designed to completely wet the entire curtain.

Curtains of other designs and materials, when not obviously of greater fire resistance than specified in this standard, shall before acceptance be subjected to the standard fire test specified in Chapter 43 of the Building Code as applicable to nonbearing partitions, except that such tests shall be continued only for a period of five minutes unless failure shall have occurred previously. The unexposed face of the curtain shall not glow within a period of 30 minutes nor shall there be any passage of smoke or flame through the curtain.

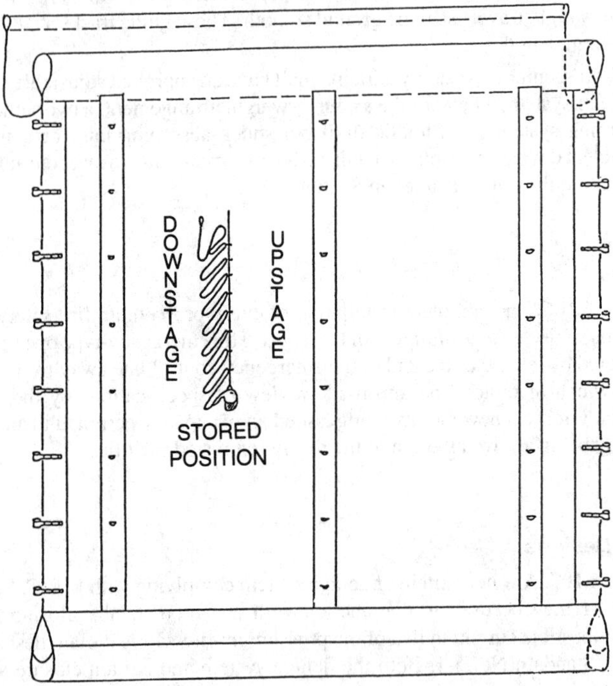
DOWNSTAGE
UPSTAGE
STORED
POSITION

FIGURE NO. 1—BRAILLE-STYLE PROSCENIUM FIRE-SAFETY CURTAIN

UNIFORM BUILDING CODE STANDARD NO. 17-1

KRAFT WATERPROOF BUILDING PAPER

Based on Federal Specification UU-B-790a (February 5, 1968)

See Sections 1701 (b) and 1708 (a), Uniform Building Code

Scope

Sec. 17.101. This standard covers building papers composed predominantly of sulfate pulp fibers intended for use as a weather-resistive barrier.

Classification

Sec. 17.102. The building papers shall be of Type I and not less than the following grades:

Grade A—High water-vapor resistance.
Grade B—Moderate water-vapor resistance.
Grade C—Water resistant.
Grade D—Water-vapor permeable.
Style 1a—Uncreped, not reinforced.
Style 1b—Uncreped, not reinforced, red rosin sized.
Style 2—Uncreped, not reinforced, saturated.
Style 3—Creped one direction, not reinforced.
Style 4—Uncreped, reinforced.

General Requirements

Sec. 17.103. (a) **Description.** The paper shall be either a single-ply or a multi-ply lamination.

(b) **Paper.** The paper shall consist of 100 percent sulfate pulp fibers, free of ground wood pulp, except as permitted in Section 17.104 (h).

(c) **Construction.** Lapped papers shall be securely cemented together throughout the seam area and shall have a minimum lap of 4 inches. Laminated paper shall contain no area of more than ½ inch, measured from the longitudinal edge of the combined sheet, which is devoid of the laminating agent. The paper shall not stick together to such an extent as to cause tearing when unrolled.

(d) **Treatment.** The paper shall be treated by the addition of asphalt, asphalt waxes, wax blends, wet-strength resins, rosins, fire-retarding salts or any combining agent, to impart the necessary characteristics to the paper.

(e) **Reinforcing.** When reinforcing is provided, the paper shall be reinforced by imbedding cords or strands of vegetable or inorganic fibers in the combining agent of the lamination.

Specific Requirements

Sec. 17.104. (a) **General.** Except for Style 2, the paper shall not crack when bent over a 1/16-inch mandrel at the temperature of 32°F. If reinforced, the cords or strands shall average not less than 10 per foot in each direction.

(b) **Grade A, High Water-Vapor Resistant.** Grade A paper shall have the dry tensile strength, water resistance and water-vapor transmission properties shown in Table No. 17-1-A.

(c) **Grade B, Moderate Water-Vapor Resistant.** Grade B paper shall have the dry tensile strength, water resistance and water-vapor transmission properties shown in Table No. 17-1-A.

(d) **Grade C, Water Resistant.** Grade C paper shall have the dry tensile strength and water-resistance properties shown in Table No. 17-1-A.

(e) **Grade D, Water-Vapor Permeable.** Grade D paper shall have the dry tensile strength, water resistance and water-vapor transmission properties shown in Table No. 17-1-A.

(f) **Style 1a, Uncreped, Unreinforced.** Style 1a paper shall be uncreped and shall not be reinforced.

(g) **Style 1b, Uncreped, Unreinforced, Red Rosin Sized.** Style 1b paper shall be uncreped, not reinforced, and shall be coated with red rosin sizing.

(h) **Style 2, Uncreped, Unreinforced, Saturated.** Style 2 paper shall be uncreped, not reinforced, and shall be saturated or infused with asphalt on both sides. Ground wood pulp may be included in the paper.

(i) **Style 3, Creped One Direction, Unreinforced.** Style 3 paper shall be creped in one direction, not reinforced, and shall have a minimum elongation (stretch) of 15 percent.

(j) **Style 4, Uncreped, Reinforced.** Style 4 paper shall be uncreped and reinforced.

Sec. 17.105. (a) **Test Specimens.** Test specimens shall be of the size designated by the applicable test or as otherwise provided herein.

The specimens shall be cut from the interior of the sample roll so that no specimen edge is nearer than 3 inches to the original sample edge. A minimum of 10 specimens, five in each direction of the paper, shall be cut from each sample for fire-resistance tests. Five specimens, each 5 inches square, shall be cut from each sample for water-repellency tests. One specimen, 6 inches by 1 inch in the machine direction of the paper, shall be cut from each sample for the pliability test.

(b) **Grade Requirement.** Grade requirement tests shall be made. Nonconformance to grade requirements of Table No. 17-1-A shall constitute failure of this test.

TABLE NO. 17-1-A—GRADE REQUIREMENTS[1]

PHYSICAL PROPERTY REQUIREMENT	GRADE			
	A	B	C	D
Dry tensile strength: minimum, pounds per inch width, both directions	20	20	20	20
Water resistance: permeation of water through papers, hours minimum	24	16	8	1/6
Water-vapor transmission: grams per sq. meter per 24 hours				
Maximum	4	6	—	—
Minimum	—	—	—	35

[1]**Approved test methods shall be used.**

UNIFORM BUILDING CODE STANDARD NO. 17-2

TEST METHOD TO DETERMINE POTENTIAL HEAT OF BUILDING MATERIALS

Test Standard of the International Conference of Building Officials

See Sections 1701 (b), 1713 (d) and 1713 (e) 2, Uniform Building Code

Scope

Sec. 17.201. (a) **General.** This method of test defines a means of determining the potential release of heat of materials (typically involved in building fires) under specified conditions. The method is applicable to a variety of materials including metals and especially materials with low combustible content. Determinations may be made on simple materials or on composite assemblies of materials from a which a representative sample can be taken and pulverized into a homogeneous mixture.

(b) **Definition of Potential Heat.** Potentional heat of a material is the difference between the heat of combustion of a representative specimen of the material and the heat of combustion of any residue remaining after exposure to a specified standard fire using combustion, calorimetric techniques.

Test Procedures

Sec. 17.202. (a) **General.** One of two specimens removed from the material to be tested shall be pulverized, pelleted and burned in a high-pressure-oxygen atmosphere in accordance with approved standard procedures for determination of the heat of combustion. Caution should be observed when performing bomb calorimetric measurements on materials containing significant proportions of metallic ingredients. Apart from the high reaction temperatures which may occur with the resulting possible involvement of portions of the bomb, consideration should be given to the possibility of electrical shorts in the ignition system.

(b) **Test Specimens.** Two air-dry specimens representative of the material or assembly involved are required for each determination. A specimen is considered "air dry" when it has reached constant weight in an atmosphere maintained at 73°F. ± 2°F. and 50 ± 5 percent relative humidity. The two specimens are subject to separate test procedures as set forth in Subsections (c) and (d) below.

(c) **Procedure for Direct Bomb Test.** The following steps shall be used for the direct bomb test:

Step 1. All or a representative portion of this specimen shall be pulverized into a form suitable to pass a No. 60 sieve.

Step 2. A 1-gram pellet of a representative sample of the powder formed in Step 1 is prepared.

Step 3. The pellet formed in Step 2 shall be used as the test specimen following the procedures described in Section 17.202 (a). The usual sulfur and acid corrections shall be made. These take into account the oxidation of sulfur and nitrogen, if present, which would not normally occur during fire exposure.

Step 4. If after being fired in the oxygen bomb the pellet is found to have burned completely or to have left no significant amount of residue or ash, the heat of combustion on an air-dry basis shall be computed and Steps 5, 6 and 7 shall be omitted.

Step 5. If the pellet does not burn or a residue remains after the firing, another 1-gram pellet shall be prepared with a mixture of the powdered sample and a standard sample of benzoic acid combustion promoter in approximately equal weight proportions.

Step 6. The pellet prepared in Step 5 shall be used as a test specimen following the same procedures as for the original specimen.

Step 7. A correction for the heat of combustion of the benzoic acid present in the pellet is supplied to the measured heat release by the specimen. The heat of combustion of the specimen material on an air-dry basis is then computed.

(d) **Procedure for Muffle Furnace and Bomb Test.** The following steps shall be used for the muffle furnace and bomb test:

Step 1. An air-dry specimen representative of the test material or assembly shall be cut in the form of a rectangular prism ½ inch by ¾ inch by 3 inches. Sheet materials may be folded or laminated to these dimensions.

Step 2. The muffle furnace is preheated to 1382°F. ± 18°F. The weighed specimen is supported in a fused silica or ceramic container of 1¼-inch inside diameter by 4 inches in length. The specimen, container cap and the tube for supply air to the bottom of the container are assembled. The assembly is then placed on a firebrick support within the electric muffle furnace. Firing is continued for two hours with a regulated air flow of ¹⁄₁₀ cubic foot per minute measued under laboratory conditions to assist in oxidation of the specimen. In cases where ignition occurs immediately, application of air is delayed until initial flaming has stopped.

Step 3. The container with the specimen shall be cooled in a desiccator, after which the weight of the residue is determined.

Step 4. If the residue from the muffle-firing procedure is less than 5 percent of the initial weight of the specimen, Steps 5 through 7 following shall be omitted, and the heat of combustion previously determined under the direct bomb test shall be reported as the potential heat of the material.

Step 5. If the residue after the muffle firing is in excess of 5 percent of the original specimen weight, the residue shall be pulverized, mixed with an equal weight of benzoic acid and treated as specified in the procedure for direct bomb test. The resulting heat of combustion is reported as that of the residue.

Step 6. The heat of combustion of the residue is multiplied by the ratio of the residue weight to the original specimen weight.

Step 7. The resulting difference in the heats of combustion is a measure of the gross heat release during the firing process in the muffle furnace and is reported as the potential heat.

(e) **Reporting Potential Heat.** The potential heat determined either as a result of Step 4 or 7 of Subsection (d) shall be reported as the potential heat of the material. The potential heat shall be reported in either Btu per pound or Btu per cubic foot.

UNIFORM BUILDING CODE STANDARD NO. 17-3

TEST METHOD FOR THE EVALUATION OF THERMAL BARRIERS

Standard of the International Conference of Building Officials

See Sections 1701 (b) and 1712 (d), Uniform Building Code

Scope

Sec. 17.301. This method of test for thermal barriers is applicable to building construction assemblies which incorporate foamed plastics which are required to be covered by a protective membrane.

The purpose of the test is to evaluate the temperature use or thermal transmission performance of the thermal barrier when the assembly is subjected to a standard fire exposure condition. This method does not evaluate the performance of the thermal barrier material with respect to its ability to remain in place under all actual fire exposure conditions.

Test Specimen

Sec. 17.302. The thermal barrier material and method of securing the thermal barrier shall be representative of the construction for which the thermal barrier index rating is required.

If the thermal barrier material incorporates joints, at least one such joint shall be incorporated in the test specimen.

Specimen Conditioning

Sec. 17.303. Prior to fire test, assemblies shall be conditioned so as to provide a moisture conditioning within the specimen approximately representative of that likely to exist in similar construction in buildings. For that purpose of standardization, this condition is to be considered as that which would be established at equilibrium resulting from conditioning in an ambient atmosphere of 50 ± 5 percent relative humidity and 73.4 ± 5°F.

Test Conditions

Sec. 17.304. (a) **General.** The dimensions of the furnace shall be as shown in Figure No. 17-3-1 entitled "Small-scale Horizontal Exposure Furnace."

The thermal barrier shall be installed in a manner representative of the construction for which the thermal barrier index rating is required. The specimen exposed to the fire shall have minimum horizontal dimensions of 28 inches by 28 inches.

The calcium silicate board shall be installed as shown in Figure No. 17-3-2, shall have a thickness of 1/2 inch and a density of 46 pounds per cubic foot.

(b) **Furnace Temperature.** The furnace temperature, as recorded by the thermocouples specified in Section 17.304 (c), shall follow the standard time-temperature curve specified in U.B.C. Standard No. 43-1 for which the temperatures at 5, 10 and 15 minutes following the commencement of the test are as given in Table No. 17-3-A.

(c) **Accuracy of Furnace Control.** The accuracy of the furnace control shall be such that the area under the time-temperature curve given by the average of the specified thermocouples shall be within 10 percent of the corresponding area under the standard time-temperature curve specified in Section 17.304 (b).

(d) **Thermocouple Location.** The furnace temperature shall be registered by three or more thermocouples located so as to monitor the uniformity of the exposure to the thermal barrier. They shall be located 12 inches away from the face of the specimen and shall have a length of lead exposed within the furnace of not less than 12 inches. They shall be enclosed in sealed porcelain tubes ¾ inch in outside diameter and ⅛ inch in wall thickness or, as an alternative in the case of base metal thermocouples, enclosed in sealed, standard-weight, ½-inch black wrought-steel or black wrought-iron pipe.

The temperature of the interface of the thermal barrier and the calcium silicate board shall be sensed by at least nine thermocouples as shown in Figure No. 17-3-2 located at the center of the specimen, at the center of each quarter of the specimen and at potentially critical locations such as joints in the material. The leads to each thermocouple shall be in the plane of this interface for a length of not less than 1½ inches. The wires for the thermocouples shall be not heavier than No. 20 AWG (.032 inch).

(e) **Furnace Pressures.** Furnace pressures shall be kept as close to atmospheric pressure as possible during the test.

(f) **Duration of Test.** The test shall be continued for 15 minutes or until the thermal barrier has fallen away or disintegrated.

(g) **Recording Temperatures.** Throughout the period of test, the temperature registered at each of the thermocouples required by Section 17.304 (d) shall be recorded at intervals not exceeding one minute.

Determination of Thermal Barrier Index

Sec. 17.305. The thermal barrier index shall be determined as the number of minutes at which the temperature rise above initial temperature at the interface of the thermal barrier and the calcium silicate board has not exceeded 250°F. average or 325°F. at any one of the thermocouples specified in Section 17.304 (d).

TABLE NO. 17-3-A—FURNACE TEMPERATURES

TIME	TEMPERATURE	
	°F.	°C.
5 minutes	1000	538
10 minutes	1300	704
15 minutes	1399	760

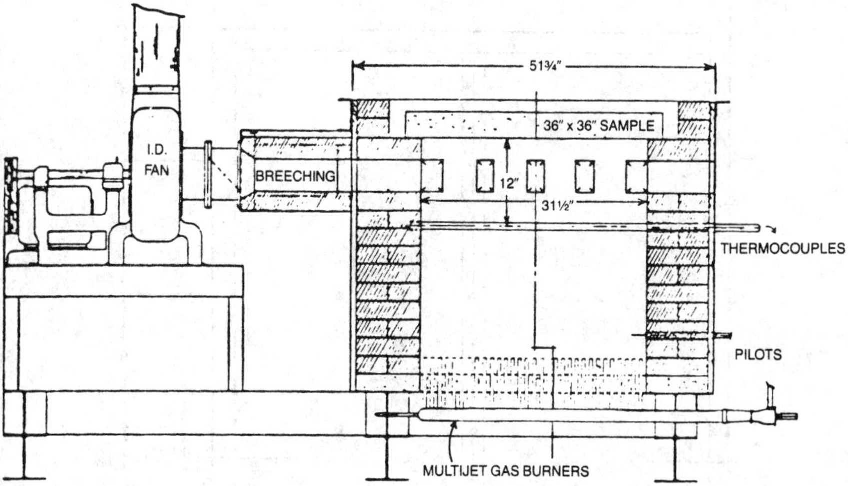
51¾″
36″ x 36″ SAMPLE
I.D.
FAN
BREECHING
12″
31½″
THERMOCOUPLES
PILOTS
MULTIJET GAS BURNERS

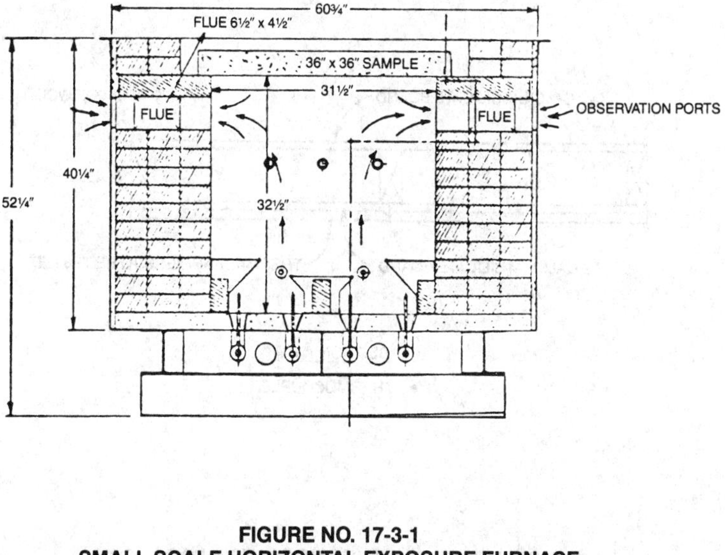
60¾″
FLUE 6½″ x 4½″
36″ x 36″ SAMPLE
31½″
FLUE
FLUE
OBSERVATION PORTS
40¼″
52¼″
32½″

FIGURE NO. 17-3-1
SMALL-SCALE HORIZONTAL EXPOSURE FURNACE

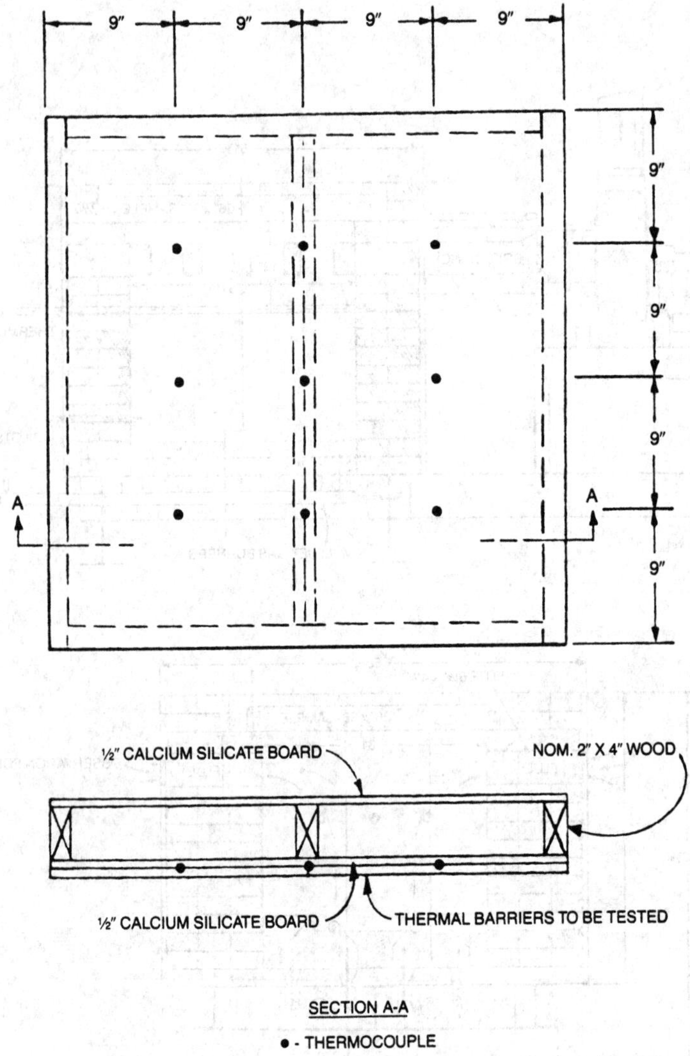
9″
9″
9″
9″
9″
9″
9″
9″
A
A
½″ CALCIUM SILICATE BOARD
NOM. 2″ X 4″ WOOD
½″ CALCIUM SILICATE BOARD
THERMAL BARRIERS TO BE TESTED
SECTION A-A
● - THERMOCOUPLE

FIGURE NO. 17-3-2—THERMOCOUPLE LOCATIONS

UNIFORM BUILDING CODE STANDARD NO. 17-5

ROOM FIRE TEST STANDARD FOR INTERIOR OF FOAM PLASTIC SYSTEMS

Test Standard of the International Conference of Building Officials

See Sections 1701 (b) and 1713 (f), Uniform Building Code

Scope

Sec. 17.501. This standard details a test method to evaluate the burning characteristics of foam plastic assemblies in a standard room configuration. It is intended to be a test for use under Section 1713 (f) of the Uniform Building Code.

Fire Test Structure

Sec. 17.502. The fire test structure shall consist of a room 8 feet by 12 feet having a ceiling height of 8 feet located in an enclosed building. A doorway 2 feet 6 inches by 7 feet 0 inches shall be centered in one of the 8-foot-long walls of the test structure. See Figure No. 1.

The wall test area shall consist of wall sections 8 feet square intersecting at the corner opposite the doorway. Ceiling specimens shall cover an area 8 feet square with two edges resting on or adjoining the intersecting wall test sections. Vertical and horizontal joints shall be included in the test wall and ceiling specimens to represent field conditions.

Except for composite panels, the construction of the walls and ceiling beyond the test area or which serve as a substrate for foam plastic shall consist of ½-inch asbestos cement board supported by suitable framing.

Composite wall and ceiling or roof panels with structural foam plastic cores shall be installed without a substrate and in the manner intended for use, including connections along all joints and perimeters. Panels intended to support superimposed loads shall be fire tested with the panels loaded in a manner resulting in conditions of maximum allowable stress.

> **EXCEPTION:** Testing under loaded conditions may be waived in Type V construction when the panels need not be fire resistive.

When the test concerns nonstructural protective material, the foam plastic base shall be applied to the maximum thickness anticipated and have a minimum flame-spread rating of 75.

Material and fabrication of test assemblies must be certified by the testing agency as complying with descriptions or details that are a part of the report of tests.

The building containing the test structure shall have a temperature between 60°F. and 90°F. at the start of the fire test and shall be free of excessive drafts.

Test Procedure

Sec. 17.503. (a) **Cribs.** The fuel for the room test shall be a wood crib constructed of 1½-inch square white fir sticks cut to 15-inch lengths. At a 12 percent moisture content, the crib shall weigh 30 pounds and be 15 inches square in plan. One 8d nail shall be driven at each corner of each tier. Each interior stick shall be attached at each end to a perimeter stick with one 8d nail. Approximately 45 to 50 sticks will be involved and must be assembled in nine or ten tiers with five sticks in each tier. The placement of sticks in each tier shall be oriented at 90 degrees to sticks in adjacent tiers. After fabrication the crib shall be conditioned to a maximum constant moisture content of 8 percent. Standard bricks cut in half and placed at each corner of the crib shall be used to support the crib not less than 3 inches above the floor located as described in Subsection (c) below.

(b) **Starter Material.** One pound of shredded, fluffed wood excelsior is distributed around the bricks with the excelsior extending from the wall surfaces and covering an area approximately 21 inches by 21 inches. To start the test, the wood excelsior is soaked with 4 ounces of reagent ethyl alcohol or absolute ethyl alcohol, except for a triangular area approximately 6 inches by 6 inches diametrically opposite the intersection of the walls. The crib is then located 1 inch from the intersecting wall surfaces on the bricks.

(c) **Ignition.** A match is placed in the excelsior to initiate burning. Under proper conditions for ignition, flames typically progress slowly through the dry excelsior for only ten seconds until the soaked alcohol portion is reached, whereupon flames flash through the entire excelsior, providing uniform application of the ignition flame beneath the entire crib.

(d) **Extinguishment.** Fire extinguishment is permitted 15 minutes after crib ignition. Charring of the test panels must not be affected by the extinguishing procedures.

(e) **Temperature Readings.** Temperature readings at locations shown in Figure No. 2 shall be taken at maximum two-minute intervals and at 15 minutes from crib ignition with properly calibrated thermocouples of the type described in U.B.C. Standard No. 43-1.

(f) **Smoke Measurement.** Smoke generated during the 15-minute test period shall be measured by photoelectric instrumentation if there is sufficient available data to establish a basis of acceptance. In lieu of this, the test report shall include films taken during the test.

Conditions of Acceptance

Sec. 17.504. A foam plastic wall or ceiling assembly shall be considered as meeting the requirements for acceptable performance within the following conditions:

1. Charring of the foam plastic shall not extend to the outer extremities of the test area within a 15-minute period after ignition of the excelsior. Discoloration extending not more than ¼ inch into the foam plastic shall not be considered as charring.
2. Smoke levels generated during the test period shall not be excessive.
3. Structural panels shall sustain the applied load during the test period.

Report of Test

Sec. 17.505. The report of test shall include the following:

1. A detailed description of the foam plastic assembly including specifications on all components and manner of fabrication and installation.
2. A statement by the testing agency that preparation, fabrication and installation of the foam plastic assembly was in accordance with Item No. 1 and this standard.
3. A statement of compliance or specific points of deviation from test procedures set forth in this standard.
4. An account of visual observation of the foam plastic assemblies during the test.
5. Location and extent of charring in the foam plastic assemblies at the conclusion of the test.
6. Temperature readings during the test as set forth in Section 17.502 (c).
7. Smoke measurement during the test or films of the test.

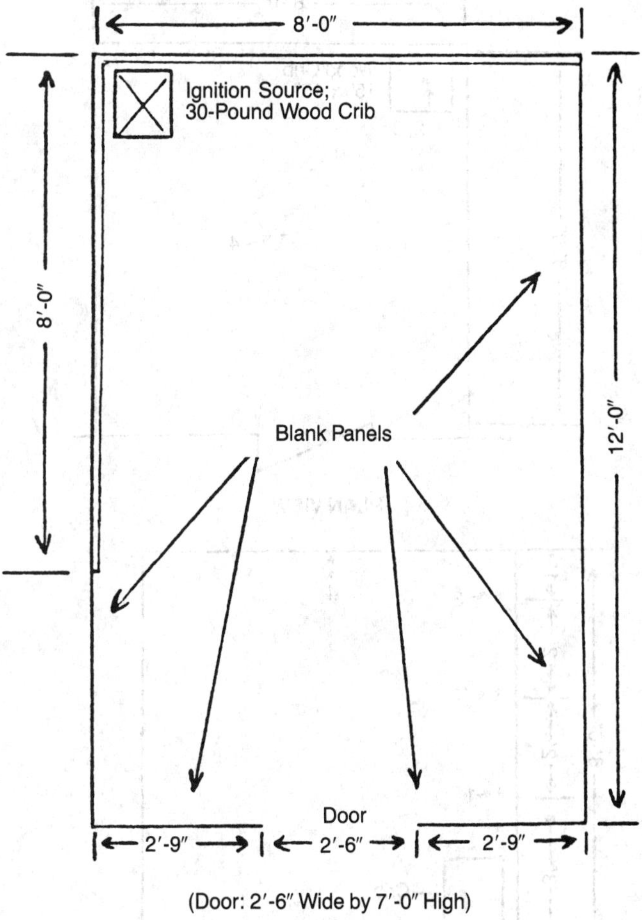
8′-0″
Ignition Source;
30-Pound Wood Crib
8′-0″
12′-0″
Blank Panels
Door
2′-9″
2′-6″
2′-9″
(Door: 2′-6″ Wide by 7′-0″ High)

FIGURE NO. 1
ROOM TEST CONFIGURATION

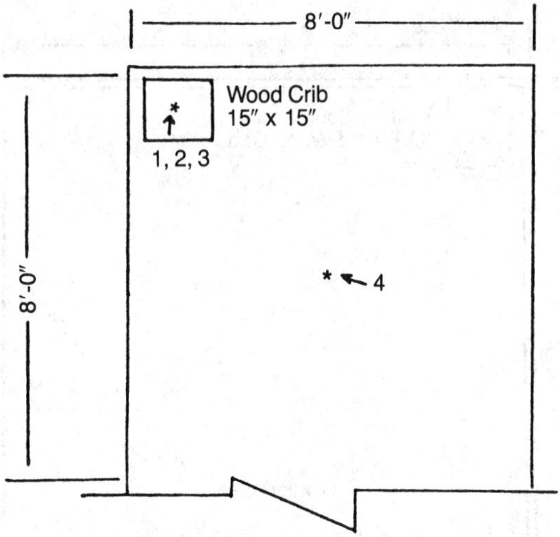
8′-0″
Wood Crib
15″ x 15″
1, 2, 3
4
8′-0″

PLAN VIEW

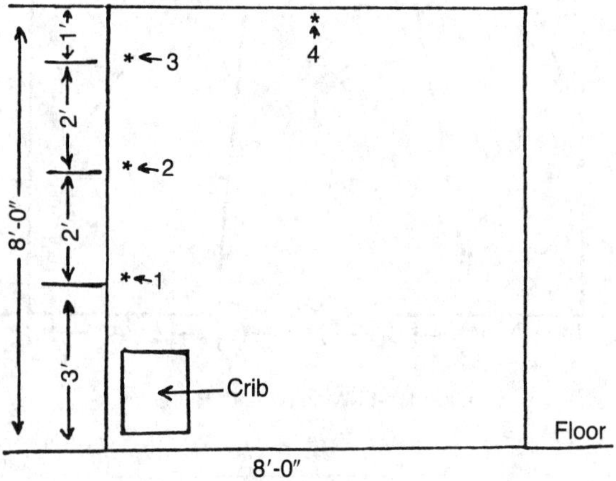
1′
2′
2′
3′
8′-0″
3
2
1
4
Crib
Floor
8′-0″

ELEVATION

*Thermocouple locations

NOTES: 1. Thermocouples 1, 2 and 3 located 3 inches from adjacent wall surfaces.

2. Thermocouple 4 located 1 inch below the ceiling, 4 feet from each of three walls.

FIGURE NO. 2
THERMOCOUPLE LOCATIONS

UNIFORM BUILDING CODE STANDARD NO. 17-6

METHOD OF TEST FOR THE EVALUATION OF FLAMMABILITY CHARACTERISTICS OF EXTERIOR, NONLOAD-BEARING WALL PANEL ASSEMBLIES USING FOAM PLASTIC INSULATION

Test Standard of the International Conference of Building Officials See Sections 1701 (b) and 1713 (e) 2, Uniform Building Code

Scope

Sec. 17.601. This test provides a method of determining the flammability characteristics of foam plastic insulated, exterior, nonload-bearing wall panel assemblies. The test structure is intended to simulate a "full-scale" multistory building installation. Test assemblies are evaluated on a "full-scale" basis.

The primary performance characteristics to be evaluated are:

1. Capability of the test panels to resist vertical spread of flame within the core of the panel from one story to the next;
2. Capability to resist flame propagation over the exterior face of the panels;
3. Capability to resist vertical spread of flame over the interior (room side) surface of the panels from one story to the next; and
4. Capability to resist lateral spread of flame from the compartment of fire origin to adjacent spaces.

Fire Test Structure

Sec. 17.602. The fire test structure shall consist of a two-story, 24-foot-high building having inside room dimensions of 15 feet wide by 15 feet deep. See Figure No. 17-6-1. Floor-to-floor height shall be 12 feet. Floors and roof shall be of reinforced concrete construction supported on a steel frame. The first floor shall be a slab 12 inches thick whereas the second floor and roof shall be 8 inches thick. Spandrel beams (W10 by 11.5), designed to be replaceable, are supported on steel columns. Permanent walls of the structure are of 8-inch concrete block. The concrete block wall shall completely close two walls of the test structure, except for a 3-foot 4-inch access opening at the first- and second-floor levels.

Test panels shall be secured to the test structure using a girt system of replaceable 4-inch by 4-inch by 3/16-inch steel angles. The test panels shall completely close the two walls of the test structure, except for a window opening in one wall. Test panels shall be fabricated with a 4-foot-high by 8-foot-long window opening in the first story. The window opening shall be the only opening in the first-story burn room enclosure at the time of test.

Test panels shall be secured to the test structure using a method of fastening including all joints and perimeters to represent actual field conditions. Details of erection shall follow the manufacturer's instructions and shall be typical of actual product use. When a product may have vertical or horizontal joints, joints typical of normal construction, including caulking, backing and other details as appropriate, shall be incorporated in the test panels.

Prior to the start of a test, access opening shall be closed using an assembly having a minimum of three layers of 5/8-inch-thick Type X gypsum wallboard on the burn room side of any supports. The door opening in the second story may remain open during testing.

In the first-floor burn room prior to each test, the two concrete block walls and the ceiling are protected with three layers of 5/8-inch Type X gypsum wallboard. The floor is protected with two layers of 5/8-inch Type X gypsum wallboard. The steel column located within the burn room is wrapped with two layers of ceramic fiber blanket insulation (1 inch thick) and boxed in with one layer of 1/2-inch-thick Marinite board. Spandrel beams are wrapped with one layer of ceramic fiber blanket insulation and boxed in with one layer of 1/2-inch-thick Marinite board. The outriggers and the girt angles are not protected.

In the second story, prior to each test, the concrete block walls and ceiling are protected by one layer of 1/2-inch-thick Marinite board. The floor is protected by one layer of 5/8-inch-thick Type X gypsum wallboard. The interior steel column is wrapped with one layer of ceramic fiber blanket insulation (1 inch thick). Girt angles are left unprotected.

Material and fabrication of test assemblies must be certified by the testing agency as complying with the description or details that are a part of the report of test.

A windshield shall be utilized (see Figure No. 17-6-2) to minimize wind action across the face of the test structure.

Instrumentation and Documentation

Sec. 17.603. (a) **Instrumentation.** In this procedure, test instrumentation consists primarily of temperature measurements placed in the following locations:

1. Inside room of fire origin—underside of second-story floor and underside of structural steel members.
2. Window opening—6 inches below top of window opening.
3. On exterior face of wall panels.
4. On interior face of wall panels—at floors and in panel cores at second-floor level and above.

Temperature measurements are made using 20-gauge Type K thermocouples.

Specific thermocouple locations are provided in Figures Nos. 17-6-3 through 17-6-7. Temperatures shall be recorded at intervals not to exceed 15 seconds.

(b) **Documentation.** Documentation of tests is provided by:

1. Color video tape of exterior,
2. Color 16-mm film of exterior, and
3. Color 35-mm slides of exterior.

In order to facilitate documentation of flame penetration (if any) into the second-floor level, a black and white video camera is placed inside the second floor. The camera is aimed at the test wall/floor intersection and observations relating to flame penetration and/or smoke development are made.

After the test is terminated by extinguishment of the fire in the wood crib, special note shall be made of the extent and duration of any residual burning in the test panel.

After the cooling period, the interior and exterior sides of the test walls shall be described as to visual appearance and shall be photographed. The test walls shall then be dismantled and dissected to determine height and depth of char damage within the cavity and condition of panel facings.

Test Procedure

Sec. 17.604. (a) **Crib Fire Exposure.** The burn room shall be provided with a fuel load which when burned produces the standard time/temperature curve described in Sections 43.102 and 43.103 of U.B.C. Standard No. 43-1 as measured inside the burn room for a period of not less than 30 minutes. The crib shall generate fire exposure producing an intermittent flame plume similar to that generated in an actual fire discharging out of the burn room window. The plume shall attach itself to and shall expose the face of the test panel for a minimum of 5 feet above the top of the burn room window. Makeup air for combustion of the crib shall be supplied solely through the 4-foot by 8-foot window opening. No other ventilation is provided. Control temperatures are measured at the underside of the second floor and at the underside of the spandrel beams.

The fuel for the fire exposure shall be a 1285-pound wood crib. The crib shall be constructed of dried 2-inch by 4-inch Douglas fir members having a moisture content of 11 percent plus or minus 1 percent. Crib members are cut into 4-foot and 8-foot lengths. The 2-inch by 4-inch members shall be nailed into a lattice-type crib consisting of full tiers and one partial tier of three 8-foot 2 by 4's. Overall crib dimensions shall be 48 inches deep, 96 inches wide and 28 1/2 inches high. See Figure No. 17-6-8.

The crib shall be centered on the burn room window but located off center toward the window. See Figure No. 17-6-9.

The crib shall be supported above floor level by 8-inch concrete blocks. A layer of 5/8-inch-thick Type X gypsum wallboard is placed between the crib and the concrete block support. See Figure No. 17-6-10.

(b) **Starter Material.** Prior to ignition, 1 gallon of kerosene is equally divided into eight pans (7 1/4 inches in diameter, 15/16 inch deep) and the pans are placed under the crib. The pans are interconnected using kerosene-soaked rags that have been soaked sufficiently to facilitate ignition. Additionally, 2 pints of kerosene are poured over the crib. The kerosene is to provide quick ignition of the crib and also cause an initial rapid increase in temperature within the burn room.

(c) **Ignition.** After proper operation of all instrumentation and documentation equipment is verified, the pans containing kerosene are placed under the crib, the kerosene is poured over the crib and the test is begun.

A match is used to ignite a kerosene-soaked rag which, in turn, causes flames to spread to the kerosene in the eight pans located under the crib. The fire develops quickly with flames reaching the ceiling of the burn room within one to three minutes. Flames begin to emerge from the burn room window in three to five minutes.

(d) **Duration.** The test is continued for 30 minutes. At the conclusion of the test, the crib fire is extinguished using a hose line. The test structure is allowed to cool naturally. Any residual burning in or on the surface of the test panels shall be noted and panels shall be allowed to burn freely until self-extinguishment occurs or fire spreads to the limits of the test panels.

(e) **Weather Conditions.** The test shall not be conducted if at the start of the test the average wind velocity exceeds 10 miles per hour, if the relative humidity is 100 percent or if there is fog or precipitation present at the test site.

Conditions of Acceptance

Sec. 17.605. The performance of a test assembly shall be judged on the basis of visual observations both during and after the test in conjunction with temperature data. An exterior wall assembly shall be considered as meeting the requirements for acceptable performance if during the 30-minute test period:

1. Flames do not propagate beyond the immediate area of flame impingement on the exterior face of the wall panels.
2. Flame propagation does not occur vertically or laterally through the core insulation to the limits of the test panels. Flame propagation may be judged to occur within the test panels when temperatures within the insulation core outside the region of direct flame exposure exceed 750°F. above ambient.
3. Flame propagation shall not occur to the first-floor wall panels extending beyond the concrete block walls of the test fixture either through core insulation or over the exterior or interior panel surfaces. Where the flame cannot be directly observed, flame propagation shall be assumed to occur where the temperatures within the insulation core exceed 750°F. above ambient.

4. Temperatures measured 1 inch from the interior surfaces of the wall assembly within the second story do not exceed 350°F. above ambient.
5. Flames do not enter the second-story room.

Report of Test

Sec. 17.606. The report of test shall contain the following:

1. Description of test wall assembly to include:
   a. Drawings showing structural design, plan, elevation, principal cross section plus other sections as needed for clarity and joint locations and details.
   b. Details of attachment of walls to test facility.
   c. Flame-spread and smoke-developed values of foam plastic per U.B.C. Standard No. 42-1.
   d. Ignition temperature of foam plastic
2. Location of thermocouples.
3. General ambient condition at test time.
4. Temperature data obtained during the test for all thermocouple locations.
5. Visual observations made during the test.
6. Photographs of the following:
   a. Test walls prior to test.
   b. Test in progress.
   c. Test walls exterior—post test.
   d. Test walls interior—post test.
   e. Core insulation of both walls—post test.
7. Performance of wall system with respect to:
   a. Damage to the walls and core.
   b. Flame advance over exterior faces.
   c. Flame advance over interior faces.
   d. Flame penetration into second floor.
   e. Smoke accumulation inside the second-story room.

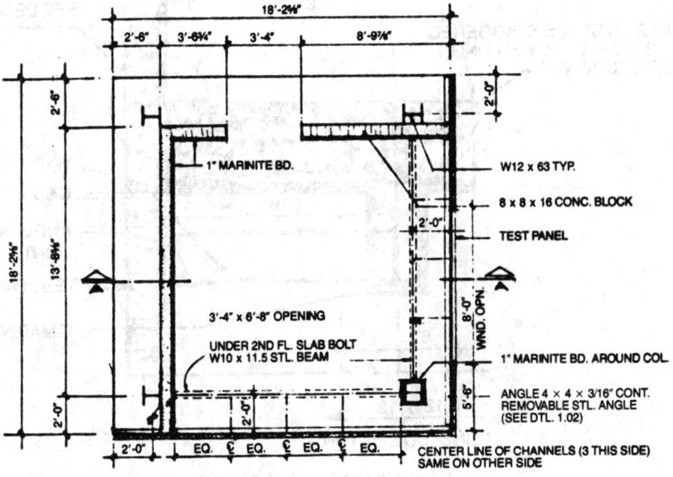
18'-2¾"
2'-6"
3'-6¾"
3'-4"
8'-9⅞"
2'-0"
1" MARINITE BD.
W12 x 63 TYP.
8 x 8 x 16 CONC. BLOCK
2'-0"
TEST PANEL
18'-2⅝"
13'-8⅝"
3'-4" x 6'-8" OPENING
8'-0" WND. OPN.
UNDER 2ND FL. SLAB BOLT W10 x 11.5 STL. BEAM
1" MARINITE BD. AROUND COL.
ANGLE 4 × 4 × 3/16" CONT. REMOVABLE STL. ANGLE (SEE DTL. 1.02)
5'-6"
2'-0"
EQ.
CENTER LINE OF CHANNELS (3 THIS SIDE) SAME ON OTHER SIDE

SCALE: ¼" = 1'-0"

FIRST/SECOND FL. PLAN

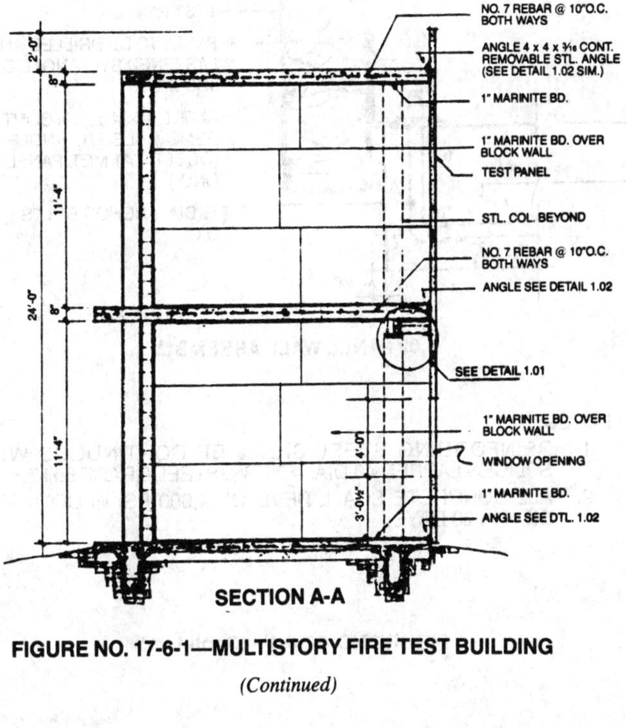
NO. 7 REBAR @ 10"O.C. BOTH WAYS
ANGLE 4 x 4 x 3/16 CONT. REMOVABLE STL. ANGLE (SEE DETAIL 1.02 SIM.)
1" MARINITE BD.
1" MARINITE BD. OVER BLOCK WALL
TEST PANEL
STL. COL. BEYOND
NO. 7 REBAR @ 10"O.C. BOTH WAYS
ANGLE SEE DETAIL 1.02
SEE DETAIL 1.01
1" MARINITE BD. OVER BLOCK WALL
WINDOW OPENING
1" MARINITE BD.
ANGLE SEE DTL. 1.02
2'-0"
8"
11'-4"
24'-0"
8"
11'-4"
4'-0"
3'-0½"

SECTION A-A

FIGURE NO. 17-6-1—MULTISTORY FIRE TEST BUILDING

(Continued)

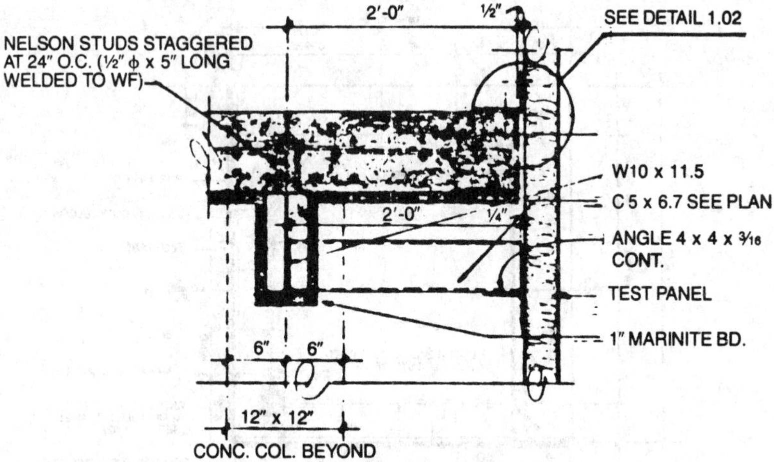
2'-0"
½"
SEE DETAIL 1.02
NELSON STUDS STAGGERED AT 24" O.C. (½" ϕ x 5" LONG WELDED TO WF)
W10 x 11.5
C 5 x 6.7 SEE PLAN
2'-0"
¼"
ANGLE 4 x 4 x 3/16 CONT.
TEST PANEL
1" MARINITE BD.
6"
6"
12" x 12"
CONC. COL. BEYOND

1.01 SECTION DETAIL

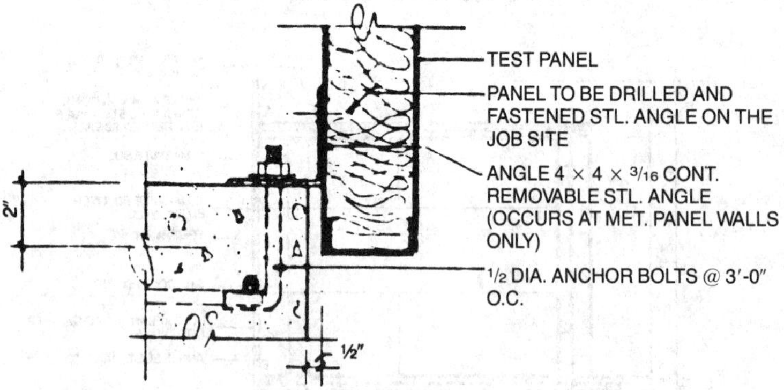
TEST PANEL
PANEL TO BE DRILLED AND FASTENED STL. ANGLE ON THE JOB SITE
ANGLE 4 × 4 × 3/16 CONT. REMOVABLE STL. ANGLE (OCCURS AT MET. PANEL WALLS ONLY)
1/2 DIA. ANCHOR BOLTS @ 3'-0" O.C.
2"
½"

1.02 PANEL WALL ASSEMBLY

NOTES:

1. REINFORCING STEEL SHALL BE CONTINUOUS WITH SPLICES LAPPED 40 DIAMETERS. STEEL GRADE 60 KSI.
2. ALL CONCRETE SHALL DEVELOP 4,000 PSI IN COMPRESSION IN 28 DAYS.

FIGURE NO. 17-6-1—(Continued)

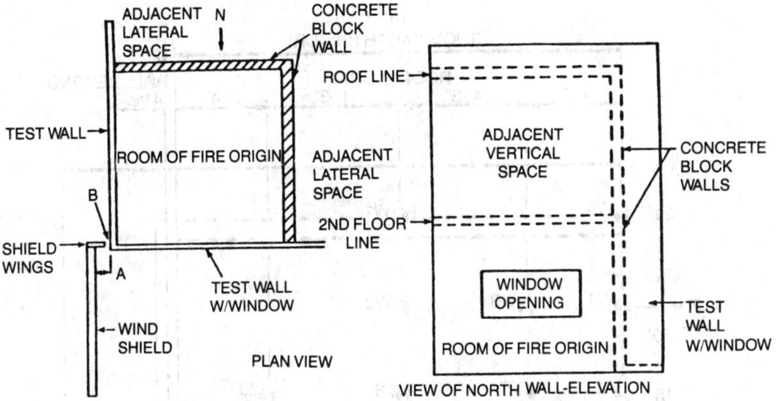
ADJACENT LATERAL SPACE
N
CONCRETE BLOCK WALL
TEST WALL
ROOM OF FIRE ORIGIN
ADJACENT LATERAL SPACE
B
SHIELD WINGS
A
TEST WALL W/WINDOW
WIND SHIELD
PLAN VIEW
ROOF LINE
ADJACENT VERTICAL SPACE
CONCRETE BLOCK WALLS
2ND FLOOR LINE
WINDOW OPENING
TEST WALL W/WINDOW
ROOM OF FIRE ORIGIN
VIEW OF NORTH WALL-ELEVATION

FIGURE NO. 17-6-2—TEST ARRANGEMENT

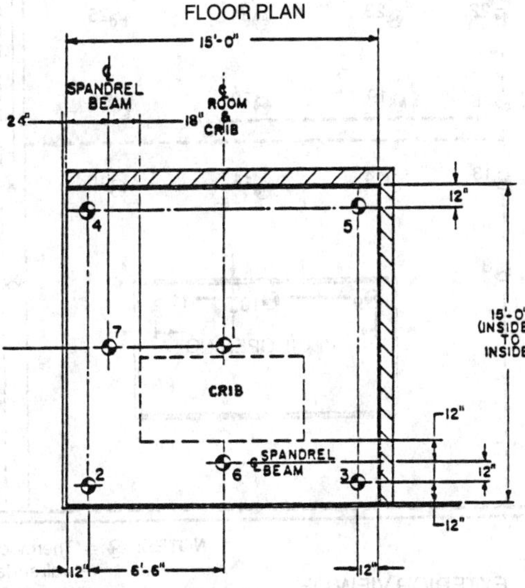
FLOOR PLAN
15'-0"
℄ SPANDREL BEAM
℄ ROOM & CRIB
24"
18"
12"
4
5
15'-0" (INSIDE TO INSIDE)
7
1
CRIB
12"
SPANDREL BEAM
6
2
3
12"
12"
12"
6'-6"
12"

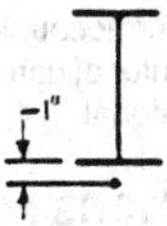
1"

Thermocouple Layout

- Thermocouples 1 and 5 are 6 inches below ceiling.
- Thermocouples 2, 3 and 4 are 2 inches below spandrel beam and centered between wall and beam.
- Thermocouples 6 and 7 are 1 inch below bottom surface of spandrel beam.

BURN ROOM—PLAN VIEW

FIGURE NO. 17-6-3—THERMOCOUPLE LOCATIONS

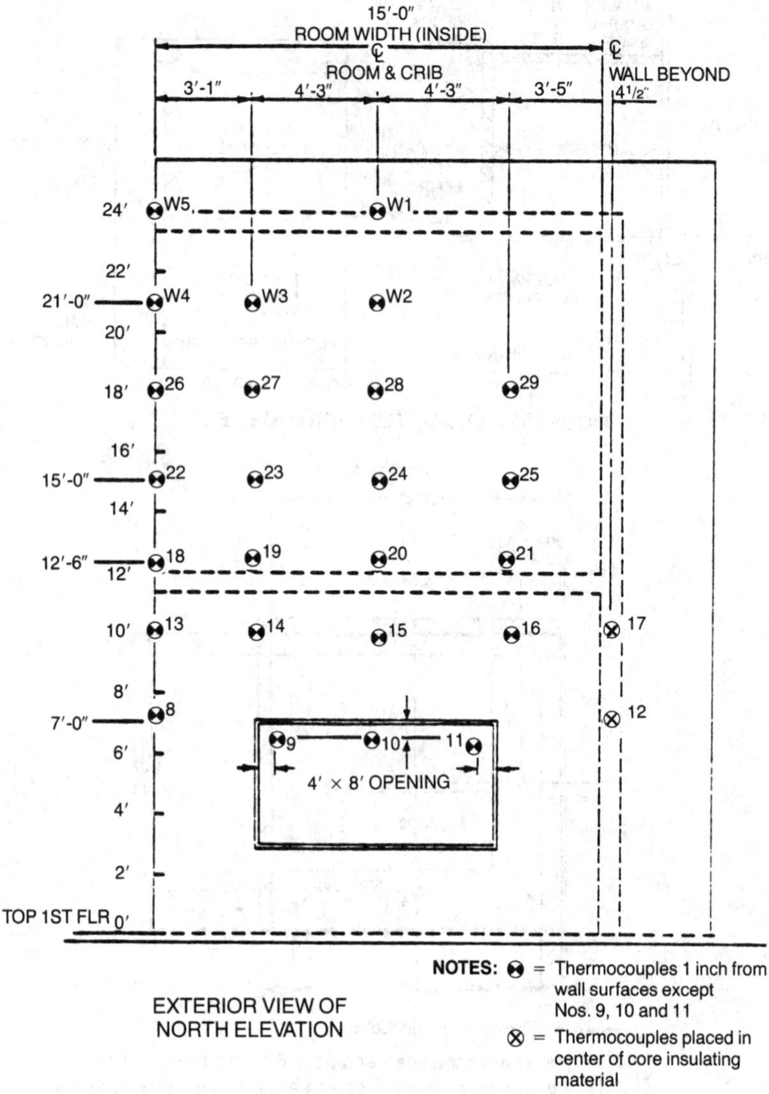
15′-0″
ROOM WIDTH (INSIDE)
℄
ROOM & CRIB
℄
WALL BEYOND
3′-1″
4′-3″
4′-3″
3′-5″
4 1/2″
24′
W5
W1
22′
21′-0″
W4
W3
W2
20′
18′
26
27
28
29
16′
15′-0″
22
23
24
25
14′
12′-6″
18
19
20
21
12′
10′
13
14
15
16
17
8′
7′-0″
8
12
9
10
11
6′
4′ × 8′ OPENING
4′
2′
TOP 1ST FLR 0′
EXTERIOR VIEW OF NORTH ELEVATION
NOTES: ⊗ = Thermocouples 1 inch from wall surfaces except Nos. 9, 10 and 11
⊗ = Thermocouples placed in center of core insulating material

FIGURE NO. 17-6-4—THERMOCOUPLE LOCATIONS

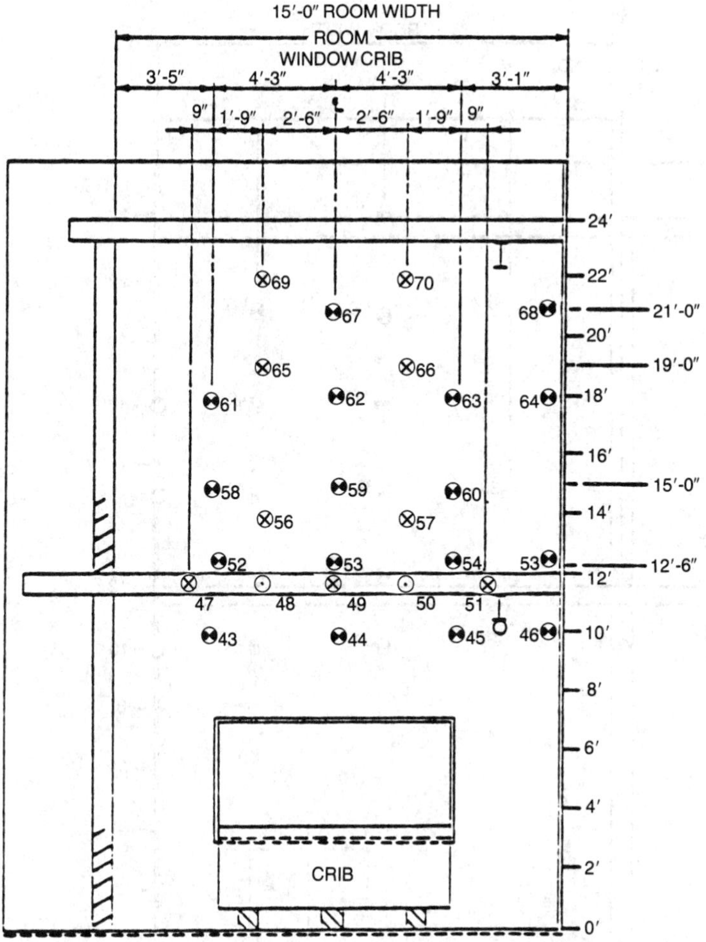
15′-0″ ROOM WIDTH
ROOM
WINDOW CRIB
3′-5″
4′-3″
4′-3″
3′-1″
9″
1′-9″
2′-6″
2′-6″
1′-9″
9″
24′
22′
21′-0″
20′
19′-0″
18′
16′
15′-0″
14′
12′-6″
12′
10′
8′
6′
4′
2′
0′
69
70
67
68
65
66
61
62
63
64
58
59
60
56
57
52
53
54
53
47
48
49
50
51
43
44
45
46
CRIB

NOTES: ⊗ = Thermocouples placed 1 inch from wall surfaces

⊗ = Thermocouples placed in center of core insulating material

⊙ = Thermocouples placed in center of safing material—center of floor level

INSIDE VIEW OF NORTH ELEVATION

FIGURE NO. 17-6-5—THERMOCOUPLE LOCATIONS

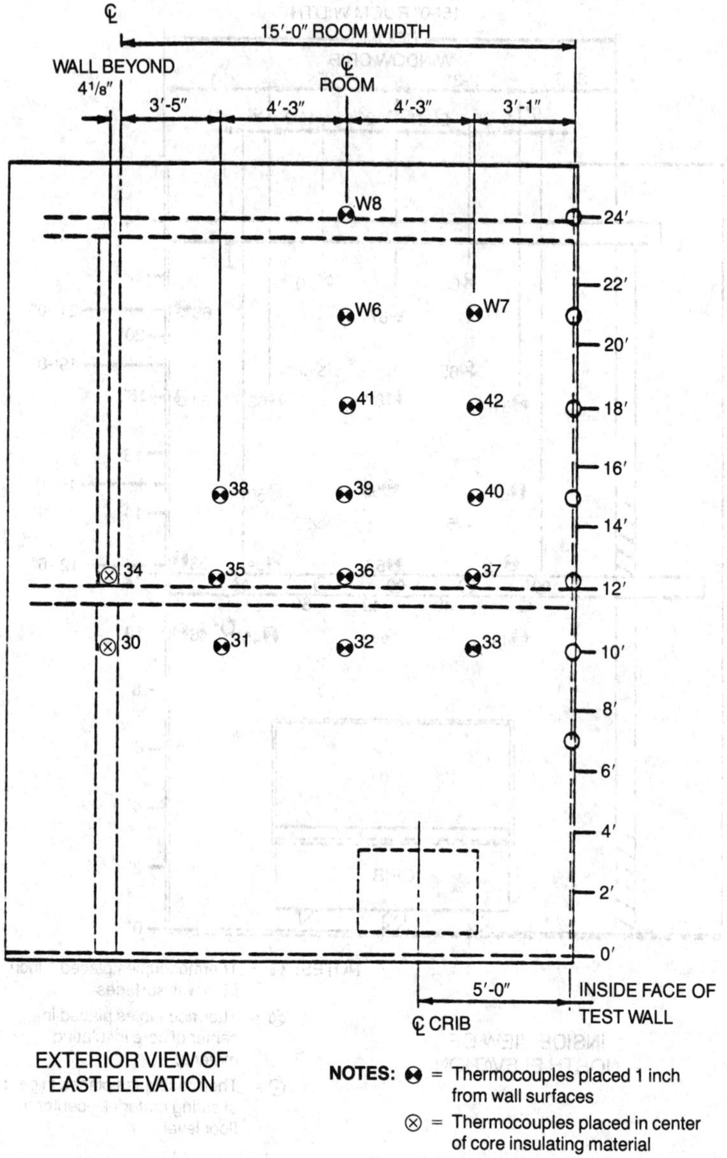

℄
15′-0″ ROOM WIDTH
WALL BEYOND
4 1/8″
℄
ROOM
3′-5″
4′-3″
4′-3″
3′-1″
W8
24′
22′
W6
W7
20′
41
42
18′
16′
38
39
40
14′
34
35
36
37
12′
30
31
32
33
10′
8′
6′
4′
2′
0′
5′-0″
INSIDE FACE OF
TEST WALL
℄ CRIB
EXTERIOR VIEW OF
EAST ELEVATION
NOTES: = Thermocouples placed 1 inch from wall surfaces
⊗ = Thermocouples placed in center of core insulating material

FIGURE NO. 17-6-6—THERMOCOUPLE LOCATIONS

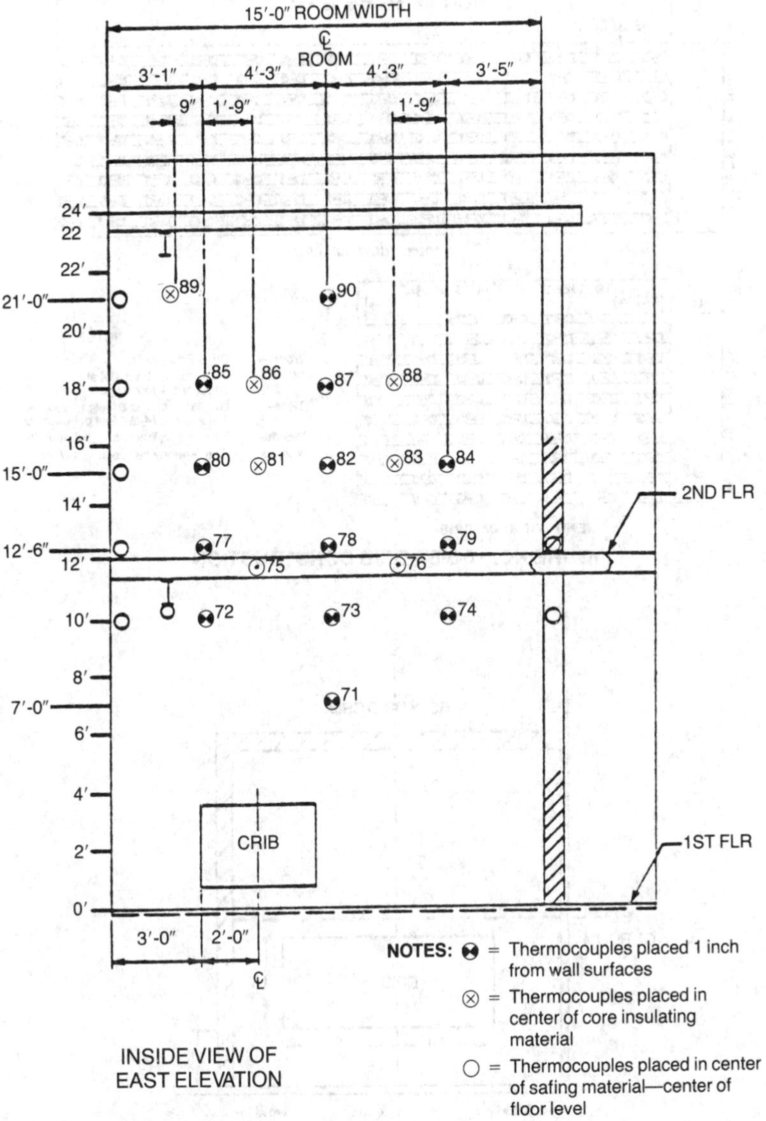
15′-0″ ROOM WIDTH
℄ ROOM
3′-1″
4′-3″
4′-3″
3′-5″
9″
1′-9″
1′-9″
24′
22
22′
21′-0″
20′
18′
16′
15′-0″
14′
12′-6″
12′
10′
8′
7′-0″
6′
4′
2′
0′
89
90
85
86
87
88
80
81
82
83
84
77
78
79
75
76
72
73
74
71
CRIB
2ND FLR
1ST FLR
3′-0″
2′-0″
℄
NOTES: = Thermocouples placed 1 inch from wall surfaces
= Thermocouples placed in center of core insulating material
= Thermocouples placed in center of safing material—center of floor level
INSIDE VIEW OF EAST ELEVATION

FIGURE NO. 17-6-7—THERMOCOUPLE LOCATIONS

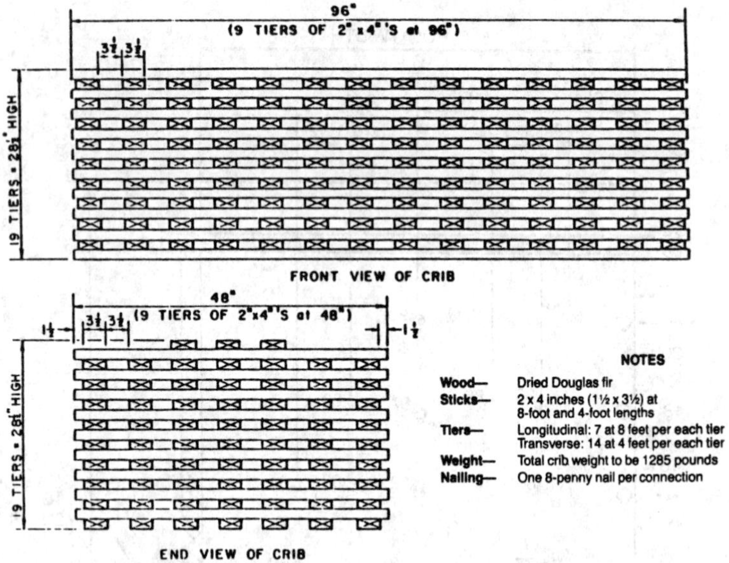
96"
(9 TIERS OF 2"x4"'S at 96")
3½ 3½
19 TIERS = 28½" HIGH
FRONT VIEW OF CRIB
48"
(9 TIERS OF 2"x4"'S at 48")
3½ 3½
1½
1½
19 TIERS = 28½" HIGH
END VIEW OF CRIB
NOTES
Wood— Dried Douglas fir
Sticks— 2 x 4 inches (1½ x 3½) at 8-foot and 4-foot lengths
Tiers— Longitudinal: 7 at 8 feet per each tier
Transverse: 14 at 4 feet per each tier
Weight— Total crib weight to be 1285 pounds
Nailing— One 8-penny nail per connection

FIGURE NO. 17-6-8—CRIB CONSTRUCTION

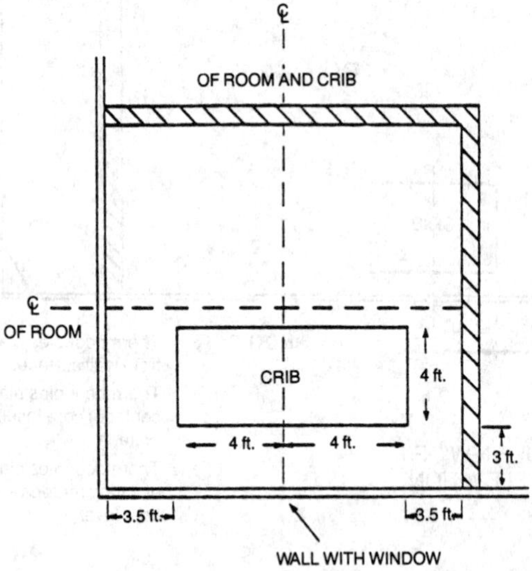
℄
OF ROOM AND CRIB
℄
OF ROOM
CRIB
4 ft.
4 ft.
4 ft.
3 ft.
3.5 ft.
3.5 ft.
WALL WITH WINDOW

FIGURE NO. 17-6-9—PLACEMENT OF CRIB IN ROOM

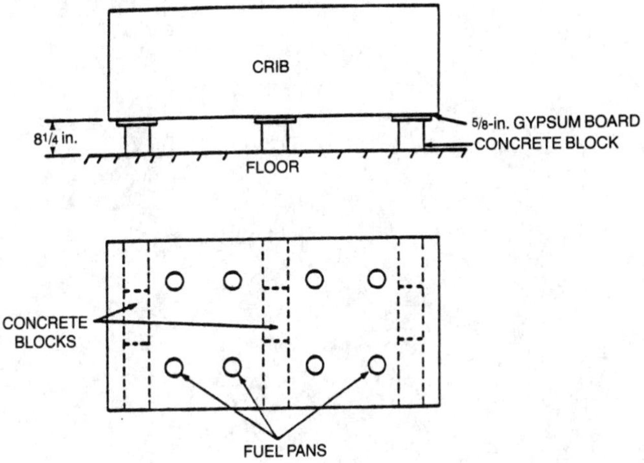
CRIB
8¼ in.
5/8-in. GYPSUM BOARD
CONCRETE BLOCK
FLOOR
CONCRETE BLOCKS
FUEL PANS

FIGURE NO. 17-6-10—CRIB ARRANGEMENT

UNIFORM BUILDING CODE STANDARD NO. 18-1

FIRE ALARM AND STANDBY POWER GENERATING SYSTEMS FOR HIGH-RISE BUILDINGS

Installation Standard of the International Conference of Building Officials

See Sections 1807 (i) and Appendix Section 716 of the Uniform Building Code

Sec. 18.101. This standard outlines requirements governing the installation of fire alarm and standby power generating systems in high-rise buildings where such systems are required by the provisions of Section 1807 or 1907 of the Uniform Building Code.

Fire Alarms

Sec. 18.102. (a) **Operating Characteristics.** 1. **General.** The fire alarm system shall be an approved, electrically supervised direct wire, radio or combination thereof consisting of an interior fire alarm and voice communication system.

2. **Visual signals.** The system's design shall be so arranged that the operation of any station or detector will identify its location at the central control station and at any other location designated by the fire department. This identification signal shall be accompanied by a visual information display at the central control station, which shall be manually resettable from the central control station.

3. **Audible signal.** Audible signal devices indicating operation of the fire alarm signal system shall also be provided at the central control station and at any other location designated by the fire department. Provisions shall be made for silencing the audible signal and transferring this signal to lamp indication.

4. **Automatic alarm operation.** Automatic alarm systems shall be operable by the actuation of approved fire or smoke detecting equipment located upon the ceiling (or on the walls near the ceiling) and spaced in accordance with the terms of their approval.

5. **Detector interconnection.** The activation of detectors installed at location required by Section 1807 (d) of the Uniform Building Code shall cause the voice alarm signal system to operate in accordance with Section 1807 (e) of the Uniform Building Code and this standard. Such activation shall also operate the visual information display in the central control station required by Section 1807 (f) of the Uniform Building Code.

6. **Equipment.** All equipment for the alarm system shall be approved for that particular purpose.

(b) **Location and Installation.** 1. **General.** A manual fire alarm sending station shall be located adjacent to each exit door into a stairway shaft and at each elevator lobby. Additional stations shall be installed so that no point on any floor shall be more than 200 feet (measured in the line of travel) from the nearest station.

2. **Identification.** Doors of manual fire alarm sending stations shall be of an approved design, readily identifiable and simple in operation. Instructions for operating the station shall be permanently affixed or be an integral part of the station. Designation number of station shall be prominently displayed on an instruction card or on the cover of the station.

3. **Testing.** Provisions shall be made for a silent test of manual fire alarm sending-station mechanisms without operating the signaling devices. Such test devices shall be designed to prevent any person, except those in authority, from operating the same and to prevent the possibility of the box being left inoperative after the test.

4. **Alarm sounding devices.** Approved speakers shall be provided as the sounding devices The alarm sound shall be a vocal signal of intelligible instructions. The speakers

shall be located not more than 10 feet from the entrance to each required exit and at other designated locations so as to ensure proper coverage of the audible voice signal. Speakers shall not be mounted more than 20 feet above floor.

5. **Wiring.** All wiring for fire alarm systems shall be installed in an approved manner in conformance with approved nationally recognized standards for fire alarm systems. It shall be properly identified or marked and protected to avoid interruption of service.

(c) **Condition of Approval.** Prior to the installation of any equipent or wiring for a fire alarm system, complete plans, details, design data and other information shall be submitted to and approved by the building official.

(d) **Tests.** Upon completion of the installation, tests demonstrating adequate performance of the system shall be made a requirement by the building official.

(e) **Power Supply.** The fire alarm system shall have at least two sources of power supply. The primary supply shall be a commercial or municipal power and light service. The secondary power supply shall be an approved standby power generation system conforming to the provisions specified in Section 1807 (i) of the Uniform Building Code and this standard.

Standby Power Generating System

Sec. 18.103. (a) **General.** On-site standby power generating systems shall be installed in accordance with Section 1807 of the Uniform Building Code, this section and the Electrical Code.

(b) **Wiring and Transfer Equipment.** Wiring and transfer equipment shall be designed and installed to prevent the inadvertent interconnection of normal and standby supply in any operation of the transfer equipment. The wiring of this system may occupy the same raceways, boxes, cabinets and panelboards with other wiring but shall not occupy the same raceways, boxes or cabinets as wiring for emergency sytems listed in Section 1807 (i), Item 3.

(c) **Testing.** The standby power generating system shall be tested after installation and periodically thereafter on the schedule approved by the fire department.

UNIFORM BUILDING CODE STANDARD NO. 24-1

BUILDING BRICK, FACING BRICK AND HOLLOW BRICK (MADE FROM CLAY OR SHALE)

Based on Standard Specifications C 62-87, C 216-86 and C 652-87a of the American Society for Testing and Materials. Extracted, with permission, from the Annual Book of ASTM Standards, copyright American Society for Testing and Materials, 1916 Race Street, Philadelphia, PA 19103.

See Section 2402 (b) 4, Uniform Building Code

Scope

Sec. 24.101. (a) **General.** This standard covers brick made from clay or shale and subjected to heat treatment at elevated temperatures (firing), and intended for use in brick masonry. In addition, this standard covers dimension and distortion tolerances for facing brick to be used in load-bearing or shear walls.

(b) **Definition. BRICK** is a solid clay masonry unit.

(c) **Grades.** Three grades of brick are covered.

Grade SW. Brick intended for use where a high and uniform degree of resistance to disintegration by weathering is desired and the exposure is such that the brick may be frozen when saturated with water.

Grade MW. Brick intended for use where it may be exposed to temperatures below freezing and the units are unlikely to be saturated with water or where a moderate degree of resistance to frost action is permissible.

Grade NW. Brick intended for use as backup or interior masonry; or, if exposed, for use where no frost action occurs; or if frost action occurs, where the annual precipitation is less than 20 inches.

(d) **Grade Requirements for Face Exposure.** The selection of the grade of brick for face exposure of vertical or horizontal surfaces shall conform to Table No. 24-1-A and Figure No. 24-1-1.

Physical Properties

Sec. 24.102. (a) **Durability.** The brick shall conform to the physical requirements for the grade specified, as prescribed in Table No. 24-1-B.

(b) **Substitution of Grades.** Grades SW and MW may be used in lieu of Grade NW, and Grade SW in lieu of Grade MW.

(c) **Waiver of Saturation Coefficient.** The saturation coefficient shall be waived provided the average cold-water absorption of a random sample of five bricks does not exceed 8 percent, no more than one brick of the sample exceeds 8 percent and its cold-water absorption must be less than 10 percent.

(d) **Freezing and Thawing.** The requirements specified in this standard for water absorption (five-hour boiling) and saturation coefficient shall be waived, provided a sample of five bricks, meeting all other requirements, complies with the following requirements when subjected to 50 cycles of the freezing-and-thawing test:

Grade SW	No breakage and not greater than 0.5 percent loss in dry weight of any individual brick.

Brick is not required to conform to the provisions of this section, and these do not apply unless the sample fails to conform to the requirements for absorption and saturation coefficient prescribed in Table No. 24-1-B or the absorption requirements in Section 24.102 (c).

A particular lot or shipment shall be given the same grading as a previously tested lot, without repeating the freezing-and-thawing test, provided the brick is made by the same manufacturer from similar raw materials and by the same method of forming; and provided also that a sample of five bricks selected from the particular lot has an average and individual minimum strength not less than a previously graded sample, and has average and individual maximum water absorption and saturation coefficient not greater than those of the previously tested sample graded according to the freezing-and-thawing test.

(e) **Waiver of Durability Requirements.** If brick is intended for use exposed to weather where the weathering index is less than 50 (see Figure No. 24-1-1), unless otherwise specified, the requirements given in Section 24.102 (a) for water absorption (five-hour boiling) and for saturation coefficient shall be waived and a minimum average strength of 2,500 pounds per square inch shall apply.

Size, Coring and Frogging

Sec. 24.103. (a) **Tolerances on Dimensions.** The maximum permissible variation in dimensions of individual units shall not exceed those given in Table No. 24-1-C.

(b) **Coring.** The net cross-sectional area of cored brick in any plane parallel to the bearing surface shall be at least 75 percent of the gross cross-sectional area measured in the same plane. No part of any hole shall be less than $^3/_4$ inch from any edge of the brick.

(c) **Frogging.** One bearing face of each brick may have a recess or panel (frog) not exceeding $^3/_8$ inch in depth, except that in brick containing deep frogs any cross section through the frogs parallel to the bearing surface shall conform to the requirements of subsection (b). No part of the recess shall be less than $^3/_4$ inch from any edge of the brick.

Visual Inspection

Sec. 24.104. (a) The brick shall be free of defects, deficiencies and surface treatments, including coatings, that would interfere with the proper setting of the brick or significantly impair the strength or performance of the construction.

(b) Minor indentations or surface cracks incidental to the usual method of manufacture, or the chipping resulting from the customary methods of handling in shipment and delivery should not be deemed grounds for rejection.

Sampling and Testing

Sec. 24.105. The brick shall be sampled and tested in accordance with U.B.C. Standard No. 24-24.

Facing Brick

Sec. 24.106. (a) **General.** Facing brick shall be of Grade SW or MW and shall comply with the degree of mechanical perfection and size variations specified in this section. Grade SW may be used in lieu of Grade MW.

(b) **Types.** Three types of facing brick are covered:

Type FBS. Brick for general use in exposed exterior and interior masonry walls and partitions where wider color ranges and greater variation in sizes are permitted than are specified for Type FBX.

Type FBX. Brick for general use in exposed exterior and interior masonry walls and partitions where a high degree of mechanical perfection, narrow color range, and minimum permissible variation in size are required.

Type FBA. Brick manufactured and selected to produce characteristic architectural effects resulting from nonuniformity in size, color and texture of individual units.

When the type is not specified, the requirements for Type FBS shall govern.

(c) **Tolerances on Dimensions.** The brick shall not depart from the specified size to be used by more than the individual tolerance for the type specified set forth in Table No. 24-1-B. Tolerances on dimensions for Type FBA shall be as specified by the purchaser.

(d) **Warpage.** Tolerances for distortion or warpage of face or edges of individual brick from a plane surface and from a straight line, respectively, shall not exceed the maximum for the type specified as set forth in Table No. 24-1-E. Tolerances on distortion for Type FBA shall be as specified by the purchaser.

(e) **Coring.** Brick may be cored. The net cross-sectional area of cored brick in any plane parallel to the bearing surface shall be at least 75 percent of the gross cross-sectional area measured in the same plane. No part of any hole shall be less than $^3/_4$ inch from any edge of the brick.

(f) **Frogging.** One bearing face of each brick may have a recess or panel (frog) not exceeding $^3/_8$ inch in depth, except that in brick containing deep frogs, any cross section through the frogs parallel to the bearing surface shall conform to the requirements of Section 24.106 (d). No part of the recess shall be less than $^3/_4$ inch from any edge of the brick.

(g) **Visual Inspection.** In addition to the requirements of Section 24.104, brick used in exposed wall construction shall have faces which are free of cracks or other imperfections detracting from the appearance of the designated sample when viewed from a distance of 15 feet for Type FBX and a distance of 20 feet for Types FBS and FBA.

Hollow Brick

Sec. 24.107. (a) **General.** Hollow brick shall be of Grade SW or MW and comply with the physical requirements in Table No. 24-1-B and other requirements of this section. Grade SW may be used in lieu of Grade MW.

(b) **Definitions. HOLLOW BRICK** is a clay masonry unit whose net cross-sectional area (solid area) in any plane parallel to the bearing surface is less than 75 percent of its gross cross-sectional area measured in the same plane.

CORES are void spaces having a gross cross-sectional area equal to or less than $1^1/_2$ square inches.

CELLS are void spaces having a gross cross-sectional area greater than $1^1/_2$ square inches.

(c) **Types.** Four types of hollow brick are covered:

Type HBS. Hollow brick for general use in exposed exterior and interior masonry walls and partitions where wider color ranges and greater variation in size are permitted than is specified for Type HBX.

Types HBX. Hollow brick for general use in exposed exterior and interior masonry walls and partitions where a high degree of mechanical perfection, narrow color range and minimum permissible variation in size are required.

Type HBA. Hollow brick manufactured and selected to produce characteristic architectural effects resulting from nonuniformity in size, color and texture of the individual units.

Types HBB. Hollow brick for general use in masonry walls and partitions where color and texture are not a consideration and a greater variation in size is permitted than is specified for Type HBX.

When the type is not specified, the requirements for Type HBS shall govern.

(d) **Class.** Two classes of hollow brick are covered:

Class H40V. Hollow brick intended for use where void areas or hollow spaces greater than 25 percent, but not greater than 40 percent, of the gross cross-sectional area of the unit measured in any plane parallel to the bearing surface. The void spaces, web thicknesses and shell thicknesses shall comply with the requirements of Section 24.107 (e) and (f).

Class H60V. Hollow brick intended for use where larger void areas are desired. The sum of these void areas shall be greater than 40 percent, but not greater than 60 percent, of the gross cross-sectional area of the unit measured in any plane parallel to the bearing surface. The void spaces, web thicknesses and shell thicknesses shall comply with the requirements of Section 24.107 (e) and (f) and to the minimum requirements of Table No. 24-1-F.

When the class is not specified, the requirements for Class H40V shall govern.

(e) **Hollow Spaces.** Core holes shall not be less than $^5/_8$ inch from any edge of the brick, except for cored-shell hollow brick. Cored-shell hollow brick shall have a minimum shell thickness of $1^1/_2$ inches. Cores greater than 1 square inch in cored shells shall not be less than $^1/_2$ inch from any edge. Cores not greater than 1 square inch in shells cored not more than 35 percent shall not be less than $^3/_8$ inch from any edge.

Cells shall not be less than $^3/_4$ inch from any edge of the brick except for double-shell hollow brick.

Double-shell hollow brick with inner and outer shells not less than $^1/_2$ inch thick may not have cells greater than $^5/_8$ inch in width or 5 inches in length between the inner and outer shell.

(f) **Webs.** The thickness for webs between cells shall not be less than $^1/_2$ inch, $^3/_8$ inch between cells and cores or $^1/_4$ inch between cores. The distance of voids from unexposed edges, which are recessed not less than 1/2 inch, shall not be less than 1/2 inch.

(g) **Frogging.** One bearing face of each brick may have a recess or panel (frog) not exceeding 3/8 inch in depth. No part of the recess shall be less than 5/8 inch from any edge of the brick, except that brick containing deep frogs shall comply with other requirements of Section 24.107 (b) for void area and Section 24.107 (e) for hollow spaces.

(h) **Tolerances on Dimensions.** The hollow brick shall not depart from the specified size by more than the individual tolerance for specified size by more than individual tolerances for the type specified as set forth in Table No. 24-1-G. Tolerances and dimensions for Type HBA shall be as specified by the purchaser.

(i) **Warpage.** Tolerances for distortion or warpage of face or edges of individual hollow brick from a plane surface and from a straight line, respectively, shall not exceed the maximum for the type specified in Table No. 24-1-H. Tolerances on dimensions for Type HBA shall be as specified by the purchaser.

(j) **Visual Inspection.** In addition to the requirements of Section 24.104, brick used in exposed wall construction shall have faces which are free of cracks or other imperfections detracting from the appearance of a sample wall when viewed from a distance of 15 feet for Type HBX and a distance of 20 feet for Types HBS and HBA.

TABLE NO. 24-1-A—GRADE REQUIREMENTS FOR FACE EXPOSURE

EXPOSURE	WEATHERING INDEX		
	Less than 50	50 to 500	500 and greater
In vertical surfaces:			
In contact with earth	MW	SW	SW
Not in contact with earth	MW	SW	SW
In other than vertical surfaces:			
In contact with earth	SW	SW	SW
Not in contact with earth	MW	SW	SW

TABLE NO. 24-1-B—PHYSICAL REQUIREMENTS FOR TYPES OF UNIT MASONRY

TYPE OF MASONRY	GRADE	MINIMUM FACE SHELL THICKNESS (Inches)	MINIMUM[1] COMPRESSIVE STRENGTH PSI AVERAGE GROSS AREA		MAXIMUM WATER ABSORPTION By Five-hour Boiling (percent)		MAXIMUM SATURATION COEFFICIENT[2]		WATER ABSORPTION Maximum Pounds per Cubic Foot	MOISTURE CONTENT Maximum Percentage of Total Absorption	MINIMUM MODULUS OF RUPTURE	
			Average of Five Tests	Individual	Average of Five Tests	Individual	Average of Five Tests	Individual			Average of Five Tests	Individual
			(brick flatwise)								(brick flatwise) psi Average Gross Area	
24-1. Building Brick Made from Clay or Shale[3]	SW		3000	2500	17	20	.78	.80				
	MW		2500	2200	22	25	.88	.90				
	NW		1500	1250	no limit							
			(net area)[4]									
Hollow Brick[3]	SW	See Table No. 24-1-F	3000	2500	17	20	.78	.80				
	MW		2500	2000	22	25	.88	.90				
24-2. Sand-Lime Building Brick	SW		4500	3500							600	400
	MW		2500	2000							450	300
			Based on Net Area (psi)[4]						Based on % of Dry Wt.			
24-14. Unburned Clay Masonry Units			300	250					2.5%	4.0%	50	35

[1]Gross area of a unit shall be determined by multiplying the horizontal face dimension of the unit as placed in the wall by its thickness.

[2]The saturation coefficient is the ratio of absorption by 24-hour submersion in cold water to that after five-hour submersion in boiling water.

[3]If the average cold-water absorption of a random sample of five bricks does not exceed 8.0 percent, when no more than one brick unit of the sample exceeds 8.0 percent and its cold-water absorption must be less than 10.0 percent, the saturation coefficient shall be waived.

[4]Based on net area of a unit which shall be taken as the area of solid material in shells and webs actually carrying stresses in a direction parallel to the direction of loading.

[5]The range in percentage absorption for tile delivered to any one job shall be not more than 12.

TABLE NO. 24-1-C—TOLERANCES ON DIMENSIONS

SPECIFIED DIMENSION	MAXIMUM PERMISSIBLE VARIATION FROM SPECIFIED DIMENSION, PLUS OR MINUS (Inch)
Up to 3, incl.	3/32
Over 3 to 4, incl.	1/8
Over 4 to 6, incl.	3/16
Over 6 to 8, incl.	1/4
Over 8 to 12, incl.	5/16
Over 12 to 16, incl.	3/8

TABLE NO. 24-1-D—TOLERANCES ON DIMENSIONS

SPECIFIED DIMENSION (Inches)	MAXIMUM PERMISSIBLE VARIATION FROM SPECIFIED DIMENSION, PLUS OR MINUS (Inch)	
	Type FBX	Type FBS
3 and under	1/16	3/32
Over 3 to 4, incl.	3/32	1/8
Over 4 to 6, incl.	1/8	3/16
Over 6 to 8, incl.	5/32	1/4
Over 8 to 12, incl.	7/32	5/16
Over 12 to 16, incl.	9/32	3/8

TABLE NO. 24-1-E—TOLERANCES ON DISTORTION

MAXIMUM FACE DIMENSION (Inches)	MAXIMUM PERMISSIBLE DISTORTION (Inch)	
	Type FBX	Type FBS
8 and under	1/16	3/32
Over 8 to 12, incl.	3/32	1/8
Over 12 to 16, incl.	1/8	5/32

TABLE NO. 24-1-F—HOLLOW BRICK (Class H60V) MINIMUM THICKNESS OF FACE SHELLS AND WEBS

NOMINAL WIDTH OF UNIT (Inches)	FACE SHELL THICKNESS (Inches)		END SHELLS OR WEBS (Inches)	WEB THICKNESS PER FOOT, TOTAL (Inches per Foot)[1]
	Solid	Cored or Double Shell		
3 and 4	3/4	—	3/4	15/8
6	1	11/2	1	21/4
8	11/4	11/2	1	21/4
10	13/8	15/8	11/8	21/2
12	11/2	2	11/8	21/2

[1]The sum of the measured thickness of all webs in the unit, multiplied by 12, and divided by the length of the unit. In the case of open-ended units where the open-end portion is solid grouted, the length of that open-ended portion shall be deducted from the overall length of the unit.

TABLE NO. 24-1-G—TOLERANCES ON DIMENSIONS

SPECIFIED DIMENSION (Inches)	MAXIMUM PERMISSIBLE VARIATION FROM SPECIFIED DIMENSION, PLUS OR MINUS (Inch)	
	Type HBX	Type HBS and HBB
3 and under	1/16	3/32
Over 3 to 4, incl.	3/32	1/8
Over 4 to 6, incl.	1/8	3/16
Over 6 to 8, incl.	5/32	1/4
Over 8 to 12, incl.	7/32	5/16
Over 12 to 16, incl.	9/32	3/8

TABLE NO. 24-1-H—TOLERANCES ON DISTORTION

MAXIMUM FACE DIMENSION (Inches)	MAXIMUM PERMISSIBLE DISTORTION (Inch)	
	Type HBX	Type HBS and HBB
8 and under	1/16	3/32
Over 8 to 12, incl.	3/32	1/8
Over 12 to 16, incl.	1/8	5/32

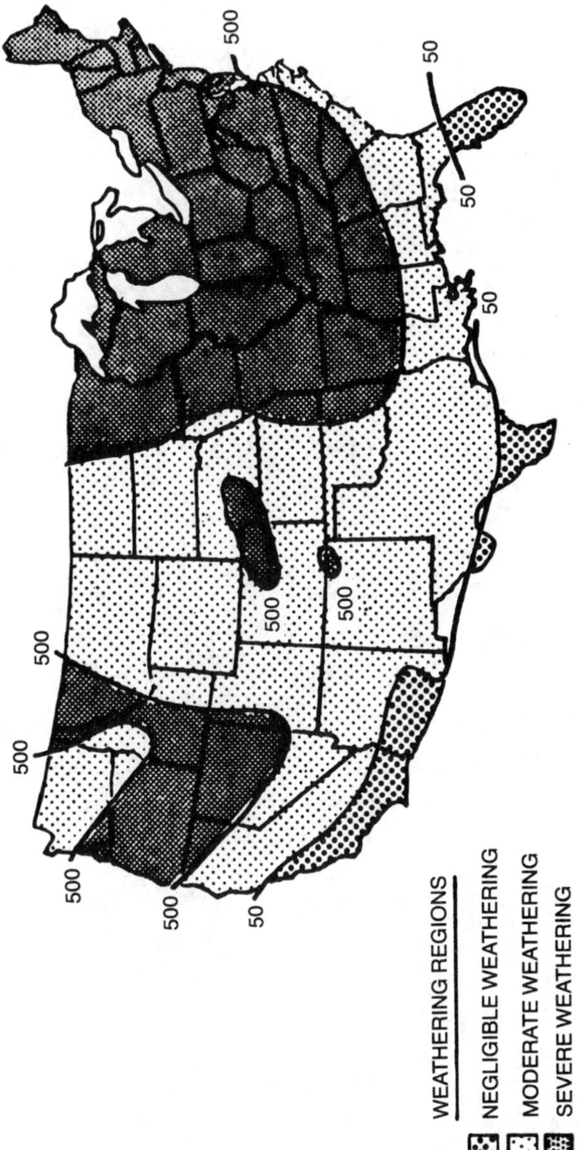
500
500
500
500
500
500
500
50
50
50
50
WEATHERING REGIONS
NEGLIGIBLE WEATHERING
MODERATE WEATHERING
SEVERE WEATHERING

FIGURE NO. 24-1-1—WEATHERING INDEXES IN THE UNITED STATES

UNIFORM BUILDING CODE STANDARD NO. 24-2

CALCIUM SILICATE FACE BRICK (SAND-LIME BRICK)

Based on Standard Specification C 73-75 of the American Society for Testing and Materials. Extracted, with permission, from the Annual Book of ASTM Standards, copyright American Society for Testing and Materials, 1916 Race Street, Philadelphia, PA 19103.

See Section 2402 (b) 6, Uniform Building Code

Scope

Sec. 24.201. (a) **Grades.** This standard covers brick made from sand and lime and intended for use in brick masonry. Two grades of brick are covered:

1. **Grade SW.** Brick intended for use where exposed to temperatures below freezing in the presence of moisture.

2. **Grade MW.** Brick intended for use where exposed to temperature below freezing but unlikely to be saturated with water.

(b) **Definition.** The term "brick" used in this standard shall mean brick or a solid sand-lime masonry unit.

Physical Properties

Sec. 24.202. (a) **Durability.** The brick shall conform to the physical requirements for the grade specified as prescribed in Table No. 24-2-A.

(b) **Substitution of Grades.** Unless otherwise specified, brick of Grade SW shall be accepted in lieu of Grade MW.

Size

Sec. 24.203. The size of the brick shall be as specified by the purchaser, and the average size of brick furnished shall approximate the size specified in the invitation for bids.

No overall dimension (width, height and length) shall differ by more than 1/8 inch from the specified standard dimension. Standard dimensions of units are the manufacturer's designated dimensions.

Visual Inspection

Sec. 24.204. Brick shall pass a visual inspection for soundness, compact structure, reasonably uniform shape, and freedom from the following: cracks, warpage, large pebbles, balls of clay, or particles of lime that would affect the serviceability or strength of the brick.

TABLE NO. 24-2-A
PHYSICAL REQUIREMENTS FOR SAND-LIME BUILDING BRICK

TYPE OF MASONRY	GRADE	MINIMUM COMPRESSIVE STRENGTH PSI AVERAGE GROSS AREA		MINIMUM MODULUS OF RUPTURE (Brick Flatwise) psi Average Gross Area	
		Average of Five Tests	Individual	Average of Five Tests	Individual
Sand-Lime Building Brick	SW	4500	3500	600	400
	MW	2500	2000	450	300

Gross area of a unit shall be determined by multiplying the horizontal face dimension of the unit as placed in the wall by its thickness.

UNIFORM BUILDING CODE STANDARD NO. 24-3
CONCRETE BUILDING BRICK

Based on Standard Specification C 55-75 (1980) of the American Society for Testing and Materials. Extracted, with permission, from the Annual Book of ASTM Standards, copyright American Society for Testing and Materials, 1916 Race Street, Philadelphia, PA 19103.

See Section 2402 (b) 5 of the Uniform Building Code

Scope

Sec. 24.301. This standard covers concrete building brick and similar solid units made from portland cement, water and suitable mineral aggregates with or without the inclusion of other materials.

Classification

Sec. 24.302. (a) **Types.** Two types of concrete brick in each of two grades are covered, as follows:

1. **Type I, moisture-controlled units.** Concrete brick designated as Type I (Grades N-I and S-I) shall conform to all requirements of this standard, including the requirements of Table No. 24-3-A.

2. **Type II, nonmoisture-controlled units.** Concrete brick designated as Type II (Grades N-II and S-II) shall conform to all requirements of this standard except the requirements of Table No. 24-3-A.

(b) **Grades.** Concrete brick manufactured in accordance with this standard shall conform to two grades as follows:

1. **Grade N.** For use as architectural veneer and facing units in exterior walls and for use where high strength and resistance to moisture penetration and severe frost action are desired.

2. **Grade S.** For general use where moderate strength and resistance to frost action and moisture penetration are required.

Materials

Sec. 24.303. (a) **Cementitious Materials.** Materials shall conform to the following applicable U.B.C. Standards:

1. Portland Cement—U.B.C. Standard No. 26-1 modified as follows:

   Limitation on insoluble residue—1.5 percent.

   Limitation on air content of mortar,

   Volume percent—22 percent maximum.

   Limitation on loss on ignition—7 percent maximum.

   Limestone with a minimum 85 percent calcium carbonate ($CaCO_3$) content may be added to the cement, provided the requirements of U.B.C. Standard No. 26-1 as modified above are met.

2. Blended Cements—U.B.C. Standard No. 26-1.

3. Hydrated Lime, Type S—U.B.C. Standard No. 24-18.

(b) **Other Constituents.** Air-entraining agents, coloring pigments, integral water repellents, finely ground silica, etc., shall be previously established as suitable for use in concrete or shall be shown by test or experience not to be detrimental to the durability of the concrete.

Physical Requirements

Sec. 24.304. At the time of delivery to the work site the concrete brick shall conform to the physical requirements prescribed in Table No. 24-3-B.

The moisture content of Type I concrete brick at the time of delivery shall conform to the requirements prescribed in Table No. 24-3-A.

Dimensions and Permissible Variations

Sec. 24.305. Overall dimensions (width, height, or length) shall not differ by more than $^1/_8$ inch from the specified standard dimensions.

NOTE: Standard dimensions of concrete brick are the manufacturer's designated dimensions. Nominal dimensions of modular size concrete brick are equal to the standard dimensions plus $^3/_8$ inch, the thickness of one standard mortar joint. Nominal dimensions of nonmodular size concrete brick usually exceed the standard dimensions by $^1/_8$ to $^1/_4$ inch.

Variations in thickness of architectural units such as split-faced or slumped units will usually vary from the specified tolerances.

Visual Inspection

Sec. 24.306. (a) **General.** All concrete brick shall be sound and free of cracks or other defects that would interfere with the proper placing of the unit or impair the strength or permanence of the construction. Minor cracks incidental to the usual method of manufacture, or minor chipping resulting from customary methods of handling in shipment and delivery, shall not be deemed grounds for rejection.

(b) **Brick in Exposed Walls.** Where concrete brick are to be used in exposed wall construction, the face or faces that are to be exposed shall be free of chips, cracks or other imperfections when viewed from 20 feet, except that if not more than 5 percent of a shipment contains slight cracks or small chips not larger than $^1/_2$ inch, this shall not be deemed grounds for rejection.

TABLE NO. 24-3-A—MOISTURE CONTENT REQUIREMENTS FOR TYPE I CONCRETE BRICK

LINEAR SHRINKAGE, PERCENT	MOISTURE CONTENT, MAX. PERCENT OF TOTAL ABSORPTION (Average of 3 Concrete Brick)		
	Humidity[1] Conditions at Jobsite or Point of Use		
	Humid	Intermediate	Arid
0.03 or less	45	40	35
From 0.03 to 0.045	40	35	30
0.045 to 0.065, max.	35	30	25

[1]Arid—Average annual relative humidity less than 50 percent.
Intermediate—Average annual relative humidity 50-75 percent.
Humid—Average annual relative humidity above 75 percent.

TABLE NO. 24-3-B—STRENGTH AND ABSORPTION REQUIREMENTS

COMPRESSIVE STRENGTH, MIN., psi (Concrete Brick Tested Flatwise)			WATER ABSORPTION, MAX, (Avg. of 3 Brick) WITH OVEN-DRY WEIGHT OF CONCRETE Lb./Ft.^{3}		
Average Gross Area			Weight Classification		
Grade	Avg. of 3 Concrete Brick	Individual Concrete Brick	Lightweight Less Than 105	Medium Weight Less Than 125 to 105	Normal Weight 125 or More
N-I	3500	3000	15	13	10
N-II	3500	3000	15	13	10
S-I	2500	2000	18	15	13
S-II	2500	2000	18	15	13

UNIFORM BUILDING CODE STANDARD NO. 24-4

HOLLOW AND SOLID LOAD-BEARING CONCRETE MASONRY UNITS

Based on Standard Specification C 90-86 of the American Society for Testing and Materials. Extracted, with permission, from the Annual Book of ASTM Standards, copyright American Society for Testing and Materials, 1916 Race Street, Philadelphia, PA 19103.

Scope

Sec. 24.401. This standard covers solid (units with 75 percent or more net area) and hollow load-bearing concrete masonry units made from portland cement, water and mineral aggregates with or without the inclusion of other materials.

Classification

Sec. 24.402. (a) **Grades.** Concrete masonry units manufactured in accordance with this standard shall conform to two grades as follows:

1. **Grade N.** Units having a weight classification of 85 pcf or greater, for general use such as in exterior walls below and above grade that may or may not be exposed to moisture penetration or the weather and for interior walls and backup.

2. **Grade S.** Units having a weight classification of less than 85 pcf, for uses limited to above grade installation in exterior walls with weather-protective coatings and in walls not exposed to the weather.

(b) **Types.** Two types of concrete masonry units in each of two grades are covered as follows:

1. **Type I, moisture-controlled units.** Units designated as Type I (Grades N-I and S-I) shall conform to all requirements of this standard including the moisture content requirements of Table No. 24-4-A.

2. **Type II, nonmoisture-controlled units.** Units designated as Type II (Grades N-II and S-II) shall conform to all requirements of this standard except the moisture content requirements of Table No. 24-4-A.

Materials

Sec. 24.403. (a) **Cementitious Materials.** Materials shall conform to the following applicable standards:

1. Portland Cement—U.B.C. Standard No. 26-1 modified as follows:

   Limitation on insoluble residue—1.5 percent maximum.

   Limitation on air content of mortar,

   Volume percent—22 percent maximum.

   Limitation on loss on ignition—7 percent maximum.

   Limestone with a minimum 85 percent calcium carbonate ($CaCO_3$) content may be added to the cement, provided the requirements of U.B.C. Standard No. 26-1 as modified above are met.

2. Blended Cements—U.B.C. Standard No. 26-1.

3. Hydrated Lime, Type S—U.B.C. Standard No. 24-18.

(b) **Other Constituents.** Air-entraining agents, coloring pigments, integral water repellents, finely ground silica, etc., shall be previously established as suitable for use in concrete or shall be shown by test or experience to not be detrimental to the durability of the concrete.

Physical Requirements

Sec. 24.404. At the time of delivery to the work site the units shall conform to the physical requirements prescribed in Table No. 24-4-B. The moisture content of Type I concrete masonry units at time of delivery shall conform to the requirements prescribed in Table No. 24-4-A.

Minimum Face-shell and Web Thicknesses

Sec. 24.405. Face-shell (FST) and web (WT) thicknesses shall conform to the requirements listed in Table No. 24-4-C.

Permissible Variations in Dimensions

Sec. 24.406. (a) **Precision Units.** For precision units, no overall dimension (width, height and length) shall differ by more than $^1/_8$ inch from the specified standard dimensions.

(b) **Particular Feature Units.** For particular feature units, dimensions shall be in accordance with the following:

1. For molded face units, no overall dimension (width, height and length) shall differ by more than $^1/_8$ inch from the specified standard dimension. Dimensions of molded features (ribs, scores, hex-shapes, patterns, etc.) shall be within $^1/_{16}$ inch of the specified standard dimensions and shall be within $^1/_{16}$ inch of the specified placement of the unit.

2. For split-faced units, all non-split overall dimensions (width, height and length) shall differ by no more than $^1/_8$ inch from the specified standard dimensions. On faces that are split, overall dimensions will vary. Local suppliers should be consulted to determine dimensional tolerances achievable.

3. For slumped units, no overall height dimension shall differ by more than $^1/_8$ inch from the specified standard dimension. On faces that are slumped, overall dimensions will vary. Local suppliers should be consulted to determine dimension tolerances achievable.

NOTE: Standard dimensions of units are the manufacturer's designated dimensions. Nominal dimensions of modular size units, except slumped units, are equal to the standard dimensions plus $^3/_8$ inch, the thickness of one standard mortar joint. Slumped units are equal to the standard dimensions plus $^1/_2$ inch, the thickness of one standard mortar joint. Nominal dimensions of nonmodular size units usually exceed the standard dimensions by $^1/_8$ to $^1/_4$ inch.

Visual Inspection

Sec. 24.407. All units shall be sound and free of cracks or other defects that would interfere with the proper placing of the unit or impair the strength or permanence of the construction. Units may have minor cracks incidental to the usual method of manufacture, or minor chipping resulting from customary methods of handling in shipment and delivery.

Units that are intended to serve as a base for plaster or stucco shall have a sufficiently rough surface to afford a good bond.

Where units are to be used in exposed wall construction, the face or faces that are to be exposed shall be free of chips, cracks or other imperfections when viewed from 20 feet, except that not more than 5 percent of a shipment may have slight cracks or small chips not larger than 1 inch.

TABLE NO. 24-4-A—MOISTURE CONTENT REQUIREMENTS FOR TYPE I UNITS

LINEAR SHRINKAGE, PERCENT	MOISTURE CONTENT, MAX. PERCENT OF TOTAL ABSORPTION (Average of 3 Units) — Humidity Conditions at Jobsite or Point of Use: Humid[1]	Intermediate[2]	Arid[3]
0.03 or less	45	40	35
From 0.03 to 0.045	40	35	30
0.045 to 0.065, max.	35	30	25

[1]Average annual relative humidity above 75 percent.

[2]Average annual relative humidity 50 to 75 percent.

[3]Average annual relative humidity less than 50 percent.

TABLE NO. 24-4-B—STRENGTH AND ABSORPTION REQUIREMENTS

COMPRESSIVE STRENGTH, MIN., psi			WATER ABSORPTION, MAX., (Avg. of 3 units) WITH OVEN-DRY WEIGHT OF CONCRETE Lb./Cu. Ft.			
Average Net Area			Weight Classification			
			Lightweight		Medium Weight	Normal Weight
Grade	Avg. of 3 Units	Individual Unit	Less than 85	Less than 105	Less than 125 to 105	125 or more
N-I	1900	1500	—	18	15	13
N-II	1900	1500	—	18	15	13
S-I[1]	1300	1100	20	—	—	—
S-II[1]	1300	1100	20	—	—	—

[1]Limited to use above grade in exterior walls with weather-protective coatings and in walls not exposed to the weather.

NOTE: To prevent water penetration, protective coating should be applied on the exterior face of basement walls and when required on the face of exterior walls above grade.

TABLE NO. 24-4-C—MINIMUM THICKNESS OF FACE-SHELLS AND WEBS

NOMINAL WIDTH (W) OF UNITS, In.	FACE-SHELL THICKNESS (FST) MIN., In.[1] [4]	WEB THICKNESS (WT.)	
		Webs[1] Min., In.	Equivalent Web Thickness, Min. In./Lin.Ft.[2]
3 and 4	3/4	3/4	1 5/8
6	1	1	2 1/4
8	1 1/4	1	2 1/4
10	1 3/8 1 1/4[3]	1 1/8	2 1/2
12	1 1/2 1 1/4[3]	1 1/8	2 1/2

[1]Average of measurements on three units taken at the thinnest point.

[2]Sum of the measured thickness of all webs in the unit, multiplied by 12, and divided by the length of the unit. In the case of open-ended units where the open-ended porton is solid grouted, the length of that open-ended portion shall be deducted from the overall length of the unit.

[3]This face-shell thickness (FST) is applicable where allowable design load is reduced in proportion to the reduction in thicknesses shown, except that allowable design load on solid-grouted units shall not be reduced.

[4]For split-faced units, a maximum of 10 percent of a shipment may have face-shell thicknesses less than those shown, but in no case less than 3/4 inch.

UNIFORM BUILDING CODE STANDARD NO. 24-6

NONLOAD-BEARING CONCRETE MASONRY UNITS

Based on Standard Specification C 129-75 (1980) of the American Society for Testing and Materials. Extracted, with permission, from the Annual Book of ASTM Standards, copyright American Society for Testing and Materials, 1916 Race Street, Philadelphia, PA 19103.

See Section 2402 (b) 5, Uniform Building Code

Scope

Sec. 24.601. This standard covers hollow and solid nonload-bearing concrete masonry units made from portland cement, water, and mineral aggregates with or without the inclusion of other materials. Such units are intended for use in nonload-bearing partitions but under certain conditions may be suitable for use in nonload-bearing exterior walls above grade, where effectively protected from the weather.

Classification

Sec. 24.602. (a) **Weight Classifications.** Nonload-bearing concrete masonry units manufactured in accordance with this standard shall conform to one of three weight classifications and two types as follows:

WEIGHT CLASSIFICATION	OVEN-DRY WEIGHT OF CONCRETE lb./cu.ft.
Lightweight	105 max.
Medium weight	105 - 125
Normal weight	125 min.

(b) **Types.** Nonload-bearing concrete masonry units shall be of two types as follows:

1. **Type I, moisture-controlled units.** Type I units shall conform to all requirements of this standard, including the requirements of Table No. 24-6-A.

2. **Type II, nonmoisture-controlled units.** Type II units shall conform to all requirements of this standard, except the requirements listed in Table No. 24-6-A.

Materials

Sec. 24.603. (a) **Cementitious Materials.** Cementitious materials shall conform to the following applicable U.B.C. standards:

1. Portland Cement—U.B.C. Standard No. 26-1 modified as follows:

   Limitation on insoluble residue—1.5 percent.

   Limitation on air content of mortar,

   Volume percent—22 percent maximum.

   Limitation on loss on ignition—7 percent maximum.

   Limestone with a minimum 85 percent calcium carbonate ($CaCO_3$) content may be added to the cement, provided the requirements of U.B.C. Standard No. 26-1 as modified above are met.

2. Blended Cements—U.B.C. Standard No. 26-1.
3. Hydrated Lime, Type S—U.B.C. Standard No. 24-18.

(b) **Other Constituents.** Air-entraining agents, coloring pigments, integral water repellents, finely ground silica, etc., shall be previously established as suitable for use in concrete or shall be shown by test or experience not to be detrimental to the durability of the concrete.

Physical Requirements

Sec. 24.604. At the time of delivery to the work site the units shall conform to the strength requirements prescribed in Table No. 24-6-B.

The moisture content of Type I concrete masonry units at the time of delivery shall conform to the requirements prescribed in Table No. 24-6-A.

Dimensions and Permissible Variations

Sec. 24.605. Minimum face-shell thickness shall not be less than $^1/_2$ inch.

No overall dimension (width, height or length) shall differ by more than $^1/_8$ inch from the specified standard dimensions.

NOTE: Standard dimensions of units are the manufacturer's designated dimensions. Nominal dimensions of modular size units are equal to the standard dimensions plus $^3/_8$ inch, the thickness of one standard mortar joint. Nominal dimensions of nonmodular size units usually exceed the standard dimensions by $^1/_8$ to $^1/_4$ inch.

Variations in thickness of architectural units such as split-faced or slumped units will usually exceed the specified tolerances.

Visual Inspection

Sec. 24.606. (a) **General.** All units shall be sound and free of cracks or other defects that would interfere with the proper placing of the units or impair the strength or permanence of the construction. Units may have minor cracks incidental to the usual method of manufacture, or minor chipping resulting from customary methods of handling in shipment and delivery.

(b) **Exposed Units.** Where units are to be used in exposed wall construction, the face or faces that are to be exposed shall be free of chips, cracks or other imperfections when viewed from 20 feet, except that not more than 5 percent of a shipment may have slight cracks or small chips not larger than 1 inch.

(c) **Identification.** Nonloading concrete masonry units shall be clearly marked in a manner to preclude their use as load-bearing units.

TABLE NO. 24-6-A—MOISTURE CONTENT REQUIREMENTS FOR TYPE I UNITS

LINEAR SHRINKAGE, PERCENT	MOISTURE CONTENT, MAX. PERCENT OF TOTAL ABSORPTION (Average of 3 Units)		
	Humidity[1] Conditions at Jobsite or Point of Use		
	Humid	Intermediate	Arid
0.03 or less	45	40	35
From 0.03 to 0.045	40	35	30
0.045 to 0.065, max.	35	30	25

[1]Arid—Average annual relative humidity less than 50 percent.
Intermediate—Average annual relative humidity 50 to 75 percent.
Humid—Average annual relative humidity above 75 percent.

TABLE NO. 24-6-B—STRENGTH REQUIREMENTS

	COMPRESSIVE STRENGTH (Average Net Area) Min., psi
Average of 3 units	600
Individual units	500

UNIFORM BUILDING CODE STANDARD NO. 24-7

IN-PLACE MASONRY SHEAR TESTS

Test Standard of the International Conference of Building Officials

See Appendix Chapter 1, Sections A106 (c) 3 and A107 (b), Uniform Code for Building Conservation

Scope

Sec. 24.701. This standard applies when the Uniform Code for Building Conservation requires in-place testing of the quality of masonry mortar.

Preparation of Sample

Sec. 24.702. The bed joints of the outer wythe of the masonry shall be tested in shear by laterally displacing a single brick relative to the adjacent bricks in the same wythe. The head joint opposite the loaded end of the test brick shall be carefully excavated and cleared. The brick adjacent to the loaded end of the test brick shall be carefully removed by sawing or drilling and excavating to provide space for a hydraulic ram and steel loading blocks.

Application of Load and Determination of Results

Sec. 24.703. Steel blocks, the size of the end of the brick, shall be used on each end of the ram to distribute the load to the brick. The blocks shall not contact the mortar joints. The load shall be applied horizontally, in the plane of the wythe, until either a crack can be seen or slip occurs. The strength of the mortar shall be calculated by dividing the load at the first cracking or movement of the test brick by the nominal gross area of the sum of the two bed joints.

UNIFORM BUILDING CODE STANDARD NO. 24-8

TESTS OF ANCHORS IN UNREINFORCED MASONRY WALLS

Test Standard of the International Conference of Building Officials

See Appendix Chapter 1, Section A107 (c) and (d), Uniform Code for Building Conservation

Scope

Sec. 24.801. Shear and tension anchors in existing masonry construction shall be tested in accordance with this standard when required by the Uniform Code for Building Conservation.

Existing Anchors

Sec. 24.802. The test apparatus shall be supported by the masonry wall. The distance between the anchor and the test apparatus support shall not be less than the wall thickness. Existing wall anchors shall be given a preload of 300 pounds prior to establishing a datum for recording elongation. The tension test load reported shall be recorded at $^1/_8$-inch relative movement of the anchor and the adjacent masonry surface. Results of all tests shall be reported. The report shall include the test results as related to the wall thickness and joist orientation.

Combined Shear and Tension Bolts

Sec. 24.803. Combined shear and tension bolts embedded in unreinforced masonry walls shall be tested using a torque-calibrated wrench to the following minimum torques:

$^1/_2$-inch-diameter bolts—40 foot pounds

$^5/_8$-inch-diameter bolts—50 foot pounds

$^3/_4$-inch-diameter bolts—60 foot pounds

All nuts shall be installed over malleable iron or plate washers when bearing on wood and heavy cut washers when bearing on steel.

UNIFORM BUILDING CODE STANDARD NO. 24-9

POINTING OF UNREINFORCED MASONRY WALLS

Construction Specification of the International Conference of Building Officials

See Appendix Chapter 1, Section A106 (c) 3 B, Uniform Code for Building Conservation

Scope

Sec. 24.901. Pointing of deteriorated mortar joints when required by the Uniform Code for Building Conservation shall be in accordance with this standard.

Joint Preparation

Sec. 24.902. The old or deteriorated mortar joint shall be cut out, by means of a toothing chisel or nonimpact power tool, to a uniform depth of $^3/_4$ inch until sound mortar is reached. Care shall be taken not to damage the brick edges. After cutting is complete, all loose material shall be removed with a brush, air or water stream.

Mortar Preparation

Sec. 24.903. The mortar mix shall be Type N or Type S proportioned as required by the construction specifications. The pointing mortar shall be prehydrated by first thoroughly mixing all ingredients dry and then mixing again, adding only enough water to produce a damp unworkable mix which will retain its form when pressed into a ball. The mortar shall be kept in a damp condition for one and one-half hours; then sufficient water shall be added to bring it to a consistency that is somewhat drier than conventional masonry mortar.

Packing

Sec. 24.904. The joint into which the mortar is to be packed shall be damp but without freestanding water. The mortar shall be tightly packed into the joint in layers not exceeding $^1/_4$ inch in depth until it is filled; then it shall be tooled to a smooth surface to match the original profile.

UNIFORM BUILDING CODE STANDARD NO. 24-14

UNBURNED CLAY MASONRY UNITS AND STANDARD METHODS OF SAMPLING AND TESTING UNBURNED CLAY MASONRY UNITS

Test Standard of the International Conference of Building Officials

See Section 2402 (b) 6, Uniform Building Code

Part I—Unburned Clay Masonry

Scope

Sec. 24.1401. This standard covers unburned clay masonry units made from a suitable mixture of soil, clay and stabilizing agent, and intended for use in brick masonry.

Composition of Units

Sec. 24.1402. (a) **Soil.** The soil used shall contain not less than 25 percent and not more than 45 percent of material passing a No. 200 mesh sieve. The soil shall contain sufficient clay to bind the particles together, but shall contain not more than 0.2 percent of water-soluble salts.

(b) **Stabilizer.** The stabilizing agent shall be emulsified asphalt. The stabilizing agent shall be uniformly mixed with the soil in amounts sufficient to provide the required resistance to absorption.

Physical Requirements

Sec. 24.1401. The units shall conform to the physical requirements prescribed in Table No. 24-1-B.

Shrinkage Cracks

Sec. 24.1404. No units shall contain more than three shrinkage cracks, and no shrinkage crack shall exceed 3 inches in length or ⅛ inch in width.

Part II—Sampling and Testing of Unburned Clay Masonry Units

Scope

Sec. 24.1405. These methods cover procedures for the sampling and testing of unburned clay masonry units for compressive strength, modulus of rupture, absorption and moisture content.

Sampling

Test Specimens

Sec. 24.1406. For each of the tests prescribed in this standard, five sample units shall be selected at random from each lot of 5000 units or fraction thereof.

Identification

Sec. 24.1407. Each specimen shall be marked so that it may be identified at any time. Markings shall cover not more than 5 percent of the superficial area of the specimen.

Compressive Strength

Procedure

Sec. 24.1408. Five full-size specimens shall be tested for compressive strength according to the following procedure:

1. Dry the specimens at a temperature of 85° ± 15°F. in an atmosphere having a relative humidity of not more than 50 percent. Weigh the specimens at one-day intervals until constant weight is attained.

2. Test the specimens in the position in which the unburned clay masonry unit is designed to be used, and bed on and cap with a felt pad not less than 1/8 inch nor more than 1/4 inch in thickness.

3. The specimens may be suitably capped with calcined gypsum mortar or the bearing surfaces of the tile may be planed or rubbed smooth and true. When calcined gypsum is used for capping, conduct the test after the capping has set and the specimen has been dried to constant weight in accordance with Item 1 of this section.

4. The loading head shall completely cover the bearing area of the specimen and the applied load shall be transmitted through a spherical bearing block of proper design. The speed of the moving head of the testing machine shall be not more than 0.05 inch per minute.

5. Calculate the average compressive strength of the specimens tested and report this as the compressive strength of the block.

Modulus of Rupture

Procedure

Sec. 24.1409. Five full-size specimens shall be tested for modulus of rupture according to the following procedure:

1. Cured specimen shall be positioned on cylindrical supports 2 inches in diameter, located 2 inches from each end, and extending across the full width of the specimen.

2. A cylinder 2 inches in diameter shall be positioned on the specimen midway between and parallel to the cylindrical supports.

3. Load shall be applied to the cylinder at the rate of 500 pounds per minute until failure occurs.

4. Calculate modulus of rupture from the formula $S = \frac{3WL}{2Bd^2}$

WHERE:

S = Modulus of rupture, psi.

W = Load at failure.

L = Distance between supports.

B = Width of specimen.

d = Thickness of specimen.

Absorption

Procedure

Sec. 24.1410. A 4-inch cube cut from a sample unit shall be tested for absorption according to the following procedure:

1. Dry specimen to a constant weight in a ventilated oven at 212°F.-239°F.

2. Place specimen on a constantly water-saturated porous surface for seven days. Weigh specimen.

3. Calculate absorption as a percentage of the initial dry weight.

Moisture Content

Procedure

Sec. 24.1411. Five representative specimens shall be tested for moisture content according to the following procedure:

1. Obtain weight of each specimen immediately upon receiving.
2. Dry all specimens to constant weight in a ventilated oven at 212°F.-239°F. and obtain dry weight.
3. Calculate moisture content as a percentage of the initial dry weight.

UNIFORM BUILDING CODE STANDARD NO. 24-15

JOINT REINFORCEMENT FOR MASONRY

Specification Standard of the International Conference of Building Officials

See Sections 2402 (b), 2404 (h), 2407 (h) 4 and 2603 (b) 4, Uniform Building Code

Part I—Joint Reinforcement for Masonry

Scope

Sec. 24.1501. This standard covers joint reinforcement fabricated from cold-drawn steel wire for reinforcing masonry.

Description

Sec. 24.1502. Joint reinforcement consists of deformed longitudinal wires welded to cross wires (Figure No. 24-15-1) in sizes suitable for placing in mortar joints between masonry courses.

Configuration and Size of Longitudinal and Cross Wires

Sec. 24.1503. (a) **General.** The distance between longitudinal wires and the configuration of cross wires connecting the longitudinal wires shall conform to the design.

(b) **Longitudinal Wires.** The diameter of longitudinal wires shall not be less than 0.148 inch (No. 9 gauge) nor more than one-half the mortar joint thickness.

(c) **Cross Wires.** The diameter of cross wires shall not be less than (No. 9 gauge) 0.148 inch diameter nor more than the diameter of the longitudinal wires. Cross wires shall not project beyond the outside longitudinal wires by more than 1/8 inch.

(d) **Width.** The width of joint reinforcement shall be the out-to-out distance between outside longitudinal wires. Variation in the width shall not exceed 1/8 inch.

(e) **Length.** The length of pieces of joint reinforcement shall not vary more than 1/2 inch or 1.0 percent of the specified length, whichever is less.

Material Requirements

Sec. 24.1504. (a) **Tensile Properties.** Wire of the finished product shall meet the following requirements:

Tensile strength, minimum	75,000 psi
Yield strength, minimum	60,000 psi
Reduction of area, minimum	30 percent

For wire testing over 100,000 psi, the reduction of area shall not be less than 25 percent.

(b) **Bend Properties.** Wire shall not break or crack along the outside diameter of the bend when tested in accordance with Section 24.1508.

(c) **Weld Shear Properties.** The least weld shear strength in pounds shall be not less than 25,000 multiplied by the specified area of the smaller wire in square inches.

Fabrication

Sec. 24.1505. Wire shall be fabricated and finished in a workmanlike manner, shall be free from injurious imperfections and shall conform to this standard.

The wires shall be assembled by automatic machines or by other suitable mechanical means which will assure accurate spacing and alignment of all members of the finished product.

Longitudinal and cross wires shall be securely connected at every intersection by a process of electric-resistance welding.

Longitudinal wires shall be deformed. One set of four deformations shall occur around the perimeter of the wire at a maximum spacing of 0.7 times the diameter of the wire but not less than eight sets per inch of length. The overall length of each deformation within the set shall be such that the summation of gaps between the ends of the deformations shall not exceed 25 percent of the perimeter of the wire. The height or depth of the deformations shall be 0.012 inch for $3/16$ inch diameter or larger wire, 0.011 for No. 8 gauge wire (0.162-inch diameter) and 0.009 inch for No. 9 gauge wire (0.148-inch diameter).

Tension Tests

Sec. 24.1506. Tension tests shall be made on individual wires cut from the finished product across the welds.

Tension tests across a weld shall have the welded joint located approximately at the center of the wire being tested.

Tensile strength shall be the average of four test values determined by dividing the maximum test load by the specified cross-sectional area of the wire.

Reduction of area shall be determined by measuring the ruptured section of a specimen which has been tested.

Weld Shear Strength Tests

Sec. 24.1507. Test specimens shall be obtained from the finished product by cutting a section of wire which includes one weld.

Weld shear strength tests shall be conducted using a fixture of such design as to prevent rotation of the cross wire. The cross wire shall be placed in the anvil of the testing device which is secured in the tensile machine and the load then applied to the longitudinal wire.

Weld shear strength shall be the average test load in pounds of four tests.

Bend Tests

Sec. 24.1508. Test specimens shall be obtained from the finished product by cutting a section of wire without welds.

The test specimens shall be bent cold through 180 degrees around a pin, the diameter of which is equal to the diameter of the specimen.

The specimen shall not break nor shall there be visual cracks on the outside diameter of the bend.

Frequency of Tests

Sec. 24.1509. One set of Tension Tests, Weld Strength Shear Tests and Bend Tests, shall be performed for each 2,000,000 lineal feet of joint reinforcement, but not less than monthly.

Corrosion Protection

Sec. 24.1510. When corrosion protection of joint reinforcement is provided, it shall be in accordance with one of the following:

1. **Brite Basic.** No coating.
2. **Mill Galvanized.** Zinc coated, by the hot-dipped method, with no minimum thickness of zinc coating. The coating may be applied before fabrication.
3. **Class I Mill Galvanized.** Zinc coated, by the hot-dipped method, with a minimum of 0.40 ounces of zinc per square foot of surface area. The coating may be applied before fabrication.
4. **Class III Mill Galvanized.** Zinc coated, by the hot-dipped method, with a minimum of 0.80 ounces of zinc per square foot of surface area. The coating may be applied before fabrication.
5. **Hot-dipped Galvanized.** Zinc coated, by the hot-dipped method, with a minimum of 1.50 ounces of zinc per square foot of surface area. The coating shall be applied after fabrication.

Part II

COLD-DRAWN STEEL WIRE FOR CONCRETE REINFORCEMENT

Based on Standard Specification A 82-88 of the American Society for Testing and Materials. Extracted, with permission, from the Annual Book of ASTM Standards, copyright American Society for Testing and Materials, 1916 Race Street, Philadelphia, PA 19103.

See Sections 2402 (b), 2404 (h), 2407 (h) 4 and 2603 (b) 4, Uniform Building Code

Scope

Sec. 24.1511. This standard covers cold-drawn steel wire to be used as such or in fabricated form, for the reinforcement as follows:

SIZE NUMBER	NOMINAL DIAMETER (Inch)	NOMINAL AREA (Square Inch)
W 31	0.628	0.310
W 30	0.618	0.300
W 28	0.597	0.280
W 26	0.575	0.260
W 24	0.553	0.240
W 22	0.529	0.220
W 20	0.505	0.200
W 18	0.479	0.180
W 16	0.451	0.160
W 14	0.422	0.140
W 12	0.391	0.120
W 10	0.357	0.100
W 8	0.319	0.080
W 6	0.276	0.060
W 5.5	0.265	0.055
W 5	0.252	0.050
W 4.5	0.239	0.045
W 4	0.226	0.040
W 3.5	0.211	0.035
W 2.9	0.192	0.029
W 2.5	0.178	0.025
W 2	0.160	0.020
W 1.4	0.134	0.014
W 1.2	0.124	0.012
W 0.5	0.080	0.005

Process

Sec. 24.1512. The steel shall be made by one or more of the following processes: open hearth, electric furnace or basic oxygen.

The wire shall be cold drawn from rods that have been hot rolled from billets.

Unless otherwise specified, the wire shall be "as cold drawn," except wire smaller than size number W 1.2 for welded fabric, which shall be galvanized at finish size.

Tensile Properties

Sec. 24.1513. The material, except as specified in this section, shall conform to the following tensile property requirements based on nominal area of wire:

Tensile strength, minimum, psi	80,000
Yield strength, minimum, psi	70,000
Reduction of area, minimum, percent	30

For material testing over 100,000 pounds per square inch tensile strength, the reduction of area shall not be less than 25 percent.

For material to be used in the fabrication of welded fabric, the following tensile and yield strength properties based on nominal area of wire shall apply:

	SIZE W. 1.2 AND LARGER	SMALLER THAN SIZE W 1.2
Tensile strength, minimum, psi	75,000	70,000
Yield strength, minimum, psi	65,000	56,000

The yield strength shall be determined at an extension of 0.005 inch per inch of gage length.

The material shall not exhibit a definite yield point as evidenced by a distinct drop of the beam or halt in the gage of the testing machine prior to reaching ultimate tensile load.

Bending Properties

Sec. 24.1514. The bend test specimen shall stand being bent cold through 180 degrees without cracking on the outside of the bent portion, as follows:

SIZE NUMBER OF WIRE	BEND TEST
W 7 and smaller	Bend around a pin, the diameter of which is equal to the diameter of the specimen.
Larger than W 7	Bend around a pin, the diameter of which is equal to twice the diameter of the specimen.

Test Specimens

Sec. 24.1515. Tension and bend test specimens shall be of the full section of the wire and shall be obtained from ends of wire coils.

Number of Tests

Sec. 24.1516. One tension test and one bend test shall be made from each 10 tons or less of each size of wire or fraction thereof in a lot, or a total of seven samples, whichever is less. A lot shall consist of all the coils of a single size offered for delivery at the same time.

If any test specimen shows imperfections or develops flaws, it may be discarded and another specimen substituted.

Permissible Variations in Wire Diameter

Sec. 24.1517. The permissible variation in the diameter of the wire shall conform to the following:

SIZE NUMBER	PERMISSIBLE VARIATION PLUS AND MINUS (Inch)
Smaller than W 5	0.003
W 5 to W 12, inclusive	0.004
Over W 12 to W 20, inclusive	0.006
Over W 20	0.008

The difference between the maximum and minimum diameter, as measured on any given cross section of the wire, shall he more than the tolerances shown above for the given wire size.

Finish

Sec. 24.1518. The wire shall be free from injurious imperfections and shall have a workmanlike finish with smooth surface.

Galvanized wire shall be completely covered in a workmanlike manner with a zinc coating.

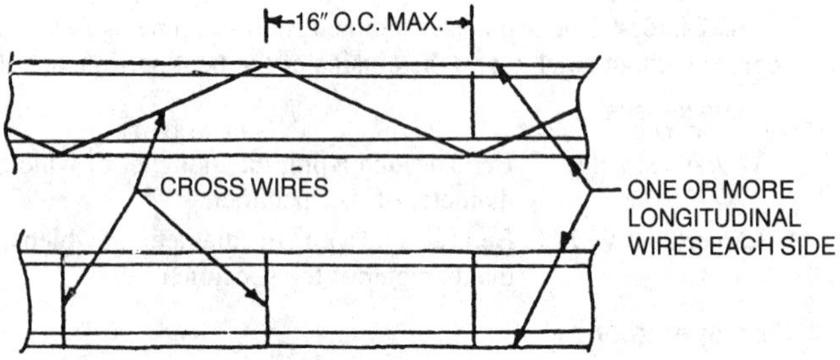
16" O.C. MAX.
CROSS WIRES
ONE OR MORE LONGITUDINAL WIRES EACH SIDE

FIGURE NO. 24-15-1
JOINT REINFORCEMENT

UNIFORM BUILDING CODE STANDARD NO. 24-16

CEMENT, MASONRY

Based on Standard Specification C 91-87a of the American Society for Testing and Materials. Extracted, with permission, from the Annual Book of ASTM Standards, copyright American Society for Testing and Materials, 1916 Race Street, Philadelphia, PA 19103.

See Section 2402 (b) 2 and Table No. 24-A, Uniform Building Code

Scope

Sec. 24.1601. This standard covers three types of masonry cement for use in masonry mortars.

Classifications

Sec. 24.1602. (a) **General.** Masonry cement complying with this standard shall be classified as one of the types set forth in this section.

(b) **Type N.** Type N cement is for use as the cementitious material in the preparation of U.B.C. Standard No. 24-20 Type N and Type O mortars. It is for use in combination with portland or blended hydraulic cements in the preparation of Type S or Type M mortars.

(c) **Type S.** Type S cement is for use as the cementitious material in the preparation of U.B.C. Standard No. 24-20 Type S mortar.

(d) **Type M.** Type M cement is for use as the cementitious material in the preparation of U.B.C. Standard No. 24-20 Type M mortar.

Physical Requirements

Sec. 24.1603. Masonry cement shall conform to the requirements set forth in Table No. 24-16-A for its classifications.

Package Labeling

Sec. 24.1604. Masonry cement packages shall carry a statement indicating that the product conforms to requirements of this standard and shall include the brand, name of manufacturer, type of masonry cement and net weight of the package in pounds.

Certification

Sec. 24.1605. Certification shall be submitted upon request of the building official and shall certify compliance with the requirements of this standard.

Sampling and Testing

Sec. 24.1606. Every 90 days, each masonry cement producer shall retain an approved agency to obtain a random sample from a local point of supply in the market area served by the producer.

The agency shall test the masonry cement for compliance with the provisions of this standard.

Upon request of the building official, the producer shall furnish (at no cost) test results to the building official, architect, structural engineer, general contractor and masonry contractor.

Temperature and Humidity

Sec. 24.1607. The temperature of the air in the vicinity of the mixing slab and dry materials, molds, base plates and mixing bowl shall be maintained between 68°F. and 81.5°F. The temperature of the mixing water, moist cabinet or moist room, and water in the storage tank shall not vary from 73.4°F. by more than 3 degrees.

The relative humidity of the laboratory air shall not be less than 50 percent. The moist cabinet or moist room atmosphere shall have a relative humidity of not less than 90 percent.

The moist cabinet or moist room shall conform to applicable standards.

Fineness

Sec. 24.1608. The fineness of the cement shall be determined from the residue on the No. 325 sieve.

Normal Consistency

Sec. 24.1609. Determine normal consistency by the Vicat apparatus.

Autoclave Expansion

Sec. 24.1610. The autoclave expansion shall be determined. After molding, store the bars in the moist cabinet or room for 48 hours ± 30 minutes before removal from the molds for measurement and test in the autoclave. Calculate the difference in the lengths of the test specimen before and after autoclaving to the nearest 0.01 percent of the effective gage length and report as the autoclave expansion of the masonry cement.

Time of Setting

Sec. 24.1611. The time of setting shall be determined by the Gilmore needle method.

Density

Sec. 24.1612. The density of the masonry cement shall be determined by using kerosene as the liquid. Use the density so determined in the calculation of the air content of the mortars.

Apparatus for Mortar Tests

Sec. 24.1613. The apparatus for mortar tests shall be in accordance with applicable standards.

Blended Sand

Sec. 24.1614. The sand shall be a blend of equal parts by weight of graded standard sand and standard 20-30 sand.

Preparation of Mortar

Sec. 24.1615. (a) **Proportions for Mortar.** Mortar for air entrainment, compressive strength and water-retention tests shall be proportioned to contain the weight of cement, in grams, equal to six times the printed bag weight in pounds (13.228 times the printed bag weight in kilograms) and 1,440 grams of sand. The sand shall consist of 720 grams of graded Ottawa sand and 720 grams of standard 20-30 sand. The quantity of water, measured in milliliters, shall be such as to produce a flow of 110 ± 5 as determined by the flow table.

(b) **Mixing of Mortars.** The mortar shall be mixed in accordance with the applicable standards.

(c) **Determination of Flow.** The flow shall be determined in accordance with applicable standards.

Air Entrainment

Sec. 24.1616. (a) **Procedure.** If the mortar has the correct flow, use a separate portion of the mortar for the determination of entrained air. Determine the mass of 400 ml of the mortar.

(b) **Calculation.** Calculate the air content of the mortar and report it to the nearest 0.1 percent as follows:

$$D = (W_1 + W_2 + V_w)\ [(W_1/S_1) + (W_2/S_2) + V_w]$$

$$A = 100 - (w_m/4D)$$

WHERE:

D = density of air-free mortar, g/ml.
W_1 = mass of cement, g.
W_2 = mass of sand, g.
V_w = milliliters-grams of water used.
S_1 = density of cement, g/ml.
S_2 = density of standard sand, 2.65 g/ml.
A = volume percent of entrained air.
W_m = mass of 400 ml.

Compressive Strength

Sec. 24.1617. (a) **Test Specimens.** 1. **Molding.** Immediately after determining the flow and the mass of 400 ml or mortar, return all the mortar to the mixing bowl and remix for 15 seconds at the medium speed. Then mold test specimens in accordance with applicable standards, except that elapsed time for mixing mortar, determining flow, determining air entrainment and starting the molding of cubes shall be within 8 minutes.

2. **Storage.** Store all test specimens immediately after molding in the molds on plane plates in a moist cabinet or moist room for 48 to 52 hours, in such a manner

that the upper surfaces shall be exposed to the moist air. Then remove the cubes from the molds and place in the moist cabinet or moist room for 5 days in such a manner as to allow free circulation of air around at least five faces of the specimens. At the age of 7 days, immerse the cubes for the 28-day tests in saturated lime water in storage tanks of noncorrodible materials.

(b) **Procedure.** Test the cube specimens immediately after their removal from the moist cabinet or moist room for 7-day specimens, and immediately after their removal from storage water for all other specimens. If more than one specimen at a time is removed from the moist cabinet or moist room for 7-day tests, cover these cubes with a damp cloth until time of testing. If more than one specimen at a time is removed from the storage water for testing, place these cubes in a pan of water at a temperature of 73.4°F. ± 3°F., and of sufficient depth to completely immerse each cube until time of testing.

The remainder of the testing procedure shall conform to applicable standards.

Water Retention

Sec. 24.1618. (a) **Apparatus.** The water-retention test shall conform to applicable standards.

(b) **Procedure.** Adjust the mercury relief column to maintain a vacuum of 51 ± 3 mm as indicated by the manometer. Seat the perforated dish on the greased gasket or greased rim of the funnel. Place a wetted filter paper in the bottom of the dish. Turn the stopcock to apply the vacuum to the the funnel and check the apparatus for leaks and to determine that the required vacuum is obtained. Then turn the stopcock to shut off the vacuum from the funnel.

Mix the mortar to a flow of 110 ± 5 percent in accordance with applicable standards. Immediately after making the flow test, return the mortar on the flow table to the mixing bowl and remix the entire batch for 15 seconds at medium speed. Immediately after remixing the mortar, fill the perforated dish with the mortar to slightly above the rim. Tamp the mortar 15 times with the tamper. Apply ten of the tamping strokes at approximately uniform spacing adjacent to the rim of the dish and with the long axis of the tamping face held at right angles to the radius of the dish. Apply the remaining five tamping strokes at random points distributed over the central area of the dish. The tamping pressure shall be just sufficient to ensure filling of the dish. On completion of the tamping, the top of the mortar will extend slightly above the rim of the dish. Smooth off the mortar by drawing the flat side of the straightedge (with the leading edge slightly raised) across the top of the dish. Then cut off the mortar to a plane surface flush with the rim of the dish by drawing the straightedge with a sawing motion across the top of the dish in two cutting strokes, starting each cut from near the center of the dish. If the mortar is pulled away from the side of the dish during the process of drawing the straightedge across the dish, gently press the mortar back into contact with the side of the dish using the tamper.

Turn the stopcock to apply the vacuum to the funnel. The time elapsed from the start of mixing the cement and water to the time of applying the vacuum shall not exceed 8 minutes. After suction for 60 seconds, quickly turn the stopcock to expose the funnel to atmospheric pressure. Immediately slide the perforated dish off from the funnel, touch it momentarily on a damp cloth to remove droplets of water, and set the dish on the table. Then, using the bowl scraper, plow and mix the mortar in the dish for 15 seconds. Upon completion of mixing, place the mortar in the flow mold and determine the flow. The entire operation shall be carried out without interruption and as quickly as possible, and shall be completed within an elapsed time of 11 minutes after the start of mixing the cement and water for the first flow determination. Both flow determinations shall be made in accordance with applicable standards.

(c) **Calculation.** Calculate the water-retention value for the mortar as follows:

Water-retention value = $(A/B) \times 100$

WHERE:

A = flow after suction.

B = flow immediately after mixing.

TABLE NO. 24-16-A—PHYSICAL REQUIREMENTS

MASONRY CEMENT TYPE	N	S	M
Fineness, residue on a No. 325 sieve, maximum percent . . .	24	24	24
Soundness:			
Autoclave expansion, maximum, percent	1.0	1.0	1.0
Time of setting, Gilmore method:			
Initial set, minimum hour	2	$1^1/_2$	$1^1/_2$
Final set, maximum hour	24	24	24
Compressive strength (average of 3 cubes): Initial compressive strength of mortar cubes, composed of 1 part cement and 3 parts blended sand (half Graded Ottawa sand, and half Standard 20-30 Ottawa sand) by volume, prepared and tested in accordance with this specification shall be equal to or higher than the values specified for the ages indicated below:			
7 days, psi	500	1300	1800
28 days, psi	900	2100	2900
Air content of mortar:			
Minimum percent by volume	8	8	8
Maximum percent by volume	22	20	20
Water retention, flow after suction, minimum, percent of original flow	70	70	70

UNIFORM BUILDING CODE STANDARD NO. 24-17

QUICKLIME FOR STRUCTURAL PURPOSES

Based on Standard Specification C 5-79 (1984) of the American Society for Testing and Materials. Extracted, with permission, from the Annual Book of ASTM Standards, copyright American Society for Testing and Materials, 1916 Race Street, Philadelphia, PA 19103.

See Section 2402 (b) 3, Uniform Building Code

Scope

Sec. 24.1701. This standard covers all classes of quicklime, such as crushed lime, granular lime, ground lime, lump lime, pebble lime and pulverized lime, used for structural purposes.

General Requirements

Sec. 24.1702. Quicklime shall be slaked and aged in accordance with the printed directions of the manufacturer. The resulting lime putty shall be stored until cool.

Chemical Composition

Sec. 24.1703. The quicklime shall conform to the following requirements as to chemical composition, calculated to the nonvolatile basis:

	CALCIUM LIME	MAGNESIUM LIME
Calcium oxide, minimum, percent	75	—
Magnesium oxide, minimum, percent	—	20
Calcium and magnesium oxides, minimum, percent	95	95
Silica, alumina, and oxide of iron, maximum, percent	5	5
Carbon dioxide, maximum, percent:		
If sample is taken at the place of manufacture	3	3
If sample is taken at any other place	10	10

Residue

Sec. 24.1704. The quicklime shall contain not more than 15 percent by weight of residue.

Quality Control

Sec. 24.1705. Every 90 days, each lime producer shall retain an approved agency to obtain a random sample from a local point of supply in the market area served by the producer.

The agency shall test the lime for compliance with the provisions of this standard.

Upon request of the building official, the producer shall furnish (at no cost) test results to the building official, architect, structural engineer, general contractor and masonry contractor.

UNIFORM BUILDING CODE STANDARD NO. 24-18

HYDRATED LIME FOR MASONRY PURPOSES

Based on Standard Specification C 207-79 (Reapproved 1984) of the American Society for Testing and Materials. Extracted, with permission, from the Annual Book of ASTM Standards, copyright American Society for Testing and Materials, 1916 Race Street, Philadelphia, PA 19103.

See Section 2402 (b) 3, Uniform Building Code

Scope

Sec. 24.1801. This standard covers four types of hydrated lime. Types N and S are suitable for use in mortar, in the scratch and brown coats of cement plaster, for stucco, and for addition to portland-cement concrete. Types NA and SA are air-entrained hydrated limes that are suitable for use in any of the above uses where the inherent properties of lime and air entrainment are desired. The four types of lime sold under this specifications shall be designated as follows:

Type N—Normal hydrated lime for masonry purposes.

Type S—Special hydrated lime for masonry purposes.

Type NA—Normal air-entraining hydrated lime for masonry purposes.

Type SA—Special air-entraining hydrated lime for masonry purposes.

Note: Type S, special hydrated lime, and Type SA, special air-entraining hydrated lime, are differentiated from Type N, normal hydrated lime, and Type NA, normal air-entraining hydrated lime, principally by their ability to develop high, early plasticity and higher water retentivity and by a limitation on their unhydrated oxide content.

Definitions

Sec. 24.1802. HYDRATED LIME. The hydrated lime covered by Type N or S in this standard shall contain no additives for the purpose of entraining air. The air content of cement-lime mortars made with Type N or S shall not exceed 7 percent. Types NA and SA shall contain an air-entraining additive as specified by Section 24.1805. The air content of cement-lime mortars made with Type NA or SA shall have a minimum of 7 percent and a maximum of 14 percent.

Additions

Sec. 24.1803. Types NA and SA hydrated lime covered by this standard shall contain additives for the purpose of entraining air.

Manufacturer's Statement

Sec. 24.1804. Where required, the nature, amount and identity of the air-entraining agent used and of any processing addition that may have been used shall be provided, as well as test data showing compliance of such air-entraining addition.

Chemical Requirements Composition

Sec. 24.1805. Hydrated lime for masonry purposes shall conform to the requirements as to chemical composition set forth in Table No. 24-18-A.

TABLE NO. 24-18-A—CHEMICAL REQUIREMENTS

	HYDRATE TYPES			
	N	NA PERCENT	S	SA
Calcium and magnesium oxides (nonvolatile basis), min.	95	95	95	95
Carbon dioxide (as-received basis), max.				
If sample is taken at place of manufacture	5	5	5	5
If sample is taken at any other place	7	7	7	7
Unhydrated oxides (as-received basis), max.	—	—	8	8

Residue, Popping and Pitting

Sec. 24.1806. The four types of hydrated lime for masonry purposes shall conform to one of the following requirements:

1. The residue retained on a No. 30 sieve shall not be more than 0.5 percent, or

2. If the residue retained on a No. 30 sieve is over 0.5 percent, the lime shall show no pops and pits when tested.

Plasticity

Sec. 24.1807. The putty made from Types S, special hydrate, or Type SA, special air-entraining hydrate, shall have a plasticity figure of not less than 200 when tested commencing within 30 minutes after mixing with water.

Water Retention

Sec. 24.1808. Hydrated lime mortar made with Type N, normal hydrated lime, or Type NA, normal air-entraining hydrated lime, after suction for 60 seconds, shall have a water-retention value of not less than 75 percent when tested in a standard mortar made from the dry hydrate or from putty made from the hydrate which has been soaked for a period of 16 to 24 hours.

Hydrated lime mortar made with Type S, special hydrated lime, or Type SA, special air-entraining hydrated lime, after suction for 60 seconds, shall have a water-retention value of not less than 85 percent when tested in a standard mortar made from the dry hydrate.

Special Marking

Sec. 24.1809. When Type NA or SA air-entraining hydrated lime is delivered in packages, the type under this standard and the words "air-entraining" shall be plainly indicated thereon or, in case of bulk shipments, so indicated on shipping notices.

Quality Control

Sec. 24.1810. Every 90 days, each lime producer shall retain an approved agency to obtain a random sample from a local point of supply in the market area served by the producer.

The agency shall test the lime for compliance with the provisions of this standard.

Upon request of the building official, the producer shall furnish (at no cost) test results to the building official, architect, structural engineer, general contractor and masonry contractor.

UNIFORM BUILDING CODE STANDARD NO. 24-19
MORTAR CEMENT
Test Standard of the International Conference of Building Officials
See Section 2402 (b) 2, Uniform Building Code

Scope

Sec. 24.1901. This standard covers mortar cement for use in masonry mortars.

Classifications

Sec. 24.1902. There are three types of mortar cement:

1. **Type N.** For use as the cementitious material in the preparation of U.B.C. Standard No. 24-20 Type N or Type O mortars. For use in combination with portland or blended hydraulic cements in the preparation of Type S or Type M mortars.

2. **Type S.** For use as the cementitious material in the preparation of U.B.C. Standard No. 24-20 Type S mortar.

3. **Type M.** For use as the cementitious material in the preparation of U.B.C. Standard No. 24-20 Type M mortar.

Physical Requirements

Sec. 24.1903. Mortar cement shall conform to the requirements set forth in Table No. 24-19-A for its classification.

Constituent Materials

Sec. 24.1904. Upon request of the building official, the constituent materials shall be provided to the building official and engineer of record.

Restricted Materials

Sec. 24.1905. Materials used in mortar cement shall conform to the requirements set forth in Table No. 24-19-B.

Deleterious Material

Sec. 24.1906. Materials listed in Table No. 24-19-C shall not be used in mortar cement.

Package Labeling

Sec. 24.1907. Mortar cement packages shall carry a statement indicating that the product conforms to requirements of this standard and shall include the brand, name of manufacturer, type of mortar cement and net weight of package in pounds.

Certification

Sec. 24.1908. Certification shall be submitted upon request of the building official and shall certify compliance with the requirements of this standard.

Sampling and Testing

Sec. 24.1909. Every 90 days, each mortar cement producer shall retain an approved agency to obtain a random sample from a local point of supply in the market area served by the producer.

The agency shall test the mortar cement for compliance with the provisions of this standard.

Upon request of the building official, the producer shall furnish (at no cost) test results to the building official, architect, structural engineer, general contractor and masonry contractor.

Temperature and Humidity

Sec. 24.1910. The temperature of the air in the vicinity of the mixing slab and dry materials, molds, base plates and mixing bowl shall be maintained between 68° and 81.5°F. The temperature of the mixing water, moist cabinet or moist room, and water in the storage tank shall not vary from 73.4°F. by more than 3°F.

The relative humidity of the laboratory air shall be not less than 50 percent. The moist cabinet or moist room atmosphere shall have a relative humidity of not less than 90 percent.

The moist cabinet or moist room shall conform to applicable standards.

Fineness

Sec. 24.1911. Determine the residue on the No. 325 sieve.

Normal Consistency

Sec. 24.1912. Determine normal consistency by the Vicat apparatus.

Autoclave Expansion

Sec. 24.1913. Determine autoclave expansion. After molding, store bars in the moist cabinet or room for 48 hours, plus or minus 30 minutes, before removal from the molds for measurement and test in the autoclave. Calculate the difference in length of the test specimen before and after autoclaving to the nearest 0.01 percent of the effective gauge length and report as the autoclave expansion of the mortar cement.

Time of Setting

Sec. 24.1914. Determine the time of setting by the Gillmore needle method.

Density

Sec. 24.1915. Determine the density of the mortar cement using kerosene as the liquid. Use the density so determined in the calculation of the air content of the mortars.

Apparatus for Mortar Tests

Sec. 24.1916. Apparatus shall be in accordance with applicable standards.

Blended Sand

Sec. 24.1917. The sand shall be a blend of equal parts by weight of graded Ottawa sand and Standard 20-30 Ottawa sand.

Preparation of Mortar

Sec. 24.1918. (a) **Proportions for Mortar.** Mortar for air entrainment, compressive strength and water-retention tests shall be proportioned to contain the weight of cement, in grams, equal to six times the printed bag weight in pounds (13.228 times the printed bag weight in kilograms) and 1440g of sand. The sand shall consist of 720g of graded Ottawa sand and 720g of Standard 20-30 sand. The quantity of water, measured in milliliters shall be such as to produce a flow of 110 plus or minus 5 as determined by the flow table.

(b) **Mixing of Mortars.** Mix the mortar in accordance with applicable standards.

(c) **Determination of Flow.** Determine the flow in accordance with applicable standards.

Air Entrainment

Sec. 24.1919. (a) **Procedure.** If the mortar has the correct flow, use a separate portion of the mortar for the determination of entrained air. Determine the weight of 400cm3 of mortar.

(b) **Calculation.** Calculate the air content of the mortar and report it to the nearest 0.1 percent as follows:

$$D = (W_1 + W_2 + V_w)/[(W_1/S_1) + (W_2/S_2) + V_w]$$

$$A = 100 - (W_m/4D)$$

WHERE:

D = density of air-free mortar, g/cm3.
W_1 = weight of cement, g.
W_2 = weight of sand, g.
V_w = milliliters-grams of water used.
S_1 = density of cement, g/cm3.
S_2 = density of standard sand, 2.65g/cm3.
A = volume percent of entrained air.
W_m = weight of 400 ml of mortar, g.

Compressive Strength of Test Specimens

Sec. 24.1920. (a) **Molding.** Immediately after determining the flow and the weight of 400 cm3 of mortar, return all the mortar to the mixing bowl and remix for 15 seconds at the medium speed. Then mold test specimens in accordance with applicable standards, except that the elapsed time for mixing mortar, determining flow, determining air entrainment and starting the molding of cubes shall be within 8 minutes.

(b) **Storage.** Store all test specimens immediately after molding in the molds on plane plates in a moist cabinet maintained at a relative humidity of 90 percent or more for 48 to 52 hours in such a manner that the upper surfaces shall be exposed to the moist air. Then remove the cubes from the molds and place in the moist cabinet for 5 days in such a manner as to allow free circulation of air around at least five faces of the specimens. At the age of 7 days, immerse the cubes for the 28-day tests in saturated lime water in storage tanks of noncorrodible materials.

Procedure

Sec. 24.1921. Test the cube specimens immediately after their removal from the moist cabinet for 7-day specimens, and immediately after their removal from storage water for all other specimens. If more than one specimen at a time is removed from the moist closet for 7-day tests, cover these cubes with a damp cloth until time of testing. If more than one specimen at a time is removed from the storage water for testing, place these cubes in a pan of water at a temperature of 73.4°F. plus or minus 3°F. and of sufficient depth to completely immerse each cube until time of testing.

The remainder of the testing procedure shall conform to applicable standards.

Water Retention

Sec. 24.1922. (a) **Water-retention Apparatus.** For the water-retention test, an apparatus essentially the same as that shown in Figure No. 24-19-1 shall be used. This apparatus consists of a water aspirator or other source of vacuum controlled by a mercury-relief column and connected by way of a three-way stopcock to a funnel upon which rests a perforated dish. The perforated dish shall be made of metal not attacked by masonry mortar. The metal in the base of the dish shall have a thickness of 1.7 to 1.9 mm and shall conform to the requirements given in Figure No. 24-19-1. The bore of the stopcock shall have a 4 mm plus or minus 0.5 mm diameter, and the connecting glass tubing shall have a minimum inside diameter of 4 mm. A mercury manometer, connected as shown in Figure No. 24-19-1, indicates the vacuum. The contact surface of the funnel and perforated dish shall be plane and shall be lapped to ensure intimate contact. An air-tight seal shall be maintained between the funnel and the dish during a test. This shall be accomplished by either of the following procedures: (1) a synthetic (grease-resistant) rubber gasket may be permanently sealed to the top of the funnel, using petrolatum or light grease to ensure a seal between the funnel and dish, or (2) the top of the funnel may be lightly coated with petrolatum or light grease to ensure a seal between the funnel and dish. Care should be taken to ensure that none of the holes in the perforated dish are clogged from the grease. Hardened, very smooth, not rapid filter paper shall be used. It shall be of such diameter that it will lie flat and completely cover the bottom of the dish.

A steel straightedge not less than 8 inches long and not less than 1/16 inch nor more than 1/8-inch thickness shall be used.

Other apparatus required for the water-retention tests shall conform to the applicable requirements of Section 24.1916.

(b) **Procedure.** Adjust the mercury-relief column to maintain a vacuum of 50.8 mm as measured on the manometer. Seat the perforated dish on the greased gasket of the funnel. Place a wetted filter paper in the bottom of the dish. Turn the stopcock to apply the vacuum to the funnel and check the apparatus for leaks and to determine that the required vacuum is obtained. Then turn the stopcock to shut off the vacuum from the funnel.

Mix the mortar to a flow of 110 plus or minus 5 percent in accordance with applicable standards. Immediately after making the flow test, return the mortar on the flow table to the mixing bowl and remix the entire batch for 15 seconds at medium speed. Immediately after remixing the mortar, fill the perforated dish with the mortar to slightly above the rim. Tamp the mortar 15 times with the tamper. Apply ten of the tamping strokes at approximately uniform spacing adjacent to the rim of the dish and with the long axis of the tamping face held at right angles to the radius of the dish. Apply the remaining five tamping strokes at random points distributed over the central area of the dish. The tamping pressure shall be just sufficient to ensure filling of the dish. On completion of the tamping, the top of the mortar should extend slightly above the rim of the dish. Smooth off the mortar by drawing the flat side of the straightedge (with the leading edge slightly raised) across the top of the dish. Then cut off the mortar to a plane surface flush with the rim of the dish by drawing the straightedge with a sawing motion across the top of the dish in two cutting strokes, starting each cut from near the center of the dish. If the mortar is pulled away from the side of the dish during the process of drawing the straightedge across the dish, gently press the mortar back into contact with the side of the dish using the tamper.

Turn the stopcock to apply the vacuum to the funnel. The time elapsed from the start of mixing the cement and water to the time of applying the vacuum shall not exceed 8 minutes. After suction for 60 seconds, quickly turn the stopcock to expose the funnel to atmospheric pressure. Immediately slide the perforated dish off from the funnel, touch it momentarily on a damp cloth to remove droplets of water, and set the dish on the table. Then, using the bowl scraper, in accordance with applicable standards, plow and mix the mortar in the dish for 15 seconds. Upon completion of mixing, place the mortar in the flow mold and determine the flow. The entire operation shall be carried out without interruption and as quickly as possible, and shall be completed within an elapsed time of 11 minutes after the start of mixing the cement and water for the first flow determination. Both flow determinations shall be made in accordance with applicable standards.

(c) **Calculation.** Calculate the water-retention value for the mortar as follows:

Water retention value = $(a/b) \times 100$

WHERE:

a = flow after suction, and

b = flow immediately after mixing.

TABLE NO. 24-19-A—PHYSICAL REQUIREMENTS

MORTAR CEMENT TYPE	N	S	M
Fineness, residue on a No. 325 sieve Maximum, percent	24	24	24
Autoclave expansion Maximum, percent	1.0	1.0	1.0
Time of setting, Gillmore Method Initial set, minimum, hour Final set, maximum, hour	 2 24	 1 1/2 24	 1 1/2 24
Compressive strength[1] 7 days, minimum, psi 28 days, minimum, psi	 500 900	 1300 2100	 1800 2900
Flexural bond strength[2] 28 days, minimum, psi	71	104	116
Air content of mortar Minimum percent by volume Maximum percent by volume	 8 16	 8 14	 8 14
Water retention Minimum, percent	70	70	70

[1]Compressive strength shall be based on the average of 3 mortar cubes composed of 1 part mortar cement and 3 parts blended sand (half graded Ottawa sand, and half standard 20-30 Ottawa sand) by volume and tested in accordance with this standard.

[2]Flexural bond strength shall be determined in accordance with U.B.C. Standard No. 24-30.

TABLE NO. 24-19-B

RESTRICTED MATERIALS	
Material	**Maximum Limit**
Chloride Salts	0.06%
Caboxylic Acids	0.25%
Sugars	1.00%
Glycols	1.00%
Lignin and derivatives	0.50%
Stearates	0.50%
Fly Ash	No Limit
Clay (except fireclay)	5.00%

TABLE NO. 24-19-C

DELETERIOUS MATERIALS NOT PERMITTED IN MORTAR CEMENT
Epoxy Resins and Derivatives Phenols Asbestos Fiber Fireclays

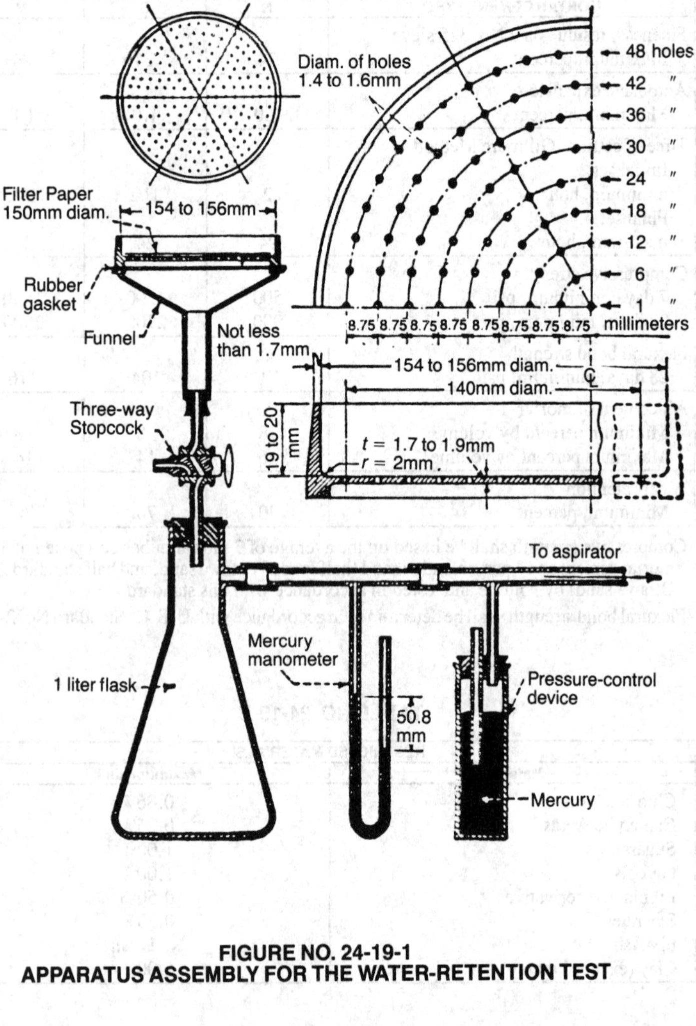
Diam. of holes
1.4 to 1.6mm
48 holes
42 "
36 "
30 "
24 "
18 "
12 "
6 "
1 "
8.75 8.75 8.75 8.75 8.75 8.75 8.75 8.75 millimeters
Filter Paper
150mm diam.
154 to 156mm
Rubber gasket
Funnel
Not less than 1.7mm
154 to 156mm diam.
140mm diam.
19 to 20 mm
t = 1.7 to 1.9mm
r = 2mm
Three-way Stopcock
To aspirator
Mercury manometer
1 liter flask
50.8 mm
Pressure-control device
Mercury

FIGURE NO. 24-19-1
APPARATUS ASSEMBLY FOR THE WATER-RETENTION TEST

UNIFORM BUILDING CODE STANDARD NO. 24-20

MORTAR FOR UNIT MASONRY AND REINFORCED MASONRY OTHER THAN GYPSUM

Based on Standard Specifications C 161-44T and C 270-59T of the American Society for Testing and Materials. Extracted, with permission, from the Annual Book of ASTM Standards, copyright American Society for Testing and Materials, 1916 Race Street, Philadelphia, PA 19103.

See Section 2402 (b) 8, Uniform Building Code

Scope

Sec. 24.2001. These specifications cover the required properties of mortars determined by laboratory tests for use in the construction of reinforced brick masonry structures and unit masonry structures. Two alternative specifications are covered as follows:

1. **Property specifications.** Property specifications are those in which the acceptability of the mortar is based on the properties of the ingredients (materials) and the properties (water retention and compressive strength) of samples of the mortar mixed and tested in the laboratory.

2. **Proportion specifications.** Proportion specifications are those in which the acceptability of the mortar is based on the properties of the ingredients (materials) and a definite composition of the mortar consisting of fixed proportions of these ingredients.

Unless data are presented to show that the mortar meets the requirements of the physical property specifications, the proportion specifications shall govern. For field tests of grout and mortars see U.B.C. Standard No. 24-22.

Property Specifications

Materials

Sec. 24.2002. (a) **General.** Materials used as ingredients in the mortar shall conform to the requirements specified in the pertinent U.B.C. Standards.

(b) **Cementitious Materials.** Cementitious materials shall conform to the following specifications:

1. **Portland cement.** Type I, IA, II, IIA, III or IIIA of U.B.C. Standard No. 26-1.

2. **Mortar cement.** U.B.C. Standard No. 24-19.

3. **Masonry cements.** U.B.C. Standard No. 24-16.

4. **Quicklime.** U.B.C. Standard No. 24-17.

5. **Hydrated lime.** U.B.C. Standard No. 24-18.

(c) **Water.** Water shall be clean and free of deleterious amounts of acids, alkalies or organic materials.

(d) **Admixtures or Mortar Colors.** Admixtures or mortar colors shall not be added to the mortar at the time of mixing unless provided for in the contract specifications and, after the material is so added, the mortar shall conform to the requirements of the property specifications.

Only pure mineral mortar colors shall be used.

(e) **Antifreeze Compounds.** No antifreeze liquid, salts or other substances shall be used in the mortar to lower the freezing point.

(f) **Storage of Materials.** Cementitious materials and aggregates shall be stored in such a manner as to prevent deterioration or intrusion of foreign material. Any material that has become unsuitable for good construction shall not be used.

Mixing Mortar

Sec. 24.2003. Mortar blended on the jobsite shall be mixed for a minimum period of three minutes, with the amount of water required to produce the desired workability, in a drum-type batch mixer. Factory-dry blended mortar shall be mixed with water in a mechanical mixer until workable but not to exceed 10 minutes.

Mortar

Sec. 24.2004. (a) **Mortar for Unit Masonry.** Mortar conforming to the proportion specifications shall consist of a mixture of cementitious material and aggregate conforming to the requirements of Section 24.2002, and the measurement and mixing requirements of Section 24.2003, and shall be proportioned within the limits given in Table No. 24-20-B for each mortar type specified.

(b) **Mortar for Reinforced Masonry.** In mortar used for reinforced masonry the following special requirements shall be met: Sufficient water has been added to bring the mixture to a plastic state. The volume of aggregate in mortar shall be at least two and one-fourth times but not more than three times the volume of cementitious materials.

(c) **Aggregate Ratio.** The volume of damp, loose aggregate in mortar used in brick masonry shall be not less than two and one-fourth times or more than three times the total separate volumes of cementitious materials used.

(d) **Water Retention.** Mortar shall conform to the water retention requirements of Table No. 24-20-A.

(e) **Air Content.** Mortar shall conform to the air content requirements of Table No. 24-20-A.

Compressive Strength

Sec. 24.2005. The average compressive strength of three 2-inch cubes of mortar (before thinning) shall not be less than the strength given in Table No. 24-20-A for the mortar type specified.

Proportion Specifications

Materials

Sec. 24.2006. (a) **General.** Materials used as ingredients in the mortar shall conform to the requirements of Section 24.2002 and to the requirements of this section.

(b) **Mortar Cement.** Mortar cement shall conform to the requirements of U.B.C. Standard No. 24-19.

(c) **Masonry Cement.** Masonry cement shall conform to the requirements of U.B.C. Standard No. 24-16.

(d) **Hydrated Lime.** Hydrated lime shall conform to either of the two following requirements:

1. The total free (unhydrated) calcium oxide (CaO) and magnesium oxide (MgO) shall not be more than 8 percent by weight (calculated on the as-received basis for hydrates).

2. When the hydrated lime is mixed with portland cement in the proportion set forth in Table No. 24-20-B, the mixture shall give an autoclave expansion of not more than .50 percent.

Hydrated lime intended for use when mixed dry with other mortar ingredients shall have a plasticity figure of not less than 200 when tested 15 minutes after adding water.

(e) **Lime Putty.** Lime putty made from either quicklime or hydrated lime shall be soaked for a period sufficient to produce a plasticity figure of not less than 200 and shall conform to either the requirements for limitation on total free oxides of calcium and magnesium or the autoclave test specified for hydrated lime in Subsection (b).

Mortar

Sec. 24.2007. Mortar shall consist of a mixture of cementitious materials and aggregate conforming to the requirements specified in Section 24.2004, mixed in one of the proportions shown in Table No. 24-20-B, to which sufficient water has been added to reduce the mixture to a plastic state.

TABLE NO. 24-20-A—PROPERTY SPECIFICATIONS FOR MORTAR[1]

MORTAR	TYPE	AVERAGE COMPRESSIVE STRENGTH OF 2-INCH CUBES AT 28 DAYS (Min., psi)	WATER RETENTION (Min., percent)	AIR CONTENT (Max., percent)[2]	AGGREGATE MEASURED IN A DAMP LOOSE CONDITION
Cement-lime or Mortar Cement	M	2500	75	12	Not less than $2^1/_4$ and not more than $3^1/_2$ times the sum of the separate volumes of cementitious materials.
	S	1800	75	12	
	N	750	75	14[3]	
	O	350	75	14[3]	
Masonry cement	M	2500	75	18	
	S	1800	75	18	
	N	750	75	18	
	O	350	75	18	

[1]Laboratory-prepared mortar only.

[2]Determined in accordance with applicable standards.

[3]When structural reinforcement is incorporated in cement-lime mortar or mortar-cement mortar, the maximum air content shall be 12 percent.

Table No. 24-20-B, page 82. Revise as follows:

TABLE NO. 24-20-B—MORTAR PROPORTIONS FOR UNIT MASONRY

MORTAR	TYPE	PROPORTIONS BY VOLUME (CEMENTITIOUS MATERIALS)								AGGREGATE MEASURED IN A DAMP, LOOSE CONDITION
		PORTLAND CEMENT OR BLENDED CEMENT[1]	MASONRY CEMENT[2]			MORTAR CEMENT[3]			HYDRATED LIME OR LIME PUTTY[1]	
			M	S	N	M	S	N		
Cement-lime	M	1	—	—	—	—	—	—	1/4	Not less than 2 1/4 and not more than 3 times the sum of the separate volumes of cementitious materials.
	S	1	—	—	—	—	—	—	over 1/4 to 1/2	
	N	1	—	—	—	—	—	—	over 1/2 to 1 1/4	
	O	1	—	—	—	—	—	—	over 1 1/4 to 2 1/2	
Mortar cement	M	1	—	—	—	—	—	1	—	
	M	—	—	—	—	1	—	—	—	
	S	1/2	—	—	—	—	—	1	—	
	S	—	—	—	—	—	1	—	—	
	N	—	—	—	—	—	—	1	—	
Masonry cement	M	1	—	—	1	—	—	—	—	
	M	—	1	—	—	—	—	—	—	
	S	1/2	—	—	1	—	—	—	—	
	S	—	—	1	—	—	—	—	—	
	N	—	—	—	1	—	—	—	—	
	O	—	—	—	1	—	—	—	—	

[1]When plastic cement is used in lieu of portland cement, hydrated lime or putty may be added, but not in excess of one tenth of the volume of cement.

[2]Masonry cement conforming to the requirements of U.B.C. Standard No. 24-16.

[3]Mortar cement conforming to the requirements of U.B.C. Standard No. 24-19.

UNIFORM BUILDING CODE STANDARD NO. 24-22

FIELD TESTS SPECIMENS FOR MORTAR

Test Standard of the International Conference of Building Officials

See Section 2402 (b) 8, Uniform Building Code

Field Compressive Test Specimen for Mortar

Sec. 24.2201. Spread mortar on the masonry units 1/2 inch to 5/8 inch thick, and allow to stand for one minute, then remove mortar and place in a 2-inch by 4-inch cylinder in two layers, compressing the mortar into the cylinder using a flat-end stick or fingers. Lightly tap mold on opposite sides, level off and immediately cover molds and keep them damp until taken to the laboratory. After 48 hours' set, have the laboratory remove molds and place them in the fog room until tested in damp condition.

Requirements

Sec. 24.2202. Each such mortar test specimen shall exhibit a minimum ultimate compressive strength of 1500 pounds per square inch.

UNIFORM BUILDING CODE STANDARD NO. 24-26

TEST METHOD FOR COMPRESSIVE STRENGTH OF MASONRY PRISMS

Based on Standard Test Method E 447-80 of the American Society for Testing and Materials. Extracted, with permission, from the Annual Book of ASTM Standards, copyright American Society for Testing and Materials, 1916 Race Street, Philadelphia, PA 19103.

See Sections 2402 (b) 6 and 2405 (c) 1 and 2, Uniform Building Code

Scope

Sec. 24.2601. This standard covers procedures for masonry prism construction, testing and procedures for determining the compressive strength of masonry.

Sec. 24.2602. Prisms shall be constructed on a flat, level base. Masonry units used in the prism shall be representative of the units used in the corresponding construction. Each prism shall be built in an opened moisture-tight bag which is large enough to enclose and seal the completed prism. The orientation of units, where top and bottom cross sections vary due to taper of the cells, or where the architectural surface of either side of the unit varies, shall be the same orientation as used in the corresponding construction. Prisms shall be a single wythe in thickness and laid up in stack bond (see Figure No. 24-26-1).

The length of masonry prisms may be reduced by saw cutting; however, prisms composed of regular shaped hollow units shall have at least one complete cell with one full-width cross web on either end. Prisms composed of irregular-shaped units shall be cut to obtain as symmetrical a cross section as possible. The minimum length of saw-cut prisms shall be 4 inches.

Masonry prisms shall be laid in a full mortar bed (mortar bed both webs and face shells). Mortar shall be representative of that used in the corresponding construction. Mortar joint thickness, the tooling of joints and the method of positioning and aligning units shall be representative of the corresponding construction.

Prisms shall be a minimum of two units in height, but the total height shall not be less than 1.3 times the least actual thickness or more than 5.0 times the least actual thickness. Immediately following the construction of the prism, the moisture-tight bag shall be drawn around the prism and sealed.

Where the corresponding construction is to be solid grouted, prisms shall be solid grouted. Grout shall be representative of that used in the corresponding construction. Grout shall be placed not less than one day nor more than two days following the construction of the prism. Grout consolidation shall be representative of that used in the construction. Additional grout shall be placed in the prism after reconsolidation and settlement due to water loss, but prior to the grout setting. Excess grout shall be screeded off level with the top of the prism. Where open-end units are used, additional masonry units shall be used as forms to confine the grout during placement. Masonry unit forms shall be sufficiently braced to prevent displacement during grouting. Immediately following the grouting operation, the moisture-tight bag shall be drawn around the prism and resealed.

Where the corresponding construction is to be partially grouted, two sets of prisms shall be constructed; one set shall be grouted solid and the other set shall not be grouted.

Where the corresponding construction is of multiwythe composite masonry, masonry prisms representative of each wythe shall be built and tested separately.

Prisms shall be left undisturbed for at least two days after construction.

Transporting Masonry Prisms

Sec. 24.2603. Prior to transporting each prism, strap or clamp the prism together to prevent damage during handling and transportation. Secure prism to prevent jarring, bouncing or falling over during transporting.

Curing

Sec. 24.2604. Prisms shall remain sealed in the moisture-tight bag until two days prior to testing; the moisture-tight bag shall then be removed and curing continued in laboratory air maintained at a temperature of 75°F. plus or minus 15°F. Prisms shall be tested at 28 days after constructing the prism or at test age designated.

Preparation for Testing

Sec. 24.2605. (a) **Capping the Prism.** Cap top and bottom of the prism prior to testing with sulfur-filled capping or with high-strength gypsum plaster capping (such as "Hydrostone" or "Hyprocal White"). Sulfur-filled capping material shall be 40 to 60 percent by weight sulfur, the remainder being ground fireclay or other suitable inert material passing a No. 100 sieve, with or without a plasticizer. Spread the capping material over a level surface which is plane within 0.003 inch in 16 inches. Bring the surface to be capped into contact with the capping paste; firmly press down the specimen, holding it so that its axis is at right angles to the capping surfaces. The average thickness of the cap shall not exceed $^1/_8$ inch. Allow caps to age at least two hours before testing.

(b) **Measurement of the Prism.** Measure the length and thickness of the prism to the nearest 0.01 inch by averaging three measurements taken at the center and quarter points of the height of the specimen. Measure the height of the prism, including caps, to the nearest 0.1 inch.

Test Procedure

Sec. 24.2606. (a) **Test Apparatus.** The test machine shall have an accuracy of plus or minus 1.0 percent over the load range. The upper bearing shall be spherically seated, hardened metal block firmly attached at the center of the upper head of the machine. The center of the sphere shall lie at the center of the surface held in its spherical seat, but shall be free to turn in any direction, and its perimeter shall have at least $^1/_4$-inch clearance from the head to allow for specimens whose bearing surfaces are not exactly parallel. The diameter of the bearing surface shall be at least 5 inches. A hardened metal bearing block may be used beneath the specimen to minimize wear of the lower platen of the machine. The bearing block surfaces intended for contact with the specimen shall have a hardness not less than 60 HRC (620 HB). These surfaces shall not depart from plane surfaces by more than 0.001 inch in any 6-inch dimension. When the bearing area of the spherical bearing block is not sufficient to cover the area of the specimen, a steel plate with surfaces machined to true planes within plus or minus 0.001 inch in any 6-inch dimension, and with a thickness equal to at least the distance from the edge of the spherical bearings to the most distant corner, shall be placed between the spherical bearing block and the capped specimen.

(b) **Installing the Prism in the Test Machine.** Wipe clean the bearing faces of the upper and lower platens or bearing blocks and of the test specimen and place the test specimen on the lower platen or bearing block. Align both centroidal axes of the specimen with the center of thrust of the test machine. As the spherically seated block is brought to bear on the specimen, rotate its movable portion gently by hand so that uniform seating is obtained.

(c) **Loading.** Apply the load, up one half of the expected minimum load, at any convenient rate, after which adjust the controls of the machine so that the remaining load is applied at a uniform rate in not less than one or more than two minutes.

(d) **Observations.** Describe the mode of failure as fully as possible or illustrate crack patterns, spalling, etc., on a sketch, or both. Note whether failure occurred on one side or one end of the prism prior to failure of the opposing side or end of the prism.

Calculations

Sec. 24.2607. Calculations of test results shall be as follows:

1. **Net cross-sectional area.** Determine the net cross-sectional area (square inches) of solid grouted prisms by multiplying the average measured width dimension (inches) by the average measured length dimension (inches). The net cross-sectional area of ungrouted prisms shall be taken as the net cross-sectional area of masonry units determined from a representative sample of units.

2. **Masonry prism strength.** Determine the compressive strength of each prism (psi) by dividing the maximum compressive load sustained (pounds) by the net cross-sectional area of the prism (square inches).

3. **Compressive strength of masonry.** The compressive strength of masonry (psi) for each set of prisms shall be the lesser of the average strength of the prisms in the set, or 1.25 times the least prism strength multiplied by the prism height to thickness correction factor from Table No. 24-26-A. Where a set of grouted and nongrouted prisms are tested, the compressive strength of masonry shall be determined for the grouted set and for the nongrouted set separately. Where a set of prisms is tested for each wythe of a multiwythe wall, the compressive strength of masonry shall be determined for each wythe separately.

TABLE NO. 24-26-A

Prisms h/t_p[1]	1.30	1.50	2.00	2.50	3.00	4.00	5.00
Correction factor	0.75	0.86	1.00	1.04	1.07	1.15	1.22

[1] h/t_p—ratio of prism height to least actual lateral dimension of prism.

Masonry Prism Test Report

Sec. 24.2608. The test report shall include the following:

1. Name of testing laboratory and name of professional engineer responsible for the tests.

2. Designation of each prism tested and description of prism, including width, height and length dimensions, mortar type, grout and masonry unit used in the construction.

3. Age of prism at time of test.

4. Maximum compressive load sustained by each prism, net cross-sectional area of each prism and net area compressive strength of each prism.

5. Test observations for each prism in accordance with Section 24.2606.

6. Compressive strength of masonry for each set of prisms.

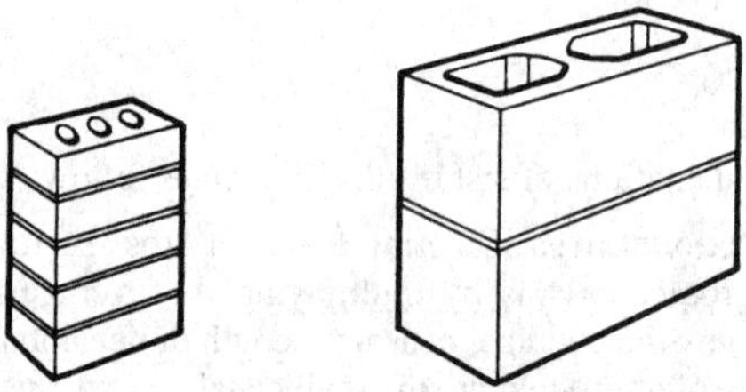

FIGURE NO. 24-26-1

UNIFORM BUILDING CODE STANDARD NO. 24-28

METHOD OF SAMPLING AND TESTING GROUT

Based on Standard Method C 1019-84 of the American Society for Testing and Materials. Extracted, with permission, from the Annual Book of ASTM Standards, copyright American Society for Testing and Materials, 1916 Race Street, Philadelphia, PA 19103.

See Section 2402 (b) 9 and Table No. 24-B, Uniform Building Code

Scope

Sec. 24.2801. This method covers procedures for both field and laboratory sampling and compression testing of grout used in masonry construction.

Apparatus

Sec. 24.2802. (a) **Maximum-Minimum Thermometer.**

(b) **Straightedge.** A steel straightedge not less than 6 inches long and not less than 1/16 inch in thickness.

(c) **Tamping Rod.** A nonabsorbent smooth rod, either round or square in cross section nominally 5/8 inch in dimension with ends rounded to hemispherical tips of the same diameter. The rod shall be a minimum length of 12 inches.

(d) **Wooden Blocks.** Wooden squares with side dimensions equal to one-half the desired grout specimen height, within a tolerance of 5 percent, and of sufficient quantity or thickness to yield the desired grout specimen height, as shown in Figures Nos. 24-28-A and 24-28-B.

Wooden blocks shall be soaked in limewater for 24 hours, sealed with varnish or wax, or covered with an impermeable material prior to use.

Sampling

Sec. 24.2803. (a) **Size of Sample.** Grout samples to be used for slump and compressive strength tests shall be a minimum of 1/2 $ft.^3$.

(b) **Field Sample.** Take grout samples as the grout is being placed into the wall. Field samples may be taken at any time except for the first and last 10 percent of the batch volume.

Test Specimen and Sample

Sec. 24.2804. (a) Each grout specimen shall be a square prism, nominally 3 inches or larger on the sides and twice as high as its width. Dimensional tolerances shall be within 5 percent of the nominal width selected.

(b) Three specimens constitute one sample.

Procedure

Sec. 24.2805. (a) Select a level location where the molds can remain undisturbed for 48 hours.

(b) **Mold Construction.** 1. The mold space should simulate the grout location in the wall. If the grout is placed between two different types of masonry units, both types should be used to construct the mold.

2. Form a square prism space, nominally 3 inches or larger on each side and twice as high as its width, by stacking masonry units of the same type and moisture condition as those being used in the construction. Place wooden blocks, cut to proper size and of the proper thickness or quantity, at the bottom of the space to achieve the necessary height of specimen. Tolerance on space and specimen dimensions shall be within 5 percent of the specimen width. See Figures Nos. 24-28-A and 24-28-B.

3. Line the masonry surfaces that will be in contact with the grout specimen with a permeable material, such as paper towel, to prevent bond to the masonry units.

(c) Measure and record the slump of the grout.

(d) Fill the mold with grout in two layers. Rod each layer 15 times with the tamping rod penetrating 1/2 inch into the lower layer. Distribute the strokes uniformly over the cross section of the mold.

(e) Level the top surface of the specimen with a straightedge and cover immediately with a damp absorbent material such as cloth or paper towel. Keep the top surface of the sample damp by wetting the absorbent material and do not disturb the specimen for 48 hours.

(f) Protect the sample from freezing and variations in temperature. Store an indicating maximum-minimum thermometer with the sample and record the maximum and minimum temperatures experienced prior to the time the specimens are placed in the moist room.

(g) Remove the masonry units after 48 hours. Transport field specimens to the laboratory, keeping the specimens damp and in a protective container.

(h) Store in a moist room conforming to nationally recognized standards.

(i) Cap the specimens in accordance with the applicable requirements of U.B.C. Standard No. 24-26.

(j) Measure and record the width of each face at midheight. Measure and record the height of each face at midwidth. Measure and record the amount out of plumb at midwidth of each face.

(k) Test the specimens in a damp condition in accordance with the applicable requirements of U.B.C. Standard No. 24-26.

Calculations

Sec. 24.2806. The report shall include the following:

(a) Mix design.

(b) Slump of the grout.

(c) Type and number of units used to form mold for specimens.

(d) Description of the specimens—dimensions, amount out of plumb—in percent.

(e) Curing history, including maximum and minimum temperatures and age of specimen, when transported to laboratory and when tested.

(f) Maximum load and compressive strength of the sample.

(g) Description of failure.

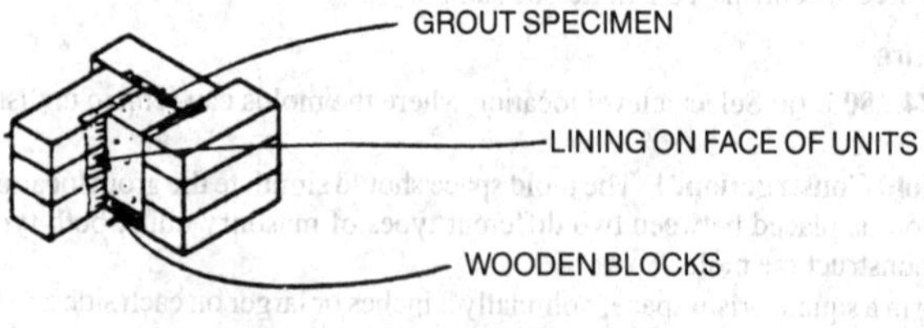
GROUT SPECIMEN
LINING ON FACE OF UNITS
WOODEN BLOCKS

Note: Front masonry unit stack not shown to allow view of specimen.

FIGURE NO. 24-28-A
Grout Mold (Units 6 inches or Less in Height, 21/4-inch-high Brick Shown)

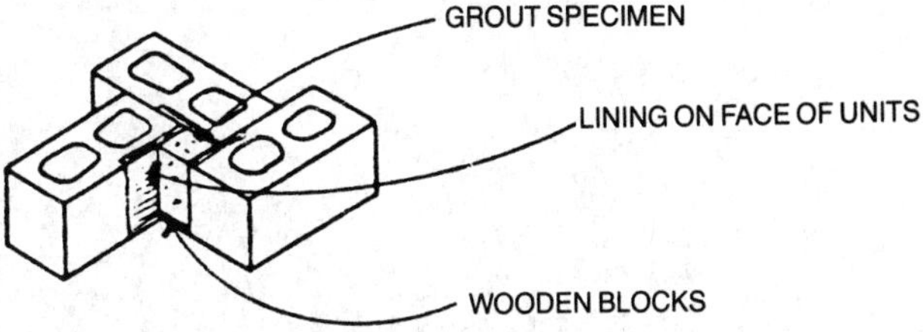
GROUT SPECIMEN
LINING ON FACE OF UNITS
WOODEN BLOCKS

Note: Front masonry unit not shown to allow view of specimen.

FIGURE NO. 24-28-B
Grout Mold (Units Greater than 6 inches High, 8-inch-high Concrete Masonry Unit Shown)

UNIFORM BUILDING CODE STANDARD NO. 24-29

GROUT FOR MASONRY

Based on Standard Specification C 476-83 of the American Society for Testing and Materials. Extracted, with permission, from the Annual Book of ASTM Standards, copyright American Society for Testing and Materials, 1916 Race Street, Philadelphia, PA 19103.

See Section 2402 (b) 8, Uniform Building Code

Scope

Sec. 24.2901. This standard covers grout for use in the construction of reinforced and nonreinforced masonry structures.

Materials

Sec. 24.2902. Materials used as ingredients in grout shall conform to the following:

1. **Cementitious Materials.** Cementitious materials shall conform to one of the following standards:

A. Portland Cement—Types I, II and III of U.B.C. Standard No. 26-1.

B. Blended Cement—Type IS, IS(MS) or IP of U.B.C. Standard No. 26-1.

C. Quicklime—U.B.C. Standard No. 24-17.

D. Hydrated lime—Type S of U.B.C. Standard No. 24-18.

2. **Water.** Water shall be clean and potable.

3. **Admixtures.** Additives and admixtures to grout shall not be used unless approved by the building official.

4. **Antifreeze Compounds.** No antifreeze liquids, chloride salts or other substances shall be used in grout.

5. **Storage of Materials.** Cementitious materials and aggregates shall be stored in such a manner as to prevent deterioration or intrusion of foreign material or moisture. Any material that has become unsuitable for good construction shall not be used.

Measurement Of Materials

Sec. 24.2903. The method of measuring materials for the grout used in construction shall be such that the specified proportions of the grout materials can be controlled and accurately maintained.

Grout

Sec. 24.2904. Grout shall consist of cementitious material and aggregate that have been mixed thoroughly fora minimum of five minutes in a mechanical mixer with sufficient water to bring the mixture to the desired consistency. The grout proportions and any additives shall be based on laboratory or field experience considering the grout ingredients and the masonry units to be used, or the grout shall be proportioned within the limits given in Table No. 24-B of the Uniform Building Code, or the grout shall have a minimum compressive strength when tested in accordance with U.B.C. Standard No. 24-28 equal to its specified strength, but not less than 2,000 psi.

EXCEPTION: Dry mixes for grout which are blended in the factory and mixed at the jobsite shall be mixed in mechanical mixers until workable, but not to exceed ten minutes.

UNIFORM BUILDING CODE STANDARD NO. 24-30

STANDARD TEST METHOD FOR FLEXURAL BOND STRENGTH OF MORTAR CEMENT

Test Standard of the International Conference of Building Officials

See Section 2402 (b) 8, Uniform Building Code, and U.B.C. Standard No. 24-19, Table No. 24-19-A

Scope

Sec. 24.3001. This method covers the laboratory evaluation of the flexural bond strength of a standardized mortar and a standardized masonry unit.

Apparatus

Sec. 24.3002. The test apparatus consists of a metal frame designed to support a prism as shown in Figures Nos. 24-30-1 and 24-30-2. The prism support system shall be adjustable to support prisms ranging in height from 2 to 7 masonry units. The upper clamping bracket that is clamped to the top masonry unit of the prism shall not come into contact with the lower clamping bracket during the test.

Materials

Sec. 24.3003. (a) **Masonry Units.** Masonry units used shall be standard masonry units selected for the purpose of determining the flexural bond strength properties of mortar cement mortars. The standard unit shall be in accordance with the following requirements:

1. Dimensions of units shall be 3[5]/[8] inches wide by 2[1]/[4] inches high by 7[5]/[8] inches long within a tolerance of plus or minus [1]/[8] inch and shall be 100 percent solid.

2. The unit material shall be concrete masonry manufactured with the following material proportions by volume:

1 part portland cement to 8 parts aggregate

3. Aggregate used in the manufacture of the unit shall be as follows:

Bulk Specific Gravity	2.6 to 2.7
Gradation	**Percent Retained by Weight**
3/8-inch sieve	0
No. 4 sieve	0 to 5
No. 8 sieve	20 to 30
No. 16 sieve	20 to 30
No. 30 sieve	15 to 25
No. 50 sieve	5 to 15
No. 100 sieve	5 to 10
Pan	5 to 10

4. Density of the unit shall be 125 to 135 pounds per cubic foot.

5. Unit shall be cured in a 100 percent relative humidity environment at 140°F. ± 10°F. at atmospheric pressure for 10 to 20 hours. Additional curing, under covered atmospheric conditions, shall continue for at least 28 days. Unit shall be loose stacked in the cube (separated by a [1]/[4]-inch gap) to allow air to circulate during drying.

6. At the time of fabricating the prisms, units shall have a moisture content in the range of 25 percent to 35 percent.

7. Upon delivery units shall be stored in the laboratory at normal temperature and humidity. Units shall not be wetted or surface treated prior to or during prism fabrication.

(b) **Mortar.** Mortar shall be prepared in accordance with the following:

1. Mortar proportions shall be in accordance with Table No. 24-30-A. The aggregate shall consist of a blend of one-half graded Ottawa sand and one-half Standard 20-30 Ottawa sand.

2. Mortar materials shall be mixed in a drum-type batch mixer for five minutes.

3. Determine mortar flow in accordance with applicable standards and adjust water until a flow of 125 ±5 is achieved.

4. Determine mortar density, air content and initial cone penetration immediately after mixing the mortar in accordance with applicable standards. Mortar shall not be used when cone penetration is less than 80 percent of the initial cone penetration value.

Test Specimens

Sec. 24.3004. (a) **Number.** Test specimens shall consist of one set of six prisms constructed with the mortar cement mortar. Each prism shall be six units in height.

(b) **Prism Construction.** (1) Each prism shall be built in an opened moisture-tight bag which is large enough to enclose and seal the completed prism. Set the first unit of each prism on a firm, horizontal surface without the use of mortar. An alignment device shall be used to ensure plumbness and joint thickness uniformity. (2) Place a full mortar bed on all units without furrowing. (3) Immediately place the next course on the mortar bed and tap it to proper level and a $^3/_8$-inch joint thickness. One face of each prism shall be in a nearly true plane. (4) Repeat (2) and (3) until the prisms are complete. (5) Joints shall be cut flush after the prism is completely built. Joints shall not be tooled. (6) One hour, ±15 minutes after completion of construction, place two masonry units of the type used to construct the prism upon the top course. (7) Identify all prisms using a water-resistant marker. (8) Draw and seal the moisture-tight bag around the prism. (9) All prisms should be cured for 28 days. Two days prior to testing remove the moisture-tight bag and continue curing in the laboratory air, maintained at a temperature of 75°F. ± 15°F., with a relative humidity between 30 and 70 percent.

Test Procedure

Sec. 24.3005. Place the prism vertically in the support frame as shown in Figure No. 24-30-1 and clamp firmly into a locked position using the lower clamping bracket. Orient the prism so that the face of the joint intended to be subjected to flexural tension is on the same side of the specimen as the clamping screws. The prism shall be positioned at the required elevation that results in a single unit projecting above the lower clamping bracket. A soft bearing material (for example, polystyrene) at least $^1/_2$-inch thick shall be placed between the bottom of the prism and the adjustable prism base support.

Attach the upper clamping bracket to the top unit as shown in Figure No. 24-30-1. Tighten each clamping bolt using a torque not greater than 20 pounds per inch.

Apply the load at a uniform rate so that the total load is applied in not less than 1 minute or more than 3 minutes. Measure load to an accuracy of ±2 percent with maximum error of 5 pounds.

Calculations

Sec. 24.3006. Calculate the modulus of rupture of each mortar joint as follows:

$$f_r = \frac{6(PL + P_1L_1)}{bd^2} - \frac{(P + P_1)}{bd}$$

WHERE:

f_r = modulus of rupture, psi.
P = maximum applied load, pounds.
P_1 = weight of loading arm, pounds.
L = distance from center of prism to loading point, inches.
L_1 = distance from center of prism to centroid of loading arm, inches.
b = average width of cross section of failure surface, inches.
d = average thickness of cross section of failure surface, inches.

The flexural bond strength of mortar shall be determined as the average modulus of rupture of 30 joints minus 1.28 times the standard deviation of the sample which yields a value that will equal or exceed a mortar joint's modulus of rupture 9 out of 10 times.

Report

Sec. 24.3007. The report shall include the manufacturer of the mortar cement being evaluated, the source of manufacture, type of mortar cement, date of testing, laboratory name and laboratory personnel.

Report mortar density, air content, flow and cone penetration test data. Report the following data for the mortar cement mortar being evaluated:

PRISM NO.	PRISM WEIGHT (lbs.)	JOINT NO.	TEST LOAD (lbs.)	MOMENT (in.-lbs.)	MODULUS OF RUPTURE, psi			
					fr psi	Mean psi	Std. Dev. psi[1]	COV %
		1	—	—	—			
		2	—	—	—			
1	—	3	—	—	—	—	—	—
		4	—	—	—			
		5	—	—	—			

[1]Also, report the standard deviation for all 6 prisms (30 joints).

Report the flexural bond strength (determined in accordance with Section 24.3006) of the mortar cement mortar.

TABLE NO. 24-30-A—MORTAR PROPORTIONS BY VOLUME FOR EVALUATING FLEXURAL BOND

MORTAR	MORTAR CEMENT TYPE	PROPORTIONS	
		Mortar Cement	Aggregate
Type N	N	1	3
Type S	S	1	3
Type M	M	1	3

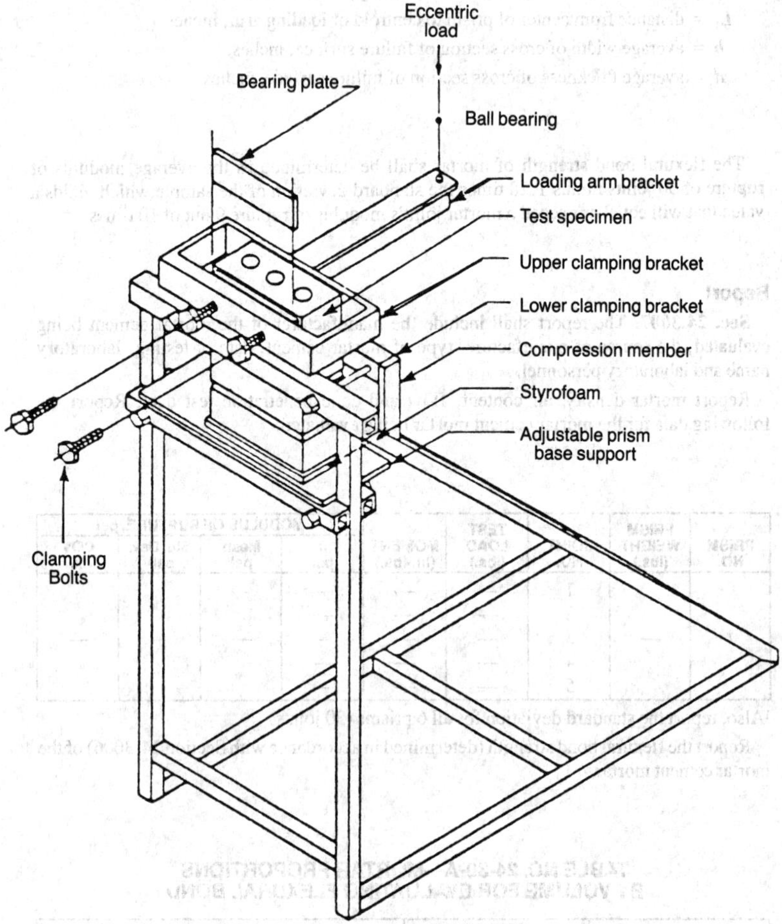
Eccentric
load
Bearing plate
Ball bearing
Loading arm bracket
Test specimen
Upper clamping bracket
Lower clamping bracket
Compression member
Styrofoam
Adjustable prism
base support
Clamping
Bolts

FIGURE NO. 24-30-1
BOND WRENCH TEST APPARATUS

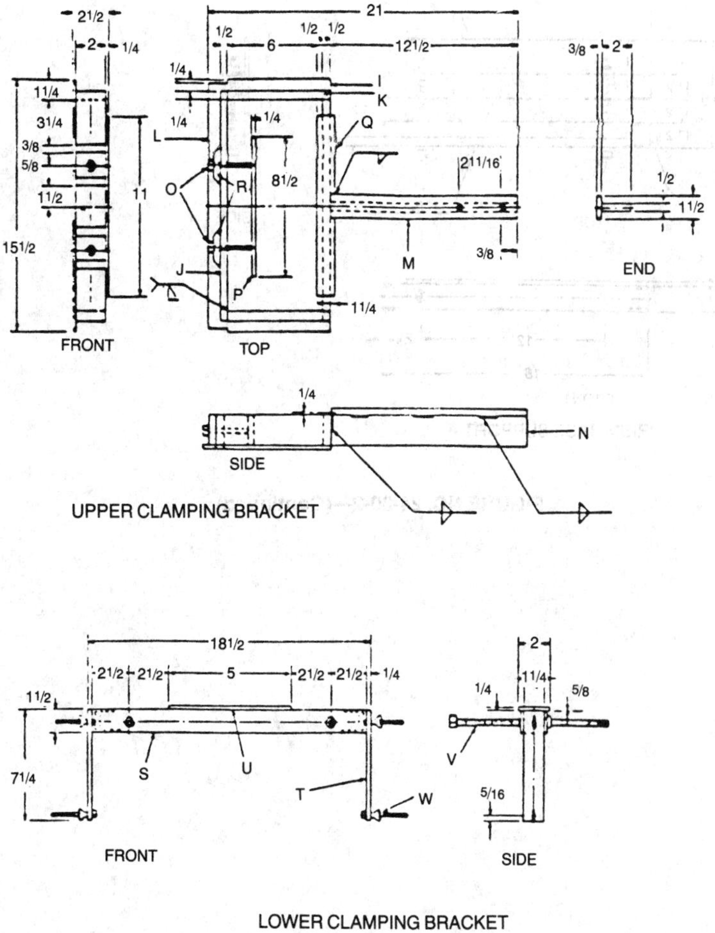
FRONT
TOP
END
SIDE
UPPER CLAMPING BRACKET
I
J
K
L
M
N
O
P
Q
R
21
6
12 1/2
8 1/2
11
15 1/2
FRONT
SIDE
LOWER CLAMPING BRACKET
S
T
U
V
W
18 1/2
7 1/4
5

FIGURE NO. 24-30-2
DETAIL DRAWINGS
OF BOND WRENCH

(Continued)

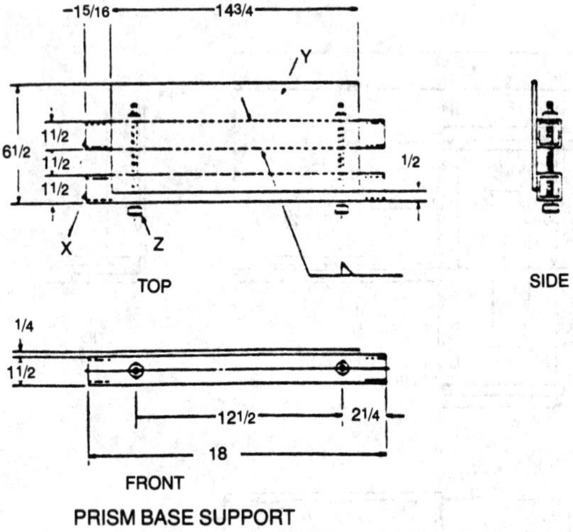

15/16
143/4
Y
61/2
11/2
11/2
11/2
1/2
X
Z
TOP
SIDE
1/4
11/2
121/2
21/4
18
FRONT
PRISM BASE SUPPORT

FIGURE NO. 24-30-2—(Continued)

UNIFORM BUILDING CODE STANDARD NO. 25-1

CLASSIFICATION, DEFINITION AND METHODS OF GRADING FOR ALL SPECIES OF LUMBER

Based on Standard Methods D 245-70 and D 2555-70 of the American Society for Testing and Materials. Extracted, with permission, from the Annual Book of ASTM Standards, copyright American Society for Testing and Materials, 1916 Race Street, Philadelphia, PA 19103; Handbook No. 72 of the U.S. Department of Agriculture, American Softwood Lumber Standard PS20-70 and National Grading Rule for Dimension Lumber of the National Grading Rule Committee.

See Sections 2501 (a) and 2502 (a), and Tables Nos. 25-A-1 and 25-A-2, Uniform Building Code

Scope

Sec. 25.101. This standard sets forth general grading rules for all of the species of lumber referred to in Uniform Building Code Tables Nos. 25-A-1 and 25-A-2 and contains common grading rules referred to in Uniform Building Code Standards Nos. 25-2 through 25-8. Allowable stresses for species or grades of lumber not referred to in Table No. 25-A-1 or 25-A-2 of the Uniform Building Code shall be established, based on approved principles for conversion of clear wood strength values to safe working stresses.

Definitions

Sec. 25.102. The standard commercial names, or their commonly accepted trade names, for lumber cut from the principal species of softwoods, as shown in Appendix A of this standard, shall be used in the formulation of lumber grading rules.

The limitations of any grade of lumber described in certified grading rules shall be expressed within the terms of the definitions in Appendix B of this standard.

The interpretation of terms used describing the factors influencing strength shall be within the meaning of terms and definitions of Section 25.108 and Appendix B of this standard.

Classification

Sec. 25.103. (a) **Use Classification.** Softwood lumber shall be classified as follows:

1. **Yard lumber.** Lumber of those grades, sizes and patterns which are generally intended for ordinary construction and general building purposes.

2. **Structural lumber.** Lumber that is 2 inches or more in thickness and width for use where working stresses are required.

3. **Factory and shop lumber.** Lumber that is produced or selected primarily for remanufacturing purposes.

(b) **Manufacturing Classifications.** Softwood lumber shall be classified according to extent of manufacture as follows:

1. **Rough lumber.** Lumber which has not been dressed (surfaced) but which has been sawed, edged and trimmed at least to the extent of showing saw marks or equivalent in the wood on the four longitudinal surfaces of each piece for its overall length.

2. **Dressed (surfaced) lumber.** Lumber that has been dressed by a planing machine (for purpose of attaining smoothness of surface and uniformity of size) on one side (S1S), two

sides (S2S), one edge (S1E), two edges (S2E), or a combination of sides and edges (S1S1E, S1S2E, S2S1E, S4S).

3. **Worked lumber.** Lumber which, in addition to being dressed, has been matched, shiplapped or patterned.

(i) **Matched lumber.** Lumber that has been worked with a tongue on one edge of each piece and a groove on the opposite edge to provide a close tongue-and-groove joint by fitting two pieces together; when end matched, the tongue and groove are worked in the ends also.

(ii) **Shiplapped lumber.** Lumber that has been worked or rabbeted on both sides of each piece to provide a close-lapped joint by fitting two pieces together.

(iii) **Patterned lumber.** Lumber that is shaped to a pattern or to a molded form, in addition to being dressed, matched or shiplapped, or any combination of these workings.

(c) **Size Classification.** Softwood lumber is classified according to size as follows:

1. **Boards.** Lumber less than 2 inches in nominal thickness and 2 or more inches in nominal width. Boards less than 6 inches may be classified as strips.

2. **Dimension.** Lumber from 2 inches to, but not including, 5 inches in nominal width. Dimension may be classified as framing, joists, planks, rafters, studs, small timbers, etc.

3. **Timbers.** Lumber 5 or more inches nominally in least dimension. Timber may be classified as beams, stringers, posts, caps, sills, girders, purlins, etc.

(d) **Rough-dry Size.** The minimum rough-dry thickness of finish, common boards, and dimension of sizes 1 or more inches nominal thickness shall be not less than 1/8 inch thicker than the corresponding minimum finished dry thickness, except that 20 percent of a shipment may be not less than 3/32 inch thicker than the corresponding minimum finished dry thickness. The minimum rough-dry widths of finish, common strip boards, and dimension shall be not less than 1/8 inch wider than the corresponding minimum finished dry width.

(e) **Dressed Sizes.** Dressed sizes of lumber shall equal or exceed the minimum sizes shown in Tables Nos. 25-1-A, 25-1-B, 25-1-C, 25-1-D and 25-1-E. See also Section 25.109.

NOTE: The actual sizes of all lumber dimensions referenced in this standard in terms of "nominal" sizes are set forth in Tables Nos. 25-1-A, 25-1-B, 25-1-D and 25-1-E. The use of "nominal" sizes in the language of the standard is for convenience and follows the practice of the industry. No inference should be drawn that the "nominal" sizes are actual sizes.

Standards for Grading Rules

Sec. 25.104. (a) **General.** To the extent to which differences in the characteristics of species, in the quality of logs, in conditions of manufacture, and in the uses to which the product is put will permit, in practical application, the basic provisions for the grading of lumber shall be uniform. Grading rules shall be sufficiently explicit to establish a maximum of 5 percent below grade as a reasonable variation between graders. If any grading rules indicate that a grade qualifies under two use classifications, the grade provisions shall satisfy the requirements for both classifications.

(b) **Yard Lumber.** 1. **Grade classifications.** The grading of yard lumber shall be based upon the uses for which the particular grade is designed, and shall be applied to each kind with reference to its size and length when graded, without consideration to further manufacture. On the basis of quality, yard lumber shall be classified Select, that is, lumber of good appearance and finishing qualities, or Common, that is, lumber which is suitable for general construction and utility purposes.

2. **Grade characteristics.** The method of determining the extent and limitations of the characteristics permitted in the poorest pieces admissible in each grade of yard lumber shall be stated in an approved rule, except in the lowest grade of each classification. A grade shall be representative, however, and shall not comprise only low-line pieces.

3. **Grade sizes.** The dressed thicknesses and widths of yard lumber as specified in Section 25.103 (b) shall be considered as minimum standards for the corresponding nominal sizes as shown. Lumber of standard size, rough or dressed, may be described by its nominal dimension, provided net sizes are also shown.

4. **Grading faces.** Timbers and dimension shall be graded from all four faces. All other yard lumber and yard boards may be graded from the face or best side only.

(c) **Structural Lumber.** 1. **Development of working stress and MOE values.** Working stress and modulus of elasticity (MOE) values contained in grading rules shall be developed in accordance with approved standards and other technically sound criteria.

2. **Mechanical grading.** The grading of structural lumber by mechanical means is recognized as an acceptable method of grading, but all such grading equipment and methods are subject to approval.

3. **Grading faces.** Timbers and dimension shall be graded from all four faces.

(d) **General Grade Provisions.** 1. **Grade characteristics.** Characteristics permitted and limitations for rough lumber shall be the same as those prescribed in grading rules for dressed lumber of like kind and grade and, in addition, such others as will disappear in standard dressing shall be allowed. If characteristics other than those described in grading rules are encountered, they shall be appraised in relation to the characteristics permitted or limitations prescribed for the grade under consideration and shall be allowed if regarded as equivalent or less damaging in effect on the strength, appearance or other utility value of the piece. The size of characteristics and limitations in any grade or species shall not exceed that permitted in the respective grading rules.

2. **Special provisions.** When heartwood, sapwood, grain classifications and other optional provisions are specified, and the lumber conforms to the requirements of such special provisions as well as of the regular grade designated, it may be regarded as of standard quality.

3. **Mixed grades.** Mixed grades other than the two highest established grades for each species shall not be included in grading rules.

4. **Nonstandard grades.** When nonstandard grades, sizes or workings are specified or when particular provisions of a standard grade are waived or changed, inspection shall be made accordingly, but all of the other provisions of the standard grading rules shall apply.

(e) **Seasoning.** The grading rules shall include clear definitions for dry lumber, under 5-inch nominal thickness, which shall be based on 19 percent or lower maximum moisture content. The grade marking of green or dry lumber of any item shall be as specified in U.B.C. Standards Nos. 25-2 through 25-8.

1. **Moisture content determinations.** Moisture content determinations shall be made with electric meters of an approved type, and the procedures to be used in making such determinations shall be in accordance with a nationally recognized method.

2. **Dry size requirements.** The grading rules shall require all lumber under 5-inch nominal thickness, sold as dry, to be 19 percent or less in moisture content at the time of dressing, and to be not less than dry dressed thickness and width at 19 percent moisture content as specified in this standard, or at such lower maximum moisture content as may be applicable to the lumber at the time of dressing. The minimum dressed dry sizes shall be as shown in Tables Nos. 25-1-A, 25-1-B, 25-1-C, 25-1-D and 25-1-E. Shrinkage that may occur after dressing to standard dry size shall be recognized through allowance of tolerance below minimum dry sizes on the basis of 1 percent shrinkage for each four points of moisture content reduction below the applicable maximum 0.7 percent shrinkage for redwood, western red cedar and northern white cedar for each four points of moisture content reduction.

3. **Green size requirements.** The green sizes specifically stated in the rules shall not be less than the green sizes shown in Tables Nos. 25-1-C, 25-1-D and 25-1-E.

4. **Size differentials.** When the grading rules permit lumber under 5-inch nominal thickness to be dressed green, the rules shall require the lumber to be dressed to sizes specifically stated in the rules, which sizes shall provide differentials both in thickness and width, as set forth in Tables Nos. 25-1-A, 25-1-B, 25-1-C, 25-1-D and 25-1-E.

5. **Grade marking.** When grading rules provide for grade marking of lumber under 5-inch nominal thickness, the rules shall contain a provision for standardized marking of such lumber so as to indicate whether the lumber was green or dry at time of dressing.

Structural Lumber Classification

Sec. 25.105. (a) **Size and Use Categories.** The effects of knots, deviations of grain, shakes and checks on the strength of a member vary with the loading to which the piece is subjected. Also, the effect of seasoning varies with the size of the member. Structural lumber is therefore often classified according to its size and use.

(b) **Dimension Lumber.** 1. Lumber which is 2 inches to 4 inches thick and 2 inches to 4 inches wide classified Structural Light Framing, Light Framing, Appearance Framing and Stud. There are four grades in this category.

2. Lumber which is 2 inches to 4 inches thick, 5 inches and wider, classified for use as Structural Joist and Planks and Appearance Framing. There are four grades in this category. (See Section 25.107.)

3. Machine stress-rated lumber 2 inches and less in thickness and 2 inches and wider that has been evaluated by mechanical stress-rating equipment to determine the modulus of elasticity and is visually graded to limit certain characteristics and imperfections.

(c) **Beams and Stringers.** Timbers of rectangular cross section 5 inches by 8 inches and up, graded for strength in bending when loaded on the narrow face.

(d) **Posts and Timbers.** Timbers of square or nearly square cross section, 5 inches by 5 inches and larger, graded primarily to provide high compression values for use as posts or columns but adapted to miscellaneous uses in which bending strength is not especially important.

(e) **Decking and Wall and Roof Planks.** Pieces 2 inches to 4 inches thick and 4 inches to 8 inches wide, graded for strength in bending when loaded on the wide face.

(f) **Structural Boards.** Lumber of 1-inch thickness used in lightweight trusses or other structural elements, and 2 inches net or thinner and 3 inches and wider used in glued-laminated structural members where the principal stresses are in axial compression or tension. Boards for common purposes such as sheathing, finish or boxes are not included.

General Requirements for Stress Grades

Sec. 25.106. (a) **General Quality of Lumber.** Only sound wood, free from any form of decay, shall be permitted unless otherwise specified. Unsound knots and limited amounts of decay in its early stages are permitted in some of the lower stress-rated grades.

In stress grading, all four faces and the ends shall be considered.

(b) **Slope of Grain.** Slope of grain resulting from either diagonal sawing or from spiral or twisted grain in the tree is measured by the angle between the direction of the fibers and the edge of the piece. The angle is expressed as a slope.

When both diagonal and spiral grain are present, the combined slope of grain is taken as the effective slope.

Slope of grain is measured and limited at the zone in the length of a structural timber that shows the greatest slope. It shall be measured over a distance sufficiently great to define the general slope, disregarding such short local deviations as those around knots except as indicated in this section.

In 1-inch boards, or similar small sizes of lumber, a general slope of grain anywhere in the length shall not pass completely through the thickness of the piece in a longitudinal distance in inches less than the number expressing the specified permissible slope. Where such a slope varies across the width of the board, its average may be taken.

Local deviations must be considered in small sizes, and if a local deviation occurs in a piece less than 4 inches nominal in width or on the narrow face of a piece less than 2 inches nominal in thickness, and is not associated with a permissible knot in the piece, the measurement of slope shall include the local deviation.

(c) **Knots.** 1. **General.** Cluster knots are prohibited in stress grades. Two or more knots closely spaced, with the fibers deflected around each knot individually, are not a cluster.

Holes associated with knots are measured and limited in the same way as knots.

A knot on the wide face of a bending or tension member is considered to be at the edge of the wide face if the center of the knot lies within two thirds of the knot diameter from the edge.

2. **Knots in joists and planks.** Knots in joists and planks may be measured by displacement method, in which the proportion of the cross section of the knot to the cross section of the piece is multiplied by actual face width to establish the equivalent knot size.

Alternatively, knots in joists and planks may be measured on the surface of the piece. Methods of measuring knots by this alternative are given in the following paragraphs.

The size of a knot on a narrow face of a joist or plank is its width between lines enclosing the knot and parallel to the edges of the piece (see Figure No. 25-1-1). A narrow-face knot that appears also in the wide face of a side-cut joist (but does not contain the intersection of those faces) is measured and graded on the wide face.

The size of a knot on a wide face is the average of its largest and smallest dimensions (see Figure No. 25-1-1) unless otherwise specified.

Any knot that contains the intersection of two faces, including a knot extending entirely across the width of a face in a side-cut joist, is a corner knot. A corner knot is measured on its end between lines parallel to the edges of the piece and is graded with respect to the face on which it is measured (see Figure No. 25-1-1). A corner knot in a joist containing the pith is measured either by its width on the narrow face between lines parallel to the edge, or by its smallest diameter on the wide face, whichever is more restrictive (see Figure No. 25-1-1). If a corner knot appears also on an opposite face, its limitation there as well as on the corner is necessary.

The sum of the sizes of all knots in any 6 inches of length of piece shall not exceed twice the size of the largest permitted knot. Two or more knots of maximum or near maximum permissible size shall not be allowed in the same 6 inches of length on a face. Any combination of knots that will make the piece unfit for its intended use shall not be admitted.

In the grading and measurement of knots in 3-inch by 4-inch and 4-inch by 4-inch sizes, each of the four faces is graded as a narrow face. For sizes 3-inch by 3-inch and smaller all knots shall be limited as if they were wide-face edge knots in the face on which they appear.

The size of knots on wide faces may be increased proportionately from the size permitted at the edge to the size permitted at the center line (see Figure No. 25-1-1).

3. **Knots in beams and stringers.** The size of a knot on a narrow face of a beam or stringer is its width between lines enclosing the knot and parallel to the edges of the piece (see Figure No. 25-1-3). When a knot on a narrow face of a side-cut piece extends into the adjacent one fourth of the width of a wide face, it is measured on the wide face.

The size of a knot on the wide face is measured by its smallest diameter (see Figure No. 25-1-3). An edge knot on the wide face is limited to the same size as a knot on the narrow face.

A corner knot in a beam or stringer containing the pith is measured either by its width on the narrow face between lines parallel to the edges or by its smallest diameter on the wide face, whichever is greater (see Figure No. 25-1-3). A corner knot in a side-cut piece is measured by whichever of these two is least.

The sum of the sizes of all knots within the middle one half of the length of a face, in a beam 20 feet or less in length, when measured as specified for the face under consideration, shall not exceed four times the size of the largest knot allowed on that face. This restriction in a beam longer than 20 feet shall apply to any 10 feet of length within the middle one half of the length.

Where the grade is used for single-span bending applications only, the sizes of knots on narrow faces and at the edges of wide faces may be increased proportionately from the size permitted in the middle one third of the length to twice that size at the ends of the piece, except that the size of no knot shall exceed the size permitted at the center of the wide face. The size of knots on wide faces may be increased proportionately from the size permitted at the edge to the size permitted at the center line (see Figure No. 25-1-2).

Where the grade is to be used on continuous spans, the restrictions for knots in the middle one third of their lengths shall be applied to the middle two thirds of the length of pieces continuous on three supports, and to the full length of pieces continuous on four or more supports.

4. **Knots in posts and timbers.** The size of a knot on any face of a post or timber is taken as the diameter of a round knot, the lesser of the two diameters of an oval knot, or the greatest diameter perpendicular to the length of a spike knot (see Figure No. 25-1-4).

A corner knot is measured wherever the measurement will represent the true diameter of the branch causing the knot.

The sum of the sizes of all knots in any 6 inches of length of a post or timber shall not exceed twice the size of the largest permitted knot. Two or more knots of maximum or near maximum permissible size shall not be allowed in the same 6 inches of length on a face.

In compression members with greater width than thickness, the sizes of knots in both the narrow and the wide faces are allowed up to the size permitted in the wide face.

5. **Knots in 1-inch boards.** Measured the same as for joists and planks.

(d) **Shakes, Checks and Splits.** Shakes are measured at the ends of the piece. The size of a shake is the distance between lines enclosing the shake and parallel to the wide face of the piece.

Splits and checks are treated as "equivalent shakes." The size of a side check is its average depth of penetration into the piece, measured from and perpendicular to the surface of the wide face on which it appears. The size of an end split or end check is one third of its average length measured along the length of the piece, except as noted below.

In single-span bending members, shakes, checks and splits are restricted only for a distance from each end equal to three times the width of the wide face, and within the critical zone, only in the middle one half of the wide face. For multiple-span bending members, shakes, checks and splits are restricted throughout the length in the middle one half of the wide face.

Where a combination of two checks in opposite faces, a check and a split, a check and a shake, or a split and a shake may later become a single horizontal shear plane, the sum of the sizes in the combination is restricted to the allowable size of shakes. Where such a combination is not additive in this way, only the largest single characteristic is considered.

(e) **Wane.** Wane is permissible in all grades of bending members as far as strength properties are concerned, but "free from wane" may be specified when required by appearance or bearing, or other factors of use.

(f) **Specific Gravity Selection.** Lumber may be selected as dense by grain characteristics for Douglas fir and southern pine. To be classified dense the wood shall average on one end or the other of each piece not less than six annual rings per inch and one third or more summerwood (the darker, harder portion of the annual ring) measured on a representative radial line. Pieces that average not less than four annual rings per inch shall be accepted as dense if they average one half or more summerwood. The contrast in color between springwood and summerwood in either case shall be distinct.

To ensure a representative radial line, measurement shall be made over a continuous length of 3 inches or as nearly 3 inches as is available. The length shall be centrally located in side-cut pieces. In pieces containing the pith, the measurement may exclude an inner portion of the radius amounting to approximately one fourth of the least dimension of the piece.

Dense material of any species may be selected by methods other than described above, provided that such methods are approved.

Lumber may be selected as close grain for Douglas fir from the Coast Region, redwood and southern pine. To be classified as close grain the wood shall average on one end or the other of each piece not less than six nor more than 30 annual rings per inch, measured on a representative radial line. To ensure a representative radial line, measurement shall be made as in the second paragraph of this subsection. Pieces averaging at least five, or more than 30, rings per inch shall be accepted as close grained if the measurement shows one third or more summerwood. Visually selected close-grained redwood shall average in each piece not less than eight nor more than 40 annual rings per inch.

Close-grained wood of any species may be selected by methods other than described above, provided that such methods are approved.

Medium-grained wood shall average on one end or the other of each piece not less than four annual rings per inch, measured on a representative radial line.

Grading Rules for Dimension Lumber

Sec. 25.107. (a) **Scope.** This section applies to dimension lumber referred to in Table No. 25-A-1 of the Uniform Building Code. Dimension lumber covered in this section is structural lumber as classified in Section 25.105 (b).

(b) **General.** The major characteristics encountered in grading of softwood lumber shall be as specified in Section 25.104. Minor characteristics unique to a single species which are not listed in the grade descriptions shall be assessed in comparison with the most similar characteristic listed in the grades and permitted or limited in the same fashion as the listed characteristic. All grade descriptions set forth the limiting characteristics that may occur in lumber in each grade. All or nearly all of the permissible characteristics of the grade shall not be present in maximum size or number in any one piece. Any piece with an unusual combination of characteristics which seriously affects normal serviceability is excluded from the grade.

Knots, checks, shakes and slope of grain shall be measured in accordance with the provisions of Section 25.106, except that no increase in slope of grain or size of knots shall be permitted outside the middle one third of length. Except as otherwise provided herein, knots appearing on narrow faces shall be limited to the same displacement as knots specified at edges of wide faces. The limitations on knot sizes and other characteristics governing strength shall not be exceeded. Compression wood is prohibited in all grades if present in readily identifiable and damaging form based on ordinary visual inspection.

Dimension lumber of the classification and grades which follow are limited in characteristics that affect strength and stiffness values to a fiber strength in bending of the percentage indicated of that allowed for clear, straight-grained wood.

2 to 4 Inches Thick, 2 to 4 Inches Wide
STRUCTURAL LIGHT FRAMING

Grade Name (and Abbreviation)

67% Bending Strength Ratio—Select Structural (Sel Str)
55% Bending Strength Ratio— 1
45% Bending Strength Ratio— 2
26% Bending Strength Ratio— 3

LIGHT FRAMING

34% Bending Strength Ratio—Construction (Const)
19% Bending Strength Ratio—Standard (Stand)
9% Bending Strength Ratio—Utility (Util)

The bending strength ratio for Construction, Standard and Utility applies only to 2 x 4, 3 x 4 and 4 x 4.

2 to 4 Inches Thick, 2 to 6 Inches Wide, 10 Feet and Shorter
STUDS

26% Bending Strength Ratio-Stud

2 to 4 Inches Thick, 5 Inches and Wider
STRUCTURAL JOISTS AND PLANKS

Grade Name (and Abbreviation)

65% Bending Strength Ratio—Select Structural (Sel Str)
55% Bending Strength Ratio— 1
45% Bending Strength Ratio— 2
26% Bending Strength Ratio— 3

2 to 4 Inches Thick, 2 Inches and Wider
APPEARANCE FRAMING

Grade Name (and Abbreviation)

55% Bending Strength Ratio—Appearance (A)

(c) **Structural Light Framing.** 1. **Select structural.** Two inches to 4 inches thick, 2 inches to 4 inches wide.

Characteristics permitted and limiting provisions shall be:

Checks—Surface seasoning checks, not limited. Through checks at ends are limited as splits.

Grain, for redwood—Close grain. For redwood open grain—Open grain. For Douglas fir dense—Dense. For Douglas fir, larch and southern pine—Medium.

Knots—Sound, firm, encased and pith knots, if tight and well spaced, are permitted in sizes not to exceed the following, or equivalent, displacement:

NOM. WIDTH	AT EDGE WIDE FACE	CENTER LINE WIDE FACE	UNSOUND OR LOOSE KNOTS & HOLES (ANY CAUSE)	
2″	3/8″	3/8″	3/8″	One hole or equivalent smaller per 4 linear feet
3″	1/2″	1/2″	1/2″	
4″[1]	3/4″	7/8″	3/4″	

[1]In 3 × 4 and 4 × 4 sizes, a 7/8-inch knot is permitted anywhere on the 4-inch face.

Manufacture—Standard "E."

Pitch and pitch streaks—Not limited.

Pockets, pitch or bark—Not limited.

Shake—On ends, limited to one half the thickness. Away from ends, several heart shakes up to 2 feet long, none through.

Skips—Hit-and-miss skips in 10 percent of the pieces.

Slope of grain—1 in 12.

Splits—Equal in length to the width of the piece.

Stain—Stained sapwood. Firm heart stain or firm red heart limited to 10 percent of the piece.

Wane—One fourth the thickness, one fourth the width; 5 percent of the pieces may have wane up to one half the thickness and one third the width for one fourth the length.

Warp—One half of medium.

Heartwood—In redwood all heartwood shall appear in "Select Heart Structural."

2. **No. 1.** Two inches to 4 inches thick, 2 inches to 4 inches wide:

Characteristics permitted and limiting provisions shall be:

Checks—Surface seasoning checks, not limited. Through checks at ends are limited as splits.

Grain, for redwood—Close grain. For redwood open grain—Open grain. For Douglas fir and southern pine dense—Dense. For Douglas fir, larch and southern pine—Medium.

Knots—Sound, firm, encased and pith knots, if tight and well spaced, are permitted in sizes not to exceed the following, or equivalent, displacement:

NOM. WIDTH	AT EDGE WIDE FACE	CENTER LINE WIDE FACE	UNSOUND OR LOOSE KNOTS & HOLES (ANY CAUSE)	
2″	1/2″	1/2″	1/2″	One hole or equivalent smaller per 3 linear feet
3″	3/4″	3/4″	3/4″	
4″[1]	1″	1 1/2″	1″	

[1]In 3 × 4 and 4 × 4 sizes, a 1 1/2-inch knot is permitted anywhere on the 4-inch face.

Manufacture—Standard "E."

Pitch and pitch streaks—Not limited.

Pockets, pitch or bark—Not limited.

Shake—On ends, limited to one half the thickness. Away from ends, several heart shakes up to 2 feet long, none through.

Skips—Hit-and-miss skips in 10 percent of pieces.

Slope of Grain—1 in 10.

Splits—Equal in length to width of the piece.

Stain—Stained sapwood. Firm heart stain or firm red heart.

Wane—One fourth the thickness, one fourth the width; 5 percent of the pieces may have wane up to one half the thickness and one third the width for one fourth the length.

Warp—One half of medium.

Heartwood, in redwood "No. 1 Heart Structural"—All heartwood.

3. **No. 2.** Two inches to 4 inches thick, 2 inches to 4 inches wide:

Characteristics permitted and limiting provisions shall be:

Checks—Seasoning checks not limited. Through checks at ends are limited as splits.

Grain, for redwood close grain—Close grain. For redwood open grain—Open grain. For Douglas fir and southern pine dense—Dense. For Douglas fir and larch—Medium.

Knots—Well-spaced knots of any quality are permitted in sizes not to exceed the following or equivalent displacement:

NOM. WIDTH	AT EDGE WIDE FACE	CENTER LINE WIDE FACE	HOLES (ANY CAUSE)	
2″	5/8″	5/8″	5/8″	One hole or equivalent smaller per 2 linear feet
3″	7/8″	7/8″	7/8″	
4″[1]	1 1/4″	2″	1 1/4″	

[1]In 3 × 4 and 4 × 4 sizes, a 2-inch knot is permitted anywhere on the 4-inch face.

Manufacture—Standard "F."

Pitch and pitch streaks—Not limited.

Pockets, pitch or bark—Not limited.

Shake—On ends limited to one half the thickness. Away from ends, through heart shakes up to 2 feet long, well separated. If not through, single shakes may be 3 feet long or up to one fourth the length, whichever is greater.

Skips—Hit and miss; and, in addition, 5 percent of the pieces may be hit-or-miss or heavy skip not longer than 2 feet.

Slope of grain—1 in 8.

Splits—Equal in length to one and one-half times the width of the piece.

Stain—Stained sapwood. Firm heart stain or firm red heart. Not limited.

Unsound wood—Not permitted in thicknesses over 2 inches; but in 2-inch thickness, heart center streaks not over one third of the width or thickness, or small spots or streaks of firm honeycomb or peck equal to one sixth the width are permitted.

Wane—One third the thickness, one third the width; 5 percent of the pieces may have wane up to two thirds the thickness and one half the width for one fourth the length.

Warp—Light.

White speck—Firm, one third the face or equivalent.

Heartwood, in redwood "No. 2 Heart Structural"—All heartwood.

4. **No. 3.** Two inches to 4 inches thick, 2 inches to 4 inches wide:

Characteristics permitted and limiting provisions shall be:

Checks—Seasoning checks not limited. Through checks at ends are limited as splits.

Grain, for redwood—Close grain. For redwood open grain—Open grain. For southern pine dense—Dense.

Knots—Not restricted as to quality and are permitted in the following sizes or their equivalent displacement:

NOM. WIDTH	AT EDGE WIDE FACE	CENTER LINE WIDE FACE	HOLES (ANY CAUSE)	
2″	3/4″	3/4″	3/4″	One hole or equivalent smaller per 1 linear foot
3″	1 1/4″	1 1/4″	1 1/4″	
4″[1]	1 3/4″	2 1/2″	1 3/4″	

[1]In 3 × 4 and 4 × 4 sizes, a 2 1/2-inch knot is permitted anywhere on the 4-inch face.

Manufacture—Standard "F."

Pitch and pitch streaks—Not limited.

Pockets, pitch or bark—Not limited.

Shake—Surface shakes permitted. If through at edges or ends, limited as splits. Elsewhere through shakes one third the length. Several such scattered along the length.

Skips—Hit or miss; in addition, 10 percent of pieces may have heavy skip.

Slope of Grain—1 in 4.

Splits—Equal to one sixth the length of the piece.

Stain—Stained wood. Not limited.

Unsound wood—In spots or streaks limited to one third the cross section at any point along the length. Must not destroy nailing edge.

Wane—One half the thickness, one half the width. Five percent of the pieces may have up to seven eighths the thickness and three fourths the width for one fourth the length.

Warp—Medium.

White Speck and Honeycomb—Firm.

Heartwood, in redwood "No. 3 Heart Structural"—All heartwood.

(d) **Light Framing.** 1. **Construction.** Two inches to 4 inches thick, 2 inches to 4 inches wide.

Characteristics permitted and limiting provisions are:

Checks—Surface seasoning checks not limited. Through checks at ends are limited as splits.

Knots—Sound, firm, encased and pith knots must be tight and are permitted in the following sizes or their equivalent displacement:

NOM. WIDTH	ANYWHERE ON WIDE FACE	UNSOUND OR LOOSE KNOTS AND HOLES	
2″	3/4″	5/8″	One hole or equivalent smaller per 3 linear feet
3″	1 1/4″	3/4″	
4″	1 1/2″	1″	

Knots spiked entirely across the wide face are limited to a displacement of approximately one-fourth the cross section.

Manufacture—Standard "E."

Pitch and pitch streaks—Not limited.

Pockets, pitch or bark—Not limited.

Shake—Several heart shakes up to 2 feet long, similar to seasoning checks, none through.

Skips—Hit and miss on 10 percent of the pieces.

Slope of Grain—1 in 6.

Splits—Equal in length to the width of the piece.

Stain—Stained sapwood. Firm heart stain or firm red heart.

Wane—One fourth the thickness, one fourth the width. Five percent of the pieces may have wane up to one half the thickness and one third the width for one fourth the length.

Warp—One half of medium.

2. **Standard.** Two inches to 4 inches thick, 2 inches to 4 inches wide.

Characteristics permitted and limiting provisions are:

Checks—Seasoning checks not limited. Through checks at ends are limited as splits.

Knots—Not restricted as to quality and are permitted in the following sizes or their equivalent displacement:

NOM. WIDTH	ANYWHERE ON WIDE FACE	HOLES	
2″	1″	3/4″	One hole or equivalent smaller per 2 linear feet
3″	1 1/2″	1″	
4″	2″	1 1/4″	

Knots spiked entirely across the wide face are limited to a displacement of approximately one-third the cross section.

Manufacture—Standard "F."

Pitch and pitch streaks—Not limited.

Pockets, pitch or bark—Not limited.

Shake—On ends limited to one-half the thickness. Away from ends through heart shakes up to 2 feet long, well separated. If not through, single shakes may be 3 feet long or up to one-fourth the length, whichever is greater.

Skips—Hit and miss. In addition, 5 percent of pieces may be hit or miss, or heavy skip not longer than 2 feet.

Slope of grain—1 in 4.

Splits—Equal in length to one and one-half times the width of the piece.

Stain—Stained sapwood. Firm heart stain or firm red heart. Not limited.

Unsound wood—Heart center streaks not over one-third the thickness or width, or small spots or streaks of firm honeycomb or peck equal to one-sixth the width are permitted.

Wane—One-third the thickness, one-third the width. Five percent of pieces may have wane up to two-thirds the thickness and one-half the width for one-fourth the length.

Warp—Light.

White speck—Firm, one-third the face or equivalent.

3. **Utility.** Two inches to 4 inches thick, 2 inches to 4 inches wide.

Characteristics permitted and limiting provisions are:

Checks—Seasoning checks not limited. Through checks at ends are limited as splits.

Knots—Not restricted as to quality and are permitted in the following sizes or their equivalent displacement:

NOM. WIDTH	ANYWHERE ON WIDE FACE	HOLES	
2″	1 1/4″	1″	One hole or equivalent smaller per 1 linear foot
3″	2″	1 1/4″	
4″	2 1/2″	1 1/2″	

Knots spiked entirely across the wide face are limited to a displacement of approximately one-half the cross section.

Manufacture—Standard "F."

Pitch and pitch streaks—Not limited.

Pockets, pitch or bark—Not limited.

Shake—Surface shakes permitted. If through at edges or ends, limited as splits. Elsewhere through shakes one third the length. Several such scattered along the length.

Skips—Hit or miss. In addition, 10 percent of the pieces may have heavy skips.

Slope of grain—1 in 4.

Splits—Equal to one sixth of the length of the piece.

Stain—Stained wood, not limited.

Unsound wood—In spots or streaks limited to one third the cross section at any point along the length. Must not destroy nailing edge.

Wane—One half the thickness, one half the width. Five percent of the pieces may have wane up to seven eighths the thickness and three fourths the width for one fourth the length.

Warp—Medium.

White speck and honeycomb—Firm.

(e) **Studs.** Two inches to 4 inches thick, 2 inches to 6 inches wide, 10 feet and shorter.

Characteristics permitted and limiting provisions are:

Checks—Seasoning checks not limited. Through checks at ends are limited as splits.

Knots—Not limited as to quality, but are well spaced and are permitted in the following sizes or their equivalent displacement:

NOM. WIDTH	AT EDGE WIDE FACE	CENTER LINE WIDE FACE[1]	HOLES	
2″	3/4″	3/4″	3/4″	One hole or equivalent smaller per 1 linear foot
3″	1 1/4″	1 1/4″	1 1/4″	
4″	1 3/4″	2 1/2″	1 1/2″	
5″	2 1/4″	3″	1 3/4″	
6″	2 3/4″	3 3/4″	2″	

[1]In 3 × 4 and 4 × 4, knot size shown for center line of wide face is permitted anywhere on 4-inch face.

Manufacture—Standard "F."

Pitch and pitch streaks—Not limited.

Pockets, pitch or bark—Not limited.

Shake—If through at ends, limited as splits. Elsewhere through shakes one third the length.

Skips—Hit or miss on any face. In addition, 10 percent of the pieces may have heavy skips on wide faces only.

Slope of grain—1 in 4.

Splits—Equal in length to twice the width of the piece.

Stain—Stained sapwood. Firm heat stain or firm red heart.

Unsound wood—In spots or streaks limited to one third the cross section at any point along the length. Must not destroy nailing edge.

Wane—One half the width and one third the thickness without length limit, or equivalent, more for 2 feet if not exceeding three fourths the width and one half the thickness.

Warp—One half of medium.

White speck and honeycomb—Firm.

(f) **Structural Joists and Planks.** Two inches to 4 inches thick, 5 inches and wider.

1. **Select structural.** Characteristics permitted and limiting provisions shall be:

Checks—Surface seasoning checks, not limited. Through checks at ends are limited as splits.

Grain, for redwood select structural—Close grain. For redwood select structural open grain—Open grain. For Douglas fir and southern pine dense—Dense. For Douglas fir, larch and southern pine—Medium.

Knots—Sound, firm, encased and pith knots, if tight and well spaced, are permitted in sizes not to exceed the following or equivalent displacement:

NOM. WIDTH	AT EDGE WIDE FACE	CENTER LINE WIDE FACE	UNSOUND OR LOOSE KNOTS & HOLES (ANY CAUSE)
5″	1″	1 1/2″	7/8″
6″	1 1/8″	1 7/8″	1″
8″	1 1/2″	2 1/4″	1 1/4″ One hole or equivalent smaller per 4 linear feet
10″	1 7/8″	2 5/8″	1 1/4″
12″	2 1/4″	3″	1 1/4″
14″	2 3/8″	3 1/4″	1 1/4″

Manufacture—Standard "E."

Pitch and pitch streaks—Not limited.

Pockets, pitch or bark—Not limited.

Shake—On ends, limited to one half the thickness. Away from ends, several heart shakes up to 2 feet long, none through.

Skips—Hit and miss in 10 percent of pieces.

Slope of grain—1 in 12.

Splits—Equal in length to the width of the piece.

Stain—Stained sapwood. Firm heart stain or firm red heart limited to 10 percent of the piece.

Wane—One fourth the thickness, one fourth the width. Five percent of the pieces may have wane up to one half the thickness and one third the width for one fourth the length.

Warp—One half of medium.

Heartwood, in redwood "Select Heart Structural"—All heartwood.

2. **No. 1.** Characteristics permitted and limiting provisions shall be:

Checks—Surface seasoning checks, not limited. Through checks at ends are limited as splits.

Grain, for redwood—Close grain. For redwood open grain—Open grain. For Douglas fir and southern pine dense—Dense. For Douglas fir, larch and southern pine—Medium.

Knots—Sound, firm, encased and pith knots, if tight and well spaced, are permitted in sizes not to exceed the following or equivalent displacement:

NOM. WIDTH	AT EDGE WIDE FACE	CENTER LINE WIDE FACE	UNSOUND OR LOOSE KNOTS & HOLES (ANY CAUSE)	
5″	1 1/4″	1 7/8″	1 1/8″	
6″	1 1/2″	2 1/4″	1 1/4″	
8″	2″	2 3/4″	1 1/2″	One hole or equivalent smaller per 3 linear feet
10″	2 1/2″	3 1/4″	1 1/2″	
12″	3″	3 3/4″	1 1/2″	
14″	3 1/8″	4″	1 1/2″	

Manufacture—Standard "E."

Pitch and pitch streaks—Not limited.

Pockets, pitch or bark—Not limited.

Shake—On ends limited to one half the thickness. Away from ends, several heart shakes up to 2 feet long, none through.

Skips—Hit-and-miss skips in 10 percent of pieces.

Slope of grain—1 in 10.

Splits—Equal in length to width of the piece.

Stain—Stained sapwood. Firm heart stain or firm red heart.

Wane—One fourth the thickness, one fourth the width. Five percent of the pieces may have wane up to one half the thickness and one third the width for one fourth the length.

Warp—One half of medium.

Heartwood, for redwood "No. 1 Heart Structural"—All heartwood.

3. **No. 2.** Characteristics permitted and limiting provisions shall be:

Checks—Seasoning checks not limited. Through checks at ends are limited as splits.

Grain, for redwood—Close grain. For redwood open grain—Open grain. For Douglas fir and southern pine dense—Dense. For Douglas fir and larch—Medium.

Knots—Well-spaced knots of any quality are permitted in sizes not to exceed the following or equivalent displacement:

NOM. WIDTH	AT EDGE WIDE FACE	CENTER LINE WIDE FACE	HOLES (ANY CAUSE)	
5″	1 5/8″	2 3/8″	1 3/8″	
6″	1 7/8″	2 7/8″	1 1/2″	
8″	2 1/2″	3 1/2″	2″	One hole or equivalent smaller per 2 linear feet
10″	3 1/4″	4 1/4″	2 1/2″	
12″	3 3/4″	4 3/4″	3″	
14″	4 1/8″	5 1/4″	3 1/2″	

Manufacture—Standard "F."

Pitch and pitch streaks—Not limited.

Pockets, pitch or bark—Not limited.

Shake—On ends, limited to one half the thickness. Away from ends through heart shakes up to 2 feet long, well separated. If not through, single shakes may be 3 feet long or up to one fourth the length, whichever is greater.

Skips—Hit and miss and, in addition, 5 percent of the pieces may be hit or miss or heavy skip not longer than 2 feet.

Slope of grain—1 in 8.

Splits—Equal in length to one and one-half times the width of the piece.

Stain—Stained sapwood. Firm heart stain or firm red heart not limited.

Unsound wood—Not permitted in thicknesses over 2 inches but in 2-inch thickness, heart center streaks not over one third the width or thickness, or small spots or streaks of firm honeycomb or peck equal to one sixth the width are permitted.

Wane—One third the thickness, one third the width. Five percent of the pieces may have wane up to two thirds the thickness and one half the width for one fourth the length.

Warp—Light.

White speck—Firm, one third the face or equivalent.

Heartwood, for redwood "No. 2 Heart Structural"—All heartwood.

4. **No. 3.** Characteristics permitted and limiting provisions shall be:

Checks—Seasoning checks not limited. Through checks at ends are limited as splits.

Grain, for redwood—Close grain. For redwood open grain—Open grain. For southern pine dense—Dense.

Knots—Well-spaced knots of any quality are permitted in the following sizes or their equivalent displacement:

NOM. WIDTH	AT EDGE WIDE FACE	CENTER LINE WIDE FACE	HOLES (ANY CAUSE)	
5″	2 1/4″	3″	1 7/8″	One hole or equivalent smaller per 1 linear foot
6″	2 3/4″	3 3/4″	2″	
8″	3 1/2″	4 1/2″	2 1/2″	
10″	4 1/2″	5 1/2″	3″	
12″	5 1/2″	6 1/2″	3 1/2″	
14″	6″	7″	4″	

Manufacture—Standard "F."

Pitch and pitch streaks—Not limited.

Pockets, pitch or bark—Not limited.

Shake—Surface shakes permitted. If through at edges or ends, limited as splits. Elsewhere through shakes one third the length. Several such scattered along the length.

Skips—Hit or miss and, in addition, 10 percent of pieces may have heavy skip.

Slope of grain—1 in 4.

Splits—Equal to one sixth of the length of the piece.

Stain—Stained wood, not limited.

Unsound wood—In spots or streaks limited to one third the cross section at any point along the length. Must not destroy nailing edge.

Wane—One half the thickness, one half the width. Five percent of the pieces may have wane up to seven eighths the thickness and three fourths the width for one fourth the length.

Warp—Medium.

White speck and honeycomb—Firm.

Rate of growth—Close grain. "Open grain" may be specified on an optional basis.

Heartwood, for redwood "No. 3 Heart Structural"—All heartwood.

(g) **Appearance Framing.** 1. Two inches to 4 inches thick, 2 inches and wider.

Characteristics permitted and limiting provisions are:

Checks—Seasoning, medium.

Free of heart center (FOHC).

Grain—Medium.

Knots—Sound, tight and well-spaced knots are permitted in the following sizes or their equivalent displacement:

NOMINAL WIDTH	ANYWHERE ON WIDE FACE
2″	1/2″
3″	3/4″
4″	1″
5″	1 1/4″
6″	1 1/2″
8″	2″
10″	2 1/2″
12″	3″
14″	3 1/8″

Manufacture—Standard "C."

Pitch—Light.

Pitch streak—Small.

Pith—Free of pith.

Pockets—Medium, well scattered.

Skips—Two very light, 6 inches in length, based on 12-foot length.

Slope of grain—1 in 10.

Splits—Equal in length to the width of the piece.

Stain—Stained sapwood, medium. Firm heart stain or firm red heart.

Wane—One twelfth the thickness, one twelfth the width for one sixth the length.

Warp—Very light.

(h) **Mechanically Stress-rated Lumber.** Each piece of mechanically stress-rated lumber shall be tested and marked to indicate the modulus of elasticity and shall comply with the following visual grading requirements:

Checks—Seasoning checks not limited. Through checks at ends limited as splits.

Shake—On ends, limited to one half the thickness. Away from ends, through heart shakes up to 2 feet long, well separated. If not through, single shakes may be 3 feet or up to one fourth the length, whichever is greater.

Skips—Hit and miss and, in addition, 5 percent of the pieces may be hit-or-miss or heavy skip not longer than 2 feet.

Splits—Equal in length to one and one-half times the width of the piece.

Wane—One third the thickness, one third the width; 5 percent of pieces may have wane up to two thirds the thickness and one half the width for one fourth the length.

Warp—Light.

In addition to the visual limitations listed, knots, knotholes, burls, distorted grain or decay, partially or wholly at edges of wide faces, must not occupy more of the net cross section than:

½ for 900 F_b and lower

⅓ for 950 F_b to and including 1450 F_b

¼ for 1500 F_b to 2050 F_b

⅙ for 2100 F_b and over

Definitions Applicable to Grading Rules

Sec. 25.108. Terms, words and phrases used in Section 25.107 shall be construed as follows and as defined in Appendix B.

1. **BIRD'S-EYE.** A small central spot with the wood fibers arranged around it in the form of an ellipse, so as to give the appearance of an eye. Bird's-eye, unless open or checked, is not considered a defect.

2. **BURL.** A distortion of grain, usually caused by abnormal growth due to injury of the tree. The effect of burls is assessed in relation to knots.

3. **CHECKS.** A separation of the wood normally occurring across or through the rings of annual growth and usually as a result of seasoning.

(i) A surface check occurs only on one surface of a piece.

(ii) A through check extends from one surface of a piece to the opposite or adjoining surface.

(iii) Small checks are not over 1/32 inch wide and not over 4 inches long.

(iv) Medium checks are not over 1/32 inch wide and not over 10 inches long.

(v) Large checks are larger than medium.

(vi) A roller check is a crack in the wood structure caused by a piece of cupped lumber being flattened in passing between the machine rollers.

A light roller check is a perceptible opening not over 2 feet long.

A medium roller check is a perceptible opening over 2 feet long but not exceeding 4 feet in length.

A heavy roller check is over 4 feet in length.

4. **COMPRESSION WOOD.** Abnormal wood that forms on the underside of leaning and crooked coniferous trees. It is characterized, aside from its distinguishing color, by being hard and brittle and by its relatively lifeless appearance. It is not permitted in readily identifiable and damaging form in stress grades nor where specifically limited.

5. **DECAY.** A disintegration of the wood substance due to action of wood-destroying fungi, and is also known as dote, rot and unsound wood.

(i) Heart center decay is a localized decay developing in the living tree along the pith in some species.

(ii) White specks are small white pits or spots in wood caused by the fungus "Fomes pini." It develops in the living tree and does not develop further in wood in service.

(iii) Honeycomb is similar to white speck but the pockets are larger.

(iv) Peck is channeled or pitted areas or pockets as sometimes found in cedar and cypress.

6. **DISPLACEMENT** is the amount of clear wood displaced by a knot and considered in its relation to the amount it reduces the strength of the cross section of the piece of lumber under consideration.

7. **EDGE.** There are three meanings for edge: the narrow face of rectangular-shaped pieces; or the corner of a piece at the intersection of two longitudinal faces; or, usually in stress grades, that part of the wide face nearest the corner of the piece.

(i) Eased edges means slightly rounded surfacing on pieces of lumber to remove sharp corners. Lumber 4 inches or less in thickness is frequently shipped with eased edges unless otherwise specified. Lumber of 1-inch and 2-inch thickness may be rounded to a radius of no more than 1/16 and 1/8 inch, respectively.

(ii) Square edged means free from wane without eased edges.

(iii) Free of wane means without wane but may have eased edges. (See WANE definition.)

(iv) Square corners means without eased edges but may permit wane allowance.

8. **GRAIN.** The stratification of fibers in wood composed of summerwood and springwood (see Appendix B).

(i) **Dense.** In Douglas fir and southern pine tree species of longleaf, slash, shortleaf and loblolly, an average of approximately six or more annual rings per inch on either end of a piece and one third or more summerwood. Rings are to be measured on a representative radial line and the contrasting color between summerwood and springwood must be distinctive; also, Douglas fir pieces averaging less than six annual rings but not less than four annual rings per inch and southern pine of specified species averaging not less than four annual rings per inch. Such averaging must be one half or more summerwood.

(ii) **Medium grain.** In applicable grades, an average of approximately four annual rings per inch measured on a representative radial line on either end of a piece. In Douglas fir, larch and southern pine tree species of longleaf, slash, shortleaf and loblolly, an average of approximately four or more annual rings per inch measured on a representative radial line; also, in Douglas fir and larch, pieces averaging less than four rings per inch and one third or more summerwood.

(iii) **Close grain.** In applicable species, an average of approximately six but not more than approximately 30 annual rings per inch on either end of a piece measured on a representative radial line. In Douglas fir and larch, pieces averaging five rings or more than 30 rings per inch are accepted as close grain if averaging one third or more summerwood. In southern pine, longleaf species, pieces shall average on either end not less than six annual rings per inch and one third or more summerwood measured on a representative radial line.

In redwood, an average ring count of not less than eight rings per inch.

(iv) **Open grain.** In all species, pieces with an unrestricted rate of growth as to rings per inch.

(v) Slope of grain is the deviation of the line of fibers from a straight line parallel to the sides of the piece.

(vi) Vertical grain (VG) (Edge grain EG) (Rift grain) lumber is a piece sawn at approximately right angles to the annual growth rings so that the rings form an angle of 45 degrees or more with the surface of the piece.

(vii) Flat grain (FG) (Slash grain SG) lumber is a piece or pieces sawn approximately parallel to the annual growth rings so that all or some of the rings form an angle of less than 45 degrees with the surface of the piece.

(viii) Mixed grain (MG) lumber may be either or both vertical and flat grain.

(ix) Spiral grain is a deviation in the slope of rain caused when the fibers in a tree take a spiral course around the trunk of the tree instead of the normal vertical course.

(x) Diagonal grain is a deviation in the slope of grain caused by sawing at an angle with the bark of the tree.

EXCEPTION: In redwood, grain is considered vertical when the rings of annual growth form an angle of 45 degrees or more with the surface of the piece. Any lumber that will not qualify as vertical grain is flat grain.

9. **HEART.** The portion of the tree contained within the sapwood. It is sometimes used to mean the pith.

(i) Boxed heart means with the pith enclosed in the piece.

(ii) Heart center is the pith or center core of the log.

(iii) Free of heart centers (FOHC) means without pith (side cut). When a piece has been sawn so as to eliminate the pith (heart center), an occasional piece showing pith on the surface for not more than one fourth the length may be accepted.

10. **HOLES.** Holes may extend partially or entirely through a piece and may be from any cause. Holes that extend only partially through the piece may also be designated as surface

pits. Unless otherwise specified, holes are measured the same as knots. Holes are classified by size as follows:

A pinhole is not over 1/16 inch in diameter.

A medium (small) hole is not over ¼ inch in diameter.

A large hole is not over 1 inch in diameter.

A very large hole is over 1 inch in diameter.

11. **KNOTS.** A portion of a branch or limb that has become incorporated in a piece of lumber. In lumber, knots are classified as to form, size, quality and occurrence. A red knot is one that results from a live branch growth in the tree and is intergrown with the surrounding wood. A black knot is one that results from a dead branch which the wood growth of the tree has surrounded.

A round knot is a knot cut at right angles to the length of the knot (limb).

An oval knot is a knot cut at slightly more than right angles to the length of the knot (limb).

A spike knot is a knot cut either lengthwise of the knot or diagonally across it.

A pin knot is not over ½ inch.

A small knot is not over ¾ inch.

A medium knot is not over 1½ inches.

A large knot is over 1½ inches.

A sound knot contains no decay. It may be red or black.

A pith knot is sound in all respects except it contains a pith hole not over ¼ inch in diameter.

A hollow knot is an apparently sound knot in all respects except it contains a hole over ¼ inch in diameter, and a through opening in a hollow knot may be of a size equal to other holes permitted.

An unsound knot contains decay.

A firm knot is solid across its face but contains incipient decay.

A tight knot is so fixed by growth, shape or position that it retains its place in the piece. It may be red or black.

An intergrown knot is one whose growth rings are partially or completely intergrown on one or more faces with the growth rings of the surrounding wood.

A watertight knot has its growth rings completely intergrown with those of the surrounding wood on one surface and is sound on that surface.

An encased knot is one which is not intergrown with the growth rings of the surrounding wood.

A loose or "not firmly fixed" knot is one not held tightly in place by growth, shape or position.

A fixed knot will retain its place in dry lumber under ordinary conditions but can be moved under pressure though not easily pushed out.

A knot cluster is two or more knots grouped together as a unit with the fibers of the wood deflected around the entire unit.

A star-check knot has radial checks.

Well-scattered knots are not in clusters and each knot is separated from any other by a distance at least equal to the diameter of the smaller of the two.

"Well-spaced" knots means that the sum of the sizes of all knots in any 6 inches of length of a piece must not exceed twice the size of the largest knot permitted. More than one knot of maximum permissible size must not be in the same 6 inches of length and the combination of knots must not be serious.

12. **MANUFACTURING IMPERFECTIONS.** Means all imperfections or blemishes

which are the result of manufacturing, such as the following:

(i) Chipped grain is a barely perceptible irregularity in the surface of a piece caused when particles of wood are chipped or broken below the line of cut. It is too small to be classed as torn grain and as usually found is not considered unless in excess of 25 percent of the surface involved.

(ii) Torn grain is an irregularity in the surface of a piece where wood has been torn or broken out by surfacing. Torn grain is described as follows:

Very light torn grain—not over 1/64 inch deep.

Light torn grain—not over 1/32 inch deep.

Medium torn grain—not over 1/16 inch deep.

Heavy torn grain—not over 1/8 inch deep.

Very heavy torn grain—over 1/8 inch deep.

(iii) Raised grain is an unevenness between springwood and summerwood on the surface of dressed lumber. Slight raised grain is an unevenness somewhat less than 1/64 inch.

Very light raised grain is not over 1/64 inch.

Light raised grain is not over 1/32 inch.

Medium raised grain is not over 1/16 inch.

Heavy raised grain is not over 1/8 inch.

(iv) Loosened grain is a grain separation or loosening between springwood and summerwood without displacement.

Very light loosened grain is not over 1/64-inch separation.

Light loosened grain is not over 1/32-inch separation.

Medium loosened grain is not over 1/16-inch separation.

Heavy loosened grain is not over 1/8-inch separation.

Very heavy loosened grain is over 1/8-inch separation.

(v) Skips are areas on a piece that failed to surface clean. Skips are described as follows with equivalent areas being permissible:

Very light skip is not over 1/64 inch deep.

Light skip is not over 1/32 inch deep.

Medium skip is not over 1/16 inch deep.

Heavy skip is not over 1/8 inch deep.

(vi) "Hit and miss" is a series of skips not over 1/16 inch deep with surfaced area between.

(vii) Hit or miss means completely surfaced or partly surfaced or entirely rough. Scantness may be 1/16 inch

(viii) Mismatch is an uneven fit in worked lumber when adjoining pieces do not meet tightly at all points of contact or when the surfaces of adjoining pieces are not in the same plane.

Slight mismatch is a barely evident trace of mismatch.

Very light mismatch is not over 1/64 inch.

Light mismatch is not over 1/32 inch.

Medium mismatch is not over 1/16 inch.

Heavy mismatch is not over 1/8 inch.

(ix) Machine burn is a darkening of the wood due to overheating by machine knives or rolls when pieces are stopped in machine.

(x) Machine bite is a depressed cut of the machine knives at the end of the piece.

Very light machine bite is not over 1/64 inch deep.

Light machine bite is not over 1/32 inch deep.

Medium machine bite is not over 1/16 inch deep.

Heavy machine bite is not over ⅛ inch deep.

Very heavy machine bite is over ⅛ inch deep.

(xi) Machine gouge is a groove cut by the machine below the desired line.

Slight machine gouge is less than 1/64 inch deep.

Very light machine gouge is not over 1/64 inch deep.

Light machine gouge is not over 1/32 inch deep.

Medium machine gouge is not over 1/16 inch deep.

Heavy machine gouge is not over ⅛ inch deep.

(xii) A machine offset is an abrupt dressing variation in the edge surface which usually occurs near the end of the piece and without reducing the width or without changing the plane of the wide surface.

Very light machine offset is a variation not over 1/64 inch.

Light machine offset is a variation not over 1/32 inch.

Medium machine offset is a variation not over 1/16 inch.

Heavy machine offset is a variation not over ⅛ inch.

Very heavy machine offset is a variation over ⅛ inch.

(xiii) Chip marks are shallow depressions or indentations on or in the surface of dressed lumber caused by shavings or chips getting embedded in the surface during dressing.

Slight chip marks are less than 1/64 inch deep.

Very light chip marks are not over 1/64 inch deep.

Light chip marks are not over 1/32 inch deep.

Medium chip marks are not over 1/16 inch deep.

Heavy chip marks are not over ⅛ inch deep.

(xiv) Knife marks are the imprints or markings of the machine knives on the surface of dressed lumber.

Very slight knife marks are visible only from a favorable angle and are perfectly smooth to the touch.

Slight knife marks are readily visible but evidence no unevenness to the touch.

(xv) Wavy dressing involves more uneven dressing than knife marks.

Very slight wavy dressing evidences unevenness that is barely perceptible to the touch.

Slight wavy dressing evidences perceptible unevenness that is somewhat less than 1/64 inch deep.

Very light wavy dressing is not over 1/64 inch deep.

Light wavy dressing is not over 1/32 inch deep.

Medium wavy dressing is not over 1/16 inch deep.

Heavy wavy dressing is not over ⅛ inch deep.

Very heavy wavy dressing is over ⅛ inch deep.

13. **CLASSIFICATIONS OF MANUFACTURING IMPERFECTIONS.** (i) Standard "A" Manufacture admits: Very light torn grain; occasional slight chip marks; very slight knife marks.

(ii) Standard "B" Manufacture admits: Very light torn grain; very light raised grain; very light loosened grain; slight chip marks; average of one slight chip mark per lineal foot but not more than two in any lineal foot; slight knife marks; very slight mismatch.

(iii) Standard "C" Manufacture admits: Medium torn grain; light raised grain; light loosened grain; very light machine bite; very light machine gouge; very light machine offset; light chip marks if well scattered; occasional medium chip marks; very slight knife marks; very slight mismatch.

(iv) Standard "D" Manufacture admits: Heavy torn grain; medium raised grain; very heavy loosened grain; light machine bite; light machine gouge; light machine offset; medium chip marks; slight knife marks; very light mismatch.

(v) Standard "E" Manufacture admits: Torn grain; raised grain; very heavy loosened grain; medium machine bite; machine gouge; medium machine offset; chip marks; knife marks; light wavy dressing; light mismatch.

(vi) Standard "F" Manufacture admits: Very heavy torn grain; raised grain; very heavy loosened grain; heavy machine bite; machine gouge; heavy machine offset; chip marks; knife marks; medium wavy dressing; medium mismatch.

14. **MOISTURE CONTENT.** The weight of the water in wood expressed in percentage of the weight of the oven-dry wood.

(i) Surfaced green "S-GRN"—Lumber which at the time of surfacing had a moisture content in excess of 19 percent.

(ii) Surfaced dry "S-DRY"—Lumber which at the time of surfacing had a moisture content of 19 percent or less.

(iii) Moisture content of 15 percent "MC 15" or "KD"—Lumber which is kiln or air dried and which at the time of surfacing had a moisture content of 15 percent or less.

EXCEPTION: Occasional pieces may have a moisture content greater than that specified above.

15. **OCCASIONAL PIECES.** Means not more than 10 percent of the pieces in a parcel or shipment.

16. **PITCH STREAK.** Is a well-defined accmulation of pitch in the wood cells in a more or less regular streak. Pitch streaks are described approximately as follows, with equivalent areas being permissible:

(i) Very small pitch streak ⅜ inch in width and 15 inches in length.

(ii) Small pitch streak one twelfth the width and one sixth the length of the piece.

(iii) Medium pitch streak one sixth the width and one third the length of the piece.

(iv) A large pitch streak is not over one fourth the width by one half the length of the surface.

(v) A very large pitch streak is over one fourth the width by one half the length of the surface.

(vi) A pitch seam is a shake or check which contains pitch.

17. **PITH.** Pith is the small soft core in the structural center of a log.

(i) Very small pith is not over ⅛ inch wide and occupies on face surface not over ¼ square inch (⅛ inch wide by 2 inches long, or ¹⁄₁₆ inch by 4 inches).

(ii) Small pith occupies not over ¾ square inch (⅛ inch by 3 inches, ³⁄₁₆ inch by 4 inches, ⅛ inch by 6 inches, or ¹⁄₁₆ inch by 12 inches).

(iii) Free of pith means that pith on or within the body of the piece is prohibited.

18. **POCKET.** A well-defined opening between the rings of annual growth which develops during the growth of the tree. It usually contains pitch or bark.

Pockets are described approximately as follows with equivalent areas being permissible:

(i) Very small pocket is ¹⁄₁₆ inch in width and 3 inches in length, or ⅛ inch in width and 2 inches in length.

(ii) Small pocket is ¹⁄₁₆ inch in width and 6 inches in length, or ⅛ inch in width and 4 inches in length, or ¼ inch in width and 2 inches in length.

(iii) Medium pocket is ¹⁄₁₆ inch in width and 12 inches in length, or ⅛ inch in width and 8 inches in length, or ⅜ inch in width and 4 inches in length.

(iv) A large pocket is not over 4 square inches in area.

(v) A very large pocket is over 4 square inches in area.

19. **PLUGS AND FILLERS.** Wood plugs and fillers are inserted into pieces of lumber to improve their appearance and usefulness. Quality of the inserts and workmanship must be in keeping with the quality of the grade. In dimension and other lumber graded for strength, inserts are limited to the same size and location as knots.

20. **SAPWOOD.** Outer layers of growth between the bark and the heartwood which contain the sap. In redwood, the layers of the cream-colored wood between the bark and heartwood.

(i) Bright sapwood shows no stain and is not limited in any grade except as specifically provided.

(ii) Sapwood restrictions waived means that any restrictions in a rule on the amount of sapwood permitted in pieces graded under that rule are not to apply.

(iii) Bright sapwood no defect (BSND) means that bright sapwood is permitted in each piece in any amount.

(iv) Bright sapwood, unless specifically restricted, is not limited in any grade. It is not limited if treated with anti-stain solution, kiln dried or air dried.

21. **SAW-SIZED.** Lumber sawn to size but permitting in 20 percent of the pieces a manufacturing tolerance of 1/32 inch under; in addition, an oversize tolerance of 1/8 inch is permitted.

Sized dimension lumber is uniformly manufactured to the net surfaced sizes and may be rough, surface or partially surfaced on one or more faces. When opposing faces are rough, a variation over size of 1/32 inch is permitted in No. 2 and better and Standard and better and, in addition, a variation of 1/32 inch undersize in 20 percent of the pieces is permitted. In Stud, Utility and No. 3, a variation of 1/6 inch over or under is acceptable in 20 percent of the pieces. When grade-stamped, sized dimension lumber must be identified as sized (SZD).

22. **SHAKE.** A lengthwise separation of the wood which usually occurs between or through the rings of annual growth.

(i) A light shake is not over 1/32 inch wide.

(ii) A medium shake is not over 1/8 inch wide.

(iii) A surface shake occurs on only one surface of a piece. A fine shake is one with a barely perceptible opening.

(iv) A through shake extends from one surface of a piece to the opposite or to an adjoining surface.

(v) A pith shake (or heart shake or heart check) extends through the growth rings from or through the pith toward the surface of a piece, and can be distinguished from a season check by the fact that its greatest width is nearest the pith whereas the greatest width of a season check in a pith-centered piece is farthest from the pith.

(vi) A ring shake occurs between the growth rings to partially or wholly encircle the pith.

23. **SPLITS.** A separation of the wood due to the tearing apart of the wood cells.

(i) A very short split is equal in length to one half the width of the piece.

(ii) A short split is equal in length to the width of the piece and in no case exceeds one sixth the length.

(iii) A medium split is equal in length to twice the width of the piece and in no case exceeds one sixth the length.

(iv) A long split is longer than a medium split.

24. **STRESS GRADES.** Lumber grades having assigned working stress and modulus of elasticity values in accordance with accepted basic principles of strength grading.

25. **TRIMMING.** The act of crosscutting a piece to a given length.

26. **WANE DIP.** A dip extending across a surface to occupy full surface for a part of length.

(i) A very short wane dip occupies full surface for not over 4 inches of length.

(ii) A short wane dip occupies full surface for not over 16 inches of length.

27. **WARP.** Any deviation from a true or plane surface, including bow, crook, cup and twist or any combination thereof. Warp restrictions are based on the average form of warp as it occurs normally, and any variation from this average form, such as short kinks, shall be appraised according to its equivalent effect. Pieces containing two or more forms shall be appraised according to the combined effect in determining the amount permissible. In these rules warp is classified as very light, light, medium and heavy, and applied to each width and length as set forth in the various grades in accordance with the following provisions and tables:

(i) Bow is a deviation flatwise from a straight line drawn from end to end of a piece. It is measured at the point of greatest distance from the straight line. The amount permitted according to the grade is as follows: If under 2 inches thick, three times as much as crook permitted for 2-inch faces. If 2 inches thick and under 3 inches, twice as much as crook permitted for 2-inch faces. If 3 inches thick and over, the same as the amount of crook permitted for that thickness.

(ii) Crook is a deviation edgewise from a straight line drawn from end to end of a piece. It is measured at the point of greatest distance from the straight line. For amount permitted, see Table No. 25-1-F.

(iii) Cup is a deviation in the face of a piece from a straight line drawn from edge to edge of a piece. It is measured at the point of greatest distance from the straight line. The amount of cup shall not exceed the following:

	FACE WIDTH			
	2″ & 3″	4″	5″ & 6″	8″
Very Light	1/32″	1/32″	1/32″	1/16″
Light	1/32″	1/32″	1/16″	1/8″
Medium	1/32″	1/16″	1/8″	3/16″
Heavy	1/16″	1/8″	3/16″	1/4″
	10″	12″	14″ AND WIDER	
Very Light	3/32″	1/8″	Proportionately	
Light	3/16″	1/4″	more	
Medium	1/4″	3/8″	″	
Heavy	3/8″	1/2″	″	

(iv) Twist is a deviation flatwise, or a combination of flatwise and edgewise, in the form of a curl or spiral, and the amount is the distance an edge of a piece at one end is raised above a flat surface against which both edges at the opposite end are resting snugly. For amount permitted, see Table No. 25-1-G.

Grade Marking

Sec. 25.109. (a) **The Grade Mark.** Lumber which is grade marked under this standard shall be subject to the following:

(i) The grade mark shall signify that the lumber conforms to the size, grade and seasoning provisions of the rules under which it is graded. When green lumber thinner than 5-inch nominal is graded and grade marked under the applicable grading rules, it shall comply with the green size requirements of such rules. If lumber is dressed to a size below minimum requirements or below the minimum sizes set forth in the applicable grading rules, the stamp must show size, and if thinner than 5-inch nominal, in addition, must state whether the lumber was dry or green when dressed. If lumber is dressed to less than the standard thickness of 1-inch nominal, the stamp must show the dressed thickness and whether the lumber was green or dry when dressed.

(ii) An approved easily distinguishable mark or insignia, registered and symbolizing grading supervision by an approved agency, shall be used in conjunction with the grade mark for each agency.

(iii) All pieces of a given grade shall be grade marked.

(iv) Mixed grades other than the two highest recognized grades for each species shall not be grade marked with a combination grade designation; if grade marking is required, each piece of a grade shall be marked as of its actual grade.

(v) The grade mark for structural lumber, except machine graded lumber, shall include an identification or designation of the commercial name of the species from which the lumber was produced. The identification of species will not be required when the agency symbol also indicates the species from which the lumber was produced. Where grading rules contain provisions for the grouping of species, each individual species included in a group shall be identified in the rules and the grade mark will include the designation assigned to the group.

(vi) A certified agency may provide further regulations for the use of its grade mark, provided the basic provisions of this section are observed.

(b) **Delegation of Grading Authority.** Permission to grade mark may be delegated by any approved agency to operate a mill supervisory service to those mills which are able to prove their ability to conform and their conformance currently with the grading rules for the species and grades which they manufacture and which agree to maintain the established standards of size and grade and to submit their lumber to inspection by the supervisory agency, both at the mill and upon complaint at destination.

TABLE NO. 25-1-A—NOMINAL AND MINIMUM-DRESSED DRY SIZES OF FINISH, FLOORING, CEILING, PARTITION, AND STEPPING AT 19 PERCENT MAXIMUM-MOISTURE CONTENT

(The thicknesses apply to all widths and all widths to all thicknesses except as modified.)

ITEM	THICKNESSES		FACE WIDTHS	
	NOMINAL[1]	MINIMUM DRESSED (Inches)	NOMINAL	MINIMUM DRESSED (Inches)
Flooring[1]	3/8	5/16	2	1 1/8
	1/2	7/16	3	2 1/8
	5/8	9/16	4	3 1/8
	1	3/4	5	4 1/8
	1 1/4	1	6	5 1/8
	1 1/2	1 1/4		
Partition[1]	1	23/32	3	2 1/8
			4	3 1/8
			5	4 1/8
			6	5 1/8

[1]In tongued-and-grooved flooring 7/16-inch, and 9/16-inch dressed thicknesses, the tongue or lap shall be 3/16 inch wide, with the overall widths 3/16 inch wider than the face widths shown. In all other worked lumber of dressed thicknesses of 5/8 inch to 1 1/4 inches, the tongue shall be 1/4 inch wide or wider and the overall widths shall be not less than the dressed face widths shown in the above table plus the width of the tongue or lap.

TABLE NO. 25-1-B—NOMINAL AND MINIMUM-DRESSED DRY SIZES OF SIDING AT 19 PERCENT MAXIMUM-MOISTURE CONTENT

(The thicknesses apply to all widths and all widths to all thicknesses)

ITEM	THICKNESSES		FACE WIDTHS	
	Nominal	Minimum dressed (Inches)	Nominal	Minimum dressed (Inches)
Bevel siding	½	7/16 butt, 3/16 tip	4	3½
	9/16	15/32 butt, 3/16 tip	5	4½
	⅝	9/16 butt, 3/16 tip	6	5½
	¾	11/16 butt, 3/16 tip	8	7¼
	1	3/4 butt, 3/16 tip	10	9¼
			12	11¼
Bungalow siding	¾	11/16 butt, 3/16 tip	8	7¼
			10	9¼
			12	11¼
Rustic and drop siding (shiplapped, ⅜-in. lap)	⅝	9/16	4	3
	1	23/32	5	4
			6	5
Rustic and drop siding (shiplapped, ½-in. lap)	⅝	9/16	4	2⅞
	1	23/32	5	3⅞
			6	4⅞
			8	6⅝
			10	8⅝
			12	10⅝
Rustic and drop siding (dressed and matched)	⅝	9/16	4	3⅛
	1	23/32	5	4⅛
			6	5⅛
			8	6⅞
			10	8⅞

TABLE NO. 25-1-C—NOMINAL AND MINIMUM-DRESSED SIZES OF BOARDS, DIMENSION, AND TIMBERS

(The thicknesses apply to all widths and all widths to all thicknesses)

ITEM	THICKNESSES			FACE WIDTHS		
	Nominal	Minimum dressed		Nominal	Minimum dressed	
		Dry (Inches)	Green (Inches)		Dry (Inches)	Green (Inches)
Boards[1]	1	¾	25/32	2	1½	1 9/16
	1¼	1	1 1/32	3	2½	2 9/16
	1½	1¼	1 9/32	4	3½	3 9/16
				5	4½	4⅝
				6	5½	5⅝
				7	6½	6⅝
				8	7¼	7½
				9	8¼	8½
				10	9¼	9½
				11	10¼	10½
				12	11¼	11½
				14	13¼	13½
				16	15¼	15½
Dimension	2	1½	1 9/16	2	1½	1 9/16
	2½	2	2 1/16	3	2½	2 9/16
	3	2½	2 9/16	4	3½	3 9/16
	3½	3	3 1/16	5	4½	4 5/8
				6	5½	5⅝
				8	7¼	7½
				10	9¼	9½
				12	11¼	11½
				14	13¼	13½
				16	15¼	15½
Dimension	4	3½	3 9/16	2	1½	1 9/16
	4½	4	4 1/16	3	2½	2 9/16
				4	3½	3 9/16
				5	4½	4⅝
				6	5½	5⅝
				8	7¼	7½
				10	9¼	9½
				12	11¼	11½
				14	—	13½
				16	—	15½
Timbers	5 and thicker	—	½ off	5 and wider	—	½ off

[1]Boards less than the minimum thickness for 1-inch nominal but ⅝ inch or greater thickness dry (11/16 inch green) may be regarded as American Standard Lumber, but such boards shall be marked to show the size and condition of seasoning at the time of dressing. They shall also be distinguished from 1-inch boards on invoices and certificates.

TABLE NO. 25-1-D—NOMINAL AND MINIMUM-DRESSED SIZES OF (2 INCH AND UNDER) SHIPLAP, CENTERMATCH, AND D&M
(The thicknesses apply to all widths and all widths to all thicknesses)

ITEM	THICKNESSES			FACE WIDTHS		
	Nominal	Minimum dressed		Nominal	Minimum dressed	
		Dry (Inches)	Green (Inches)		Dry (Inches)	Green (Inches)
Shiplap, ⅜-inch lap	1	¾	25/32	4	3⅛	3 3/16
				6	5⅛	5¼
				8	6⅞	7⅛
				10	8⅞	9⅛
				12	10⅞	11⅛
				14	12⅞	13⅛
				16	14⅞	15⅛
Shiplap, ½-inch lap	1	¾	25/32	4	3	3 1/16
				6	5	5⅛
				8	6¾	7
				10	8¾	9
				12	10¾	11
				14	12¾	13
				16	14¾	15
Centermatch, ¼-inch tongue	1	¾	25/32	4	3⅛	3 3/16
	1¼	1	1 1/32	5	4⅛	4¼
	1½	1¼	1 9/32	6	5⅛	5¼
				8	6⅞	7⅛
				10	8⅞	9⅛
				12	10⅞	11⅛
2″ D & M, ⅜-inch tongue	2	1½	1 9/16	4	3	3 1/16
				6	5	5⅛
				8	6¾	7
				10	8¾	9
				12	10¾	11
2″ Shiplap, ½-inch lap	2	1½	1 9/16	4	3	3 1/16
				6	5	5⅛
				8	6¾	7
				10	8¾	9
				12	10¾	11

TABLE NO. 25-1-E—WORKED LUMBER SUCH AS FACTORY FLOORING, HEAVY ROOFING, DECKING, AND SHEET PILING

(The thicknesses apply to all widths and all widths to all thicknesses) (See Note)

THICKNESSES[1]			FACE WIDTHS		
Nominal	Minimum dressed (Inches)		Nominal	Minimum dressed (Inches)	
TONGUED AND GROOVED					
	Dry	Green		Dry	Green
2½	2	2 1/16	4	3	3 1/16
3	2½	2 9/16	6	5	5⅛
3½	3	3 1/16	8	6¾	7
4	3½	3 9/16	10	8¾	9
4½	4	4 1/16	12	10¾	11
SHIPLAP					
	Dry	Green		Dry	Green
2½	2	2 1/16	4	3	3 1/16
3	2½	2 9/16	6	5	5⅛
3½	3	3 1/16	8	6¾	7
4	3½	3 9/16	10	8¾	9
4½	4	4 1/16	12	10¾	11
GROOVED FOR SPLINES					
	Dry	Green		Dry	Green
2½	2	2 1/16	4	3½	3 9/16
3	2½	2 9/16	6	5½	5⅝
3½	3	3 1/16	8	7¼	7½
4	3½	3 9/16	10	9¼	9½
4½	4	4 1/16	12	11¼	11½

NOTE: In worked lumber of nominal thicknesses of 2 inches and over, the tongue shall be ⅜ inch wide in tongued-and-grooved lumber and the lap ½ inch wide in shiplapped lumber, with the overall widths ⅜ inch and ½ inch wider, respectively, than the face widths shown. Double tongued-and-grooved decking may be manufactured with a 5/16-inch tongue.

[1]See Table No. 25-1-C for information on 2-inch dimension.

TABLE NO. 25-1-F—CROOK

Length in feet	Description	WIDTH OF PIECE						
		2″	3″	4″	5″,6″	8″	10″	12″
4 & 6	Very Light	1/8	1/8	1/8	1/8	1/16	1/16	1/16
	Light	1/4	1/4	1/4	3/16	1/8	1/16	1/16
	Medium	3/8	3/8	3/8	1/4	3/16	1/8	1/8
	Heavy	1/2	1/2	1/2	3/8	1/4	3/16	3/16
8	Very Light	1/4	1/4	1/16	1/8	1/8	1/16	1/16
	Light	3/8	3/8	3/8	5/16	1/4	3/16	1/8
	Medium	1/2	1/2	1/2	1/2	3/8	1/4	3/16
	Heavy	3/4	3/4	3/4	5/8	1/2	3/8	1/4
10	Very Light	3/8	3/16	1/4	3/16	3/16	1/8	1/8
	Light	3/4	3/8	1/2	7/16	3/8	1/4	3/16
	Medium	1 3/8	1	3/4	5/8	1/2	7/16	3/8
	Heavy	1 3/4	1 1/4	1 1/8	1	7/8	3/4	5/8
12	Very Light	1/2	3/8	3/8	5/16	1/4	1/4	3/16
	Light	1	3/4	11/16	5/8	1/2	7/16	3/8
	Medium	1 1/2	1 1/8	1	7/8	13/16	3/4	9/16
	Heavy	2	1 1/2	1 3/8	1 1/4	1 1/8	1	13/16
14	Very Light	5/8	1/2	7/16	3/8	5/16	1/4	3/16
	Light	1 1/4	1	7/8	3/4	5/8	1/2	3/8
	Medium	2	1 1/2	1 1/4	1 1/8	1	7/8	3/4
	Heavy	2 3/4	2	1 3/4	1 1/2	1 1/4	1 1/8	1
16	Very Light	3/4	5/8	1/2	7/16	3/8	5/16	1/4
	Light	1 5/8	1 1/4	1	7/8	3/4	5/8	1/2
	Medium	2 1/2	1 7/8	1 1/2	1 3/8	1 1/8	1	7/8
	Heavy	3 1/4	2 1/2	2	1 3/4	1 1/2	1 1/4	1 1/8
18	Very Light	1	3/4	5/8	1/2	7/16	3/8	5/16
	Light	2	1 3/8	1 1/8	1	7/8	3/4	5/8
	Medium	3	2 1/16	1 5/8	1 1/2	1 1/4	1 1/8	1
	Heavy	4	2 3/4	2 1/4	2	1 3/4	1 1/2	1 1/4
20	Very Light	1 1/8	7/8	3/4	5/8	1/2	7/16	3/8
	Light	2 1/4	1 1/2	1 3/8	1 1/4	1	7/8	3/4
	Medium	3 3/8	2 1/4	2 1/16	1 7/8	1 1/2	1 5/16	1 1/8
	Heavy	4 1/2	3	2 3/4	2 1/2	2	1 3/4	1 1/2
22	Very Light	1 1/4	1	7/8	3/4	5/8	1/2	7/16
	Light	2 1/2	1 3/4	1 5/8	1 1/2	1 1/4	1	7/8
	Medium	3 3/4	2 5/8	2 7/16	2 1/4	1 7/8	1 1/2	1 1/4
	Heavy	5	3 1/2	3 1/4	3	2 1/2	2	1 3/4
24	Very Light	1 1/2	1 1/8	1	7/8	3/4	5/8	1/2
	Light	3	2	1 7/8	1 3/4	1 1/2	1 1/4	1
	Medium	4 1/2	3	2 3/4	2 5/8	2 1/4	1 7/8	1 5/8
	Heavy	6	4	3 3/4	3 1/2	3	2 1/2	2 1/4

TABLE NO. 25-1-G—TWIST

Length in feet	Description	FACE WIDTH 2″	3″,4″	5″,6″	8″	10″	12″
4	Very Light	1/16	1/8	3/16	1/4	5/16	3/8
	Light	1/8	1/4	3/8	1/2	5/8	3/4
	Medium	3/16	3/8	1/2	3/4	7/8	1 1/8
	Heavy	1/4	1/2	3/4	1	1 1/4	1 1/2
6	Very Light	3/32	3/16	5/16	3/8	7/16	9/16
	Light	3/16	3/8	1/2	3/4	7/8	1 1/8
	Medium	9/32	1/2	3/4	1 1/8	1 3/8	1 5/8
	Heavy	3/8	3/4	1 1/8	1 1/2	1 7/8	2 1/4
8	Very Light	1/8	1/4	3/8	1/2	5/8	3/4
	Light	1/4	1/2	3/4	1	1 1/4	1 1/2
	Medium	3/8	3/4	1 1/8	1 1/2	1 7/8	2 1/4
	Heavy	1/2	1	1 1/2	2	2 1/2	3
10	Very Light	5/32	5/16	7/16	5/8	3/4	15/16
	Light	5/16	5/8	7/8	1 1/4	1 1/2	1 7/8
	Medium	1/2	7/8	1 3/8	1 7/8	2 3/8	2 3/4
	Heavy	5/8	1 1/4	1 7/8	2 1/2	3 1/8	3 3/4
12	Very Light	3/16	3/8	9/16	3/4	15/16	1 1/8
	Light	3/8	3/4	1 1/8	1 1/2	1 7/8	2 1/4
	Medium	9/16	1 1/8	1 5/8	2 1/4	2 3/4	3 3/8
	Heavy	3/4	1 1/2	2 1/4	3	3 3/4	4 1/2
14	Very Light	7/32	7/16	5/8	7/8	1 1/16	15/16
	Light	7/16	7/8	1 1/4	1 3/4	2 1/8	2 5/8
	Medium	5/8	1 1/4	1 7/8	2 5/8	3 1/4	3 7/8
	Heavy	7/8	1 3/4	2 5/8	3 1/2	4 3/8	5 1/4
16	Very Light	1/4	1/2	3/4	1	1 1/4	1 1/2
	Light	1/2	1	1 1/2	2	2 1/2	3
	Medium	3/4	1 1/2	2 1/4	3	3 3/4	4 1/2
	Heavy	1	2	3	4	5	6
18	Very Light	5/16	9/16	11/16	1 1/8	1 7/16	1 11/16
	Light	9/16	1 1/8	1 5/8	2 1/4	2 3/4	3 3/8
	Medium	7/8	1 5/8	2 1/2	3 3/8	4 1/4	5
	Heavy	1 1/8	2 1/4	3 3/8	4 1/2	5 5/8	6 3/4
20 and Longer	Very Light	5/16	5/8	15/16	1 1/4	1 9/16	1 7/8
	Light	5/8	1 1/4	1 7/8	2 1/2	3 1/8	3 3/4
	Medium	1	1 7/8	2 3/4	3 3/4	4 5/8	5 5/8
	Heavy	1 1/4	2 1/2	3 3/4	5	6 1/4	7 1/2

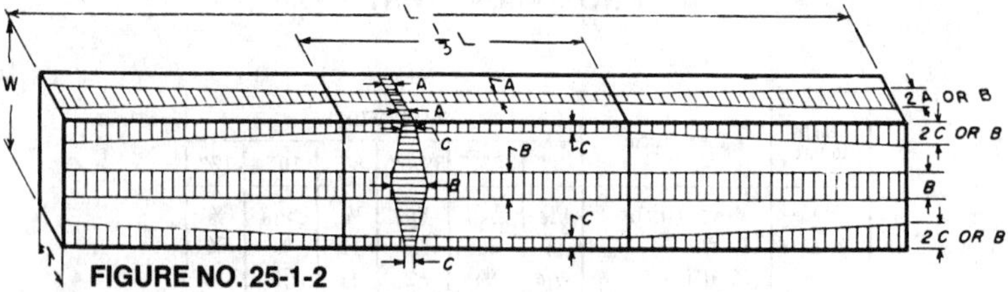
L
1/3 L
W
A
A
A
C
B
C
B
C
C
2A OR B
2C OR B
B
2C OR B
T

FIGURE NO. 25-1-2

Maximum Size of Knots Permitted in Various Parts of Joists and Planks, and Beams and Stringers:

A, maximum size on narrow face in middle third of length with a uniform increase to 2A but not to exceed B, at the ends.

B, maximum size at center of wide face.

C, maximum size at edge of wide face in middle third of length with a uniform increase to 2C but not to exceed B at the ends and a uniform increase to B at the center of the wide face. In beams and stringers, A and C are equal.

L, length.

W, width of side face.

T, width of narrow face.

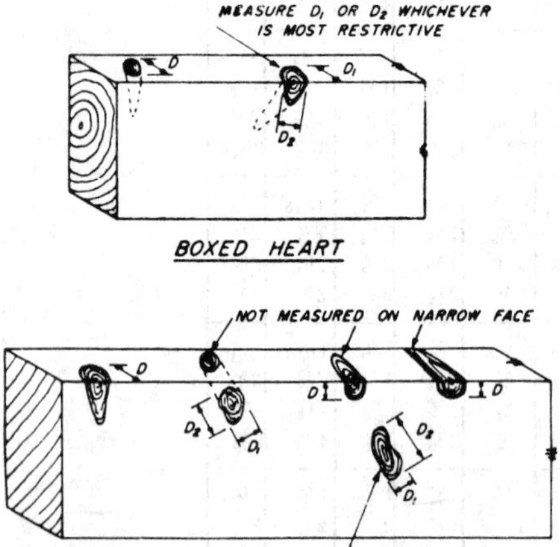
MEASURE D1 OR D2 WHICHEVER IS MOST RESTRICTIVE
D
D1
D2
BOXED HEART
NOT MEASURED ON NARROW FACE
D
D
D
D2
D1
D2
D1
MEASURE AVERAGE OF D1 AND D2

FIGURE NO. 25-1-1

Measurement of Knots in Joists and Planks

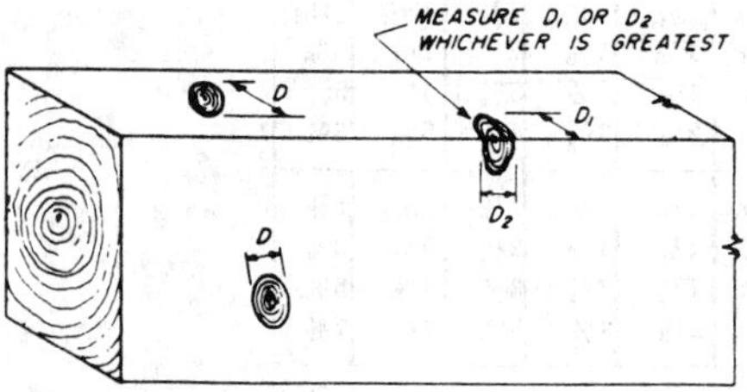
MEASURE D1 OR D2 WHICHEVER IS GREATEST
D
D1
D2
D

FIGURE NO. 25-1-3

Measurement of Knots in Beams and Stringers

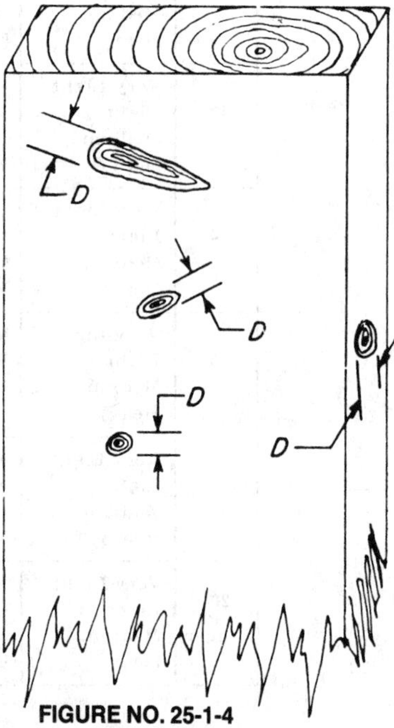
D
D
D
D

FIGURE NO. 25-1-4

Measurement of Knots in Posts and Timbers or Other Compression Members

APPENDIX A—NOMENCLATURE OF COMMERCIAL SOFTWOODS

The following commercial names for lumber cut from the principal species of softwoods should be used in grading rule description and in specifications.

COMMERCIAL NAMES FOR LUMBER	OFFICIAL COMMON TREE NAMES	BOTANICAL NAMES
Alaska Cedar	Alaska cedar	*Chamaecyparis nootkatensis.*
Incense Cedar	incense cedar	*Libocedrus decurrens.*
Port Orford Cedar	Port Orford cedar	*Chamaecyparis lawsoniana.*
Eastern Red Cedar	eastern red cedar	*Juniperus virginiana.*
	southern red cedar	*Juniperus silicicola.*
Western Red Cedar	western red cedar	*Thuja plicata.*
Northern White Cedar	northern white cedar	*Thuja occidentalis.*
Southern White Cedar	Atlantic white cedar	*Chamaecyparis thyoides.*
Balsam Fir	balsam fir	*Abies balsamea.*
	Fraser fir	*Abies fraseri.*
Douglas Fir	Douglas fir	*Pseudotsuga taxifolia.*
Noble Fir	noble fir	*Abies procera.*
White Fir	alpine fir	*Abies lasiocarpa.*
	California red fir	*Abies magnifica.*
	grand fir	*Abies grandis.*
	noble fir	*Abies procera.*
	Pacific silver fir	*Abies amabilis.*
	white fir	*Abies concolor.*
Eastern Hemlock	Carolina hemlock	*Tsuga caroliniana.*
	eastern hemlock	*Tsuga canadensis.*
Mountain Hemlock	mountain hemlock	*Tsuga mertensiana.*
West Coast Hemlock	western hemlock	*Tsuga heterophylla.*
Western Juniper	alligator juniper	*Juniperus deppeana.*
	Rocky Mountain juniper	*Juniperus scopulorum.*
	Utah juniper	*Juniperus osteosperma.*
	western juniper	*Juniperus occidentalis.*
Western Larch	western larch	*Larix occidentalis.*
Jack Pine	jack pine	*Pinus banksiana.*
Lodgepole Pine	lodgepole pine	*Pinus contorta.*
Norway Pine	red pine	*Pinus resinosa.*
Ponderosa Pine	ponderosa pine	*Pinus ponderosa.*
Sugar Pine	sugar pine	*Pinus lambertiana.*
Idaho White Pine	western white pine	*Pinus monticola.*
Northern White Pine	eastern white pine	*Pinus strobus.*
Longleaf Yellow Pine	longleaf pine	*Pinus palustris.*
	slash pine	*Pinus caribaea.*
Southern Yellow Pine	loblolly pine	*Pinus taeda.*
	longleaf pine	*Pinus palustris.*
	pitch pine	*Pinus rigida.*
	shortleaf pine	*Pinus echinata.*
	slash pine	*Pinus caribaea.*
	Virginia pine	*Pinus virginiana.*
Redwood	redwood	*Sequoia sempervirens.*
Eastern Spruce	black spruce	*Picea mariana.*
	red spruce	*Picea rubens.*
	white spruce	*Picea glauca.*
Engelmann Spruce	blue spruce	*Picea pungens.*
	Engelmann spruce	*Picea engelmanni.*
Sitka Spruce	Sitka spruce	*Picea sitchensis.*
Pacific Yew	Pacific yew	*Taxus brevifolia.*

APPENDIX B

A Glossary of Lumber Terms

(See also Section 25.108)

A

AIR DRIED, seasoned by exposure to the atmosphere, in the open or under cover, without artificial heat.

ALL-HEART, of heartwood throughout; that is, free of sapwood.

ANNUAL RING, growth put on in a single year.

B

BARK POCKET, patch or bark partially or wholly enclosed in the wood. Classified as are pitch pockets.

BLEMISH, anything marring the appearance of lumber.

BOXED PITH, where the pith is enclosed within the four sides of the piece.

BRIGHT, unstained.

C

CHARACTERISTICS, distinguishing features which by their extent and number determine the quality of a piece of lumber.

CLEAR, free or practically free of all blemishes, characteristics, or defects.

COMPRESSION WOOD, abnormal wood that forms on the under side of leaning and crooked coniferous trees. It is characterized, aside from its distingushing color, by being hard and brittle and by its relatively lifeless appearance.

CORNER, the intersection of two adjacent faces.

CROOK, see WARP.

CROSS BREAK, separation of the wood across the width.

CROSSCUTTING, cutting with a saw across the width.

CUP, see WARP.

CUTTING, resulting pieces after crosscutting and/or ripping.

D

DEGRADES, pieces which on reinspection prove of lower quality than the grade in which they were shipped.

DIAGONAL GRAIN, a deviation of the grain from a line parallel to the edges, which results from sawing a piece of lumber at an angle other than parallel with the bark.

DOUBLE END TRIMMED, trimmed reasonably square by a saw on both ends.

F

FIRM RED HEART, a stage of incipient decay characterized by a reddish color in the heartwood, which does not unfit the wood for the majority of yard purposes. (Not to be confused with natural red heartwood in some species.)

G

GROWTH RING, the growth put on in a single year.

GUM POCKET, an opening between growth rings which usually contains or has contained resin or bark, or both.

GUM SEAM, check or shake filled with gum.

GUM SPOT, accumulation of gumlike substance occurring as a small patch. May occur in conjunction with a bird-peck or other injury to the growing wood.

GUM STREAK, well-defined accumulation of gum in more or less regular streak. Classified as are pitch streaks.

H

HEART FACE, face side free of sapwood.

HEARTWOOD, inner core of the tree trunk comprising the annual rings containing non-living elements; usually darker in color than sapwood.

HONEYCOMB (DECAY), honeycomb is indicated by large pits in the wood.

K

KILN-DRIED, seasoned in a chamber by means of artificial heat.

KNOT, branch or limb embedded in the tree and cut through in the process of lumber manufacture; classified according to size, quality, and occurrence. To determine the size of a knot, average the maximum length and maximum width, unless otherwise specified.

PIN KNOT, not over ½ inch in diameter.

SMALL KNOT, over ½ inch, but not over ¾ inch in diameter.

MEDIUM KNOT, over ¾ inch, but not over 1½ inches in diameter.

LARGE KNOT, over 1½ inches in diameter.

P

PECK, channeled or pitted areas or pockets as sometimes found in cedar and cypress.

PITCH, accumulaton of resin in the wood cells in a more or less irregular patch.

LIGHT PITCH, lightly evident presence of pitch.

MEDIUM PITCH, trace of pitch slightly more evident than light pitch.

(Continued)

HEAVY PITCH, very evident presence of pitch showing by its color and consistency.

MASSED PITCH, clearly defined accumulation of solid pitch in a body by itself.

PITCH POCKET, an opening between growth rings which usually contains or has contained resin or bark, or both.

VERY SMALL PITCH POCKET, not over ⅛ inch in width and not over 2 inches in length.

SMALL PITCH POCKET, not over ⅛ inch in width and not over 4 inches in length, or not over ¼ inch in width and not over 2 inches in length.

MEDIUM PITCH POCKET, not over ⅛ inch in width and not over 8 inches in length; or not over ⅜ inch in width and not over 4 inches in length.

LARGE PITCH POCKET, width or length exceeds the maximum permissible for medium pitch pocket.

CLOSED PITCH POCKET, does not show an an opening on both sides of the piece.

OPEN (THROUGH) PITCH POCKET, is cut across on both sides of the piece.

PITCH SEAM, shake or check filled with pitch.

PITH, small soft core in the structural center of a log.

BOXED PITH, where the pith is within the four faces of an end of a piece.

PITH FLECK, narrow streak resembling pith on the surface of a piece, usually brownish, up to several inches in length, resulting from burrowing of larvae in the growing tissue of the tree.

R

RAISED GRAIN, roughened condition of the surface of dressed lumber in which the hard summerwood is raised above the softer springwood, but not torn loose from it.

S

SAPWOOD, outer layers of growth in a tree, exclusive of bark, which contain living elements; usually lighter in color than heartwood.

SAW BUTTED, trimmed by a saw on both ends.

SEASONING, evaporation or extraction of moisture from green or partially dried wood.

SIDE CUT, where the pith is not enclosed within the four sides of the piece.

SLOPE OF GRAIN, cross grain or deviation of the fiber from a line parallel to the sides of the piece, and may consist of diagonal grain, spiral grain, or both.

STRAIGHT GRAIN, slope of grain limited to 1 inch each 20 inches of length.

SLIGHT CROSS GRAIN, slope of grain not more than 1 inch in a length of 15 inches.

MEDIUM CROSS GRAIN, slope of grain more than 1 inch in a length of 15 inches, but not more than 1 inch in a length of 8 inches.

STEEP CROSS GRAIN, slope of grain more than 1 inch in a length of 8 inches.

SMOKE-DRIED, seasoned by exposure to the heat and smoke of fire maintained beneath or within the stacks of lumber.

SOFTWOOD, one of the group of trees which have needle-like or scale-like leaves. The term has no specific reference to the softness of the wood.

SOUND, free of decay.

SPIRAL GRAIN, fibers that extend spirally about instead of vertically along the bole of a tree.

SPRINGWOOD, more or less open and porous tissue marking the inner part of each annual ring, formed early in the period of growth.

STAIN, discoloration on or in lumber other than its natural color.

LIGHT STAIN, slight difference in color wnich will not materially impair the appearance of the piece if given a natural finish.

MEDIUM STAIN, pronounced difference in color which, although it does not obscure the grain of the wood, is customarily objectionable in a natural but not in a painted finish.

HEAVY STAIN, difference in color so pronounced as practically to obscure the grain of the wood.

SUMMERWOOD, denser fibrous outer portion of each annual ring, usually without conspicuous pores, formed late in the growing period, not necessarily in summer.

U

UNSOUND, decayed.

V

VARIATION IN SAWING, a deviation from the line of cut. Slight variation is not over 1/16 inch scant in 1 inch lumber, ⅛ inch in 2 inch, 3/16 in 3 inch to 7 inch, and ¼ inch in 8 inch and up.

W

WANE, this is bark or lack of wood from any cause on the edge or corner of a piece.

SLIGHT WANE, not over ¼ inch wide on the surface on which it appears for one sixth of the length and one fourth of the thickness of the piece.

MEDIUM WANE, over ¼ inch, but not over ½ inch wide on the surface on which it appears, for one sixth of the length and one fourth of the thickness of the piece.

LARGE WANE, over ½ inch wide on the surface on which it appears, or over one sixth of the length and one fourth of the thickness of the piece, or both.

WARP, any variation from a true or plane surface, includes bow, crook, cup, or any combination thereof.

BOW, deviation flatwise from a straight line from end to end of a piece, measured at the point of greatest distance from the straight line.

CROOK, deviation edgewise from a straight line from end to end of a piece, measured at the point of greatest distance from the straight line; and classified as slight, small, medium and large. Based on a piece 4 inches wide and 16 feet long, the distance for each degree of crook shall be: slight crook, 1 inch; small crook, 1½ inches; medium crook, 3 inches; and large crook, over 3 inches. For wider pieces it shall be ⅛ inch less for each additional 2 inches of width. Shorter or longer pieces may have the same curvature.

CUP, deviation flatwise from a straight line across the width of a piece, measured at the point of greatest distance from the line; and classified as slight, medium and deep. Based on a piece 12 inches wide, the distance from each degree of cup shall be: slight cup, ¼ inch; medium cup, ⅜ inch; and deep cup, ½ inch. Narrower or wider pieces may have the same curvature.

UNIFORM BUILDING CODE STANDARD NO. 25-9

CONSTRUCTION AND INDUSTRIAL PLYWOOD

Based on Product Standard PS 1-83 (for Construction and Industrial Plywood) of the U.S. Department of Commerce, and National Bureau of Standards Calculation of Diaphragm Action, an Engineering Standard of the International Conference of Building Officials

See Sections 2501 (a), 2501 (e), 2502 (a), 2513 (a) and 2513 (c), and Tables Nos. 25-B, 25-J-1, 25-K-1, 25-S-2 and 47-J, Uniform Building Code

Scope

Sec. 25.901. (a) **General.** This standard covers construction and industrial plywood for both Exterior and Interior types. This standard also covers construction and industrial hardwood plywood of red and white lauan (Philippine mahogany), tanoak, red alder and western poplar.

(b) **Wood Species.** Plywood produced under this standard considers four species classifications: Groups 1, 2, 3 and 4. The species used for the face and back plies are at the option of the manufacturer. When face and back veneers are of the same species group, the panels shall be identified as being of that species group. The species covered in each group are set forth in Table No. 25-9-A. In addition, other softwood or hardwood species having an average specific gravity of 0.41 or more, based on green volume and oven dry weight, may be used for inner plies except as required for premium grades in Section 25.905.

Definitions

Sec. 25.902. General definitions not included in the following section are to be interpreted as defined in U.B.C. Standard No. 25-1.

BACK is the side of a panel that is of lower veneer quality on any panel whose outer plies are of different veneer grades.

BORER HOLES are voids made by wood-boring insects, such as grubs or worms.

BROKEN GRAIN is a (leafing, shelling, grain separation) separation on veneer surface between annual rings.

CENTERS are inner plies whose grain direction runs parallel to that of the outer plies. May be of parallel laminated plies.

CHECK is a lengthwise separation of wood fibers, usually extending across the rings of annual growth caused chiefly by strains produced in seasoning.

CLASS I, CLASS II are terms used to identify different species group combinations of B-B concrete form panels. The standard provides for two classes, Class I and Class II, as described in Subsection 25.905 (c).

CORE. Sometimes referred to as a crossband.

CROSSBAND. Inner layers whose grain direction runs perpendicular to that of the outer plies. May be of parallel laminated plies. Sometimes referred to as core.

CROSSBAND GAP and **CENTER GAP.** An open joint extending through or partially through a panel, which results when crossband or center veneers are not tightly butted.

DEFECTS, OPEN, are irregularities such as splits, open joints, knotholes, or loose knots, that interrupt the smooth continuity of the veneer.

DELAMINATION is a visible separation between plies that would normally receive glue at their interface and be firmly contacted in the pressing operation. Wood characteristics, such as checking, leafing, splitting and broken grain, are not to be construed as delamination. See corresponding definition for those terms.

(a) For purposes of reinspection, areas coinciding with open knotholes, pitch pockets, splits and gaps and other voids or characteristics permitted in the panel grade are not considered in evaluating ply separation of Interior-type panels bonded with interior or intermediate glue.

(b) In evaluating Interior panels bonded with exterior glue, delamination in any glueline shall not exceed 3 square inches except where directly attributable to defects permitted in the grade as follows:
Delamination associated with:
1. Knots and knotholes—shall not exceed the size of the defect plus a surrounding band not wider than 3/4 inch.
2. All other forms of permissible defects—shall not exceed the size of the defect.

(c) In evaluating Exterior-type panels for ply separation, the area coinciding with the grade characteristics noted in Item (a) are considered, and a panel is considered delaminated if visible ply separation at a single glueline in such area exceeds 3 square inches.

EDGE SPLITS are wedge-shaped openings in the inner plies caused by splitting of the veneer before pressing.

FACE is the better side of any panel whose outer plies are of different veneer grades; also either side of a panel where the grading rules draw no distinction between faces.

GROUP is the term used to classify species covered by this standard in an order that provides a basis for simplified marketing and efficient utilization. Species covered by the standard are classified as Groups 1, 2, 3 and 4. See Table No. 25-9-A for listing of species in individual groups.

HEARTWOOD is the nonactive core of a log generally distinguishable from the outer portion (sapwood) by its darker color.

INNER PLIES are other than exposed face and back plies in a panel construction.

JOINTED INNER PLIES. Crossband and center veneer that has had edges machine-squared to permit tightest possible layup.

KNOT is a natural characteristic of wood that occurs where a branch base is embedded in the trunk of a tree. Generally the size of a knot is distinguishable by (1) a difference in color of limbwood and surrounding trunkwood; (2) abrupt change in growth ring width between knot and bordering trunkwood; and (3) diameter of circular or oval shape described by points where checks on the face of a knot that extend radially from its center to its side experience abrupt change in direction.

KNOTHOLES are voids produced by the dropping of knots from the wood in which they are originally embedded.

LAP is a condition where the veneers are so placed that one piece overlaps the other.

LAYER is a single veneer ply or two or more plies laminated with grain direction parallel. Two or more plies laminated with grain direction parallel is a parallel laminated layer.

NOMINAL THICKNESS is full "designated" thickness. For example, 1/10-inch nominal veneer is 0.10 inch thick. Nominal 1/2-inch-thick panel is 0.50 inch thick. Also, commercial size designation, subject to acceptable tolerances.

PATCHES are insertions of sound wood or synthetic material in veneers or panels for replacing defects. "Boat" patches are oval shaped with sides tapering in each direction to a point or to a small rounded end. "Router" patches have parallel sides and rounded ends. "Sled" patches are rectangular with feathered ends.

PITCH POCKET is a well-defined opening between rings of annual growth, usually containing, or which has contained, pitch, either solid or liquid.

PITCH STREAK is a localized accumulation of resin in coniferous woods which permeates the cells forming resin soaks, patches or streaks.

PLUGS are sound wood of various shapes, including, among others, circular and dog-bone, for replacing defective portions of veneer used to fill openings and provide a smooth, level, durable surface. Plugs usually are held in veneer by friction until veneers are bonded into plywood.

PLY is a single veneer lamina in a glued plywood panel. (See also layer.)

PLYWOOD is a flat panel, built up of sheets of veneer called plies, united under pressure by a bonding agent to create a panel with an adhesive bond between plies as strong as or stronger than the wood. Plywood is constructed of an odd number of layers with grain of adjacent layers perpendicular. Layers may consist of a single ply or two or more plies laminated with grain direction parallel. Outer layers and all odd-numbered layers generally have the grain direction oriented parallel to the long dimension of the panel. The odd number of layers with alternating grain direction equalizes strains, prevents splitting and minimizes dimensional change and warping of the panel.

Interior type—Plywood of this type is moisture resistant. It is intended for all interior applications as well as applications where it may be temporarily exposed to the elements. Table No. 25-9-D lists the grades within this type. Adhesive performance requirements are provided in Section 25.907.

Intermediate glue (IMG) type—Plywood of this type is bonded with adhesives that possess high-level bacteria, mold and moisture resistance. It is plywood suitable for protected construction and industrial uses where delays in providing protection may be expected. Adhesive performance requirements are provided in Section 25.907. (The grades of IMG-type plywood generally available are given in Table No. 25-9-D.)

Exterior type—Plywood of this type is produced with a C grade veneer or better throughout and is bonded with completely waterproof adhesives. It is a plywood that will retain its glue bond when repeatedly wetted and dried or otherwise subjected to the weather, and is therefore intended for permanent exterior exposure. Table No. 25-9-E lists the grades within this type. Adhesive performance requirements are provided in Section 25.907.

Overlaid plywood is Exterior-type plywood to which has been added a resin-treated fiber surfacing material on one or both sides. It is made in two standard categories, "High Density" and "Medium Density," and a "Special" category, all of which refer to the surfacing materials. The overlay surfaces are permanently fused to the base panel under heat and pressure. Although designed for all types of moisture exposure and service, all overlaid plywood is made only in the Exterior type. This refers to the base panel and to the overlay itself.

REPAIR is any patch, plug or shim.

SAPWOOD is the living wood of lighter color occurring in the outer portion of a log. Sometimes referred to as "sap."

SHIM is a long narrow repair of wood or suitable synthetic not more than 3/16 inch wide.

SHOP CUTTING PANELS are panels which have been rejected as not conforming to grade requirements of standard grades in this standard. Identification of these panels shall be with a separate mark that makes no reference to this standard and contains the notation, "Shop Cutting Panel—All Other Marks Void." Blistered panels are not considered as coming within the category covered by this stamp.

SPAN RATING is a set of numbers used in marking sheathing and combination subfloor underlayment (single floor) grades of plywood as described in Section 25.909.

SPLIT is lengthwise separation of wood fibers completely through the veneer caused chiefly by manufacturing process or handling.

STREAKS are synonymous with "pitch streaks."

STRUCTURAL I, II are names used to identify panels that provide for greatest refinement of engineering properties which may be important in the use of plywood for structural components and other sophisticated engineered applications. Manufacturing requirements include special provisions for species, panel construction and veneer grade characteristics as described in Section 25.905 (d).

TORN GRAIN. (See **BROKEN GRAIN.**)

TOUCH-SANDING is a sizing operation consisting of a light surface sanding in a sander. Sander skips to any degree are admissible.

VENEER. Thin sheets of wood of which plywood is made. Also referred to as plies in the glued panel.

WATERPROOF ADHESIVE is glue capable of bonding plywood in a manner to satisfy the exterior performance requirements given herein.

WHITE POCKET is a form of decay (*Fomes pini*) that attacks most conifers but has never been known to develop in wood in service. In plywood manufacture, routine drying of veneer effectively removes any possibility of decay surviving.

Light white pockets are advanced beyond incipient or stain stage to the point where the pockets are present and plainly visible, mostly small and filled with white cellulose and generally distributed with no heavy concentrations. Pockets for the most part are separate and distinct with few to no holes through the veneer.

Heavy white pockets may contain a great number of pockets, in dense concentrations, running together and at times appearing continuous. Holes may extend through the veneer but wood between pockets appears firm. At any cross section extending across the width of the affected area, sufficient wood fiber shall be present to develop not less than 40 percent of the strength of clear veneer. Brown cubical and similar forms of decay which have caused the wood to crumble are prohibited.

WOOD FAILURE (PERCENT) is the area of wood fiber remaining at the glueline following completion of the specified shear test. Determination is by means of visual examination and expressed as a percent of the 1-square-inch test area. (See Section 25.914 for test.)

Requirements

Sec. 25.903. (a) **Workmanship.** Unless otherwise specified, sanded plywood shall be surfaced on two sides. Faces and backs of panels shall be full width and full length except that C grade and D grade backs may be narrow on one edge or short on one end only, but by not more than 1/8 inch for half the panel length or width, respectively. Inner plies shall be full width and length except that one edge or end void not exceeding 1/8 inch in depth or 8 inches in length per panel will be acceptable. Crossband veneers not exceeding 1/8 inch in thickness may be lapped but by not more than 3/16 inch when adjacent to faces, or 1/2 inch when adjacent to backs, and provided such laps create no adjacent visible opening. Sanding defects resulting from crossband laps shall not be permitted in panel faces.

C or D grade veneers may be lapped by not more than 1/2 inch, provided such laps create no adjacent visible opening. All plies of CD panels only shall be full length and full width except that no more than half the length of one edge nor half the width of one end may contain short or narrow plies. This is contingent on such plies not being short or narrow by more than 3/16 inch, the aggregate area in the plane of the plies of such edge characteristics not exceeding 6 square inches in the entire panel, and such edge characteristics not occurring in more than one ply at any panel cross section.

In grades other than CD, backs may be narrow on one edge or short on one end only, but by not more than 1/8 inch for half the panel length or width, respectively; inner plies shall be full width and length, except that one edge or end void not exceeding 1/8 inch in depth or 8 inches in length per panel will be acceptable.

Crossband gaps or center gaps, except as noted for plugged crossband and jointed crossband shall not exceed 1 inch in width for a depth of 8 inches (measured from panel edge) and the average of all gaps occurring in a panel shall not exceed 1/2 inch. Every effort shall be made to produce closely butted core joints.

Where plugged inner plies are specified, inner plies shall be of C-Plugged veneer and gaps between adjacent pieces of inner plies shall not exceed 1/2 inch. Where jointed inner plies are specified, gaps between pieces of inner plies shall not exceed 3/8 inch, and the average of all gaps occurring in a panel shall not exceed 3/16 inch.

Unless otherwise specified, plugged core (also referred to as solid core) shall be core and center construction of C-Plugged veneer, and gaps between adjacent pieces of core shall not exceed 1/2 inch. When jointed core is specified, gaps between pieces of core shall not exceed 3/8 inch, and the average of all gaps occurring in a panel shall not exceed 3/16 inch.

Plywood shall be clean, well manufactured, and free from blisters, laps and other defects, except as expressly permitted herein. Panels shall have no continuous holes or through openings from face to back.

End butt joints may be used only under the following conditions:

1. Decorative grades as provided in Section 25.905 (b).
2. Butt joints having a total aggregate width not exceeding the width of the panel may occur in the center ply of five-ply, five-layer panels. The butt joints must be perpendicular to the grain of the panel face and back plies. The use of butt-jointed centers is allowed in Interior sanded grades in thicknesses up to and including 1/2 inch, and in C-D and C-D Plugged thicknesses up to and including 3/4 inch. End butt joints shall not be used in Structural I or II panels. Panels with butt joints in center plies shall be marked "butt-jointed center."

Plywood panels shall be constructed in the grades and veneer combinations as set forth in Tables No. 25-9-D and No. 25-9-E. All terms used herein shall be interpreted as described in Section 25.902. Constructions for all panels shall conform to the minimum number of plies and layers as set forth in Table No. 25-9-C. The proportion of wood with grain perpendicular to panel face grain shall be not less than 33 percent nor more than 70 percent of the total panel thickness. The combined thickness of inner layers in panels having four or more plies shall be not less than 45 percent of the total panel thickness. For application of the above requirements, the panel thickness shall be actual finished panel thickness and veneer thickness shall be the dry veneer thickness before layup. The grain of all layers shall be at right angles to the grain of adjacent layers and to the ends or edges of the panels. The entire area of each contacting surface of the adjacent veneer plies including repairs shall be bonded with an adhesive in a manner to assure satisfactory compliance with the performance requirements for its type as set forth in the tests described in this standard. Where face or back plies consist of more than one piece of edge-joined veneer, gaps between adjacent pieces shall be graded as splits. Any adhesive or bonding system that causes degradation of the wood or latent failure of bond will not be permitted.

For the purpose of veneer repairing or edge joining, strings, ribbons or tapes up to 3/8-inch maximum width can occur in a glueline and shall be considered as allowable localized defects in the evaluation of glueline test specimens. Wider strings, ribbons or tapes may be used for veneer repairing or joining if they are prequalified to show bonding equal to the required bonding for that panel. Glueline test specimens cut to include the strings, ribbons or tapes wider than 3/8 inch shall not be discarded because of the presence of these materials.

Veneer strips may be joined by string stitching, provided the punch for making holes prior to stitching has a dimension across the grain of 0.095 inch or less and the holes are spaced 1/2 inch center-to-center or greater. All veneer used for inner plies may be stitched. Stitched veneer used for outer plies is limited to panels with C or D grade faces or backs, except stitched C veneer may not be used for faces in decorative panels. Panels may have face or back plies stitched but not both.

Shims or strips of veneer shall not be used to repair panel edge voids. However, filling of permissible edge voids with approved synthetic fillers neatly applied will be admitted. Staples or pins of metal or synthetic material are prohibited. Face and back plies of exposed N, A and B veneer panels shall have the bark or tight surface out. Plies directly under surfaces of overlaid panels are not considered exposed veneers.

(b) **Tolerance.** A tolerance of +0.0 inch −1/16 inch (0.0625) shall be allowed on the specified length and/or width. Sanded panels shall have a thickness tolerance of 1/64 inch (0.0156) of the specified panel thickness of 3/4 inch and less, and ±3.0 percent of the specified thickness for panels thicker than 3/4 inch. Unsanded, touch-sanded, and overlaid panels shall fall within a plus or minus tolerance of 1/32 inch (0.0312) of the specified panel thickness for all thicknesses through 13/16 inch, and such panels greater than 13/16 inch shall have a thickness tolerance of 5 percent over or under the specified thickness. Panel thickness shall be based on a moisture content of 9 percent.

Panels shall be square within 1/64 inch per lineal foot for panels of 4-foot by 4-foot size or larger. Panels less than 4 feet in length or width shall be square within 1/16 inch measured along the short dimension. All panels shall be sawn so that a straight line drawn from one corner to the adjacent corner shall fall within 1/16 inch of panel edge.

(c) **Moisture Content.** Moisture content of panels at time of shipment shall not exceed 18 percent of oven-dry weight as determined by the oven-dry test specified in Section 25.917.

Veneer

Sec. 25.904. (a) **General.** Except as noted, veneers shall be 1/10 inch or thicker in panels 3/8 inch rough (unsanded) thickness or over; 1/12 inch or thicker in panels of lesser thickness. In no case shall veneers used in face or back layers be thicker than 1/4 inch, or veneers used in inner layers thicker than 5/16 inch.

One-twelfth-inch veneer may be used as crossbands in 5-ply, 5-layer, 1/2-inch panels and in parallel laminated layers.

One-sixteenth-inch veneer may be used for any ply in 5-ply Exterior-type panels less than 1/2 inch in thickness, as the center only in other 5-ply panels, and may be included in a parallel laminated layer.

Face and back veneers must be 1/8-inch minimum thickness for 19/32 inch and 5/8 inch, three-, four- and five-ply, three-layer panels of C-D, C-D Plugged, C-C, C-C Plugged and Underlayment grades.

For further limitations on panel layup, refer to Table No. 25-9-C panel constructions and workmanship.

The average veneer thickness shall conform to the limitations given in this standard within a tolerance of 5 percent of the specified nominal thickness measured dry before layup.

Parallel laminated outer layers may be used only in C-C, C-D, STRUCTURAL I C-C and C-D, and STRUCTURAL II C-C and C-D grades. Such layers shall consist of veneers 1/10 inch or thicker in any thickness combination not exceeding 1/4-inch total layer thickness. The face and back plies or exposed plies of outer layers shall conform to the species group and grade requirements for faces and backs, respectively, of the panel grade. The unexposed plies of outer layers, or sub-face and sub-back plies, shall conform to the species group and grade requirements for inner plies of the panel grade as specified in Section 25.904 (c) and (d).

The maximum split or gap in sub-faces and sub-backs shall be 1/4 inch under the faces of STRUCTURAL I C-C and C-D and STRUCTURAL II C-C and C-D panels, 1/2 inch under the faces of C-C and C-D grades, and 1/2 inch under D backs.

Parallel laminated inner layers in any grade shall consist of veneers 1/16 inch or thicker in any thickness combination not exceeding 7/16-inch total layer thickness. Individual plies in such layers shall conform to the species group and grade requirements for inner plies of the panel grade.

The veneers used in each ply of each panel and the completed panel shall conform with the applicable veneer grade and with the construction and workmanship requirements given herein. Additionally, the type and frequency of the characteristics shall be further limited as set forth for the grades listed in Table No. 25-9-B.

(b) **Number of Plies.** For a given thickness, the number of plies used in the panel makeup shall be not less than as provided in Table No. 25-9-C.

(c) **Species for Faces and Backs.** For purposes of this standard, veneer species are classified into the four groups given in Table No. 25-9-A. The species of face and back plies may be from any group; however, when a face or back is made of more than one piece, the entire ply shall be of the same species. Panels, other than unsanded and touch-sanded panels with span ratings which are produced with face and back veneers of the same species group shall be classified as being of that species group. Touch-sanded panels without span ratings that are manufactured with face and back plies of different species groups shall be identified by the larger numbered species group (i.e., Group 4 is larger numbered than Group 1). Sanded panels 3/8 inch or less in thickness and decorative panels of any thickness that are manufactured with face and back plies of different species groups shall be identified by the face species group number. Sanded panels greater than 3/8 inch that are manufactured with face and back plies of different species groups shall be identified by the larger numbered species group, except that sanded panels with C or D grade backs may be identified by the face species group number if backs are no more than one species group larger in number than the face and are 1/8 inch or thicker before sanding. The species classification group (except for unsanded and touch-sanded panels with span ratings) shall be set forth in the grade mark on each panel. See Section 25.909 for identification requirements for unsanded and touch-sanded panels with span ratings. Where intermixing between species groups occurs in the faces and backs of unsanded or touch-sanded panels with span ratings, provisions of Table No. 25-9-G shall be followed. [Douglas fir for the purpose . . . and loblolly (*Pinus taeda*) pines.] Because black, white and Engelmann spruce cannot be separated in veneer form by gross structure or minute anatomy, these species shall be classed as Engelmann spruce unless procedures are established for identification prior to peeling.

(d) **Species for Inner Plies.** Inner plies may be of any species or of any softwood species or any hardwood species having a published average specific gravity value of 0.41 or more, based on green volume and oven-dry weight, except as required for premium panels in Section 25.905.

(e) **Scarfed Veneers.** Scarfed veneer may be used for any face, back or inner ply except as provided in Section 25.911. Scarfed joints shall not have a slope steeper than 1 in 8, but may be specified at less than 1 in 8. Veneer in the scarf area shall not contain defects which reduce its effective cross section by more than 20 percent. Veneer scarfed joints shall be glued with a waterproof adhesive.

(f) **Classification.** All veneers used in the construction of the plywood panels shall conform to one of the following grade requirements of which N grade is the highest classification:

1. **Grade N veneer.** Grade N veneer (intended for natural finish) shall be smoothly cut 100 percent heartwood or 100 percent sapwood, free from knots, knotholes, pitch pockets,

open splits, other open defects, and stain; limited to not more than two pieces in a 48-inch width; not more than three pieces in wider panels; and well matched for color and grain.

Suitable synthetic fillers may be used to fill small cracks or checks not more than 1/32 inch wide; small splits or openings up to 1/16 inch wide if not exceeding 2 inches in length; and small chipped areas or openings not more than 1/8 inch wide by 1/4 inch long. Pitch streaks averaging not more than 3/8 inch in width and blending with color of wood are permitted.

Repairs shall be neatly made and parallel to grain and are limited to a total of six in number in any 4-foot by 8-foot face, with proportional limits for other sizes. They shall also be well matched for color and grain.

Patches are limited to three "router" patches not exceeding 1 inch in width and 31/2 inches in length.

No overlapping is permitted.

Wood shims not exceeding 3/16 inch in width and 12 inches in length that occur only at the ends of the panel are permitted.

2. **Grade A veneer.** Grade A veneer (suitable for painting) shall be firm, smoothly cut and free from knots, pitch pockets, open splits and other open defects. It shall be well joined when of more than one piece.

Suitable synthetic fillers may be used to fill, in Exterior-type panels, small cracks or checks not more than 1/32 inch wide; small splits or openings up to 1/16 inch wide, if not exceeding 2 inches in length; and small chipped areas or openings not more than 1/8 inch wide by 1/4 inch long. In Interior-type panels: small cracks or checks not more than 3/16 inch wide; openings or depressions up to 1/2 inch wide by 2 inches long or equivalent area.

Pitch streaks averaging not more than 3/8 inch in width, blending with color of wood are permitted.

Sapwood and discolorations are also permitted.

Repairs shall be wood or of synthetic patching material neatly made and parallel to grain, limited to a total of 18 in number, excluding shims, in any 4-foot by 8-foot face and shall have proportional limits on other sizes.

Patches are limited to the boat, router and sled types. Radius of ends of boat patches shall not exceed 1/8 inch. Patches shall not exceed 21/4 inches in width singly. Multiple patches consisting of not more than two patches, neither of which may exceed 7 inches in length if either is wider than 1 inch are permitted, except that there may be one multiple repair consisting of three die-cut veneer patches. Synthetic repairs shall not exceed 21/4 inches in width. Shims are permitted except over or around patches or as multiple repairs.

3. **Grade B veneer.** Grade B veneer shall be solid and free from open defects and broken grain except as noted. Slightly rough grain and minor sanding and patching defects, including sander skips not exceeding 5 percent of panel area are permitted.

Suitable synthetic filler may be used to fill, in Exterior-type panels, small splits or openings up to 1/16 inch wide if not exceeding 2 inches in length and small chipped areas or openings not more than 1/8 inch wide by 1/4 inch long. In Interior-type panels: small cracks or checks not more than 3/16 inch wide; openings or depressions up to 1/2 inch wide by 2 inches long or equivalent area.

Knots up to 1 inch measured across the grain if both sound and tight, pitch streaks averaging not more than 1 inch in width, and discolorations are permitted.

Splits not wider than 1/32 inch and vertical holes not exceeding 1/16 inch in diameter if not exceeding an average of one per square foot in number are permitted. Horizontal or surface tunnels limited to 1/16 inch across, 1 inch in length, and 12 in number in a 4-foot by 8-foot panel or proportionately in panels of other dimensions are also permitted.

Repairs shall be neatly made of wood or synthetic patching material. Repairs permitted are patches ("boat," "router" and "sled") not exceeding 3 inches in width individually where occurring in multiple repairs, or 4 inches in width where occurring singly. Synthetic veneer repairs shall not exceed 4 inches in width. Synthetic panel repairs shall not exceed 2 1/4 inches in width. Shims are permitted. Synthetic shims shall completely fill kerfs or voids; shall present a smooth level surface; and shall not crack, shrink or lose their bond under Exterior-type plywood test exposures described in Section 25.915 (b) and (c). Performance of synthetic shims under normal conditions of service shall be comparable to that of wood shims.

Synthetic plugs not exceeding dimensions specified previously which present solid, level, hard surfaces and whose performances under normal conditions of service are comparable to that of wood plugs are permitted.

4. **Grade C veneer.** Grade C veneer permits sanding defects that will not impair the strength or serviceability of the panel, knots if tight and not more than 1 1/2 inches across the grain, and knotholes up to 1 inch measured across the grain. An occasional knothole more than 1 inch but not more than 1 1/2 inches measured across the grain, occurring in any section 12 inches along the grain in which the aggregate width of all knots and knotholes occurring wholly within the section does not exceed 6 inches in a 48-inch width, and proportionately for other widths is also permitted.

Splits tapering to a point and limited to 1/2 inch by one-half panel length, 3/8 inch by any panel length are permitted, provided separation at one end does not exceed 1/16 inch where split runs full panel length, or 1/4 inch maximum width where located within 1 inch of parallel panel edge.

Voids due to missing wood on panel faces and backs not otherwise specified above shall not exceed the maximum width of knotholes permitted in the grade and the length of such voids shall not exceed 6 inches.

Repairs shall be wood or synthetic material, neatly made. Wood veneer repairs shall be die cut, and wood panel repairs shall be router or sled type. Wood repairs shall not exceed 3 inches in width individually where occurring in multiple repairs, or 4 inches in width where occurring singly; plugs (circular or "dog bone") not exceeding 3 inches in width individually where occurring in multiple repairs or 4 inches in width where occurring singly; and shims including synthetic as provided for in B grade.

Synthetic veneer repairs shall not exceed 4 inches in width.

Synthetic panel repairs shall not exceed 2 1/4 inches in width.

Shims are permitted.

C-Plugged veneer (veneer used for faces of underlayment, C-D Plugged and C-C Plugged grades, and inner plies of overlaid panels and other products if specified) may contain knotholes, worm and borer holes, and other open defects not larger than 1/4 inch by 1/2 inch, sound and tight knots up to 1 1/2 inches measured across the grain, splits up to 1/8 inch wide, broken grain, pitch pockets, if solid and tight, plugs, patches and shims. Synthetic repairs in veneer shall not exceed 4 inches in width. Synthetic panel repairs shall not exceed 2 1/4 inches in width. Where grades having C-Plugged face veneer are specified as fully sanded, sanding defects shall be the same as admitted under B grade. Sander skips to any degree shall be admissible in C-Plugged veneer.

5. **Grade D veneer.** Grade D veneer permits any number of plugs, patches, shims, worm or borer holes, sanding defects and other characteristics, provided they do not seriously impair the strength or serviceability of the panels. See also Section 25.903.

Tight knots are permitted in inner plies; and in D grade backs where limited to 2 1/2 inches measured across the grain.

In D grade backs, an occasional tight knot larger than 2 1/2 inches but not larger than 3 inches measured across the grain, occurring in any section 12 inches along the grain in which the aggregate width of all knots and knotholes occurring wholly within the section does not exceed 10 inches in a 48-inch width and proportionately for other widths is also permitted.

Knotholes up to 2 1/2 inches across the grain, an occasional knothole larger than 2 1/2 inches but not larger than 3-inch dimension occurring in any section 12 inches along the grain in which the aggregate width of all knots and knotholes occurring wholly within the section does not exceed 10 inches in a 48-inch width, and proportionately for other widths; in sanded panels, knotholes not exceeding 2 1/2 inches across the grain in veneer thicker than 1/8 inch; and knotholes not exceeding 3 1/2 inches across the grain are permitted in veneers at least two plies removed from the face and back plies of C-D and C-D Plugged grades having five or more plies.

Splits measured at a point 8 inches from their end shall not exceed 1 inch in width, tapering to not more than 1/16 inch where split runs full panel length; however, the maximum width within 8 inches of the end of the split shall not exceed the maximum width of knotholes permitted within the grade.

Splits on panel faces and backs shall not exceed 1/4 inch where located within 1 inch of parallel panel edge.

Voids due to missing wood on panel backs not otherwise specified above shall not exceed the maximum width of knotholes permitted in the grade and the length of such voids shall not exceed 6 inches.

Any area 24 inches wide across the grain and 12 inches long, in which light or heavy white pocket occurs, shall not contain more than three of the following characteristics, in any combination: 6-inch width of heavy white pocket; 12-inch width of light white pocket. One knot or knothole, 1 1/2 inches to 2 1/2 inches, or two knots or knotholes, 1 inch to 1 1/2 inches; knots or knotholes less than 1 inch shall not be considered. Size of any knot or knothole shall be measured in greatest dimension. Any repair in white pocket area shall be treated for grading purposes as a knothole.

6. **Synthetic repairs.** Synthetic fillers shall be limited to the repair of minor defects as specified in this standard. Synthetic fillers shall be of an approved type.

7. **Synthetic shims, patches and plugs.** These repairs shall completely fill kerfs or voids; shall present a smooth, level surface; and shall not crack, shrink, or lose their bond. Performance of synthetic shims, patches and plugs under normal conditions of service shall be comparable to that of wood repairs. The equivalency shall be established by testing and evaluation in accordance with approved procedures.

Premium Grades

Sec. 25.905. (a) **Marine Plywood.** Marine grade shall be of Exterior-type meeting applicable requirements of this standard, and of one of the following grades: A-A, A-B, B-B, High Density Overlay, or Medium Density Overlay, all as modified below for "Marine" plywood.

Only Douglas fir 1 and western larch veneer shall be used.

"A" faces shall be limited to a total of nine single repairs in a 4-foot by 8-foot sheet, or to a proportionate number in any other size as manufactured. "B" faces or backs where specified, and all inner plies, shall conform to "B" quality veneer requirements and shall be full length and width.

All patches shall be glued with an adhesive meeting Exterior-type performance requirements of this standard and, in addition, shall be set in the panel using a technique involving both heat and pressure.

When the inner ply veneers consist of two or more pieces of veneer, the edges shall be straight and square without lapping.

Neither edge of a panel shall have any crossband gap or edge-split in excess of 1/8 inch wide. Crossband gaps and edge-splits per 8 feet of crossband ply shall not exceed four in number. End splits and gaps on either end of a panel shall not exceed 1/8 inch in aggregate width. Filling of crossband gaps and edge-splits with crossband gaps and edge-split materials that serve to conceal the gaps or splits is prohibited.

(b) **Decorative Panels.** Specialty panels with decorative face veneer treatments in the form of striations, grooving, embossing, brushing, etc., which, except for the special face treatment, meet all of the requirements of this standard, including veneer qualities, glue bond performance and workmanship, shall be considered as conforming to the standard.

An occasional butt joint up to 6 inches in width shall be permitted for decorative effect in veneer on one panel face only. Where butt joints occur, the aggregate width of all knots and knotholes and two thirds the aggregate width of all repairs, including butt joints, shall not exceed 6 inches in any area 12 inches along the grain by 48 inches wide or proportionately for other widths.

(c) **Exterior B-B (Concrete Form) Panels.** A panel especially made for general concrete form use. Face veneers shall be not less than B grade and shall always be from the same species group. Inner plies shall be not less than C grade. (See Table No. 25-9-E for veneer grade limitations of High Density overlaid concrete form panels.) This grade of plywood is produced in two classes and panels of each class shall be identified accordingly. Panels shall be sanded two sides, edge-sealed and, unless otherwise specified, mill-oiled. Species shall be limited as follows and are applicable also to High Density overlaid exterior concrete form panels.

Class I—Faces of any Group I species, crossband of any Group 1 or Group 2 species, and centers of any Group 1, 2, 3 or 4 species.

Class II—Faces of any Group 1 or Group 2 species, and crossband and centers of any Group 1, 2, 3 or 4 species, or faces of Group 3 species of 1/8-inch minimum thickness before sanding, crossband of any Group 1, 2 or 3 species, and centers of any Group 1, 2, 3 or 4 species.

(d) **Structural Grade Panels.** Panels especially designed for engineered applications such as structural components where design properties including tension, compression, shear, cross-panel flexural properties and nail bearing may be of significant importance. In addition to the special species, grade and glue bond requirements set forth in Table No. 25-9-F, all other provisions of this standard for the specific types and grades form a part of the specifications for Structural grade panels.

(e) **Special Exterior.** A premium panel of Exterior type that may be produced of any specified species covered by this standard. It shall otherwise meet all of the requirements for Marine Exterior and be produced in one of the following grades: A-A, A-B, B-B, High Density Overlay, or Medium Density Overlay.

(f) **Underlayment, C-C Plugged.** Face veneer shall be 1/10 inch or thicker before sanding. The veneer immediately adjacent to the face ply of C-C Plugged and Underlayment shall be C grade or better with no knotholes over 1 inch across the grain, except that (1) veneer imemdiately adjacent to the face ply of Underlayment may be D grade with open defects up to 2 1/2 inches across the grain or (2) veneer immediately adjacent to the face ply of C-C Plugged may be C grade with open defects up to 1 1/2 inches across the grain, provided the face veneer is Group 1 or Group 2 species of 1/6-inch minimum thickness before sanding. Also see requirements set forth in Table No. 25-9-B.

Overlays

Sec. 25.906. (a) **General.** The standard grades of overlaid plywood are listed in Table No. 25-9-E.

(b) **High Density.** The surfacing on the finished product shall be hard, smooth and of such character that further finishing by paint or varnish is not necessary. It shall consist of a cellulose-fiber sheet or sheets, containing not less than 45 percent resin solids based on a volatile-free weight of fiber and resin. The resin shall be a thermosetting phenol or melamine type. The total resin-impregnated materials for each face shall be not less than 0.012 inch thick before pressing and shall weigh not less than 60 pounds per 1000 square feet, including both resin and fiber. The resin impregnation shall be sufficient to make a continuous bond without voids or blisters between the surfacing material and the plywood. The overlay face is usually produced in natural translucent color, but certain other colors may be used by manufacturers for identification.

Other resin-cellulose fiber overlay systems having a weight of not less than 60 pounds per 1000 square feet of single surface exclusive of glueline, and which possess performance capabilities of the above phenol system may be identified as High Density Overlay. Determination of equivalent performance shall be based on approved tests.

(c) **Medium Density.** The resin-treated facing on the finished product shall present a smooth, uniform surface intended for high-quality paint finishes. It shall consist of a cellulose-fiber sheet containing not less than 17 percent resin solids for a beater loaded sheet, or 22 percent for an impregnated sheet, both based on the volatile-free weight of resin and fiber exclusive of glueline. The resin shall be a thermo-setting phenol or melamine type. The resin-treated material shall weigh not less than 58 pounds per 1000 square feet of single face including both resin and fiber but exclusive of glueline. After application, the material shall measure not less than 0.012 inch thick. Some evidence of the underlying grain may appear. The overlay face is produced in a natural color and certain other colors.

Other resin-cellulose fiber overlay systems having a weight of 58 pounds per 1000 square feet of single surface exclusive of glueline, and which possess performance capabilities of the above phenol system may be identified as Medium Density Overlay. Determination of equivalent performance shall be based on approved test methods.

(d) **Special Overlays.** Surfacing materials having special characteristics which do not fit the exact description of High Density or Medium Density types as outlined previously. These must meet the test requirements for overlaid plywood and have a durable surface material. Panels shall be identified as "Special Overlay."

Adhesive Bond Requirements

Sec. 25.907. (a) **General.** Lots represented by test panels shall be considered as meeting the requirements of this standard if all of the following minimum requirements are met.

(b) **Interior-type Bonded with Interior Glue (Underlayment, C-D Plugged and C-D).** A panel shall be considered as meeting the requirements of the standard if three or more of the five test specimens pass. The material represented by the sampling shall be considered as meeting the requirements of this standard if 90 percent or more of the panels pass the test described in Section 25.913.

(c) **Interior-type Bonded with Exterior Glue (STRUCTURAL C-D).** When tested in accordance with Section 25.915, the average wood failure of all test specimens, regardless of the number of panels tested, shall be not less than 80 percent.

When more than one panel is tested:

1. At least 90 percent of the panels represented by the test pieces shall have 60 percent wood failure or better.
2. At least 95 percent of the panels represented by the test pieces shall have 30 percent wood failure or better.

These requirements are applicable separately and independently to the results obtained from the vacuum-pressure test and the boiling test. Specimens cut through localized defects permitted in the grade shall be discarded. Test specimens showing delamination in excess of

1/8 inch deep and 1 inch long shall be rated as 0 percent wood failure.

(d) **All Other Grades of Interior-type Plywood.** A panel shall be classed as failing if more than two of the five test specimens fail. The material represented by the sampling shall be considered as meeting the requirements of this standard if 85 percent or more of the panels pass, when tested in accordance with Section 25.913.

(e) **Mold Resistance.** Underlayment, C-D Plugged, and Standard shall be made with an adhesive possessing a mold resistance equivalent to that created by adding, to plain protein glue, 5 pounds of pentachlorophenol or its sodium salt per 100 pounds of dry glue base.

IMG-type plywood shall be made with an adhesive possessing a high degree of resistance to attack by bacteria and mold organisms. Adhesives, in order to qualify for use in the manufacture of IMG-type panels, must meet the "Bacteria Test" requirements published by the American Plywood Association. This procedure is specifically designed for adhesive qualification and is not applicable to inspection and testing, as covered in Section 25.912.

(f) **Resistance to Elevated Temperature.** Underlayment, C-D Plugged shall be made with an adhesive possessing resistance to temperatures up to 160°F. at least equal to that of plain protein glue. Urea resin glue shall not be used in these grades unless evidence is submitted indicating performance equivalent to plain protein glues.

(g) **Interior Type Bonded with Intermediate Glue (IMG-type).** When tested in accordance with Section 25.914, IMG-type plywood shall be considered as meeting the requirements of the standard if all of the following minimum conditions are met:

1. The average wood failure of all test specimens, regardless of the number of panels tested, shall be not less than 45 percent.
2. When more than one panel is tested at least 90 percent of the panels represented by the test pieces shall have 30 percent wood failure or better.

Specimens cut through localized defects permitted in the grade shall be discarded. Test specimens showing delamination in excess of 1/8 inch deep and 1 inch long shall be rated as 0 percent wood failure.

(h) **Exterior Type.** When tested in accordance with Section 25.915, Exterior-type plywood shall be considered as meeting the requirements of this standard if all of the following minimum conditions are met:

1. The average wood failure of all test specimens, regardless of the number of panels tested, shall be not less than 85 percent.
2. When more than one panel is tested:
   A. At least 75 percent of the panels represented by the test pieces shall have 80 percent wood failure or better.
   B. At least 90 percent of the panels represented by the test pieces shall have 60 percent wood failure or better.
   C. At least 95 percent of the panels represented by the test pieces shall have 30 percent wood failure or better.

These requirements are applicable separately and independently to the results obtained from the vacuum-pressure test and the boiling test. Specimens cut through localized defects permitted in the grade shall be discarded. Test specimens showing delamination in excess of 1/8 inch deep and 1 inch long shall be rated as 0 percent wood failure.

Plywood shall be tested for heat durability as described in Section 25.915. Any delamination due to combustion shall be considered as failure, except when occurring at a localized defect permitted in the grade. When testing overlaid plywood, blisters or bubbles in the surface caused by combustion shall not be considered delamination.

The bond between veneers of overlaid plywood as well as the bond between the overlay and the base panel shall meet the wood failure requirements described above for exterior. In evaluating specimens for separation of resin-treated face from the plywood, fiber failure shall be considered the same as wood failure.

Grade Marking

Sec. 25.908. All plywood shall be grade marked in accordance with Section 2501 of the Uniform Building Code. No reference shall be made to this standard in the certification or trademarking or grade marking of panels not conforming to all provisions of the standard. Each panel shall be identified with the mark of a qualified inspection and testing agency that shall designate the species group classification or span rating, glue bond type (Interior or Exterior), grade name or the grade of face and back veneers, and a symbol signifying conformance with the standard.

Panels not fully satisfying Exterior veneer requirements shall be identified as "Interior." However, the additional notation "Exterior Glue" or "Intermediate" (IMG) may be used where applicable to supplement the designation of Interior grades bonded with Exterior glue or Intermediate glue. Any further reference to adhesive bond, including those which imply premium performance or special warranty by the manufacturer, as well as manufacturer's proprietary designations, shall be separated from the grade marks or trademarks of the testing agency by not less than 6 inches.

Span Rating for Unsanded and Touch-sanded Panels

Sec. 25.909. Grade marking or trademarking of C-C, C-D, Structural C-C and Structural C-D, and of C-C Plugged and Underlayment to be used as combination subfloor underlayment (single floor) shall include a span rating for the thickness shown in Table No. 25-9-G. The numbers are presented as a fraction in the marking of sheathing grades of plywood, and as a single number for C-C Plugged and Underlayment. They describe the recommended maximum spans in inches under normal use conditions and correspond with commonly accepted criteria. For sheathing, the left-hand number refers to spacing of roof framing, and the right-hand number relates to spacing of the floor framing. The single number for Underlayment and C-C Plugged refers to spacing of the floor framing in single floor applications. The span rating number is related to species and thickness of the panel face and back veneers and panel thickness. It is established by either one of the following procedures:

1. By specification as detailed in Table No. 25-9-G.
2. By performance testing to satisfy the strength, stiffness and durability criteria as detailed in Section 25.910. Such performance testing is to be performed by a qualified testing agency.

Panels manufactured as C-C, C-D, Structural C-C and Structural C-D shall not be sanded, touch-sanded, surface textured or thickness sized by any mechanical means. However, sanded or touch-sanded panels which do not meet the grades for which they were intended may be reclassified and marked as C-C or C-D, provided the panels meet all applicable requirements for C-C or C-D and the finished face and back veneers after sanding each have a minimum net thickness equal to 90 percent of the applicable thickness in Table No. 25-9-G.

Performance Testing Qualification Requirements

Sec. 25.910. (a) **General.** Acceptance of performance-tested plywood under this standard is based upon testing of panel strength, stiffness and durability. Panels selected for testing shall be of near minimum grade and near minimum thickness. All provisions of veneer grade and panel workmanship are applicable.

(b) **Performance Testing.** Panels qualified for performance testing shall satisfy the criteria called for in this section when tested as required in Section 25.910 (c) and (d).

(c) **Structural Performance.** 1. **Concentrated loads.** A minimum of ten tests (specimens taken from at least five panels) shall be conducted for both concentrated static and impact loads according to Section 25.916. The tests shall be conducted for each exposure condition specified in Table No. 25-9-L or 25-9-N (Wet, Dry and/or Wet/Redry).

Deflection. At least 90 percent of tests shall deflect no more than the specified maximum.

Retest. If no more than two tests in a lot of ten fail to meet the deflection requirements, another lot of ten may be tested for that requirement. If no more than one test fails in this second round of testing, the requirements shall be considered satisfied.

Ultimate load. For each lot, 100 percent of tests shall support the specified minimum ultimate load.

Retest. If no more than one test in a lot of ten fails to meet the minimum ultimate load requirement, another lot of ten may be tested for that requirement. If all pass the retest, the requirements shall be considered satisfied.

2. **Uniform loads.** A minimum of ten tests (specimens taken from at least five panels) shall be conducted for uniform load capacity according to Section 25.917. The tests shall be conducted for each exposure condition specified in Table No. 25-9-M or 25-9-O.

Deflection. The average deflection shall not be greater than that specified.

Retest. If the average deflection is greater than specified, but does not exceed the requirement by 20 percent, another lot of ten may be tested for that requirement. If the average of the first and second lot taken together does not exceed that specified, the requirement shall be considered satisfied.

Ultimate load. For each lot, 100 percent of tests shall support the specified minimum ultimate load.

Retest. If no more than one test in a lot of ten fails to meet the ultimate load requirement, another lot of ten may be tested for that requirement. If all specimens pass this retest, the requirements shall be completely satisfied.

(d) **Bond Durability.** Panels shall be classed as Exposure 1 or Exterior.

1. **Exposure 1.** Panels rated as Exposure 1 shall be so identified and shall satisfy the bond requirements for Interior panels bonded with exterior glue as specified in Section 25.907 (c).

2. **Exterior.** Panels rated as Exterior shall be so identified and shall satisfy the bond requirements as specified in Section 25.907 (h).

(e) **Product Evaluation.** Upon satisfactory completion of the appropriate requirements of Sections 25.910 (c) and (d), a manufacturing specification will be written based on product evaluation under this section. This specification is to be used for quality assurance purposes by the manufacturer and his qualified testing agency. Product evaluation will be made on the same lot supplied by the manufacturer for qualification testing. Control values established during product evaluation will be the basis for quality evaluation of future production. The mill specification shall contain the following information.

1. **Panel construction.** Panels shall be defined as to veneer species and construction.

2. **Mechanical properties.** Twenty tests (specimens taken from at least 10 panels) shall be evaluated for bending stiffness both along and across the major panel axis according to the procedures of Section 25.918. The control value for each panel direction will be the sample mean and the minimum will be the lower value of a 90 percent confidence interval established on the mean.

Ten tests (specimens taken from at least 10 different panels) shall be tested for maximum bending moment both along and across the major panel axis according to the procedures of Section 25.918. The control value for each panel direction will be the minimum observed value, or the sample mean less 1.8 times the sample standard deviation, whichever is the higher value.

(f) **Re-examination.** 1. **Quarterly re-examination.** A product qualified by performance testing shall be subjected to quarterly re-examination by the manufacturer's qualified testing agency. Panels shall be tested according to the procedures of Section 25.910 (e) 2, Mechanical Properties.

2. **Resampling.** Failure to meet established control values shall result in an immediate intensive resampling of current production which will be tested for the failing property. This resampling shall consist of 20 panels.

3. **Requalification.** When results of the resampling fail to meet the applicable test requirements, a requalification for structural properties under Section 25.910 (c) shall be required.

Scarf- and Finger-jointed Panels

Sec. 25.911. (a) **General.** Neither panels with N faces nor the faces of such panels, unless longer than 10 feet, shall be scarfed or finger jointed except when specifically so ordered. Panels of other grades may be scarfed or finger jointed. Panels longer than 12 feet are necessarily scarfed. Scarf joints shall not have a slope greater than 1 to 8, but may be specified as less than 1 to 8. Joints shall be glued with a waterproof adhesive and meet the test requirements specified in this section as applicable. In addition, the adhesive shall not show creep or flow characteristics greater than unjointed wood when subject to load under any conditions of temperature and moisture.

(b) **Strength Requirements (Interior, IMG and Exterior) Scarfed and Finger-jointed Panels.** Panels shall be tested in accordance with Section 25.916 (a). If the average ultimate stress of the three test specimens of any one panel is less than 4000 psi for panels of Group 1 species, or less than 2800 psi for panels of Group 2 or Group 3 species, or 2400 psi for panels of Group 4 species, then that panel fails. The jointed panels represented by the sampling are acceptable if not more than one of the panels fails.

(c) **Scarf- and Finger-joint Durability for Interior and IMG Panels.** Panels shall be tested as outlined in Section 25.916 (b). Test specimens showing continuous delamination in excess of 1/16 inch deep and 1/2 inch long at the joint glueline shall be considered as failing. More than one failing specimen in a panel shall constitute failure of that panel. The jointed panels represented by the sampling are acceptable if not more than one of the panels fails.

(d) **Scarf-joint Durability for Exterior and Interior Panel Bonded with Exterior and Intermediate Glue.** Panels shall be tested in accordance with Subsection 25.916 (c). The material represented by the sampling shall be evaluated in accordance with Subsections 25.907 (b) and (c).

(e) **Finger-joint Durability for Exterior-type Panels and Interior-type Panels Bonded with Exterior or Intermediate Glue.** Panels shall be tested in accordance with Section 25.916. The joints shall meet the following minimum conditions:

1. The average wood failure rating of all specimens from each panel when tested in accordance with Section 25.916 shall be not less than 85 percent.
2. No single specimen from a panel (average of face and back gluelines) shall rate less than 60 percent wood failure.
3. No single face or back glueline in any specimen shall rate less than 30 percent wood failure.

Inspection and Testing

Sec. 25.912. (a) **General.** The tests specified in this section shall be used to determine the glue bond quality of plywood produced under this standard.

(b) **Inspections.** All plywood designated as complying with this standard shall be subject to inspection prior to coating or finishing, except that concrete form material may have a priming coat of oil or other clear preparation before inspection. The above requirement does not apply to Interior-type plywood bonded with exterior glue or to Exterior-type plywood when tested for glue bond quality.

(c) **Plywood Panel Grade, Size and Thickness Reinspections.** If reinspection establishes that an item is more than 5 percent below grade or out of dimensional tolerance according to the grade description, that item fails to pass the reinspection. The below-grade panels shall not be accepted. If reinspection establishes that a disputed item is 5 percent or less below grade or out of dimensional tolerance, it passes the reinspection. In addition to the above 5 percent grade and dimensional tolerance, a 5 percent tolerance shall apply separately to the inner-ply gap limitations, including the limitations applicable to the plugged crossband and jointed crossband, as specified in Section 25.903.

(d) **Plywood Glue Bond Quality Reinspections.** Reinspection of the unused panels shall be carried out following the procedures specified in Sections 25.912, 25.913, 25.914 and 25.915. If the reinspection tests establish that the glue bond quality does not meet the requirements of Section 25.907, as applicable, the panels fail to pass the reinspection. If the glue bond quality requirements are met, panels pass the reinspection. Any delaminated Exterior-type or overlaid panels are not acceptable.

(e) **Sampling for Panel Grade, Size and Thickness Reinspections.** Grade, size and thickness may include all panels of an item in dispute. However, when approved, a reduced basis for sampling consisting of at least 20 percent or 300 panels, whichever is smaller, shall be inspected for conformance to grade. For reduced sampling, the quantity of panels selected from each disputed item shall be prorated according to the number of panels. Panels found to be below grade or out of tolerance for size and thickness shall have improper grademarks obliterated and shall be remarked for appropriate classification with a special inspection mark registered by the qualified agency conducting the reinspection and applied by this agency's authorized representative.

(f) **Sampling for Glue Bond Reinspections.** For test purposes, 20 panels, or 5 percent of the panels, whichever is less, shall be selected at random from the item which is in dispute. The number of panels required shall be calculated by applying the "percent panels" to the lot size and converting part panels to whole panels by using a rounding procedure where 0.01 to 0.49 parts are considered to be the smaller whole number, while 0.50 to 0.99 parts are considered to be the larger whole number. These panels shall be selected from locations distributed as widely as practicable throughout the material being sampled. When an item, lot, or shipment involves panels with different adhesive bond requirements as provided for in Section 25.907, testing and evaluation shall apply separately to each category.

Sampling shall include no less than 20 panels of Interior-type Underlayment, C-D Plugged, and C-D. Sampling of Interior-type (including the different adhesive qualities) or Exterior-type shall be prorated on the basis of ratio of their volume to total volume (i.e., for shipment containing 50 percent Exterior, 10 Exterior panels shall be selected), but in no case shall less than 10 panels of each type or adhesive quality be selected. Shipments of Interior-type plywood bonded with exterior glue shall be sampled in the same manner as Exterior plywood.

(g) **Specimen Preparation.** One piece shall be cut from each Interior panel selected and from that piece five test specimens shall be cut. Each specimen shall be 2 inches wide by 5 inches along the grain. From each Exterior panel selected, one piece shall be cut from the panel and from that piece 10 test specimens shall be cut as described in Subsection 25.915 (a). Of the 10 specimens cut from each test piece, five shall be for vacuum pressure test, and five shall be for the boil test. From each overlaid panel selected, 10 specimens shall be cut as described for Exterior plywood. These shall be for testing the bond between veneers. A second set of 10 specimens shall be cut to test the bond between the overlay and the base panel as described in Subsection 25.915 (a).

From five of the Exterior test panels and five of the overlaid test panels, 5 1/2inch by 8-inch specimens shall be cut and tested as described in Subsection 25.915 (d).

Test for Interior-type Plywood

Sec. 25.913. The test specimens prepared as described in Subsection 25.916 (c) shall be placed in a pressure vessel and completely submerged in 110°F. water. A vacuum of 15 inches of mercury shall be drawn, maintained for 30 minutes and released. Specimens shall then be allowed to soak in the same water at atmospheric pressure for four and one half hours with no additional heating. They shall be removed and dried for 15 hours at 150°F. in an oven with fan forced air circulation of 45 to 50 air changes per minute. Specimens shall then be examined for delamination and evaluated in accordance with requirements given in the following paragraph.

Total continuous visible delamination of 1/4 inch or more in depth and 2 inches in length along the edges of a 2-inch by 5-inch test specimen shall be considered as failure. Where required, this shall be determined by probing with a suitable feeler gage not greater than 0.013 inch in thickness. When delamination occurs by reason of a localized defect permitted in the grade, other than white pocket, that test specimen shall be discarded.

Tests for IMG-type Plywood

Sec. 25.914. (a) **Preparation of Test Specimens.** Test specimens, taken as described in Subsection 25.916 (c), shall be cut 3 1/4 inches long and 1 inch wide, and kerfed one third of the length of the specimen from each end, as illustrated in Figure No. 25-9-1, so that a 1-inch square test area in the center results. Specimens shall be oriented so that the grain direction of the ply under test runs at a 90-degree angle to the length of the specimen. Kerfing shall extend two thirds of the way through the ply under test, and shall not penetrate the next glueline.

If the number of plies exceeds three, the cuts shall be made so as to test any two of the joints, but the additional plies need not be stripped except as demanded by the limitations of the width of the retaining jaws on the testing device. When desired, special jaws may be constructed to accommodate the thicker plywood. If the number of plies exceeds three, the choice of joints to be tested shall be left to the discretion of the approved inspection and testing agency, but at least one half of the tests shall include the innermost joints.

(b) **Vacuum Soak Test.** The test specimens shall be placed in a pressure vessel and submerged in water 120°F. A vacuum of 15 inches of mercury shall be drawn and maintained for 30 minutes. Following release of vacuum, specimens shall continue soaking for 15 hours at atmospheric pressure. The temperature of the water shall not drop below 75°F. at any time during the 15-hour soaking period. Specimens shall then be removed from the vessel and tested while wet by tension loading to failure in a shear testing machine operated at a maximum head travel of 16 inches per minute. Jaws of the machine shall securely grip the specimen so there is no slippage. The percentage of wood failure of the specimens shall be determined with specimens in a dry condition and evaluated as described in Subsection 25.907 (g).

Tests for Exterior- and Interior-type Bonded Exterior Glue (Includes Structural C-D and C-D with Exterior Glue)

Sec. 25.915. (a) **Preparation of Test Specimens.** Test specimens, taken as described in Subsection 25.912 (d) shall be cut 3 1/4 inches long and 1 inch wide, and kerfed one third of the length of the specimen from each end, as illustrated in Figure No. 25-9-1, so that a 1-inch square test area in the center results. Specimens shall be oriented so that the grain direction of the ply under test runs at a 90-degree angle to the length of the specimen. Kerfing shall extend two thirds of the way through the ply under test, and shall not penetrate the next glueline. Overlaid plywood specimens, taken as described in Subsection 25.912 (c) for testing of bond between veneers, shall be cut as described above for Exterior specimens. Overlaid specimens for testing the bond between the overlay and the base panel, shall be cut 1 inch wide and long enough for handling (3 inches is a convenient length) and kerfed just through the overlay 1 inch from the end, on each overlay face.

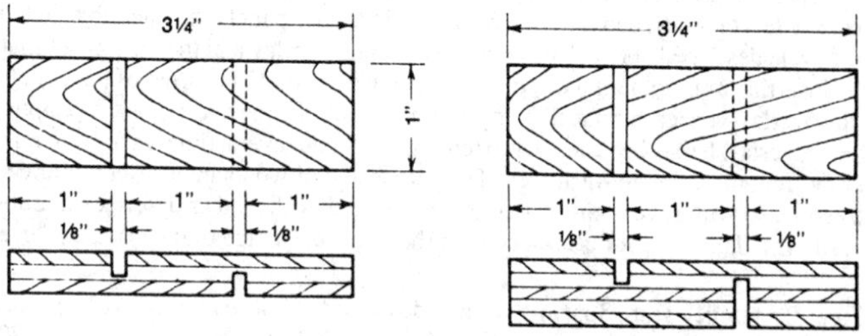
3¼"
1"
1"
1"
1"
⅛"
⅛"
3¼"
1"
1"
1"
⅛"
⅛"

(a) 3-ply Specimen

(b) 5-ply Specimen
NOTE: Orient grain direction across specimens to test inner two joints.

FIGURE NO. 25-9-1
Shear Test Specimens

If the number of plies exceeds three, the cuts shall be made so as to test any two of the joints, but the additional plies need not be stripped except as demanded by the limitations of the width of the retaining jaws on the testing device. When desired, special jaws may be constructed to accommodate the thicker plywood. If the number of plies exceeds three, the choice of joints to be tested shall be left to the discretion of the approved inspection and testing agency, but at least one half of the tests shall include the innermost joints.

(b) **Vacuum-pressure Test.** The test specimen shall be placed in a pressure vessel and submerged in cold tap water. A vacuum of 25 inches of mercury shall be drawn and maintained for 30 minutes, followed immediately with application of 65-70 psi of pressure for 30 minutes duration. Specimens shall then be removed from the vessel and tested while wet by tension loading to failure in a shear testing machine operated at a maximum head travel of 16 inches per minute. Jaws of the machine shall securely grip the specimens so there is no slippage. The percentage of wood failure of the specimens shall be determined with specimens in a dry condition and evaluated as described in Subsection 25.907 (h).

The bond between veneers in overlaid plywood shall be tested in an identical manner and evaluated as described in Subsection 25.907 (h). Specimens for testing the bond between the overlay and the base panel shall be subjected to the same test cycle described above. The bond between the overlay and the base panel shall be tested by inserting a sharp, thin blade of adequate stiffness into the corner of the 1-inch test area at the overlay-veneer interface, taking care not to cut into the overlay, and attempting to peel off the overlay. It may be necessary to reinsert the blade several times in order to remove the overlay from the 1-square-inch area. The percentage of wood and/or fiber failure shall then be estimated with specimens in a dry condition and evaluated as described in Subsection 25.907 (h). The value for each specimen shall be the average of the test areas on each face.

(c) **Boiling Test.** Test specimens shall be boiled in water for four hours and then dried for

20 hours at a temperature of 145 ± 5°F. with sufficient air circulation to lower moisture content of the specimens to a maximum of 8 percent, based on oven-dry weight. The specimens shall be boiled again for a period of four hours, cooled in water, and tested while wet by tension loading for failure in a shear testing machine operated at a maximum head travel of 16 inches per minute. Jaws of the machine shall securely grip the specimens so there is no slippage. The percentage of wood failure of the specimens shall be determined with specimens in a dry condition and evaluated as described in Subsection 25.907 (h). The bond between veneers in overlaid plywood shall be tested and evaluated in an identical manner. Specimens to test the bond between the overlay and the base panels shall be subjected to the same test cycle described above. The bond between the overlay and the base panel shall be tested by inserting a sharp, thin blade of adequate stiffness into the corner of the 1-inch test area at the overlay-veneer interface, taking care not to cut into the overlay, and attempting to peel off the overlay. It may be necessary to reinsert the blade several times in order to remove the overlay from the 1-square-inch area. The percentage of wood and/or fiber failure shall then be estimated with specimens in a dry condition and evaluated as described in Subsection 25.907 (h). The value for each specimen shall be the average of the test areas on each face.

(d) **Heat Durability Test.** Specimens cut as described in Subsection 25.912 (c) shall be placed on a stand as illustrated in Figure No. 25-9-2. It shall then be subjected to a 1472° to 1652°F. (800° to 900°C) flame from a Bunsen-type burner for a period of 10 minutes or, in the case of a thin specimen, until a brown char area appears on the backside. The burner shall be equipped with a wing top to envelop the entire width of the specimen in flame. The top of the burner shall be 1 inch from the specimen face and the flame 1 1/2 inches high. The flame shall impinge on the face of the specimen 2 inches from the bottom end. After the test, the sample shall be removed from the stand and the gluelines examined for delamination by separating the charred plies with a sharp, chisel-like instrument. Specimens shall be evaluated in accordance with Subsection 25.907 (h).

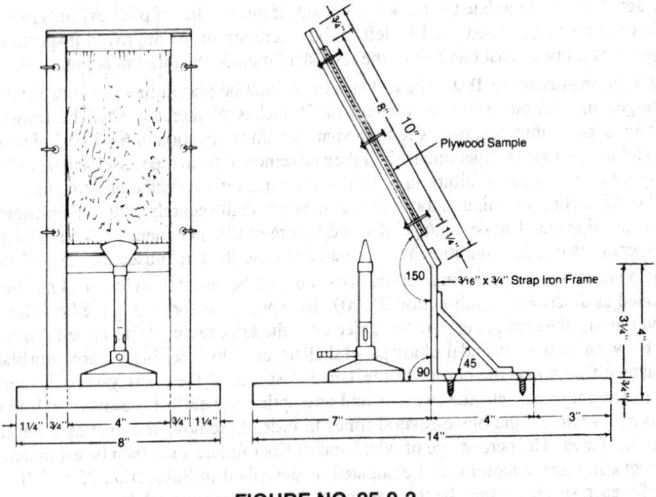
3/4"
8"
10"
Plywood Sample
1 1/4"
150
3/16" x 3/4" Strap Iron Frame
3 1/4"
4"
3/4"
90
45
1 1/4"
3/4"
4"
3/4"
1 1/4"
8"
7"
4"
3"
14"

FIGURE NO. 25-9-2
Apparatus for Heat Durability Test

Tests for Performance Under Concentrated Static and Impact Loads

Sec. 25. 916. (a) **Preparation of Test Specimens.** Samples shall be selected representative of the plywood product being evaluated. Length, L, of panels shall conform to the maximum center-to-center support spacing, S, anticipated in service, continuous over the minimum number of spans recommended for its use. See Figures Nos. 25-9-7 and 25-9-8. Width, W, of individual pieces shall be 24 inches or greater for span ratings up to 24 inches on center and 48 inches for greater span ratings.

(b) **Test Procedure.** 1. **Concentrated static.** Specimens shall be loaded at locations shown in Figure No. 25-9-7 using a 3-inch-diameter loading disc, except a 1-inch-diameter loading disc shall be used to determine strength of single-layer floor panels in the dry or redried condition.

Stiffness shall be determined by measuring deflection in 50-pound increments to 200 pounds. Strength shall be determined by loading to failure.

2. **Concentrated impact.** Specimens shall be loaded at locations shown in Figure No. 25-9-8 using an impact device 9 to 10 1/2 inches in diameter and weighing 30 pounds, except that for span ratings greater than 24 inches on center, the impact device shall weigh 60 pounds.

Strength shall be determined by impacting the specimen from the specified height at increments of 6 inches. Deflection under a 200-pound concentrated load, using a 3-inch-diameter disc, shall be measured before the test and after each impact. After the specified impact load has been reached the concentrated load shall be applied to failure.

Test for Performance Under Uniform Loads

Sec. 25.917. (a) **Apparatus.** A vacuum chamber is used consisting of a sealed box with the panel to be tested forming the top. See Figure No. 25-9-9. A 6-mil polyethylene sheet or equivalent is securely taped at the perimeter to seal the top surface. A vacuum pump reduces air pressure under the specimen such that load is measured.

(b) **Preparation of Test Specimens.** Samples shall be selected representative of the plywood product being evaluated. The specimen length perpendicular to framing shall be equal to twice the maximum center-to-center support spacing, S, anticipated in service. See Figure No. 25-9-10. The specimen width is at least 23 1/2 inches.

(c) **Test Procedure.** The specimen is mounted in the vacuum box following anticipated joist spacing and recommended nail size and spacing and sealed. The panel is loaded to the specified level. Deflections are measured at locations shown in Figure No. 25-9-10 sufficient to develop the straight-line portion of the load-deflection curve, but in no case shall the number of data points be less than six.

Test for Panel Bending

Sec. 25.918. (a) **Apparatus.** A testing machine shall be used capable of applying pure moments to opposite ends of the test panel through loading frames and measurement of moment and deformation.

(b) **Preparation of Test Specimens.** Samples shall be selected representative of the plywood product being evaluated. Specimens shall measure 4 feet by 4 feet.

(c) **Test Procedure.** Separate specimens are subjected to pure moment along and across the major axis. Deformation or curvature is measured in a manner adequate to calculate bending stiffness. Test is carried on to failure to evaluate maximum moment.

Scarf- and Finger-joint Tests

Sec. 25.919. (a) **Strength.** Three test specimens shall be cut at random along each joint from panels selected as directed in Subsection 25.919 (c). Type, grade and species of the panels shall be recorded. The specimens shall be cut so as to include the joint and shall be prepared as illustrated in Figure No. 25-9-3.

Insofar as possible, the joint test area shall contain no localized natural defects permitted within the grade. At the joint, the maximum thickness and width of plies parallel with the load shall be recorded. Each specimen shall then be placed in the tension grips of a testing machine and loaded continuously at a rate of cross-head travel of 0.030 to 0.040 inch per minute until failure, and the ultimate load recorded. The ultimate stress in pounds per square inch shall be computed using the ultimate load and area of those plies whose grain is parallel with direction of load. Moisture content of specimens at the time of testing shall not exceed 16 percent.

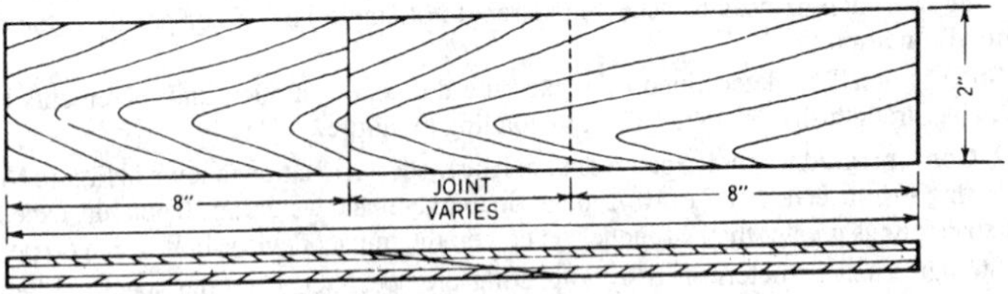
2"
8"
JOINT
VARIES
8"

FIGURE NO. 25-9-3
Tension Specimen for Scarf-jointed Panels

(b) **Scarf-joint Durability of Interior-type Panels Bonded with Interior Glue.** Ten test specimens shall be cut at random along each scarf joint from panels selected as directed in Subsection 25.916 (c), and shall be prepared following the general procedure in the same subsection, but shall be cut so that the scarf joint occurring on one surface of the panel runs across the middle of five specimens and the joint occurring on the opposite surface runs across the middle of the other five specimens. The specimens shall be subjected to the same test procedure as outlined in Section 25.912.

(c) **Scarf-joint Durability of Exterior-type Panels and Interior-type Panels Bonded with Exterior or Intermediate Glue.** Ten test specimens shall be cut at random along each joint from panels selected as directed in Subsection 25.919 (c). The specimens shall be prepared following the general procedure described in Subsection 25.921 (a), but, in addition, shall be cut so that the joints run through the test specimens as shown in Figure No. 25-9-4. For Exterior-type panels and Interior-type bonded with exterior glue, five specimens shall be subjected to the vacuum-pressure test described in Subsection 25.915 (b), and five to the boiling test of Subsection 25.915 (c). The panels shall be evaluated as described in Section 25.907.

For Interior-type panels bonded with intermediate glue (IMG), the 10 specimens shall be subjected to the vacuum soak test outlined in Subsection 25.914 (b). The panels shall be evaluated as described in Section 25.907.

(d) **Finger-joint Durabiity of Interior-type Panels Bonded with Interior Glue.** Five specimens shall be cut at random along the finger joint from each panel selected and shall be prepared following the general procedure in Section 25.911 so that the middle of the joint coincides with the middle of the five specimens. The specimens shall be subjected to the same test procedure as outlined in Section 25.919.

(e) **Finger-joint Durability of Exterior-type Panels and Interior-type Panels Bonded with Exterior or Intermediate-type Glue.** Ten specimens shall be cut at random along the finger joint from each panel selected according to Section 25.911. These specimens shall be cut so as to include the joint and shall be prepared as illustrated in Figure No. 25-9-5.

For Exterior-type panels and Interior-type panels bonded with exterior glue, five of the specimens shall be subjected to the vacuum pressure test of Subsection 25.915 (b) and five to the boiling test of Subsection 25.915 (a).

For Interior-type panels bonded with intermediate glue, the 10 specimens shall be subjected to the vacuum soak test of Section 25.914.

Upon completion of the vacuum pressure and boil tests, or vacuum soak tests, as applicable, a wedge or chisel (see Figure No. 25-9-6) shall be inserted in locations shown in Figure No. 25-9-5 in such a manner as to pry apart the scarfed portions of the joint without directly contacting the glued area. Test specimens shall be dried and percent wood failure in the test area estimated and applied separately for both the boil and vacuum pressure treatments. The panels shall be evaluated as described in Section 25.907.

Test for Determination of Moisture Content (Oven-drying Method)

Sec. 25.920. The moisture content of the plywood shall be determined as follows: A small test specimen shall be cut from each sample panel; the test specimen shall measure not less than 9 square inches in area and shall weigh not less than 20 grams (approximately 3/4 ounce). All loose splinters shall be removed from the specimen. The specimen shall be immediately weighed on a scale that is accurate to 0.5 percent, and the weight shall be recorded as original weight. The specimen shall then be dried in an oven at 212° to 221°F. (100° to 105°C.) until constant weight is attained. After drying, the specimen shall be reweighed immediately, and this weight shall be recorded as the oven-dry weight. The moisture content shall be calculated as follows:

$$\frac{\text{Original weight} - \text{Oven-dry weight}}{\text{Oven-dry weight}} \times 100 = \text{Moisture content (percent)}$$

Plywood Section Properties

Sec. 25.921. (a) **General.** Section properties set forth in Tables Nos. 25-9-H and 25-9-I shall be used with all species and grades of plywood in this standard. The section properties shall be used in determining compliance with allowable stresses set forth in Table No. 25-B of the Uniform Building Code. The properties have been adjusted to reflect "effective" section properties in each of two directions, assuming a homogenous material. As a result of these adjusted values, moment of inertia "*I*" shall be used only in stiffness calculations, with section modulus "*S*" used in bending stress calculations.

(b) **Veneer Lay-up.** Section properties listed are adjusted to allow for variations in panel veneer constructions. Properties parallel to the face grain of the plywood are based on a panel construction giving minimum values in that direction. Properties perpendicular to the face grain are based on a different panel construction, giving minimum values in that direction. Properties for the two directions, however, cannot be added to achieve properties of the full panel.

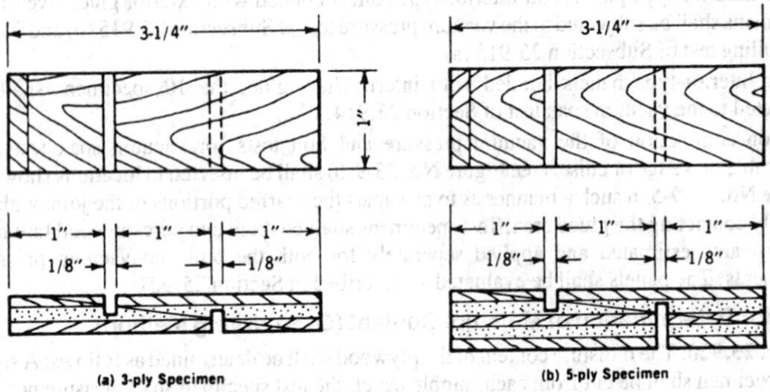
3-1/4"
1"
1"
1"
1"
1/8"
1/8"
(a) 3-ply Specimen
3-1/4"
1"
1"
1"
1/8"
1/8"
(b) 5-ply Specimen

FIGURE NO. 25-9-4—SCARF-JOINT SPECIMENS FOR VACUUM SOAK, VACUUM PRESSURE AND BOILING TESTS

Calculation of Diaphragm Deflection

Sec. 25.922. Calculations for diaphragm deflection shall account for the usual bending and shear components as well as any other factors, such as nail deformation, which will contribute to the deflection.

The deflection (Δ) of a blocked plywood diaphragm uniformly nailed throughout may be calculated by use of the following formula. If not uniformly nailed, the constant 0.188 in the third term must be modified accordingly.

$$\Delta = \frac{5vL^3}{8EAb} + \frac{vL}{4Gt} + 0.188\,Le_n + \frac{\Sigma(\Delta_c X)}{2b}$$

WHERE:

Δ = the calculated deflection, in inches.

v = maximum shear due to design loads in the direction under consideration, in pounds per lineal foot.

L = diaphragm length, in feet.

b = diaphragm width, in feet.

E = elastic modulus of chords, in pounds per square inch.

A = area of chord cross section, in square inches.

G = modulus of rigidity of plywood, in pounds per square inch (see Table No. 25-9-J.)

t = effective thickness of plywood for shear, in inches (see Tables Nos. 25-9-H and 25-9-I.)

e_n = nail deformation, in inches (see Table No. 25-9-K.)

$\Sigma(\Delta_c X)$ = sum of individual chord-splice slip values on both sides of the diaphragm, each multiplied by its distance to the nearest support.

Calculation of Shear Wall Deflection

Sec. 25.923. The deflection (Δ) of a blocked shear wall uniformly nailed throughout may be calculated by use of the following formula:

$$\Delta = \frac{8vh^3}{EAb} + \frac{vh}{Gt} + 0.75he_n + d_a$$

WHERE:

Δ = the calculated deflection, in inches.

v = maximum shear due to design loads at the top of the wall, in pounds per lineal foot.

A = area of boundary element cross section in square inches (vertical member at shear wall boundary).

h = wall height, in feet.

b = wall width, in feet.

d_a = deflection due to anchorage details (rotation and slip at tie-down bolts).

E = elastic modulus of boundary element (vertical member at shear wall boundary) in pounds per square inch.

G = modulus of rigidity of plywood, in pounds per square inch (see Table No. 25-9-J).

t = effective thickness of plywood for shear, in inches (see Tables Nos. 25-9-H and 25-9-I).

e_n = nail deformation, in inches (see Table No. 25-9-K).

Allowable Stresses for Shear Through the Thickness

Sec. 25.924. Shear-through-the-thickness stresses in Uniform Building Code Table No. 25-B are based on the most common structural applications, as where plywood is mechanically fastened to framing. If the plywood is rigidly glued to full-length, continuous (unjointed) framing around all panel edges, increase allowable shear-through-the-thickness stresses by 33 percent. If the continuous framing is glued to only two edges parallel to the face grain, increase stresses by 19 percent. When continuous framing is only at edges perpendicular to the face grain, no increase in stresses shall be taken.

In lieu of the increase in shear-through-the-thickness stresses given above for continuous glued framing, a 33-percent increase may be taken when panels are regraded to limit core gap width and placement. Contiguous core gaps in adjacent plies within a layer shall be measured as a single gap from the outermost edge of one to the opposite edge of the other. Noncontiguous core gaps in any parallel ply of the panel shall be offset by at least 1 inch, measured from innermost edges of the gaps. Gap width limitations are as follows:

1. For all three-layer panels (including three-ply and four-ply), core gaps shall not be wider than 1/4 inch.
2. For panels with five or more layers, core gaps shall be limited to 1 inch in 1/2-inch-thick panels and to 1/2 inch in thicker panels.

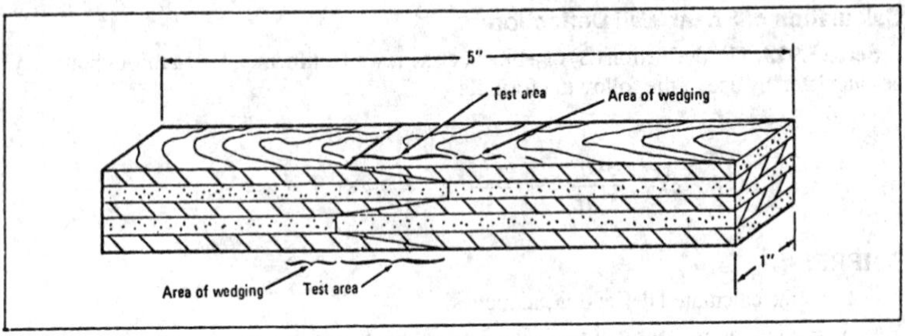
5"
Test area
Area of wedging
1"
Area of wedging
Test area

FIGURE NO. 25-9-5
CLEAVAGE TEST, TYPICAL TEST SPECIMEN

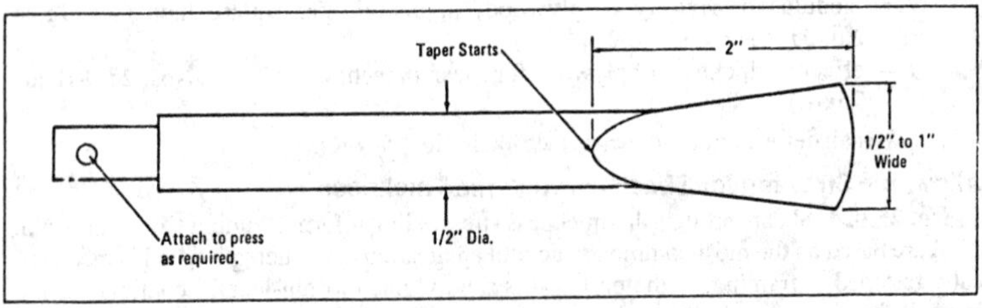
Taper Starts
2"
1/2" to 1"
Wide
Attach to press
as required.
1/2" Dia.

FIGURE NO. 25-9-6
WEDGE OR CHISEL USED FOR CLEAVAGE TEST

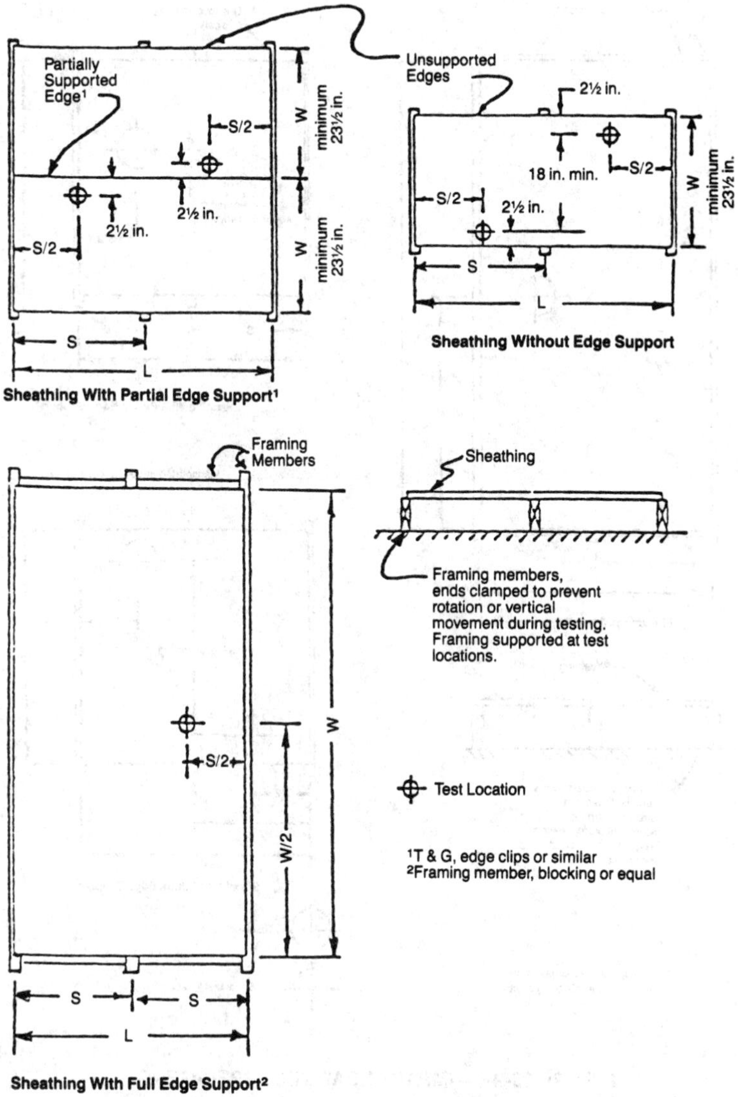
Partially Supported Edge[1]
S/2
2½ in.
2½ in.
S/2
W minimum 23½ in.
W minimum 23½ in.
S
L
Sheathing With Partial Edge Support[1]
Unsupported Edges
2½ in.
18 in. min.
S/2
S/2
2½ in.
W minimum 23½ in.
S
L
Sheathing Without Edge Support
Framing Members
S/2
W
W/2
S
S
L
Sheathing With Full Edge Support[2]
Sheathing
Framing members, ends clamped to prevent rotation or vertical movement during testing. Framing supported at test locations.
Test Location
[1]T & G, edge clips or similar
[2]Framing member, blocking or equal

FIGURE 25-9-7—CONCENTRATED STATIC LOAD TEST SPECIMENS

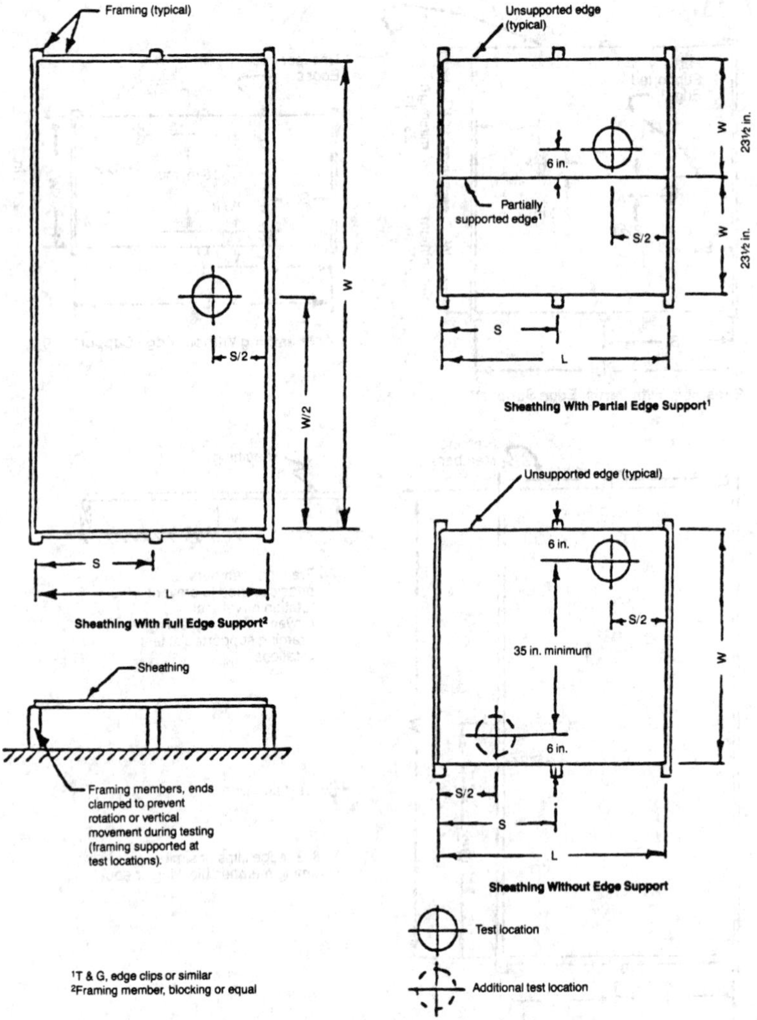

Framing (typical)
W
W/2
S/2
S
L
Sheathing With Full Edge Support²
Sheathing
Framing members, ends clamped to prevent rotation or vertical movement during testing (framing supported at test locations).
Unsupported edge (typical)
6 in.
Partially supported edge¹
S/2
W
23½ in.
W
23½ in.
S
L
Sheathing With Partial Edge Support¹
Unsupported edge (typical)
6 in.
S/2
35 in. minimum
W
6 in.
S/2
S
L
Sheathing Without Edge Support
Test location
Additional test location
¹T & G, edge clips or similar
²Framing member, blocking or equal

FIGURE 25-9-8—IMPACT LOAD TEST SPECIMENS

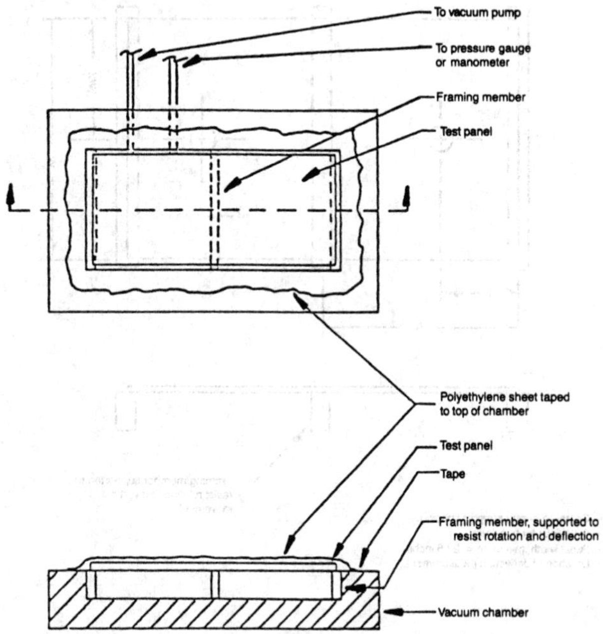
To vacuum pump
To pressure gauge or manometer
Framing member
Test panel
Polyethylene sheet taped to top of chamber
Test panel
Tape
Framing member, supported to resist rotation and deflection
Vacuum chamber

FIGURE NO. 25-9-9—VACUUM CHAMBER TEST EQUIPMENT

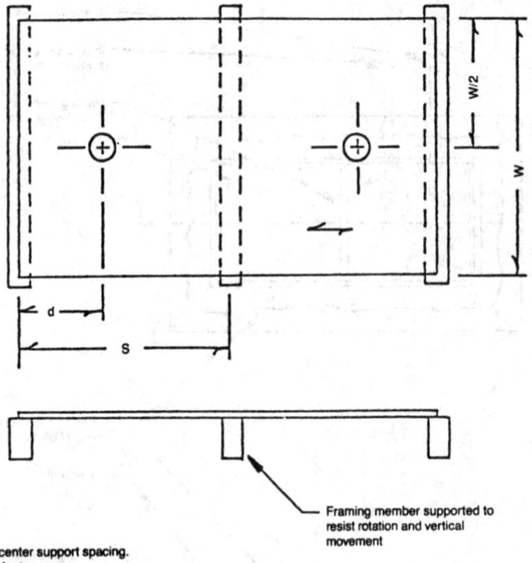
W/2
W
d
S
Framing member supported to resist rotation and vertical movement

S = Center-to-center support spacing.
d = 0.4215(S) for two span.
W = Panel width, minimum = 23.5 inches.
(+) = Location of deflection measurement.

FIGURE NO. 25-9-10—UNIFORM LOAD TEST SPECIMENS

TABLE NO. 25-9-A—CLASSIFICATION OF SPECIES

Group 1	Group 2	Group 3	Group 4

Aptiong[(a) (b)]
Beech, American
Birch
  Sweet
  Yellow
Douglas fir 1[(c)]
Kapur[(a)]
Keruing[(a) (b)]
Larch, Western
Maple, Sugar
Pine
  Caribbean
  Ocote
Pine, Southern
  Loblolly
  Longleaf
  Shortleaf
  Slash
Tanoak
	Cedar, Port Orford
	Cypress
	Douglas fir 2[(c)]
	Fir
	  Balsam
	  California Red
	  Grand
	  Noble
	  Pacific Silver
	  White
	Hemlock, Western
	Lauan
	  Almon
	  Bagtikan
	  Mayapis
	  Red Lauan
	  Tangile
	  White Lauan
	Maple, Black
	Mengkulang[(a)]
	Meranti, Red[(a) (d)]
	Mersawa[(a)]
	Pine
	  Pond
	  Red
	  Virginia
	  Western White
	Spruce
	  Black
	  Red
	  Sitka
	Sweetgum
	Tamarack
	Yellow-poplar
		Alder, Red
		Birch, Paper
		Cedar, Alaska
		Fir, Subalpine
		Hemlock, Eastern
		Maple, Bigleaf
		Pine
		  Jack
		  Lodgepole
		  Ponderosa
		  Spruce
		Redwood
		Spruce
		  Engelmann
		  White
			Aspen
			  Bigtooth
			  Quaking
			Cativo
			Cedar
			  Incense
			  Western Red
			Cottonwood
			  Eastern
			  Black (Western poplar)
			Pine
			  Eastern White
			  Sugar

(a) Each of these names represents a trade group of woods consisting of a number of closely related species.

(b) Species from the genus Dipterocarpus are marketed collectively: Aptiong if originating in the Philippines; Keruing if originating in Malaysia or Indonesia.

(c) Douglas fir from trees grown in the states of Washington, Oregon, California, Idaho, Montana, Wyoming, and the Canadian Provinces of Alberta and British Columbia shall be classed as Douglas fir No. 1. Douglas fir from trees grown in the states of Nevada, Utah, Colorado, Arizona and New Mexico shall be classed as Douglas fir No. 2.

(d) Red Meranti shall be limited to species having a specific gravity of 0.41 or more based on green volume and oven-dry weight.

TABLE NO. 25-9-B—CHARACTERISTICS PROHIBITED OR RESTRICTED IN CERTAIN PANEL GRADES

Panel Grade Designation	Description and Number of Characteristics Per Panel
N-N, N-A	No crossband laps adjacent to faces and backs
N-B	No crossband laps adjacent to N faces No more than 2 crossband laps adjacent to B grade side Laps are limited to $^3/_{16}$ inch
N-D	No crossband laps adjacent to faces No more than a total of 2 of any combination of the following: — Knothole in D veneer over $2^1/_2$ inches but not over 3 inches — Split in D veneer over $^1/_2$ inch (not over 1 inch) — Crossband lap adjacent to backs
Underlayment & C-C Plugged	No knotholes in veneer adjacent to face over 1 inch across the grain where C grade is required per Tables Nos. 25-9-D and 25-9-E No knotholes in veneer adjacent to face over $2^1/_2$ inches where D grade is permitted or $1^1/_2$ inches where C grade is permitted per Subsection 25.905 (f) No laps adjacent to face

Structural I and II C-D	No splits in faces over 1/4 inch No splits in backs over 1/2 inch No more than a total of 2 of any combination of the following: — Knothole in C veneer over 1 inch but not over 1 1/2 inches — Knot in D backs over 2 1/2 inches but not over 3 inches — Knothole in D veneer over 2 1/2 inches but not over 3 inches — Crossband lap adjacent to faces per Subsection 25.905 (d) — Crossband lap adjacent to backs per Subsection 25.905 (d)
Structural I and II C-D Plugged	No splits in backs over 1/2 inch No more than a total of 2 of any combination of the following: — Knot in D backs over 2 1/2 inches but not over 3 inches — Knothole in D veneer over 2 1/2 inches but not over 3 inches — Crossband lap adjacent to faces per Subsection 25.905 (d) — Crossband lap adjacent to backs per Subsection 25.905 (d)
Structural I and II Underlayment	No knotholes in core veneer next to face over 1 inch No crossband laps adjacent to faces No splits in backs over 1/2 inch No more than a total of 2 of any combination of the following: — Knot in D backs over 2 1/2 inches but not over 3 inches — Knothole in D veneer over 2 1/2 inches but not over 3 inches — Crossband lap adjacent to backs per Subsection 25.905 (d)

TABLE NO. 25-9-C—PANEL CONSTRUCTIONS

Panel Grades	Finished Panel NominalThickness Range (Inch)	Minimum Number of Plies	Minimum Number of Layers
Exterior Marine Special Exterior [See Subsection 25.905 (d)] B-B concrete form High Density Overlay High Density concrete form overlay	Through $\frac{3}{8}$ Over $\frac{3}{8}$, through $\frac{3}{4}$ Over $\frac{3}{4}$	3 5 7	3 5 7
Interior N-N, N-A, N-B, N-D, A-A, A-B, A-D B-B, B-D Structural I (C-D, C-D Plugged and Underlayment) Structural II (C-D, C-D Plugged and Underlayment) Exterior A-A, A-B, A-C, B-B, B-C Structural I and Structural II C-C and C-C Plugged [See Subsection 25.905 (d)] Medium Density and special overlays	Through $\frac{3}{8}$ Over $\frac{3}{8}$, through $\frac{1}{2}$ Over $\frac{1}{2}$, through $\frac{7}{8}$ Over $\frac{7}{8}$	3 4 5 6	3 3 5 5
Interior (including grades with exterior glue) Underlayment Exterior C-C Plugged	Through $\frac{1}{2}$ Over $\frac{1}{2}$, through $\frac{3}{4}$ Over $\frac{3}{4}$	3 4 5	3 3 5
Interior (including grades with exterior glue) C-D C-D Plugged Exterior C-C	Through $\frac{5}{8}$ Over $\frac{5}{8}$, through $\frac{3}{4}$ Over $\frac{3}{4}$	3 4 5	3 3 5

TABLE NO. 25-9-D—INTERIOR TYPE GRADES

Panel Grade Designations	Minimum Veneer Quality			Surface
	Face	Back	Inner Plies	
N-N	N	N	C	Sanded 2 sides
N-A	N	A	C	Sanded 2 sides
N-B	N	B	C	Sanded 2 sides
N-D	N	D	D	Sanded 2 Sides
A-A	A	A	D	Sanded 2 sides
A-B	A	B	D	Sanded 2 sides
A-D	A	D	D	Sanded 2 sides
B-B	B	B	D	Sanded 2 sides
B-D	B	D	D	Sanded 2 sides
Underlayment[1]	C Plugged	D	C & D	Touch-sanded
C-D Plugged	C Plugged	D	D	Touch-sanded
Structural I C-D	See 25.905 (d)			Unsanded[2]
Structural I C-D Plugged, Underlayment	See 25.905 (d)			Touch-sanded
Structural II C-D	See 25.905(d)			Unsanded[2]
Structural II C-D Plugged, Underlayment	See 25.905(d)			Touch-sanded
C-D	C	D	D	Unsanded[2]
C-D with exterior glue (See Sec. 25.915)	C	D	D	Unsanded[2]

[1] See Subsection 25.905 (f) for special limitations.

[2] Except for decorative grades, panels shall not be sanded, touch-sanded, surface textured or thickness sized by any mechanical means.

TABLE NO. 25-9-E—EXTERIOR TYPE GRADES[1]

Panel Grade Designations	Minimum Veneer Quality			Surface
	Face	Back	Inner Plies	
Marine, A-A, A-B, B-B, HDO, MDO		See 25.905 (a)		See regular grades
Special Exterior, A-A, A-B, B-B, HDO, MDO		See 25.905 (e)		See regular grades
A-A	A	A	C	Sanded 2 sides
A-B	A	B	C	Sanded 2 sides
A-C	A	C	C	Sanded 2 sides
B-B (concrete form)		See 25.905 (c)		
B-B	B	B	C	Sanded 2 sides
B-C	B	C	C	Sanded 2 sides
C-C Plugged [2]	C Plugged	C	C	Touch-sanded
C-C	C	C	C	Unsanded [3]
A-A High Density Overlay	A	A	C Plugged	
B-B High Density Overlay	B	B	C Plugged [4]	
B-B High Density Concrete Form Overlay [See 25.905 (c)]	B	B	C Plugged	
B-B Medium Density Overlay	B	B	C	
Special Overlays	C	C	C	

1Available also in Structural I and Structural II Classifications as provided in Subsection 25.905 (d).

2See Subsection 25.905 (f) for special limitations.

3Except for decorative grades, panels shall not be sanded, touch-sanded, surface textured or thickness sized by any mechanical means.

4C centers may be used in panels of five or more plies.

TABLE NO. 25-9-F—PREMIUM GRADES

GRADE	GLUE BOND	SPECIES
Structural I C-D[(a)] C-D Plugged[1] Underlayment[1]	Shall meet the requirements of Sec. 25.915	Face, back and all inner plies limited to Group 1 species
Structural II C-D[(a)] C-D Plugged[1] Underlayment[1]	Shall meet the requirements of Sec. 25.915	Face, back and all inner plies may be of any Group 1, 2, or 3 species
Structural I All Exterior grades (see Table 25-9-E)	Exterior	Face, back and all inner plies limited to Group 1 species
Structural II All Exterior grades (see Table 25-9-E)	Exterior	Face, back and all inner plies may be of any Group 1, 2, or 3 species

[1]Special limitations applying to Structural (C-D, C-D Plugged, Underlayment) grade panels are:

(a) In D grade veneers white pocket in any area larger than the size of the largest knothole, pitchpocket or split specifically permitted in D grade shall not be permitted in any ply.

(b) Sound tight knots in D grade shall not exceed 2½ inches measured across the grain, except as provided in Table No. 25-9-B.

(c) Plugs, including multiple repairs, shall not exceed 4 inches in width.

(d) Panel construction shall be as specified in Subsection 25.903 (a).

TABLE NO. 25-9-G—SPAN RATINGS FOR SHEATHING AND SINGLE-FLOOR PANELS

[For special ply-layer and species requirements applicable to STRUCTURAL panels, see Subsection 25.905 (d) and Tables Nos. 25-9-C and 25-9-F. For crossband and total inner ply thickness proportion requirements, see Subsection 25.903 (a)]

SPAN RATING[a]	NOMINAL PANEL THICKNESS (In.)[b]	MINIMUM NUMBER OF PLIES-LAYERS	MINIMUM FACE AND BACK VENEER THICKNESS BEFORE PRESSING, FOR SPECIES GROUP[c] (In.)				INNER PLY SPECIES GROUP
			1	2	3	4	
SHEATHING PANELS (C-D, C-C)							
12/0	5/16	3-3	1/12	1/12	1/12	1/12	1, 2, 3 or 4
16/0	5/16	3-3	1/12	1/12	1/12	(d)	1, 2, 3 or 4
	11/32	3-3	1/12	1/12	1/12	1/12	1, 2, 3 or 4
20/0	5/16	3-3	1/12	(d)	(d)	(d)	1, 2, 3 or 4
	11/32	3-3	1/12	1/12	1/10	(d)	1, 2, 3 or 4
	3/8	3-3	1/10	1/10	1/10	1/10	1, 2, 3 or 4
24/0	3/8	3-3	1/10	(d)	(d)	(d)	1, 2, 3 or 4
	13/32	3-3	1/10	1/10	(d)	(d)	1, 2, 3 or 4
	1/2	3-3	1/10	1/10	1/10	1/10	1, 2, 3 or 4
32/16	1/2	3-3	1/10	1/6	(d)	(d)	1, 2, 3 or 4
	17/32	3-3	1/10	1/10	1/6	(d)	1, 2, 3 or 4
	5/8	3-3	(e)	(e)	(e)	(e)	1, 2, 3 or 4
40/20	5/8	3-3	(e)	1/6	(d)	(d)	1, 2, 3 or 4
	21/32	3-3	1/10	1/8	1/6	(d)	1, 2, 3 or 4
	3/4	4-3	1/10	1/10	1/10	1/8	1, 2, 3 or 4
	25/32	4-3	1/10	1/10	1/10	1/10	1, 2, 3 or 4
48/24	3/4	4-3	1/10	1/6	(d)	(d)	1, 2, 3 or 4
	25/32	4-3	1/10	1/8	1/6	(d)	1, 2, 3 or 4
	7/8	5-5	1/10	1/10	1/10	(d)	1, 2, 3 or 4
	29/32	5-5	1/10	1/10	1/10	1/8	1, 2, 3 or 4

SPAN RATING[a]	NOMINAL PANEL THICKNESS (in.)[b]	MINIMUM NUMBER OF PLIES-LAYERS	MINIMUM FACE AND BACK VENEER THICKNESS BEFORE PRESSING, FOR SPECIES GROUP[c] (in.)				INNER PLY SPECIES GROUP
			1	2	3	4	
SINGLE-FLOOR PANELS (UNDERLAYMENT, C-C PLUGGED)							
16 o.c.	1/2	3-3	1/10	(d)	(d)	(d)	1, 2, 3 or 4
	19/32	4-3	(e)	(e)	(e)	1/6	1, 2, 3 or 4
	5/8	4-3	(e)	(e)	(e)	(e)	1, 2, 3 or 4
20 o.c.	19/32	4-3	(e)	1/6	(d)	(d)	1, 2, 3 or 4
	5/8	4-3	(e)	1/8	1/6	(d)	1, 2, 3 or 4
	23/32	4-3	1/10	1/10	1/10	1/8	1, 2, 3 or 4
	3/4	4-3	1/10	1/10	1/10	1/10	1, 2, 3 or 4
24 o.c.	23/32	4-3	1/10	1/6	3/16	(d)	1, 2, 3 or 4
	3/4	4-3	1/10	1/8	1/6	(d)	1, 2, 3 or 4
	7/8	5-5	1/10	1/10	1/10	1/8	1, 2, 3 or 4
48 o.c.	1 1/8	7-5	1/8	1/6	(d)	(d)	1 or 2
	1 1/8	7-5	1/7	1/6	(d)	(d)	1, 2 or 3
	1 1/8	7-7	1/10	1/6	3/16	(d)	1
	1 1/8	7-7	1/8	1/6	3/16	(d)	1, 2 or 3

[a]See Section 25.909 for description.

[b]Panels for which there is no span rating shall be identified by largest species group number of the face and back, or by the span rating of the next thinner comparable panel. Sheathing panels manufactured 1/32-inch over standard thickness may be identified as the standard thickness.

[c]Intermixing between species groups and/or thicknesses in the faces and backs of panel is permitted. Use the lowest applicable span rating to identify the panel.

[d]Not permitted.

[e]1/8 inch minimum for 3-, 4- and 5-ply three-layer panels per Section 25.904 (a). May be 1/10 minimum for 5-ply five-layer panels.

TABLE NO. 25-9-H—FACE PLIES OF DIFFERENT SPECIES GROUP THAN INNER PLIES
(Includes all standard grades except those noted in Table No. 25-9-I)

Nominal Thickness (in.)	Approximate Weight (psf)	Effective Thickness for Shear (in.)	STRESS APPLIED PARALLEL TO FACE GRAIN				STRESS APPLIED PERPENDICULAR TO FACE GRAIN			
			A Area ($in.^2/ft.$)	*I* Moment of Inertia ($in.^4/ft.$)	*KS* Eff. Section Modulus ($in.^3/ft.$)	*Ib/Q* Rolling Shear Constant ($in.^2/ft.$)	*A* Area ($in.^2/ft.$)	*I* Moment of Inertia ($in.^4/ft.$)	*KS* Eff. Section Modulus ($in.^3/ft.$)	*Ib/Q* Rolling Shear Constant ($in.^2/ft.$)
UNSANDED PANELS										
$^5/_{16}$-U	1.0	0.268	1.491	0.022	0.112	2.569	0.660	0.001	0.023	4.497
$^3/_8$-U	1.1	0.278	1.866	0.037	0.154	3.110	0.799	0.002	0.031	5.444
$^{15}/_{32}$ & $^1/_2$-U	1.5	0.298	2.292	0.074	0.247	3.921	1.007	0.004	0.051	2.450
$^{19}/_{32}$ & $^5/_8$-U	1.8	0.319	2.330	0.146	0.355	5.273	1.354	0.010	0.091	3.126
$^{23}/_{32}$ & $^3/_4$-U	2.2	0.445	3.247	0.227	0.496	6.544	1.563	0.033	0.208	3.613
$^7/_8$-U	2.6	0.607	3.509	0.340	0.678	7.175	1.950	0.112	0.397	5.097
1-U	3.0	0.842	3.916	0.493	0.859	9.244	3.611	0.210	0.660	7.115
$1^1/_8$-U	3.3	0.859	4.725	0.676	1.047	9.960	3.079	0.288	0.768	8.821

Nominal Thickness (in.)	Approximate Weight (psf)	Effective Thickness for Shear (in.)	STRESS APPLIED PARALLEL TO FACE GRAIN				STRESS APPLIED PERPENDICULAR TO FACE GRAIN			
			A Area (in.²/ft.)	*I* Moment of Inertia (in.⁴/ft.)	*KS* Eff. Section Modulus (in.³/ft.)	*Ib/Q* Rolling Shear Constant (in.²/ft.)	*A* Area (in.²/ft.)	*I* Moment of Inertia (in.⁴/ft.)	*KS* Eff. Section Modulus (in.³/ft.)	*Ib/Q* Rolling Shear Constant (in.²/ft.)
SANDED PANELS										
1/4-S	0.8	0.267	0.996	0.008	0.059	2.010	0.348	0.001	0.009	2.019
11/32-S	1.0	0.284	0.996	0.019	0.093	2.765	0.417	0.001	0.016	2.589
3/8-S	1.1	0.288	1.307	0.027	0.125	3.088	0.626	0.002	0.023	3.510
15/32-S	1.4	0.421	1.947	0.066	0.214	4.113	1.251	0.006	0.067	2.832
1/2-S	1.5	0.425	1.947	0.077	0.236	4.466	1.409	0.009	0.087	3.099
19/32-S	1.7	0.546	2.423	0.115	0.315	5.471	1.389	0.021	0.137	2.861
5/8-S	1.8	0.550	2.475	0.129	0.339	5.824	1.528	0.027	0.164	3.119
23/32-S	2.1	0.563	2.822	0.179	0.389	6.717	1.737	0.050	0.231	3.818
3/4-S	2.2	0.568	2.884	0.197	0.412	7.121	2.084	0.063	0.285	4.079
7/8-S	2.6	0.586	2.942	0.278	0.515	8.182	2.841	0.122	0.470	5.078
1-S	3.0	0.817	3.721	0.423	0.664	8.882	3.163	0.185	0.591	7.031
1 1/8-S	3.3	0.836	3.854	0.548	0.820	9.883	3.180	0.271	0.744	8.428
TOUCH-SANDED PANELS										
1/2-T	1.5	0.342	2.698	0.083	0.271	4.252	1.159	0.006	0.061	2.746
19/32 & 5/8-T	1.8	0.408	2.354	0.122	0.291	5.350	1.555	0.017	0.138	3.220
23/32 & 3/4-T	2.2	0.439	2.715	0.196	0.398	6.589	2.014	0.032	0.219	3.635
1 1/8-T	3.3	0.839	4.548	0.633	0.977	11.258	4.067	0.272	0.743	8.535

TABLE NO. 25-9-I—STRUCTURAL I AND MARINE WITH ALL PLIES FROM SAME SPECIES GROUP

Nominal Thickness (in.)	Approximate Weight (psf)	Effective Thickness for Shear (in.)	STRESS APPLIED PARALLEL TO FACE GRAIN				STRESS APPLIED PERPENDICULAR TO FACE GRAIN			
			A Area (in.²/ft.)	*I* Moment of Inertia (in.⁴/ft.)	*KS* Eff. Section Modulus (in.³/ft.)	*Ib/Q* Rolling Shear Constant (in.²/ft.)	*A* Area (in.²/ft.)	*I* Moment of Inertia (in.⁴/ft.)	*KS* Eff. Section Modulus (in.³/ft.)	*Ib/Q* Rolling Shear Constant (in.²/ft.)
UNSANDED PANELS										
5/16-U	1.0	0.356	1.619	0.022	0.126	2.567	1.188	0.002	0.029	6.037
3/8-U	1.1	0.371	2.226	0.041	0.195	3.107	1.438	0.003	0.043	7.307
15/32 & 1/2-U	1.5	0.535	2.719	0.074	0.279	4.206	2.175	0.014	0.127	2.408
19/32 & 5/8-U	1.8	0.707	3.464	0.154	0.437	5.685	2.742	0.045	0.240	3.072
23/32 & 3/4-U	2.2	0.739	4.219	0.241	0.572	6.148	2.813	0.064	0.299	3.540
7/8-U	2.6	0.776	4.388	0.346	0.690	6.948	3.510	0.192	0.584	5.086
1-U	3.0	1.088	5.200	0.529	0.922	8.512	6.500	0.366	0.970	7.052
1 1/8-U	3.3	1.118	6.654	0.751	1.164	9.061	5.542	0.503	1.131	8.755
SANDED PANELS										
1/4-S	0.8	0.342	1.280	0.012	0.083	2.009	0.626	0.001	0.013	2.723
11/32-S	1.0	0.365	1.280	0.026	0.133	2.764	0.751	0.001	0.023	3.397
3/8-S	1.1	0.373	1.680	0.038	0.177	3.086	1.126	0.002	0.033	4.927
15/32-S	1.4	0.537	1.947	0.067	0.247	4.107	2.251	0.009	0.093	2.807
1/2-S	1.5	0.545	1.947	0.078	0.271	4.457	2.536	0.014	0.123	3.076
19/32-S	1.7	0.709	3.018	0.116	0.338	5.566	2.501	0.034	0.199	2.811
5/8-S	1.8	0.717	3.112	0.131	0.361	5.934	2.751	0.045	0.238	3.073
23/32-S	2.1	0.741	3.735	0.183	0.439	6.707	3.126	0.085	0.338	3.780
3/4-S	2.2	0.748	3.848	0.202	0.464	7.146	3.751	0.108	0.418	4.047
7/8-S	2.6	0.778	3.952	0.288	0.569	7.539	5.114	0.212	0.692	5.046
1-S	3.0	1.091	5.215	0.479	0.827	7.978	5.693	0.321	0.870	6.981
1 1/8-S	3.3	1.121	5.593	0.623	0.955	8.841	5.724	0.474	1.098	8.377

Nominal Thickness (in.)	Approximate Weight (psf)	Effective Thickness for Shear (in.)	STRESS APPLIED PARALLEL TO FACE GRAIN				STRESS APPLIED PERPENDICULAR TO FACE GRAIN			
			A Area (in.^{2}/ft.)	*I* Moment of Inertia (in.^{4}/ft.)	*KS* Eff. Section Modulus (in.^{3}/ft.)	*Ib/Q* Rolling Shear Constant (in.^{2}/ft.)	*A* Area (in.^{2}/ft.)	*I* Moment of Inertia (in.^{4}/ft.)	*KS* Eff. Section Modulus (in.^{3}/ft.)	*Ib/Q* Rolling Shear Constant (in.^{2}/ft.)
TOUCH-SANDED PANELS										
$^1/_2$-T	1.5	0.543	2.698	0.084	0.282	4.511	2.486	0.020	0.162	2.720
$^{19}/_{32}$ & $^5/_8$-T	1.8	0.707	3.127	0.124	0.349	5.500	2.799	0.050	0.259	3.183
$^{23}/_{32}$ & $^3/_4$-T	2.2	0.739	4.059	0.201	0.469	6.592	3.625	0.078	0.350	3.596

TABLE NO. 25-9-J—VALUES OF *G* FOR USE WITH EFFECTIVE THICKNESS FOR SHEAR (TABLES NOS. 25-9-H AND 25-9-I) IN CALCULATING DEFLECTION OF PLYWOOD DIAPHRAGMS

PLYWOOD GRADES OR SPECIES GROUP NOS.	G—(MODULUS OF RIGIDITY—PSI)[1]
Group 1	90,000
Group 2	75,000
Group 3	60,000
Group 4	50,000
STRUCTURAL I	90,000
STRUCTURAL II	60,000
Exterior C-C and C-D with Exterior glue The combination of Identification Index designation and panel thickness determine the minimum species group and, therefore, the modulus of rigidity to be used: 5/16 — 20/0; 3/8 — 24/0; 15/32, 1/2 — 32/16; 19/32, 5/8 — 42/20; 23/32, 3/4 — 48/24	90,000
All other combinations of C-C and C-D with Exterior glue	50,000

[1]Values of "G" shown apply to plywood bonded with Exterior glue. For plywood bonded with Interior glue, multiply by 0.91.

TABLE NO. 25-9-K—"e_n" VALUES (INCHES) FOR USE IN CALCULATING DIAPHRAGM DEFLECTION DUE TO NAIL SLIP (STRUCTURAL I)[1]

LOAD PER NAIL (Pounds)	NAIL DESIGNATION		
	6d	8d	10d
60	0.012	0.008	0.006
80	0.020	0.012	0.010
100	0.030	0.018	0.013
120	0.045	0.023	0.018
140	0.068	0.031	0.023
160	0.102	0.041	0.029
180	–––	0.056	0.037
200	–––	0.074	0.047
220	–––	0.096	0.060
240	–––	–––	0.077

[1]Increase "e_n" values 20 percent for plywood grades other than STRUCTURAL I.
Values apply to common wire nails.
Load per nail = maximum shear per foot divided by the number of nails per foot at interior panel edges.
Decrease values 50 percent for seasoned lumber.

TABLE NO. 25-9-L—CONCENTRATED STATIC AND IMPACT TEST PERFORMANCE CRITERIA FOR PANELS TESTED ACCORDING TO SECTION 25.916—SHEATHING

END USE—SPAN RATING	TEST EXPOSURE CONDITIONS[a]	PERFORMANCE REQUIREMENTS		
		Minimum Ultimate Load (Lb.)		Maximum Deflection (In.) Under 200-Lb. Load[b]
		Static	Following Impact[d]	
Roof—16	Dry	400	300	7/16 (.438)
	Wet	400	300	(c)
Roof—20	Dry	400	300	15/32 (.469)
	Wet	400	300	(c)
Roof—24	Dry	400	300	1/2 (.500)
	Wet	400	300	(c)
Roof—32	Dry	400	300	1/2 (.500)
	Wet	400	300	(c)
Roof—40	Dry	400	300	1/2 (.500)
	Wet	400	300	(c)
Roof—48	Dry	400	300	1/2 (.500)
	Wet	400	300	(c)
Subfloor—16	Dry	400	400	3/16 (.188)
	Wet/Redry	400	400	3/16 (.188)
Subfloor—20	Dry	400	400	7/32 (.219)
	Wet/Redry	400	400	7/32 (.219)
Subfloor—24	Dry	400	400	1/4 (.250)
	Wet/Redry	400	400	1/4 (.250)

[a]Wet/redry is exposure to three days continuous wetting followed by testing dry. Wet conditioning is exposure to three days continuous wetting and tested wet.

[b]Criteria apply under static concentrated load according to Section 25.916. They do not apply following impact.

[c]Not applicable.

[d]Impact shall be 75 ft.-lb. for span ratings up to 24 o.c., 90 ft.-lb. for 32 o.c., 120 ft.-lb. for 40 o.c., and 150 ft.-lb. for 48 o.c.

TABLE NO. 25-9-M—UNIFORM LOAD PERFORMANCE CRITERIA FOR PANELS TESTED ACCORDING TO SECTION 25.917—SHEATHING

END USE—SPAN RATING	TEST EXPOSURE CONDITIONS[a]	PERFORMANCE REQUIREMENTS	
		Average Deflection (In.) Under Load (psf)	Minimum Ultimate Uniform Load (psf)
Roof—16	Dry	0.067 at 35 psf	150
Roof—20	Dry	0.080 at 35 psf	150
Roof—24	Dry	0.100 at 35 psf	150
Roof—32	Dry	0.133 at 35 psf	150
Roof—40	Dry	0.167 at 35 psf	150
Roof—48	Dry	0.200 at 35 psf	150
Subfloor—16	Dry	0.044 at 100 psf	330
	Wet/Redry	0.044 at 100 psf	330
Subfloor—20	Dry	0.053 at 100 psf	330
	Wet/Redry	0.053 at 100 psf	330
Subfloor—24	Dry	0.067 at 100 psf	330
	Wet/Redry	0.067 at 100 psf	330

[a]Wet/redry is exposure to three days continuous wetting followed by testing dry.

TABLE NO. 25-9-N—CONCENTRATED STATIC AND IMPACT TEST PERFORMANCE CRITERIA FOR PANELS TESTED ACCORDING TO SECTION 25.916—SINGLE FLOOR

SPAN RATING	TEST EXPOSURE CONDITIONS[a]	PERFORMANCE REQUIREMENTS		
		Minimum Ultimate Load (Lb.)		Maximum Deflection (In.) Under 200-Lb. Load[b]
		Static	Following 75 Ft.-Lb. Impact	
16	Dry	550	400	$\frac{5}{64}$ (.078)
	Wet/Redry	550	400	$\frac{5}{64}$ (.078)
20	Dry	550	400	$\frac{6}{64}$ (.094)
	Wet/Redry	550	400	$\frac{6}{64}$ (.094)
24	Dry	550	400	$\frac{7}{64}$ (.108)
	Wet/Redry	550	400	$\frac{7}{64}$ (.108)

[a]Wet/redry is exposure to three days continuous wetting followed by testing dry.

[b]Criteria apply under static concentrated load and following a 75 ft.-lb. impact according to Section 25.916.

TABLE NO. 25-9-O—UNIFORM LOAD PERFORMANCE CRITERIA FOR PANELS TESTED ACCORDING TO SECTION 25.917—SINGLE FLOOR

SPAN RATING	TEST EXPOSURE CONDITIONS[a]	PERFORMANCE REQUIREMENTS	
		Average Deflection (In.) Under Load (psf)	Minimum Ultimate Uniform Load (psf)
16	Dry or Wet/Redry	0.044 at 100 psf	330
20	Dry or Wet/Redry	0.053 at 100 psf	330
24	Dry or Wet/Redry	0.067 at 100 psf	330

[a]Wet/redry is exposure to three days continuous wetting followed by testing dry.

UNIFORM BUILDING CODE STANDARD NO. 25-15

SPACED WOOD COLUMN DESIGN

Based on National Design Specification for Wood Construction (1982), including the 1982 Supplement, National Forest Products Association

See Sections 2501 (a), 2507 (a) 2 and 2507 (b), Uniform Building Code

Scope

Sec. 25.1501. This standard shall cover requirements for spaced column design, in accordance with Chapter 25 of the Uniform Building Code.

Spaced Wood Columns

Sec. 25.1502. Wood columns shall be designed in accordance with the following formulas and requirements:

A = area of column cross section, square inches.

F_c = allowable unit stress in compression parallel to grain as given in Table No. 25-A of the Uniform Building Code.

F'_c = allowable unit stress in compression parallel to grain adjusted to l/d ratio.

d = dimension of least side of individual members of spaced columns, inches.

d_2 = dimension of wide face of individual member, inches.

E = modulus of elasticity.

l_1 and l_2 = distances from center to center of lateral supports of continuous spaced columns, and from end to end of simple spaced columns, inches.

l_3 = distance in spaced column from center of connector in end blocks to center of spacer block, inches.

P = total load, pounds.

P/A = maximum load per unit of cross-sectional area.

Columns, Connector Joined

Sec. 25.1503. Spaced columns are formed of two or more individual members with their longitudinal axis parallel, separated at the ends and middle points of their length by blocking and joined at the ends by timber connectors capable of developing the required shear resistance.

Spaced columns shall be classifed as to end fixity, either as condition "a" or condition "b," as follows:

Condition a. The centroid of connectors or a connector group in the end block shall be within $1/20$ of the length l_1 from the column end.

Condition b. The centroid of connectors or a connector group in the end block shall be between $1/20$ and $1/10$ of the length l_1 from the column end.

Limitations

Sec. 25.1504. For individual members of a spaced column:

1. l_1/d_1 shall not exceed 80, where l_1 is the distance between lateral supports that provide restraint perpendicular to the wide faces of the individual members.
2. l_2/d_2 shall not exceed 50, where l_2 is the distance between lateral supports that provide restraint in a direction parallel to the wide faces of the individual members.

3. l_3/d_1 shall not exceed 40, where l_3 is the distance between the centroid of connectors in an end block and the center of the spacer block.

Location of Spacer and End Blocks

Sec. 25.1505. A single spacer block shall be located within the middle one tenth of the column length l and, if so located, connectors are not required for this block. If there are two or more spacer blocks, the distance between any two blocks shall not exceed one half the distance between centers of connectors in the end blocks. The requirements for connectors in spacer blocks when two or more blocks are used are the same as for end blocks.

End blocks shall be so placed that sufficient end and edge distances and spacings for the required minimum size and number of connectors are maintained in both end blocks and individual members, and connectors so placed that they comply with conditions "a" or "b" (Figure No. 25-15-1), depending on fixity factor assumed.

For spaced columns used as members of a truss, e.g., compression chords, a panel point which is stayed laterally shall be considered as the end of the spaced column and the portion of the web members between the individual pieces making up a spaced column may be considered as the end blocks. For spaced column web members, joints at the tension chord may be considered stayed laterally by the tautness of the tension chord and by customary lateral braces between trusses.

If there are two or more connectors in a contact face, the position of the center of gravity of the group of connectors shall be used in measuring the distance from connectors in the end block to the end of the column for determining fixity condition "a" or "b" (Figure No. 25-15-1).

Dimensions of Spacer and End Blocks

Sec. 25.1506. The thickness of spacer and end blocks shall be not less than that of the individual members of the spaced column nor shall the thickness, width and length of spacer and end blocks be less than that required for installation of connectors of a size and number capable of carrying a load equal to that computed from Table No. 25-15-A.

Load Capacity of Connectors in End Spacer Blocks

Sec. 25.1507. To obtain spaced-column action the connectors in each pair of mutually contacting surfaces of end blocks and individual members at each end of a spaced column shall be of a size and number to provide a connector load capacity in pounds equal to the cross-sectional area in square inches of one of the individual members times the appropriate end-spacer block constant in Table No. 25-15-A.

If connector-joined spaced columns are used in locations other than dry, the connector loads should be adjusted for such conditions.

If spaced columns are a part of a truss system or other similar framing, the connectors required by joint design may be sufficient for end block connectors but should be checked against Table No. 25-15-A.

Allowable Loads for Spaced Columns

Sec. 25.1508. The total allowable load for a spaced column is the sum of the allowable loads for each of its individual members determined as follows, except that the unit load for the individual members shall not exceed the allowable unit stresses in compression parallel to grain appropriately modified as provided in Chapter 25 of the Uniform Building Code, nor shall such load exceed that permitted for net section for connectors.

Maximum design values F'_c in psi of cross-sectional area of individual members of spaced columns shall be determined in accordance with the following formulas:

1. **Short columns.** For spaced columns with individual members having an l_1/d_1 ratio of 11 or less:

$$F'_c = F_c$$

2. **Intermediate columns.** For spaced columns with individual members having an l_1/d_1 ratio greater than 11 but less than K:

$$F'_c = F_c\left[1 - \frac{1}{3}\left(\frac{l_1/d_1}{K}\right)^4\right]$$

WHERE:

$K = 0.671\sqrt{C_x E/F_c}$

3. **Long columns.** For spaced columns with individual members having an l_1/d_1 ratio of K or greater:

$$F'_c = \frac{0.30 C_x E}{(l_1/d_1)^2}$$

WHERE:

C_x = 2.5 for fixity condition "a."
C_x = 3.0 for fixity condition "b."

Where the design values F'_c for the two individual members of a spaced column are different because the members are of different species, grades or thicknesses, the lesser value of F'_c shall apply to both members.

The design values shall not exceed the design values for the individual members taken as simple solid columns without regard to fixity, when determined with Section 2507 by using dimensions d_2 and length l_2, where l_2 is the distance between the lateral supports which provide restraint in a direction parallel to dimension d_2.

TABLE NO. 25-15-A—END SPACER BLOCK CONSTANTS FOR CONNECTOR JOINED SPACED COLUMNS

l/d RATIO OF INDIVIDUAL MEMBER IN THE SPACED COLUMN[1]	END SPACER BLOCK CONSTANT			
	Group A Connector Loads	Group B Connector Loads	Group C Connector Loads	Group D Connector Loads
0 to 11	0	0	0	0
15	38	33	27	21
20	86	73	61	48
25	134	114	94	75
30	181	155	128	101
35	229	195	162	128
40	277	236	195	154
45	325	277	229	181
50	372	318	263	208
55	420	358	296	234
60 to 80	468	399	330	261

[1]Constants for intermediate l/d ratios may be obtained by straight line interpolation.

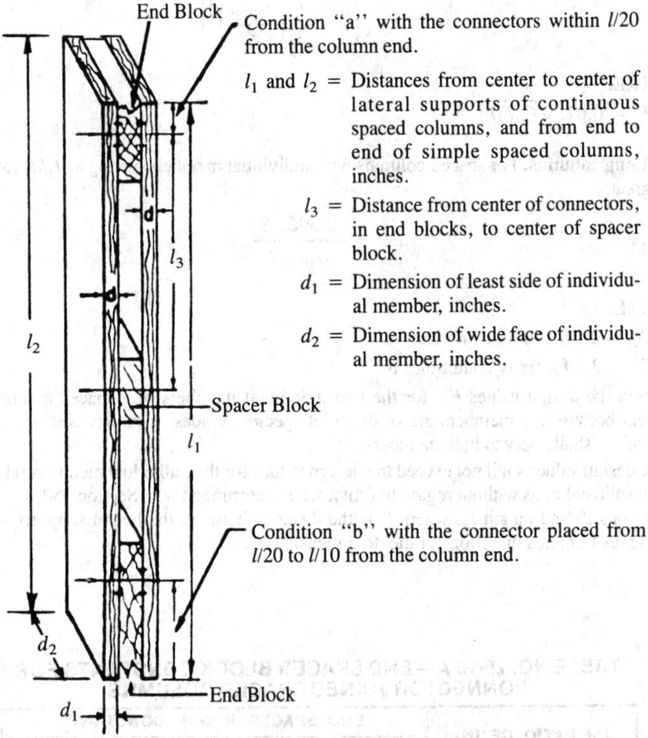
End Block
Condition "a" with the connectors within $l/20$ from the column end.
l_1 and l_2 = Distances from center to center of lateral supports of continuous spaced columns, and from end to end of simple spaced columns, inches.
l_3 = Distance from center of connectors, in end blocks, to center of spacer block.
d_1 = Dimension of least side of individual member, inches.
d_2 = Dimension of wide face of individual member, inches.
d
l_3
d
l_2
Spacer Block
l_1
Condition "b" with the connector placed from $l/20$ to $l/10$ from the column end.
d_2
End Block
d_1

FIGURE NO. 25-15-1—SPACED COLUMN, CONNECTOR JOINED

UNIFORM BUILDING CODE STANDARD NO. 25-17

TIMBER CONNECTOR JOINTS, BOLTED JOINTS, DRIFT BOLTS AND WOOD SCREWS, AND LAG SCREWS; METAL PLATE CONNECTED WOOD TRUSS DESIGN, AND NAILS AND STAPLES

Based on the National Design Specification for Wood Construction (1986), including the 1986 Supplement, of the National Forest Products Association; Design Specifications for Metal Plate Connected Wood Truss, TPI-85; Design Specification for Metal Plate Connected Parallel Chord Wood Trusses, PCT-80 of the Truss Plate Institute; and Federal Specification No. FF-N-105B, dated March 17, 1971

See Sections 2501 (a); 2504 (c); 2510 (a), (b), (d) and (f); 2513 (b); 2516 (s) 1; 4702; Tables Nos. 25-F, 25-G, 25-H, 25-J-1, 25-J-2, 25-K-1, 25-K-2, 25-O, 32-B-1, 32-B-2, 32-D-1, 32-D-2, 43-B, 43-C, 47-H, 47-I; and Appendix Table No. A-24-4, Uniform Building Code

Part I—Timber Connectors, Bolts, Screws, and Nails and Staples Based on the National Design Specifications for Wood Construction, 1986 Edition, of the National Forest Products Association

Scope

Sec. 25.1701. This part sets forth basic design considerations and limitations for purposes of specifying allowable loads for timber connectors, bolts, lag screws, drift bolts, nails, spikes and wood screws.

General Conditions

Sec. 25.1702. Where members of structural frames are composed of two or more layers or sections, the effect of inelastic deformations shall be considered in design. Composite constructions such as wood-concrete, wood-steel, lumber-plywood and glued-laminated timber-plywood composites shall be designed using the appropriate fastener values specified in Chapter 25 and in this standard. Care shall be taken at joints and splices to assure that connections will distribute proportional stresses to each individual piece and that consideration is given to stresses resulting from moment in joints.

The design values for fastenings in a given species apply to all grades of that species unless otherwise provided and to a moisture content of 19 percent or less. Design values for fasteners installed in fire-retardant-treated wood are subject to modification specified in Chapter 25, Section 2504 (c) 3.

Design values tabulated are the maximum for loads of normal duration and are subject to modification as provided in Chapter 25, Section 2504 (c) 4. Providing the wood is unseasoned or partially seasoned at the time of fabrication, design values shall be multiplied by the appropriate factor from Table No. 25-17-R or Table No. 25-17-S. When joints are to be exposed to weather or used where wood will remain wet in service, design values shall be multiplied by the appropriate factor from Table No. 25-17-R.

Design

Sec. 25.1703. (a) **Stresses in Members at Joints.** Members shall be checked for load-carrying capacity at the critical net section at joints, reducing the gross section area for holes or other removed wood.

In tension and compression members, the required net area, in square inches, shall be determined by dividing the total load transferred through the critical net section by the applicable design value in tension, F_t, or compression parallel to grain, F_c, for the species and grade of material used. Where timber connectors are staggered, adjacent connectors, with parallel-to-grain spacing equal to or less than one connector diameter, shall be considered as occurring at the same critical section. For parallel-to-grain loading with staggered bolts or lag screws, adjacent bolts or lag screws shall be considered as being placed at the critical section unless bolts in a row are spaced a minimum of eight diameters.

(b) **Eccentric Joints.** Timber connectors, bolts or lag screw joints that induce tension perpendicular to grain stresses in the wood shall not be used unless tested or analyzed to assure that all loads will be carried.

(c) **Group of Fastenings.** Design values for fastenings tabulated are for one fastening unit. When a joint contains two or more fastenings of the same type, each of the same or miscellaneous sizes, the design value for the joint shall be the sum of the design values for each individual fastening, except that for timber connectors, bolts or lag screws loaded laterally. In this case, the sum of the design values shall be limited as specified under the following Subsection (d).

(d) **Reduction for Lateral Loading of Groups.** A group of fastenings consists of one or more rows of connector units, bolts or lag screws arranged symmetrically with respect to the axis of the load. A row of fastenings consists of the following aligned with the direction of load:

1. Two or more timber connector units, or
2. Two or more bolts of the same diameter loaded in single or multiple shear, or
3. Two or more lag screws of the same type and size loaded in single shear.

Allowable Design Loads

Sec. 25.1704. Allowable design loads are the tabulated values which are for one fastening unit loaded as described at the head of columns and adjusted in accordance with Sections 25.1702 and 25.1703. Where a joint contains two or more fastenings of the same type, each of the same or miscellaneous sizes, the design value for the joint shall be the sum of the design values for each individual fastening, except that for timber connectors, bolts or lag screws loaded laterally, the sum of the design values shall be limited as specified in the following paragraphs.

The design value for a row of fasteners of the same size and type shall be not greater than the value of P_r (pounds) as determined by the following:

$$P_r = P_s K$$

WHERE:

P_s = the summation of the design values for individual fasteners in a row (pounds).

K = the modification factor appropriate for the type of side member, member sizes and number of fasteners in a row, as given in Tables Nos. 25-17-U and 25-17-V.

The design value for a group of fasteners is the sum of the design values for the rows in the group.

Gross cross-sectional areas shall be used, with no reductions for net section, in calculating cross-sectional area ratios for Tables Nos. 25-17-U and 25-17-V.

When a member is loaded perpendicular to grain direction, its equivalent cross- sectional area shall be the product of the thickness of the member and the overall width of the fastener group for calculating cross-sectional area ratios. When only one row of fasteners is used, the width of the fastener group shall be considered as the minimum parallel-to-grain spacing of the fasteners.

When fasteners in adjacent rows are staggered, and the distance between adjacent rows is less than one-fourth the distance between the closest fasteners in adjacent rows measured parallel to the rows, the adjacent rows shall be considered as one row for purposes of determining the design value for the group. For groups of fasteners having even numbers of rows, this principle shall apply to each pair. For groups of fasteners having odd numbers of rows, the more conservative interpretation shall apply. (See Figures Nos. 25-17-1 and 25-17-2.)

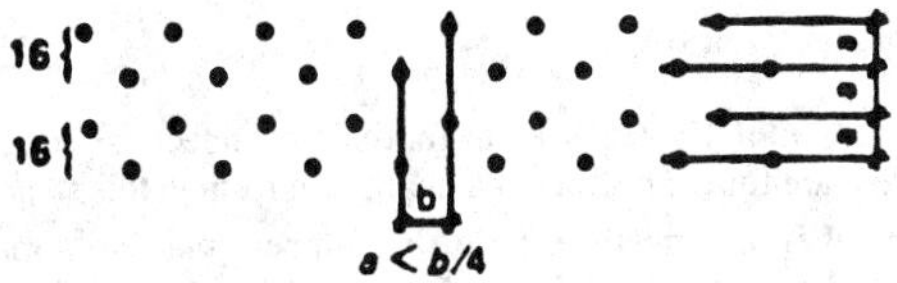
16
16
b
a < b/4

Consider as 2 rows of 16 fasteners
FIGURE NO. 25-17-1

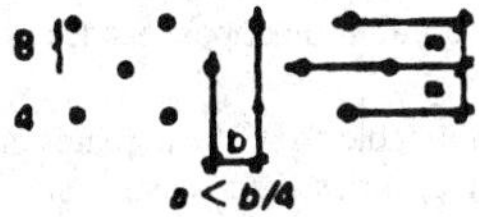
8
4
b
a < b/4

Consider as 1 row of 8 fasteners and 1 row of 4 fasteners
FIGURE NO. 25-17-2

Part II—Timber Connector Joints

Based on the National Design Specifications for Wood Construction (1986), of the National Forest Products Association

Scope

Sec. 25.1705. This standard covers detailed design considerations and limitations for purposes of specifying allowable connector loads for the following types of connectors:

1. One split ring with its bolt in single shear; or

2. Two shear plates used back-to-back in the contact faces of a timber-to-timber joint with their bolt in single shear; or one shear plate with its bolt in single shear used in conjunction with a steel strap or shape in a timber-to-metal joint.

Materials

Sec. 25.1706. (a) **Quality.** Specifications for timber connectors and tabulated loads and modifications thereof are for connectors of a quality set forth in this standard.

(b) **Split-ring Timber Connectors.** Split-ring timber connectors manufactured from hot-rolled carbon steel approved for this use. Each ring shall form a closed true circle with the principal axis of the cross section of the ring metal parallel to the geometric axis of the ring. The ring shall fit snugly in the precut groove. This may be accomplished with a ring, the metal section of which is beveled from the central portion toward the edges to a thickness less than at midsection, or by any other method which will accomplish equivalent performance. It shall be cut through in one place in its circumference to form a tongue and slot.

(c) **Shear Plate Timber Connectors.** Shear plate timber connectors are of the following types:

1. **Pressed-steel type**—Pressed-steel shear plates manufactured from hot-rolled carbon steel approved for this use. Each plate shall be a true circle with a flange around the edge, extending at right angles to the face of the plate and extending from one face only, the plate portion having a central bolt hole, with an integral hub concentric to the hole or without an integral hub, and two small perforations on opposite sides of the hole and midway from the center and circumference.

2. **Malleable-iron type**—Malleable-iron shear plates manufactured under approved specifications for malleable iron castings. Each casting shall consist of a perforated round plate with a flange around the edge extending at right angles to the face of the plate and projecting from one face only, the plate portion having a central bolt hole with an integral hub extending from the same face as the flange.

(d) **Tolerances.** The tolerances in dimensions of the connector shall not be greater than those conforming to standard practices for the machine operations involved in manufacturing the connector.

Installation

Sec. 25.1707. In installation of connectors and bolts, a nut shall be placed on each bolt, and washers not smaller than the size set forth in Table No. 25-17-A shall be placed between the outside wood member and the bolt head, and between the outside wood member and the nut. When an outside member is a steel strap or shape, the washer may be omitted except when needed to extend bolt length to prevent metal plate or shape from bearing on threaded portion of bolt when used in conjunction with shear plates.

Methods of Measurement

Sec. 25.1708. (a) **Edge Distance.** Edge distance is the distance from edge of member to center of connector closest to the edge of the member measured perpendicular to the edge. (See Figures Nos. 25-17-3 and 25-17-4.)

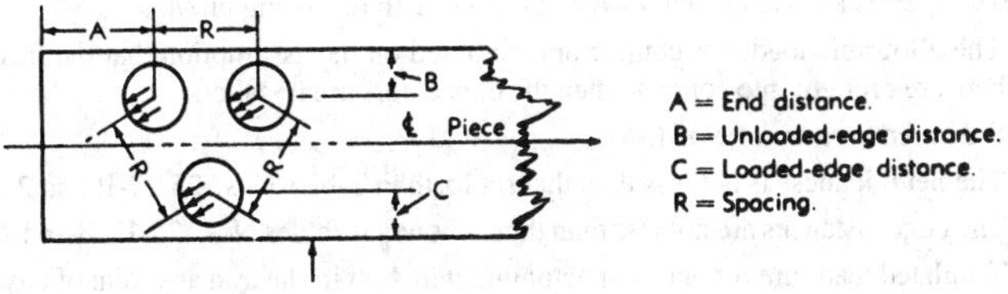
A
R
B
℄ Piece
C
A = End distance.
B = Unloaded-edge distance.
C = Loaded-edge distance.
R = Spacing.

FIGURE NO. 25-17-3
END DISTANCE, EDGE DISTANCE AND SPACING

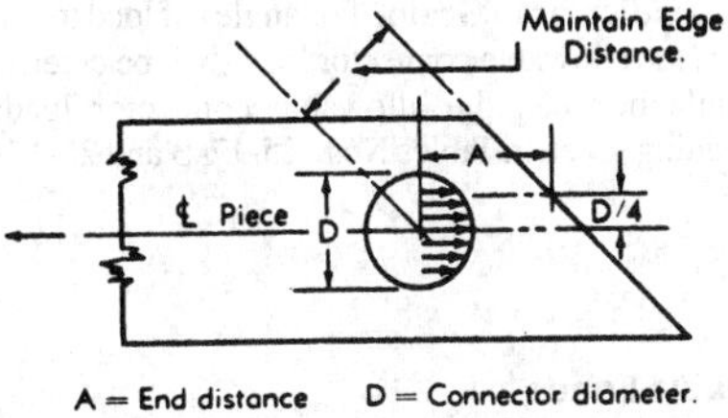
Maintain Edge Distance.
A
℄ Piece
D
D/4
A = End distance
D = Connector diameter.

FIGURE NO. 25-17-4
END DISTANCE FOR MEMBER WITH SLOPING END CUT

(b) **Grooves, Daps and Bolt Holes.** Grooves, daps and bolt holes of dimensions and shapes given in Table No. 25-17-A as appropriate for the type and size of the connector used, shall be accurately cut or bored to conform to the bolts and connectors and shall be oriented in contacting faces.

When lumber is not seasoned to the moisture content normal to the conditions of service, the joints should be drawn up by turning down the nuts on the bolts periodically until moisture equilibrium is reached so as to keep the adjacent faces of the members in contact.

(c) **Spacing.** Spacing is the distance between centers of connectors measured along a line joining their centers.

(d) **Load at Angle to Grain.** The angle of load to grain is the angle between the direction of the load acting on the member and the longitudinal axis of the member.

(e) **End Distance.** End distance is the distance measured parallel to the grain from center of connector to the square cut end of the member. (See Figure No. 25-17-3.)

Allowable Loads

Sec. 25.1709. (a) **General.** The tabulated loads for lumber in Tables Nos. 25-17-B and 25-17-C, specified in this section, apply to stress grades (Table No. 25-A, Uniform Building Code) of species as listed in Table No. 25-17-D, with following provisions:

1. The allowable loads for connectors are based on the assumption that the faces of the members are brought into contact when the connectors are installed.
2. Side members are of wood.
3. The net thickness is not less than that set forth in Tables Nos. 25-17-B and 25-17-C.
4. The edge distances are not less than those shown in Tables Nos. 25-17-B and 25-17-C.
5. Tabulated loads are for one connector unit with bolt in shear in any joint of any number of members.

(b) **Parallel or Perpendicular to Grain.** Allowable connector loads for loading parallel or perpendicular to grain given in Tables Nos. 25-17-B and 25-17-C, are applicable for the connectors described in Section 25.1706 for all conditions other than those for which specific exceptions are made.

(c) **Not Parallel or Perpendicular to Grain.** For angles of load to grain between parallel and perpendicular to grain, the allowable connector load shall be determined by application of the Hankinson formula between the allowable connector loads for parallel and perpendicular-to-grain loading given in Tables Nos. 25-17-B and 25-17-C, except for shear plates.

Modification of Allowable Loads

Sec. 25.1710. (a) **Species and Grades.** Tabulated loads for groups A, B, C and D woods in Tables Nos. 25-17-B and 25-17-C, apply to stress-graded lumber of the species as listed in Table No. 25-17-D.

(b) **Condition of Lumber.** For connectors used in joints exposed to weather or where the wood will remain wet in service, the allowable connector loads shall be modified in accordance with Table No. 25-17-R.

For connectors in lumber which has been pressure-impregnated with fire-retardant chemicals and dried after treatment, 90 percent of the tabulated loads, shall apply for lumber so treated and not dried after treatment, the requirements of the second paragraph of this subsection shall apply.

(c) **Connectors in End Grain.** When connectors are installed in a surface that is not parallel to the general direction of the grain of the member, such as the end of a square-cut member, or the sloping surface of a member cut at an angle to its axis, or the surface of a glued-laminated timber cut at an angle to the direction of laminations, design values shall be determined in accordance with this subsection.

The following definitions and notations apply to this subsection:

AXIS OF CUT defines the direction of a sloping surface relative to the general direction of the wood fibers. For a sloping cut symmetrical about one of the major axes of the members, as in Figures Nos. 25-17-6, 25-17-9, 25-17-10 and 25-17-11, the axis of cut is parallel to a major axis. For an asymmetrical sloping surface (i.e., one that slopes relative to both major axes of the member), the axis of cut is the direction of a line defining the intersection of the sloping surface with any plane that is both normal to the sloping surface and also is aligned with the general direction of the wood fibers. (See Figures Nos. 25-17-6 and 25-17-7.)

SIDE-GRAIN SURFACE means a surface parallel to the general direction of the wood fibers ($\alpha = 0°$), such as the top, bottom and sides of a straight member.

SLOPING SURFACE means a surface cut at an angle, α , other than 0 degrees or 90 degrees to the general direction of the wood fibers.

SQUARE-CUT SURFACE means a surface perpendicular to the general direction of the wood fibers ($\alpha = 90°$).

α = the least angle formed between a sloping surface and the general direction of the wood fibers (i.e., the acute angle between the axis of cut and the general direction of the fibers. (Sometimes called the slope of the cut.) (See Figures Nos. 25-17-6 through 25-17-11.)

Θ = the angle between the direction of applied load and the axis of cut of a sloping surface, measured in the plane of the sloping surface. (See Figure No. 25-17-11.)

P = design value for a connector unit in a side-grain surface, when loaded in a parallel-to-grain direction ($\alpha = 0°, \Theta = 0°$).

Q = design value for a connector unit in a side-grain surface, when loaded in a perpendicular-to-grain direction ($\alpha = 0°, \Theta = 90°$).

Q_{90} = design value for a connector unit in a square-cut surface, when loaded in any direction in the plane of the surface ($\alpha = 90°$).

$P\alpha$ = design value for a connector unit in a sloping surface, when loaded in a direction parallel to the axis of cut ($0° < \alpha < 90°, \Theta = 90°$).

$Q\alpha$ = design value for a connector unit in a sloping surface, when loaded in a direction perpendicular to the axis of cut ($0° < \alpha < 90°, \Theta = 90°$).

$N\alpha$ = design value for a connector unit in a sloping surface, when direction of load is at an angle Θ from the axis of cut.

For connectors installed in square-cut or sloping surfaces, design values shall be determined from the following applications of the Hankinson formula:

1. Square-cut surface; loaded in any direction ($\alpha = 90°$). (See Figure No. 25-17-8.)

$$Q_{90} = 0.60\,Q$$

2. Sloping surface, loaded parallel to axis of cut ($0° < \alpha < 90°, \Theta = 0°$). (See Figure No. 25-17-9.)

$$P\alpha = \frac{PQ_{90}}{P \sin^2 \alpha + Q_{90} \cos^2 \alpha}$$

3. Sloping surface; loaded perpendicular to axis of cut ($0° < \alpha < 90°, \Theta = 90°$). (See Figure No. 25-17-10.)

$$Q\alpha = \frac{QQ_{90}}{Q \sin^2 \alpha + Q_{90} \cos^2 \alpha}$$

4. Sloping surface; loaded at angle Θ to axis of cut ($0° < \alpha < 90°, 0° < \Theta < 90°$). (See Figure No. 25-17-11.)

$$N\alpha = \frac{P\alpha Q\alpha}{P\alpha \sin^2 \Theta + Q\alpha \cos^2 \Theta}$$

The provisions for edge distance, end distance and spacing for connectors in side-grain surfaces, shall apply to connectors in square-cut surfaces and sloping surfaces, as follows:

5. Square-cut surface, loaded in any direction—apply provisions for perpendicular-to-grain loading.

6. Sloping surface with α from 45 degrees to 90 degrees, loaded in any direction—apply provisions for perpendicular-to-grain loading.

7. Sloping surface with α less than 45 degrees, loaded parallel to axis of cut—apply provisions for parallel-to-grain loading.

8. Sloping surface with α less than 45 degrees, loaded perpendicular to axis of cut—apply provisions for perpendicular-to-grain loading.

9. Sloping surface with α less than 45 degrees, loaded at angle Θ to axis of cut—apply provisions for members loaded at angles to grain other than 0 degrees and 90 degrees.

(d) **Type or Arrangement.** 1. **Two or more connectors.** For a joint assembly in which two or more connector units of the same sizes are used in the contact faces with the connectors concentric with the same bolt axis, or in which two or more bolts are used with connectors on separate bolts, the total allowable connector load shall be the sum of the allowable connector loads given for each connector unit used. This provision applies to all conditions except that connectors shall not be placed concentrically on the same bolt in the same timber surface except as provided in Subsection 2 of this section.

2. **Metal side plates.** If metal side plates instead of wood side plates are used, the tabulated allowable connector loads for parallel-to-grain loading shall be modified in accordance with the notes for Table No. 25-17-C.

Design of Member

Sec. 25.1711. (a) **Design of Joints in Shear.** Timber connector and bolted joints and beams supported by connectors or bolts shall be designed so F_v in the following formula does not exceed the allowable unit stresses in horizontal shear.

$$F_v = \frac{3V}{2bd_e}$$

WHERE:

de (with connectors) = the depth of the member less the distance from the unloaded edge of member to the nearest edge of the nearest connector.

de (with bolts only) = the depth of the member less the distance from the unloaded edge of the member to the center of the nearest bolt.

Allowable unit stresses in shear for joints involving bolts or connectors loaded perpendicular to grain may be 50 percent greater than the horizontal shear values set forth in Tables Nos. 25-A and 25-C of the Uniform Building Code, provided that the joint occurs at least five times the depth of the member from its end. Where joints occur within five times the depth of the member from its end, the strength of the joint shall be evaluated not only for the bolt or connector load but also as a notched beam, considering the notch to extend from the unloaded edge of the member to the center of the nearest bolt or the nearest edge of the nearest connector.

(b) **Net Section.** The net section shall be determined by subtracting from the full cross-sectional area of the timber the projected area of that portion of the connector groove within the member and that portion of the bolt hole not within the connector groove, located at the critical plane. (See Table No. 25-17-A.)

If knots occur at the critical section, the cross-sectional area of the knots outside the area deducted for connectors and bolts should also be deducted in determining the net section.

In tension and compression members the required net area, in square inches, shall be determined by dividing the total load transferred through the critical section by the allowable F_t for tension members, or by the allowable F_c for compression members, for the species and grade of lumber used.

EXCEPTION: Where fabrication of timber connector joints is subjected to supervision by the designer, required net area may be determined as provided in Table No. 25-17-Q.

(c) **Eccentric Joints.** Eccentric timber connector, bolt or lag screw joints that induce tension-perpendicular-to-grain stresses in the wood shall not be used unless appropriate engineering procedures or tests are employed in the design of such joints to ensure that all service loads will be safely carried.

Use of Lag Screws Instead of Bolts with Timber Connectors

Sec. 25.1712. (a) **Type of Screw.** The lag screw shall have a cut thread, not a rolled thread.

(b) **Diameter of Lag Screw.** The shank of the lag screw shall have the same diameter as the bolt specified for the connector.

(c) **Hole for Shank and Threaded Portion.** The hole for the shank shall be the same diameter as the shank.

The hole for the threaded portion of the lag screw shall have a diameter equal to approximately 75 percent of that of the shank.

(d) **Allowable Loads.** When lag screws are used with connectors, the full allowable load (the load for one connector unit with bolt) may be used for 2 1/2-inch and 4-inch split rings and 4-inch shear plates when the minimum penetration of the lag screw into the member receiving the point is seven diameters for Group I woods, eight diameters for Group II, 10 diameters for Group III and 11 diameters for Group IV. For 2 5/8-inch shear plates, the full allowable load may be used when the minimum penetration is four diameters for Group I woods, five diameters for Group II, seven diameters for Group III and eight diameters for Group IV. (See Table No. 25-17-I.)

The allowable load for 2 1/2-inch and 4-inch split rings and 2 5/8-inch and 4-inch shear plates, when used with lag screws, shall vary uniformly from the full allowable load with penetration as specified in this section, to 75 percent of the full allowable load with penetration of three diameters for Group I woods, three and one-half diameters for Group II, four diameters for Group III and four and one-half diameters for Group IV. When metal side plates are used with 2 5/8-inch shear plates, the full allowable load may be used for the minimum penetrations specified.

Part III—Bolted Joints

Based on National Design Specification for Wood Construction (1986), including the 1986 Supplement of the National Forest Products Association

Scope

Sec. 25.1713. This standard covers detailed design considerations and limitations of bolted joints. Tabulated allowable bolt loads are the maximum for normal loading. Pertinent adjustments of stresses and provisions for lumber in Chapter 25 of the Uniform Building Code, except as otherwise provided in this standard, apply likewise to the tabulated bolt loads given in this standard.

Allowable Loads

Sec. 25.1714. (a) **Number of Bolts.** Tabulated loads are for one common bolt in double shear in a three-member joint.

For bolt lengths in the main member intermediate to those shown in Table No. 25-17-G, the bolt design value may be calculated by linear interpolation between the next lower and next higher bolt lengths.

(b) **Number of Members in Joint.** Tabulated loads are for a joint consisting of three members (double shear). Length of bolt is measured in the main member, i.e., thickness of the piece.

(c) **Exposure to Weather.** Tabulated loads apply for joints used indoors or in a location always dry.

(d) **Nuts and Washers.** Loosening of nuts, resulting from any shrinkage, is assumed and allowed for in the tabulated bolt loads.

Tabulated bolt loads shall also apply for tight nuts.

(e) **Placement of Bolts in Joint.** The l/d of bolt is the ratio of its length, l, in main member, to its diameter, d.

(f) **Side Members—Dimensions.** Tabulated loads apply when side members of wood are each one half the thickness of the main member.

(g) **Side Members—Materials.** Tabulated bolt loads are for side members of wood. Bearing thrust on side plates is assumed to be parallel to fibers.

(h) **Load at Angle with Axis of Bolt.** Tabulated loads are for loading acting perpendicular to axis of bolt.

Loads for more than one bolt, each of the same or miscellaneous sizes, are the sum of the loads permitted for each bolt. Spacings, end distances and edge distances shall be sufficient to develop the full strength of each bolt.

(i) **Loads Neither Parallel nor Perpendicular to Grain.** Allowable bolt loads acting in a direction inclined to grain shall be determined from the Hankinson formula, which for total bolt loads may be stated as follows:

$$N = \frac{PQ}{P \sin^2 \theta + Q \cos^2 \theta}$$

WHERE:

N = allowable load per bolt in a direction at inclination θ with the direction of the grain.

P = allowable load per bolt in compression parallel to grain.

Q = allowable load per bolt in compression perpendicular to grain.

θ = angle between the direction of the load and the direction of the grain.

(j) **Different Angle to Grain Between Side and Main Members.** Tabulated values apply when side and main members are loaded in the same grain direction. When side members are loaded at a different direction to the grain from the main member, the design value shall be taken as the lesser of (1) the tabulated design values for the main member, or (2) the tabulated design value for a piece twice the thickness of the side members and loaded in the same direction as the side members.

Modification of Allowable Loads

Sec. 25.1715. (a) **Condition of Lumber.** For bolts used in joints exposed to weather or where the wood will remain wet in service, the allowable bolt loads shall be modified in accordance with Table No. 25-17-R.

(b) **Treated Lumber.** For lumber pressure impregnated with fire-retardant chemicals and dried after treatment, 90 percent of the tabulated bolt loads shall apply. For lumber so treated and not dried after treatment, the 90 percent value shall be reduced in accordance with Subsection (a) of this section.

(c) **Wood Plates.** When wood splice plates are used, the allowable load perpendicular to grain shall not exceed the load parallel to grain for any given size and quality of timbers.

(d) **Steel Plates.** When steel plates are used for side members, the tabulated loads for parallel-to-grain loading shall be increased by 75 percent for joints made with bolts 1/2 inch or less in diameter, 25 percent for joints made with bolts 1 1/2 inches in diameter, and proportionately for intermediate diameters. No increase shall be allowed for perpendicular-to-grain loads. Steel plates shall be of ample strength.

When steel plates are used for main members, the tabulated values for parallel-to-grain loading for a piece twice the thickness of one of the side members shall be increased 75 percent for joints made with bolts 1/2 inch or less in diameter, 25 percent for joints made with bolts 1 1/2 inches in diameter, and proportionately for intermediate diameters. No increase in tabulated values for perpendicular-to-grain loading shall be made for joints having steel plates as side or main members. Steel plates shall be of ample strength.

(e) **Side Members.** 1. **Double shear.** If side members are thicker than one half the thickness of the main member, no increase in tabulated loads is permissible.

When the side members are less than one half the thickness of the main member, the tabulated loads indicated for a main member, which is twice the thickness of thinnest side members used, shall apply. For example, with 2-inch side members and a 10-inch center member, the tabulated loads for 4-inch center member shall be used.

2. **Single shear.** When a joint consists of two members (single shear) of equal thickness, one half the tabulated load for a piece the thickness of one of the members shall apply.

When members of a two-member joint are of unequal thickness, the allowable load shall be determined from the lesser of:

1. One half the tabulated load for the thicker member, or
2. One half the tabulated load for a piece twice the thickness of the thinner member.

When a joint consists of a wood member connected to a metal plate, one-half the tabulated design value for a piece the thickness of the wood member shall apply subject to the adjustments in Subsection (d) above.

For single shear joints in which one member is loaded parallel to grain and the other member is loaded at an angle to the grain, the design value shall be the lesser of:

1. One-half the tabulated design value for the thickness of the parallel-to-grain loaded member, or
2. The value obtained from application of the Hankinson Formula using one-half the tabulated parallel-to-grain and perpendicular-to-grain design values for a piece the

thickness of the angle-to-grain loaded member for P and Q, respectively.

(f) **Multiple Members.** For multiple-member joints other than two or three members, of which the pieces are of equal thickness, the allowable load shall vary as the number of shear planes involved; the allowable load for each shear plane shall be equal to one half the tabulated load for a piece the thickness of the member involved. Thus, when a joint consists of four members of equal thickness, one and one-half times the tabulated load for a piece the thickness of one of the members shall apply.

For a joint with four or more members not of equal thickness, the allowable load may be determined from the tabulated loads for the individual shear planes as follows:

1. Resolve the multimember joint into the maximum number of contiguous three-member joints.
2. For each such three-member joint, determine the applicable allowable load in accordance with standard procedures and assign one half of the load to each shear plane in the joint.
3. For those shear planes to which two different tabulated loads have been assigned, the allowable load shall be the lesser of the two loads.
4. For assemblies in which the load is shared equally among the members, or in which the distribution of load among members is indeterminate, the allowable load for the multimember joint shall be the least tabulated load for any one shear plane times the number of shear planes in the joint.
5. For assemblies in which the load on each member is known, the bolt allowable load for any member in the joint shall be the sum of the individual bolt allowable load for each of the two shear planes acting on that member, as determined in Items Nos. 1 through 3 above.

(g) **Load at an Angle with Axis of Bolt.** Tabulated design values are for loading acting perpendicular to axis of bolt. If the load in a two-member joint acts at an angle with the axis of a bolt, with the length of bolt in the two members designated l_1 and l_2 (Figure No. 25-17-11), respectively, the component of the design value acting at 90 degrees with the bolt axis shall be determined in accordance with Subsections (e) and (f) above, whichever is applicable for a joint in which two members at 90 degrees with the bolt axis have thicknesses l_2 and l_1. Ample bearing area under washers or plates shall be provided to resist the load component acting parallel to the axis of the bolt.

(h) **Mixed Species.** Design values for joints made with side members of different species from the main member shall be taken as the lesser of (1) the value determined for a comparable joint having all members made of the side member species or (2) the value determined for a comparable joint having all members of the main member species.

Materials

Sec. 25.1716. (a) **Quality of Bolts.** Tabulated loads are for common bolts.

(b) **Species of Lumber.** Tabulated loads apply to species given in Table No. 25-17-G.

(c) **Grade of Lumber.** Tabulated loads apply to species irrespective of grade of lumber used.

(d) **Condition of Lumber.** Tabulated loads are for bolts in lumber seasoned to a moisture content approximately equal to that to which it will eventually come in service.

Installation Requirements

Sec. 25.1717. (a) **Bolt Holes.** Bolt holes of a diameter permitting bolts to be driven easily, and careful centering of holes in main members and splice plates are assumed.

Bolt holes in unseasoned lumber shall be $^{1}/_{32}$ inch minimum to $^{1}/_{16}$ inch maximum larger than the bolt, depending on the size of the bolt.

Tight fit requiring forcible driving of bolts is not recommended.

(b) **Washers.** A washer not less than a standard cut washer, or a metal plate or strap in lieu thereof, shall be between the wood and the bolt head, and between the wood and the nut.

(c) **Spacing.** All spacings and distances given are measured from center of bolt.

(d) **End Distance.** End distance is the distance from the end of a bolted timber to the center of the bolt hole nearest the end.

For parallel-to-grain loading, the end distance shall be as follows:

1. In tension, seven times the bolt diameter for softwoods and five times for hardwoods.
2. In compression, four times the bolt diameter.

End distances specified for parallel- or perpendicular-to-grain loading may be reduced when the full design load on the joint is reduced in proportion to the reduction in end distance, except no end distance less than one half of those specified shall be used.

For perpendicular-to-grain loading, the end distance shall be not less than four times the bolt diameter. When members abut at a joint, the strength of the joint shall be evaluated not only for the bolt load but also as a beam supported by fastening as specified in Section 25.1711 (a).

For a joint loaded in tension at an angle to the axis of the bolt, the end distance shall be such that the shear area is equal to that for a parallel member joint. The shear area for a parallel member is the product of the length of the bolt in the main member and the minimum end distance for the full design load. For a joint loaded in tension at an angle to the axis of the bolt, the equivalent shear area is the area of the member up to the center line of the bolt.

Shear area requirements for parallel- and perpendicular-to-grain loadings may be reduced when the full design load on a joint loaded in tension at an angle to the bolt is reduced in proportion to the reduction in shear area, except, no shear area less than one-half that calculated for an equivalent parallel member joint shall be used.

(e) **Spacing of Bolts in a Row.** 1. **Row of bolts.** Row of bolts means a number of bolts placed in a line parallel to the direction of the load when parallel or perpendicular to grain.

2. **Parallel-to-grain loading.** For parallel-to-grain loading, the minimum spacing is four times bolt diameter *d*.

3. **Perpendicular-to-grain loading.** If the design load approaches bolt-bearing capacity of side members, spacing shall be same as parallel to grain.

If design load is less than bolt-bearing capacity of side members, spacing may be reduced proportionately but not less than three times the bolt diameter in the case of perpendicular-to-grain loading.

(f) **Spacing Between Rows of Bolts.** 1. **Parallel-to-grain loading.** For parallel-to-grain loading, the spacing across the grain between rows of bolts shall be at least one and one-half bolt diameters.

2. **Perpendicular-to-grain loading.** For perpendicular-to-grain loading, the spacing shall be at least two and one-half times bolt diameter for l/d ratios of two, and five times bolt diameter for l/d ratios of six or more. For ratios between two and six, the spacing shall be obtained by straight-line interpolation.

3. The spacing between rows of bolts paralleling the member shall not exceed 5 inches unless separate splice plates are used for each row of bolts.

(g) **Edge Distance.** Edge distance is the distance from the edge of the timber to the center of the nearest bolt hole.

For parallel-to-grain loading in tension or compression, the edge distance shall be at least one and one-half times the bolt diameter, except that for *l/d* ratios more than six, use one half the distance between the rows of bolts.

For perpendicular-to-grain loading, the edge margin toward which load is acting shall be at least four times the bolt diameter and the margin on the opposite edge shall be at least one and one-half bolt diameters.

Design

Sec. 25.1718. (a) **Critical Section.** The critical section is that section of the member, taken at right angles to the direction of the load, which gives the maximum stress in the member based on the net area remaining after reducing it for bolt holes at that section.

In tension and compression members, the required net area in square inches shall be determined by dividing the total load which is transferred through the critical section by the allowable F_t for tension members, or by the allowable F_c for compression members for the species and grade of lumber used.

(b) **Staggered Bolts.** For parallel-to-grain loading with staggered bolts, adjacent bolts shall be considered as being placed at the critical section unless spaced a minimum of eight diameters.

For perpendicular-to-grain loading, if design load for main member is less than bolt-bearing capacity of side timbers, staggering may be employed.

(c) **Bolting for Loads at Angle to Grain.** Since general requirements regarding the alignment, spacing and distances of bolts to cover all possible directions of applied load cannot be set up, uniform stress in main members and a uniform distribution of load to all bolts require that the gravity axis of the members shall pass through the center of resistance of the bolt groups.

(d) **Design of Eccentric Joints and Beam Supports.** For design of eccentric bolted joints and bolt-supported beams, see Section 25.1711.

Part IV—Nail, Staple, Spike, Drift Bolt and Wood Screw Joints

Based on Federal Specification FF-N-105B dated March 17, 1971, with Interim Amendment 4 dated August 23, 1977, and National Design Specification for Wood Construction (1986), including the 1986 Supplement of the National Forest Products Association

Scope

Sec. 25.1719. The following provisions apply to staples, wire nails and spikes, and to threaded, hardened steel nails and spikes which shall conform to the minimum sizes set forth in Table No. 25-17-H. Tabulated diameters apply to fasteners before application of any protective coating.

Nails, Staples and Spikes

Sec. 25.1720. (a) **Steel Wire.** Steel wire shall be of good commercial quality, entirely suitable for the purpose and sufficiently ductile to ensure that the finished product shall withstand, without fracture, cold bending through 180 degrees over a diameter not greater than the diameter of the wire. Except as specified for hardened steel, the cold bend test will not be applied to barbed nails, or nails having mechanically formed or deformed shanks.

(b) **Hardened Steel.** Hardened steel nails shall be heat treated to a minimum hardness of Rockwell C37. The finished product shall withstand, without fracture, cold bending through 20 degrees over a diameter not greater than the diameter of the wire.

(c) **Copper.** Copper nails shall contain a minimum of 98 percent pure copper. Copper nails shall withstand, without fracture, cold bending through 180 degrees over a diameter not greater than the diameter of thickness of the nail.

(d) **Aluminum Alloy Wire.** Aluminum alloy wire shall conform to alloy 5056 having a minimum ultimate tensile strength of 60,000 psi or alloy 6061 having a minimum ultimate tensile strength of 63,000 psi. Smooth shank nails shall be chemically treated to remove all grease, oil and foreign matter and to microscopically roughen the surface. Barbed and mechanically deformed nails shall be cleaned to remove all grease and foreign matter. Finished, smooth shank nails shall withstand, without fracture, cold bending through 90 degrees over a diameter not greater than the diameter of the wire.

(e) **Brass Wire.** Brass wire shall be of good commercial quality, entirely suitable for the purpose. The finished product shall withstand, without fracture, cold bending through 180 degrees over a diameter not greater than the diameter of the wire.

(f) **Stainless Steel Wire.** Stainless steel wire shall be of a commercial quality entirely suitable for the purpose of forming fasteners, and shall include stainless steel Types 302, 302, 304 and 316. The wire shall withstand without fracture cold bending through 180 degrees over a mandrel of a diameter not greater than the diameter of the wire so tested.

Finishes

Sec. 25.1721. (a) **Zinc Coating.** Hand-driven staples or nails required to be zinc coated shall be cut and formed from hot-dip galvanized steel wire or cut from uncoated (bright) steel wire and shall be hot-dip galvanized, electrodeposited zinc coated or mechanically deposited zinc coated.

Power or mechanically driven staples required to be zinc coated shall be cut and formed from hot-dip galvanized, asbestos-wiped steel wire, electrogalvanized steel wire or mechanically deposited zinc-coated steel wire.

Power or mechanically driven nails required to be zinc coated shall be cut and formed from hot-dip galvanized, asbestos-wiped steel wire, electrogalvanized steel wire, mechanically deposited zinc-coated steel wire or cut from uncoated (bright) steel wire and shall be hot-dip galvanized, electrodeposited zinc coated or mechanically deposited zinc coated.

Zinc-coated fasteners shall be reasonably smooth and shall be free from black and uncoated spots, fins and lumps. Any one of the following methods may be used for zinc coating:

1. **Galvanizing.** Hot-dip galvanizing of wire shall produce coating weights in accordance with Table No. 25-17-T.

2. **Mechanically deposited.** Mechanically deposited zinc coating shall produce coating weights in accordance with Table No. 25-17-T.

3. **Electrogalvanized.** Electrogalvanizing of wire or electrogalvanizing after forming shall produce coating weights in accordance with Table No. 25-17-T.

(b) **Cement Coating.** Cement coatings shall be reasonably even and shall not be tacky or gummy at normal temperatures or atmospheric conditions.

(c) **Chemical Etching.** Nails of all styles may be chemically etched.

Mechanically Deformed Shanks

Sec. 25.1722. Mechanically deformed shanks may be of either the screw type or the annular-ring (complete circle) type.

Dimensions

Sec. 25.1723. (a) **Measurement.** Nails with flat heads or with square shoulders under the heads shall be measured from under the head to the tip of the point and, except as otherwise specified, all other nails shall be measured overall, i.e., top of head to tip of point.

Cement-coated nails, except common box nails, standard cement-coated nails and cooler nails shall be measured overall, i.e., top of head to end of point.

Power-driven staples are referred to by "crown width" and "leg length." The crown width is an approximate measurement outside of the legs, dependent on the gage of the material. The inside measurement is critical for the staple gun. Staples shall fit the make and model of gun specified. The leg length is measured from the top of the crown to the tip of the point.

(b) **Lengths.** Lengths are in inches and common fractions; diameters are in common fractions when in multiples of 1/64 inch, otherwise diameters are given in decimals of an inch.

(c) **Tolerances.** Variation in the diameter of shanks of nails and staples from the dimensions specified shall not exceed ±.004 inch for diameters .076 inch or larger, and ±.002 inch for diameters smaller than .076 inch. Measurement of diameters shall not include coatings except for copper-clad staples. Diameters of pointed nails shall be measured immediately below the gripper marks, variation in length shall not exceed ±1/32 inch for lengths up to and including 1 inch; ±1/16 inch for lengths over 1 inch up to and including 21/2 inches; ±3/32 inch for lengths over 21/2 inches up to and including 7 inches and ±1/8 inch for lengths over 7 inches. These tolerances apply to all staples and nails. Diameters of mechanically deformed shanks shall be measured before deformation. The head diameter of roofing nails shall be plus or minus 10 percent of the nominal head diameter (mean of two readings 90 degrees apart) and the head diameters for other nails shall be plus or minus 10 percent of the nominal head diameter (individual measurement). The difference in diameter across the long axis of a roofing nailhead shall not exceed that across the short axis by more than 20 percent. For other nails the difference in diameter across the long axis should not exceed that across the short axis by more than 10 percent. A fillet must be provided under the head, an angle fillet is acceptable in lieu of a radius. Heads must be well centered.

(d) **Mechanically Driven Nails.** Nailheads for mechanically driven nails shall be either "T" headed or with or without altered round heads. These nails shall be suitable for use in the make and model of gun specified by the manufacturer including the head tolerances.

(e) **Types.** Nails specified for use in the Uniform Building Code shall conform to the physical requirements of Table No. 25-17-H. Tabulated diameters apply to fasteners before application of any protective coating.

Allowable Loads: Nails and Spikes

Sec. 25.1724. (a) **Threaded, Hardened Steel Nails.** Threaded or hardened steel nails meeting the requirements of this standard may be used with the same loads as given for common wire nails of corresponding pennyweight size except as provided in Sections 25.1725 (a) and 25.1726 (a).

(b) **Multiple Nails.** When more than one nail or spike is used in a joint, the total allowable load in withdrawal or lateral resistance is the sum of the allowable loads for the individual nail or spike.

(c) **Bored Holes.** When using a bored hole having a diameter not exceeding nine tenths of that of the nail or spike for Group I species, or three fourths for Groups II, III and IV species (see Table No. 25-17-I), the allowable load for the same size fastener, without a bored hole, applies in withdrawal and lateral resistance.

(d) **Treated Lumber.** For lumber pressure impregnated with fire-retardant chemicals and kiln-dried after treatment, 90 percent of the tabulated loads for nails and spikes shall apply. For lumber so treated and not kiln-dried after treatment, the 90 percent value shall be reduced in accordance with Sections 25.1725 (a) and 25.1726 (a).

(e) **Type of Load.** Allowable loads given for nails and spikes in Table No. 25-17-J are the maximum for normal loading, except that for nails and spikes used in a diaphragm construction the loads, adjusted as provided in Section 25.1726 (a), may be increased 30 percent. These loads are subject to duration of load adjustment, as provided for lumber in these standards.

Withdrawal Resistance: Nails and Spikes

Sec. 25.1725. (a) **Condition of Lumber.** For nails and spikes used in joints exposed to weather or where the wood will remain wet in service, the allowable loads shall be modified in accordance with Table No. 25-17-R.

The allowable withdrawal load in toenailed joints, for all conditions of seasoning, is equivalent to two thirds of that permitted in this subsection.

(b) **End Grain.** Structural design shall be such that nails and spikes are not loaded in withdrawal from end grain of wood.

Lateral Resistance: Nails and Spikes

Sec. 25.1726. (a) **Side Grain.** The allowable loads in lateral resistance, when driven in side grain of seasoned wood with load applied in any lateral direction, are given in Table No. 25-17-J. These loads apply only where the depth of penetration into the member holding the point is not less than 10 diameters for Group I species, 11 diameters for Group II species, 13 diameters for Group III species, and 14 diameters for Group IV species. When penetration is less than that specified, the allowable load may be determined by straight-line interpolation between zero and the tabulated load, except that penetration shall be not less than one third of that specified. Design values shall not be increased when the penetration of nails into the main member holding the point is larger than those specified above.

For nails or spikes in double shear and fully penetrating all members in a three-member joint, the allowable lateral load may be increased one third when each side member is not less than one third the thickness of the center member and may be increased two thirds when each side member is equal in thickness to the center member. For any intermediate thickness of side members, the increase in allowable load shall be determined by straight-line interpolation. The provisions on penetration in the previous paragraph apply to the center member in a three-member joint.

For nails or spikes in double shear with side members at least 3/8 inch thick, the allowable load may be doubled for nails not exceeding 12d in size when the nail extends at least three diameters beyond the side member and is clinched, except threaded, hardened steel nails need not be clinched.

For nails and spikes used in joints exposed to weather or where the wood will remain wet in service, the allowable loads shall be modified in accordance with Table No. 25-17-R.

The allowable lateral load in a toenailed joint is equivalent to five sixths of that permitted in this subsection.

Where properly designed metal side plates are used, the allowable loads given in paragraph 1 of this subsection may be increased 25 percent.

When connected members are sawn lumber from different fastener species groups, the design value shall be based on the higher numbered species group in Table No. 25-17-I.

(b) **End Grain.** The allowable load in lateral resistance for a nail or spike driven in the end grain (parallel to fibers) shall be two thirds of that given for lateral resistance in side grain.

Allowable Loads: Wood Screws

Sec. 25.1727. (a) **General.** 1. **Scope.** For wood screw joints with stress-grade lumber and the wood screws defined in this standard, the provisions of this section and the tabulated values apply.

2. **Type of load.** Allowable loads given in Tables No. 25-17-K and No. 25-17-L for wood screws are the maximum for normal loading. They are subject to duration of load adjustments as provided for in this standard.

3. **Number of wood screws.** Loads given are for one wood screw either in withdrawal or in lateral resistance in a two-member joint.

Loads for more than one wood screw each of the same or miscellaneous sizes are the sum of the loads permitted for each wood screw, provided that spacings, end distances and edge distances are sufficient to develop the full strength of each wood screw.

4. **Grade of lumber.** The allowable loads for wood screws in a given species apply to all grades of that species.

5. **Condition of lumber.** The allowable loads given in Tables No. 25-17-K and No. 25-17-L are for wood screws in seasoned lumber. For lumber pressure-impregnated with fire-retardant chemicals and dried after treatment, 90 percent of the tabulated loads shall apply. For lumber so treated and not dried after treatment, the 90 percent value shall be reduced in accordance with Section 25.1728 (b)— Exposure.

6. **Penetration.** For lateral resistance, the length of screw in main member shall be approximately seven times the shank diameter for the allowable loads in Table No. 25-17-K. If the penetration is less than seven diameters, the allowable load shall be reduced proportionately, but a penetration of less than four diameters shall not be used.

(b) **Allowable Loads for Lateral Resistance with Wood Screws in Side Grain.** The allowable loads for lateral resistance to any angle of load to grain when the wood screw is inserted perpendicular to the fibers (i.e., in side grain of main member), and a wood side piece is used, are given in Table No. 25-17-K.

(c) **Allowable Loads for Lateral Resistance When Loads Act Perpendicular to the Grain and the Wood Screw Is Inserted in End Grain.** The allowable loads for lateral resistance, when the loads act perpendicular to grain and the wood screw is inserted parallel to the fibers (i.e., in the end grain of the main member), shall be two thirds of those for lateral resistance given in Table No. 25-17-K.

(d) **Withdrawal Resistance.** 1. **General.** The structural design shall be such that wood screws are not loaded in withdrawal. When this condition cannot be avoided, the withdrawal loads given in Table No. 25-17-L apply when the following conditions are met:

1. The allowable tensile strength of the wood screw at net (root) section shall not be exceeded.
2. Wood screws shall not be loaded in withdrawal from end grain of wood.

For withdrawal resistance, the effective penetration used to determine total load capacity shall be the length of the threaded portion of the screw in the member receiving the point.

Modification of Allowable Loads: Wood Screws

Sec. 25.1728. (a) **Steel Side Piece.** Where steel side plates rather than wood side pieces are used, the allowable load for wood screws in lateral resistance of any angle of load to grain may be increased by 25 percent.

(b) **Condition of Lumber.** For wood screws used in joints exposed to weather or where the wood will remain wet in service, the allowable loads shall be modified in accordance with Table No. 25-17-R.

(c) **Depth of Penetration.** If the depth of penetration is less than seven times the diameter of the shank, the allowable load for lateral resistance shall be reduced in proportion to the length of penetration, but a length of penetration of less than four times the shank diameter shall not be used.

Installation: Wood Screws

Sec. 25.1729. (a) **Lead Holes.** Lead holes shall be prebored as follows:

1. **Withdrawal resistance.** For Group I species, the lead hole shall have a diameter of 90 percent of the root diameter of the wood screw.

For Groups II, III and IV species, the lead hole shall have a diameter of 70 percent of the root diameter of the wood screw.

2. **Lateral resistance.** For Group I species, the part of the lead hole receiving the shank shall have the same diameter as the shank, and that receiving the threaded portion shall have the same diameter as the root of the thread.

For Groups II, III and IV species, the part of the lead hole receiving the shank shall be seven eighths the diameter of the shank and that for the threaded portion shall be seven eighths the diameter of the screw at the root of the thread.

(b) **Insertion.** The screw shall be inserted in its lead hole by turning with a screw driver or other tool, not by driving with a hammer.

(c) **Lubrication.** Soap or other lubricant may be used on the screws to facilitate insertion and to prevent damage to screw.

(d) **Location.** Spacings, end distances and edge distances for wood screw joints shall be such as to prevent unusual splitting.

Materials: Wood Screws

Sec. 25.1730. (a) **Quality of Wood Screws.** The allowable loads are for any wood screw of sufficient strength to cause failure in the wood rather than the metal.

(b) **Lumber.** 1. **Seasoning.** The allowable loads determined by the provisions in this standard are for wood screws in seasoned lumber except as otherwise specifically provided.

2. **Service condition.** Allowable loads apply for joints used indoors or in a location always dry.

Allowable Load: Drift Bolts

Sec. 25.1731. (a) **Allowable Withdrawal of Driftpins or Drift Bolts from Side Grain.** The allowable withdrawal load per linear inch of penetration of a round drift bolt or pin from side grain when driven into a prebored hole having a diameter 1/8 inch less than that of the bolt diameter shall be determined from the formula:

$$p = 1200\,G2D$$

WHERE:

p = allowable withdrawal load per linear inch of penetration.
G = specific gravity of oven-dry wood (see Table No. 25-17-I).
D = diameter of drift bolt in inches.

(b) **Lateral Resistance of Drift Bolts.** The allowable load in lateral resistance for a drift bolt or pin driven in the side grain of wood shall not exceed 75 percent of the design values for a common bolt of the same diameter and length in main member. When possible, additional penetration of pin into members shall be provided in lieu of washers, head and nut on a common bolt.

Part V—Lag Screws

Based on National Design Specifications for Wood Construction (1982), including the 1982 Supplement of the National Forest Products Association

Design

Sec. 25.1732. (a) **General.** Allowable loads for lag screws given in this standard are the maximum for normal loading. Pertinent adjustment of stresses and provisions of Chapter 25 of the Uniform Building Code for lumber except as otherwise provided in this standard apply likewise to loads for lag screws given in this standard.

(b) **Number of Lag Screws.** Loads given are for one lag screw either in withdrawal or in lateral resistance in single shear in a two-member joint.

Loads for more than one lag screw, each of the same or miscellaneous sizes, are the sum of the loads permitted for each lag screw, provided that spacings, end distances and edge distances are sufficient to develop the full strength of each lag screw.

(c) **Grade of Lumber.** The allowable loads for lag screws in a given species apply to all grades of that species. Species groups are given in Table No. 25-17-I.

(d) **Condition of Lumber.** The allowable loads given are for lag screws in lumber seasoned to a moisture content approximately equal to that to which it will eventually come in service.

(e) **Exposure to Weather.** Allowable loads given apply for joints used indoors or in a location always dry.

Allowable Loads

Sec. 25.1733. (a) **Lateral Loads Parallel to Grain.** Loads for lag screws inserted perpendicular to the fiber (i.e., in side grain of main member) shall not exceed the values set forth in Tables No. 25-17-N and No. 25-17-O.

(b) **Lateral Loads Perpendicular to Grain.** Loads for lag screws inserted perpendicular to the fiber (i.e., in side grain of main member) shall not exceed the values set forth in Tables No. 25-17-N and No. 25-17-O.

(c) **Lateral Loads at Angles Other than Zero Degrees and 90 Degrees.** When the load acts at an angle other than zero degrees and 90 degrees with the grain, the lag screw is inserted perpendicular to the fiber (i.e., in side grain of main member) and either wood or metal side piece is used, the allowable loads for lag screws under lateral loading shall be determined from the Hankinson formula. See Section 25.1714 (i).

(d) **Lateral Loads Perpendicular to Grain in End Grain.** Allowable loads for lateral resistance, when the loads act perpendicular to grain and the lag screw is inserted parallel to the fibers (i.e., in the end grain of the main member) and shall be two-thirds of those for lateral resistance when the loads act perpendicular to the grain and the lag screw is inserted perpendicular to the grain (i.e., in the side grain of the main member).

(e) **Withdrawal Loads in Side Grain.** The allowable load for lag screws in withdrawal from side grain is dependent upon the specific gravity of the species, given in Table No. 25-17-I. The allowable loads in withdrawal from side grain, with the axis of the lag screw perpendicular to the fibers, are given in Table No. 25-17-M.

(f) **Withdrawal Loads in End Grain.** The design shall be such that lag screws are not loaded in withdrawal from end grain of wood. When this condition cannot be avoided, the allowable load withdrawal from end grain shall not be taken as more than three fourths of that for withdrawal from side grain.

(g) **Combined Lateral and Withdrawal Loads.** When a lag screw is subjected to a combined lateral and withdrawal loading, as when the lag screw is inserted perpendicular to the fiber and the load acts at an angle to the wood surface, it shall be analyzed separately for its resistance to lateral and withdrawal loads. The withdrawal component of the applied load shall not exceed the recommended design value in withdrawal and the lateral component of the applied load shall not exceed the recommended lateral load design value.

Modification of Allowable Loads

Sec. 25.1734. (a) **Condition of Lumber.** For lag screws used in joints exposed to weather or where the wood will remain wet in service, the allowable loads shall be modified in accordance with Table No. 25-17-R.

(b) **Pressure-impregnated Lumber.** Lumber pressure impregnated with fire-retardant chemicals and dried after treatment, shall be permitted 90 percent of the tabulated lag-screw loads. For lumber so treated and not dried after treatment, the 90 percent value shall be reduced in accordance with Section 25.1734 (a).

(c) **Steel Side Pieces.** The allowable lateral loads for lag screws, where metal side pieces are used, are given in Table No. 25-17-O. The loads are for metal plates up to 1/2 inch thick.

If metal side pieces of greater thickness are used, the loads for lag screws shall be reduced in proportion to the lesser penetration of the lag screw.

The stresses induced in the steel plate and at bearing of lag bolt on plate shall not exceed the allowable stresses for the metal used.

Quality of Lag Screw

Sec. 25.1735. Allowable loads are based on lag screws of metal having a yield point of 45,000 pounds per square inch and a tensile strength of 77,000 pounds per square inch.

For other metal, the values herein may be adjusted in proportion to the tensile strength of the metal for maximum allowable loads in withdrawal and in proportion to square roots of the yield point stresses of the metal for allowable loads in lateral resistance.

Installation

Sec. 25.1736. (a) **Placement of Lag Screws in Joint.** The spacings, end distances, edge distances and net section for lag-screw joints shall be the same as for joints with bolts of a diameter equal to the shank diameter of the lag screw used. See Part III.

(b) **Lead Holes.** Lead holes shall be prebored as follows:

1. The lead hole for the shank shall have the same diameter as the shank and the same depth as the length of unthreaded shank.

2. The lead hole for the threaded portion shall have a diameter equal to 65 percent to 85 percent of the shank diameter in Group I species, 60 percent to 75 percent in Group II species, and 40 percent to 70 percent in Groups III and IV species, and a length equal to at least the length of the threaded portion. The larger figure in each range shall apply to screws of the greater diameters.

(c) **Insertion.** The threaded portion of the screw shall be inserted in its lead hole by turning with a wrench, not by driving with a hammer.

Soap or other lubricant shall be used on the screws or in the lead hole to facilitate insertion and prevent damage to screw.

(d) **Penetration of Threaded Portion of Lag Screw.** In determining the penetration of threaded portion of lag screw into a member, the reduced portion (threaded or gimlet point) shall not be considered as part of the threaded portion.

Part VI—Light Metal Plate Connected Wood Truss Design

Based on Design Specification for Light Metal Plate Connected Wood Trusses, TPI-85 of the Truss Plate Institute

Scope

Sec. 25.1737. This standard shall cover requirements for the manufacture of light metal plate connectors and the design and fabrication of metal plate connected wood trusses in accordance with Chapter 25 of the Uniform Building Code.

Materials

Sec. 25.1738. (a) **Lumber.** Species and grades of lumber shall be clearly defined for each member of the truss. Design stresses used shall conform to the working stresses published in Chapter 25 of the Uniform Building Code.

(b) **Connector Plates.** 1. **General.** Metal connector plates shall be fabricated from galvanized steel sheet conforming to the requirements established for A446, Grade A, in U.B.C. Standard No. 27-1 or any higher grade of steel.

2. **Plate marking.** Whenever separately applied nails or fasteners are to be used with a plate, the plate shall be provided with some positive means to indicate the locations of the separate fasteners used.

3. **Manufacturing tolerances.** All connector plates shall be manufactured with all holes, plugs, teeth or prongs uniformly spaced and properly formed.

4. **Identification.** All plates shall be identified by the plate manufacturer's name.

Heel Joint Designs

Sec. 25.1739. The effects of eccentric loading shall be considered in the design of heel joints. For roof trusses spaced not more than 24 inches on center and spanning not more than

35 feet, heel joint connector plates may be designed with sufficient capacity to resist the direct axial stresses imposed on both top and bottom chord members by their respective nail, tooth or plug groups using the reduced allowable connector loads for eccentric loading as shown in Table No. 25-17-P.

Connector Plate Evaluation

Sec. 25.1740. (a) **Lateral Load Evaluation.** 1. **General.** Basic normal load values for use in designing wood joints using metal connector plate, per tooth or nail, plug or square inch or other unit shall be determined in accordance with the test procedure described herein. This procedure is based on the proportional limit value at 0.015-inch slip, with a further limitation based on the factor of safety at ultimate load. Figure No. 25-17-5 details the limits for dimensions of the test specimens and alternate test arrangements. Critical slip of 0.015 inch is measured from connector plate to each active wood member.

2. **Wood test specimens.** Test specimens shall be fabricated from clear wood specimens having a moisture content of not less than 11 percent nor more than 19 percent. Specimens shall be commercially available grades of the species of wood intended to be used in the trusses to be fabricated using the connectors. A range of ring counts and specific gravities shall be used in the test specimens and these properties of the test specimens shall be recorded with other test data. Five specimens of each of three species shall be tested. Two of the three species may be from the same species group of Table No. 25-17-I. Test specimens shall be cut and matchmarked so that the connector interacts with wood of substantially equal chracteristics on each side of the test joint. These five specimens shall be referred to as "uncycled" specimens.

3. **Aging.** To simulate the effects of aging and cycling of moisture content, five additional specimens of each species, matching those described in paragraph 2 above, shall be subject to an accelerated change in moisture content and shall be referred to as "cycled" specimens. The moisture-cycling procedure shall require that specimens be fabricated at not less than 17 percent moisture content. Specimens shall then be dried to 7 percent moisture content within five days and shall be tested at a moisture content of not less than 10 percent. Results shall be compared with those obtained from the "uncycled" specimens referred to in paragraph 2 above.

4. **Methods of test.** Each tensile specimen shall be tested to failure in a calibrated testing machine by an approved independent testing agency. Test specimen arrangement may be either two-dial or four-dial setup as shown in Figure No. 25-17-5. Certification of calibration of the testing machine shall be made available on request. The test shall be conducted to achieve maximum load in about 10 minutes, but reach maximum load in not less than five nor more than 20 minutes. A rate of motion of the movable crosshead of 0.035 inch in one minute, + or − 50 percent will usually permit reaching maximum load in the prescribed time. Record the speed used. Readings shall be taken so as to obtain not less than three increments of load before the proportional limit slip of 0.030 inch (wood to wood) has been reached. Readings shall include total load applied and amount of slip indicated by each dial gage. Applications of load shall continue at the original rate of application until failure occurs. Type of failure shall be noted for each specimen.

5. **Evaluation of test result.** The basic normal plate value per tooth, nail, plug or square inch shall be the least of the values determined as follows:

1. The uncycled proportional limit slip divided by 1.6;
2. The cycled proportional limit slip divided by 1.33;
3. The uncycled ultimate load at failure divided by 4.0; or
4. The cycled ultimate load at failure divided by 3.33.

(b) **Net Section.** 1. **General.** Five perforated truss plates of each plate width shall be selected randomly from production. In addition, five solid plates shall be taken from the stock steel coil utilized to make the perforated plates.

The width and thickness of each specimen shall be measured to the nearest 0.001 inch and recorded before testing.

2. **Procedure.** Tension tests on the solid plates shall be made and the ultimate load shall be recorded for each specimen.

Tension tests of the perforated truss plate shall be made by adequately clamping a single truss plate in a testing machine and holding it in place by a system so that universal movement of the test specimen is allowed.

The ultimate load shall be recorded for each specimen.

3. **Ultimate tensile strength.** The cross-sectional area shall be computed for each specimen and divided into the ultimate load for each specimen. This value will be the ultimate tensile stress in pounds per square inch.

The ultimate tensile stress shall be averaged for the perforated truss plates and for solid steel plates.

4. **Efficiency ratio.** The efficiency ratios shall be computed by dividing the average solid plate tensile stress into the average perforated plate tensile stress.

This efficiency ratio, when multiplied by the basic design value of steel, times the total cross-sectional area of the plate, yields the maximum safe load that may be carried by the truss plate net section in tension.

Full-scale Load Tests

Sec. 25.1741. (a) **General.** Full-scale load tests may be required at the option of the building official to verify the deflection and ultimate load or both characteristics of wood trusses at crucial spans. Any new type of connector system shall be substantiated by full-scale load tests of at least three substantially different designs to establish performance characteristics. Load tests shall be furnished on the longest span or most critical of each distinct series, configuration or type of unit. All tests shall conform to the requirements set forth herein and all test trusses shall be truly representative of the production and design.

Whenever possible, load testing shall be conducted under cover. When this is not possible or feasible, adequate weather protection shall be furnished to prevent adverse effects of moisture on the wood trusses and to prevent variation of the load caused by the absorption of water by the loading units. Loading units shall be separated to prevent the possibility of each action.

Trusses may be tested in pairs or singly; however, in either case a minimum of three units would be tested when done singly; three setups when done in pairs.

Trusses shall be fabricated at least one week prior to testing.

(b) **Testing in Pairs.** The test units shall be supported on firm stable reactors. They shall be spaced at the spacing for which they were designed. Experience has shown that properly securing the trusses to the reactors is recommended for safety. Use of strapping or metal framing connectors is suggested to resist tipping of the units during the load application. The top chords shall be sheathed with 4- to 6-foot lengths of any of the generally accepted sheathing materials (boards, plywood, reconstituted panel products, etc.). In any case, each piece shall be separated at least 1/8 inch. A recommended practice is to use cross-bracing between the trusses to stablize the setup; however, the trusses shall not be braced by tying the setup to adjacent permanent supports or other supports which may affect the free deflection of the trusses.

Deflection readings shall be taken and recorded for each truss as required for the purpose of the tests. For laboratory and investigative testing, it may be necessary to record deflection at all panel points, at the center of the trusses and at the midpoint of each lower chord panel, and at other locations that may be specified. Deflection readings may be averaged between each pair of trusses at corresponding locations.

Deflection measurements may be taken by any one of several methods; however, experience has shown that more accuracy is obtained when the gauges are independent of the support reactions. This is best accomplished by line scale and mirror arrangement. The line is supported on free-rolling bearings and kept under tension by means of weights. When the tests are conducted where temperature conditions change, using a braided fish line is recommended. Under controlled laboratory conditions, piano wire or monofilament line will suffice. Deflector readings are taken by reading on the scale which is attached to the truss adjacent to the line. Adjusting the eye position so that the line covers its image in the mirror removes parallax from the scale reading. Scale readings may then be referenced to either the top or bottom edge of the line. Dial gauges may be used to measure deflection; however, a precise measurement must be taken of settlement at the supports.

The other deflection readings are then subject to correction for settlement.

(c) **Testing Singly.** The trusses (a minimum of three trusses) may be tested as single units in either a vertical or horizontal position in a properly designed test facility. The loads may be applied uniformly or at concentrated points along the chords. Wood strips may be attached along the top chords, or frictionless brackets or attachments may be used to prevent the load brackets from slipping down the top chords on steep-sloped trusses.

Deflection measurements shall be similar to the procedures described in Subsection (b).

(d) **Load-deflection Test Procedures.** Apply one-half design load and hold for five minutes. This application allows the truss to be settled and provides an opportunity for checking alignment, equipment positioning and overall setup. This initial preliminary load shall be removed and deflection readings taken within 5 to 10 minutes. The design dead load is then applied, and after a minimum hold period of five minutes, the deflection readings are taken. Optionally, this dead load may be left in place 24 to 48 hours to establish a basic dead load position.

With the dead load applied, increase the load to one-fourth, one-half, three-fourths and full design live load. Apply the incremental loads at a uniform rate of loading with a minimum of 5 minutes hold at each increment. In any event, a minimum of 15 minutes is required to reach design live load.

Continue to load the truss incrementally in quarter live load units to dead load plus 2.0 times the design live load. The truss shall sustain this loading for at least 30 minutes without exceeding a deflection of $L_s/180$ or $l_s/120$, respectively, for plaster and drywall ceilings.

Remove all live load and, within 30 minutes, the truss must recover to a position of $L_s/360$ or $L_s/240$, respectively, relative to basic dead load. If deflections due to the loads of preceding paragraph remain within $L_s/360$ or $L_s/240$, respectively, the loading may be increased per Subsection (e) without removing the live load. **Note:** With single truss test using hydraulic cylinders, the dead load may be partially removed so the cylinders retract properly. Then immediately return to basic dead load.

(e) **Load to Failure Test.** Load to failure tests as herein described may be desired after the above load deflection test has been completed.

If Subsection (d) has been satisfied, continue loading in one-fourth load increments at five-minute intervals or longer at manufacturer's option, until failure occurs. At basic dead load plus 3.0 times design total load, the truss shall sustain the load for five minutes.

(f) **Reporting Test Results.** The written report shall include method and location of testing and personnel performing tests. The report shall include the lumber grades, lumber moisture content at time of tests, plate type and size at each location. A detailed drawing of the truss, pictures of the setup and failure location, if it occurred, is required.

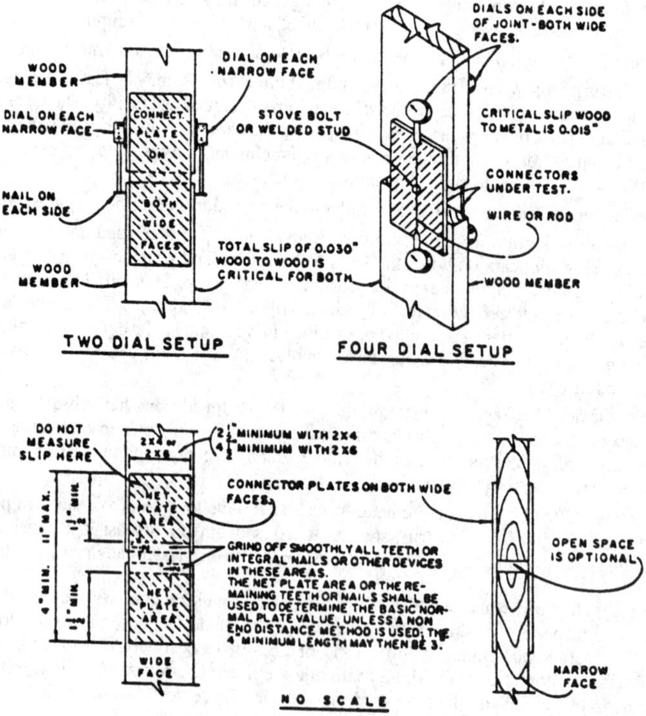
WOOD MEMBER
DIAL ON EACH NARROW FACE
CONNECT PLATE ON BOTH WIDE FACES
NAIL ON EACH SIDE
WOOD MEMBER
DIAL ON EACH NARROW FACE
STOVE BOLT OR WELDED STUD
TOTAL SLIP OF 0.030" WOOD TO WOOD IS CRITICAL FOR BOTH
TWO DIAL SETUP
DIALS ON EACH SIDE OF JOINT-BOTH WIDE FACES.
CRITICAL SLIP WOOD TO METAL IS 0.015"
CONNECTORS UNDER TEST.
WIRE OR ROD
WOOD MEMBER
FOUR DIAL SETUP
DO NOT MEASURE SLIP HERE
2X4 or 2X6
2 1/2" MINIMUM WITH 2X4
4 1/2" MINIMUM WITH 2X6
11" MAX.
4" MIN.
1 1/2" MIN.
1 1/2" MIN.
NET PLATE AREA
NET PLATE AREA
WIDE FACE
CONNECTOR PLATES ON BOTH WIDE FACES.
GRIND OFF SMOOTHLY ALL TEETH OR INTEGRAL NAILS OR OTHER DEVICES IN THESE AREAS.
THE NET PLATE AREA OR THE REMAINING TEETH OR NAILS SHALL BE USED TO DETERMINE THE BASIC NORMAL PLATE VALUE, UNLESS A NON END DISTANCE METHOD IS USED; THE 4" MINIMUM LENGTH MAY THEN BE 3.
OPEN SPACE IS OPTIONAL
NARROW FACE
NO SCALE

STANDARD CONNECTOR EVALUATION TENSION TEST

FIGURE NO. 25-17-5

Marking

Sec. 25.1742. Each truss shall be legibly branded, marked or otherwise have permanently affixed thereto the following information:

1. Identity of the company manufacturing the truss.
2. The design load.
3. The spacing of trusses.

Fabrication Quality

Sec. 25.1743. (a) **General.** This section shall be used in conjunction with an in-plant quality assurance procedure and an engineered truss design. Truss manufacturers and inspection agencies shall establish filing methods which document the proper application of quality assurance procedures throughout the manufacturing and inspection process.

(b) **Engineering.** Truss engineering is an essential part of the quality assurance procedure. Truss engineering shall be provided for every structural truss setup manufactured.

Truss engineering design shall include reference to the design criteria used, lumber requirements, plating requirements, design loading, adjustments to metal connector plate and lumber design values and truss engineer's registered seal.

(c) **Lumber.** 1. **Grade, size and species.** Truss lumber shall be the grade, size species specified by the design engineer. Truss lumber of a higher stress grade of the same size and species combination may be substituted for the stress grade, size and species combination specified by the design engineer. Manufactured lumber may be approved within the appropriate jurisdiction. Changes in size and/or species or conversion to manufactured lumber shall require additional analysis by the design engineer to provide equivalency. Grademarks and/or other identification shall be preserved as much as possible during the manufacturing process for verification in the complete truss unit.

2. **Moisture content.** All lumber, including pressure-treated lumber, used in the manufacture of wood trusses shall have a moisture content (MC) of less than or equal to 19 percent at time of fabrication, unless engineering design specifically states that the moisture content may be higher. If green lumber (over 19 percent MC) is used, the engineering design shall clearly show that lumber values were reduced for higher moisture content. Basic plate design values shall be reduced 20 percent when the plates are to be installed in lumber having a moisture content greater 19 percent at time of fabrication. Pressure-preservative-treated lumber shall bear the quality mark of an approved inspection agency which maintains continued supervision, testing and inspection over the treating and redrying of the lumber product. The quality mark shall indicate the material has been treated and redried to 19 percent MC or less.

3. **Characteristics.** Lumber shall not have characteristics which would interfere with the proper placement of metal connector plates, or the fabrication of uniformly consistent trusses.

4. **Fire retardants.** Lumber pressure impregnated with fire-retardant chemicals shall be identified by the quality mark of a code-approved inspection agency which maintains continued supervision, testing and inspection over the quality of the treatment and drying process and design value adjustments. The quality mark shall indicate the material has been treated and redried to 19 percent MC or less, and in conformance to those procedures established by the manufacturer which were used in the evaluation and qualification of that treatment. The quality shall indicate that the design value adjustments are in accordance with U.B.C. Standard No. 25-29.

(d) **Special Markings.** 1. **Installation.** Bottom chord bearing parallel chord trusses shall be clearly marked in a manner which will avoid inverted installation and shall permit visual verification of proper orientation after installation.

2. **Bearing locations.** Trusses having bearing locations other than at the end of heel locations shall have bearing points clearly marked in a manner which permits verification during and after installation.

3. **Lateral bracing.** All truss chord and web members which require special lateral bracing to prevent lateral buckling (such as, but not limited to, top chords of piggy-back trusses, long compression webs and bottom chords at cantilevers) due to engineering analysis shall be clearly marked to call attention to the need for such field bracing during and after installation.

4. **Alternatives.** In lieu of marking trusses, it shall be acceptable to document the location of special bearing conditions, permanent bracing and orientation of trusses by means of engineering drawings, erection plans and/or special details.

(e) **Plating.** 1. **Tests.** Metal connector plates used in the manufacture of wood trusses shall be manufactured and evaluated in accordance with Section 25.1740. Metal connector plates used in the manufacture of wood trusses shall be of the gauge, type and minimum size specified by the truss design engineer. Substituting larger metal connector plates is acceptable per the provisions of Section 25.1743 (e) 7 and (h).

2. **Positioning.** The metal connector plate sizes shall be determined by engineering analysis; metal connector plates shall be placed on both faces of the truss at each joint and positioned in accordance with the engineered design dimensions. The positioning shall be defined in either of two ways:

A. Symmetrical positioning (as shown in Figure No. 25-17-10).

B. Nonsymmetrical positioning (as shown in Figure No. 25-17-11).

3. **Effective metal connector plate contact area.** The engineer-specified metal connector plate positioning and metal connector plate contact area is developed with the provision that 10 percent of the specified metal connector plate contact area is ineffective due to metal connector plate misplacement, partial embedment, tooth flattening, gaps between joined members and on-grade lumber characteristics (knots, wane, pitch pockets and holes).

4. **The 10 percent rule.** The 10 percent area rule is derived from a manufacturing adjustment factor used in the establishment of basic allowable design properties for metal connector plate teeth stressed in lateral withdrawal. The derivation of allowable metal connector plate properties is referenced in Section 25.1740.

5. **Combinations.** To assess a plated connection for sufficient (90 percent or better) clear wood-plate contact area, the following manufacturing characteristics (knots, wane, pitch pockets, holes, gaps and metal connector plate misplacement) can be found in combination in the metal connector plate contact area. These characteristics shall not reduce the engineer-specified metal connector plate contact area by more than 10 percent.

6. **Tolerances.** The allowable tolerance for metal connector plate positioning shall be as shown in Figure No. 25-17-12. The tolerance shall apply to the nearside metal connector plate, provided the far-side metal connector plate is positioned without variance. Tolerances shall be halved if the near- and far-side metal connector plates are equally mislocated. The metal connector plate location tolerance shown in Figure No. 25-17-12 is a field air calibrated to the 10 percent area rule and shall apply to the metal connector plate misplacement characteristic only. Joints that exhibit knots, wane, pitch pockets, holes and gaps in addition to metal connector plate misplacement shall not use Figure No. 25-17-12. The 10 percent rule for these characteristics in combination shall apply. Increased metal connector plate sizes may be used to increase placement tolerances, provided Section 25.1743 (e) 7 and (h) is followed.

7. **Overplating.** A metal connector plate with larger dimensions in one or both directions and of the same type and gauge may be substituted for the specified size, provided its placement does not interfere with other design aspects or the function of the truss as shown in Figure No. 25-17-13.

8. **Storage and handling.** Metal connector plates shall be protected from damage during storage and shall be in an undamaged condition when they are used. Trusses shall be adequately plated to prevent damage during manufacturing and delivery.

9. **Tooth flattening.** Metal connector plates showing visible evidence of flattening of more than 5 percent of the teeth for each connected member shall not be acceptable unless approved by the design engineer. Flattening is defined as one fourth of tooth length or greater than is visible within the tooth opening as shown in Figure No. 25-17-14. The 5 percent evidence of flattening is a maximum tolerance as it pertains to the 10 percent rule; it shall not be used in combination with any other manufacturing characteristics [see Section 25.1743 (h) 3.]

(f) **Assembly.** 1. **Accuracy.** Trusses shall have wood members that are accurately cut, so that assembly into the design configuration will result in wood to wood bearing between truss wood members at the interface, and uniformity between completed, similarly designed truss units. The location of chords, webs and joints shall be as specified in the engineered design.

2. **Splices.** More than one splice in a panel is not permitted.

3. **Cutting.** Members shall be cut in accordance with the design specifications.

4. **Tolerances.** Truss manufacturing tolerances resulting from engineering design specifications shall not exceed the variance shown in Table No. 25-17-Y.

5. **Gaps.** Trusses shall have close-fitting wood members at every joint. Gaps in joints resulting from inaccuracies in cutting and assembly shall be limited to no more than two joints or 20 percent of the total number of joints, whichever is greater.

6. **Repair.** Correction of gaps exceeding the tolerances in Section 25.1743 (f) 4 are shown in Section 25.1743 (h).

7. **Camber.** Truss camber shall be provided as specified in the engineered design.

8. **Plating over lumber characteristics.** Plating over off-grade knots or other lumber characteristics between panel points and other joints (splices) to strengthen or reinforce the wood member is not permitted unless so specified by the truss engineer. Such plating requirements shall conform to Section 25.1743 (f) 9 and (h).

9. **The 10 percent rule.** On-grade lumber characteristics, such as knots, wane, pitch pockets, holes and gaps, in the metal connector plate area shall be permitted provided such characteristics do not affect more than 10 percent of the minimum engineer-required metal connector plate area or required number of effective teeth in the affected member. Required area of effective teeth calculations are shown in Figure No. 25-17-18.

10. **Embedment.** All trusses shall have fully embedded metal connector plates at every joint. The bottom surface of the metal connector plates shall be in firm contact with the wood surfaces. The embedment tolerance shall not exceed a gap of no greater than 10 percent of the tooth length, or $^1/_{16}$ inch, whichever is greater, for no more than one third of the minimum required metal connector plate contact area, for each member as shown in Figures Nos. 25-17-19 and 25-17-20. However, no less than two thirds of the minimum required metal connector plate contact area for each member shall be in firm contact with the wood. Tooth length is measured from the tip of the tooth to the nearest face of the metal connector plate from which it is formed. If a metal connector plate has more than one length of teeth, the shortest tooth length shall be used. The metal connector plate embedment tolerance as shown in Figures Nos. 25-17-29 and 25-17-20 is a maximum tolerance as it pertains to the 10

percent rule; it shall not be used in combination with any other manufacturing characteristics.

11. **Rejection.** More than one maximum allowable tolerance in any given joint shall be cause for rejection of that joint.

12. **Splitting.** Excessive splitting in any wood member by the metal connector plate teeth shall not be acceptable. Splits resulting from the manufacturing process shall not exceed those permitted for the grade and species of lumber used.

13. **Documentation.** Fabrication inaccuracies exceeding the allowable tolerances are acceptable per the provisions of Section 25.1743 (h), (i) and (j), and/or upon approval and follow-up documentation by a registered engineer. Any necessary repair authorization shall be documented by a registered engineer subject to the approval of the building official.

(g) **Handling.** 1. **Structural integrity.** Trusses shall not be subjected to any external force effect during manufacturing, packaging, storage and delivery which may impair their structural integrity.

2. **Fire-retardant-treated lumber.** Fire-retardant-treated (FRT) lumber shall not be subjected to impact load which may impair the structural integrity of the trusses manufactured from FRT lumber.

(h) **Overplating.** 1. **Prior to plating.** Embedment areas prior to plating that exhibit any combination of knots, wane, pitch pockets, holes and gaps shall be evaluated to determine if the engineer-specified metal connector plate size per member has 90 percent or better of clear wood contact area. A metal connector plate with larger dimensions as shown in Figures Nos. 25-17-13 and 25-17-21 in one or both directions and of the same type and gage may be substituted for the specified size to achieve 90 percent or better of the specified clear wood plate contact area. This check applies to all joints; however, certain joints exhibiting gaps as defined in Section 25.1743 (i) shall require shimming in addition.

2. **Embedded metal connector plates.** Embedded metal connector plates that exhibit any combination of knots, wane, pitch pockets, holes, gaps and misplacement shall be evaluated to determine if the clear wood-plate contact area has 90 percent or better of the engineer-specified clear wood-plate contact area. Embedded metal connector plates not exhibiting 90 percent or better of the engineer-specified clear wood-plate contact area shall be removed and overplated in accordance with Section 25.1743 (h) 1. This check applies to all joints; however, certain joints exhibiting gaps as defined in Section 25.1743 (i) shall require shimming in addition.

3. **Tooth flattening.** Metal connector plates exhibiting flattened teeth in excess of the 5 percent minimum required teeth (i.e., metal connector plate contact area) per member shall be removed. A larger metal connector plate meeting the provisions of Section 25.1743 (e) 7 and (h) 1 shall be affixed provided the larger metal connector plate exhibits firm embedment and no flattened teeth.

(i) **Shimming.** The use of galvanized metal shims, as shown in Figure No. 25-17-22, or alternatives acceptable to a registered engineer to obtain firm bearing between members at open compression joints (spices, peaks and web-chord interfaces) is acceptable provided the number of open joints so treated does not exceed two per truss or 20 percent of the total number of joints, whichever is greater, and the gaps prior to shimming do not exceed the tolerances in Section 25.1743 (f) 4. Metal shims shall be long enough to bend over at least 1 inch along the member being shimmed. The shim shall be fixed in position with a 6d deformed shank nail to prevent accidental loss or removal (see Figure No.s 25-17-22) and shall be documented by a professional engineer.

(j) **Repressing.** Embedded metal connector plates exceeding the tolerances in Section 25.1743 (f) 10 shall be repressed. Other manufacturing characteristics are acceptable in the metal connector plate contact area per Section 25.1743 (h) and (i) provided the repressed metal connector plate exhibits firm embedment and no flattened teeth.

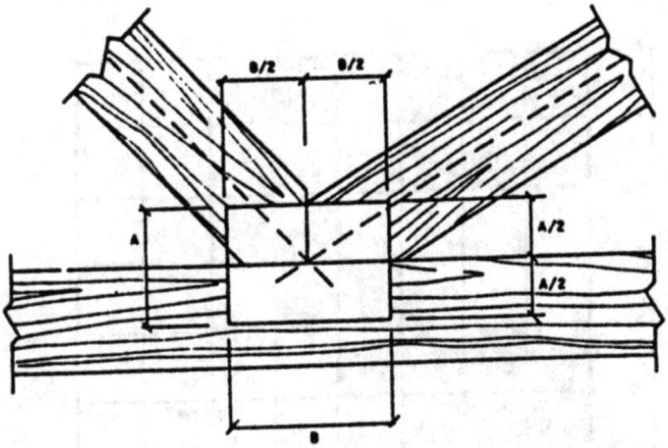
B/2
B/2
A
A/2
A/2
B

FIGURE NO. 25-17-10—SYMMETRICAL POSITIONING

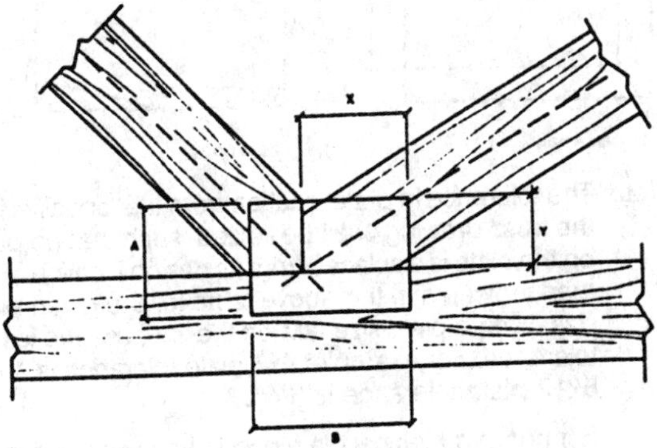
X
A
Y
B

FIGURE NO. 25-17-11—NONSYMMETRICAL POSITIONING

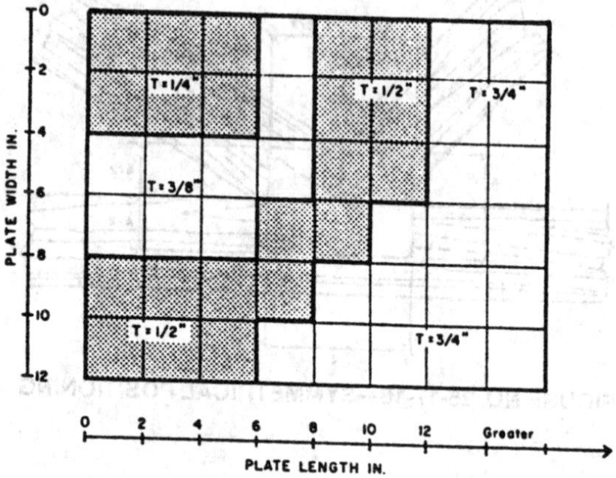
PLATE WIDTH IN.
0
2
4
6
8
10
12
T=1/4"
T=1/2"
T=3/4"
T=3/8"
T=1/2"
T=3/4"
0
2
4
6
8
10
12
Greater
PLATE LENGTH IN.

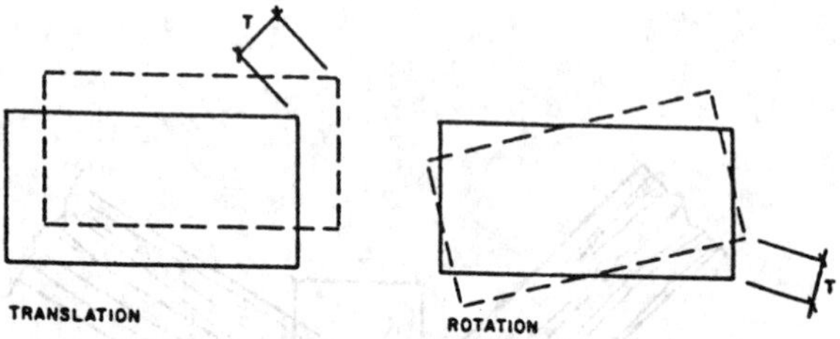
T
TRANSLATION
T
ROTATION

Note: The tolerance in plate location from that specified on the truss drawing shall be limited, such that no point on the plate is displaced from its design location more than indicated in the above table for the given plate size. Where plate size falls on the line, use the lesser tolerance. For example: 4x6 plate tolerance is 1/4", 8x12 plate tolerance is 3/4".

For non symmetrical plate positioning use the dimension of the smallest contact area per member as the plate dimension for the plate location tolerance that shall govern.

FIGURE NO. 25-17-12—METAL CONNECTOR PLATE LOCATION TOLERANCE (T)

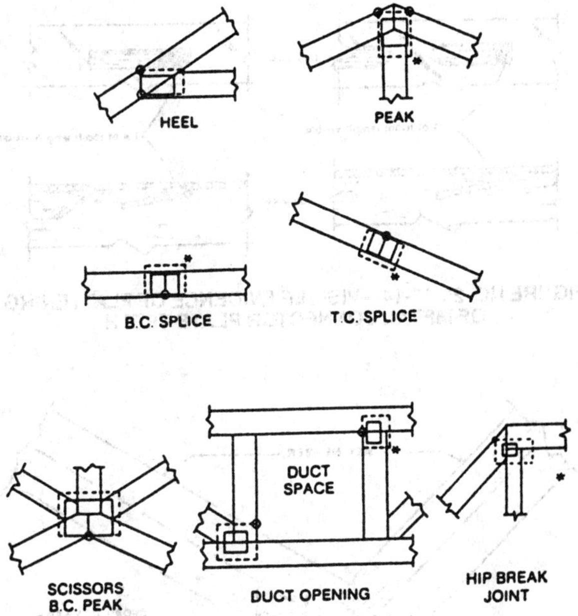
HEEL
PEAK
B.C. SPLICE
T.C. SPLICE
DUCT SPACE
SCISSORS B.C. PEAK
DUCT OPENING
HIP BREAK JOINT

⊙—Indicates control point beyond which plate shall not extend.

*—Indicates extension of plate which shall be checked for interference before substitution of larger plate.

FIGURE NO. 25-17-13—EXAMPLES OF SUBSTITUTION OF LARGER METAL CONNECTOR PLATES THAN SPECIFIED SIZE

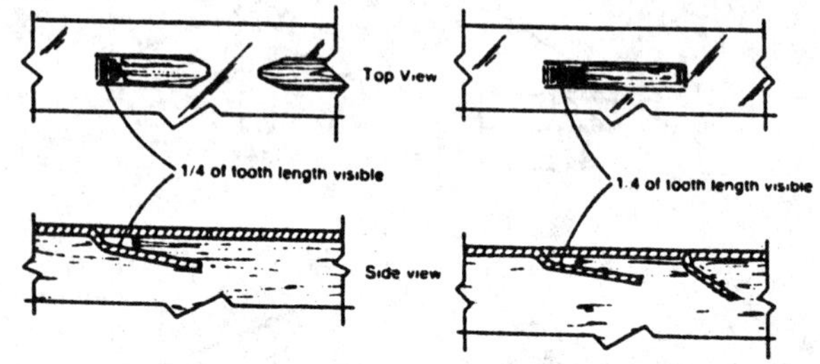
Top View
1/4 of tooth length visible
1/4 of tooth length visible
Side view

FIGURE NO. 25-17-14—VISIBLE EVIDENCE OF FLATTENING OF METAL CONNECTOR PLATE TEETH

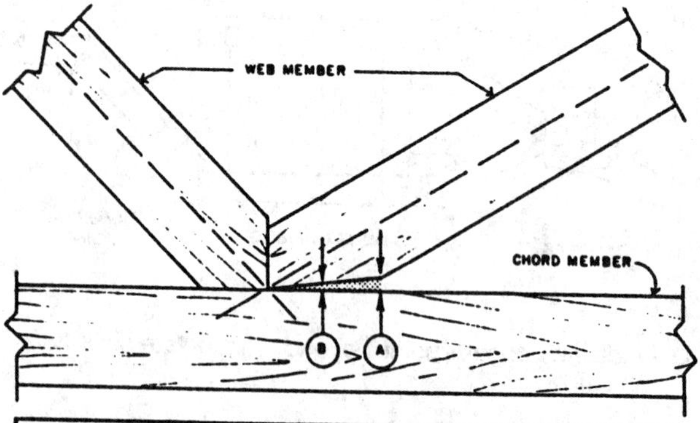
WEB MEMBER
CHORD MEMBER
B > A

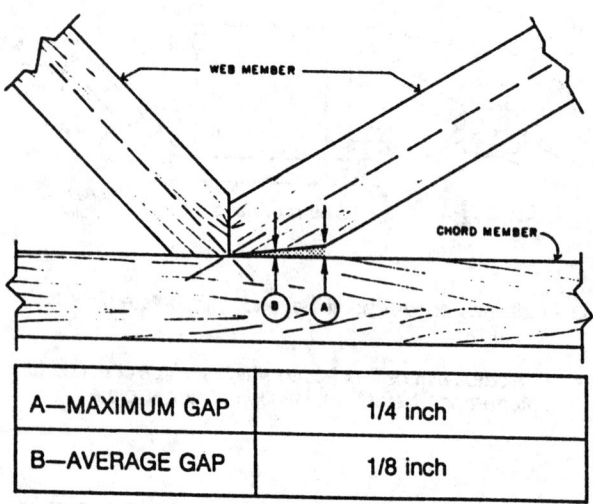

A—MAXIMUM GAP	1/4 inch
B—AVERAGE GAP	1/8 inch

FIGURE NO. 25-17-15—INTERIOR JOINT TOLERANCES

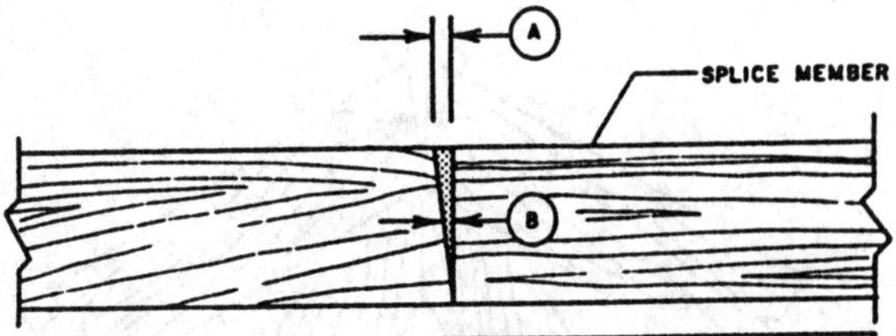
A
SPLICE MEMBER
B

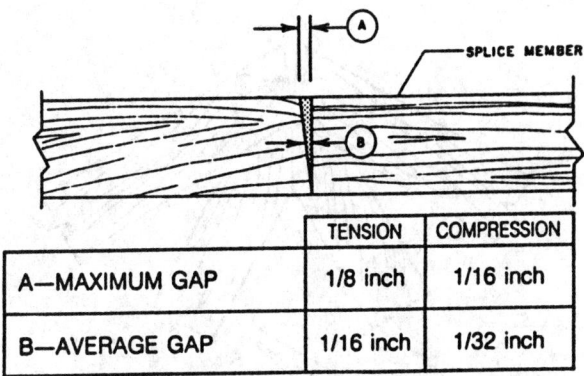

	TENSION	COMPRESSION
A—MAXIMUM GAP	1/8 inch	1/16 inch
B—AVERAGE GAP	1/16 inch	1/32 inch

Note: Compression splice joints not meeting these joint tolerances shall be shimmed with metal shims or alternatives acceptable to the truss design engineer.

FIGURE NO. 25-17-16—SPLICE JOINT TOLERANCES

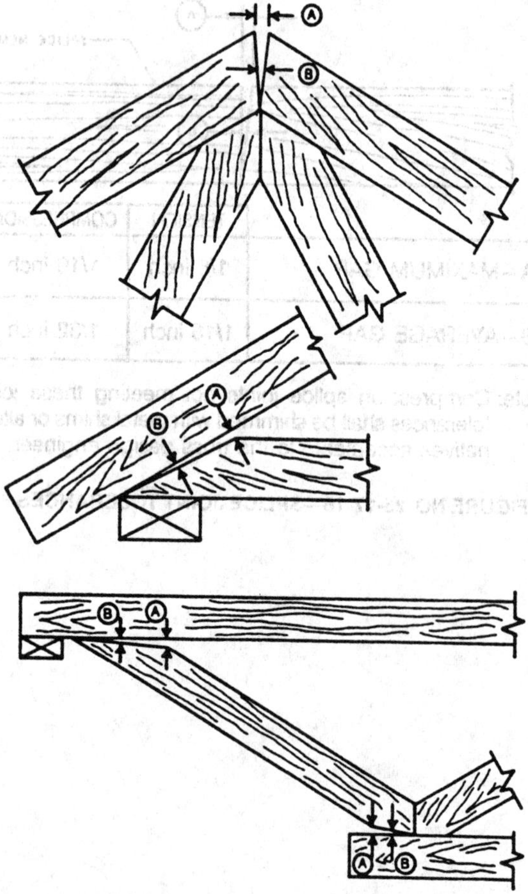
A
B
A
B
B
A
A
B

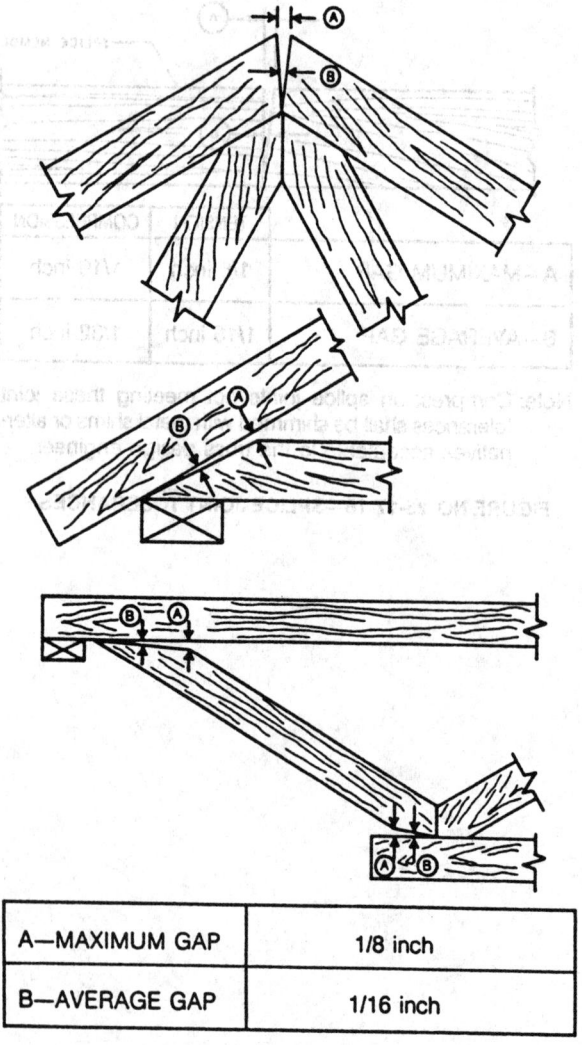

A—MAXIMUM GAP	1/8 inch
B—AVERAGE GAP	1/16 inch

FIGURE NO. 25-17-17—EXTERIOR JOINT TOLERANCES

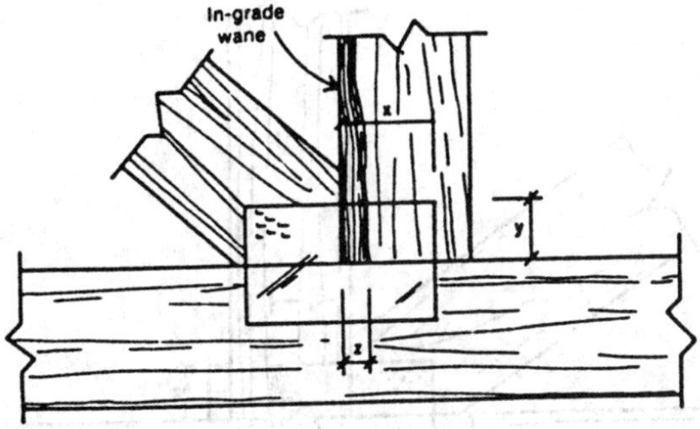
In-grade wane
x
y
z

Note: If xy = required area, then zy ≤ 0.1 xy.

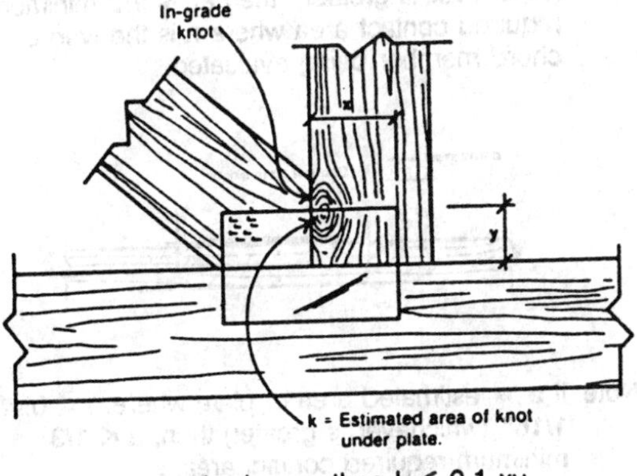
In-grade knot
x
y
k = Estimated area of knot under plate.

Note: If xy = required area, then k ≤ 0.1 xy.

FIGURE NO. 25-17-18—WANE AND KNOTS IN METAL CONNECTOR PLATE AREA

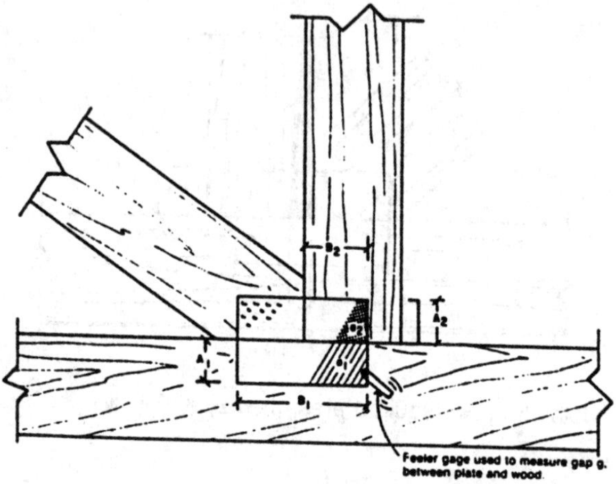
B_2
A_2
a_2
A_1
a_1
B_1
Feeler gage used to measure gap g. between plate and wood.

Note: a_n is the estimated area of plate, per member contact area (A_n B_n), where g ≤ 0.1ℓ or 1/16″ (whichever is greater), then a_n ≤ 1/3 minimum required contact area where n is the web or chord member being evaluated.

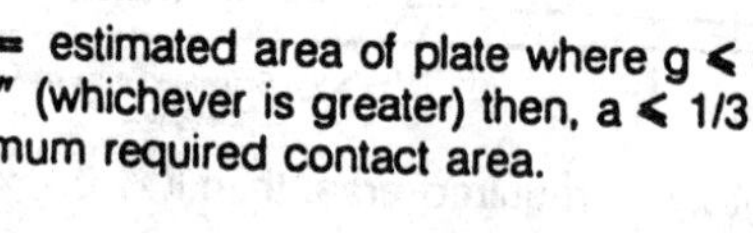
ℓ Shortest tooth length
ℓ
g

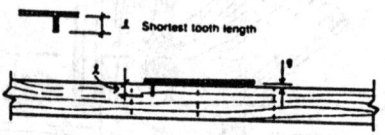

Note: If a = estimated area of plate where g ≤ 0.1ℓ or 1/16″ (whichever is greater) then, a ≤ 1/3 minimum required contact area.

FIGURE NO. 25-17-19—METAL CONNECTOR PLATE EMBEDMENT TOLERANCES

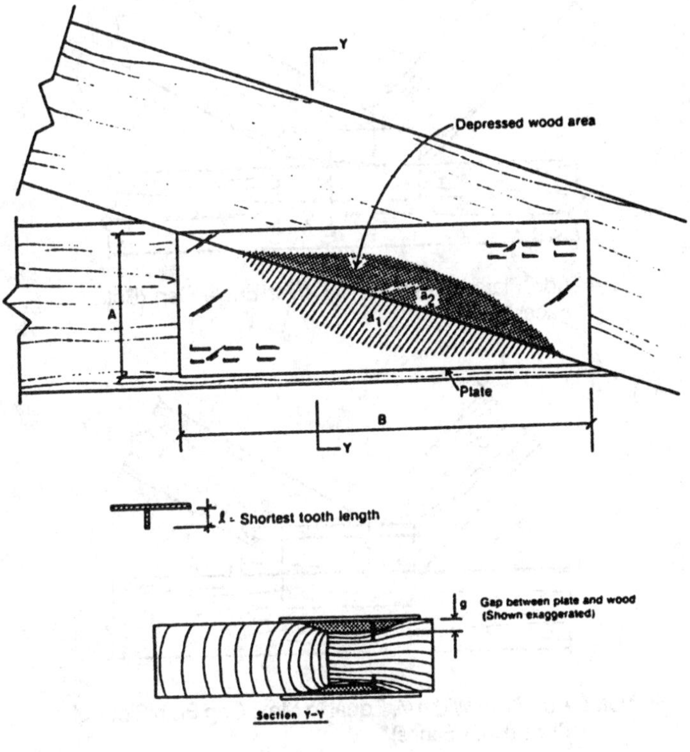
Y
Depressed wood area
a_2
a_1
A
Plate
B
Y
ℓ - Shortest tooth length
g Gap between plate and wood
(Shown exaggerated)
Section Y-Y

Note: If a_n is the estimated area of plate, per member contact area, where $g \leq 0.1\ell$ or 1/16" (whichever is greater), then, $a_n \leq 1/3$ minimum required plate contact area.

FIGURE NO. 25-17-20—METAL CONNECTOR PLATE EMBEDMENT TOLERANCES

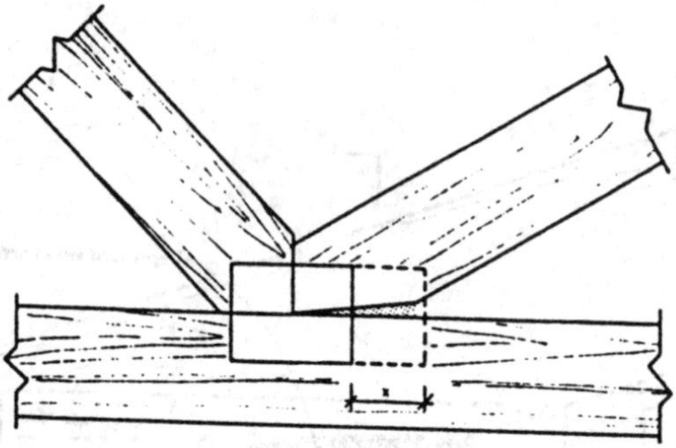

Note: Add Plate Length X, To Cover Entire Gap (Both Faces).

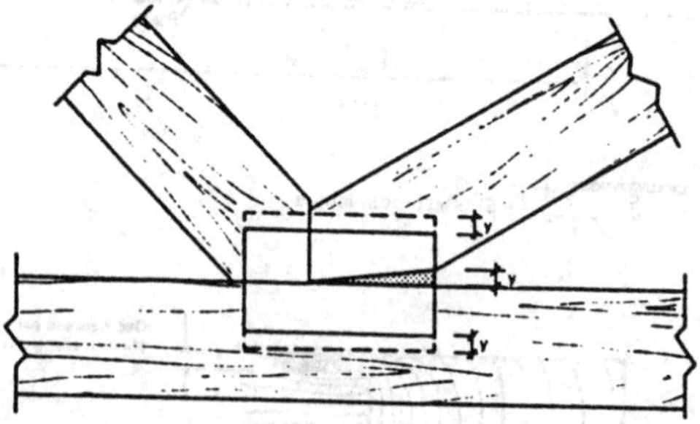
Y
Y
Y

Note: Add Plate Width Y, Equal to Max. Gap Both Sides of Plate (Both Faces).

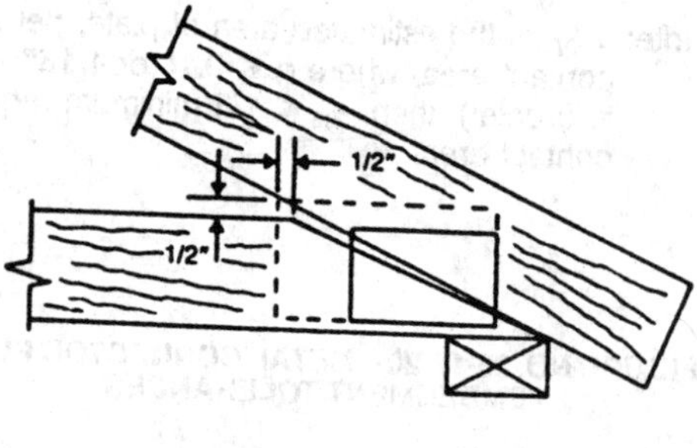
1/2"
1/2"

Note: Increase Plate Length and Width 1/2" past scarf cut (Both Faces).

(Continued)

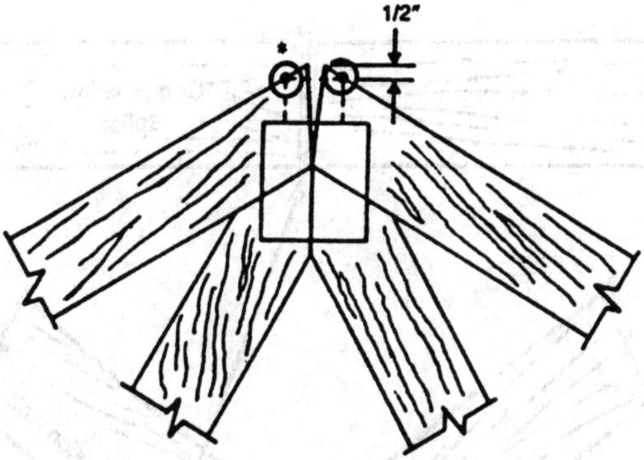
1/2"
*

Note: Add Additional Plate to Within 1/2" of Peak (Both Faces).

*—Indicates extension of plate which shall be checked for interference before substitution of larger plate.

FIGURE NO. 25-17-21—CORRECTION OF JOINT TOLERANCE

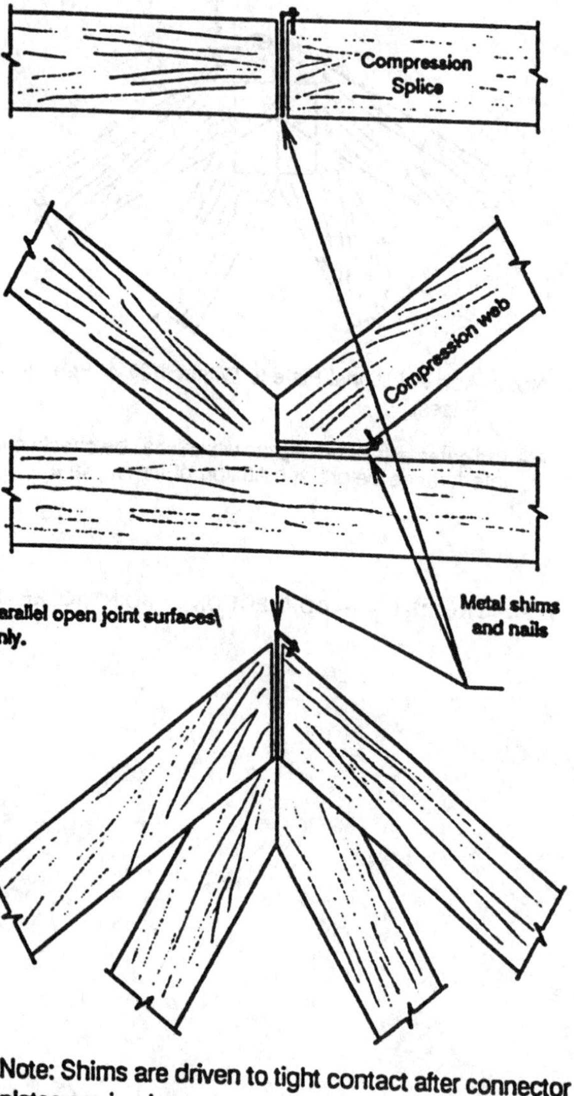
Compression Splice
Compression web
Parallel open joint surfaces\ only.
Metal shims and nails

Note: Shims are driven to tight contact after connector plates are in place.

FIGURE NO. 25-17-22—COMPRESSION JOINT REPAIR

TABLE NO. 25-17-Y—MANUFACTURING TOLERANCE FOR FINISHED TRUSS UNITS

LENGTH[2] OF FINISHED TRUSS UNIT	VARIANCE FROM DESIGN DIMENSIONS	HEIGHT[3] OF FINISHED TRUSS UNIT	VARIANCE FROM FROM DESIGN DIMENSIONS
PITCHED[1] TRUSS UNITS			
Up to 30 feet	1/4 inch	Up to 5 feet	1/8 inch
30 to 50 feet	3/8 inch	5 to 12 feet	1/4 inch
Over 50 feet	1/2 inch	Over 12 feet	3/8 inch
PARALLEL CHORD[4] TRUSS UNITS			
Up to 30 feet	1/4 inch	Up to 24 inches	1/8 inch
Over 30 feet	3/8 inch	24 to 60 inches	1/4 inch
		Over 60 inches	3/8 inch

1 Pitched trusses are defined as having differences in slopes between top and bottom chords greater than 1:12.

2 Length, for fabrication tolerance purposes, is the overall length of the truss unit, excluding overhangs or extensions.

3 Height, for fabrication tolerance purposes, is the overall height of the truss unit measured from the top of the top chord to the bottom of the bottom chord at the highest point of the truss, excluding projections above the top chord and below the bottom chord, overhangs and extensions.

4 Parallel chord trusses are defined as having differences in slopes between top and bottom chords less than or equal to 1:12.

In-plant Inspection

Sec. 25.1744. Periodic Nonscheduled Inspection. Each truss manufacturer shall retain an approved agency having no financial interest in the plant being inspected to make nonscheduled inspections of truss fabrication and delivery operations. The inspections shall cover all phases of the truss operation including: lumber storage, handling, cutting, fixtures, presses or rollers, fabrication bundling and banding, handling and delivery.

Parallel Chord Truss Design

Sec. 25.1745. (a) **General.** The design standard shall be applicable to parallel chord wood trusses that have the major cross section of 2 by 4 lumber members oriented horizontally.

(b) **Notations and Symbols.**

WHERE:

A = Cross-sectional area of member
b = Width of member
D = Overall depth of truss
DL = Dead Load
d = Critical thickness or width of members in buckling
d' = Distance between centroids of chords
E = Modulus of elasticity
F_b = Design value for extreme fiber in bending
F_c = Design value for compression parallel to grain
F'_c = Design value for compression parallel to grain adjusted for L'/d
F_t = Design value for tension parallel to grain
G = Concentrated load
h = Thickness of member
I_c = Moment of inertia of chord
I_e = Equivalent moment of inertia of the truss
J = Unitless factor used in the interaction equation for combined bending and axial compression
K = Largest slenderness ratio (L'/d) at which the intermediate column formula applies for determining design value in compression parallel to grain
K_b = Load and span effect constant
L = Nominal panel length of chords used in computing bending moment
L_c = Length of cantilever
L_o = Width of the rectangular opening measured from center of vertical web to center of vertical web
L_p = Center-to-center spacing of purlins
L_s = Clear span length measured from face-to-face of supports
L_w = Buckling length of web member
L' = Effective buckling length
LL = Live load
M = Bending moment
M_e = Moment of an equivalent beam at the location under investigation
M_o = Moments produced at a rectangular opening due to shear
M_p = Moment due to loads acting on chord between panel points; panel moments may be at midpanel or panel points
M_s = Secondary moment
P = Axial load
S = Section modulus

V_e = Shear of the equivalent beam

w = Uniformly distributed load

WL = Wind load

X = Offset of center line of rectangular opening from center line of truss

Δ = Deflection of truss

(c) **Truss Loading.** Uniformly distributed loads on top and bottom chords shall be considered as equivalent concentrated loads applied at panel points for determination of axial forces.

Trusses having concentrated loads shall be designed specifically to carry these loads in addition to any other loading which may be applied to the truss within the allowable stresses defined in this standard.

A nonbearing partition may be neglected in design, provided:

1. Trusses are not over 24 inches on centers.
2. Top chord panel length of supporting truss system does not exceed 30 inches.
3. Design live load of supporting truss system results from a residential occupancy and is not less than 40 psf.
4. Partition weight does not exceed 60 pounds per lineal foot.
5. When partitions parallel to supporting trusses are not located on or immediately adjacent to a truss, the subfloor shall be adequate for the partition load.

Trusses are to be designed for the most critical combination of gravity dead load, live load and/or wind load.

(d) **Axial Forces.** For the purpose of determining the axial forces in a truss all members may be assumed to have pinned joints. Forces are assumed to act along the centroids of the chord members. The effective depth d' of the truss is the distance between the centroids of the chords.

The vertical component of the minimum design force in any diagonal web shall not be less than one sixth of the simple span total load.

The minimum design force for any member shall not be less than 375 pounds.

(e) **Bending Moments in Chords.** For the purpose of determining the bending moments in the chords, the chord members shall be modeled as continuous beams with the web members pin connected to the chords.

Any accurate engineering method may be used, provided the method accounts for:

1. The bending moments due to the loads acting on the chords between panel points (joints); henceforth called the panel moments.
2. The bending moments induced into the chords by the overall deformation of the truss; henceforth called the secondary moments.
3. The bending moments produced at a rectangular opening due to the transfer of vertical load (shear) across the opening, henceforth called the open-panel moments.

The simplified method refers to an equivalent beam. The moments and shears referred to are those of a beam with the same span, points of support and loading conditions as the truss under investigation. The sign convention used is one that gives the following results to a uniformly, downward-loaded simple-span beam:

1. Positive moment throughout.
2. Positive shear on the left half of the beam and negative shear on the right half of the beam. See Figure No. 25-17-12.

The simplified method applies only to trusses that meet the following conditions:

1. All concentrated loads shall be located at joints.
2. The uniform load w shall not differ by more than 20 percent (of the larger loading) in adjacent panels.
3. Rectangular openings shall not exceed 24 inches clear width.
4. All rectangular openings shall be located within 15 inches of midspan or within 15 inches of the location of zero shear on an equivalent beam. The offset shall be measured from the center of the rectangular opening.
5. No more than one rectangular opening shall be present in each span.
6. If a rectangular opening is present and this opening is offset greater than 4 inches from the location of zero shear on an equivalent beam, then the moment of inertia of the top chord at the rectangular opening shall be equal to that of the bottom chord at the opening.

The panel moment M_p shall be determined at the joints (panel point moment) and between the joints (midpanel moment). The moments determined shall be based on the uniform load acting downward. If the uniform load acts upward, the signs of the moments given shall be reversed.

The panel point moments shall be taken as follows:

M_p = zero for end joints.

$M_p = -wL2/9$ for joints located at one panel from the end of the chord.

$M_p = -wL2/12$ for all other interior joints.

Where L is the largest of the following:

1. The average length of the two panels adjacent to the joint under investigation.
2. Ninety percent of the longer of the two panels adjacent to the joint under investigation.

The midpanel moments shall be taken as:

$M_p = +wL2/13$ for end panels.

$M_p = +wL2/24$ for interior panels.

Where L is the length of the panel under investigation.

The secondary moments shall be taken as:

$$M_s = \frac{I_c}{I_e} \times M_e$$

WHERE:

1. I_c is the moment of inertia of the chord member under investigation.
2. I_e is the equivalent moment of inertia of the truss at the location under investigation.
3. M_e is the moment of an equivalent beam at the location under investigation.

The sign of the secondary moment shall be the same as that of the equivalent beam.

The open-panel moments shall be considered to act at all joints adjacent to the rectangular opening only. The open-panel moment shall have a magnitude of:

$$M_o = \frac{V_e \times L_o}{4}$$

WHERE:

V_e is the shear of the equivalent beam at the same location as the center of the rectangular opening.

L_o is the width of the rectangular opening measured from center of vertical web to center of vertical web.

When the shear on the equivalent beam V_e is positive, the moment M_o at the joints to the left of the open panel shall be taken as negative and the moment M_o at joints to the right of the open panel shall be taken as positive. When the shear on the equivalent beam V_e is negative, the above convention shall be reversed.

The total moment at a given panel point is the absolute value of the sum of the panel-point moment, the secondary moment and the open-panel moment.

$$M = M_p + M_s + M_o$$

The total moment at a given midpanel is the absolute value of the sum of the midpanel moment and the secondary moment.

$$M = M_p + M_s$$

The moment used in Subsection (f) for a given panel shall be the larger of:

1. The total moment at the panel point at the left of the panel.
2. The total moment at the midpanel.
3. The total moment at the panel point at the right of the panel.

(f) **Member Design.** All members subject to axial tension shall be so proportioned that:

$$\frac{P}{A} \leqslant F_t$$

All members subject to axial compression shall be so proportioned that:

$$\frac{P}{A} \leqslant F'_c$$

and F'_c is calculated as shown in Table No. 25-17-W.

All members subject to bending only shall be so proportioned that:

$$\frac{M}{S} \leqslant F_b$$

All members subject to both bending and axial tension shall be so proportioned that:

$$\frac{P/A}{F'_c} + \frac{M/S}{F_b \bullet J(P/A)} \leqslant 1.00$$

Where F'_c is defined in Table No. 25-17-W, and

$$J = \frac{(L'/d) - 11}{K - 11}$$

except that J shall not be less than zero or greater than one.

Lumber design values may be adjusted for duration of load in accordance with U.B.C. Section 2504 (c) 4.

The L'/d for compression members shall not exceed 50, and L'/d for tension members, including tension members subject to reversal of stress, shall not exceed 80. For chords and webs the effective buckling length shall be as shown in Table No. 25-17-X. See Figure No. 25-17-13.

Where three or more trusses are positioned side by side and spaced no farther than 24 inches apart and are joined by properly attached roof sheathing or flooring and/or strong-backs or other effective load-distributing elements which are properly attached to the trusses, the allowable stress in bending may be increased 15 percent.

In accordance with Table No. 25-A-1 criteria, an additional 10 percent increase in allowable bending stress is permitted for 2 by 4 lumber used flatwise. This stress increase is not dependent upon being part of a repetitive member system.

(g) **Joint Design.** Connector plates shall be designed for installation on both faces of each joint with sufficient plate area or wood-to-wood contact in compression or bearing to resist the critical forces or minimum forces described in Subsection (d).

Connector plates shall have the minimum properties as set forth in Section 25.1740.

When the net plate area method is used to determine the connector plate design rating, all plates shall be designed using a 1/2-inch end distance measured parallel to the member and a 1/4-inch edge distance measured perpendicular to the member.

When the gross area method is used to determine the connector plate design rating, 85 percent of the wide face test values shall be used for plating on 1.5-inch surfaces.

Plate basic design values (lateral resistance) established in accordance with Section 25.1740 shall be reduced 20 percent when the plates are to be installed in lumber having a moisture content greater than 19 percent at the time of fabrication.

The basic design values of plated (lateral resistance) may be adjusted for various durations of load in accordance with U.B.C. Section 2504 (c) 4.

The net section of plates for all tension joints shall be designed using the basic tensile design value of the metal adjusted for the plate efficiency factor. Plate tensile design values may be increased by 33.3 percent for wind or earthquake loads, but in no case shall the tensile design values be exceeded for dead load and other live loads.

The net shear section of plates for all joints involving shear shall be designed using the plate shear design value adjusted for the plate shear efficiency factor. Plate shear design values may be increased by 33.3 percent for wind or earthquake loads, but in no case shall the shear design values be exceeded for dead load and other live loads.

(h) **Bearings.** Either top chord or bottom chord bearing trusses are acceptable.

Bearing area shall be sized to develop the full design reactions in accordance with the design value in compression perpendicular to grain.

Truss bearing (either top or bottom chord bearing) must extend a distance of not less than 3 inches over the support. Engineered anchorage may be substituted for the 3-inch minimum support.

For top chord supported trusses the clearance between the outside edge of the first connector plate and the inside edge of the bearing shall not exceed the following:

1. For single 4 by 2 top chord, 1/2 inch maximum.
2. For double 4 by 2 top chord, 1 inch maximum.

(i) **Bridging.** Continuous cross and/or horizontal bridging between trusses shall be provided at spacings of approximately 10 feet for floors and 16 feet for roofs. Cross bridging shall be minimum 1 by 3s with two 8d nails each end. Horizontal bridging shall be minimum 2 x 6 strongbacks (on edge) attached to each truss with three 10d nails.

Strongbacks shall be attached to walls at their outer ends or restrained by other means.

(j) **Deflection.** Deflection calculations shall be based on full live load and may be determined using beam formulas. If two grades of chord lumber having different *E* values are used, deflection calculations may be based on the average E value. Other accepted methods of calculating deflections may be used, provided adjustments for web shear and joint slippage are considered.

For uniformly loaded, simply supported, parallel chord trusses, deflection may be calculated as follows:

$$\Delta = \frac{1.33\,K_b}{EI_e} \quad (1 + .015\,X)$$

$$K_b = \frac{5\,wL_s^4}{384}$$

WHERE:

Δ = Deflection at center line of truss in inches.

w = Uniform load in pounds per lineal inch.

L_s = Clear span in inches.

I_e = Moment of inertia of the cross-sectional areas of the top and bottom chords about the N.A. of the truss. See Figure No. 25-17-14.

E = Average modulus of elasticity of chord lumber (psi).

K_b = Load and span effect constant.

X = Offset of centerline of opening from centerline of truss in inches. See Figure No. 25-17-15. (Not to exceed 15 inches for this deflection formula.)

Maximum live load deflection for floor trusses shall be limited to $L_s/360$.

The portion of the total truss deflection due to live load shall not exceed $L_s/360$ when plaster is used nor $L_s/240$ when flexible type ceiling such as drywall or a suspended ceiling is used. The deflection of roof trusses without a finished ceiling shall not exceed $L_s/180$.

(k) **Camber.** The minimum recommended camber between supports shall equal the dead load deflection.

TABLE NO. 25-17-A—TYPICAL DIMENSIONS FOR TIMBER CONNECTORS SPLIT RINGS
(Dimensions in Inches)

	2 1/2	4
Split ring:		
Inside diameter at center when closed	2.500	4.000
Thickness of metal at center	.163	.193
Depth of metal (width of ring)	.750	1.000
Groove:		
Inside diameter	2.56	4.08
Width	.18	.21
Depth	.375	.50
Bolt hole:		
Diameter	9/16	13/16

	2 1/2	4
Washers, standard:		
Round, cast or malleable iron, diameter	2 5/8	3
Round, wrought iron (minimum):		
Diameter	1 3/8	2
Thickness	3/32	5/32
Square plate:		
Length of side	2	3
Thickness	1/8	3/16
Projected area:		
Portion of one ring within member, sq. in.	1.10	2.24

	2 5/8	2 5/8	4	4
Shear plate:				
Material	Pressed steel	Light gauge	Malleable iron	Malleable iron
Diameter of plate	2.62	2.62	4.03	4.03
Diameter of bolt hole	0.81	0.81	0.81	0.94
Thickness of plate	0.172	0.12	0.20	0.20
Depth of flange	0.42	0.35	0.64	0.64
Circular dap—dimensions:				
A	2.63	2.63	4.03	4.03
B		1.07	1.55	1.55
C	0.81	0.81	0.81	0.94
D		0.65	0.97	0.97
E	0.19	0.13	0.27	0.27
F	0.45	0.38	0.64	0.64
G	0.25	0.14	0.22	0.22
H		0.34	0.50	0.50
I	2.25	2.37	3.49	3.49

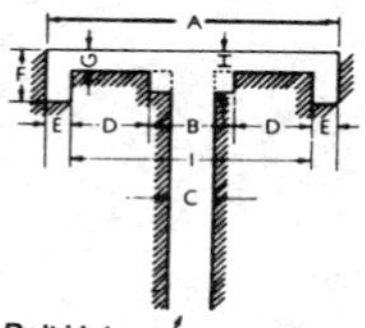
A
B
C
D
E
F
G
H
I
Bolt Hole

	2 5/8	2 5/8	4	4
Steel strap or shapes for use with shear plates:				
Steel straps or shapes, for use with shear plates, shall be designed in accordance with accepted engineering practices.				
Hole diameter in straps or shapes for bolts	13/16	13/16	13/16	15/16
Bolt hole—diameter in timber	13/16	13/16	13/16	15/16
Washers, standard:				
Round, cast or malleable iron, diameter	3	3	3	3 1/2
Round, wrought iron, min.				
Diameter	2	2	2	2 1/4
Thickness	5/32	5/32	5/32	11/64
Square plate:				
Length of side	3	3	3	3
Thickness	1/4	1/4	1/4	1/4
Projected area:				
Portion of one shear plate within member, sq. in.	1.18	1.00	2.58	2.58

TABLE NO. 25-17-B—ALLOWABLE LOADS FOR ONE SPLIT RING AND BOLT IN SINGLE SHEAR

**(The allowable loads below are for normal loading conditions.
See other provisions of this standard for adjustments of these tabulated allowable loads.)**

Split-Ring diam. (inches)	Bolt diam. (inches)	Number of faces of piece with connectors on same bolt	Thickness (net) of lumber (inches)	Loaded parallel to grain (0°): Edge distance min. (inches)	Loaded parallel to grain (0°): Allowable load per connector unit and bolt (pounds)				Loaded perpendicular to grain (90°): Edge distance (inches)		Loaded perpendicular to grain (90°): Allowable load per connector unit and bolt (pounds)			
					Group A woods	Group B woods	Group C woods	Group D woods	Unloaded edge min.	Loaded-edge	Group A woods	Group B woods	Group C woods	Group D woods
2½	½	1	1 min.	1¾	2630	2270	1900	1640	1¾	1¾ min.	1580	1350	1130	970
										2¾ or more	1900	1620	1350	1160
			1½ or more	1¾	3160	2730	2290	1960	1¾	1¾ min.	1900	1620	1350	1160
										2¾ or more	2280	1940	1620	1390
		2	1½ min.	1¾	2430	2100	1760	1510	1¾	1¾ min.	1460	1250	1040	890
										2¾ or more	1750	1500	1250	1070
			2 or more	1¾	3160	2730	2290	1960	1¾	1¾ min.	1900	1620	1350	1160
										2¾ or more	2280	1940	1620	1390
4	¾	1	1 min.	2¾	4090	3510	2920	2520	2¾	2¾ min.	2370	2030	1700	1470
										3¾ or more	2840	2440	2040	1760
			1½ or more	2¾	6020	5160	4280	3710	2¾	2¾ min.	3490	2990	2490	2150
										3¾ or more	4180	3590	2990	2580
		2	1½ min.	2¾	4110	3520	2940	2540	2¾	2¾ min.	2480	2040	1700	1470
										3¾ or more	2980	2450	2040	1760
			2	2¾	4950	4250	3540	3050	2¾	2¾ min.	2870	2470	2050	1770
										3¾ or more	3440	2960	2460	2120
			2½	2¾	5830	5000	4160	3600	2¾	2¾ min.	3380	2900	2410	2080
										3¾ or more	4050	3480	2890	2500
			3 or more	2¾	6140	5260	4380	3790	2¾	2¾ min.	3560	3050	2540	2190
										3¾ or more	4270	3660	3050	2630
4	3/4	1	15/8 or more	23/4	6140	5260	4380	3790	23/4	23/4 min.	3560	3050	2540	2190
										33/4 or more	4270	3660	3050	2630

TABLE NO. 25-17-C—ALLOWABLE LOADS FOR ONE SHEAR-PLATE UNIT AND BOLT IN SINGLE SHEAR

Shear-Plate diam. (inches)	Bolt diam. (inches)	Number of faces of piece with connectors on same bolt	Thickness (net) of lumber (inches)	Loaded parallel to grain (0°)					Loaded perpendicular to grain (90°)					
				Edge distance min. (inches)	Allowable load per connector unit and bolt (pounds)				Edge distance (inches)		Allowable load per connector unit and bolt (pounds)			
					Group A woods	Group B woods	Group C woods	Group D woods	Unloaded edge min.	Loaded-edge	Group A woods	Group B woods	Group C woods	Group D woods
2⅝	¾	1	1½ min	1¾	3110[1]	2760	2220	2010	1¾	1¾ min.	1810	1550	1290	1110
										2¾ or more	2170	1860	1550	1330
		2	1½ min	1¾	2420	2080	1730	1500	1¾	1¾ min.	1410	1210	1010	870
										2¾ or more	1690	1450	1210	1040
			2	1¾	3190[1]	2730	2270	1960	1¾	1¾ min.	1850	1590	1320	1140
										2¾ or more	2220	1910	1580	1370
			2½ or more	1¾	3330[1]	2860	2380	2060	1¾	1¾ min.	1940	1660	1380	1200
										2¾ or more	2320	1990	1650	1440
4	¾ or ⅞	1	1½ min.	2¾	4370	3750	3130	2700	2¾	2¾ min.	2540	2180	1810	1550
										3¾ or more	3040	2620	2170	1860
			1¾ or more	2¾	5090[1]	4360	3640	3140	2¾	2¾ min.	2950	2530	2110	1810
										3¾ or more	3540	3040	2530	2200
		2	1¾ min.	2¾	3390	2910	2420	2090	2¾	2¾ min.	1970	1680	1400	1250
										3¾ or more	2360	2020	1680	1410
			2	2¾	3790	3240	2700	2330	2¾	2¾ min.	2200	1880	1570	1360
										3¾ or more	2640	2260	1880	1630
			2½	2¾	4310	3690	3080	2660	2¾	2¾ min.	2500	2140	1780	1540
										3¾ or more	3000	2550	2140	1850
			3	2¾	4830	4140	3450	2980	2¾	2¾ min.	2800	2400	2000	1720
										3¾ or more	3360	2880	2400	2060
			3 or more	2¾	5030[1]	4320	3600	3110	2¾	2¾ min.	2920	2500	2090	1800
										3¾ or more	3500	3000	2510	2160

1. Loads followed by "1" in the above table exceed those permitted by Note 3, but are needed for proper determination of loads for other angles of load to grain. Note 3 limitations apply in all cases.

2. For metal side plates, tabulated loads apply except that, for 4-inch shear plates, the parallel-to-grain (not perpendicular) loads for wood side plates shall be increased 18, 11, 5 and 0 percent for groups A, B, C and D woods, respectively, but loads shall not exceed those permitted by Note 3.

3. The allowable loads for all loadings, except wind, shall not exceed 2900 pounds for 2⅝-inch shear plates; 4970 pounds and 6760 pounds for 4-inch shear plates with ¾-inch and ⅞-inch bolts, respectively; or, for wind loading, shall not exceed 3870 pounds, 6630 pounds and 9020 pounds, respectively. If bolt threads are in bearing on the shear plate, reduce the preceding values by one-ninth.

4. Metal side plates, when used, shall be designed in accordance with accepted metal practices. For steel, the following unit stresses, in pounds per square inch, are suggested for all loadings except wind: net section in tension, 20,000; shear, 12,500; double-shear bearing, 28,125; single-shear bearing, 22,500; for wind, these values may be increased one-third; if bolt threads are in bearing, reduce the preceding shear and bearing values by one-ninth.

TABLE NO. 25-17-D—CONNECTOR LOAD GROUPING OF SPECIES WHEN STRESS GRADED

Connector load grouping	Species	
Group A	Ash, Commercial White Beech Birch, Sweet & Yellow Douglas Fir-Larch (Dense)[1]	Hickory & Pecan Maple, Black & Sugar Oak, Red & White Southern Pine (Dense)
Group B	Douglas Fir-Larch[1] Southern Pine (Med. Grain)	Sweetgum & Tupelo
Group C	California Redwood (Close grain) Douglas Fir, South Eastern Hemlock-Tamarack[1] Eastern Spruce Hem-Fir[1] Lodgepole Pine Mountain Hemlock	Northern Aspen Northern Pine Ponderosa Pine Ponderosa Pine—Sugar Pine Red Pine Sitka Spruce Southern Cypress Spruce-Pine-Fir Western Hemlock Yellow Poplar
Group D	Aspen Balsam Fir Black Cottonwood California Redwood (Open grain) Coast Sitka Spruce Cottonwood, Eastern Eastern White Pine[1]	Englemann Spruce-Alpine Fir Idaho White Pine Northern White Cedar Subalpine Fir Western Cedars[1] Western White Pine

[1]Also applies when species name includes the designation "North."

TABLE NO. 25-17-E—CONNECTOR SPACINGS AND END DISTANCES

(With corresponding percentages of tabulated loads)

SPLIT RING DIAM. (Inches)	SHEAR PLATE DIAM. (Inches)	SPACING PARALLEL TO GRAIN		SPACING PERPENDICULAR TO GRAIN		END DISTANCE		
		Spacing	Percentage of Tabulated Load	Minimum	Percentage of Tabulated Load	Tension Member	Compression Member	Percentage of Tabulated Load
		(Inches)	(Percent)	(Inches)	(Percent)	(Inches)	(Inches)	(Percent)
Parallel to grain loading								
2-1/2	2-5/8	6-3/4	100	3-1/2 min.	100	5-1/2	* 4	100
2-1/2	2-5/8	3-1/2 min.	50	3-1/2 min.	100	2-3/4 min.	* 2-1/2 min.	62.5
4	4	9	100	5 min.	100	7	* 5-1/2	100
4	4	5 min.	50	5 min.	100	3-1/2 min.	* 3-1/4 min.	62.5
Perpendicular to grain loading								
2-1/2	2-5/8	3-1/2 min.		4-1/4	100	5-1/2	5-1/2	100
2-1/2	2-5/8	3-1/2 min.		3-1/2 min.	50	2-3/4 min.	2-3/4 min.	62.5
4	4	5 min.		6	100	7	7	100
4	4	5 min.		5 min.	50	3-1/2 min.	3-1/2 min.	62.5

*No reduction in end distance is permitted for compression members loaded parallel to grain.

TABLE NO. 25-17-F—SPACINGS FOR MEMBERS LOADED AT ANGLE OF GRAIN OTHER THAN ZERO DEGREES AND 90 DEGREES

1 TYPE AND SIZE OF CONNECTOR	2 ANGLE OF LOAD TO GRAIN (θ)	3 *A*	4 *B*	5 *C* (50 percent value)
	Degrees	Inches	Inches	Inches
$2^1/_2$-inch split ring or $2^5/_8$-inch shear plate.	0	$6^3/_4$	$3^1/_2$	$3^1/_2$
	15	6	$3^3/_4$	$3^1/_2$
	30	$5^1/_8$	$3^7/_8$	$3^1/_2$
	45	$4^1/_4$	$4^1/_8$	$3^1/_2$
	60—90	$3^1/_2$	$4^1/_4$	$3^1/_2$
4-inch split ring or 4-inch shear plate.	0	9	5	5
	15	8	$5^1/_4$	5
	30	7	$5^1/_2$	5
	45	6	$5^3/_4$	5
	60—90	5	6	5

TABLE NO. 25-17-G—BOLT DESIGN VALUES

Design values, in pounds, on one bolt loaded at both ends (double shear)[1] for following species.
For bolt lengths in the main member intermediate to those shown below, the bolt design value may be calculated by linear interpolation between the next lower and next higher bolt lengths.

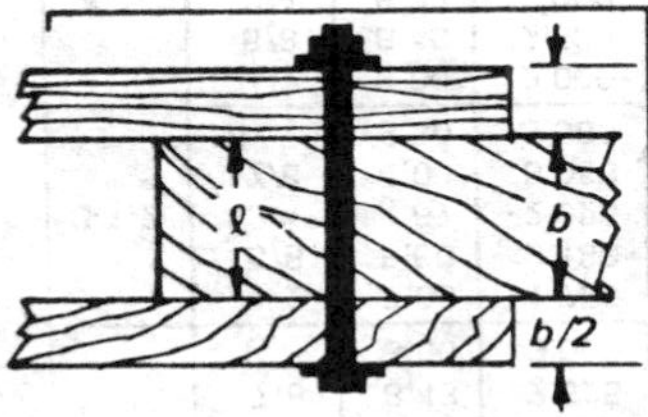
ℓ
b
b/2

				1		2		3		4		5		6	
				DOUGLAS FIR-LARCH (Dense), SOUTHERN PINE (Dense)		ASH, Commercial White, HICKORY		CALIFORNIA REDWOOD (Close grain), DOUGLAS FIR-LARCH, SOUTHERN PINE, SOUTHERN CYPRESS		BEECH, BIRCH, Sweet & Yellow, MAPLE, Black & Sugar		OAK, Red & White		DOUGLAS FIR SOUTH	
Length of bolt in main member ℓ	Diameter of bolt D	ℓ/D	Projected area of bolt A=ℓxD	Parallel to grain P	Perpendicular to grain Q	Parallel to grain P	Perpendicular to grain Q	Parallel to grain P	Perpendicular to grain Q	Parallel to grain P	Perpendicular to grain Q	Parallel to grain P	Perpendicular to grain Q	Parallel to grain P	Perpendicular to grain Q
1-1/2	1/2	3.00	.750	1100	500	1080	780	940	430	900	480	830	650	870	370
	5/8	2.40	.938	1380	570	1360	880	1180	490	1130	540	1050	730	1090	420
	3/4	2.00	1.125	1660	630	1630	980	1420	540	1360	600	1260	820	1310	470
	7/8	1.71	1.313	1940	700	1910	1080	1660	600	1590	670	1470	900	1530	520
	1	1.50	1.500	2220	760	2180	1170	1890	650	1820	730	1690	980	1750	570
2	1/2	4.00	1.000	1370	670	1340	1030	1170	570	1120	640	1040	870	1140	500
	5/8	3.20	1.250	1810	760	1780	1170	1550	650	1480	720	1380	980	1450	560
	3/4	2.67	1.500	2200	840	2170	1300	1880	720	1810	810	1680	1090	1750	630
	7/8	2.29	1.750	2580	930	2540	1430	2210	790	2120	890	1960	1200	2040	690
	1	2.00	2.000	2960	1010	2910	1560	2520	870	2420	970	2250	1310	2330	750
2-1/2	1/2	5.00	1.250	1480	830	1450	1280	1260	720	1210	800	1120	1070	1290	620
	5/8	4.00	1.563	2140	950	2100	1460	1820	810	1750	900	1620	1220	1780	710
	3/4	3.33	1.875	2700	1050	2650	1630	2310	900	2210	1010	2050	1360	2180	790
	7/8	2.86	2.188	3210	1160	3150	1790	2740	990	2630	1110	2440	1500	2550	860
	1	2.50	2.500	3680	1270	3620	1960	3150	1080	3020	1210	2800	1640	2920	940

[1]Three-member joint with side and main members of the same species.

(Continued)

TABLE NO. 25-17-G—BOLT DESIGN VALUES—(Continued)

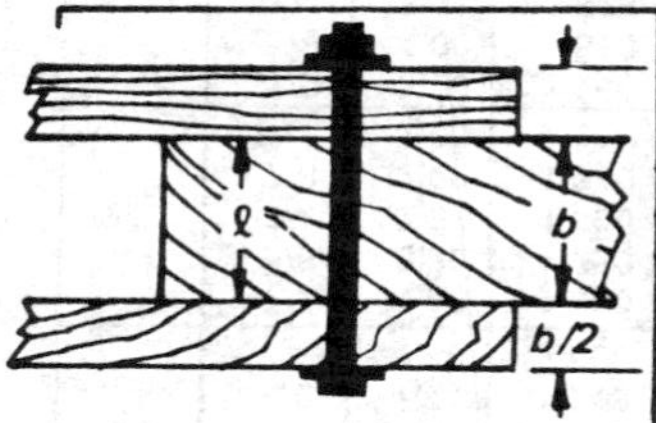

ℓ
b
b/2

Length of bolt in main member ℓ	Diameter of bolt D	ℓ/D	Projected area of bolt A=ℓxD	1 DOUGLAS FIR-LARCH (Dense), SOUTHERN PINE (Dense) Parallel to grain P	1 Perpendicular to grain Q	2 ASH, Commercial White, HICKORY Parallel to grain P	2 Perpendicular to grain Q	3 CALIFORNIA REDWOOD (Close grain), DOUGLAS FIR-LARCH, SOUTHERN PINE, SOUTHERN CYPRESS Parallel to grain P	3 Perpendicular to grain Q	4 BEECH, BIRCH, Sweet & Yellow, MAPLE, Black & Sugar Parallel to grain P	4 Perpendicular to grain Q	5 OAK, Red & White Parallel to grain P	5 Perpendicular to grain Q	6 DOUGLAS FIR SOUTH Parallel to grain P	6 Perpendicular to grain Q
3	1/2	6.00	1.500	1490	970	1460	1460	1270	860	1220	960	1130	1130	1330	750
	5/8	4.80	1.875	2290	1130	2250	1750	1960	970	1880	1090	1740	1460	1980	850
	3/4	4.00	2.250	3080	1270	3020	1950	2630	1080	2520	1210	2340	1630	2560	940
	7/8	3.43	2.625	3760	1390	3700	2150	3220	1190	3080	1330	2860	1800	3040	1040
	1	3.00	3.000	4390	1520	4310	2350	3750	1300	3600	1450	3340	1960	3500	1130
3-1/2	1/2	7.00	1.750	1490	1120	1460	1460	1270	980	1220	1090	1130	1130	1330	850
	5/8	5.60	2.188	2320	1310	2280	2020	1980	1130	1900	1270	1770	1690	2060	990
	3/4	4.67	2.625	3280	1470	3220	2270	2800	1260	2690	1410	2490	1900	2820	1100
	7/8	4.00	3.063	4190	1630	4120	2510	3580	1390	3430	1550	3180	2100	3480	1210
	1	3.50	3.500	5000	1770	4920	2740	4270	1520	4100	1690	3800	2290	4050	1320
4	1/2	8.00	2.000	1490	1010	1460	1460	1270	1010	1220	1130	1130	1130	1330	880
	5/8	6.40	2.500	2330	1410	2290	2180	1990	1290	1910	1440	1770	1770	2080	1120
	3/4	5.33	3.000	3340	1690	3280	2600	2850	1440	2740	1610	2540	2180	2950	1260
	7/8	4.57	3.500	4440	1850	4360	2860	3790	1590	3640	1770	3370	2390	3800	1380
	1	4.00	4.000	5470	2030	5380	3130	4670	1730	4480	1940	4160	2620	4540	1510

4-1/2	5/8	7.20	2.813	2330	1440	2290	2230	1990	1400	1910	1560	1770	1770	2070	1220
	3/4	6.00	3.375	3350	1830	3290	2820	2860	1620	2750	1810	2550	2360	2980	1410
	7/8	5.14	3.938	4540	2110	4460	3260	3880	1790	3720	2000	3450	2720	3980	1560
	1	4.50	4.500	5770	2280	5670	3520	4930	1950	4730	2180	4390	2940	4920	1700
	1-1/4	3.60	5.625	7970	2670	7830	4120	6810	2280	6530	2550	6060	3450	6490	1990
5-1/2	5/8	8.80	3.438	2330	1390	2290	2150	1990	1410	1910	1570	1770	1770	2080	1220
	3/4	7.33	4.125	3350	1930	3300	2980	2860	1880	2750	2100	2550	2490	2990	1630
	7/8	6.29	4.813	4570	2400	4490	3710	3900	2180	3740	2430	3470	3100	4070	1900
	1	5.50	5.500	5930	2760	5830	4260	5070	2380	4860	2660	4510	3560	5270	2080
	1-1/4	4.40	6.875	8930	3260	8780	5040	7630	2790	7320	3120	6790	4210	7580	2430
7-1/2	5/8	12.00	4.688	2330	1210	2290	1870	1990	1260	1910	1410	1770	1560	2070	1100
	3/4	10.00	5.625	3350	1930	3290	2710	2860	1820	2750	2030	2550	2260	2990	1580
	7/8	8.57	6.563	4560	2410	4480	3720	3900	2420	3740	2700	3470	3110	4060	2110
	1	7.50	7.500	5950	3090	5850	4760	5080	3030	4880	3390	4520	3980	5300	2640
	1-1/4	6.00	9.375	9310	4290	9150	6620	7950	3800	7630	4250	7080	5530	8290	3310
9-1/2	3/4	12.67	7.125	3350	1570	3290	2420	2860	1640	2740	1840	2540	2030	2990	1430
	7/8	10.86	8.313	4560	2180	4480	3360	3890	2270	3740	2540	3470	2810	4070	1980
	1	9.50	9.500	5950	2890	5850	4460	5080	2960	4880	3310	4520	3730	5310	2580
	1-1/4	7.60	11.875	9310	4510	9150	6960	7950	4450	7630	4970	7070	5820	8290	3870
	1-1/2	6.33	14.250	13420	6070	13190	9370	11470	5520	11000	6170	10200	7830	11960	4810
11-1/2	7/8	13.14	10.062	4560	1960	4490	3050	3900	2060	3750	2300	3470	2550	4070	1790
	1	11.50	11.500	5950	2650	5850	4080	5080	2770	4880	3090	4520	3410	5310	2410
	1-1/4	9.20	14.375	9310	4280	9160	6610	7960	4360	7630	4870	7080	5530	8300	3800
	1-1/2	7.67	17.250	13410	6210	13180	9590	11450	6140	10990	6860	10190	8010	11940	5350
13-1/2	1	13.50	13.500	5960	2390	5850	3730	5280	2530	4880	2830	4520	3120	5322	2190
	1-1/4	10.80	16.875	9300	3980	9150	6150	7950	4160	7630	4650	7070	5140	8300	3620
	1-1/2	9.00	20.250	13400	5950	13180	9190	11450	6040	10990	6750	10190	7680	11950	5260

(Continued)

TABLE NO. 25-17-G—BOLT DESIGN VALUES—(Continued)

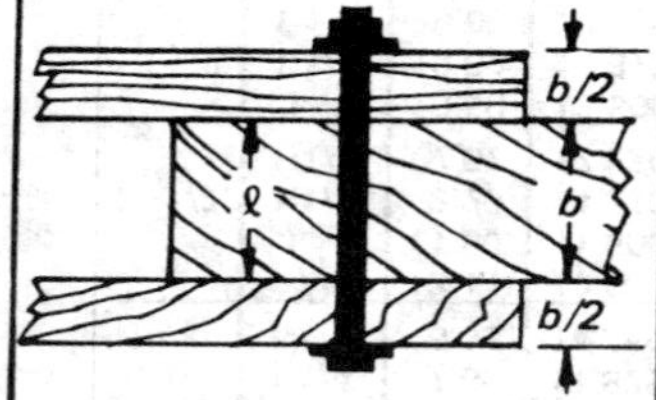
b/2
ℓ
b
b/2

				7 SWEETGUM & TUPELO		8 EASTERN HEMLOCK-TAMARACK, CALIFORNIA REDWOOD (Open grain), HEM-FIR, WESTERN HEMLOCK		9 MOUNTAIN HEMLOCK, WESTERN CEDARS, NORTHERN PINE		10 SPRUCE-PINE-FIR, SITKA SPRUCE, YELLOW POPLAR, EASTERN SPRUCE, LODGEPOLE PINE		11 RED PINE, WESTERN WHITE PINE, PONDEROSA PINE-SUGAR PINE, EASTERN WHITE PINE, BALSAM FIR, IDAHO WHITE PINE		12 ASPEN, EASTERN COTTONWOOD, ENGELMANN SPRUCE-ALPINE FIR, NORTHERN WHITE CEDAR	
Length of bolt in main member ℓ	Diameter of bolt D	ℓ/D	Projected area of bolt A=ℓxD	Parallel to grain P	Perpendicular to grain Q	Parallel to grain P	Perpendicular to grain Q	Parallel to grain P	Perpendicular to grain Q	Parallel to grain P	Perpendicular to grain Q	Parallel to grain P	Perpendicular to grain Q	Parallel to grain P	Perpendicular to grain Q
1-1/2	1/2	3.00	.750	810	410	800	270	750	300	680	280	630	190	530	210
	5/8	2.40	.938	1010	460	1000	310	930	340	850	320	790	210	660	230
	3/4	2.00	1.125	1220	510	1200	350	1120	370	1020	350	950	240	800	260
	7/8	1.71	1.313	1420	560	1400	380	1310	410	1190	390	1110	260	930	290
	1	1.50	1.500	1620	620	1600	420	1490	450	1360	420	1260	290	1060	310
2	1/2	4.00	1.000	1050	540	1040	370	970	400	900	370	840	250	700	280
	5/8	3.20	1.250	1350	610	1330	410	1240	450	1130	420	1050	280	880	310
	3/4	2.67	1.500	1620	680	1600	460	1490	500	1360	470	1260	320	1060	350
	7/8	2.29	1.750	1890	750	1870	510	1740	550	1580	520	1480	350	1240	380
	1	2.00	2.000	2160	820	2130	550	1990	600	1810	560	1690	380	1420	420
2-1/2	1/2	5.00	1.250	1190	680	1180	460	1100	500	1080	470	1010	310	840	340
	5/8	4.00	1.563	1640	770	1620	520	1510	560	1410	530	1310	360	1100	390
	3/4	3.33	1.875	2020	850	1990	580	1860	620	1700	590	1580	400	1330	430
	7/8	2.86	2.188	2360	940	2330	630	2180	690	1980	650	1840	440	1550	480
	1	2.50	2.500	2700	1030	2670	690	2490	750	2260	700	2110	480	1770	520

3	1/2	6.00	1.500	1230	810	1210	550	1130	590	1160	560	1080	380	910	410
	5/8	4.80	1.875	1830	920	1810	620	1690	670	1640	630	1520	430	1280	470
	3/4	4.00	2.250	2370	1030	2340	690	2180	750	2030	700	1890	480	1590	520
	7/8	3.43	2.625	2820	1120	2780	760	2600	820	2380	780	2210	520	1860	570
	1	3.00	3.000	3240	1230	3200	830	2990	900	2710	850	2530	570	2120	620
3-1/2	1/2	7.00	1.750	1230	920	1210	640	1130	690	1160	650	1080	440	910	480
	5/8	5.60	2.188	1910	1070	1890	720	1760	780	1790	740	1660	500	1400	550
	3/4	4.67	2.625	2610	1200	2570	810	2400	870	2310	820	2150	560	1800	610
	7/8	4.00	3.063	3220	1320	3180	890	2970	960	2760	900	2570	610	2160	670
	1	3.50	3.500	3760	1440	3710	970	3460	1050	3170	990	2950	670	2480	730
4	1/2	8.00	2.000	1230	960	1210	700	1130	760	1160	720	1080	500	910	550
	5/8	6.40	2.500	1920	1220	1900	830	1770	900	1820	840	1690	570	1420	620
	3/4	5.33	3.000	2730	1370	2690	920	2510	1000	2520	940	2350	630	1970	690
	7/8	4.57	3.500	3520	1500	3470	1010	3240	1100	3090	1030	2880	700	2420	760
	1	4.00	4.000	4210	1640	4150	1110	3880	1200	3600	1130	3360	760	2820	830
4-1/2	5/8	7.20	2.813	1920	1320	1900	930	1770	1010	1820	950	1690	640	1420	700
	3/4	6.00	3.375	2760	1540	2730	1040	2550	1120	2610	1060	2440	710	2050	780
	7/8	5.14	3.938	3680	1690	3630	1140	3390	1240	3360	1160	3130	790	2630	860
	1	4.50	4.500	4560	1850	4500	1250	4200	1350	3990	1270	3710	860	3120	940
	1-1/4	3.60	5.625	6010	2160	5930	1460	5540	1580	5080	1490	4740	1000	3980	1100
5-1/2	5/8	8.80	3.438	1920	1330	1900	1010	1770	1090	1820	1030	1690	750	1420	820
	3/4	7.33	4.125	2770	1780	2730	1260	2550	1360	2620	1280	2440	870	2050	950
	7/8	6.29	4.813	3770	2060	3720	1400	3470	1510	3560	1420	3320	960	2790	1050
	1	5.50	5.500	4890	2260	4820	1520	4500	1650	4550	1550	4240	1050	3560	1150
	1-1/4	4.40	6.875	7020	2640	6930	1780	6470	1930	6110	1820	5690	1230	4780	1340
7-1/2	5/8	12.00	4.688	1920	1200	1890	950	1770	1030	1820	960	1690	730	1420	800
	3/4	10.00	5.625	2770	1720	2730	1320	2550	1430	2620	1340	2440	1010	2050	1110
	7/8	8.57	6.563	3770	2290	3720	1730	3470	1870	3560	1760	3320	1280	2780	1400
	1	7.50	7.500	4910	2870	4850	2060	4520	2230	4650	2100	4330	1430	3640	1560
	1-1/4	6.00	9.375	7680	3600	7580	2430	7070	2630	7260	2480	6770	1670	5680	1830

(Continued)

TABLE NO. 25-17-G—BOLT DESIGN VALUES—(Continued)

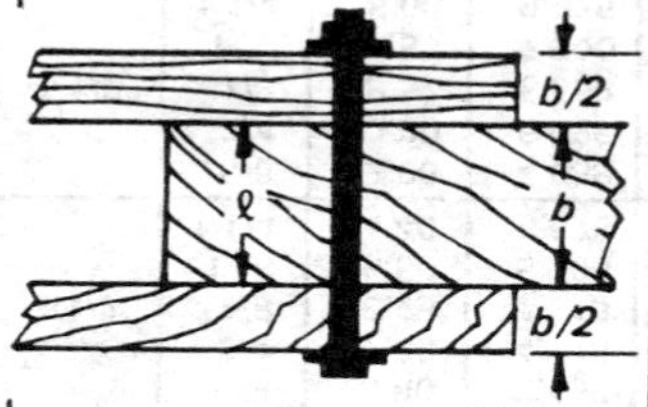
b/2
ℓ
b
b/2

Length of bolt in main member ℓ	Diameter of bolt D	ℓ/D	Projected area of bolt A=ℓxD	7 SWEETGUM & TUPELO Parallel to grain P	7 Perpendicular to grain Q	8 EASTERN HEMLOCK-TAMARACK, CALIFORNIA REDWOOD (Open grain), HEM-FIR, WESTERN HEMLOCK Parallel to grain P	8 Perpendicular to grain Q	9 MOUNTAIN HEMLOCK, WESTERN CEDARS, NORTHERN PINE Parallel to grain P	9 Perpendicular to grain Q	10 SPRUCE-PINE-FIR, SITKA SPRUCE, YELLOW POPLAR, EASTERN SPRUCE, LODGEPOLE PINE Parallel to grain P	10 Perpendicular to grain Q	11 RED PINE, WESTERN WHITE PINE, PONDEROSA PINE-SUGAR PINE, EASTERN WHITE PINE, BALSAM FIR, IDAHO WHITE PINE Parallel to grain P	11 Perpendicular to grain Q	12 ASPEN, EASTERN COTTONWOOD, ENGELMANN SPRUCE-ALPINE FIR, NORTHERN WHITE CEDAR Parallel to grain P	12 Perpendicular to grain Q
9-1/2	3/4	12.67	7.125	2770	1560	2730	1250	2550	1350	2620	1270	2440	970	2050	1060
	7/8	10.86	8.313	3770	2150	3720	1660	3470	1790	3560	1690	3320	1280	2790	1400
	1	9.50	9.500	4920	2800	4850	2130	4530	2300	4650	2170	4330	1630	3640	1780
	1-1/4	7.60	11.875	7680	4210	7580	3030	7070	3280	7270	3090	6770	2120	5690	2320
	1-1/2	6.33	14.250	11080	5250	10930	3540	10200	3830	10470	3610	9760	2440	8190	2660
11-1/2	7/8	13.14	10.062	3770	1950	3700	1590	3460	1730	3570	1630	3330	1230	2790	1350
	1	11.50	11.500	4920	2620	4860	2040	4530	2210	4650	2080	4330	1580	3640	1730
	1-1/4	9.20	14.375	7690	4130	7590	3140	7080	3400	7270	3200	6780	2380	5690	2600
	1-1/2	7.67	17.250	11070	5820	10920	4210	10190	4550	10470	4280	9750	2950	8190	3230
13-1/2	1	13.50	13.500	4920	2400	4850	1970	4540	2140	4670	2020	4350	1530	3650	1680
	1-1/4	10.80	16.875	7690	3940	7590	3030	7080	3280	7260	3080	6770	2340	5680	2560
	1-1/2	9.00	20.250	11070	5720	10930	4340	10200	4700	10460	4420	9750	3280	8190	3580

TABLE NO. 25-17-H—PROPERTIES OF NAILS

DESIGNATION	LENGTH (In Inches)	WIRE DIAMETER (In Inches)	HEAD DIAMETER (In Inches)
Box Nails—Broad Flat Head, Diamond-point, Barbed or Smooth, Bright or Cement-coated			
2d	1	.067	3/16
3d	1 1/4	.076	7/32
4d	1 1/2	.080	7/32
5d	1 3/4	.080	7/32
6d	2	.099	17/64
7d	2 1/4	.099	17/64
8d	2 1/2	.113	19/64
9d	2 3/4	.113	19/64
10d	3	.128	5/16
12d	3 1/4	.128	5/16
16d	3 1/2	.135	11/32
20d	4	.148	3/8
30d	4 1/2	.148	3/8
40d	5	.162	13/32
Casing Nails—Deep Countersunk Head, Diamond Point			
6d	2	.099	.142
8d	2 1/2	.113	.155
10d	3	.128	.170
Cooler Nails—Cement-coated, Standard, Flat Head, Diamond-point			
2d	1	.062	11/64
3d	1 1/8	.067	3/16
4d	1 3/8	.080	7/32
5d	1 5/8	.086	15/64
6d	1 7/8	.092	1/4
7d	2 1/8	.099	17/64
8d	2 3/8	.113	9/32
9d	2 5/8	.113	9/32
10d	2 7/8	.120	19/64
Wallboard Nail—Concave Head, Phosphate Etched Diamond Point			
3 1/4d	1 3/16	.080	1/4
4d	1 3/8	.080	1/4
5d	1 5/8	.086	9/32
6d	1 7/8	.0915	19/64
7d	2 1/8	.099	5/16
8d	2 3/8	.113	3/8
Common Wire Nails			
6d	2	.113	.266
8d	2 1/2	.131	.281
10d	3	.148	.312
12d	3 1/4	.148	.312
16d	3 1/2	.162	.344
20d	4	.192	.406
30d	4 1/2	.207	.438
40d	5	.226	.469
50d	5 1/2	.244	.500
60d	6	.262	.531

(Continued)

TABLE NO. 25-17-H—PROPERTIES OF NAILS—(Continued)

DESIGNATION	LENGTH (In Inches)	WIRE DIAMETER (In Inches)	HEAD DIAMETER (In Inches)
Threaded, Hardened Steel Nails and Spikes[1]			
6d	2	.120	9/32
8d	2½	.120	9/32
10d	3	.135	5/16
12d	3¼	.135	5/16
16d	3½	.148	5/16
20d	4	.177	3/8
40d	5	.177	3/8
60d	6	.177	3/8
70d	7	.207	½
80d	8	.207	½
Plasterboard Blued Nails—Steel Flat Head, Diamond-point			
	1½	.0915	19/64
	1¼	.0915	19/64
Spikes—Flat Head or Oval Head—Diamond Point			
40d	5	.263	17/32
50d	5½	.283	9/16
60d	6	.283	9/16
5/16	7	.312	5/8
3/8	8½	.375	3/4

[1]Nails and spikes made of high-carbon steel wire, headed, pointed, annularly or helically threaded, and heat treated and tempered to provide greater strength than is developed by common wire nails of corresponding size.

TABLE NO. 25-17-I—GROUPING OF SPECIES FOR DETERMINING ALLOWABLE LOADS FOR LAG SCREWS, NAILS, SPIKES, WOOD SCREWS, DRIFT BOLTS

GROUP	SPECIES OF WOOD	SPECIFIC (G)[1]
I	Ash, Commercial White	.62
	Mixed Hardwoods	.71
	Mixed Oak	.71
	Northern Red Oak	.68
	Red Oak	.68
	White Oak	.74
II	Double Fir-Larch[2]	.51
	Mixed Maple	.59
	Red Maple	.57
	Southern Pine	.55
	Sweetgum & Tupelo	.54
	Virginia Pine-Pond Pine	.54
III	California Redwood (Close Grain)	.42
	Douglas Fir, South	.48
	Eastern Hemlock	.43
	Eastern Hemlock—Tamarack[2]	.45
	Eastern Softwoods	.42
	Eastern Spruce	.43
	Englemann Spruce-Lodgepole Pine (MSR)[3]	.46
	Hem-Fir[2]	.42
	Lodgepole Pine	.44
	Mountain Hemlock	.47
	Mountain Hemlock-Hem-Fir	.44
	Northern Aspen	.42
	Northern Pine	.46
	Ponderosa Pine[3]	.49
	Ponderosa Pine-Sugar Pine	.42
	Red Pine	.42
	Sitka Spruce	.43
	Southern Cypress	.48
	Spruce-Pine-Fir	.42
	Western Hemlock	.48
	Yellow Poplar	.46

(Continued)

TABLE NO. 25-17-I—GROUPING OF SPECIES FOR DETERMINING ALLOWABLE LOADS FOR LAG SCREWS, NAILS, SPIKES, WOOD SCREWS, DRIFT BOLTS—(Continued)

GROUP	SPECIES OF WOOD	SPECIFIC (G)[1]
IV	Aspen	.40
	Balsam Fir	.38
	Black Cottonwood	.33
	California Redwood (Open Grain)	.37
	Coast Sitka Spruce	.39
	Coast Species	.39
	Cottonwood, Eastern	.41
	Eastern White Pine[2]	.38
	Eastern Woods	.38
	Engelmann Spruce-Alpine Fir	.36
	Idaho White Pine	.40
	Northern Species	.35
	Northern White Cedar	.31
	West Coast Woods (Mixed Species)	.35
	Western Cedars[2]	.35
	Western White Pine	.40
	White Woods (Western Woods)	.35

[1]Based on weight and volume when oven dry.
[2]Also applies when species name includes the designation "North."
[3]Applies to grades of $1650F_b$-$1.5E$ and higher machine stress-rated (MSR) lumber.

TABLE NO. 25-17-J-1—NAILED AND SPIKED JOINTS—ALLOWABLE WITHDRAWAL LOADS—NORMAL DURATION
(See Table No. 25-17-I for Species of Wood)

Allowable load in withdrawal in pounds per inch of penetration into side grain of member holding point. d = penny weight of nail or spike. G = specific gravity of the wood based on weight and volume when oven dry.

Specific gravity G	Size of common nail (d)										Size of threaded nail (d)[1]						
Penny wt. / Diam.	6d 0.113	8d 0.131	10d 0.148	12d 0.148	16d 0.162	20d 0.192	30d 0.207	40d 0.225	50d 0.244	60d 0.263	30d 0.177	40d 0.177	50d 0.177	60d 0.177	70d 0.207	80d 0.207	90d 0.207
0.75	76	88	99	99	109	129	139	151	164	177	129	129	129	129	151	151	151
0.68	59	69	78	78	85	101	109	118	128	138	101	101	101	101	118	118	118
0.67	57	66	75	75	82	97	105	114	124	133	97	97	97	97	114	114	114
0.66	55	64	72	72	79	94	101	110	119	128	94	94	94	94	110	110	110
0.62	47	55	62	62	68	80	86	94	102	110	80	80	80	80	94	94	94
0.55	35	41	46	46	50	59	64	70	76	81	59	59	59	59	70	70	70
0.54	33	39	44	44	48	57	61	67	72	78	57	57	57	57	67	67	67
0.51	29	34	38	38	42	49	53	58	63	67	49	49	49	49	58	58	58
0.49	26	30	34	34	38	45	48	52	57	61	45	45	45	45	52	52	52
0.48	25	29	33	33	36	42	46	50	54	58	42	42	42	42	50	50	50
0.47	24	27	31	31	34	40	43	47	51	55	40	40	40	40	47	47	47
0.46	22	26	29	29	32	38	41	45	48	52	38	38	38	38	45	45	45
0.45	21	25	28	28	30	36	39	42	46	49	36	36	36	36	42	42	42
0.44	20	23	26	26	29	34	37	40	43	47	34	34	34	34	40	40	40
0.43	19	22	25	25	27	32	35	38	41	44	32	32	32	32	38	38	38
0.42	18	21	23	23	26	30	33	35	38	41	30	30	30	30	35	35	35
0.41	17	19	22	22	24	29	31	33	36	39	29	29	29	29	33	33	33
0.40	16	18	21	21	23	27	29	31	34	37	27	27	27	27	31	31	31
0.39	15	17	19	19	21	25	27	29	32	34	25	25	25	25	29	29	29
0.38	14	16	18	18	20	24	25	28	30	32	24	24	24	24	28	28	28
0.37	13	15	17	17	19	22	24	26	28	30	22	22	22	22	26	26	26
0.36	12	14	16	16	17	21	22	24	26	28	21	21	21	21	24	24	24
0.35	11	13	15	15	16	19	21	23	24	26	19	19	19	19	23	23	23
0.33	10	11	13	13	14	17	18	19	21	23	17	17	17	17	19	19	19
0.31	8	10	11	11	12	14	15	17	18	19	14	14	14	14	17	17	17

[1]Loads for threaded, hardened steel nails, in 6d to 20d sizes, are the same as for common nails.

TABLE NO. 25-17-J-1—NAILED AND SPIKED JOINTS—ALLOWABLE WITHDRAWAL LOADS—NORMAL DURATION—(Continued)

(See Table No. 25-17-I for Species of Wood)

Specific gravity G	Penny wt. Diam.	Size of common spike (d)										Size of box nail (d)							
		10d 0.192	12d 0.192	16d 0.207	20d 0.225	30d 0.244	40d 0.263	50d 0.283	60d 0.283	5/16" 0.312	3/8" 0.375	6d 0.099	8d 0.113	10d 0.128	12d 0.128	16d 0.135	20d 0.148	30d 0.148	40d 0.162
0.75		129	129	139	151	164	177	190	190	210	252	67	76	86	86	91	99	99	109
0.68		101	101	109	118	128	138	149	149	164	197	52	59	67	67	71	78	78	85
0.67		97	97	105	114	124	133	144	144	158	190	50	57	65	65	68	75	75	82
0.66		94	94	101	110	119	128	138	138	152	183	48	55	63	63	66	72	72	79
0.62		80	80	86	94	102	110	118	118	130	157	41	47	53	53	56	62	62	68
0.55		59	59	64	70	76	81	88	88	97	116	31	35	40	40	47	46	46	50
0.54		57	57	61	67	72	78	84	84	92	111	29	33	38	38	40	44	44	48
0.51		49	49	53	58	63	67	73	73	80	96	25	29	33	33	35	38	38	42
0.49		45	45	48	52	57	61	66	66	72	87	23	26	30	30	31	34	34	38
0.48		42	42	46	50	54	58	62	62	69	83	22	25	28	28	30	33	33	36
0.47		40	40	43	47	51	55	59	59	65	78	21	24	27	27	28	31	31	34
0.46		38	38	41	45	48	52	56	56	62	74	20	22	25	25	27	29	29	32
0.45		36	36	39	42	46	49	53	53	58	70	19	21	24	24	25	28	28	30
0.44		34	34	37	40	43	47	50	50	55	66	18	20	23	23	24	26	26	29
0.43		32	32	35	38	41	44	47	47	52	63	17	19	21	21	23	25	25	27
0.42		30	30	33	35	38	41	45	45	49	59	16	18	20	20	21	23	23	26
0.41		29	29	31	33	36	39	42	42	46	56	15	17	19	19	20	22	22	24
0.40		27	27	29	31	34	37	40	40	44	52	14	16	18	18	19	21	21	23
0.39		25	25	27	29	32	34	37	37	41	49	13	15	17	17	18	19	19	21
0.38		24	24	25	28	30	32	35	35	38	46	12	14	16	16	17	18	18	20
0.37		22	22	24	26	28	30	33	33	36	43	11	13	15	15	16	17	17	19
0.36		21	21	22	24	26	28	30	30	33	40	11	12	14	14	14	16	16	17
0.35		19	19	21	23	24	26	28	28	31	38	10	11	13	13	14	15	15	16
0.33		17	17	18	19	21	23	24	24	27	32	9	10	11	11	12	13	13	14
0.31		14	14	15	17	18	19	21	21	23	28	7	8	9	9	10	11	11	12

TABLE NO. 25-17-J-2—NAILS AND SPIKES—LATERAL LOAD DESIGN VALUES

Design values for lateral loads (single shear) for nails and spikes penetrating not less than 10 diameters in Group I species, 11 diameters in Group II species, 13 in diameters in Group III species, and 14 diameters in Group IV species, into the member holding the point. Nail size in pennyweight. Diameters and lengths in inches. Loads in pounds.

	BOX NAILS									
Penny weight	*6d*	*8d*	*10d*	*12d*	*16d*	*20d*	*30d*	*40d*		
Length	2	2½	3	3¼	3½	4	4½	5		
Diameter	0.099	0.113	0.128	0.128	0.135	0.148	0.148	0.162		
10 Diameters	0.99	1.13	1.28	1.28	1.35	1.48	1.48	1.62		
11 Diameters	1.09	1.24	1.41	1.41	1.49	1.63	1.63	1.78		
13 Diameters	1.29	1.47	1.66	1.66	1.76	1.92	1.92	2.11		
14 Diameters	1.39	1.58	1.79	1.79	1.89	2.07	2.07	2.27		
Species group I	64	77	93	93	101	116	116	133		
Species group II	51	63	76	76	82	94	94	108		
Species group III	42	51	62	62	67	77	77	88		
Species group IV	34	41	49	49	54	61	61	70		
	COMMON WIRE NAILS									
Penny weight	*6d*	*8d*	*10d*	*12d*	*16d*	*20d*	*30d*	*40d*	*50d*	*60d*
Length	2	2½	3	3¼	3½	4	4½	5	5½	6
Diameter	0.113	0.131	0.148	0.148	0.162	0.192	0.207	0.225	0.244	0.263
10 Diameters	1.13	1.31	1.48	1.48	1.62	1.92	2.07	2.25	2.44	2.63
11 Diameters	1.24	1.44	1.63	1.63	1.78	2.11	2.28	2.48	2.68	2.89
13 Diameters	1.47	1.70	1.92	1.92	2.11	2.50	2.69	2.93	3.17	3.42
14 Diameters	1.58	1.83	2.07	2.07	2.27	2.69	2.90	3.15	3.42	3.68
Species group I	77	97	116	116	133	172	192	218	246	275
Species group II	63	78	94	94	108	139	155	176	199	223
Species group III	51	64	77	77	88	114	127	144	163	182
Species group IV	41	51	61	61	70	91	102	115	130	146

(Continued)

TABLE NO. 25-17-J-2—NAILS AND SPIKES—LATERAL LOAD DESIGN VALUES—(Continued)

THREADED HARDENED STEEL NAILS AND SPIKES													
Penny weight	*6d*	*8d*	*10d*	*12d*	*16d*	*20d*	*30d*	*40d*	*50d*	*60d*	*70d*	*80d*	*90d*
Length	2	2½	3	3¼	3½	4	4½	5	5½	6	7	8	9
Diameter	0.120	0.120	0.135	0.135	0.148	0.177	0.177	0.177	0.177	0.177	0.207	0.207	0.207
10 Diameters	1.20	1.20	1.35	1.35	1.48	1.77	1.77	1.77	1.77	1.77	2.07	2.07	2.07
11 Diameters	1.32	1.32	1.49	1.49	1.63	1.95	1.95	1.95	1.95	1.95	2.28	2.28	2.28
13 Diameters	1.56	1.56	1.76	1.76	1.92	2.30	2.30	2.30	2.30	2.30	2.69	2.69	2.69
14 Diameters	1.68	1.68	1.89	1.89	2.07	2.48	2.48	2.48	2.48	2.48	2.90	2.90	2.90
Species group I	77	97	116	116	133	172	172	172	172	172	218	218	218
Species group II	63	78	94	94	108	139	139	139	139	139	176	176	176
Species group III	51	64	77	77	88	114	114	114	114	114	144	144	144
Species group IV	41	51	61	61	70	91	91	91	91	91	115	115	115
COMMON WIRE SPIKES													
Penny weight			*10d*	*12d*	*16d*	*20d*	*30d*	*40d*	*50d*	*60d*	5/16"	3/8"	
Length			3	3¼	3½	4	4½	5	5½	6	7	8½	
Diameter			0.192	0.192	0.207	0.225	0.244	0.263	0.283	0.283	0.312	0.375	
10 Diameters			1.92	1.92	2.07	2.25	2.44	2.63	2.83	2.83	3.12	3.75	
11 Diameters			2.11	2.11	2.28	2.48	2.68	2.89	3.11	3.11	3.43	4.13	
13 Diameters			2.50	2.50	2.69	2.93	3.17	3.42	3.68	3.68	4.06	4.88	
14 Diameters			2.69	2.69	2.90	3.15	3.42	3.68	3.96	3.96	4.37	5.25	
Species group I			172	172	192	218	246	275	307	307	356	468	
Species group II			139	139	155	176	199	223	248	248	288	379	
Species group III			114	114	127	144	163	182	203	203	235	310	
Species group IV			91	91	102	115	130	146	163	163	188	248	

TABLE NO. 25-17-K—WOOD SCREWS—ALLOWABLE LATERAL LOADS—NORMAL DURATION

Allowable lateral loads (shear) in pounds for screws embedded to approximately seven times the shank diameter into the member holding the point. For less penetration, reduce loads in proportion. Penetration should not be less than four times the shank diameter.

(For Species in Each Group see Table No. 25-17-I)	SIZE OF SCREW											
	g =	6	7	8	9	10	12	14	16	18	20	24
	D =	0.138	0.151	0.164	0.177	0.190	0.216	0.242	0.268	0.294	0.320	0.372
	7D =	.966	1.057	1.148	1.239	1.330	1.512	1.694	1.876	2.058	2.240	2.604
	4D =	.552	.604	.656	.708	.760	.864	.968	1.072	1.176	1.280	1.488
Group I	=	91	109	129	150	173	224	281	345	415	492	664
Group II	=	75	90	106	124	143	185	232	284	342	406	548
Group III	=	62	74	87	101	117	151	190	233	280	332	448
Group IV	=	48	58	68	79	91	118	148	181	218	258	349

TABLE NO. 25-17-L—WOOD-SCREW[1] JOINTS—ALLOWABLE WITHDRAWAL LOADS—NORMAL DURATION

(See Table No. 25-17-I for Species of Wood)

Allowable load in withdrawal in pounds per inch of penetration of threaded part into side grain of member holding point. g = gage of screw. D = shank diameter in inches. G = specific gravity of the wood based on weight and volume when oven-dry.

Specific gravity G	SIZE										
	g =	6	7	8	9	10	12	14	16	18	20	24
	D =	0.138	0.151	0.164	0.177	0.190	0.216	0.242	0.268	0.294	0.320	0.372
.75		222	242	263	284	306	347	388	430	471	514	597
.68		182	199	216	233	251	285	319	353	387	422	490
.67		177	193	210	227	243	276	310	343	376	410	476
.66		171	188	204	220	236	268	300	333	365	397	461
.62		151	166	180	194	208	237	265	294	322	351	407
.55		118	130	141	152	164	186	208	231	253	275	320
.54		114	126	136	147	158	180	201	224	245	266	310
.51		102	112	121	131	141	160	179	199	218	237	276
.48		91	99	108	116	125	142	159	176	193	210	244
.47		87	95	103	111	120	136	152	169	185	201	234
.46		83	91	99	107	115	130	146	162	177	193	224
.45		80	87	95	102	110	125	140	155	170	185	215
.44		76	83	91	97	105	119	133	148	162	177	205
.43		73	80	86	93	100	114	127	141	155	169	196
.42		69	76	82	89	95	109	121	135	148	161	187
.41		66	72	79	85	91	103	116	128	141	153	178
.40		65	71	77	83	89	102	113	126	138	151	175
.39		61	66	72	78	84	95	106	118	130	141	164
.38		57	62	67	73	78	89	99	110	121	132	153
.37		54	59	64	69	74	84	94	104	115	125	145
.36		51	56	60	65	70	80	89	99	109	118	137
.34		46	50	54	58	63	71	80	88	97	105	123
.31		38	42	45	48	53	59	67	73	81	88	103

[1]Approximately two thirds of the length of a standard wood screw is threaded.

TABLE NO. 25-17-M—LAG BOLTS OR LAG SCREWS—ALLOWABLE WITHDRAWAL LOADS—NORMAL DURATION
(See Table No. 25-17-I for Species of Wood)

Allowable load in withdrawal in pounds per inch of penetration of threaded part into side grain of member holding point. D = the shank diameter in inches. G = specific gravity of the wood based on weight and volume when oven-dry.

Specific gravity G	SIZE (D)											
	¼	5/16	⅜	7/16	½	9/16	⅝	¾	⅞	1	1⅛	1¼
	0.250	0.3125	0.375	0.4375	0.500	0.5625	0.625	0.750	0.875	1.000	1.125	1.250
.75	414	488	561	630	697	760	824	944	1060	1172	1282	1388
.68	357	422	484	543	601	655	710	814	914	1010	1103	1194
.67	349	412	472	531	587	640	693	795	893	986	1078	1166
.66	342	403	462	519	574	626	678	778	873	965	1054	1141
.62	311	367	421	473	523	570	618	708	795	878	960	1038
.55	264	312	356	402	443	484	524	601	675	745	815	881
.54	256	304	348	391	432	473	512	586	660	728	796	860
.51	232	274	313	352	389	425	460	528	593	655	716	774
.48	212	251	287	322	357	389	421	483	542	599	655	709
.47	205	242	278	312	345	376	407	467	525	580	633	685
.46	199	235	269	302	334	364	395	453	508	562	613	664
.45	192	227	260	292	323	353	382	438	492	544	594	643
.44	186	220	252	283	313	341	369	424	476	526	574	621
.43	180	213	244	274	303	331	358	411	461	509	556	602
.42	173	205	235	263	291	318	344	395	443	490	535	579
.41	167	197	226	254	281	306	332	340	427	472	515	558
.40	162	191	220	246	273	296	324	368	414	458	500	542
.39	156	184	211	237	262	284	311	354	397	439	480	520
.38	149	176	202	227	251	273	298	339	381	421	460	498
.37	143	169	194	218	241	263	285	326	367	405	442	479
.36	138	163	186	209	231	252	273	313	352	389	425	460
.34	126	149	171	192	212	231	251	287	323	356	389	421
.31	107	127	145	163	180	196	213	244	274	302	330	358

TABLE NO. 25-17-N—LAG SCREWS—LATERAL LOAD DESIGN VALUES WITH WOOD SIDE PIECES

Normal load duration, dry service conditions

Thickness of side member (inches)	Length of lag screw (inches)	Diameter of lag screw shank (inches)	Species Group (See Table No. 25-17-I)							
			GROUP I		GROUP II		GROUP III		GROUP IV	
			Total lateral load per lag screw in single shear (pounds)		Total lateral load per lag screw in single shear (pounds)		Total lateral load per lag screw in single shear (pounds)		Total lateral load per lag screw in single shear (pounds)	
			Parallel to grain	Perpendicular to grain	Parallel to grain	Perpendicular to grain	Parallel to grain	Perpendicular to grain	Parallel to grain	Perpendicular to grain
1½"	4"	1/4	200	200	170	170	130	130	100	100
		5/16	290	240	220	180	150	130	120	110
		3/8	330	250	250	190	180	140	140	110
		7/16	370	260	280	190	200	140	160	110
		1/2	390	250	290	190	210	140	170	110
		5/8	470	280	360	210	260	160	200	120
	5"	1/4	240	230	200	200	180	180	160	160
		5/16	340	290	290	250	240	200	190	160
		3/8	440	340	380	290	270	210	220	170
		7/16	550	380	420	290	300	210	240	170
		1/2	580	380	440	280	310	200	250	160
		5/8	710	420	530	320	380	230	310	180

1½"	6"	1/4	270	260	230	220	210	200	180	180
		5/16	380	320	330	280	290	250	260	220
		3/8	490	370	420	320	370	280	300	230
		7/16	600	420	520	360	410	280	330	230
		1/2	700	460	600	390	430	280	340	220
		5/8	850	510	710	430	510	310	410	250
	7"	1/4	280	270	240	230	210	210	190	180
		5/16	400	340	350	300	310	270	280	230
		3/8	530	400	460	350	410	310	360	270
		7/16	650	450	560	390	500	350	420	300
		1/2	760	490	660	430	550	360	440	290
		5/8	910	540	780	470	640	380	510	310
2½"	6"	3/8	450	340	380	290	270	210	220	170
		7/16	590	410	440	310	320	220	250	180
		1/2	620	410	470	310	340	220	270	180
		5/8	730	440	550	330	390	240	320	190
		3/4	830	460	630	350	450	250	360	200
		7/8	950	490	720	370	510	270	410	210
		1	1060	530	800	400	570	290	460	230

(Continued)

TABLE NO. 25-17-N—LAG SCREWS—LATERAL LOAD DESIGN VALUES WITH WOOD SIDE PIECES—(Continued)

Thickness of side member (inches)	Length of lag screw (inches)	Diameter of lag screw shank (inches)	Species Group (See Table No. 25-17-I) GROUP I Total lateral load per lag screw in single shear (pounds)		GROUP II Total lateral load per lag screw in single shear (pounds)		GROUP III Total lateral load per lag screw in single shear (pounds)		GROUP IV Total lateral load per lag screw in single shear (pounds)	
			Parallel to grain	Perpendicular to grain	Parallel to grain	Perpendicular to grain	Parallel to grain	Perpendicular to grain	Parallel to grain	Perpendicular to grain
2½″	7″	3/8	500	380	430	330	380	290	300	230
		7/16	670	470	580	410	430	300	350	240
		1/2	830	540	650	420	460	300	370	240
		5/8	1000	600	750	450	540	320	430	260
		3/4	1120	620	850	470	610	330	490	270
		7/8	1280	660	970	500	690	360	550	290
		1	1440	720	1090	540	780	390	620	310
	8″	3/8	560	420	480	370	430	330	380	290
		7/16	730	510	630	440	560	390	450	320
		1/2	890	580	770	500	600	390	480	310
		5/8	1230	740	970	580	700	420	560	340
		3/4	1440	790	1090	600	780	430	630	340
		7/8	1610	840	1220	630	870	450	700	360
		1	1810	910	1370	690	980	490	790	390
	9″	3/8	600	460	520	400	470	350	410	310
		7/16	790	550	680	480	610	430	540	380
		1/2	960	630	830	540	740	480	600	390
		5/8	1310	790	1130	680	860	520	690	420
		3/4	1680	920	1350	740	960	530	770	430
		7/8	1940	1010	1470	760	1050	550	840	[illegible]

TABLE NO. 25-17-O—LAG SCREWS—LATERAL LOAD DESIGN VALUES WITH METAL SIDE PIECES UP TO 1/2 INCH THICK

Normal load duration, dry service conditions

Length of lag screw (inches)	Diameter of lag screw shank (inches)	Species Group (See Table No. 25-17-I)							
		GROUP I		GROUP II		GROUP III		GROUP IV	
		Total lateral load per lag screw in single shear (pounds)		Total lateral load per lag screw in single shear (pounds)		Total lateral load per lag screw in single shear (pounds)		Total lateral load per lag screw in single shear (pounds)	
		Parallel to grain	Perpendicular to grain	Parallel to grain	Perpendicular to grain	Parallel to grain	Perpendicular to grain	Parallel to grain	Perpendicular to grain
3″	1/4	240	190	210	160	160	120	130	100
	5/16	350	240	270	180	190	130	150	100
	3/8	420	250	320	190	230	140	180	110
	7/16	480	270	360	200	260	140	210	120
	1/2	540	280	400	210	290	150	230	120
	5/8	650	310	490	230	350	170	280	130
4″	1/4*	270	210	240	180	210	160	190	150
	5/16	410	280	350	240	290	200	230	160
	3/8	570	350	480	290	340	210	280	170
	7/16	730	410	550	310	390	220	310	180
	1/2	810	420	610	320	440	230	350	180
	5/8	980	470	740	360	530	250	430	200
5″	5/16	440	300	380	260	340	230	300	200
	3/8	620	380	530	320	470	290	380	230
	7/16	810	460	700	390	530	300	430	240
	1/2	1040	540	840	440	600	310	480	250
	5/8	1330	640	1010	480	720	350	580	280
	3/4	1550	680	1170	520	840	370	670	300

(Continued)

TABLE NO. 25-17-O—LAG SCREWS—LATERAL LOAD DESIGN VALUES WITH METAL SIDE PIECES UP TO 1/2 INCH THICK—(Continued)

Normal load duration, dry service conditions

Length of lag screw (inches)	Diameter of lag screw shank (inches)	Species Group (See Table No. 25-17-I)							
		GROUP I		GROUP II		GROUP III		GROUP IV	
		Total lateral load per lag screw in single shear (pounds)		Total lateral load per lag screw in single shear (pounds)		Total lateral load per lag screw in single shear (pounds)		Total lateral load per lag screw in single shear (pounds)	
		Parallel to grain	Perpendicular to grain	Parallel to grain	Perpendicular to grain	Parallel to grain	Perpendicular to grain	Parallel to grain	Perpendicular to grain
6″	5/16*	450	300	390	260	340	230	300	210
	3/8	630	390	550	330	490	300	430	260
	7/16	850	480	730	410	660	370	540	300
	1/2	1100	570	950	490	760	400	610	320
	5/8	1640	790	1290	620	920	440	740	350
	3/4	1990	870	1500	660	1070	470	860	380
7″	3/8*	640	390	560	340	500	300	440	270
	7/16	870	490	750	420	670	380	590	330
	1/2	1120	580	970	500	870	450	740	380
	5/8	1710	820	1480	710	1130	540	900	430
	3/4	2380	1050	1840	810	1310	580	1050	460
8″	7/16*	880	490	760	420	680	380	600	330
	1/2	1140	590	980	510	880	460	780	400
	5/8	1750	840	1510	720	1320	630	1060	510
	3/4	2470	1090	2130	940	1560	690	1250	550
	7/8	3260	1360	2480	1030	1770	740	1420	590
9″	1/2*	1150	600	990	510	890	460	780	410
	5/8	1770	850	1530	730	1370	660	1210	580
	3/4	2510	1100	2160	950	1790	790	1440	630
	7/8	3360	1400	2880	1200	2060	860	1650	690

10″	5/8*	1790	860	1550	740	1380	660	1220	590
	3/4	2550	1120	2200	970	1970	870	1630	720
	7/8	3430	1420	2960	1230	2340	970	1880	780
	1	4410	1770	3680	1470	2640	1050	2110	850
11″	3/4*	2570	1130	2220	980	1990	880	1750	770
	7/8	3470	1440	3000	1250	2620	1090	2100	870
	1	4490	1800	3880	1550	2960	1180	2370	950
12″	7/8	3490	1450	3020	1260	2700	1120	2320	960
	1	4520	1810	3900	1560	3260	1310	2620	1050
	1-1/8	5670	2270	4890	1960	3630	1450	2910	1170
13″	7/8*	3510	1460	3030	1260	2710	1130	2390	1000
	1	4550	1820	3930	1570	3520	1410	2870	1150
	1-1/8	5710	2280	4930	1970	3980	1590	3200	1280
14″	1	4570	1830	3950	1580	3530	1410	3110	1250
	1-1/8	5750	2300	4960	1980	4330	1730	3470	1390
	1-1/4	7030	2810	6070	2430	4750	1900	3810	1520
15″	1	4590	1830	3960	1580	3540	1420	3130	1250
	1-1/8	5770	2310	4990	1990	4460	1780	3750	1500
	1-1/4	7070	2830	6110	2440	5130	2050	4120	1650
16″	1*	4590	1830	3960	1580	3540	1420	3130	1250
	1-1/8*	5790	2320	5000	2000	4480	1790	3950	1580
	1-1/4*	7120	2850	6150	2460	5500	2200	4430	1770

*Greater lengths do not provide higher loads.

TABLE NO. 25-17-P

ROOF SLOPE	PERCENTAGE OF ALLOWABLE CONNECTOR VALUE TO BE USED
Less than 3 in 12	85 percent
3 in 12, less than 4 in 12	80 percent
4 in 12, less than 5 in 12	75 percent
5 in 12, to include 5½ in 12	70 percent
Greater than 5½ in 12	65 percent

TABLE NO. 25-17-Q—CONSTANTS FOR USE IN DETERMINING REQUIRED NET SECTION[1] IN SQUARE INCHES

DURATION OF LOADING	THICKNESS OF WOOD MEMBER IN INCHES	CONSTANTS FOR EACH CONNECTOR LOAD GROUP			
		GROUP A	GROUP B	GROUP C	GROUP D
Normal	4 inches or less	2350	2000	1650	1300
	Over 4 inches	1850	1600	1300	1050
Permanent	4 inches or less	2100	1800	1500	1200
	Over 4 inches	1700	1450	1200	950
Snow	4 inches or less	2700	2300	1900	1500
	Over 4 inches	2150	1850	1500	1200
Wind or earthquake	4 inches or less	3100	2650	2200	1750
	Over 4 inches	2500	2150	1750	1400

[1]For grouping of species, see Table No. 25-17-D.

TABLE NO. 25-17-R—FASTENER LOAD MODIFICATION FACTORS FOR MOISTURE CONTENT

Type of fastener	Condition of wood[1]		Factor
	At time of fabrication	In service	
Timber connectors[2]	Dry	Dry	1.0
	Partially seasoned[3]	Dry	See Note 3
	Wet	Dry	0.8
	Dry or wet	Partially seasoned or wet	0.67
Bolts or lag screws	Dry	Dry	1.0
	Partially seasoned[3] or wet	Dry	See Table No. 25-17-S
	Dry or wet	Exposed to weather	0.75
	Dry or wet	Wet	0.67
Drift bolts or pins - Laterally loaded	Dry or wet	Dry	1.0
	Dry or wet	Partially seasoned or wet, or subject to wetting and drying	0.70
Wire nails and spikes —Withdrawal loads	Dry	Dry	1.0
	Partially seasoned or wet	Will remain wet	1.0
	Partially seasoned or wet	Dry	0.25
	Dry	Subject to wetting and drying	0.25
—Lateral loads	Dry	Dry	1.0
	Partially seasoned or wet	Dry or wet	0.75
	Dry	Partially seasoned or wet	0.75
Threaded, hardened steel nails	Dry or wet	Dry or wet	1.0
Wood screws	Dry or wet	Dry	1.0
	Dry or wet	Exposed to weather	0.75
	Dry or wet	Wet	0.67
Metal plate connectors	Dry	Dry	1.0
	Partially seasoned or wet	Dry or wet	0.8

[1]Condition of wood definitions applicable to fasteners are:

"Dry" wood has a moisture content of 19 percent or less.

"Wet" wood has a moisture content at or above the fiber saturation point (approximately 30 percent).

"Partially seasoned" wood, for the purposes of this table, has a moisture content greater than 19 percent but less than the fiber saturation point (approximately 30 percent).

"Exposed to weather" implies that the wood may vary in moisture content from dry to partially seasoned, but is not expected to reach the fiber saturation point at times when the joint is under full design load.

"Subject to wetting and drying" implies that the wood may vary in moisture content from dry to partially seasoned or wet, or vice versa, with consequent effects on the tightness of the joint.

[2]For the timber connectors, moisture content limitations apply to a depth of 3/4 inch from the surface of the wood.

[3]When timber connectors, bolts or laterally loaded lag screws are installed in wood that is partially seasoned at the time of fabrication but that will be dry before full design load is applied, proportional intermediate values may be used.

TABLE NO. 25-17-S—MODIFICATION FACTORS FOR LATERALLY LOADED BOLTS AND LAG SCREWS IN TIMBER SEASONED IN PLACE

Factors apply when wood is at or above the fiber saturation point (wet) at time of fabrication but dries to a moisture content of 19 percent or less (dry) before full design load is applied. For wood partially seasoned when fabricated, adjusted intermediate values may be used.

Arrangement of bolts or lag screws	Type of splice plate	Modification factor
–One fastener only, or –Two or more fasteners placed in a single line parallel to grain, or –Fasteners placed in two or more lines parallel to grain with separate splice plates for each line	Wood or metal	1.0
–All other arrangements	Wood or metal	0.4

TABLE NO. 25-17-T—MINIMUM WEIGHT OF ZINC PER UNIT AREA OF UNCOATED WIRE SURFACE

WIRE DIAMETER[1] (in.)	COATING WEIGHT (oz./ft.^{2})[2]
0.035, 0.041	0.10
0.048 - 0.072	0.15
0.076	0.20
0.080	0.25
0.092 - 0.135	0.30
0.148 - 0.177	0.40
0.192	0.50
0.207 and larger	0.65

[1]Diameters, other than those shown above, are produced with zinc coating equivalent to those of the next smaller size.

[2]The coating weight for hot-dipped zinc-coated nails used in connection with treated wood foundations (see U.B.C. Standard No. 29-3) shall be at least 2.00 for the average of specimens tested and 1.70 for any individual specimen.

TABLE NO. 25-17-U—WOOD SIDE PLATE MODIFICATION FACTORS FOR CONNECTOR, BOLT AND LATERALLY LOADED LAG-SCREW JOINTS

A_1/A_2	A_1 (in^2)†	Number of fasteners in a row										
		2	3	4	5	6	7	8	9	10	11	12
	<12	1.00	0.92	0.84	0.76	0.68	0.61	0.55	0.49	0.43	0.38	0.34
	12 – 19	1.00	0.95	0.88	0.82	0.75	0.68	0.62	0.57	0.52	0.48	0.43
	>19 – 28	1.00	0.97	0.93	0.88	0.82	0.77	0.71	0.67	0.63	0.59	0.55
0.5	>28 – 40	1.00	0.98	0.96	0.92	0.87	0.83	0.79	0.75	0.71	0.69	0.66
*	>40 – 64	1.00	1.00	0.97	0.94	0.90	0.86	0.83	0.79	0.76	0.74	0.72
‡	>64	1.00	1.00	0.98	0.95	0.91	0.88	0.85	0.82	0.80	0.78	0.76
	<12	1.00	0.97	0.92	0.85	0.78	0.71	0.65	0.59	0.54	0.49	0.44
	12 – 19	1.00	0.98	0.94	0.89	0.84	0.78	0.72	0.66	0.61	0.56	0.51
	>19 – 28	1.00	1.00	0.97	0.93	0.89	0.85	0.80	0.76	0.72	0.68	0.64
1.0	>28 – 40	1.00	1.00	0.99	0.96	0.92	0.89	0.86	0.83	0.80	0.78	0.75
*	>40 – 64	1.00	1.00	1.00	0.97	0.94	0.91	0.88	0.85	0.84	0.82	0.80
‡	>64	1.00	1.00	1.00	0.99	0.96	0.93	0.91	0.88	0.87	0.86	0.85

Notes: 1. A_1 = cross-sectional area of main member(s) before boring or grooving.
2. A_2 = sum of the cross-sectional areas of side members before boring or grooving.

*When A_1/A_2 exceeds 1.0, use A_2/A_1.

†When A_1/A_2 exceeds 1.0, use A_2 instead of A_1.

‡For A_1/A_2 between 0 and 1.0, interpolate or extrapolate from the tabulated values.

TABLE NO. 25-17-V—METAL SIDE PLATE MODIFICATION FACTORS FOR CONNECTOR, BOLT AND LATERALLY LOADED LAG-SCREW JOINTS

A_1/A_2	A_1 (in^2)	Number of fasteners in a row										
		2	3	4	5	6	7	8	9	10	11	12
2–12	5 – 8	1.00	0.78	0.64	0.54	0.46	0.40	0.35	0.30	0.25	0.20	0.15
	> 8 - 16	1.00	0.85	0.73	0.63	0.54	0.48	0.42	0.38	0.34	0.30	0.26
	> 16 - 24	1.00	0.91	0.83	0.74	0.66	0.5[illegible]	0.53	0.48	0.43	0.38	0.33
	> 24 - 39	1.00	0.94	0.87	0.80	0.73	0.6[illegible]	0.61	0.56	0.51	0.46	0.42
	> 39 - 64	1.00	0.96	0.92	0.87	0.81	0.75	0.70	0.66	0.62	0.58	0.55
	> 64 - 119	1.00	0.98	0.95	0.91	0.87	0.82	0.78	0.75	0.72	0.69	0.66
	119 - 199	1.00	0.99	0.97	0.95	0.92	0.8[illegible]	0.86	0.84	0.81	0.79	0.78
12–18	17 – 24	1.00	0.94	0.88	0.81	0.74	0.67	0.61	0.55	0.49	0.43	0.37
	> 24 - 39	1.00	0.96	0.91	0.86	0.80	0.74	0.68	0.62	0.56	0.50	0.44
	> 39 - 64	1.00	0.98	0.94	0.90	0.85	0.80	0.75	0.70	0.67	0.62	0.58
	> 64 - 119	1.00	0.99	0.96	0.93	0.90	0.86	0.82	0.79	0.75	0.72	0.69
	>119 - 199	1.00	1.00	0.98	0.96	0.94	0.92	0.89	0.86	0.83	0.80	0.78
	200 or more	1.00	1.00	1.00	0.98	0.97	0.95	0.93	0.91	0.90	0.88	0.87
18–24	40 – 64	1.00	1.00	0.96	0.93	0.89	0.84	0.79	0.74	0.69	0.64	0.59
	> 64 - 119	1.00	1.00	0.97	0.94	0.92	0.89	0.86	0.83	0.80	0.76	0.73
	>119 - 199	1.00	1.00	0.99	0.98	0.96	0.94	0.92	0.90	0.88	0.86	0.85
	200 or more	1.00	1.00	1.00	1.00	0.98	0.96	0.95	0.93	0.92	0.92	0.91
24–30	40 – 64	1.00	0.98	0.94	0.90	0.85	0.80	0.74	0.69	0.65	0.61	0.58
	> 64 - 119	1.00	0.99	0.97	0.93	0.90	0.86	0.82	0.79	0.76	0.73	0.71
	>119 - 199	1.00	1.00	0.98	0.96	0.94	0.92	0.89	0.87	0.85	0.83	0.81
	200 or more	1.00	1.00	0.99	0.98	0.97	0.95	0.93	0.92	0.90	0.89	0.89
30–35	40 – 64	1.00	0.96	0.92	0.86	0.80	0.74	0.68	0.64	0.60	0.57	0.55
	>119 - 199	1.00	0.98	0.95	0.90	0.86	0.81	0.76	0.72	0.68	0.65	0.62
	> 64 - 119	1.00	0.99	0.97	0.95	0.92	0.88	0.85	0.82	0.80	0.78	0.77
	200 or more	1.00	1.00	0.98	0.97	0.95	0.93	0.90	0.89	0.87	0.86	0.85
35–42	40 – 64	1.00	0.95	0.89	0.82	0.75	0.69	0.63	0.58	0.53	0.49	0.46
	> 64 - 119	1.00	0.97	0.93	0.88	0.82	0.77	0.71	0.67	0.63	0.59	0.56
	>119 - 199	1.00	0.98	0.96	0.93	0.89	0.85	0.81	0.78	0.76	0.73	0.71
	200 or more	1.00	0.99	0.98	0.96	0.93	0.90	0.87	0.84	0.82	0.80	0.78

Notes: 1. A_1 = Cross-sectional area of main member before boring or grooving.
2. A_2 = Sum of cross-sectional areas of metal side plates before drilling.

TABLE NO. 25-17-W—FORMULAS FOR DETERMINING F'_c [1, 2, 3]

L'/d RATIO	VISUALLY GRADED LUMBER	MACHINE STRESS RATED LUMBER
$L'/d \leq 11$	$F'_c = F_c$	$F'_c = F_c$
$11 < L'/d < K$	$F'_c = F_c \left[1 - \frac{1}{3}\left(\frac{L'/d}{K}\right)^4\right]$ where $K = 0.671 \sqrt{\frac{E}{F_c}}$	$F'_c = F_c \left[1 - \frac{1}{3}\left(\frac{L'/d}{K}\right)^4\right]$ where $K = 0.792 \sqrt{\frac{E}{F_c}}$
$L'/d > K$	$F'_c = \frac{0.30E}{(L'/d)^2}$	$F'_c = \frac{0.418E}{(L'/d)^2}$

[1]See Table No. 25-17-X for L'.
[2]See U.B.C. Section 2507.
[3]Duration of load adjustment factors apply only to F_c. Values of F_c and E may be subject to other appropriate modifications for conditions of use or types of treatment. Calculated values F'_c are not subject to further adjustment for these conditions.

TABLE NO. 25-17-X—EFFECTIVE LENGTH IN BUCKLING

POSSIBLE CRITICAL *L'/d*			
MEMBER	EFFECTIVE DIMENSION *(d)*	EFFECTIVE BUCKLING LENGTH *(L')*	
Chords	*h*	1 or 2 panels	1.00 *L*
		3 or more panels	0.55 *L*
	b	L_p for top chord[1]	
		L_p for bottom chord[1]	
Webs	*h*	$0.8\,L_w$	

[1]Where sheathing or ceiling material is nailed directly to a compression chord, lateral support of the axis may be assumed to be continuous and $L'/d = L_p/b$ may be neglected.

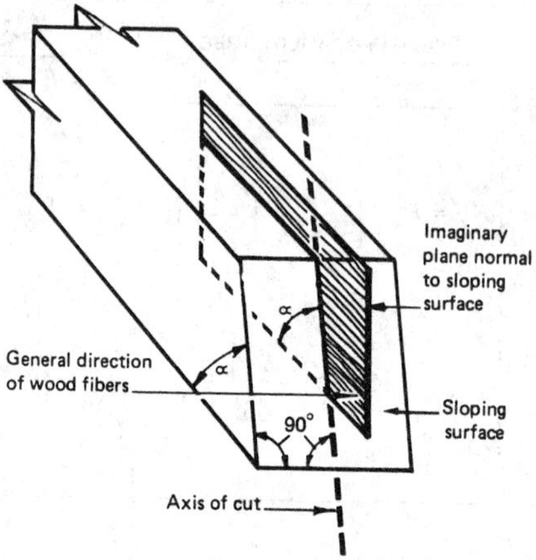
Imaginary
plane normal
to sloping
surface
General direction
of wood fibers
90°
Sloping
surface
Axis of cut

Figure No. 25-17-6

Axis of cut for symmetrical sloping end; cut at angle α

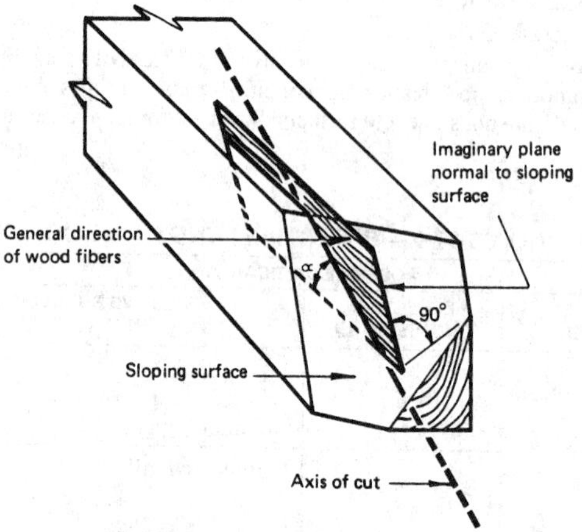
Imaginary plane
normal to sloping
surface
General direction
of wood fibers
90°
Sloping surface
Axis of cut

Figure No. 25-17-7

Axis of cut for asymmetrical compound sloped end cut.

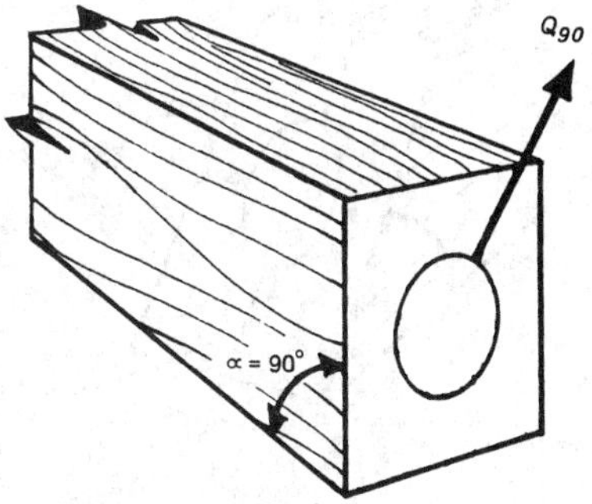
Q_{90}
α = 90°

Figure No. 25-17-8

Square-cut end, $\alpha = 90$ degrees

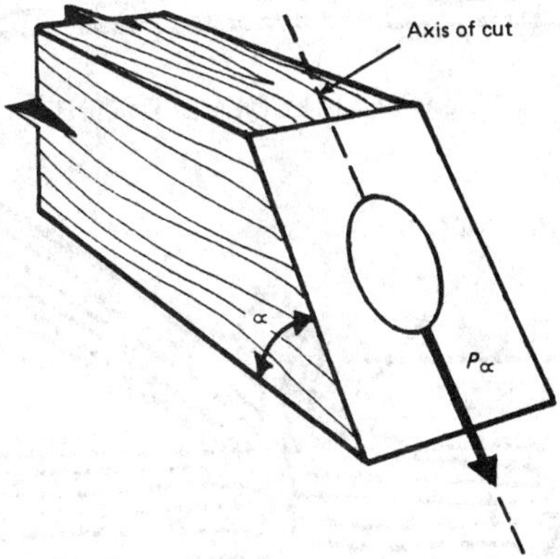
Axis of cut
α
P_α

Figure No. 25-17-9

Load parallel to axis of cut; $\Theta = 0$ degrees

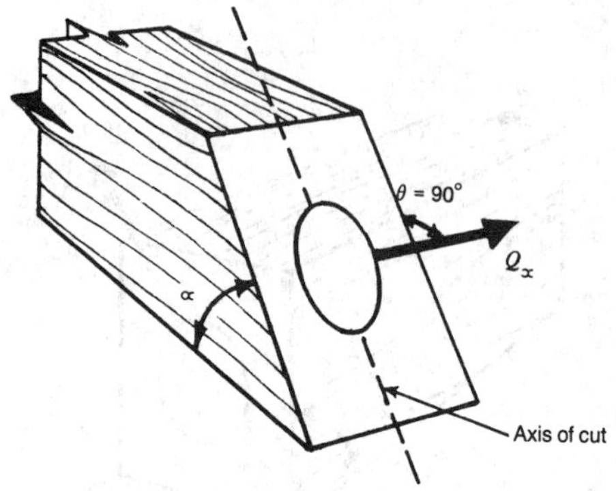
θ = 90°
Q_α
α
Axis of cut

FIGURE NO. 25-17-10

Load perpendicular to axis of cut; Θ = 90 degrees

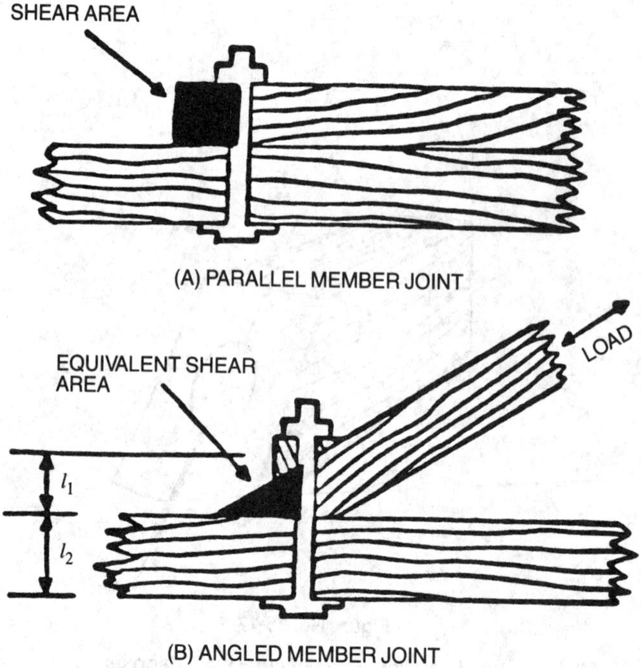
SHEAR AREA
(A) PARALLEL MEMBER JOINT
EQUIVALENT SHEAR AREA
LOAD
l_1
l_2
(B) ANGLED MEMBER JOINT

FIGURE NO. 25-17-11

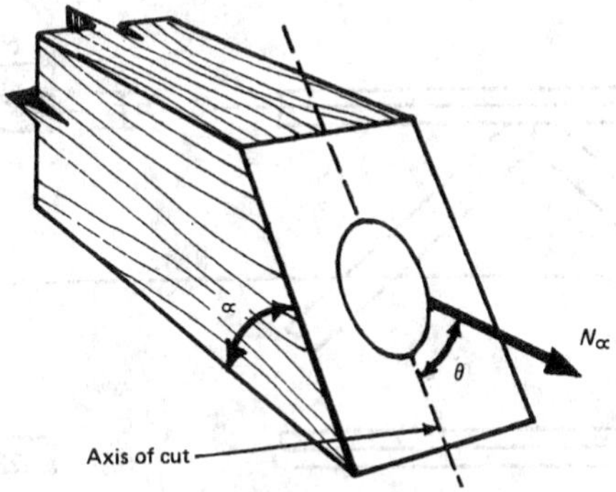
α
θ
Nα
Axis of cut

FIGURE NO. 25-17-12
Load at angle Θ to axis of cut.

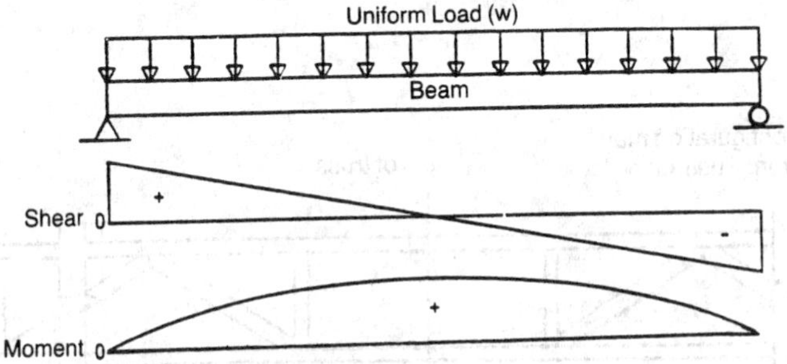
Uniform Load (w)
Beam
Shear 0
+
-
Moment 0
+

FIGURE NO. 25-17-13—SIGN CONVENTION FOR EQUIVALENT BEAM.

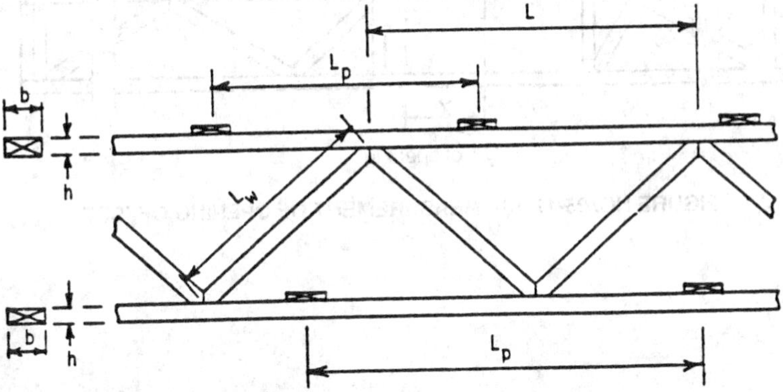
L
Lp
b
h
Lw
b
h
Lp

FIGURE NO. 25-17-14—DIMENSIONS USED TO DETERMINE *L′/d*.

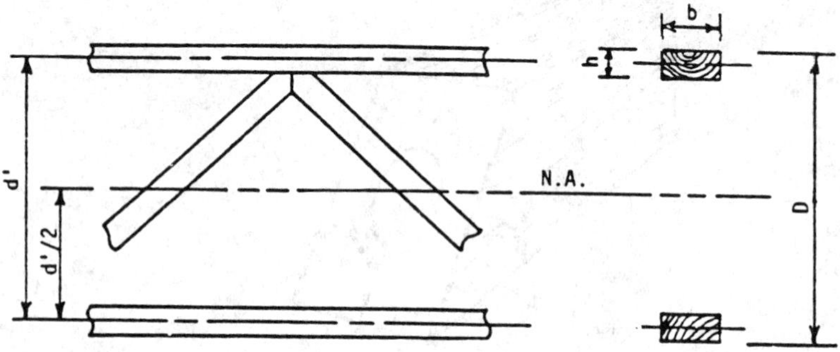
b
h
d'
N.A.
d'/2
D

FIGURE NO. 25-17-15—DIMENSIONS USED TO DETERMINE l_o.

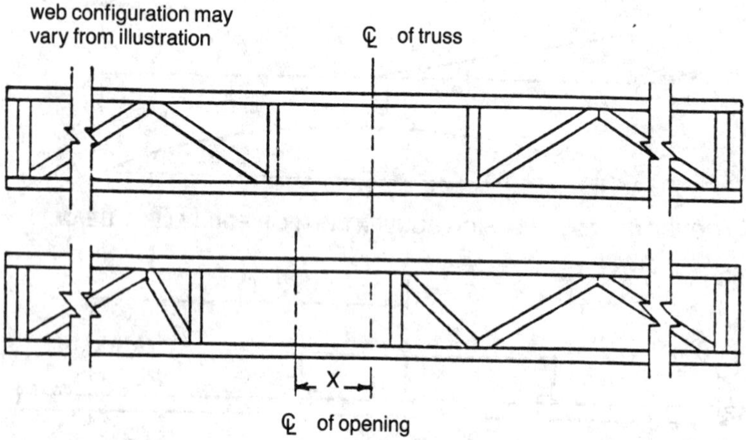
web configuration may
vary from illustration
℄ of truss
X
℄ of opening

FIGURE NO. 25-17-16—MEASUREMENT OF OPENING OFFSET.

UNIFORM BUILDING CODE STANDARD NO. 25-18

STRUCTURAL GLUED BUILT-UP MEMBERS— PLYWOOD COMPONENTS

Based on Design and Fabrication Specifications of American Plywood Association

See Sections 2501 (a) and 2512, Uniform Building Code

Part I—Plywood Stressed Skin Panels

Scope

Sec. 25.1801. This standard covers requirements for the design of plywood stressed skin panels as referred to in Section 2512 of the Uniform Building Code.

Definition

Sec. 25.1802. A panel with stressed covers, or a stressed skin panel, is one in which the covering acts integrally with the framing members to resist bending loads in proportion to its effective moment of inertia. It consists of several longitudinal framing members or ribs spaced by headers and covered on top alone or top and bottom with plywood panels.

Design

Sec. 25.1803. (a) **Spacing of Ribs.** The clear distance between ribs shall not exceed twice the basic spacing set forth in Table No. 25-18-A.

(b) **Skin Bending.** The stressed skin shall be capable of resisting bending stresses due to loads normal to the skin with allowance for direction of the face grain.

(c) **Determination of Section Properties.** For determination of bending stresses, the section properties shall be calculated considering that only the ribs or plies of the ribs and the plies in the stressed skin with grain parallel to the span of the ribs are effective. If the clear distance between ribs is less than the basic spacing "*b*" as set forth in Table No. 25-18-A, the effective width of the skin is equal to the full panel width. If the clear distance between ribs is greater than the basic spacing "*b*" the effective width of the skins equals the sum of the widths of the ribs in contact with the stressed skin plus a portion of the skin extending a distance equal to 0.5 "*b*" each side of each rib.

For determination of horizontal shear, rolling shear, deflection and splice stresses, the section properties shall be based on the gross section of all material having its grain parallel with the direction of the principal stress. The modulus of elasticity used to calculate deflection shall be based on the modulus of elasticity of the plywood stressed skins.

(d) **Method of Design.** Stressed skin panels shall be designed in accordance with accepted engineering formulas, without exceeding the allowable stresses specified in Section 25.1804.

(e) **Splices.** The stressed skin panels and ribs shall be continuous in the longitudinal direction, except where adequately spliced and designed in accordance with Section 25.1804.

Allowable Stresses

Sec. 25.1804. (a) **Panel Stresses.** 1. **Direct stress from bending.** The allowable working stresses in the stressed skin flanges shall not exceed the values set forth in Table No. 25-B of the Uniform Building Code for tension or compression when multiplied by the factor "*F*":

b = the clear distance between ribs in inches.

"b" = the basic spacing shown in Table No. 25-18-A in inches.

For $b/$ "b" equal or less than 0.5, F equals 1.

For $b/$ "b" greater than 0.5 and less than 1.0

$F = 0.67\,(2 - b/\text{"}b\text{"})$.

For $b/$ "b" equal or greater than 1.0 and not greater than 2.0

$F = 0.67$.

2. **Rolling shear.** The shear between interior ribs and plywood skin shall not exceed the values set forth in Table No. 25-B of the Uniform Building Code for rolling shear. The allowable working stresses shall be reduced 50 percent at exterior ribs. This reduction applies to exterior stringers whose clear distance to the panel edge is less than half the clear distance between stringers.

3. **Stress in plywood skin splices.** A. **Scarf-jointed splice in compression.** The allowable stress in the skin at the splice shall not exceed the values specified in Section 25.1804 (a) 1. The slope of the scarf shall not be steeper than one in five.

B. **Butt-jointed splice in compression.** Where a splice plate is installed on one side of the joint, the allowable stress in the skin at the splice shall not exceed the values specified in Section 25.1804 (a) 1, provided said values are reduced in proportion to the ratio of the width of the splice plate to the width of the stressed skin. The splice plate shall be at least equal in thickness and grade to the skin being spliced. The splice plate shall be centered over the joint with the face grain parallel to the face grain of the skin. The minimum length of the splice plate, measured parallel to the span, shall be not less than the values set forth in Table No. 25-18-B. Splice plates shall be preglued to the skins prior to assembly of the panel. No percentage reduction is taken for compressive stress.

C. **Scarf-jointed splice in tension.** The allowable stress in the skin at the splice shall not exceed the values specified in Section 25.1804 (a) 1. The slope of scarf shall not be steeper than 1 in 8.

D. **Butt-jointed splice in tension.** Where a splice plate is installed the allowable stress in the skin at the splice shall not exceed the values set forth in Table No. 25-18-C. The splice plate thickness, position, orientation to face grain, installation and length shall conform to Section 25.1804 (a) 3 B.

(b) **Rib or Longitudinal Stresses.** 1. **Bending.** Bending stresses shall not exceed the values set forth in Table No. 25-A-1 or No. 25-A-2 of the Uniform Building Code.

2. **Horizontal shear.** Horizontal shear shall not exceed the values set forth in Table No. 25-A-1 or No. 25-A-2 of the Uniform Building Code.

3. **Splices in ribs or longitudinal members.** Accurately fitted and well-glued scarf or finger joints are permitted provided the maximum stress in bending does not exceed the percentages of the basic flexural stress shown in Section 25.1003, Item No. 3, of U.B.C. Standard No. 25-10. In the finger joint, the portion of the joint occupied by the tips of the fingers at that cross section shall not be considered as effective. Finger joints and other nonstandard configurations of scarf joints may be prequalified in accordance with U.B.C. Standard No. 25-10. The effective slope of the joint shall be determined as shown in Section 25.1003.

Fabrication

Sec. 25.1805. The plywood stressed skins shall be fabricated in accordance with the procedures specified in Part V of this standard.

Part II—Plywood Curved Panels

Scope

Sec. 25.1806. This standard covers requirements for the design of plywood curved panels as referred to in Section 2512 of the Uniform Building Code. Fabrication procedure shall be in accordance with the requirements of Part V of this standard.

General Design

Sec. 25.1807. Curved panels may be designed as either curved flexural panels or arch panels. The curved flexural panels act as a simple beam, without developing horizontal thrust. Bearing details are designed accordingly, with provision for horizontal deflection. Tie rods are not required. Arch panels are stressed both in compression and in flexure. They exert horizontal thrust at the supports and therefore require tie rods or abutments.

Definition

Sec. 25.1808. Core Types. Curved plywood panels consist of full-length plywood faces top and bottom spaced by and joined with glue to a structural core capable of resisting the shearing forces. The core may consist of one or more layers of plywood, butt-jointed or full-length, glued over the full areas to the faces or spaced ribs constructed of single-piece or laminated plywood or lumber strips, spaced as required, either preglued or glued during panel assembly.

Allowable Stresses

Sec. 25.1809. (a) **Plywood Core.** The allowable working stresses in plywood core type of construction in flexure, compression and tension shall not exceed the values set forth in Table No. 25-C of the Uniform Building Code, and reduced for curvature by multiplication by the following curvature factor:

$$1 - 2000\left[\frac{t}{R}\right]^2$$

WHERE:

t = thickness, out-to-out of plies parallel with the stress, inches.

R = radius of curvature at center line of member, inches.

$\frac{t}{R}$ = shall not exceed 1/125.

(b) **Spaced Ribs.** The allowable working stresses in compression and tension shall be established as specified in Section 25.1809 (a). In addition, the allowable stresses shall be further reduced as for stressed skin panels as specified in Part I of this standard.

(c) **Radial Stresses.** The radial stresses induced by bending moment in a curved spaced rib or plywood core panel shall be computed by the formula:

$$S_R = \frac{3M}{2Rbh}$$

WHERE:

S_R = actual stress in a radial direction, pounds per square inch.

M = bending moment, in pounds, on a width of panel equal to the rib spacing.

R = radius of curvature at center line of member, inches.

b = width of stringer, inches.

h = overall height of panel, inches.

When M is in the direction tending to decrease curvature (increase the radius) the stress is in tension and S_R for plywood shall be limited to one half the values shown for rolling shear in the plane of the plies in Table No. 25-B of the Uniform Building Code. S_R for lumber ribs shall be limited to one third the values shown for horizontal shear in Table No. 25-A-1 of the

Uniform Building Code. When M is in the direction tending to increase curvature (decrease the radius) the stress is in compression and S_R for plywood shall be limited to the values shown for compression perpendicular to the grain in Table No. 25-B of the Uniform Building Code. S_R for lumber ribs shall be limited to the values shown for compression perpendicular to the grain in Table No. 25-A-1 or No. 25-A-2 of the Uniform Building Code.

Effective Cross Section

Sec. 25.1810. (a) **Direction of Grain.** All plywood and lumber having its grain parallel with the direction of stress shall be considered effective in resisting the stress, except for spaced-rib panels which should be as outlined in Part I of this standard.

(b) **Scarfed Plywood Joints.** The slope of scarfed joints shall not be steeper than one in eight in order to fully develop the strength of the plywood elements.

(c) **Glued-plywood Butt Joints With Splice Plates.** Butt joints with splice plates shall be designed in accordance with Part I of this standard. Splice plates shall be preglued to the skins prior to assembly of the panel.

(d) **Butt Joints Without Splice Plates.** The effective strength of solid plywood core panels and of laminated ribs in a spaced rib panel at a section containing a butt joint in any lamination shall be determined by ignoring the butted lamination and any other lamination containing a butt joint closer than 50 times the lamination thickness.

(e) **Deflection.** The deflection of curved panels containing butt joints in either the core or the faces may be based on the gross section of all material having its grain parallel with the direction of principal stress, provided all butt joints are staggered at least 10 times the lamination thickness.

Design of Curved Flexural Panels

Sec. 25.1811. Curved flexural panels shall be designed as simple beams in accordance with the applicable parts of this standard, with provisions to permit horizontal displacement at supports. The extent of this displacement shall be determined in accordance with accepted engineering practice.

Design of Arch Panels

Sec. 25.1812. (a) **General.** Arch panels shall be designed in accordance with this standard as arches which are subjected to combined bending and direct stress. Determination of vertical and horizontal reactions and maximum axial loads, moments and shears shall be based on accepted engineering practice.

(b) **Bending and Direct Stress.** Combined bending and direct stress shall be calculated by the formula:

$$\frac{P}{Ac} + \frac{M}{Sf} = lc = \frac{0.3E}{(l/d)^2}$$

WHERE:

P = direct force, pounds per foot width of arch.

M = moment, in inch-pounds per foot width of arch.

A = area in square inches of arch cross section per foot width of arch of plies with their grain parallel to the direction of the stress.

S = section modulus, inches cubed per foot width of arch, of plies with their grain parallel to the direction of the stress.

l = chord length in inches between points of zero moment.

d = thickness, out-to-out, of plies with their grain parallel to the direction of the stress in inches.

E = modulus of elasticity of skins in pounds per square inch.

c = allowable unit compressive stress in pounds per square inch, as indicated by the above formula but not to exceed the values in Tables No. 25-A-1 and No. 25-A-2 of the Uniform Building Code.

f = allowable stress in extreme fiber, pounds per square inch, tension or compression, modified by Sections 25.1809 (a) and 25.1804 (a) as applicable.

(c) **Shear Stresses.** Shear stresses shall be calculated by the following formula:

$$S = \frac{VQ}{Ib}$$

WHERE:

S = shear stress, pounds per square inch, either rolling shear in plywood, or horizontal shear in rib.

V = shear acting normal to the slope of the arch, pounds per foot of arch width, or per rib section.

Q = first moment about neutral axis of area of parallel grain material from panel face in to plane at which shear stress is to be calculated, inches cubed per foot width of arch panel, or per rib section.

I = moment of inertia of arch panel, inches to the fourth power, per foot width of arch panel, or per rib section.

b = width of rib, inches.

(b = 12 inches for solid plywood core panel.)

(d) **Connections.** Connections of panels to supporting members shall be with nails, lag screws, bolts, or other means adequate to resist the maximum horizontal thrust and uplift, as well as any shear developed by assumed diaphragm action.

(e) **Supports.** The horizontal members supporting arch panels shall be adequate to resist vertical and horizontal loads between supports without deflection sufficient to alter the design basis of the arch panels. Horizontal thrust shall be resisted by properly designed tie rods, struts or abutments.

Where tie rods are used to resist thrust, such rods or other effective means of resisting thrust shall be placed in all bays.

Where abutments are used at the outer edges of exterior bays, struts or other means of resisting thrust, such as shear walls, shall be placed in all bays. Spacing shall be as required by the interior panel supporting members. Such struts are required to provide for unbalanced loads when all bays are not equally loaded.

(f) **Buckling.** Adequate design provisions shall be provided to ensure stability against buckling due to axial and/or shear forces.

Part III—Plywood Beams

Scope

Sec. 25.1813. This standard covers requirements for design of plywood beams as referred to in Section 2512 of the Uniform Building Code.

Definition

Sec. 25.1814. Plywood beams are structural units consisting of one or more vertical plywood webs which are attached to lumber flanges. The lumber flanges carry the bending forces while the plywood webs transmit the shear. At intervals along the beam, stiffeners, inserted between the flanges and attached to the webs, serve to distribute concentrated loads and resist web buckling.

Flanges

Sec. 25.1815. (a) **Design.** 1. **Bending in symmetrical sections.** The allowable resisting moment for a symmetrical section shall not exceed the values established by the following formula:

$$M = \frac{2tI}{h}$$

WHERE:

M = resisting moment in inch-pounds.

t = allowable working stress in pounds per square inch in tension parallel to the grain of the flange lumber. Also see Section 25.1815 (a) 3 and 5.

I = net moment of inertia in inches to the fourth power of all the continuous parallel grain material in the flange and web section. Location of the neutral axis shall be calculated without considering butt joints.

h = depth of the beam in inches.

2. **Bending in unsymmetrical sections.** The allowable resisting moment for an unsymmetrical beam section shall not exceed the value established by the following formula:

$$M = \frac{fI}{Z}$$

WHERE:

M = resisting moment in inch-pounds.

f = allowable working stress in pounds per square inch. Note that the allowable working stress for the tension flange and compression flange corresponds to allowable values for t and c, respectively. Also see Section 25.1815 (a) 3 and 5.

I = net moment of inertia in inches to the fourth power of all continuous parallel grain material in the flange and web section.

Z = distance from the neutral axis to an outer flange fiber in inches. Location of the neutral axis shall be calculated without considering butt joints.

3. **Lateral support of compression flange.** The actual stress in the compression flange shall not exceed the allowable stress established by the following formula and in no case shall exceed the allowable unit stress for compression parallel to the grain:

$$\frac{P}{A} = \frac{.3E}{\left(\frac{L}{d}\right)^2}$$

WHERE:

P/A = allowable compression stress parallel to the grain in pounds per square inch.

E = modulus of elasticity in pounds per square inch (see Table No. 25-A-1 of the Uniform Building Code).

L = distance between lateral supports of the compression flange in inches.

d = width of the upper flange in inches.

Bracing elements and their connections providing restraint for the compression flange shall be capable of resisting a force F applied in a horizontal direction of not less than that established by the following formula:

$$F = .02\ A\ (c')\ \frac{L}{Lm}$$

WHERE:

F = force applied in a horizontal direction in pounds.

A = area of the compression flange in square inches.

c' = the allowable compressive stress or the actual stress in compression in pounds per square inch as governed by Section 25.1815 (a).

Lm = maximum permissible bracing for the actual stress.

When the member is not symmetrical about the vertical neutral axis, due consideration shall be taken in the design for adequate lateral restraint.

4. **Lateral stability of deep narrow beam.** The ratio I_x/I_y of the gross moment of inertia of all parallel grain material about the horizontal neutral axis to that about the vertical axis shall determine the type of bracing required as set forth in Table No. 25-18-D.

5. **Flange splices.** Scarf joints in tension and compression flanges may be assumed fully effective for the determination of moment of inertia. Scarf joints in adjacent laminations shall be spaced no closer than 16 times the lamination thickness, measured center to center, except that the spacing may be reduced to zero where the design indicates no bending stress.

Butt joints shall not be permitted in tension flanges except where the butted lamination is omitted in determination of the moment of inertia at that section. In addition, the moment of inertia shall be reduced at the above section where butted joints occur in adjacent laminations based upon the area reduction factors set forth in Table No. 25-18-E.

The allowable stress in tension flanges having butt joints shall not exceed 80 percent of the allowable code values. Compression flanges having butt joints shall be designed as required for tension flanges except that a reduction in stress is not required.

The allowable stress in flanges having finger joints shall not exceed 2200 pounds per square inch. The portion of the joint occupied by the tips of the fingers at the cross section shall not be considered as effective.

Approved finger joints based on the performance tests set forth in U.B.C. Standard No. 25-10, with the exception that the low test value be limited to twice the design stress, may be used in lieu of the preceding requirement.

(b) **Fabrication.** Flanges shall consist of one or more laminations of Douglas fir (Coast Region), West Coast hemlock or southern pine dry lumber not more than 2 inches thick which is stress-graded in accordance with U.B.C. Standard No. 25-3 or No. 25-6. Finger joints may be used in lieu of scarf joints. All provisions of U.B.C. Standard No. 25-3 are applicable except as further limited by Section 25.1815 (a) 5.

Plywood Webs

Sec. 25.1816. (a) **Design.** 1. **Horizontal shear.** The allowable shear on the plywood web shall not exceed the value established by the following formula:

$$V = \frac{vI\Sigma t}{Q}$$

WHERE:

V = allowable total shear on the section in pounds.

v = allowable plywood shear stress through the panel thickness in pounds per square inch. See Table No. 25-B of the Uniform Building Code and Section 25.1816 (a) 4.

I = total moment of inertia in inches to the fourth power about the neutral axis of all parallel grain material regardless of any butt joints.

Σt = total shear thickness of all webs at the section in inches.

Q = statical moment about the neutral axis of all parallel grain material regardless of any butt joints lying above (or below) the neutral axis in inches to the third power.

2. **Flange—web shear (rolling shear).** For beams having one or two webs, the allowable flange—web shear on pressure-glued or nail-glued systems shall not exceed the value established by the following formula:

$$V = \left(\frac{nsdI}{Q_{fl}}\right)$$

WHERE:

V = allowable total shear on the section in pounds.

n = number of contact surfaces between web and flange.

s = one half of the allowable plywood rolling shear stress in pounds per square inch as given in Table No. 25-B of the Uniform Building Code. Shear values shall not be assigned to the nails in the nail-glued systems.

d = depth of contact area between flange and plywood web in inches.

I = total moment of inertia about the neutral axis of all parallel grain material, regardless of any butt joints in inches to the fourth power.

Q_{fl} = statical moment about the neutral axis of all parallel grain material, regardless of any butt joints, in the upper (or lower) flanges in inches to the third power.

3. **Stiffeners for concentrated loads.** Stiffeners shall be placed over reactions and where other heavy concentrated loads occur. They shall fit tightly against the flanges and their attachment to the webs shall be capable of transmitting the concentrated load or reaction. The width of the stiffeners shall be equal to the lumber flange width at the section. Their dimension parallel to the beam span shall be not less than "w."

$$w = \frac{P}{c \perp b}$$

WHERE:

P = concentrated load or reaction in pounds.

b = flange width in inches.

$c\perp$ = allowable stress in compression perpendicular to grain for the flange lumber as set forth in Table No. 25-A-1 or No. 25-A-2 of the Uniform Building Code.

4. **Intermediate stiffeners to prevent web buckling.** Intermediate stiffeners shall be spaced not to exceed 48 inches on center. The width of the stiffeners shall be equal to the lumber flange width at the section and shall be of not less than 2-inch nominal dimensioned lumber.

In regions of high shear, where shear stress is 100 percent of values set forth in Table No. 25-A-2 of the Uniform Building Code, the spacing of the stiffeners specified above shall be reduced in accordance with Table No. 25-18-F.

Where the webs are stressed to less than 100 percent of the shear strength, the stiffener spacing b shall be calculated by the following formula, except that where the shear stress is

90 percent or less of the shear strength of the webs, the intermediate stiffeners may be spaced at 48 inches on center. In no case shall the spacing exceed 48 inches.

$$b' = b\left(1 + \frac{100 - p}{25}\right)$$

WHERE:

b = stiffener spacing in inches from Table No. 25-18-F.

p = actual percentage of allowable plywood shear stress existing at the section.

b' = actual stiffener spacing.

5. **Tapered beams.** Where the depth of the beam is tapered, the net vertical component of the direct forces in the flanges shall be added to or subtracted from the external shear to obtain the net shear acting at a section of web. This vertical component shall be calculated as follows:

$$P_r = \frac{M}{L_l}$$

WHERE:

P_v = vertical component of flange in pounds.

M = bending moment acting on section in inch-pounds.

L_l = distance from section to the intersection of the flange center lines in inches.

6. **Web splices.** Scarfed and butt end joints in plywood webs shall be designed in accordance with Part I of this standard. Joints subject to more than one type of stress or to stress reversal shall be designed for the most severe case. The slope of scarf joints, 1 in 8 or flatter, and splice plate lengths in Table No. 25-18-B of this standard are adequate to transmit 100 percent of the shear strength of the plywood webs being spliced, provided that the provisions of Section 25.1804 (a) 3 B of Part I of this standard, regarding splice plate thickness, grade and orientation, are adhered to.

All end joints in plywood webs shall be staggered at least 24 inches with intermediate stiffeners at each joint.

Part IV—Plywood Sandwich Panels

Scope

Sec. 25.1817. This standard covers requirements for the design of plywood sandwich panels as referred to in Section 2512 of the Uniform Building Code.

Definition

Sec. 25.1818. A structural sandwich panel is an assembly consisting of a lightweight core securely laminated between two relatively thin, strong facings. Axial compression forces are carried by compression in the facings, stabilized by the core material against buckling; bending moments are resisted by an internal couple composed of forces in the facings; shearing forces are resisted by the core.

General Design

Sec. 25.1819. (a) **Material.** For purposes of this standard, facings are assumed to be plywood meeting the requirements of U.B.C. Standard No. 25-9. Cores may be a variety of material, including polystyrene foams, polyurethane foams and paper honeycombs.

(b) **Bond Between Faces and Core.** Core may be glued to faces, or in the case of some foam materials, may adhere directly to the faces during expansion. In exterior wall panels, the bond shall be waterproof. The combination of core material and bond shall be such as not to creep excessively under the long-term loads and temperatures.

(c) **Trial Section.** A trial section of an exterior wall sandwich panel shall be determined as described below. It shall then be investigated for all possible modes of failure.

Faces and Cores

Sec. 25.1820. (a) **Plywood Faces.** The required parallel-grain plywood area shall be determined by the following formula:

$$A_1 + A_2 = \frac{P}{F_c}$$

WHERE:

A_1 = parallel-grain area of outside (top) skin in in.^{2}/ft. of width.

A_2 = parallel-grain area of inside (bottom) skin in in.^{2}/ft.

P = axial load in pounds per foot of panel width.

F_c = allowable compressive stress in parallel plies of plywood in pounds per square inch.

(b) **Core Thickness.** The minimum core thickness for structural purposes shall satisfy the following formula. In practice, core thickness is usually chosen on the basis of required insulating value.

$$S = \frac{M}{F_c} = \frac{A(h + c)^2}{4h}$$

WHERE:

S = section modulus of panel in in.^{3}/ft. of width.

M = maximum bending moment applied to panel, in lb.-in. per foot of panel width (for simply supported end conditions, $M = 1.5wL^2$).

w = normal loading in pounds per square foot.

L = panel span in feet.

A = parallel-grain area of skin in in.^{2}/ft. of panel width, $= A_1 = A_2$.

h = total panel thickness in inches.

C = core thickness in inches.

Analysis

Sec. 25.1821. (a) **Neutral Axis.** The location of the neutral axis for the panel shall be calculated from the following formula:

$$\bar{y} = \frac{A_1\left(h - \frac{t_1}{2}\right) + A_2\left(\frac{t_2}{2}\right)}{A_1 + A_2}$$

WHERE:

$\bar{y}$ = distance from bottom (or inside) of panel to neutral axis in inches.

t_1 = thickness of outside (top) skin in inches.

t_2 = thickness of inside (bottom) skin in inches.

(b) **Moment of Inertia and Section Modulus.** Moment of inertia and section modulus shall be calculated from the following formulas:

$$I = \frac{A_1A_2(h + c)^2}{4(A_1 + A_2)}$$

$$S_1 = \frac{I}{h - \bar{y}}, \quad S_2 = \frac{I}{\bar{y}}$$

WHERE:

I = panel moment of inertia in inches^4 per foot of width.

S_1 = section modulus calculated from the compression side of the panel, in in.^{3}.

S_2 = section modulus calculated from the tension side of the panel, in in.^{3}.

(c) **Column Buckling.** Allowable axial load shall be no larger than the value calculated from the following formula:

$$P_{cr} = \frac{\pi^2 EI}{(12L)^2\left[1 + \frac{\pi^2 EI}{(12L)^2 \times 6(h + c)G_c}\right]}$$

WHERE:

P_{cr} = theoretical column buckling load in pounds per foot of panel width.

E = modulus of elasticity of plywood in pounds per square inch. This value should include a 10 percent increase over published data to restore an allowance made when shear deflection is not computed separately.

G_c = modulus of rigidity of core in direction of span, in pounds per square inch.

(d) **Skin Buckling.** Stress tending to cause buckling of skin shall be no larger than that given in the following formula:

$$C_{cr} = 0.5\sqrt[3]{EE_cG_c}$$

WHERE:

C_{cr} = theoretical skin buckling stress in pounds per square inch.

E_c = modulus of elasticity of the core perpendicular to the skin, in pounds per square inch.

(e) **Deflection.** The maximum deflection shall conform to Table No. 23-D of the Uniform Building Code. Deflection shall be calculated according to the following formulas:

Deflection due to transverse loading only is equal to

$$\Delta = \Delta_b + \Delta_s = \frac{5wL^4 \times 1728}{384EI} + \frac{wL^2}{4(h + c)G_c}$$

WHERE:

Δ = total deflection in inches.

Δ_b = deflection due to loading.

Δ_s = deflection due to shear.

Total deflection including effects of axial load is approximately equal to:

$$\Delta_{max} = \frac{\Delta}{1 - P/P_{cr}}$$

WHERE:

Δ_{max} = Maximum deflection in inches.

(f) **Bending Stress.** Bending stress shall be calculated using the following formula. This stress includes the bending due to the axial load through the initial transverse load deflection.

$$f_{b\ max} = \frac{1.5wL^2 + P\Delta_{max}}{S_1}$$

WHERE:

$f_{b\ max}$ = applied bending stress in the facings.

(g) **Combined Stress.** Maximum combined stress will occur at midlength or midheight of the panel. It is the sum of the axial stress and the compressive bending stress in the concave side of the panel. It shall be calculated in accordance with the following formula:

$$f_{c\ max} = \frac{P}{A_1 + A_2} + f_{b\ max}$$

WHERE:

$f_{c\ max}$ = maximum combined stress in pounds per square inch (compression). This stress shall be less than F_c and less than $\frac{1}{3}C_{cr}$

(h) **Shear Stress.** Shear stress shall be computed by the formula:

$$f_v = \frac{wL}{(h + c)12} \leqq F_v$$

WHERE:

f_v = applied shear stress in the core, in pounds per square inch.

F_v = allowable shear stress in the core, in pounds per square inch.

Part V—Fabrication of Plywood Components

Scope

Sec. 25.1822. This standard applies to the fabrication of glued plywood-lumber structural assemblies such as stressed skin panels, curved panels, beams, etc., that have been designed in accordance with accepted engineering principles, including U.B.C. Standard No. 25-18, Parts I, II and III, for stressed skin panels, curved panels and beams.

Materials

Sec. 25.1823. (a) **Plywood.** 1. **General.** Plywood shall be as specified in the design and conform to U.B.C. Standard No. 25-9. Each original panel shall bear the grade-trademark of an approved independent inspection and testing agency.

2. **Type.** When the equilibrium moisture content of the member in use exceeds 16

percent or if any edge or surface of the plywood is permanently exposed to the weather, the plywood affected shall be exterior type. Otherwise, it may be interior type with exterior glue.

3. **Moisture content.** At time of gluing the plywood shall be conditioned to a moisture content of approximately that which it will attain in service, but shall be between 7 percent and 16 percent. Difference in average moisture content between panels glued to each other in any member shall not exceed 5 percent.

4. **Surface requirements.** Surfaces of plywood to be glued shall be clean and free from oil, dust, paper tape and other material which would be detrimental to satisfactory gluing.

Medium density overlaid surfaces shall not be relied on for a structural glue bond.

5. **Dimensional tolerances.** Scarfed panels of plywood shall be square, as measured on the diagonals, within ⅛ inch for a 4-foot-wide panel, and proportionately for other widths.

(b) **Lumber.** 1. **Grading.** Lumber shall be uniformly manufactured and shall be of the grade required by the design. Lumber shall be graded and grade marked in accordance with applicable U.B.C. Standards for the species to be used, except as modified herein.

When lumber is resawn, it shall be regraded and grade marked on the basis of the new size.

2. **Knotholes.** Knotholes to the same size as the sound and tight knots specified for the grade by applicable U.B.C. Standards may be permitted.

3. **Moisture content.** At time of gluing, the lumber shall be conditioned to a moisture content of approximately that which it will attain in service, but shall be between 7 percent and 16 percent.

The range of moisture content of the various pieces assembled into a single panel or flange of a beam shall not exceed 5 percent.

4. **Surface requirements.** Surfaces of lumber to be glued shall be clean and free from oil, dust and other foreign matter which would be detrimental to satisfactory gluing.

Each piece of lumber shall be machine finished, but not sanded, to a smooth surface with a maximum allowable variation of 1/64 inch in the surface to be glued.

Warp, twist, cup or other characteristics which would prevent intimate contact of adjacent glued surfaces shall not be permitted.

5. **Flanges.** Lumber for laminated flanges of beams and ribs for curved panels shall conform with the applicable requirements of U.B.C. Standard No. 25-10 regardless of the number of laminations.

6. **Transverse members.** Lumber for headers, blocking and stiffeners shall be of minimum 2-inch nominal thickness and Standard Grade or higher Douglas fir or West Coast hemlock or equal.

(c) **Glue.** 1. **General.** Mixing, spreading, storage life, pot life and working life, and assembly time and temperature shall be in accordance with the manufacturer's recommendations.

2. **Interior type.** When the equilibrium moisture content of the member in use does not exceed 16 percent, glue may be casein type, containing a mold inhibitor, and conforming with U.B.C. Standard No. 25-19, Part I, Type II.

3. **Exterior type.** When the equilibrium moisture content of the member in use exceeds 16 percent, glue shall be of a phenol, resorcinol or melamine base and conform with U.B.C. Standard No. 25-19.

Fabrication

Sec. 25.1824. (a) **General.** Units may be assembled in a one-step process using either nail-gluing or mechanical pressure including pressure from clamps, presses, or other reasonably uniform measurable pressure, externally applied, to attach the plywood to the framing. If the unit is longer than available lengths of plywood, the skins and webs shall be spliced to full length, either with scarf joints, or butt joints with glued splice plates. Flange laminations of beams having glue lines parallel to the web may be glued at the same time as webs or preassembled. In either case, the laminating shall conform to the applicable requirements of U.B.C. Standard No. 25-10.

If more than one unit is pressed at a time, care shall be taken to prevent distortion of any core material used in the assembly.

All cutouts for openings shall be reinforced as required in the design.

(b) **Surfacing.** The edges of framing members to which plywood skins or webs are to be glued shall be surfaced prior to assembly so that the members have a maximum variation in surface of $1/64$ inch and $1/32$ inch in depth for all framing members (allowing for actual thickness of any splice plates superimposed on blocking). This variation in depth shall apply to each framing member, as well as to the entire group of framing members within a unit.

Stiffeners for glued beams shall be surfaced prior to gluing so that their surfaces are flush with those of the flanges within $1/32$ inch, allowing for any superimposed plywood splice plates.

For glued beams, flanges at all stiffener locations shall have a maximum deviation from square of $1/16$ inch in 6 inches, measured perpendicular to an accurate square gage. Twist or bow which would prevent intimate contact of webs, or would cause the beam to deform, shall not be permitted.

Surfaces of high density overlaid plywood to be glued shall be roughened, as by a light sanding, before gluing.

(c) **Glued Joints.** Plywood skins and webs shall be glued to all framing members over their full contact area, except that solid core curved panels may have the width and spacing of the contact area specified in the design.

All splice plates at butt joints in plywood skins and webs and all scarfed end joints shall be glued over their full contact area. Scarf joints shall be glued, under pressure, and those plywood surfaces in contact with the framing members shall be sanded smooth with tape removed prior to assembly.

(d) **End Joints in Lumber.** 1. **General.** End joints in stringers, ribs and flange material, including shims shall be as specified in the design for the grade and stress used.

2. **Scarf joints.** Scarf joints in the lumber flanges shall be well scattered throughout. Unless otherwise specified, in adjoining laminations they shall be spaced not closer than 16 times the lamination thickness, measured from center to center. If shown on the approved plans this spacing may be decreased to zero where the design indicates no bending stress. In flanges of three or less laminations, only one scarf joint shall be allowed at any one cross section; in flanges of four or more laminations, two scarf joints shall be allowed at the same cross section. Scarf slopes shall not be steeper than 1 in 10 unless otherwise permitted by the design.

3. **Butt joints.** Stringer, rib and flange laminations shall not be butt jointed unless specified in the design. If permitted and not otherwise stipulated in the design, they shall be spaced at least 30 times the lamination thickness in adjoining (actually touching) laminations, and at least 10 times the lamination thickness in nonadjoining laminations.

(e) **End Joints in Plywood.** 1. **Scarf joints.** When a skin or web is composed of panels less than full length, end joints shall be scarfed and glued, unless butt joints with plywood splice plates are permitted by the design. Slope of scarf joints shall not be steeper than 1 in 8.

2. **Butt joints in skins of panels.** Butt joints shall be backed with plywood splice plates glued to one side of the skin. For ribbed panels, when glued during panel assembly the splice plate shall be backed with one or more pieces of lumber blocking, accurately

machined in width so as to obtain adequate pressure. Lumber blocking by itself shall not be used for splicing skins unless shown on the approved plans.

Splice plates shall be centered over the butt joint, and shall have their grain parallel with that of the skin. Plates shall extend to within ¼ inch of the ribs; the latter shall not be notched to receive them, unless permitted by the design. Splice plates shall be at least equal in thickness to the skin, except that minimum thickness shall be ½ inch if nail- or staple-glued. Minimum splice plate lengths shall be as shown in Table No. 25-18-B.

Solid plywood core panels shall be scarf jointed to length if so specified by the design. If designated on the approved plans, joints in solid plywood core panels may be tightly butted, provided they will conform readily with the curvature of the surface. Spacing of butt joints shall be not less than 10 times the lamination thickness.

3. **Butt joints in webs of beams.** Butt joints shall be staggered at least 24 inches.

Splices at butt joints in webs shall be in accordance with the design. Unless otherwise noted in the design, at all web butt joints a plywood shear splice plate shall be centered over the joint and preglued prior to assembly. The plate shall extend to within ¼ inch of each flange on the inside of the beam, shall be at least equal in thickness to the web being spliced, of a length as specified on the approved plans, and shall have its grain parallel to that of the web. No splice plate shall consist of more than two pieces of plywood. Where the design provides for the stiffeners to act as the web splices, web butt joints shall be located over the center of the stiffener, within 1/16 inch, and webs shall be glued to the stiffener. The stiffener alone may be used as a splice plate when the web is 24 inches deep or less, and is no thicker than ⅜ inch, or carries no more shear than would be allowed on a ⅜-inch panel.

(f) **Stiffener Location for Beams.** Stiffeners shall be placed as shown on the approved plans, but in any case they shall be spaced not to exceed 4 feet on centers, and at reactions and other concentrated load joints.

Stiffeners shall be held in tight contact with the flanges by positive lateral pressure during fabrication.

(g) **Assembly.** Ribs, stringers, flanges and other framing members shall be assembled accurately and shall be square. Joints shall be made tight, and all framing members shall be of uniform thickness within 1/32 inch.

All gluing surfaces shall be flush within 1/32 inch.

Plywood may be lightly tacked to framing members so as to maintain alignment during pressing.

(h) **Tongue-and-groove Edge Joint.** Where a tongue-and-groove type edge joint for stressed skin and curved panels is specified (and not otherwise detailed), the longitudinal framing member forming the tongue shall be of at least 2-inch nominal thickness, set out ¾ inch from the plywood edge plus or minus 1/16 inch. Edges of the tongue shall be eased so as to leave a flat shoulder at least ⅜ inch wide. Any corresponding framing member forming the base of the groove shall be set back ¼ inch to 1 inch more than the amount by which the tongue protrudes. Abutting plywood edges may be chamfered. One face may be cut back 1/16 inch to provide a tight fit for the opposite face.

(i) **Nail- and Pressure-gluing.** Curved units shall be laminated over a form. Means shall be used that will provide close contact and substantially uniform pressure on panels and beams. Application of pressure or nailing may start at any point, but shall progress to an end or ends. Movement of the units shall not be permitted while the glue is setting.

Where clamping or other positive mechanical means are used, the pressure on the net framing area shall be sufficient to provide adequate contact and ensure good glue bond. Pressure shall be uniformly distributed by caul plates, beams or other effective means.

In place of mechanical pressure methods, nail-gluing may be used for bonding plywood to lumber and plywood to plywood, but shall not be used for bonding lumber to lumber.

Regardless of the method used, the resulting glue line must meet the required standards. Nails shall be at least 4d for plywood up to ⅜ inch thick, and 6d for ½-inch to ⅞-inch plywood, and 8d for 1-inch to 1⅛-inch plywood. Nails shall be spaced not to exceed 3 inches along the ribs for plywood through ⅜ inch, or 4 inches for plywood ½ inch and thicker, using one line for glue lines 2 inches wide or less, two lines for glue lines more than 2 inches wide and up to 4 inches wide, three lines for glue lines up to 10 inches wide and four lines for 12-inch-wide glue lines. (If shorter nail lengths are used in order to avoid penetrating the opposite face, spacing shall be decreased in proportion to actual penetration.)

Panels having solid plywood cores may be glued using staples or nails, following a schedule of demonstrated effectiveness, but in no case spaced farther apart than 6 inches both ways. Length of fasteners is limited by the available thickness of the laminations. Additional nailing, into temporary solid framing, may be required to provide close contact for adequate glue bonds.

In any case, it shall be the responsibility of the fabricator to produce a glue bond which meets or exceeds the requirements of this standard.

(j) **Insulation and Ventilation.** In hollow panels, insulating and vapor-barrier materials and ventilation provided as specified in the design shall be securely fastened in the assembly in such a way that they cannot interfere with the process of gluing the plywood skins to the framing members or with the ventilation pattern.

When specified, longitudinal sections shall be vented through blocking and headers on the cool side of the insulation. Provision shall be made to line up the ventholes in assembling panels, with a definite ventilation pattern leading to the outdoors. Framing members shall not be notched for ventilation, unless shown on the approved plans.

Identification

Sec. 25.1825. Each member shall be identified by the appropriate trademark of the approved independent inspection and testing agency, legibly applied so as to be clearly visible. If the strength of one surface of a beam or panel is different from the other, the top surface shall be identified.

Test Samples

Sec. 25.1826. When glue bond test samples are taken from a member and from trim, they shall be taken as cores approximately 2 inches in diameter, drilled perpendicular to the plane of the skins or webs, and no deeper than ¾ inch into any framing member. Samples at beam flanges shall be taken from the ends of the beams only. Centers of cores shall normally be located in the top corner of the beam at points within 2 inches from one edge and up to 6 inches from the other.

No samples shall be taken from the same skin or web closer together than 12 inches, except as detailed in Exception No. 2. Samples shall be taken at a distance from the panel ends not greater than the panel depth.

> **EXCEPTIONS:** 1. One sample may be taken from one of the outside longitudinal framing members, within the outer fourth points of the panel length, provided the framing member is notched no deeper than ½ inch below its edge. The other outside longitudinal framing member may be sampled similarly, but at the opposite end of the panel.
>
> 2. Two samples per butt joint at any one cross section may be taken from skin or web splice plates. They shall be located midway between longitudinal framing members, and shall be aligned longitudinally, one on each side of the butt joint.

Samples through beam web splice plates shall be taken within the middle half of the span, at the center line of the beam depth.

Where the core of curved panels consists of solid plywood or a solid core material, only one core shall be taken at any one cross section. Cross sections shall be no closer than 12 inches along the arc. Not more than four cores shall be taken from a 4-foot-wide panel, with a proportionate number limited to other widths. Ribs in such panels shall be sampled as required by this section, except that at ribs the core shall not extend more than ¾ inch into the rib.

Samples may be taken from other locations when approved by the building official.

Testing of Glued Joints

Sec. 25.1827. (a) **General.** This section shall govern all glued joints which have not been subjected to prior inspection and testing such as the glue line between plywood and lumber as contained in U.B.C. Standard No. 25-20. These joints shall be referred to as "secondary" glue lines. Glued joints subjected to prior testing such as those in plywood shall be referred to as "primary" glue lines. Before testing, specimens shall be allowed to cure.

All secondary glue line testing shall be performed by approved testing agencies. Test specimens containing localized defects permitted by the grade of the material involved shall be discarded.

(b) **Lumber-plywood Side Grain Combinations.** 1. **Selection of test samples.** Lumber-plywood side grain samples shall be taken from members selected at random. They shall consist of 2-inch-diameter core of adequate depth and location to yield sufficient material on both sides of the secondary glue line.

Members to be sampled shall be selected to include production variables such as different lots of material, glue batches, shifts and crews.

Trim may be acceptable in lieu of cores for sampling purposes if it is truly representative of the member.

2. **Dry shear strength testing.** Lumber and plywood side grain specimens shall be tested in a block shear tool with the load applied through a self-aligning seat to ensure uniform lateral distribution of the load. Rate of load application shall be 0.2 inch per minute. Ultimate load shall be read to the nearest 5 pounds and wood failure shall be determined to the nearest 5 percent.

3. **Durability testing.** A. **Interior.** This test method shall be used in all cases where the durability requirement for the completed component is Interior.

Lumber and plywood side grain specimens shall be submerged in water at room temperature for a period of four hours and then dried at a temperature between 100°F. and 105°F. for a period of 19 hours with sufficient air circulation in drying cabinet to lower moisture content of specimen to a maximum of 8 percent based on oven-dry weight. This test procedure shall be conducted through three cycles, unless all specimens have failed. All specimens shall be inspected after the first and third cycles and all failures recorded. Total continuous delamination 1 inch along the edge of the test specimen and ¼ inch deep shall be considered as failure.

B. Exterior. This test method shall be used where the test specimen contains exterior-type adhesives throughout and where the durability requirement for the completed component is Exterior.

Lumber and plywood specimens shall be cycled by one of the following methods:

(i) **Cold soak.** Test specimens shall be submerged in water at room temperature for 48 hours and then dried for eight hours at a temperature of 145°F. (plus or minus 5°F.), followed by two cycles of soaking for 16 hours and drying for eight hours under conditions described above. The specimens shall be soaked again for a period of 16 hours.

(ii) **Vacuum pressure.** Place the specimens in the pressure vessel and weight them down. Admit water at a temperature of 65°F. to 80°F. in sufficient quantity so that the specimens are completely submerged. Separate the specimens by stickers, wire screens or other means in such a manner that all end grain surfaces are freely exposed to the water. Draw a vacuum of

20 inches to 25 inches of mercury (at sea level) and hold for 30 minutes. Release the vacuum and apply a pressure of 40 plus or minus 5 pounds per square inch for two hours.

While still wet the specimens shall be tested in accordance with the method specified above in Section 25.1827 (b) 2.

4. **Performance requirements.** A. **General.** The minimum performance requirements for laboratory testing of all side grain glue joint specimens shall be as specified in this subsection. If two or more grain orientations are present in any one test run or combinations of test runs, an adjusted average shear stress performance requirement shall be computed by the weighted average method.

B. **Dry shear strength requirements.** The specimens shall have an average dry strength shear stress as set forth in Table No. 25-18-G.

C. **Interior durability requirement.** Ninety-five percent of all specimens shall pass the first cycle and 85 percent shall pass three cycles.

D. **Exterior durability requirement.** Eighty-five percent of more wood failure shall be required for the overall average. Ninety percent of all specimens tested shall show 60 percent or more wood failure, 80 percent of all specimens tested shall show 80 percent or more wood failure. Failure in any part of test specimen, except glue failure in the secondary glue bond tested, is wood failure.

(c) **Lumber End Joints.** 1. **General.** Plain scarf joints and finger joints shall be tested in accordance with the provisions of U.B.C. Standards No. 25-20 and No. 25-23.

2. **Selection of test samples.** Test samples shall be obtained from full size joints, or from scarf joints selected at random from routine production. The latter shall be taken from the center line of the lamination containing the scarf being sampled. No more than one sample shall be taken from any component cross section and scarf samples shall be not closer than 4 feet.

3. **Dry tension testing.** Specimens shall be tested in accordance with U.B.C. Standard No. 25-23.

4. **Durability testing.** A. **Interior.** Test specimens shall be submerged in water at room temperature for a period of four hours and then dried at a temperature between 100°F. and 105°F. for a period of 19 hours with sufficient air circulation in drying cabinet to lower moisture content of specimen to a maximum of 8 percent based on oven-dry weight. This test procedure shall be conducted through three cycles, unless all specimens have failed.

The specimens then shall be tested dry in accordance with U.B.C. Standard No. 25-23.

B. **Exterior.** Test specimens shall be cycled by one of the following methods:

(i) **Cold soak.** Test specimens shall be submerged in water at room temperature for 48 hours and then dried for eight hours at a temperature of 145°F. (plus or minus 5°F.), followed by two cycles of soaking for 16 hours and drying for eight hours under conditions described above. The specimens shall be soaked again for a period of 16 hours.

(ii) **Vacuum pressure.** Place the specimens in the pressure vessel and weight them down. Admit water at a temperature of 65°F. to 80°F. in sufficient quantity so that the specimens are completely submerged. Separate the specimens by stickers, wire screens, or other means in such a manner that all end grain surfaces are freely exposed to the water. Draw a vacuum of 20 inches to 25 inches of mercury (at sea level) and hold for 30 minutes. Release the vacuum and apply a pressure of 40 plus or minus 5 pounds per square inch for two hours.

The specimens shall be then tested wet in accordance with U.B.C. Standard No. 25-23.

5. **Performance requirements.** A. **General.** The minimum performance requirements for laboratory testing of all lumber end joint specimens shall be as specified in this subsection.

B. **Dry tension stress requirements.** The test specimens shall have the tension stresses set forth in Table No. 25-18-H. No test value shall be less than twice the normal allowable stress.

Dry tension wood failure requirements regardless of species shall average not less than 80 percent except tests averaging at least 10,000 pounds per square inch in tension shall have not less than 70 percent. The minimum requirement for 90 percent of the individual specimens shall be not less than 40 percent wood failure.

C. **Interior durability requirement.** Average wood failure shall be not less than 70 percent.

D. **Exterior durability requirement.** Average wood failure shall be not less than 85 percent and the minimum requirement for 90 percent of the individual specimens shall be not less than 50 percent.

(d) **Plywood End Joints.** 1. **General.** Plain plywood scarf joints shall be tested in accordance with the provisions of this subsection. Splice butt joints shall be tested as specified in Subsection 25.1827 (b).

2. **Selection of test samples.** Full width scarfs shall be selected at random from routine production. A minimum of 2 percent of the scarfs produced shall be sampled. At least 20 specimens suitable for testing shall be obtained from each 4 feet of scarf. They shall be equally distributed across the width.

3. **Dry tension.** Specimens shall be tested in a tension machine equipped with wedge-type grips. Dry tension specimens shall be loaded at a rate of 0.4 inch per minute. Ultimate load shall be read to the nearest 5 pounds and wood failure on the joined surface estimated to the nearest 5 percent. Wood failure shall be estimated on the scarf surface of the plies parallel to the direction of the tension load.

4. **Durability.** A. **Interior.** Interior durability test specimens shall be submerged in water at room temperature for a period of four hours and then dried at a temperature between 100°F. and 105°F. for a period of 19 hours with sufficient air circulation in drying cabinet to lower moisture content of specimen to a maximum of 8 percent based on oven-dry weight. This test procedure shall be conducted through three cycles, unless all specimens have failed. Test specimens showing delamination on the face or end in excess of 1/16 inch deep and 1/2 inch long at the scarf glue line shall be considered as failing.

B. **Exterior.** Exterior durability test specimens shall be cycled by one of the following methods:

(i) **Cold soak.** Test specimens shall be submerged in water at room temperature for 48 hours and then dried for eight hours at a temperature of 145°F. (plus or minus 5°F.), followed by two cycles of soaking for 16 hours and drying for eight hours under conditions described above. The specimens shall be soaked again for a period of 16 hours.

(ii) **Vacuum pressure.** Place the specimens in the pressure vessel and weight them down. Admit water at a temperature of 65°F. to 80°F. in sufficient quantity so that the specimens are completely submerged. Separate the specimens by stickers, wire screens, or other means in such a manner that all end grain surfaces are freely exposed to the water. Draw a vacuum of 20 inches to 25 inches of mercury (at sea level) and hold for 30 minutes. Release the vacuum and apply a pressure of 40 plus or minus 5 pounds per square inch for two hours.

While still wet, the specimens shall be tested in a tension machine equipped with wedge-type grips. Dry tension specimens shall be loaded at a rate of 0.4 inch per minute. Ultimate load shall be read to the nearest 5 pounds and wood failure on the joined surface estimated to the nearest 5 percent.

5. **Performance requirements.** A. **General.** The minimum performance require-

ments for laboratory testing of all lumber end joint specimens shall be as specified in this subsection.

B. **Dry tension stress.** The average tension stress for Group 1 shall be 4000 pounds per square inch; for Groups 2 and 3, 2800 pounds per square inch; and 2400 pounds per square inch for Group 4, all adjusted as required for inner ply species. Regardless of species, wood failure shall average not less than 80 percent and the minimum requirement for 90 percent of the individual test specimens shall be not less than 50 percent.

C. **Durability requirements.** 1. **Interior.** Ninety-five percent of all test specimens shall pass one cycle and 85 percent shall pass three cycles.

2. **Exterior.** Average wood failure shall be not less than 85 percent.

Part VI—All-plywood Beams

Scope

Sec. 25.1828. This part covers requirements for the design of all-plywood beams as referred to in Section 2512 of the Building Code.

Definition

Sec. 25.1829. All-plywood beams are staple-glued structural units consisting of one or more vertical layers of butt-jointed plywood for webs which resist both bending and shear forces. Plywood web splice plates located at web joints, and/or one or more vertical layers of butt-jointed plywood for flanges, may also be staple glued to the webs for added resistance to shear and bending forces, if necessary. Plywood web stiffeners are staple-glued to single-layer webs to distribute concentrated loads and resist web buckling at end supports and interior concentrated load points. (For design of plywood beams consisting of plywood webs attached to lumber flanges, see Part III of this standard.)

Allowable Stresses

Sec. 25.1830. Allowable stresses for plywood used in all-plywood beams shall not exceed the values set forth in Table No. 25-B of the Building Code, except that allowable bending stress may be multiplied by 2 for five-ply, five-layer plywood, and by 1.7 for three-, four- or five-ply, three-layer plywood. Five-ply, five-layer plywood with butt-jointed center ply shall be considered as three-layer plywood for design purposes.

Design

Sec. 25.1831. (a) **Bending.** The allowable resisting moment for a beam section shall not exceed the value established by the following formula:

$$M = \frac{fI}{Z}$$

WHERE:

M = resisting moment in inch-pounds.

f = allowable working stress in bending for plywood, in pounds per square inch. Also, see Section 25.1830.

I = the minimum net moment of inertia, in inches to the fourth power, of all continuous parallel grain material at any beam section containing a web or flange butt joint. Location of the neutral axis shall be calculated without considering butt joints in the web of flanges (if used). Also, see Section 25.1833 (b). A web splice plate (if used) shall be included in the net amount of inertia only if directly glued to the web layer containing the butt joint.

Z = distance in inches from the neutral axis to the extreme fiber in bending.

(b) **Horizontal Shear.** The allowable shear on the plywood web shall not exceed the value established by the following formula:

$$V = \frac{vI\,\Sigma t}{Q}$$

WHERE:

V = allowable total shear on the section, in pounds. Loads may be disregarded that are located within a distance from the support equal to the beam depth.

v = allowable plywood shear stress through the panel thickness, in pounds per square inch.

I = total moment of inertia, in inches to the fourth power, of all parallel grain material in the web and flanges regardless of butt joints. Stiffeners or web splice plates shall be disregarded.

Σt = total shear thickness of continuous webs (and/or web splice plates and stiffeners, if applicable) at the neutral axis of the section, in inches. Also, see Section 25.1833 (b).

Q = statical moment about the neutral axis, in inches to the third power, of all parallel grain material in the web and flanges, regardless of butt joints, lying above (or below) the neutral axis. Stiffeners or web splice plates shall be disregarded.

(c) **Flange-web Shear (Rolling Shear).** For beams containing plywood flanges, the allowable flange-web shear on glued joints shall not exceed the value established by the following formula:

$$V = \frac{nsdI}{Q_{fl}}$$

WHERE:

V = allowable total shear on the section, in pounds. Loads may be disregarded that are located within a distance from the support equal to the beam depth.

n = number of contact surfaces between web and flange.

s = one half of the allowable plywood rolling shear stress, in pounds per square inch.

d = depth of contact area between flange and web, in inches.

I = total moment of inertia, in inches to the fourth power, of all parallel grain material in the web and flanges regardless of butt joint. Stiffeners or web splice plates shall be disregarded.

Q_{fl} = statical moment about the neutral axis, in inches to the third power, of all parallel grain material in the upper (or lower) flanges, regardless of butt joints.

(d) **Lateral Stability.** The compression edges of the beam shall be positively restrained from lateral buckling, as by fastening to structural panel sheathing, framing spaced no further than 24 inches on center, and/or by ceiling material.

(e) **Connections.** Bolts, lag screws or other similar large-diameter connectors shall not be used in web or flange tension areas where bending stresses exceed the allowable values set forth in Table No. 25-B of the Building Code.

Materials

Sec. 25.1832. (a) **Plywood.** Plywood shall be as required in Section 25.1823 (a). Plywood pieces cut 4 1/2 inches or less in width for flanges shall be visually inspected after cutting for size of knots. Pieces containing knots in face or back plies larger than two thirds of the flange width shall not be used in fabricating flanges for all-plywood beams.

(b) **Glue.** Glue shall be as specified in Section 25.1823 (c).

(c) **Staples.** Staples shall be 16 gage by 7/16-inch crown, made from galvanized steel wire. Staple length shall be 1/8 inch less than the total thickness of materials joined.

Fabrication

Sec. 25.1833. (a) **General.** Plywood beams shall be fabricated with glue and staples. Plywood face grain for webs, flanges, web splice plates and stiffeners shall be oriented parallel to the span (i.e., horizontally).

(b) **Web and Flange End Joints.** End joints in plywood webs and flanges shall be located as specified in the design. Joints in any web or flange lamination shall be spaced at least 24 inches from the nearest joint in any other lamination. In single-web beams, joints in webs shall be located at least 24 inches from any end or interior support.

Butt joints at ends of plywood web or flange pieces shall be trimmed square and tightly butted (maximum gap 1/32 inch).

(c) **Adhesive Application.** Adhesive shall be spread uniformly over the full contact area of mating web and/or flange surfaces.

If web or flange laminations are glued under pressure, such pressure shall be applied by clamping or other mechanical means. Pressure shall be sufficient to provide adequate contact and ensure good glue bonds (100 to 150 psi is suggested, unless otherwise specified by the adhesive manufacturer). Movement of the members shall be prevented until the adhesive develops sufficient handling strength as recommended by the adhesive manufacturer.

In any case, it shall be the responsibility of the fabricator to produce a glue bond which meets or exceeds applicable specifications.

(d) **Staple Installation.** Staples shall be installed with their crowns parallel to the plywood face-grain direction. Staple spacing shall be as shown in Figure No. 25-18-1.

Installation of staples may start at any point but shall progress to the end or ends of each piece. Pressure may be needed during stapling to flatten webs and flanges to ensure uniform contact between mating glued surfaces.

(e) **Web Splices.** Splices at butt joints in webs shall be as specified in the design. Butt joints shall be spliced with a plywood plate centered over the joint. The splice plate shall be glued over its full contact area and stapled to the web in accordance with Figure No. 25-18-1. The plate shall extend to at least 1/4 inch of each flange (if applicable); shall be equal in thickness to the web; shall be of a length as specified in the design or in Table No. 25-18-B; and shall have its face-grain direction parallel with that of the web. In multiple-layer webs, the splice plate shall be directly glued to the web containing the butt joint.

(f) **Web Stiffeners.** Stiffeners for single-layer webs shall be located as shown in the design, but in any case they shall be placed at end supports and at interior concentrated-load points.

The stiffeners shall consist of a plywood plate glued over its full contact area and stapled to the web in accordance with Figure No. 25-18-1. The plate shall extend to at least 1/4 inch of each flange (if applicable); shall be at least equal in thickness to the web; shall be of a length as specified in the design, but in no case less than 10 inches; and shall have its face-grain direction parallel with that of the web. The end or ends of the stiffener shall extend at least 6 inches beyond the edges of the support at the end and any interior supports.

Single-layer webs shall be reinforced at cutouts with a plywood web stiffener.

Identification

Sec. 25.1834. Each member shall be identified as specified in Section 25.1825.

Test Samples

Sec. 25.1835. Test samples shall be as specified in Section 25.1826.

Testing of Glued Joints

Sec. 25.1836. Plywood splice butt joints shall be tested as specified in Section 25.1827 (b).

FIGURE NO. 25-18-1—STAPLE SPACING FOR PLYWOOD WEBS, FLANGES, SPLICE PLATES AND STIFFENERS

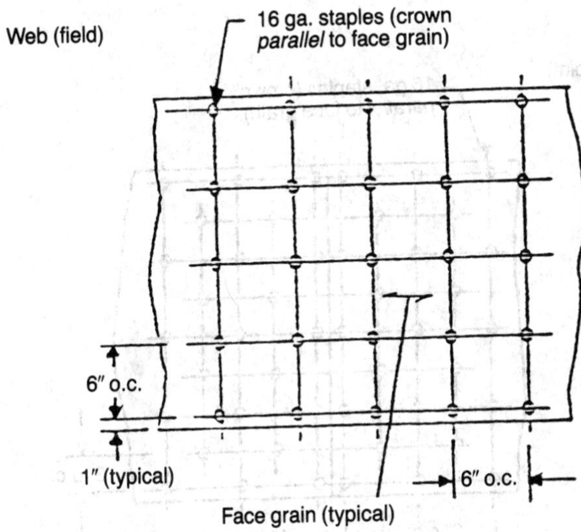
Web (field)
16 ga. staples (crown *parallel* to face grain)
6″ o.c.
1″ (typical)
6″ o.c.
Face grain (typical)

(Continued)

FIGURE NO. 25-18-1—(Continued)

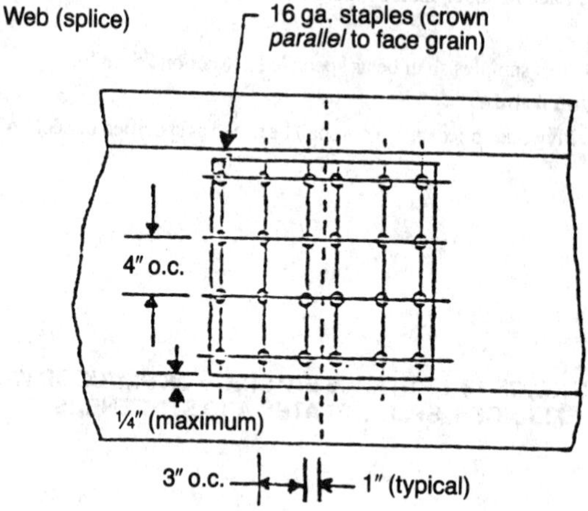
Web (splice)
16 ga. staples (crown *parallel* to face grain)
4″ o.c.
¼″ (maximum)
3″ o.c.
1″ (typical)

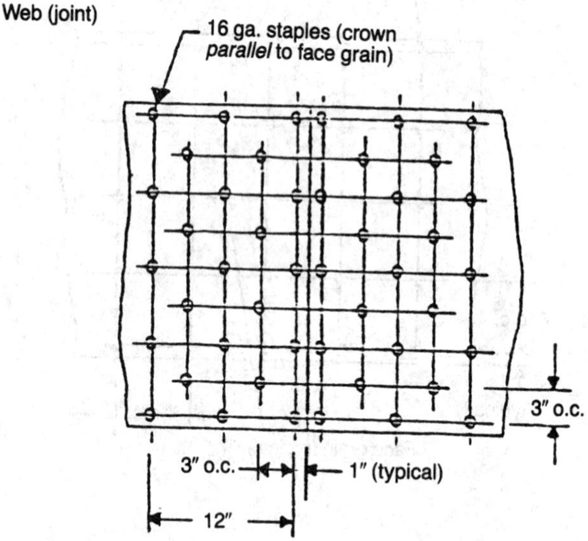
Web (joint)
16 ga. staples (crown *parallel* to face grain)
3″ o.c.
3″ o.c.
1″ (typical)
12″

FIGURE NO. 25-18-1—(Continued)

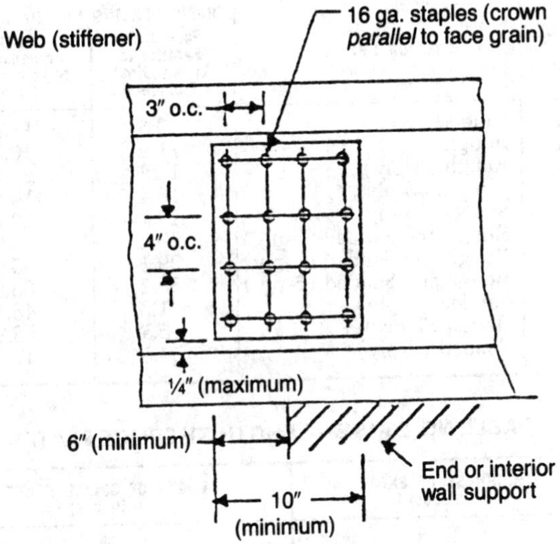
Web (stiffener)
16 ga. staples (crown *parallel* to face grain)
3″ o.c.
4″ o.c.
¼″ (maximum)
6″ (minimum)
End or interior wall support
10″ (minimum)

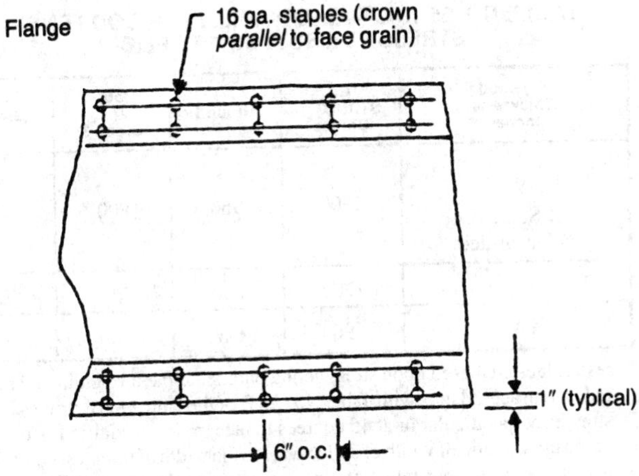
Flange
16 ga. staples (crown *parallel* to face grain)
1″ (typical)
6″ o.c.

TABLE NO. 25-18-A—BASIC SPACING

PLYWOOD THICKNESS (In Inches)	PLYWOOD FINISH	BASIC SPACING "b" (In Inches)	
		Face Grain Parallel to Longitudinal Members	Face Grain Perpendicular to Longitudinal Members
1/4	Sanded	10.3	11.6
5/16	Rough	11.9	16.8
3/8	Rough (3-ply)	14.2	20.1
3/8	Sanded (3-ply)	16.4	16.4
3/8	Sanded (5-ply)	18.1	20.2
1/2	Rough and Sanded (5-ply)	23.2	28.5
5/8	Rough and Sanded (5-ply)	29.1	35.6
3/4	Rough and Sanded (5-ply)	38.2	38.2
7/8	Sanded (7-ply)	41.6	48.1
1	Rough (7-ply)	45.5	58.9
1	Sanded (7-ply)	54.5	47.9

TABLE NO. 25-18-B—LENGTH OF SPLICE PLATES

THICKNESS OF SKIN (In Inches)	LENGTH OF SPLICE PLATE (In Inches)
1/4	6
5/16	8
3/8 (Sanded)	10
3/8 (Unsanded)	12
1/2	14
5/8	16
3/4	16

TABLE NO. 25-18-C—ALLOWABLE PLYWOOD TENSION STRESS FOR BUTT JOINT SPLICE[1]

Plywood Thickness (inches)	All STRUCT. I Grades	Group 1	Group 2 and Group 3	Group 4
1/4 5/16 3/8 Sanded 3/8 Unsanded	1200	960	800	720
1/2	1200	800	760	720
5/8 & 3/4	960	640	600	560

[1]These values are based upon stress acting parallel to the face grain and must be reduced in accordance with Table No. 25-B of the Uniform Building Code for stresses perpendicular or at 45 degrees to face grain. In addition, stresses are based upon a ratio of width of splice plate to the width of the stressed skin of 80 percent. Where other ratios are used, the allowable stress shall be adjusted accordingly. For applicable species groups for unsanded panels, refer to Footnote 1 of Table No. 25-B.

TABLE NO. 25-18-D—BRACING FOR DEEP NARROW BEAM

$\frac{I_x}{I_y}$	TYPE OF BRACING REQUIRED
Not more than 5	None required
More than 5 to not more than 10	Ends held in position at bottom flanges at supports
More than 10 to not more than 20	Ends held in position at top and bottom flanges at supports
More than 20 to not more than 30	Top or bottom flange continuously supported in accordance with Section 25.1815 (a) 3
More than 30 to not more than 40	Beam restrained by bridging or other bracing at not more than 8 feet on center
More than 40	Bridging at 8 feet on center and compression flanges continuously supported in accordance with Section 25.1815 (a) 3

TABLE NO. 25-18-E—AREA REDUCTION FACTORS

BUTT JOINT SPACING T = LAMINATION THICKNESS	PERCENT OF GROSS AREA OF ADJACENT LAMINATION EFFECTIVE
30T 20T	90 80
10T	60
Less than 10T	0

TABLE NO. 25-18-F—WEB STIFFENER SPACING

PLYWOOD WEB THICKNESS (In Inches)	CLEAR DISTANCE BETWEEN FLANGES (In Inches)					
	10	20	30	40	50	60 or More
3/8	15	15	15	15	15	15
1/2	27	22	22	22	22	22
5/8	48	29	28	28	28	28
3/4	48	38	35	34	34	34
7/8	48	48	41	39	39	39
1	48	48	48	48	46	45
1 3/16	48	48	48	48	48	48

TABLE NO. 25-18-G—DRY SHEAR STRENGTH STRESS REQUIREMENTS[1]

GRAIN ORIENTATION OF LUMBER OR PLYWOOD WITH RESPECT TO ADJACENT PLY OR LUMBER LAMINATION	AVERAGE SHEAR STRESS (Pounds per Square Inch)
(Douglas Fir and Southern Pine)	
Parallel	650
45°	500
Perpendicular	250
(Other Species)	
Parallel	520
45°	400
Perpendicular	200

[1]The minimum shear test value shall be not less than twice the normal allowable rolling shear value.

TABLE NO. 25-18-H—DRY TENSION STRESS

AVERAGE TENSION STRESS (In Pounds per Square Inch)	MINIMUM TENSION STRESS FOR AT LEAST 80 PERCENT OF SPECIMENS (In Pounds per Square Inch)
[Douglas Fir (Coast type) and Southern Pine]	
7000	6000
(Other Species)	
6000	5000

UNIFORM BUILDING CODE STANDARD NO. 25-21

SPAN TABLES FOR JOISTS AND RAFTERS

Specification Standard of the International Conference of Building Officials

See Section 2501 (a) and Tables Nos. 25-U-J-1, 25-U-J-6, 25-U-R-1, 25-U-R-2, 25-U-R-7, 25-U-R-8, 25-U-R-10, 25-U-R-11, 25-U-R-13 and 25-U-R-14, Uniform Building Code

Scope

Sec. 25.2101. This standard covers the loading (DL and LL) and deflection criteria used to establish the allowable spans in Tables Nos. 25-U-J-1 through 25-U-R-14 of the Uniform Building Code and the tables of this standard. The tables in this standard are intended for light-frame construction.

Design Criteria for Joists and Rafters

Sec. 25.2102. The allowable spans of tables of this standard and Tables Nos. 25-U-J-1 through 25-U-R-14 of Chapter 25 of the Uniform Building Code are calculated on the basis of a series of modulus of elasticity (E), and fiber stress (F_b) values. The range of values in the tables provides allowable spans for all species and grades of nominal 2-inch lumber customarily used in construction. The allowable span is the clear distance between supports. For sloping rafters the span is measured along the horizontal projection.

Lumber Stresses

Sec. 25.2103. The use of the span tables requires reference to the list of single or repetitive member bending stress values (F_b) and modulus of elasticity values (E) from Tables No. 25-A-1 and No. 25-A-2 of Chapter 25 of the Uniform Building Code.

Moisture Content

Sec. 25.2104. Tabulated spans are calculated on the basis of the dry sizes and are also applicable to the corresponding green sizes. The spans in these tables are intended for use in covered structures or where moisture content in use does not exceed 19 percent.

Lumber Size

Sec. 25.2105. Tabulated spans apply to surfaced (S4S) lumber having dimensions which conform to U.B.C. Standard No. 25-1.

Span Tables for Joists and Rafters

Sec. 25.2106. The following tables are based on the design criteria set forth in each table and of this standard.

DESIGN CRITERIA:
Deflection - For 40 pounds per square foot live load. Limited to span in inches divided by 360.
Strength - Live Load of 40 pounds per square foot plus dead load of 10 pounds per square foot determines the required fiber stress value.

TABLE NO. 25-21-J-1—FLOOR JOISTS 40 Pounds Per Square Foot Live Load

JOIST SIZE (Inches)	SPACING (Inches)	Modulus of Elasticity, *E*, in 1,000,000 psi																		
		0.4	0.5	0.6	0.7	0.8	0.9	1.0	1.1	1.2	1.3	1.4	1.5	1.6	1.7	1.8	1.9	2.0	2.2	2.4
2x6	12.0	6-9 450	7-3 520	7-9 590	8-2 660	8-6 720	8-10 780	9-2 830	9-6 890	9-9 940	10-0 990	10-3 1040	10-6 1090	10-9 1140	10-11 1190	11-2 1230	11-4 1280	11-7 1320	11-11 1410	12-3 1490
	13.7	6-6 470	7-0 550	7-5 620	7-9 690	8-2 750	8-6 810	8-9 870	9-1 930	9-4 980	9-7 1040	9-10 1090	10-0 1140	10-3 1190	10-6 1240	10-8 1290	10-10 1340	11-1 1380	11-5 1470	11-9 1560
	16.0	6-2 500	6-7 580	7-0 650	7-5 720	7-9 790	8-0 860	8-4 920	8-7 980	8-10 1040	9-1 1090	9-4 1150	9-6 1200	9-9 1250	9-11 1310	10-2 1360	10-4 1410	10-6 1460	10-10 1550	11-2 1640
	19.2	5-9 530	6-3 610	6-7 690	7-0 770	7-3 840	7-7 910	7-10 970	8-1 1040	8-4 1100	8-7 1160	8-9 1220	9-0 1280	9-2 1330	9-4 1390	9-6 1440	9-8 1500	9-10 1550	10-2 1650	10-6 1750
	24.0	5-4 570	5-9 660	6-2 750	6-6 830	6-9 900	7-0 980	7-3 1050	7-6 1120	7-9 1190	7-11 1250	8-2 1310	8-4 1380	8-6 1440	8-8 1500	8-10 1550	9-0 1610	9-2 1670	9-6 1780	9-9 1880
	32.0					6-2 1010	6-5 1090	6-7 1150	6-10 1230	7-0 1300	7-3 1390	7-5 1450	7-7 1520	7-9 1590	7-11 1660	8-0 1690	8-2 1760	8-4 1840	8-7 1950	8-10 2060
2x8	12.0	8-11 450	9-7 520	10-2 590	10-9 660	11-3 720	11-8 780	12-1 830	12-6 890	12-10 940	13-2 990	13-6 1040	13-10 1090	14-2 1140	14-5 1190	14-8 1230	15-0 1280	15-3 1320	15-9 1410	16-2 1490
	13.7	8-6 470	9-2 550	9-9 620	10-3 690	10-9 750	11-2 810	11-7 870	11-11 930	12-3 980	12-7 1040	12-11 1090	13-3 1140	13-6 1190	13-10 1240	14-1 1290	14-4 1340	14-7 1380	15-0 1470	15-6 1560
	16.0	8-1 500	8-9 580	9-3 650	9-9 720	10-2 790	10-7 850	11-0 920	11-4 980	11-8 1040	12-0 1090	12-3 1150	12-7 1200	12-10 1250	13-1 1310	13-4 1360	13-7 1410	13-10 1460	14-3 1550	14-8 1640
	19.2	7-7 530	8-2 610	8-9 690	9-2 770	9-7 840	10-0 910	10-4 970	10-8 1040	11-0 1100	11-3 1160	11-7 1220	11-10 1280	12-1 1330	12-4 1390	12-7 1440	12-10 1500	13-0 1550	13-5 1650	13-10 1750
	24.0	7-1 570	7-7 660	8-1 750	8-6 830	8-11 900	9-3 980	9-7 1050	9-11 1120	10-2 1190	10-6 1250	10-9 1310	11-0 1380	11-3 1440	11-5 1500	11-8 1550	11-11 1610	12-1 1670	12-6 1780	12-10 1880
	32.0					8-1 990	8-5 1080	8-9 1170	9-0 1230	9-3 1300	9-6 1370	9-9 1450	10-0 1520	10-2 1570	10-5 1650	10-7 1700	10-10 1790	11-0 1840	11-4 1950	11-8 2070

JOIST SIZE (IN)	SPACING (IN)	Modulus of Elasticity, E, in 1,000,000 psi																		
		0.4	0.5	0.6	0.7	0.8	0.9	1.0	1.1	1.2	1.3	1.4	1.5	1.6	1.7	1.8	1.9	2.0	2.2	2.4
2x10	12.0	11-4 450	12-3 520	13-0 590	13-8 660	14-4 720	14-11 780	15-5 830	15-11 890	16-5 940	16-10 990	17-3 1040	17-8 1090	18-0 1140	18-5 1190	18-9 1230	19-1 1280	19-5 1320	20-1 1410	20-8 1490
	13.7	10-10 470	11-8 550	12-5 620	13-1 690	13-8 750	14-3 810	14-9 870	15-3 930	15-8 980	16-1 1040	16-6 1090	16-11 1140	17-3 1190	17-7 1240	17-11 1290	18-3 1340	18-7 1380	19-2 1470	19-9 1560
	16.0	10-4 500	11-1 580	11-10 650	12-5 720	13-0 790	13-6 850	14-0 920	14-6 980	14-11 1040	15-3 1090	15-8 1150	16-0 1200	16-5 1250	16-9 1310	17-0 1360	17-4 1410	17-8 1460	18-3 1550	18-9 1640
	19.2	9-9 530	10-6 610	11-1 690	11-8 770	12-3 840	12-9 910	13-2 970	13-7 1040	14-0 1100	14-5 1160	14-9 1220	15-1 1280	15-5 1330	15-9 1390	16-0 1440	16-4 1500	16-7 1550	17-2 1650	17-8 1750
	24.0	9-0 570	9-9 660	10-4 750	10-10 830	11-4 900	11-10 980	12-3 1050	12-8 1120	13-0 1190	13-4 1250	13-8 1310	14-0 1380	14-4 1440	14-7 1500	14-11 1550	15-2 1610	15-5 1670	15-11 1780	16-5 1880
	32.0					10-4 1000	10-9 1080	11-1 1150	11-6 1240	11-10 1310	12-2 1380	12-5 1440	12-9 1520	13-0 1580	13-3 1640	13-6 1700	13-9 1770	14-0 1830	14-6 1970	14-11 2080
2x12	12.0	13-10 450	14-11 520	15-10 590	16-8 660	17-5 720	18-1 780	18-9 830	19-4 890	19-11 940	20-6 990	21-0 1040	21-6 1090	21-11 1140	22-5 1190	22-10 1230	23-3 1280	23-7 1320	24-5 1410	25-1 1490
	13.7	13-3 470	14-3 550	15-2 620	15-11 690	16-8 750	17-4 810	17-11 870	18-6 930	19-1 980	19-7 1040	20-1 1090	20-6 1140	21-0 1190	21-5 1240	21-10 1290	22-3 1340	22-7 1380	23-4 1470	24-0 1560
	16.0	12-7 500	13-6 580	14-4 650	15-2 720	15-10 790	16-5 860	17-0 920	17-7 980	18-1 1040	18-7 1090	19-1 1150	19-6 1200	19-11 1250	20-4 1310	20-9 1360	21-1 1410	21-6 1460	22-2 1550	22-10 1640
	19.2	11-10 530	12-9 610	13-6 690	14-3 770	14-11 840	15-6 910	16-0 970	16-7 1040	17-0 1100	17-6 1160	17-11 1220	18-4 1280	18-9 1330	19-2 1390	19-6 1440	19-10 1500	20-2 1550	20-10 1650	21-6 1750
	24.0	11-0 570	11-10 660	12-7 750	13-3 830	13-10 900	14-4 980	14-11 1050	15-4 1120	15-10 1190	16-3 1250	16-8 1310	17-0 1380	17-5 1440	17-9 1500	18-1 1550	18-5 1610	18-9 1670	19-4 1780	19-11 1880
	32.0					12-7 1000	13-1 1080	13-6 1150	13-11 1220	14-4 1300	14-9 1380	15-2 1450	15-6 1520	15-10 1580	16-2 1650	16-5 1700	16-9 1770	17-0 1830	17-7 1950	18-1 2070

NOTE: The required extreme fiber stress in bending F_b in pounds per square inch is shown below each span.

TABLE NO. 25-21-J-5—CEILING JOISTS
10 Pounds Per Square Foot Live Load
(Plaster Ceiling)

DESIGN CRITERIA:
Deflection - For 10 pounds per square foot live load. Limited to span in inches divided by 360.
Strength - live load of 10 pounds per square foot plus dead load of 5 pounds per square foot determines required fiber stress value.

JOIST SIZE (IN)	SPACING (IN)	Modulus of Elasticity, E, in 1,000,000 psi																	
		0.4	0.5	0.6	0.7	0.8	0.9	1.0	1.1	1.2	1.3	1.4	1.5	1.6	1.7	1.8	1.9	2.0	2.2	2.4
2x4	12.0	6-10 340	7-4 400	7-10 450	8-3 500	8-7 540	8-11 590	9-3 630	9-7 670	9-10 710	10-1 750	10-4 790	10-7 830	10-10 860	11-1 900	11-3 930	11-6 970	11-8 1000	12-1 1070	12-5 1130
	13.7	6-6 360	7-0 410	7-6 470	7-10 520	8-3 570	8-7 610	8-10 660	9-2 700	9-5 740	9-8 780	9-11 820	10-2 860	10-4 900	10-7 940	10-9 970	11-0 1010	11-2 1050	11-6 1110	11-10 1180
	16.0	6-2 380	6-8 440	7-1 490	7-6 550	7-10 600	8-1 650	8-5 690	8-8 740	8-11 780	9-2 830	9-5 870	9-8 910	9-10 950	10-0 990	10-3 1030	10-5 1060	10-7 1100	10-11 1170	11-3 1240
	19.2	5-10 400	6-3 460	6-8 520	7-0 580	7-4 630	7-8 690	7-11 740	8-2 790	8-5 830	8-8 880	8-10 920	9-1 970	9-3 1010	9-5 1050	9-8 1090	9-10 1130	10-0 1170	10-4 1250	10-7 1320
	24.0	5-5 430	5-10 500	6-2 560	6-6 630	6-10 680	7-1 740	7-4 790	7-7 850	7-10 900	8-0 950	8-3 990	8-5 1040	8-7 1090	8-9 1130	8-11 1170	9-1 1220	9-3 1260	9-7 1340	9-10 1420
2x6	12.0	10-9 340	11-7 400	12-3 450	12-11 500	13-6 540	14-1 590	14-7 630	15-0 670	15-6 710	15-11 750	16-3 790	16-8 830	17-0 860	17-4 900	17-8 930	18-0 970	18-4 1000	18-11 1070	19-6 1130
	13.7	10-3 360	11-1 410	11-9 470	12-4 520	12-11 570	13-5 610	13-11 660	14-4 700	14-9 740	15-2 780	15-7 820	15-11 860	16-3 900	16-7 940	16-11 970	17-3 1010	17-6 1050	18-1 1110	18-8 1180
	16.0	9-9 380	10-6 440	11-2 490	11-9 550	12-3 600	12-9 650	13-3 690	13-8 740	14-1 780	14-5 830	14-9 870	15-2 910	15-6 950	15-9 990	16-1 1030	16-4 1060	16-8 1100	17-2 1170	17-8 1240
	19.2	9-2 400	9-10 460	10-6 520	11-1 580	11-7 630	12-0 690	12-5 740	12-10 790	13-3 830	13-7 880	13-11 920	14-3 970	14-7 1010	14-10 1050	15-2 1090	15-5 1130	15-8 1170	16-2 1250	16-8 1320
	24.0	8-6 430	9-2 500	9-9 560	10-3 630	10-9 680	11-2 740	11-7 790	11-11 850	12-3 900	12-7 950	12-11 990	13-3 1040	13-6 1090	13-9 1130	14-1 1170	14-4 1220	14-7 1260	15-0 1340	15-6 1420

JOIST SIZE (Inches)	SPACING (Inches)	Modulus of Elasticity, E, in 1,000,000 psi																		
		0.4	0.5	0.6	0.7	0.8	0.9	1.0	1.1	1.2	1.3	1.4	1.5	1.6	1.7	1.8	1.9	2.0	2.2	2.4
2x8	12.0	14-2 340	15-3 400	16-2 450	17-0 500	17-10 540	18-6 590	19-2 630	19-10 670	20-5 710	20-11 750	21-5 790	21-11 830	22-5 860	22-11 900	23-4 930	23-9 970	24-2 1000	24-11 1070	25-8 1130
	13.7	13-6 360	14-7 410	15-6 470	16-3 520	17-0 570	17-9 610	18-4 660	18-11 700	19-6 740	20-0 780	20-6 820	21-0 860	21-5 900	21-11 940	22-4 970	22-9 1010	23-1 1050	23-10 1110	24-7 1180
	16.0	12-10 380	13-10 440	14-8 490	15-6 550	16-2 600	16-10 650	17-5 690	18-0 740	18-6 780	19-0 830	19-6 870	19-11 910	20-5 950	20-10 990	21-2 1030	21-7 1060	21-11 1100	22-8 1170	23-4 1240
	19.2	12-1 400	13-0 460	13-10 520	14-7 580	15-3 630	15-10 690	16-5 740	16-11 790	17-5 830	17-11 880	18-4 920	18-9 970	19-2 1010	19-7 1050	19-11 1090	20-4 1130	20-8 1170	21-4 1250	21-11 1320
	24.0	11-3 430	12-1 500	12-10 560	13-6 630	14-2 680	14-8 740	15-3 790	15-9 850	16-2 900	16-7 950	17-0 990	17-5 1040	17-10 1090	18-2 1130	18-6 1170	18-10 1220	19-2 1260	19-10 1340	20-5 1420
2x10	12.0	18-0 340	19-5 400	20-8 450	21-9 500	22-9 540	23-8 590	24-6 630	25-3 670	26-0 710	26-9 750	27-5 790	28-0 830	28-7 860	29-2 900	29-9 930	30-4 970	30-10 1000	31-10 1070	32-9 1130
	13.7	17-3 360	18-7 410	19-9 470	20-9 520	21-9 570	22-7 610	23-5 660	24-2 700	24-10 740	25-7 780	26-2 820	26-10 860	27-5 900	27-11 940	28-6 970	29-0 1010	29-6 1050	30-5 1110	31-4 1180
	16.0	16-5 380	17-8 440	18-9 490	19-9 550	20-8 600	21-6 650	22-3 690	22-11 740	23-8 780	24-3 830	24-10 870	25-5 910	26-0 950	26-6 990	27-1 1030	27-6 1060	28-0 1100	28-11 1170	29-9 1240
	19.2	15-5 400	16-7 460	17-8 520	18-7 580	19-5 630	20-2 690	20-11 740	21-7 790	22-3 830	22-10 880	23-5 920	23-11 970	24-6 1010	25-0 1050	25-5 1090	25-11 1130	26-4 1170	27-3 1250	28-0 1320
	24.0	14-4 430	15-5 500	16-5 560	17-3 630	18-0 680	18-9 740	19-5 790	20-1 850	20-8 900	21-2 950	21-9 990	22-3 1040	22-9 1090	23-2 1130	23-8 1170	24-1 1220	24-6 1260	25-3 1340	26-0 1420

NOTE: The required extreme fiber stress in bending F_b in pounds per square inch is shown below each span.

TABLE NO. 25-21-J-6—CEILING JOISTS
10 Pounds Per Square Foot Live Load
(Drywall Ceiling)

DESIGN CRITERIA:
Deflection - For 10 pounds per square foot live load. Limited to span in inches divided by 240.
Strength - live load of 10 pounds per square foot plus dead load of 5 pounds per square foot detemines required fiber stress value.

JOIST SIZE (Inches)	SPACING (Inches)	Modulus of Elasticity, *E*, in 1,000,000 psi																		
		0.4	0.5	0.6	0.7	0.8	0.9	1.0	1.1	1.2	1.3	1.4	1.5	1.6	1.7	1.8	1.9	2.0	2.2	2.4
2x4	12.0	7-10 450	8-5 520	8-11 590	9-5 650	9-10 710	10-3 770	10-7 830	10-11 880	11-3 930	11-7 980	11-10 1030	12-2 1080	12-5 1130	12-8 1180	12-11 1220	13-2 1270	13-4 1310	13-9 1400	14-2 1480
	13.7	7-6 470	8-1 540	8-7 610	9-0 680	9-5 740	9-9 800	10-2 860	10-6 920	10-9 970	11-1 1030	11-4 1080	11-7 1130	11-10 1180	12-1 1230	12-4 1280	12-7 1320	12-9 1370	13-2 1460	13-7 1550
	16.0	7-1 490	7-8 570	8-1 650	8-7 720	8-11 780	9-4 850	9-8 910	9-11 970	10-3 1030	10-6 1080	10-9 1140	11-0 1190	11-3 1240	11-6 1290	11-9 1340	11-11 1390	12-2 1440	12-6 1540	12-11 1630
	19.2	6-8 520	7-2 610	7-8 690	8-1 760	8-5 830	8-9 900	9-1 970	9-4 1030	9-8 1090	9-11 1150	10-2 1210	10-4 1270	10-7 1320	10-10 1380	11-0 1430	11-3 1480	11-5 1530	11-9 1630	12-2 1730
	24.0	6-2 560	6-8 660	7-1 740	7-6 820	7-10 900	8-1 970	8-5 1040	8-8 1110	8-11 1170	9-2 1240	9-5 1300	9-8 1360	9-10 1420	10-0 1480	10-3 1540	10-5 1600	10-7 1650	10-11 1760	11-3 1860
2x6	12.0	12-3 450	13-3 520	14-1 590	14-9 650	15-6 710	16-1 770	16-8 830	17-2 880	17-8 930	18-2 980	18-8 1030	19-1 1080	19-6 1130	19-11 1180	20-3 1220	20-8 1270	21-0 1310	21-8 1400	22-4 1480
	13.7	11-9 470	12-8 540	13-5 610	14-2 680	14-9 740	15-5 800	15-11 860	16-5 920	16-11 970	17-5 1030	17-10 1080	18-3 1130	18-8 1180	19-0 1230	19-5 1280	19-9 1320	20-1 1370	20-9 1460	21-4 1550
	16.0	11-2 490	12-0 570	12-9 650	13-5 720	14-1 780	14-7 850	15-2 910	15-7 970	16-1 1030	16-6 1080	16-11 1140	17-4 1190	17-8 1240	18-1 1290	18-5 1340	18-9 1390	19-1 1440	19-8 1540	20-3 1630
	19.2	10-6 520	11-4 610	12-0 690	12-8 760	13-3 830	13-9 900	14-3 970	14-8 1030	15-2 1090	15-7 1150	15-11 1210	16-4 1270	16-8 1320	17-0 1380	17-4 1430	17-8 1480	17-11 1530	18-6 1630	19-1 1730
	24.0	9-9 560	10-6 660	11-2 740	11-9 820	12-3 900	12-9 970	13-3 1040	13-8 1110	14-1 1170	14-5 1240	14-9 1300	15-2 1360	15-6 1420	15-9 1480	16-1 1540	16-4 1600	16-8 1650	17-2 1760	17-8 1860

JOIST SIZE (Inches)	SPACING (Inches)	Modulus of Elasticity, E, in 1,000,000 psi																		
		0.4	0.5	0.6	0.7	0.8	0.9	1.0	1.1	1.2	1.3	1.4	1.5	1.6	1.7	1.8	1.9	2.0	2.2	2.4
2x8	12.0	16-2 450	17-5 520	18-6 590	19-6 650	20-5 710	21-2 770	21-11 830	22-8 880	23-4 930	24-0 980	24-7 1030	25-2 1080	25-8 1130	26-2 1180	26-9 1220	27-2 1270	27-8 1310	28-7 1400	29-5 1480
	13.7	15-6 470	16-8 540	17-9 610	18-8 680	19-6 740	20-3 800	21-0 860	21-8 920	22-4 970	22-11 1030	23-6 1080	24-0 1130	24-7 1180	25-1 1230	25-7 1280	26-0 1320	26-6 1370	27-4 1460	28-1 1550
	16.0	14-8 490	15-10 570	16-10 650	17-9 720	18-6 780	19-3 850	19-11 910	20-7 970	21-2 1030	21-9 1080	22-4 1140	22-10 1190	23-4 1240	23-10 1290	24-3 1340	24-8 1390	25-2 1440	25-11 1540	26-9 1630
	19.2	13-10 520	14-11 610	15-10 690	16-8 760	17-5 830	18-2 900	18-9 970	19-5 1030	19-11 1090	20-6 1150	21-0 1210	21-6 1270	21-11 1320	22-5 1380	22-10 1430	23-3 1480	23-8 1530	24-5 1630	25-2 1730
	24.0	12-10 560	13-10 660	14-8 740	15-6 820	16-2 900	16-10 970	17-5 1040	18-0 1110	18-6 1170	19-0 1240	19-6 1300	19-11 1360	20-5 1420	20-10 1480	21-2 1540	21-7 1600	21-11 1650	22-8 1760	23-4 1860
2x10	12.0	20-8 450	22-3 520	23-8 590	24-10 650	26-0 710	27-1 770	28-0 830	28-11 880	29-9 930	30-7 980	31-4 1030	32-1 1080	32-9 1130	33-5 1180	34-1 1220	34-8 1270	35-4 1310	36-5 1400	37-6 1480
	13.7	19-9 470	21-3 540	22-7 610	23-9 680	24-10 740	25-10 800	26-10 860	27-8 920	28-6 970	29-3 1030	30-0 1080	30-8 1130	31-4 1180	32-0 1230	32-7 1280	33-2 1320	33-9 1370	34-10 1460	35-10 1550
	16.0	18-9 490	20-2 570	21-6 650	22-7 720	23-8 780	24-7 850	25-5 910	26-3 970	27-1 1030	27-9 1080	28-6 1140	29-2 1190	29-9 1240	30-5 1290	31-0 1340	31-6 1390	32-1 1440	33-1 1540	34-1 1630
	19.2	17-8 520	19-0 610	20-2 690	21-3 760	22-3 830	23-2 900	23-11 970	24-9 1030	25-5 1090	26-2 1150	26-10 1210	27-5 1270	28-0 1320	28-7 1380	29-2 1430	29-8 1480	30-2 1530	31-2 1630	32-1 1730
	24.0	16-5 560	17-8 660	18-9 740	19-9 820	20-8 900	21-6 970	22-3 1040	22-11 1110	23-8 1170	24-3 1240	24-10 1300	25-5 1360	26-0 1420	26-6 1480	27-1 1540	27-6 1600	28-0 1650	28-11 1760	29-9 1860

Note: The required extreme fiber stress in bending, F_b, in pounds per square inch is shown below each span.

TABLE NO. 25-21-R-1—LOW OR HIGH SLOPE RAFTERS
20 Pounds Per Square Foot Live Load
(Supporting Drywall Ceiling)

DESIGN CRITERIA:
Strength - 15 pounds per square foot dead load plus 20 pounds per square foot live load determines required fiber stress.
Deflection - For 20 pounds per square foot live load. Limited to span in inches divided by 240.

RAFTER SIZE (Inches)	RAFTER SPACING (Inches)	Allowable Extreme Fiber Stress in Bending F_b(psi)										
		300	400	500	600	700	800	900	1000	1100	1200	1300
2x6	12.0	6-7 0.12	7-7 0.19	8-6 0.26	9-4 0.35	10-0 0.44	10-9 0.54	11-5 0.64	12-0 0.75	12-7 0.86	13-2 0.98	13-8 1.11
	13.7	6-2 0.12	7-1 0.18	7-11 0.25	8-8 0.33	9-5 0.41	10-0 0.50	10-8 0.60	11-3 0.70	11-9 0.81	12-4 0.92	12-10 1.04
	16.0	5-8 0.11	6-7 0.16	7-4 0.23	8-1 0.30	8-8 0.38	9-4 0.46	9-10 0.55	10-5 0.65	10-11 0.75	11-5 0.85	11-10 0.96
	19.2	5-2 0.10	6-0 0.15	6-9 0.21	7-4 0.27	7-11 0.35	8-6 0.42	9-0 0.51	9-6 0.59	9-11 0.68	10-5 0.78	10-10 0.88
	24.0	4-8 0.09	5-4 0.13	6-0 0.19	6-7 0.25	7-1 0.31	7-7 0.38	8-1 0.45	8-6 0.53	8-11 0.61	9-4 0.70	9-8 0.78
2x8	12.0	8-8 0.12	10-0 0.19	11-2 0.26	12-3 0.35	13-3 0.44	14-2 0.54	15-0 0.64	15-10 0.75	16-7 0.86	17-4 0.98	18-0 1.11
	13.7	8-1 0.12	9-4 0.18	10-6 0.25	11-6 0.33	12-5 0.41	13-3 0.50	14-0 0.60	14-10 0.70	15-6 0.81	16-3 0.92	16-10 1.04
	16.0	7-6 0.11	8-8 0.16	9-8 0.23	10-7 0.30	11-6 0.38	12-3 0.46	13-0 0.55	13-8 0.65	14-4 0.75	15-0 0.85	15-7 0.96
	19.2	6-10 0.10	7-11 0.15	8-10 0.21	9-8 0.27	10-6 0.35	11-2 0.42	11-10 0.51	12-6 0.59	13-1 0.68	13-8 0.78	14-3 0.88
	24.0	6-2 0.09	7-1 0.13	7-11 0.19	8-8 0.25	9-4 0.31	10-0 0.38	10-7 0.45	11-2 0.53	11-9 0.61	12-3 0.70	12-9 0.78
2x10	12.0	11-1 0.12	12-9 0.19	14-3 0.26	15-8 0.35	16-11 0.44	18-1 0.54	19-2 0.64	20-2 0.75	21-2 0.86	22-1 0.98	23-0 1.11
	13.7	10-4 0.12	11-11 0.18	13-4 0.25	14-8 0.33	15-10 0.41	16-11 0.50	17-11 0.60	18-11 0.70	19-10 0.81	20-8 0.92	21-6 1.04
	16.0	9-7 0.11	11-1 0.16	12-4 0.23	13-6 0.30	14-8 0.38	15-8 0.46	16-7 0.55	17-6 0.65	18-4 0.75	19-2 0.85	19-11 0.96
	19.2	8-9 0.10	10-1 0.15	11-3 0.21	12-4 0.27	13-4 0.35	14-3 0.42	15-2 0.51	15-11 0.59	16-9 0.68	17-6 0.78	18-2 0.88
	24.0	7-10 0.09	9-0 0.13	10-1 0.19	11-1 0.25	11-11 0.31	12-9 0.38	13-6 0.45	14-3 0.53	15-0 0.61	15-8 0.70	16-3 0.78
2x12	12.0	13-5 0.12	15-6 0.19	17-4 0.26	19-0 0.35	20-6 0.44	21-11 0.54	23-3 0.64	24-7 0.75	25-9 0.86	26-11 0.98	28-0 1.11
	13.7	12-7 0.12	14-6 0.18	16-3 0.25	17-9 0.33	19-3 0.41	20-6 0.50	21-9 0.60	23-0 0.70	24-1 0.81	25-2 0.92	26-2 1.04
	16.0	11-8 0.11	13-5 0.16	15-0 0.23	16-6 0.30	17-9 0.38	19-0 0.46	20-2 0.55	21-3 0.65	22-4 0.75	23-3 0.85	24-3 0.96
	19.2	10-8 0.10	12-3 0.15	13-9 0.21	15-0 0.27	16-3 0.35	17-4 0.42	18-5 0.51	19-5 0.59	20-4 0.68	21-3 0.78	22-2 0.88
	24.0	9-6 0.09	11-0 0.13	12-3 0.19	13-5 0.25	14-6 0.31	15-6 0.38	16-6 0.45	17-4 0.53	18-2 0.61	19-0 0.70	19-10 0.78

Note: The required modulus of elasticity, *E*, in 1,000,000 pounds per square inch is shown below each span.

RAFTERS: Spans are measured along the horizontal projection and loads are considered as applied on the horizontal projection.

Allowable Extreme Fiber Stress in Bending F_b (psi)											RAFTER	
1400	1500	1600	1700	1800	1900	2000	2100	2200	2400	2700	SPACING (Inches)	SIZE (Inches)
14-2 1.24	14-8 1.37	15-2 1.51	15-8 1.66	16-1 1.81	16-7 1.96	17-0 2.12	17-5 2.28	17-10 2.44			12.0	2x6
13-3 1.16	13-9 1.29	14-2 1.42	14-8 1.55	15-1 1.69	15-6 1.83	15-11 1.98	16-3 2.13	16-8 2.28	17-5 2.60		13.7	
12-4 1.07	12-9 1.19	13-2 1.31	13-7 1.44	13-11 1.56	14-4 1.70	14-8 1.83	15-1 1.97	15-5 2.11	16-1 2.41		16.0	
11-3 0.98	11-7 1.09	12-0 1.20	12-4 1.31	12-9 1.43	13-1 1.55	13-5 1.67	13-9 1.80	14-1 1.93	14-8 2.20		19.2	
10-0 0.88	10-5 0.97	10-9 1.07	11-1 1.17	11-5 1.28	11-8 1.39	12-0 1.50	12-4 1.61	12-7 1.73	13-2 1.97	13-11 2.35	24.0	
18-9 1.24	19-5 1.37	20-0 1.51	20-8 1.66	21-3 1.81	21-10 1.96	22-4 2.12	22-11 2.28	23-6 2.44			12.0	2x8
17-6 1.16	18-2 1.29	18-9 1.42	19-4 1.55	19-10 1.69	20-5 1.83	20-11 1.98	21-5 2.13	21-11 2.28	22-11 2.60		13.7	
16-3 1.07	16-9 1.19	17-4 1.31	17-10 1.44	18-5 1.56	18-11 1.70	19-5 1.83	19-10 1.97	20-4 2.11	21-3 2.41		16.0	
14-10 0.98	15-4 1.09	15-10 1.20	16-4 1.31	16-9 1.43	17-3 1.55	17-8 1.67	18-2 1.80	18-7 1.93	19-5 2.20		19.2	
13-3 0.88	13-8 0.97	14-2 1.07	14-7 1.17	15-0 1.28	15-5 1.39	15-10 1.50	16-3 1.61	16-7 1.73	17-4 1.97	18-5 2.35	24.0	
23-11 1.24	24-9 1.37	25-6 1.51	26-4 1.66	27-1 1.81	27-10 1.96	28-7 2.12	29-3 2.28	29-11 2.44			12.0	2x10
22-4 1.16	23-2 1.29	23-11 1.42	24-7 1.55	25-4 1.69	26-0 1.83	26-8 1.98	27-4 2.13	28-0 2.28	29-3 2.60		13.7	
20-8 1.07	21-5 1.19	22-1 1.31	22-10 1.44	23-5 1.56	24-1 1.70	24-9 1.83	25-4 1.97	25-11 2.11	27-1 2.41		16.0	
18-11 0.98	19-7 1.09	20-2 1.20	20-10 1.31	21-5 1.43	22-0 1.55	22-7 1.67	23-2 1.80	23-8 1.93	24-9 2.20		19.2	
16-11 0.88	17-6 0.97	18-1 1.07	18-7 1.17	19-2 1.28	19-8 1.39	20-2 1.50	20-8 1.61	21-2 1.73	22-1 1.97	23-5 2.35	24.0	
29-1 1.24	30-1 1.37	31-1 1.51	32-0 1.66	32-11 1.81	33-10 1.96	34-9 2.12	35-7 2.28	36-5 2.44			12.0	2x12
27-2 1.16	28-2 1.29	29-1 1.42	29-11 1.55	30-10 1.69	31-8 1.83	32-6 1.98	33-3 2.13	34-1 2.28	35-7 2.60		13.7	
25-2 1.07	26-0 1.19	26-11 1.31	27-9 1.44	28-6 1.56	29-4 1.70	30-1 1.83	30-10 1.97	31-6 2.11	32-11 2.41		16.0	
23-0 0.98	23-9 1.09	24-7 1.20	25-4 1.31	26-0 1.43	26-9 1.55	27-5 1.67	28-2 1.80	28-9 1.93	30-1 2.20		19.2	
20-6 0.88	21-3 0.97	21-11 1.07	22-8 1.17	23-3 1.28	23-11 1.39	24-7 1.50	25-2 1.61	25-9 1.73	26-11 1.97	28-6 2.35	24.0	

Note: The required modulus of elasticity, E, in 1,000,000 pounds per square inch is shown below each span.

TABLE NO. 25-21-R-2—LOW OR HIGH SLOPE RAFTERS
30 Pounds Per Square Foot Live Load
(Supporting Drywall Ceiling)

DESIGN CRITERIA:
Strength - 15 pounds per square foot dead load plus 30 pounds per square foot live load determines required fiber stress.
Deflection - For 30 pounds per square foot live load. Limited to span in inches divided by 240.

RAFTER SIZE (IN)	SPACING (IN)	Allowable Extreme Fiber Stress in Bending F_b (psi)										
		300	400	500	600	700	800	900	1000	1100	1200	1300
2x6	12.0	5-10 0.13	6-8 0.19	7-6 0.27	8-2 0.36	8-10 0.45	9-6 0.55	10-0 0.66	10-7 0.77	11-1 0.89	11-7 1.01	12-1 1.14
	13.7	5-5 0.12	6-3 0.18	7-0 0.25	7-8 0.33	8-3 0.42	8-10 0.52	9-5 0.61	9-11 0.72	10-5 0.83	10-10 0.95	11-3 1.07
	16.0	5-0 0.11	5-10 0.17	6-6 0.24	7-1 0.31	7-8 0.39	8-2 0.48	8-8 0.57	9-2 0.67	9-7 0.77	10-0 0.88	10-5 0.99
	19.2	4-7 0.10	5-4 0.15	5-11 0.22	6-6 0.28	7-0 0.36	7-6 0.44	7-11 0.52	8-4 0.61	8-9 0.70	9-2 0.80	9-6 0.90
	24.0	4-1 0.09	4-9 0.14	5-4 0.19	5-10 0.25	6-3 0.32	6-8 0.39	7-1 0.46	7-6 0.54	7-10 0.63	8-2 0.72	8-6 0.81
2x8	12.0	7-8 0.13	8-10 0.19	9-10 0.27	10-10 0.36	11-8 0.45	12-6 0.55	13-3 0.66	13-11 0.77	14-8 0.89	15-3 1.01	15-11 1.14
	13.7	7-2 0.12	8-3 0.18	9-3 0.25	10-1 0.33	10-11 0.42	11-8 0.52	12-5 0.61	13-1 0.72	13-8 0.83	14-4 0.95	14-11 1.07
	16.0	6-7 0.11	7-8 0.17	8-7 0.24	9-4 0.31	10-1 0.39	10-10 0.48	11-6 0.57	12-1 0.67	12-8 0.77	13-3 0.88	13-9 0.99
	19.2	6-1 0.10	7-0 0.15	7-10 0.22	8-7 0.28	9-3 0.36	9-10 0.44	10-6 0.52	11-0 0.61	11-7 0.70	12-1 0.80	12-7 0.90
	24.0	5-5 0.09	6-3 0.14	7-0 0.19	7-8 0.25	8-3 0.32	8-10 0.39	9-4 0.46	9-10 0.54	10-4 0.63	10-10 0.72	11-3 0.81
2x10	12.0	9-9 0.13	11-3 0.19	12-7 0.27	13-9 0.36	14-11 0.45	15-11 0.55	16-11 0.66	17-10 0.77	18-8 0.89	19-6 1.01	20-4 1.14
	13.7	9-1 0.12	10-6 0.18	11-9 0.25	12-11 0.33	13-11 0.42	14-11 0.52	15-10 0.61	16-8 0.72	17-6 0.83	18-3 0.95	19-0 1.07
	16.0	8-5 0.11	9-9 0.17	10-11 0.24	11-11 0.31	12-11 0.39	13-9 0.48	14-8 0.57	15-5 0.67	16-2 0.77	16-11 0.88	17-7 0.99
	19.2	7-8 0.10	8-11 0.15	9-11 0.22	10-11 0.28	11-9 0.36	12-7 0.44	13-4 0.52	14-1 0.61	14-9 0.70	15-5 0.80	16-1 0.90
	24.0	6-11 0.09	8-0 0.14	8-11 0.19	9-9 0.25	10-6 0.32	11-3 0.39	11-11 0.46	12-7 0.54	13-2 0.63	13-9 0.72	14-4 0.81
2x12	12.0	11-10 0.13	13-8 0.19	15-4 0.27	16-9 0.36	18-1 0.45	19-4 0.55	20-6 0.66	21-8 0.77	22-8 0.89	23-9 1.01	24-8 1.14
	13.7	11-1 0.12	12-10 0.18	14-4 0.25	15-8 0.33	16-11 0.42	18-1 0.52	19-3 0.61	20-3 0.72	21-3 0.83	22-2 0.95	23-1 1.07
	16.0	10-3 0.11	11-10 0.17	13-3 0.24	14-6 0.31	15-8 0.39	16-9 0.48	17-9 0.57	18-9 0.67	19-8 0.77	20-6 0.88	21-5 0.99
	19.2	9-5 0.10	10-10 0.15	12-1 0.22	13-3 0.28	14-4 0.36	15-4 0.44	16-3 0.52	17-1 0.61	17-11 0.70	18-9 0.80	19-6 0.90
	24.0	8-5 0.09	9-8 0.14	10-10 0.19	11-10 0.25	12-10 0.32	13-8 0.39	14-6 0.46	15-4 0.54	16-1 0.63	16-9 0.72	17-5 0.81

Note: The required modulus of elasticity, E, in 1,000,000 pounds per square inch is shown below each span.

RAFTERS: Spans are measured along the horizontal projection and loads are considered as applied on the horizontal projection.

Allowable Extreme Fiber Stress in Bending F_b (psi)											RAFTER	
1400	1500	1600	1700	1800	1900	2000	2100	2200	2400	2700	SPACING (IN)	SIZE (IN)
12-6 1.28	13-0 1.41	13-5 1.56	13-10 1.71	14-2 1.86	14-7 2.02	15-0 2.18	15-4 2.34	15-8 2.51			12.0	2x6
11-9 1.19	12-2 1.32	12-6 1.46	12-11 1.60	13-3 1.74	13-8 1.89	14-0 2.04	14-4 2.19	14-8 2.35			13.7	
10-10 1.10	11-3 1.22	11-7 1.35	11-11 1.48	12-4 1.61	12-8 1.75	13-0 1.89	13-3 2.03	13-7 2.18	14-2 2.48		16.0	
9-11 1.01	10-3 1.12	10-7 1.23	10-11 1.35	11-3 1.47	11-6 1.59	11-10 1.72	12-2 1.85	12-5 1.99	13-0 2.26		19.2	
8-10 0.90	9-2 1.00	9-6 1.10	9-9 1.21	10-0 1.31	10-4 1.43	10-7 1.54	10-10 1.66	11-1 1.78	11-7 2.02	12-4 2.41	24.0	
16-6 1.28	17-1 1.41	17-8 1.56	18-2 1.71	18-9 1.86	19-3 2.02	19-9 2.18	20-3 2.34	20-8 2.51			12.0	2x8
15-5 1.19	16-0 1.32	16-6 1.46	17-0 1.60	17-6 1.74	18-0 1.89	18-5 2.04	18-11 2.19	19-4 2.35			13.7	
14-4 1.10	14-10 1.22	15-3 1.35	15-9 1.48	16-3 1.61	16-8 1.75	17-1 1.89	17-6 2.03	17-11 2.18	18-9 2.48		16.0	
13-1 1.01	13-6 1.12	13-11 1.23	14-5 1.35	14-10 1.47	15-2 1.59	15-7 1.72	16-0 1.85	16-4 1.99	17-1 2.26		19.2	
11-8 0.90	12-1 1.00	12-6 1.10	12-10 1.21	13-3 1.31	13-7 1.43	13-11 1.54	14-4 1.66	14-8 1.78	15-3 2.02	16-3 2.41	24.0	
21-1 1.28	21-10 1.41	22-6 1.56	23-3 1.71	23-11 1.86	24-6 2.02	25-2 2.18	25-10 2.34	26-5 2.51			12.0	2x10
19-8 1.19	20-5 1.32	21-1 1.46	21-9 1.60	22-4 1.74	22-11 1.89	23-7 2.04	24-2 2.19	24-8 2.35			13.7	
18-3 1.10	18-11 1.22	19-6 1.35	20-1 1.48	20-8 1.61	21-3 1.75	21-10 1.89	22-4 2.03	22-10 2.18	23-11 2.48		16.0	
16-8 1.01	17-3 1.12	17-10 1.23	18-4 1.35	18-11 1.47	19-5 1.59	19-11 1.72	20-5 1.85	20-10 1.99	21-10 2.26		19.2	
14-11 0.90	15-5 1.00	15-11 1.10	16-5 1.21	16-11 1.31	17-4 1.43	17-10 1.54	18-3 1.66	18-8 1.78	19-6 2.02	20-8 2.41	24.0	
25-7 1.28	26-6 1.41	27-5 1.56	28-3 1.71	29-1 1.86	29-10 2.02	30-7 2.18	31-4 2.34	32-1 2.51			12.0	2x12
24-0 1.19	24-10 1.32	25-7 1.46	26-5 1.60	27-2 1.74	27-11 1.89	28-8 2.04	29-4 2.19	30-0 2.35			13.7	
22-2 1.10	23-0 1.22	23-9 1.35	24-5 1.48	25-2 1.61	25-10 1.75	26-6 1.89	27-2 2.03	27-10 2.18	29-1 2.48		16.0	
20-3 1.01	21-0 1.12	21-8 1.23	22-4 1.35	23-0 1.47	23-7 1.59	24-2 1.72	24-10 1.85	25-5 1.99	26-6 2.26		19.2	
18-1 0.90	18-9 1.00	19-4 1.10	20-0 1.21	20-6 1.31	21-1 1.43	21-8 1.54	22-2 1.66	22-8 1.78	23-9 2.02	25-2 2.41	24.0	

Note: The required modulus of elasticity, E, in 1,000,000 pounds per square inch is shown below each span.

TABLE NO. 25-21-R-3—LOW OR HIGH SLOPE RAFTERS
40 Pounds Per Square Foot Live Load
(Supporting Drywall Ceiling)

DESIGN CRITERIA :
Strength - 15 pounds per square foot dead load plus 40 pounds per square foot live load determines required fiber stress.
Deflection - For 40 pounds per square foot live load. Limited to span in inches divided by 240.

RAFTER SIZE (IN)	RAFTER SPACING (IN)	Allowable Extreme Fiber Stress in Bending F_b (psi)										
		300	400	500	600	700	800	900	1000	1100	1200	1300
2x6	12.0	5-3 0.12	6-1 0.19	6-9 0.27	7-5 0.35	8-0 0.44	8-7 0.54	9-1 0.65	9-7 0.76	10-0 0.88	10-6 1.00	10-11 1.13
	13.7	4-11 0.12	5-8 0.18	6-4 0.25	6-11 0.33	7-6 0.42	8-0 0.51	8-6 0.61	8-11 0.71	9-5 0.82	9-10 0.93	10-3 1.05
	16.0	4-6 0.11	5-3 0.17	5-10 0.23	6-5 0.31	6-11 0.39	7-5 0.47	7-10 0.56	8-3 0.66	8-8 0.76	9-1 0.86	9-5 0.98
	19.2	4-2 0.10	4-9 0.15	5-4 0.21	5-10 0.28	6-4 0.35	6-9 0.43	7-2 0.51	7-7 0.60	7-11 0.69	8-3 0.79	8-8 0.89
	24.0	3-8 0.09	4-3 0.14	4-9 0.19	5-3 0.25	5-8 0.31	6-1 0.38	6-5 0.46	6-9 0.54	7-1 0.62	7-5 0.71	7-9 0.80
2x8	12.0	6-11 0.12	8-0 0.19	8-11 0.27	9-9 0.35	10-7 0.44	11-3 0.54	12-0 0.65	12-7 0.76	13-3 0.88	13-10 1.00	14-5 1.13
	13.7	6-6 0.12	7-6 0.18	8-4 0.25	9-2 0.33	9-11 0.42	10-7 0.51	11-2 0.61	11-10 0.71	12-5 0.82	12-11 0.93	13-6 1.05
	16.0	6-0 0.11	6-11 0.17	7-9 0.23	8-6 0.31	9-2 0.39	9-9 0.47	10-4 0.56	10-11 0.66	11-6 0.76	12-0 0.86	12-6 0.98
	19.2	5-6 0.10	6-4 0.15	7-1 0.21	7-9 0.28	8-4 0.35	8-11 0.43	9-6 0.51	10-0 0.60	10-6 0.69	10-11 0.79	11-5 0.89
	24.0	4-11 0.09	5-8 0.14	6-4 0.19	6-11 0.25	7-6 0.31	8-0 0.38	8-6 0.46	8-11 0.54	9-4 0.62	9-9 0.71	10-2 0.80
2x10	12.0	8-10 0.12	10-2 0.19	11-5 0.27	12-6 0.35	13-6 0.44	14-5 0.54	15-3 0.65	16-1 0.76	16-11 0.88	17-8 1.00	18-4 1.13
	13.7	8-3 0.12	9-6 0.18	10-8 0.25	11-8 0.33	12-7 0.42	13-6 0.51	14-3 0.61	15-1 0.71	15-10 0.82	16-6 0.93	17-2 1.05
	16.0	7-8 0.11	8-10 0.17	9-10 0.23	10-10 0.31	11-8 0.39	12-6 0.47	13-3 0.56	13-11 0.66	14-8 0.76	15-3 0.86	15-11 0.98
	19.2	7-0 0.10	8-1 0.15	9-0 0.21	9-10 0.28	10-8 0.35	11-5 0.43	12-1 0.51	12-9 0.60	13-4 0.69	13-11 0.79	14-6 0.89
	24.0	6-3 0.09	7-2 0.14	8-1 0.19	8-10 0.25	9-6 0.31	10-2 0.38	10-10 0.46	11-5 0.54	11-11 0.62	12-6 0.71	13-0 0.80
2x12	12.0	10-9 0.12	12-5 0.19	13-10 0.27	15-2 0.35	16-5 0.44	17-6 0.54	18-7 0.65	19-7 0.76	20-6 0.88	21-5 1.00	22-4 1.13
	13.7	10-0 0.12	11-7 0.18	12-11 0.25	14-2 0.33	15-4 0.42	16-5 0.51	17-5 0.61	18-4 0.71	19-3 0.82	20-1 0.93	20-11 1.05
	16.0	9-3 0.11	10-9 0.17	12-0 0.23	13-2 0.31	14-2 0.39	15-2 0.47	16-1 0.56	17-0 0.66	17-9 0.76	18-7 0.86	19-4 0.98
	19.2	8-6 0.10	9-10 0.15	10-11 0.21	12-0 0.28	12-11 0.35	13-10 0.43	14-8 0.51	15-6 0.60	16-3 0.69	17-0 0.79	17-8 0.89
	24.0	7-7 0.09	8-9 0.14	9-10 0.19	10-9 0.25	11-7 0.31	12-5 0.38	13-2 0.46	13-10 0.54	14-6 0.62	15-2 0.71	15-9 0.80

Note: The required modulus of elasticity, E, in 1,000,000 pounds per square inch is shown below each span.

RAFTERS: Spans are measured along the horizontal projection and loads are considered as applied on the horizontal projection.

Allowable Extreme Fiber Stress in Bending F_b (psi)											RAFTER	
1400	1500	1600	1700	1800	1900	2000	2100	2200	2400	2700	SPACING (IN)	SIZE (IN)
11-4 1.26	11-9 1.40	12-1 1.54	12-6 1.68	12-10 1.83	13-2 1.99	13-6 2.15	13-10 2.31	14-2 2.48			12.0	2x6
10-7 1.18	11-0 1.31	11-4 1.44	11-8 1.57	12-0 1.72	12-4 1.86	12-8 2.01	13-0 2.16	13-3 2.32			13.7	
9-10 1.09	10-2 1.21	10-6 1.33	10-10 1.46	11-1 1.59	11-5 1.72	11-9 1.86	12-0 2.00	12-4 2.15	12-10 2.45		16.0	
8-11 0.99	9-3 1.10	9-7 1.22	9-10 1.33	10-2 1.45	10-5 1.57	10-8 1.70	11-0 1.83	11-3 1.96	11-9 2.23		19.2	
8-0 0.89	8-3 0.99	8-7 1.09	8-10 1.19	9-1 1.30	9-4 1.41	9-7 1.52	9-10 1.63	10-0 1.75	10-6 2.00	11-1 2.38	24.0	
14-11 1.26	15-5 1.40	16-0 1.54	16-5 1.68	16-11 1.83	17-5 1.99	17-10 2.15	18-3 2.31	18-9 2.48			12.0	2x8
14-0 1.18	14-6 1.31	14-11 1.44	15-5 1.57	15-10 1.72	16-3 1.86	16-8 2.01	17-1 2.16	17-6 2.32			13.7	
12-11 1.09	13-5 1.21	13-10 1.33	14-3 1.46	14-8 1.59	15-1 1.72	15-5 1.86	15-10 2.00	16-3 2.15	16-11 2.45		16.0	
11-10 0.99	12-3 1.10	12-7 1.22	13-0 1.33	13-5 1.45	13-9 1.57	14-1 1.70	14-6 1.83	14-10 1.96	15-5 2.23		19.2	
10-7 0.89	10-11 0.99	11-3 1.09	11-8 1.19	12-0 1.30	12-4 1.41	12-7 1.52	12-11 1.63	13-3 1.75	13-10 2.00	14-8 2.38	24.0	
19-1 1.26	19-9 1.40	20-4 1.54	21-0 1.68	21-7 1.83	22-2 1.99	22-9 2.15	23-4 2.31	23-11 2.48			12.0	2x10
17-10 1.18	18-5 1.31	19-1 1.44	19-8 1.57	20-2 1.72	20-9 1.86	21-4 2.01	21-10 2.16	22-4 2.32			13.7	
16-6 1.09	17-1 1.21	17-8 1.33	18-2 1.46	18-9 1.59	19-3 1.72	19-9 1.86	20-2 2.00	20-8 2.15	21-7 2.45		16.0	
15-1 0.99	15-7 1.10	16-1 1.22	16-7 1.33	17-1 1.45	17-7 1.57	18-0 1.70	18-5 1.83	18-11 1.96	19-9 2.23		19.2	
13-6 0.89	13-11 0.99	14-5 1.09	14-10 1.19	15-3 1.30	15-8 1.41	16-1 1.52	16-6 1.63	16-11 1.75	17-8 2.00	18-9 2.38	24.0	
23-2 1.26	24-0 1.40	24-9 1.54	25-6 1.68	26-3 1.83	27-0 1.99	27-8 2.15	28-5 2.31	29-1 2.48			12.0	2x12
21-8 1.18	22-5 1.31	23-2 1.44	23-11 1.57	24-7 1.72	25-3 1.86	25-11 2.01	26-7 2.16	27-2 2.32			13.7	
20-1 1.09	20-9 1.21	21-5 1.33	22-1 1.46	22-9 1.59	23-5 1.72	24-0 1.86	24-7 2.00	25-2 2.15	26-3 2.45		16.0	
18-4 0.99	19-0 1.10	19-7 1.22	20-2 1.33	20-9 1.45	21-4 1.57	21-11 1.70	22-5 1.83	23-0 1.96	24-0 2.23		19.2	
16-5 0.89	17-0 0.99	17-6 1.09	18-1 1.19	18-7 1.30	19-1 1.41	19-7 1.52	20-1 1.63	20-6 1.75	21-5 2.00	22-9 2.38	24.0	

Note: The required modulus of elasticity, E, in 1,000,000 pounds per square inch is shown below each span.

TABLE NO. 25-21-R-4—LOW OR HIGH SLOPE RAFTERS
20 Pounds Per Square Foot Live Load
(Supporting Plaster Ceiling)

DESIGN CRITERIA:
Strength - 15 pounds per square foot dead load plus 20 pounds per square foot live load determines required fiber stress.
Deflection - For 20 pounds per square foot live load. Limited to span in inches divided by 360.

RAFTER SIZE (IN)	RAFTER SPACING (IN)	Allowable Extreme Fiber Stress in Bending F_b (psi)									
		300	400	500	600	700	800	900	1000	1100	1200
2x6	12.0	6-7 0.18	7-7 0.28	8-6 0.40	9-4 0.52	10-0 0.66	10-9 0.80	11-5 0.96	12-0 1.12	12-7 1.29	13-2 1.48
	13.7	6-2 0.17	7-1 0.27	7-11 0.37	8-8 0.49	9-5 0.61	10-0 0.75	10-8 0.90	11-3 1.05	11-9 1.21	12-4 1.38
	16.0	5-8 0.16	6-7 0.25	7-4 0.34	8-1 0.45	8-8 0.57	9-4 0.70	9-10 0.83	10-5 0.97	10-11 1.12	11-5 1.28
	19.2	5-2 0.15	6-0 0.22	6-9 0.31	7-4 0.41	7-11 0.52	8-6 0.63	9-0 0.76	9-6 0.89	9-11 1.02	10-5 1.17
	24.0	4-8 0.13	5-4 0.20	6-0 0.28	6-7 0.37	7-1 0.46	7-7 0.57	8-1 0.68	8-6 0.79	8-11 0.92	9-4 1.04
2x8	12.0	8-8 0.18	10-0 0.28	11-2 0.40	12-3 0.52	13-3 0.66	14-2 0.80	15-0 0.96	15-10 1.12	16-7 1.29	17-4 1.48
	13.7	8-1 0.17	9-4 0.27	10-6 0.37	11-6 0.49	12-5 0.61	13-3 0.75	14-0 0.90	14-10 1.05	15-6 1.21	16-3 1.38
	16.0	7-6 0.16	8-8 0.25	9-8 0.34	10-7 0.45	11-6 0.57	12-3 0.70	13-0 0.83	13-8 0.97	14-4 1.12	15-0 1.28
	19.2	6-10 0.15	7-11 0.22	8-10 0.31	9-8 0.41	10-6 0.52	11-2 0.63	11-10 0.76	12-6 0.89	13-1 1.02	13-8 1.17
	24.0	6-2 0.13	7-1 0.20	7-11 0.28	8-8 0.37	9-4 0.46	10-0 0.57	10-7 0.68	11-2 0.79	11-9 0.92	12-3 1.04
2x10	12.0	11-1 0.18	12-9 0.28	14-3 0.40	15-8 0.52	16-11 0.66	18-1 0.80	19-2 0.96	20-2 1.12	21-2 1.29	22-1 1.48
	13.7	10-4 0.17	11-11 0.27	13-4 0.37	14-8 0.49	15-10 0.61	16-11 0.75	17-11 0.90	18-11 1.05	19-10 1.21	20-8 1.38
	16.0	9-7 0.16	11-1 0.25	12-4 0.34	13-6 0.45	14-8 0.57	15-8 0.70	16-7 0.83	17-6 0.97	18-4 1.12	19-2 1.28
	19.2	8-9 0.15	10-1 0.22	11-3 0.31	12-4 0.41	13-4 0.52	14-3 0.63	15-2 0.76	15-11 0.89	16-9 1.02	17-6 1.17
	24.0	7-10 0.13	9-0 0.20	10-1 0.28	11-1 0.37	11-11 0.46	12-9 0.57	13-6 0.68	14-3 0.79	15-0 0.92	15-8 1.04
2x12	12.0	13-5 0.18	15-6 0.28	17-4 0.40	19-0 0.52	20-6 0.66	21-11 0.80	23-3 0.96	24-7 1.12	25-9 1.29	26-11 1.48
	13.7	12-7 0.17	14-6 0.27	16-3 0.37	17-9 0.49	19-3 0.61	20-6 0.75	21-9 0.90	23-0 1.05	24-1 1.21	25-2 1.38
	16.0	11-8 0.16	13-5 0.25	15-0 0.34	16-6 0.45	17-9 0.57	19-0 0.70	20-2 0.83	21-3 0.97	22-4 1.12	23-3 1.28
	19.2	10-8 0.15	12-3 0.22	13-9 0.31	15-0 0.41	16-3 0.52	17-4 0.63	18-5 0.76	19-5 0.89	20-4 1.02	21-3 1.17
	24.0	9-6 0.13	11-0 0.20	12-3 0.28	13-5 0.37	14-6 0.46	15-6 0.57	16-6 0.68	17-4 0.79	18-2 0.92	19-0 1.04

Note: The required modulus of elasticity, E, in 1,000,000 pounds per square inch is shown below each span.

RAFTERS: Spans are measured along the horizontal projection and loads are considered as applied on the horizontal projection.

Allowable Extreme Fiber Stress in Bending F_b (psi)									RAFTER	
1300	1400	1500	1600	1700	1800	1900	2000	2100	SPACING (IN)	SIZE (IN)
13-8 1.66	14-2 1.86	14-8 2.06	15-2 2.27	15-8 2.49					12.0	2x6
12-10 1.56	13-3 1.74	13-9 1.93	14-2 2.12	14-8 2.33	15-1 2.54				13.7	
11-10 1.44	12-4 1.61	12-9 1.79	13-2 1.97	13-7 2.15	13-11 2.35	14-4 2.55			16.0	
10-10 1.32	11-3 1.47	11-7 1.63	12-0 1.80	12-4 1.97	12-9 2.14	13-1 2.32	13-5 2.51		19.2	
9-8 1.18	10-0 1.31	10-5 1.46	10-9 1.61	11-1 1.76	11-5 1.92	11-8 2.08	12-0 2.24	12-4 2.41	24.0	
18-0 1.66	18-9 1.86	19-5 2.06	20-0 2.27	20-8 2.49					12.0	2x8
16-10 1.56	17-6 1.74	18-2 1.93	18-9 2.12	19-4 2.33	19-10 2.54				13.7	
15-7 1.44	16-3 1.61	16-9 1.79	17-4 1.97	17-10 2.15	18-5 2.35	18-11 2.55			16.0	
14-3 1.32	14-10 1.47	15-4 1.63	15-10 1.80	16-4 1.97	16-9 2.14	17-3 2.32	17-8 2.51		19.2	
12-9 1.18	13-3 1.31	13-8 1.46	14-2 1.61	14-7 1.76	15-0 1.92	15-5 2.08	15-10 2.24	16-3 2.41	24.0	
23-0 1.66	23-11 1.86	24-9 2.06	25-6 2.27	26-4 2.49					12.0	2x10
21-6 1.56	22-4 1.74	23-2 1.93	23-11 2.12	24-7 2.33	25-4 2.54				13.7	
19-11 1.44	20-8 1.61	21-5 1.79	22-1 1.97	22-10 2.15	23-5 2.35	24-1 2.55			16.0	
18-2 1.32	18-11 1.47	19-7 1.63	20-2 1.80	20-10 1.97	21-5 2.14	22-0 2.32	22-7 2.51		19.2	
16-3 1.18	16-11 1.31	17-6 1.46	18-1 1.61	18-7 1.76	19-2 1.92	19-8 2.08	20-2 2.24	20-8 2.41	24.0	
28-0 1.66	29-1 1.86	30-1 2.06	31-1 2.27	32-0 2.49					12.0	2x12
26-2 1.56	27-2 1.74	28-2 1.93	29-1 2.12	29-11 2.33	30-10 2.54				13.7	
24-3 1.44	25-2 1.61	26-0 1.79	26-11 1.97	27-9 2.15	28-6 2.35	29-4 2.55			16.0	
22-2 1.32	23-0 1.47	23-9 1.63	24-7 1.80	25-4 1.97	26-0 2.14	26-9 2.32	27-5 2.51		19.2	
19-10 1.18	20-6 1.31	21-3 1.46	21-11 1.61	22-8 1.76	23-3 1.92	23-11 2.08	24-7 2.24	25-2 2.41	24.0	

Note: The required modulus of elasticity, E, in 1,000,000 pounds per square inch is shown below each span.

TABLE NO. 25-21-R-5—LOW OR HIGH SLOPE RAFTERS
30 Pounds Per Square Foot Live Load
(Supporting Plaster Ceiling)

DESIGN CRITERIA:
Strength - 15 pounds per square foot dead load plus 30 pounds per square foot live load determines required fiber stress.
Deflection - For 30 pounds per square foot live load. Limited to span in inches divided by 360.

RAFTER SIZE (IN)	SPACING (IN)	Allowable Extreme Fiber Stress in Bending F_b (psi)									
		300	400	500	600	700	890	900	1000	1100	1200
2x6	12.0	5-10 0.19	6-8 0.29	7-6 0.41	8-2 0.54	8-10 0.68	9-6 0.83	10-0 0.99	10-7 1.15	11-1 1.33	11-7 1.52
	13.7	5-5 0.18	6-3 0.27	7-0 0.38	7-8 0.50	8-3 0.63	8-10 0.77	9-5 0.92	9-11 1.08	10-5 1.25	10-10 1.42
	16.0	5-0 0.16	5-10 0.25	6-6 0.35	7-1 0.46	7-8 0.59	8-2 0.72	8-8 0.85	9-2 1.00	9-7 1.15	10-0 1.31
	19.2	4-7 0.15	5-4 0.23	5-11 0.32	6-6 0.42	7-0 0.53	7-6 0.65	7-11 0.78	8-4 0.91	8-9 1.05	9-2 1.20
	24.0	4-1 0.13	4-9 0.21	5-4 0.29	5-10 0.38	6-3 0.48	6-8 0.58	7-1 0.70	7-6 0.82	7-10 0.94	8-2 1.07
2x8	12.0	7-8 0.19	8-10 0.29	9-10 0.41	10-10 0.54	11-8 0.68	12-6 0.83	13-3 0.99	13-11 1.15	14-8 1.33	15-3 1.52
	13.7	7-2 0.18	8-3 0.27	9-3 0.38	10-1 0.50	10-11 0.63	11-8 0.77	12-5 0.92	13-1 1.08	13-8 1.25	14-4 1.42
	16.0	6-7 0.16	7-8 0.25	8-7 0.35	9-4 0.46	10-1 0.59	10-10 0.72	11-6 0.85	12-1 1.00	12-8 1.15	13-3 1.31
	19.2	6-1 0.15	7-0 0.23	7-10 0.32	8-7 0.42	9-3 0.53	9-10 0.65	10-6 0.78	11-0 0.91	11-7 1.05	12-1 1.20
	24.0	5-5 0.13	6-3 0.21	7-0 0.29	7-8 0.38	8-3 0.48	8-10 0.58	9-4 0.70	9-10 0.82	10-4 0.94	10-10 1.07
2x10	12.0	9-9 0.19	11-3 0.29	12-7 0.41	13-9 0.54	14-11 0.68	15-11 0.83	16-11 0.99	17-10 1.15	18-8 1.33	19-6 1.52
	13.7	9-1 0.18	10-6 0.27	11-9 0.38	12-11 0.50	13-11 0.63	14-11 0.77	15-10 0.92	16-8 1.08	17-6 1.25	18-3 1.42
	16.0	8-5 0.16	9-9 0.25	10-11 0.35	11-11 0.46	12-11 0.59	13-9 0.72	14-8 0.85	15-5 1.00	16-2 1.15	16-11 1.31
	19.2	7-8 0.15	8-11 0.23	9-11 0.32	10-11 0.42	11-9 0.53	12-7 0.65	13-4 0.78	14-1 0.91	14-9 1.05	15-5 1.20
	24.0	6-11 0.13	8-0 0.21	8-11 0.29	9-9 0.38	10-6 0.48	11-3 0.58	11-11 0.70	12-7 0.82	13-2 0.94	13-9 1.07
2x12	12.0	11-10 0.19	13-8 0.29	15-4 0.41	16-9 0.54	18-1 0.68	19-4 0.83	20-6 0.99	21-8 1.15	22-8 1.33	23-9 1.52
	13.7	11-1 0.18	12-10 0.27	14-4 0.38	15-8 0.50	16-11 0.63	18-1 0.77	19-3 0.92	20-3 1.08	21-3 1.25	22-2 1.42
	16.0	10-3 0.16	11-10 0.25	13-3 0.35	14-6 0.46	15-8 0.59	16-9 0.72	17-9 0.85	18-9 1.00	19-8 1.15	20-6 1.31
	19.2	9-5 0.15	10-10 0.23	12-1 0.32	13-3 0.42	14-4 0.53	15-4 0.65	16-3 0.78	17-1 0.91	17-11 1.05	18-9 1.20
	24.0	8-5 0.13	9-8 0.21	10-10 0.29	11-10 0.38	12-10 0.48	13-8 0.58	14-6 0.70	15-4 0.82	16-1 0.94	16-9 1.07

Note: The required modulus of elasticity, E, in 1,000,000 pounds per square inch is shown below each span.

RAFTERS: Spans are measured along the horizontal projection and loads are considered as applied on the horizontal projection.

Allowable Extreme Fiber Stress in Bending F_b (psi)									RAFTER SPACING (IN)	SIZE (IN)
1300	1400	1500	1600	1700	1800	1900	2000	2100		
12-1 1.71	12-6 1.91	13-0 2.12	13-5 2.34	13-10 2.56					12.0	2x6
11-3 1.60	11-9 1.79	12-2 1.98	12-6 2.19	12-11 2.39					13.7	
10-5 1.48	10-10 1.66	11-3 1.84	11-7 2.02	11-11 2.22	12-4 2.41				16.0	
9-6 1.35	9-11 1.51	10-3 1.68	10-7 1.85	10-11 2.02	11-3 2.20	11-6 2.39	11-10 2.58		19.2	
8-6 1.21	8-10 1.35	9-2 1.50	9-6 1.65	9-9 1.81	10-0 1.97	10-4 2.14	10-7 2.31	10-10 2.48	24.0	
15-11 1.71	16-6 1.91	17-1 2.12	17-8 2.34	18-2 2.56					12.0	2x8
14-11 1.60	15-5 1.79	16-0 1.98	16-6 2.19	17-0 2.39					13.7	
13-9 1.48	14-4 1.66	14-10 1.84	15-3 2.02	15-9 2.22	16-3 2.41				16.0	
12-7 1.35	13-1 1.51	13-6 1.68	13-11 1.85	14-5 2.02	14-10 2.20	15-2 2.39	15-7 2.58		19.2	
11-3 1.21	11-8 1.35	12-1 1.50	12-6 1.65	12-10 1.81	13-3 1.97	13-7 2.14	13-11 2.31	14-4 2.48	24.0	
20-4 1.71	21-1 1.91	21-10 2.12	22-6 2.34	23-3 2.56					12.0	2x10
19-0 1.60	19-8 1.79	20-5 1.98	21-1 2.19	21-9 2.39					13.7	
17-7 1.48	18-3 1.66	18-11 1.84	19-6 2.02	20-1 2.22	20-8 2.41				16.0	
16-1 1.35	16-8 1.51	17-3 1.68	17-10 1.85	18-4 2.02	18-11 2.20	19-5 2.39	19-11 2.58		19.2	
14-4 1.21	14-11 1.35	15-5 1.50	15-11 1.65	16-5 1.81	16-11 1.97	17-4 2.14	17-10 2.31	18-3 2.48	24.0	
24-8 1.71	25-7 1.91	26-6 2.12	27-5 2.34	28-3 2.56					12.0	2x12
23-1 1.60	24-0 1.79	24-10 1.98	25-7 2.19	26-5 2.39					13.7	
21-5 1.48	22-2 1.66	23-0 1.84	23-9 2.02	24-5 2.22	25-2 2.41				16.0	
19-6 1.35	20-3 1.51	21-0 1.68	21-8 1.85	22-4 2.02	23-0 2.20	23-7 2.39	24-2 2.58		19.2	
17-5 1.21	18-1 1.35	18-9 1.50	19-4 1.65	20-0 1.81	20-6 1.97	21-1 2.14	21-8 2.31	22-2 2.48	24.0	

Note: The required modulus of elasticity, E, in 1,000,000 pounds per square inch is shown below each span.

TABLE NO. 25-21-R-6—LOW OR HIGH SLOPE RAFTERS
40 Pounds Per Square Foot Live Load
(Supporting Plaster Ceiling)

DESIGN CRITERIA:
Strength - 15 pounds per square foot dead load plus 40 pounds per square foot live load determines required fiber stress.
Deflection - For 40 pounds per square foot live load. Limited to span in inches divided by 360.

RAFTER SIZE (IN)	RAFTER SPACING (IN)	Allowable Extreme Fiber Stress in Bending F_b (psi)									
		300	400	500	600	700	800	900	1000	1100	1200
2x6	12.0	5-3 0.19	6-1 0.29	6-9 0.40	7-5 0.53	8-0 0.67	8-7 0.82	9-1 0.97	9-7 1.14	10-0 1.31	10-6 1.50
	13.7	4-11 0.18	5-8 0.27	6-4 0.38	6-11 0.50	7-6 0.62	8-0 0.76	8-6 0.91	8-11 1.07	9-5 1.23	9-10 1.40
	16.0	4-6 0.16	5-3 0.25	5-10 0.35	6-5 0.46	6-11 0.58	7-5 0.71	7-10 0.84	8-3 0.99	8-8 1.14	9-1 1.30
	19.2	4-2 0.15	4-9 0.23	5-4 0.32	5-10 0.42	6-4 0.53	6-9 0.64	7-2 0.77	7-7 0.90	7-11 1.04	8-3 1.18
	24.0	3-8 0.13	4-3 0.20	4-9 0.28	5-3 0.37	5-8 0.47	6-1 0.58	6-5 0.69	6-9 0.81	7-1 0.93	7-5 1.06
2x8	12.0	6-11 0.19	8-0 0.29	8-11 0.40	9-9 0.53	10-7 0.67	11-3 0.82	12-0 0.97	12-7 1.14	13-3 1.31	13-10 1.50
	13.7	6-6 0.18	7-6 0.27	8-4 0.38	9-2 0.50	9-11 0.62	10-7 0.76	11-2 0.91	11-10 1.07	12-5 1.23	12-11 1.40
	16.0	6-0 0.16	6-11 0.25	7-9 0.35	8-6 0.46	9-2 0.58	9-9 0.71	10-4 0.84	10-11 0.99	11-6 1.14	12-0 1.30
	19.2	5-6 0.15	6-4 0.23	7-1 0.32	7-9 0.42	8-4 0.53	8-11 0.64	9-6 0.77	10-0 0.90	10-6 1.04	10-11 1.18
	24.0	4-11 0.13	5-8 0.20	6-4 0.28	6-11 0.37	7-6 0.47	8-0 0.58	8-6 0.69	8-11 0.81	9-4 0.93	9-9 1.06
2x10	12.0	8-10 0.19	10-2 0.29	11-5 0.40	12-6 0.53	13-6 0.67	14-5 0.82	15-3 0.97	16-1 1.14	16-11 1.31	17-8 1.50
	13.7	8-3 0.18	9-6 0.27	10-8 0.38	11-8 0.50	12-7 0.62	13-6 0.76	14-3 0.91	15-1 1.07	15-10 1.23	16-6 1.40
	16.0	7-8 0.16	8-10 0.25	9-10 0.35	10-10 0.46	11-8 0.58	12-6 0.71	13-3 0.84	13-11 0.99	14-8 1.14	15-3 1.30
	19.2	7-0 0.15	8-1 0.23	9-0 0.32	9-10 0.42	10-8 0.53	11-5 0.64	12-1 0.77	12-9 0.90	13-4 1.04	13-11 1.18
	24.0	6-3 0.13	7-2 0.20	8-1 0.28	8-10 0.37	9-6 0.47	10-2 0.58	10-10 0.69	11-5 0.81	11-11 0.93	12-6 1.06
2x12	12.0	10-9 0.19	12-5 0.29	13-10 0.40	15-2 0.53	16-5 0.67	17-6 0.82	18-7 0.97	19-7 1.14	20-6 1.31	21-5 1.50
	13.7	10-0 0.18	11-7 0.27	12-11 0.38	14-2 0.50	15-4 0.62	16-5 0.76	17-5 0.91	18-4 1.07	19-3 1.23	20-1 1.40
	16.0	9-3 0.16	10-9 0.25	12-0 0.35	13-2 0.46	14-2 0.58	15-2 0.71	16-1 0.84	17-0 0.99	17-9 1.14	18-7 1.30
	19.2	8-6 0.15	9-10 0.23	10-11 0.32	12-0 0.42	12-11 0.53	13-10 0.64	14-8 0.77	15-6 0.90	16-3 1.04	17-0 1.18
	24.0	7-7 0.13	8-9 0.20	9-10 0.28	10-9 0.37	11-7 0.47	12-5 0.58	13-2 0.69	13-10 0.81	14-6 0.93	15-2 1.06

Note: The required modulus of elasticity, E, in 1,000,000 pounds per square inch is shown below each span.

RAFTERS: Spans are measured along the horizontal projection and loads are considered as applied on the horizontal projection.

Allowable Extreme Fiber Stress in Bending F_b (psi)									RAFTER SPACING (IN)	SIZE (IN)
1300	1400	1500	1600	1700	1800	1900	2000	2100		
10-11 1.69	11-4 1.89	11-9 2.09	12-1 2.31	12-6 2.53					12.0	2x6
10-3 1.58	10-7 1.77	11-0 1.96	11-4 2.16	11-8 2.36	12-0 2.57				13.7	2x6
9-5 1.46	9-10 1.63	10-2 1.81	10-6 2.00	10-10 2.19	11-1 2.38	11-5 2.58			16.0	2x6
8-8 1.34	8-11 1.49	9-3 1.65	9-7 1.82	9-10 2.00	10-2 2.18	10-5 2.36	10-8 2.55		19.2	2x6
7-9 1.19	8-0 1.33	8-3 1.48	8-7 1.63	8-10 1.79	9-1 1.95	9-4 2.11	9-7 2.28	9-10 2.45	24.0	2x6
14-5 1.69	14-11 1.89	15-5 2.09	16-0 2.31	16-5 2.53					12.0	2x8
13-6 1.58	14-0 1.77	14-6 1.96	14-11 2.16	15-5 2.36	15-10 2.57				13.7	2x8
12-6 1.46	12-11 1.63	13-5 1.81	13-10 2.00	14-3 2.19	14-8 2.38	15-1 2.58			16.0	2x8
11-5 1.34	11-10 1.49	12-3 1.65	12-7 1.82	13-0 2.00	13-5 2.18	13-9 2.36	14-1 2.55		19.2	2x8
10-2 1.19	10-7 1.33	10-11 1.48	11-3 1.63	11-8 1.79	12-0 1.95	12-4 2.11	12-7 2.28	12-11 2.45	24.0	2x8
18-4 1.69	19-1 1.89	19-9 2.09	20-4 2.31	21-0 2.53					12.0	2x10
17-2 1.58	17-10 1.77	18-5 1.96	19-1 2.16	19-8 2.36	20-2 2.57				13.7	2x10
15-11 1.46	16-6 1.63	17-1 1.81	17-8 2.00	18-2 2.19	18-9 2.38	19-3 2.58			16.0	2x10
14-6 1.34	15-1 1.49	15-7 1.65	16-1 1.82	16-7 2.00	17-1 2.18	17-7 2.36	18-0 2.55		19.2	2x10
13-0 1.19	13-6 1.33	13-11 1.48	14-5 1.63	14-10 1.79	15-3 1.95	15-8 2.11	16-1 2.28	16-6 2.45	24.0	2x10
22-4 1.69	23-2 1.89	24-0 2.09	24-9 2.31	25-6 2.53					12.0	2x12
20-11 1.58	21-8 1.77	22-5 1.96	23-2 2.16	23-11 2.36	24-7 2.57				13.7	2x12
19-4 1.46	20-1 1.63	20-9 1.81	21-5 2.00	22-1 2.19	22-9 2.38	23-5 2.58			16.0	2x12
17-8 1.34	18-4 1.49	19-0 1.65	19-7 1.82	20-2 2.00	20-9 2.18	21-4 2.36	21-11 2.55		19.2	2x12
15-9 1.19	16-5 1.33	17-0 1.48	17-6 1.63	18-1 1.79	18-7 1.95	19-1 2.11	19-7 2.28	20-1 2.45	24.0	2x12

Note: The required modulus of elasticity, E, in 1,000,000 pounds per square inch is shown below each span.

TABLE NO. 25-21-R-7—LOW SLOPE RAFTERS
Slope 3 in 12 or less—20 Pounds Per Square Foot Live Load (No Ceiling Load)

DESIGN CRITERIA:
Strength - 10 pounds per square foot dead load plus 20 pounds per square foot live load determines required fiber stress.
Deflection - For 20 pounds per square foot live load. Limited to span in inches divided by 240.

RAFTER SIZE (IN)	RAFTER SPACING (IN)	Allowable Extreme Fiber Stress in Bending F_b (psi)										
		300	400	500	600	700	800	900	1000	1100	1200	1300
2x6	12.0	7-1 0.15	8-2 0.24	9-2 0.33	10-0 0.44	10-10 0.55	11-7 0.67	12-4 0.80	13-0 0.94	13-7 1.09	14-2 1.24	14-9 1.40
	13.7	6-8 0.14	7-8 0.22	8-7 0.31	9-5 0.41	10-2 0.52	10-10 0.63	11-6 0.75	12-2 0.88	12-9 1.02	13-3 1.16	13-10 1.31
	16.0	6-2 0.13	7-1 0.21	7-11 0.29	8-8 0.38	9-5 0.48	10-0 0.58	10-8 0.70	11-3 0.82	11-9 0.94	12-4 1.07	12-10 1.21
	19.2	5-7 0.12	6-6 0.19	7-3 0.26	7-11 0.35	8-7 0.44	9-2 0.53	9-9 0.64	10-3 0.75	10-9 0.86	11-3 0.98	11-8 1.10
	24.0	5-0 0.11	5-10 0.17	6-6 0.24	7-1 0.31	7-8 0.39	8-2 0.48	8-8 0.57	9-2 0.67	9-7 0.77	10-0 0.88	10-5 0.99
2x8	12.0	9-4 0.15	10-10 0.24	12-1 0.33	13-3 0.44	14-4 0.55	15-3 0.67	16-3 0.80	17-1 0.94	17-11 1.09	18-9 1.24	19-6 1.40
	13.7	8-9 0.14	10-1 0.22	11-4 0.31	12-5 0.41	13-4 0.52	14-4 0.63	15-2 0.75	16-0 0.88	16-9 1.02	17-6 1.16	18-3 1.31
	16.0	8-1 0.13	9-4 0.21	10-6 0.29	11-6 0.38	12-5 0.48	13-3 0.58	14-0 0.70	14-10 0.82	15-6 0.94	16-3 1.07	16-10 1.21
	19.2	7-5 0.12	8-7 0.19	9-7 0.26	10-6 0.35	11-4 0.44	12-1 0.53	12-10 0.64	13-6 0.75	14-2 0.86	14-10 0.98	15-5 1.10
	24.0	6-7 0.11	7-8 0.17	8-7 0.24	9-4 0.31	10-1 0.39	10-10 0.48	11-6 0.57	12-1 0.67	12-8 0.77	13-3 0.88	13-9 0.99
2x10	12.0	11-11 0.15	13-9 0.24	15-5 0.33	16-11 0.44	18-3 0.55	19-6 0.67	20-8 0.80	21-10 0.94	22-10 1.09	23-11 1.24	24-10 1.40
	13.7	11-2 0.14	12-11 0.22	14-5 0.31	15-10 0.41	17-1 0.52	18-3 0.63	19-4 0.75	20-5 0.88	21-5 1.02	22-4 1.16	23-3 1.31
	16.0	10-4 0.13	11-11 0.21	13-4 0.29	14-8 0.38	15-10 0.48	16-11 0.58	17-11 0.70	18-11 0.82	19-10 0.94	20-8 1.07	21-6 1.21
	19.2	9-5 0.12	10-11 0.19	12-2 0.26	13-4 0.35	14-5 0.44	15-5 0.53	16-4 0.64	17-3 0.75	18-1 0.86	18-11 0.98	19-8 1.10
	24.0	8-5 0.11	9-9 0.17	10-11 0.24	11-11 0.31	12-11 0.39	13-9 0.48	14-8 0.57	15-5 0.67	16-2 0.77	16-11 0.88	17-7 0.99
2x12	12.0	14-6 0.15	16-9 0.24	18-9 0.33	20-6 0.44	22-2 0.55	23-9 0.67	25-2 0.80	26-6 0.94	27-10 1.09	29-1 1.24	30-3 1.40
	13.7	13-7 0.14	15-8 0.22	17-6 0.31	19-3 0.41	20-9 0.52	22-2 0.63	23-6 0.75	24-10 0.88	26-0 1.02	27-2 1.16	28-3 1.31
	16.0	12-7 0.13	14-6 0.21	16-3 0.29	17-9 0.38	19-3 0.48	20-6 0.58	21-9 0.70	23-0 0.82	24-1 0.94	25-2 1.07	26-2 1.21
	19.2	11-6 0.12	13-3 0.19	14-10 0.26	16-3 0.35	17-6 0.44	18-9 0.53	19-11 0.64	21-0 0.75	22-0 0.86	23-0 0.98	23-11 1.10
	24.0	10-3 0.11	11-10 0.17	13-3 0.24	14-6 0.31	15-8 0.39	16-9 0.48	17-9 0.57	18-9 0.67	19-8 0.77	20-6 0.88	21-5 0.99

Note: The required modulus of elasticity, E, in 1,000,000 pounds per square inch is shown below each span.

RAFTERS: Spans are measured along the horizontal projection and loads are considered as applied on the horizontal projection.

Allowable Extreme Fiber Stress in Bending F_b (psi)										RAFTER	
1400	1500	1600	1700	1800	1900	2000	2100	2200	2400	SPACING (IN)	SIZE (IN)
15-4 1.56	15-11 1.73	16-5 1.91	16-11 2.09	17-5 2.28	17-10 2.47					12.0	2x6
14-4 1.46	14-10 1.62	15-4 1.78	15-10 1.95	16-3 2.13	16-9 2.31	17-2 2.49				13.7	
13-3 1.35	13-9 1.50	14-2 1.65	14-8 1.81	15-1 1.97	15-6 2.14	15-11 2.31	16-3 2.48			16.0	
12-2 1.23	12-7 1.37	13-0 1.51	13-4 1.65	13-9 1.80	14-2 1.95	14-6 2.11	14-10 2.27	15-2 2.43		19.2	
10-10 1.10	11-3 1.22	11-7 1.35	11-11 1.48	12-4 1.61	12-8 1.75	13-0 1.89	13-3 2.03	13-7 2.18	14-2 2.48	24.0	
20-3 1.56	20-11 1.73	21-7 1.91	22-3 2.09	22-11 2.28	23-7 2.47					12.0	2x8
18-11 1.46	19-7 1.62	20-3 1.78	20-10 1.95	21-5 2.13	22-0 2.31	22-7 2.49				13.7	
17-6 1.35	18-2 1.50	18-9 1.65	19-4 1.81	19-10 1.97	20-5 2.14	20-11 2.31	21-5 2.48			16.0	
16-0 1.23	16-7 1.37	17-1 1.51	17-7 1.65	18-2 1.80	18-7 1.95	19-1 2.11	19-7 2.27	20-0 2.43		19.2	
14-4 1.10	14-10 1.22	15-3 1.35	15-9 1.48	16-3 1.61	16-8 1.75	17-1 1.89	17-6 2.03	17-11 2.18	18-9 2.48	24.0	
25-10 1.56	26-8 1.73	27-7 1.91	28-5 2.09	29-3 2.28	30-1 2.47					12.0	2x10
24-2 1.46	25-0 1.62	25-10 1.78	26-7 1.95	27-4 2.13	28-1 2.31	28-10 2.49				13.7	
22-4 1.35	23-2 1.50	23-11 1.65	24-7 1.81	25-4 1.97	26-0 2.14	26-8 2.31	27-4 2.48			16.0	
20-5 1.23	21-1 1.37	21-10 1.51	22-6 1.65	23-2 1.80	23-9 1.95	24-5 2.11	25-0 2.27	25-7 2.43		19.2	
18-3 1.10	18-11 1.22	19-6 1.35	20-1 1.48	20-8 1.61	21-3 1.75	21-10 1.89	22-4 2.03	22-10 2.18	23-11 2.48	24.0	
31-4 1.56	32-6 1.73	33-6 1.91	34-7 2.09	35-7 2.28	36-7 2.47					12.0	2x12
29-4 1.46	30-5 1.62	31-4 1.78	32-4 1.95	33-3 2.13	34-2 2.31	35-1 2.49				13.7	
27-2 1.35	28-2 1.50	29-1 1.65	29-11 1.81	30-10 1.97	31-8 2.14	32-6 2.31	33-3 2.48			16.0	
24-10 1.23	25-8 1.37	26-6 1.51	27-4 1.65	28-2 1.80	28-11 1.95	29-8 2.11	30-5 2.27	31-1 2.43		19.2	
22-2 1.10	23-0 1.22	23-9 1.35	24-5 1.48	25-2 1.61	25-10 1.75	26-6 1.89	27-2 2.03	27-10 2.18	29-1 2.48	24.0	

Note: The required modulus of elasticity, E, in 1,000,000 pounds per square inch is shown below each span.

TABLE NO. 25-21-R-8—LOW SLOPE RAFTERS
Slope 3 in 12 or less—30 Pounds Per Square Foot Live Load
(No Ceiling Load)

DESIGN CRITERIA:
Strength - 10 pounds per square foot dead load plus 30 pounds per square foot live load determines required fiber stress.
Deflection - For 30 pounds per square foot live load. Limited to span in inches divided by 240.

RAFTER SIZE (IN)	SPACING (IN)	Allowable Extreme Fiber Stress in Bending F_b (psi)										
		300	400	500	600	700	800	900	1000	1100	1200	1300
2x6	12.0	6-2 0.15	7-1 0.23	7-11 0.32	8-8 0.43	9-5 0.54	10-0 0.66	10-8 0.78	11-3 0.92	11-9 1.06	12-4 1.21	12-10 1.36
	13.7	5-9 0.14	6-8 0.22	7-5 0.30	8-2 0.40	8-9 0.50	9-5 0.61	10-0 0.73	10-6 0.86	11-0 0.99	11-6 1.13	12-0 1.27
	16.0	5-4 0.13	6-2 0.20	6-11 0.28	7-6 0.37	8-2 0.47	8-8 0.57	9-3 0.68	9-9 0.80	10-2 0.92	10-8 1.05	11-1 1.18
	19.2	4-10 0.12	5-7 0.18	6-3 0.26	6-11 0.34	7-5 0.43	7-11 0.52	8-5 0.62	8-11 0.73	9-4 0.84	9-9 0.95	10-1 1.08
	24.0	4-4 0.11	5-0 0.16	5-7 0.23	6-2 0.30	6-8 0.38	7-1 0.46	7-6 0.55	7-11 0.65	8-4 0.75	8-8 0.85	9-1 0.96
2x8	12.0	8-1 0.15	9-4 0.23	10-6 0.32	11-6 0.43	12-5 0.54	13-3 0.66	14-0 0.78	14-10 0.92	15-6 1.06	16-3 1.21	16-10 1.36
	13.7	7-7 0.14	8-9 0.22	9-9 0.30	10-9 0.40	11-7 0.50	12-5 0.61	13-2 0.73	13-10 0.86	14-6 0.99	15-2 1.13	15-9 1.27
	16.0	7-0 0.13	8-1 0.20	9-1 0.28	9-11 0.37	10-9 0.47	11-6 0.57	12-2 0.68	12-10 0.80	13-5 0.92	14-0 1.05	14-7 1.18
	19.2	6-5 0.12	7-5 0.18	8-3 0.26	9-1 0.34	9-9 0.43	10-6 0.52	11-1 0.62	11-8 0.73	12-3 0.84	12-10 0.95	13-4 1.08
	24.0	5-9 0.11	6-7 0.16	7-5 0.23	8-1 0.30	8-9 0.38	9-4 0.46	9-11 0.55	10-6 0.65	11-0 0.75	11-6 0.85	11-11 0.96
2x10	12.0	10-4 0.15	11-11 0.23	13-4 0.32	14-8 0.43	15-10 0.54	16-11 0.66	17-11 0.78	18-11 0.92	19-10 1.06	20-8 1.21	21-6 1.36
	13.7	9-8 0.14	11-2 0.22	12-6 0.30	13-8 0.40	14-9 0.50	15-10 0.61	16-9 0.73	17-8 0.86	18-6 0.99	19-4 1.13	20-2 1.27
	16.0	8-11 0.13	10-4 0.20	11-7 0.28	12-8 0.37	13-8 0.47	14-8 0.57	15-6 0.68	16-4 0.80	17-2 0.92	17-11 1.05	18-8 1.18
	19.2	8-2 0.12	9-5 0.18	10-7 0.26	11-7 0.34	12-6 0.43	13-4 0.52	14-2 0.62	14-11 0.73	15-8 0.84	16-4 0.95	17-0 1.08
	24.0	7-4 0.11	8-5 0.16	9-5 0.23	10-4 0.30	11-2 0.38	11-11 0.46	12-8 0.55	13-4 0.65	14-0 0.75	14-8 0.85	15-3 0.96
2x12	12.0	12-7 0.15	14-6 0.23	16-3 0.32	17-9 0.43	19-3 0.54	20-6 0.66	21-9 0.78	23-0 0.92	24-1 1.06	25-2 1.21	26-2 1.36
	13.7	11-9 0.14	13-7 0.22	15-2 0.30	16-8 0.40	18-0 0.50	19-3 0.61	20-5 0.73	21-6 0.86	22-6 0.99	23-6 1.13	24-6 1.27
	16.0	10-11 0.13	12-7 0.20	14-1 0.28	15-5 0.37	16-8 0.47	17-9 0.57	18-10 0.68	19-11 0.80	20-10 0.92	21-9 1.05	22-8 1.18
	19.2	9-11 0.12	11-6 0.18	12-10 0.26	14-1 0.34	15-2 0.43	16-3 0.52	17-3 0.62	18-2 0.73	19-0 0.84	19-11 0.95	20-8 1.08
	24.0	8-11 0.11	10-3 0.16	11-6 0.23	12-7 0.30	13-7 0.38	14-6 0.46	15-5 0.55	16-3 0.65	17-0 0.75	17-9 0.85	18-6 0.96

Note: The required modulus of elasticity, *E*, in 1,000,000 pounds per square inch is shown below each span.

RAFTERS: Spans are measured along the horizontal projection and loads are considered as applied on the horizontal projection.

Allowable Extreme Fiber Stress in Bending F_b (psi)										RAFTER	
1400	1500	1600	1700	1800	1900	2000	2100	2200	2400	SPACING (IN)	SIZE (IN)
13-3 1.52	13-9 1 69	14-2 1.86	14-8 2.04	15-1 2.22	15-6 2.41	15-11 2.60				12.0	2x6
12-5 1.42	12-10 1.58	13-3 1.74	13-8 1.90	14-1 2.08	14-6 2.25	14-10 2.43				13.7	
11-6 1.32	11-11 1.46	12-4 1.61	12-8 1.76	13-1 1.92	13-5 2.08	13-9 2.25	14-1 2.42	14-5 2.60		16.0	
10-6 1.20	10-10 1.33	11-3 1.47	11-7 1.61	11-11 1.75	12-3 1.90	12-7 2.05	12-10 2.21	13-2 2.37		19.2	
9-5 1.08	9-9 1.19	10-0 1.31	10-4 1.44	10-8 1.57	10-11 1.70	11-3 1.84	11-6 1.98	11-9 2.12	12-4 2.41	24.0	
17-6 1.52	18-2 1.69	18-9 1.86	19-4 2.04	19-10 2.22	20-5 2.41	20-11 2.60				12.0	2x8
16-5 1.42	16-11 1.58	17-6 1.74	18-1 1.90	18-7 2.08	19-1 2.25	19-7 2.43				13.7	
15-2 1.32	15-8 1.46	16-3 1.61	16-9 1.76	17-2 1.92	17-8 2.08	18-2 2.25	18-7 2.42	19-0 2.60		16.0	
13-10 1.20	14-4 1.33	14-10 1.47	15-3 1.61	15-8 1.75	16-2 1.90	16-7 2.05	16-11 2.21	17-4 2.37		19.2	
12-5 1.08	12-10 1.19	13-3 1.31	13-8 1.44	14-0 1.57	14-5 1.70	14-10 1.84	15-2 1.98	15-6 2.12	16-3 2.41	24.0	
22-4 1.52	23-2 1.69	23-11 1.86	24-7 2.04	25-4 2.22	26-0 2.41	26-8 2.60				12.0	2x10
20-11 1.42	21-8 1.58	22-4 1.74	23-0 1.90	23-8 2.08	24-4 2.25	25-0 2.43				13.7	
19-4 1.32	20-0 1.46	20-8 1.61	21-4 1.76	21-11 1.92	22-6 2.08	23-2 2.25	23-8 2.42	24-3 2.60		16.0	
17-8 1.20	18-3 1.33	18-11 1.47	19-6 1.61	20-0 1.75	20-7 1.90	21-1 2.05	21-8 2.21	22-2 2.37		19.2	
15-10 1.08	16-4 1.19	16-11 1.31	17-5 1.44	17-11 1.57	18-5 1.70	18-11 1.84	19-4 1.98	19-10 2.12	20-8 2.41	24.0	
27-2 1.52	28-2 1.69	29-1 1.86	29-11 2.04	30-10 2.22	31-8 2.41	32-6 2.60				12.0	2x12
25-5 1.42	26-4 1.58	27-2 1.74	28-0 1.90	28-10 2.08	29-7 2.25	30-5 2.43				13.7	
23-6 1.32	24-4 1.46	25-2 1.61	25-11 1.76	26-8 1.92	27-5 2.08	28-2 2.25	28-10 2.42	29-6 2.60		16.0	
21-6 1.20	22-3 1.33	23-0 1.47	23-8 1.61	24-4 1.75	25-0 1.90	25-8 2.05	26-4 2.21	26-11 2.37		19.2	
19-3 1.08	19-11 1.19	20-6 1.31	21-2 1.44	21-9 1.57	22-5 1.70	23-0 1.84	23-6 1.98	24-1 2.12	25-2 2.41	24.0	

Note: The required modulus of elasticity, E, in 1,000,000 pounds per square inch is shown below each span.

TABLE NO. 25-21-R-9—LOW SLOPE RAFTERS
Slope 3 in 12 or less—40 Pounds Per Square Foot Live Load
(No Ceiling Load)

DESIGN CRITERIA:
Strength - 10 pounds per square foot dead load plus 40 pounds per square foot live load determines required fiber stress.
Deflection — For 40 pounds per square foot live load. Limited to span in inches divided by 240.

RAFTER		Allowable Extreme Fiber Stress in Bending F_b (psi)										
SIZE (IN)	SPACING (IN)	300	400	500	600	700	800	900	1000	1100	1200	1300
2x6	12.0	5-6 0.14	6-4 0.22	7-1 0.31	7-9 0.41	8-5 0.51	9-0 0.63	9-6 0.75	10-0 0.88	10-6 1.01	11-0 1.15	11-5 1.30
	13.7	5-2 0.13	5-11 0.21	6-8 0.29	7-3 0.38	7-10 0.48	8-5 0.59	8-11 0.70	9-5 0.82	9-10 0.95	10-3 1.08	10-9 1.22
	16.0	4-9 0.12	5-6 0.19	6-2 0.27	6-9 0.35	7-3 0.44	7-9 0.54	8-3 0.65	8-8 0.76	9-1 0.88	9-6 1.00	9-11 1.12
	19.2	4-4 0.11	5-0 0.18	5-7 0.24	6-2 0.32	6-8 0.41	7-1 0.50	7-6 0.59	7-11 0.69	8-4 0.80	8-8 0.91	9-1 1.03
	24.0	3-11 0.10	4-6 0.16	5-0 0.22	5-6 0.29	5-11 0.36	6-4 0.44	6-9 0.53	7-1 0.62	7-5 0.71	7-9 0.81	8-1 0.92
2x8	12.0	7-3 0.14	8-4 0.22	9-4 0.31	10-3 0.41	11-1 0.51	11-10 0.63	12-7 0.75	13-3 0.88	13-11 1.01	14-6 1.15	15-1 1.30
	13.7	6-9 0.13	7-10 0.21	8-9 0.29	9-7 0.38	10-4 0.48	11-1 0.59	11-9 0.70	12-5 0.82	13-0 0.95	13-7 1.08	14-1 1.22
	16.0	6-3 0.12	7-3 0.19	8-1 0.27	8-11 0.35	9-7 0.44	10-3 0.54	10-11 0.65	11-6 0.76	12-0 0.88	12-7 1.00	13-1 1.12
	19.2	5-9 0.11	6-7 0.18	7-5 0.24	8-1 0.32	8-9 0.41	9-4 0.50	9-11 0.59	10-6 0.69	11-0 0.80	11-6 0.91	11-11 1.03
	24.0	5-2 0.10	5-11 0.16	6-7 0.22	7-3 0.29	7-10 0.36	8-4 0.44	8-11 0.53	9-4 0.62	9-10 0.71	10-3 0.81	10-8 0.92
2x10	12.0	9-3 0.14	10-8 0.22	11-11 0.31	13-1 0.41	14-2 0.51	15-1 0.63	16-0 0.75	16-11 0.88	17-9 1.01	18-6 1.15	19-3 1.30
	13.7	8-8 0.13	10-0 0.21	11-2 0.29	12-3 0.38	13-3 0.48	14-2 0.59	15-0 0.70	15-10 0.82	16-7 0.95	17-4 1.08	18-0 1.22
	16.0	8-0 0.12	9-3 0.19	10-4 0.27	11-4 0.35	12-3 0.44	13-1 0.54	13-11 0.65	14-8 0.76	15-4 0.88	16-0 1.00	16-8 1.12
	19.2	7-4 0.11	8-5 0.18	9-5 0.24	10-4 0.32	11-2 0.41	11-11 0.50	12-8 0.59	13-4 0.69	14-0 0.80	14-8 0.91	15-3 1.03
	24.0	6-6 0.10	7-7 0.16	8-5 0.22	9-3 0.29	10-0 0.36	10-8 0.44	11-4 0.53	11-11 0.62	12-6 0.71	13-1 0.81	13-7 0.92
2x12	12.0	11-3 0.14	13-0 0.22	14-6 0.31	15-11 0.41	17-2 0.51	18-4 0.63	19-6 0.75	20-6 0.88	21-7 1.01	22-6 1.15	23-5 1.30
	13.7	10-6 0.13	12-2 0.21	13-7 0.29	14-11 0.38	16-1 0.48	17-2 0.59	18-3 0.70	19-3 0.82	20-2 0.95	21-1 1.08	21-11 1.22
	16.0	9-9 0.12	11-3 0.19	12-7 0.27	13-9 0.35	14-11 0.44	15-11 0.54	16-11 0.65	17-9 0.76	18-8 0.88	19-6 1.00	20-3 1.12
	19.2	8-11 0.11	10-3 0.18	11-6 0.24	12-7 0.32	13-7 0.41	14-6 0.50	15-5 0.59	16-3 0.69	17-0 0.80	17-9 0.91	18-6 1.03
	24.0	7-11 0.10	9-2 0.16	10-3 0.22	11-3 0.29	12-2 0.36	13-0 0.44	13-9 0.53	14-6 0.62	15-3 0.71	15-11 0.81	16-7 0.92

Note: The required modulus of elasticity, E, in 1,000,000 pounds per square inch is shown below each span.

RAFTERS: Spans are measured along the horizontal projection and loads are considered as applied on the horizontal projection.

Allowable Extreme Fiber Stress in Bending F_b (psi)										RAFTER	
1400	1500	1600	1700	1800	1900	2000	2100	2200	2400	SPACING (IN)	SIZE (IN)
11-11 1.45	12-4 1.61	12-8 1.77	13-1 1.94	13-6 2.12	13-10 2.30	14-2 2.48				12.0	2x6
11-1 1.36	11-6 1.51	11-11 1.66	12-3 1.82	12-7 1.98	12-11 2.15	13-3 2.32	13-7 2.49			13.7	2x6
10-3 1.26	10-8 1.39	11-0 1.54	11-4 1.68	11-8 1.83	12-0 1.99	12-4 2.15	12-7 2.31	12-11 2.48		16.0	2x6
9-5 1.15	9-9 1.27	10-0 1.40	10-4 1.54	10-8 1.67	10-11 1.81	11-3 1.96	11-6 2.11	11-9 2.26	12-4 2.58	19.2	2x6
8-5 1.03	8-8 1.14	9-0 1.25	9-3 1.37	9-6 1.50	9-9 1.62	10-0 1.75	10-3 1.89	10-6 2.02	11-0 2.30	24.0	2x6
15-8 1.45	16-3 1.61	16-9 1.77	17-3 1.94	17-9 2.12	18-3 2.30	18-9 2.48				12.0	2x8
14-8 1.36	15-2 1.51	15-8 1.66	16-2 1.82	16-7 1.98	17-1 2.15	17-6 2.32	17-11 2.49			13.7	2x8
13-7 1.26	14-0 1.39	14-6 1.54	14-11 1.68	15-5 1.83	15-10 1.99	16-3 2.15	16-7 2.31	17-0 2.48		16.0	2x8
12-5 1.15	12-10 1.27	13-3 1.40	13-8 1.54	14-0 1.67	14-5 1.81	14-10 1.96	15-2 2.11	15-6 2.26	16-3 2.58	19.2	2x8
11-1 1.03	11-6 1.14	11-10 1.25	12-2 1.37	12-7 1.50	12-11 1.62	13-3 1.75	13-7 1.89	13-11 2.02	14-6 2.30	24.0	2x8
20-0 1.45	20-8 1.61	21-4 1.77	22-0 1.94	22-8 2.12	23-3 2.30	23-11 2.48				12.0	2x10
18-8 1.36	19-4 1.51	20-0 1.66	20-7 1.82	21-2 1.98	21-9 2.15	22-4 2.32	22-11 2.49			13.7	2x10
17-4 1.26	17-11 1.39	18-6 1.54	19-1 1.68	19-7 1.83	20-2 1.99	20-8 2.15	21-2 2.31	21-8 2.48		16.0	2x10
15-10 1.15	16-4 1.27	16-11 1.40	17-5 1.54	17-11 1.67	18-5 1.81	18-11 1.96	19-4 2.11	19-10 2.26	20-8 2.58	19.2	2x10
14-2 1.03	14-8 1.14	15-1 1.25	15-7 1.37	16-0 1.50	16-6 1.62	16-11 1.75	17-4 1.89	17-9 2.02	18-6 2.30	24.0	2x10
24-4 1.45	25-2 1.61	26-0 1.77	26-9 1.94	27-7 2.12	28-4 2.30	29-1 2.48				12.0	2x12
22-9 1.36	23-6 1.51	24-4 1.66	25-1 1.82	25-9 1.98	26-6 2.15	27-2 2.32	27-10 2.49			13.7	2x12
21-1 1.26	21-9 1.39	22-6 1.54	23-2 1.68	23-10 1.83	24-6 1.99	25-2 2.15	25-9 2.31	26-5 2.48		16.0	2x12
19-3 1.15	19-11 1.27	20-6 1.40	21-2 1.54	21-9 1.67	22-5 1.81	23-0 1.96	23-6 2.11	24-1 2.26	25-2 2.58	19.2	2x12
17-2 1.03	17-9 1.14	18-4 1.25	18-11 1.37	19-6 1.50	20-0 1.62	20-6 1.75	21-1 1.89	21-7 2.02	22-6 2.30	24.0	2x12

Note: The required modulus of elasticity, E, in 1,000,000 pounds per square inch is shown below each span.

TABLE NO. 25-21-R-10—HIGH SLOPE RAFTERS
Slope Over 3 in 12-20 Pounds Per Square Foot Live Load (Heavy Roof Covering)

DESIGN CRITERIA:
Strength - 15 pounds per square foot dead load plus 20 pounds per square foot live load determines required fiber stress.
Deflection - For 20 pounds per square foot live load. Limited to span in inches divided by 180.

RAFTER SIZE (IN)	RAFTER SPACING (IN)	Allowable Extreme Fiber Stress in Bending F_b (psi)											
		200	300	400	500	600	700	800	900	1000	1100	1200	1300
2x4	12.0	3-5 0.05	4-2 0.09	4-10 0.14	5-5 0.20	5-11 0.26	6-5 0.33	6-10 0.40	7-3 0.48	7-8 0.56	8-0 0.65	8-4 0.74	8-8 0.83
	13.7	3-2 0.05	3-11 0.09	4-6 0.13	5-1 0.19	5-6 0.24	6-0 0.31	6-5 0.38	6-9 0.45	7-2 0.52	7-6 0.61	7-10 0.69	8-2 0.78
	16.0	2-11 0.04	3-7 0.08	4-2 0.12	4-8 0.17	5-1 0.23	5-6 0.28	5-11 0.35	6-3 0.41	6-7 0.49	6-11 0.56	7-3 0.64	7-6 0.72
	19.2	2-8 0.04	3-4 0.07	3-10 0.11	4-3 0.16	4-8 0.21	5-1 0.26	5-5 0.32	5-9 0.38	6-0 0.44	6-4 0.51	6-7 0.58	6-11 0.66
	24.0	2-5 0.04	2-11 0.07	3-5 0.10	3-10 0.14	4-2 0.18	4-6 0.23	4-10 0.28	5-1 0.34	5-5 0.40	5-8 0.46	5-11 0.52	6-2 0.59
2x6	12.0	5-4 0.05	6-7 0.09	7-7 0.14	8-6 0.20	9-4 0.26	10-0 0.33	10-9 0.40	11-5 0.48	12-0 0.56	12-7 0.65	13-2 0.74	13-8 0.83
	13.7	5-0 0.05	6-2 0.09	7-1 0.13	7-11 0.19	8-8 0.24	9-5 0.31	10-0 0.38	10-8 0.45	11-3 0.52	11-9 0.61	12-4 0.69	12-10 0.78
	16.0	4-8 0.04	5-8 0.08	6-7 0.12	7-4 0.17	8-1 0.23	8-8 0.28	9-4 0.35	9-10 0.41	10-5 0.49	10-11 0.56	11-5 0.64	11-10 0.72
	19.2	4-3 0.04	5-2 0.07	6-0 0.11	6-9 0.16	7-4 0.21	7-11 0.26	8-6 0.32	9-0 0.38	9-6 0.44	9-11 0.51	10-5 0.58	10-10 0.66
	24.0	3-10 0.04	4-8 0.07	5-4 0.10	6-0 0.14	6-7 0.18	7-1 0.23	7-7 0.28	8-1 0.34	8-6 0.40	8-11 0.46	9-4 0.52	9-8 0.59
2x8	12.0	7-1 0.05	8-8 0.09	10-0 0.14	11-2 0.20	12-3 0.26	13-3 0.33	14-2 0.40	15-0 0.48	15-10 0.56	16-7 0.65	17-4 0.74	18-0 0.83
	13.7	6-7 0.05	8-1 0.09	9-4 0.13	10-6 0.19	11-6 0.24	12-5 0.31	13-3 0.38	14-0 0.45	14-10 0.52	15-6 0.61	16-3 0.69	16-10 0.78
	16.0	6-2 0.04	7-6 0.08	8-8 0.12	9-8 0.17	10-7 0.23	11-6 0.28	12-3 0.35	13-0 0.41	13-8 0.49	14-4 0.56	15-0 0.64	15-7 0.72
	19.2	5-7 0.04	6-10 0.07	7-11 0.11	8-10 0.16	9-8 0.21	10-6 0.26	11-2 0.32	11-10 0.38	12-6 0.44	13-1 0.51	13-8 0.58	14-3 0.66
	24.0	5-0 0.04	6-2 0.07	7-1 0.10	7-11 0.14	8-8 0.18	9-4 0.23	10-0 0.28	10-7 0.34	11-2 0.40	11-9 0.46	12-3 0.52	12-9 0.59
2x10	12.0	9-0 0.05	11-1 0.09	12-9 0.14	14-3 0.20	15-8 0.26	16-11 0.33	18-1 0.40	19-2 0.48	20-2 0.56	21-2 0.65	22-1 0.74	23-0 0.83
	13.7	8-5 0.05	10-4 0.09	11-11 0.13	13-4 0.19	14-8 0.24	15-10 0.31	16-11 0.38	17-11 0.45	18-11 0.52	19-10 0.61	20-8 0.69	21-6 0.78
	16.0	7-10 0.04	9-7 0.08	11-1 0.12	12-4 0.17	13-6 0.23	14-8 0.28	15-8 0.35	16-7 0.41	17-6 0.49	18-4 0.56	19-2 0.64	19-11 0.72
	19.2	7-2 0.04	8-9 0.07	10-1 0.11	11-3 0.16	12-4 0.21	13-4 0.26	14-3 0.32	15-2 0.38	15-11 0.44	16-9 0.51	17-6 0.58	18-2 0.66
	24.0	6-5 0.04	7-10 0.07	9-0 0.10	10-1 0.14	11-1 0.18	11-11 0.23	12-9 0.28	13-6 0.34	14-3 0.40	15-0 0.46	15-8 0.52	16-3 0.59

Note: The required modulus of elasticity, E, in 1,000,000 pounds per square inch is shown below each span.

RAFTERS: Spans are measured along the horizontal projection and loads are considered as applied on the horizontal projection.

Allowable Extreme Fiber Stress in Bending F_b (psi)												RAFTER	
1400	1500	1600	1700	1800	1900	2000	2100	2200	2400	2700	3000	SPACING (IN)	SIZE (IN)
9-0 0.93	9-4 1.03	9-8 1.14	9-11 1.24	10-3 1.36	10-6 1.47	10-10 1.59	11-1 1.71	11-4 1.83	11-10 2.09	12-7 2.49		12.0	2x4
8-5 0.87	8-9 0.96	9-0 1.06	9-4 1.16	9-7 1.27	9-10 1.37	10-1 1.48	10-4 1.60	10-7 1.71	11-1 1.95	11-9 2.33		13.7	
7-10 0.80	8-1 0.89	8-4 0.98	8-7 1.08	8-10 1.17	9-1 1.27	9-4 1.37	9-7 1.48	9-10 1.59	10-3 1.81	10-10 2.16	11-5 2.53	16.0	
7-2 0.73	7-5 0.81	7-8 0.90	7-10 0.98	8-1 1.07	8-4 1.16	8-6 1.25	8-9 1.35	8-11 1.45	9-4 1.65	9-11 1.97	10-5 2.31	19.2	
6-5 0.66	6-7 0.73	6-10 0.80	7-0 0.88	7-3 0.96	7-5 1.04	7-8 1.12	7-10 1.21	8-0 1.29	8-4 1.48	8-10 1.76	9-4 2.06	24.0	
14-2 0.93	14-8 1.03	15-2 1.14	15-8 1.24	16-1 1.36	16-7 1.47	17-0 1.59	17-5 1.71	17-10 1.83	18-7 2.09	19-9 2.49		12.0	2x6
13-3 0.87	13-9 0.96	14-2 1.06	14-8 1.16	15-1 1.27	15-6 1.37	15-11 1.48	16-3 1.60	16-8 1.71	17-5 1.95	18-5 2.33		13.7	
12-4 0.80	12-9 0.89	13-2 0.98	13-7 1.08	13-11 1.17	14-4 1.27	14-8 1.37	15-1 1.48	15-5 1.59	16-1 1.81	17-1 2.16	18-0 2.53	16.0	
11-3 0.73	11-7 0.81	12-0 0.90	12-4 0.98	12-9 1.07	13-1 1.16	13-5 1.25	13-9 1.35	14-1 1.45	14-8 1.65	15-7 1.97	16-5 2.31	19.2	
10-0 0.66	10-5 0.73	10-9 0.80	11-1 0.88	11-5 0.96	11-8 1.04	12-0 1.12	12-4 1.21	12-7 1.29	13-2 1.48	13-11 1.76	14-8 2.06	24.0	
18-9 0.93	19-5 1.03	20-0 1.14	20-8 1.24	21-3 1.36	21-10 1.47	22-4 1.59	22-11 1.71	23-6 1.83	24-6 2.09	26-0 2.49		12.0	2x8
17-6 0.87	18-2 0.96	18-9 1.06	19-4 1.16	19-10 1.27	20-5 1.37	20-11 1.48	21-5 1.60	21-11 1.71	22-11 1.95	24-4 2.33		13.7	
16-3 0.80	16-9 0.89	17-4 0.98	17-10 1.08	18-5 1.17	18-11 1.27	19-5 1.37	19-10 1.48	20-4 1.59	21-3 1.81	22-6 2.16	23-9 2.53	16.0	
14-10 0.73	15-4 0.81	15-10 0.90	16-4 0.98	16-9 1.07	17-3 1.16	17-8 1.25	18-2 1.35	18-7 1.45	19-5 1.65	20-7 1.97	21-8 2.31	19.2	
13-3 0.66	13-8 0.73	14-2 0.80	14-7 0.88	15-0 0.96	15-5 1.04	15-10 1.12	16-3 1.21	16-7 1.29	17-4 1.48	18-5 1.76	19-5 2.06	24.0	
23-11 0.93	24-9 1.03	25-6 1.14	26-4 1.24	27-1 1.36	27-10 1.47	28-7 1.59	29-3 1.71	29-11 1.83	31-3 2.09	33-2 2.49		12.0	2x10
22-4 0.87	23-2 0.96	23-11 1.06	24-7 1.16	25-4 1.27	26-0 1.37	26-8 1.48	27-4 1.60	28-0 1.71	29-3 1.95	31-0 2.33		13.7	
20-8 0.80	21-5 0.89	22-1 0.98	22-10 1.08	23-5 1.17	24-1 1.27	24-9 1.37	25-4 1.48	25-11 1.59	27-1 1.81	28-9 2.16	30-3 2.53	16.0	
18-11 0.73	19-7 0.81	20-2 0.90	20-10 0.98	21-5 1.07	22-0 1.16	22-7 1.25	23-2 1.35	23-8 1.45	24-9 1.65	26-3 1.97	27-8 2.31	19.2	
16-11 0.66	17-6 0.73	18-1 0.80	18-7 0.88	19-2 0.96	19-8 1.04	20-2 1.12	20-8 1.21	21-2 1.29	22-1 1.48	23-5 1.76	24-9 2.06	24.0	

Note: The required modulus of elasticity, E, in 1,000,000 pounds per square inch is shown below each span.

TABLE NO. 25-21-R-11—HIGH SLOPE RAFTERS
Slope Over 3 in 12—30 Pounds Per Square Foot Live Load
(Heavy Roof Covering)

Strength - 15 pounds per square foot dead load plus 30 pounds per square foot live load determines required fiber stress.
Deflection - For 30 pounds per square foot live load. Limited to span in inches divided by 180.

RAFTER SIZE (IN)	RAFTER SPACING (IN)	Allowable Extreme Fiber Stress in Bending F_b (psi)											
		200	300	400	500	600	700	800	900	1000	1100	1200	1300
2x4	12.0	3-0 0.05	3-8 0.09	4-3 0.15	4-9 0.20	5-3 0.27	5-8 0.34	6-0 0.41	6-5 0.49	6-9 0.58	7-1 0.67	7-5 0.76	7-8 0.86
	13.7	2-10 0.05	3-5 0.09	4-0 0.14	4-5 0.19	4-11 0.25	5-3 0.32	5-8 0.39	6-0 0.46	6-4 0.54	6-7 0.62	6-11 0.71	7-2 0.80
	16.0	2-7 0.04	3-2 0.08	3-8 0.13	4-1 0.18	4-6 0.23	4-11 0.29	5-3 0.36	5-6 0.43	5-10 0.50	6-1 0.58	6-5 0.66	6-8 0.74
	19.2	2-5 0.04	2-11 0.08	3-4 0.12	3-9 0.16	4-1 0.21	4-5 0.27	4-9 0.33	5-1 0.39	5-4 0.46	5-7 0.53	5-10 0.60	6-1 0.68
	24.0	2-2 0.04	2-7 0.07	3-0 0.10	3-4 0.14	3-8 0.19	4-0 0.24	4-3 0.29	4-6 0.35	4-9 0.41	5-0 0.47	5-3 0.54	5-5 0.61
2x6	12.0	4-9 0.05	5-10 0.09	6-8 0.15	7-6 0.20	8-2 0.27	8-10 0.34	9-6 0.41	10-0 0.49	10-7 0.58	11-1 0.67	11-7 0.76	12-1 0.86
	13.7	4-5 0.05	5-5 0.09	6-3 0.14	7-0 0.19	7-8 0.25	8-3 0.32	8-10 0.39	9-5 0.46	9-11 0.54	10-5 0.62	10-10 0.71	11-3 0.80
	16.0	4-1 0.04	5-0 0.08	5-10 0.13	6-6 0.18	7-1 0.23	7-8 0.29	8-2 0.36	8-8 0.43	9-2 0.50	9-7 0.58	10-0 0.66	10-5 0.74
	19.2	3-9 0.04	4-7 0.08	5-4 0.12	5-11 0.16	6-6 0.21	7-0 0.27	7-6 0.33	7-11 0.39	8-4 0.46	8-9 0.53	9-2 0.60	9-6 0.68
	24.0	3-4 0.04	4-1 0.07	4-9 0.10	5-4 0.14	5-10 0.19	6-3 0.24	6-8 0.29	7-1 0.35	7-6 0.41	7-10 0.47	8-2 0.54	8-6 0.61
2x8	12.0	6-3 0.05	7-8 0.09	8-10 0.15	9-10 0.20	10-10 0.27	11-8 0.34	12-6 0.41	13-3 0.49	13-11 0.58	14-8 0.67	15-3 0.76	15-11 0.86
	13.7	5-10 0.05	7-2 0.09	8-3 0.14	9-3 0.19	10-1 0.25	10-11 0.32	11-8 0.39	12-5 0.46	13-1 0.54	13-8 0.62	14-4 0.71	14-11 0.80
	16.0	5-5 0.04	6-7 0.08	7-8 0.13	8-7 0.18	9-4 0.23	10-1 0.29	10-10 0.36	11-6 0.43	12-1 0.50	12-8 0.58	13-3 0.66	13-9 0.74
	19.2	4-11 0.04	6-1 0.08	7-0 0.12	7-10 0.16	8-7 0.21	9-3 0.27	9-10 0.33	10-6 0.39	11-0 0.46	11-7 0.53	12-1 0.60	12-7 0.68
	24.0	4-5 0.04	5-5 0.07	6-3 0.10	7-0 0.14	7-8 0.19	8-3 0.24	8-10 0.29	9-4 0.35	9-10 0.41	10-4 0.47	10-10 0.54	11-3 0.61
2x10	12.0	8-0 0.05	9-9 0.09	11-3 0.15	12-7 0.20	13-9 0.27	14-11 0.34	15-11 0.41	16-11 0.49	17-10 0.58	18-8 0.67	19-6 0.76	20-4 0.86
	13.7	7-5 0.05	9-1 0.09	10-6 0.14	11-9 0.19	12-11 0.25	13-11 0.32	14-11 0.39	15-10 0.46	16-8 0.54	17-6 0.62	18-3 0.71	19-0 0.80
	16.0	6-11 0.04	8-5 0.08	9-9 0.13	10-11 0.18	11-11 0.23	12-11 0.29	13-9 0.36	14-8 0.43	15-5 0.50	16-2 0.58	16-11 0.66	17-7 0.74
	19.2	6-4 0.04	7-8 0.08	8-11 0.12	9-11 0.16	10-11 0.21	11-9 0.27	12-7 0.33	13-4 0.39	14-1 0.46	14-9 0.53	15-5 0.60	16-1 0.68
	24.0	5-8 0.04	6-11 0.07	8-0 0.10	8-11 0.14	9-9 0.19	10-6 0.24	11-3 0.29	11-11 0.35	12-7 0.41	13-2 0.47	13-9 0.54	14-4 0.61

Note: The required modulus of elasticity, E, in 1,000,000 pounds per square inch is shown below each span.

RAFTERS: Spans are measured along the horizontal projection and loads are considered as applied on the horizontal projection.

Allowable Extreme Fiber Stress in Bending F_b (psi)												RAFTER	
1400	1500	1600	1700	1800	1900	2000	2100	2200	2400	2700	3000	SPACING (IN)	SIZE (IN)
8-0 0.96	8-3 1.06	8-6 1.17	8-9 1.28	9-0 1.39	9-3 1.51	9-6 1.63	9-9 1.76	10-0 1.88	10-5 2.15	11-1 2.56		12.0	2x4
7-5 0.89	7-9 0.99	8-0 1.09	8-3 1.20	8-5 1.30	8-8 1.41	8-11 1.53	9-2 1.64	9-4 1.76	9-9 2.01	10-4 2.40		13.7	2x4
6-11 0.83	7-2 0.92	7-5 1.01	7-7 1.11	7-10 1.21	8-0 1.31	8-3 1.41	8-5 1.52	8-8 1.63	9-0 1.86	9-7 2.22	10-1 2.60	16.0	2x4
6-4 0.76	6-6 0.84	6-9 0.92	6-11 1.01	7-2 1.10	7-4 1.20	7-6 1.29	7-9 1.39	7-11 1.49	8-3 1.70	8-9 2.03	9-3 2.37	19.2	2x4
5-8 0.68	5-10 0.75	6-0 0.83	6-3 0.90	6-5 0.99	6-7 1.07	6-9 1.15	6-11 1.24	7-1 1.33	7-5 1.52	7-10 1.81	8-3 2.12	24.0	2x4
12-6 0.96	13-0 1.06	13-5 1.17	13-10 1.28	14-2 1.39	14-7 1.51	15-0 1.63	15-4 1.76	15-8 1.88	16-5 2.15	17-5 2.56		12.0	2x6
11-9 0.89	12-2 0.99	12-6 1.09	12-11 1.20	13-3 1.30	13-8 1.41	14-0 1.53	14-4 1.64	14-8 1.76	15-4 2.01	16-3 2.40		13.7	2x6
10-10 0.83	11-3 0.92	11-7 1.01	11-11 1.11	12-4 1.21	12-8 1.31	13-0 1.41	13-3 1.52	13-7 1.63	14-2 1.86	15-1 2.22	15-11 2.60	16.0	2x6
9-11 0.76	10-3 0.84	10-7 0.92	10-11 1.01	11-3 1.10	11-6 1.20	11-10 1.29	12-2 1.39	12-5 1.49	13-0 1.70	13-9 2.03	14-6 2.37	19.2	2x6
8-10 0.68	9-2 0.75	9-6 0.83	9-9 0.90	10-0 0.99	10-4 1.07	10-7 1.15	10-10 1.24	11-1 1.33	11-7 1.52	12-4 1.81	13-0 2.12	24.0	2x6
16-6 0.96	17-1 1.06	17-8 1.17	18-2 1.28	18-9 1.39	19-3 1.51	19-9 1.63	20-3 1.76	20-8 1.88	21-7 2.15	22-11 2.56		12.0	2x8
15-5 0.89	16-0 0.99	16-6 1.09	17-0 1.20	17-6 1.30	18-0 1.41	18-5 1.53	18-11 1.64	19-4 1.76	20-3 2.01	21-5 2.40		13.7	2x8
14-4 0.83	14-10 0.92	15-3 1.01	15-9 1.11	16-3 1.21	16-8 1.31	17-1 1.41	17-6 1.52	17-11 1.63	18-9 1.86	19-10 2.22	20-11 2.60	16.0	2x8
13-1 0.76	13-6 0.84	13-11 0.92	14-5 1.01	14-10 1.10	15-2 1.20	15-7 1.29	16-0 1.39	16-4 1.49	17-1 1.70	18-2 2.03	19-1 2.37	19.2	2x8
11-8 0.68	12-1 0.75	12-6 0.83	12-10 0.90	13-3 0.99	13-7 1.07	13-11 1.15	14-4 1.24	14-8 1.33	15-3 1.52	16-3 1.81	17-1 2.12	24.0	2x8
21-1 0.96	21-10 1.06	22-6 1.17	23-3 1.28	23-11 1.39	24-6 1.51	25-2 1.63	25-10 1.76	26-5 1.88	27-7 2.15	29-3 2.56		12.0	2x10
19-8 0.89	20-5 0.99	21-1 1.09	21-9 1.20	22-4 1.30	22-11 1.41	23-7 1.53	24-2 1.64	24-8 1.76	25-10 2.01	27-4 2.40		13.7	2x10
18-3 0.83	18-11 0.92	19-6 1.01	20-1 1.11	20-8 1.21	21-3 1.31	21-10 1.41	22-4 1.52	22-10 1.63	23-11 1.86	25-4 2.22	26-8 2.60	16.0	2x10
16-8 0.76	17-3 0.84	17-10 0.92	18-4 1.01	18-11 1.10	19-5 1.20	19-11 1.29	20-5 1.39	20-10 1.49	21-10 1.70	23-2 2.03	24-5 2.37	19.2	2x10
14-11 0.68	15-5 0.75	15-11 0.83	16-5 0.90	16-11 0.99	17-4 1.07	17-10 1.15	18-3 1.24	18-8 1.33	19-6 1.52	20-8 1.81	21-10 2.12	24.0	2x10

Note: The required modulus of elasticity, E, in 1,000,000 pounds per square inch is shown below each span.

TABLE NO. 25-21-R-12—HIGH SLOPE RAFTERS
Slope Over 3 in 12—40 Pounds Per Square Foot Live Load (Heavy Roof Covering)

DESIGN CRITERIA:
Strength - 15 pounds per square foot dead load plus 40 pounds per square foot live load determines required fiber stress.
Deflection - For 40 pounds per square foot live load. Limited to span in inches divided by 180.

RAFTER SIZE (IN)	RAFTER SPACING (IN)	Allowable Extreme Fiber Stress in Bending F_b (psi)											
		200	300	400	500	600	700	800	900	1000	1100	1200	1300
2x4	12.0	2-9 0.05	3-4 0.09	3-10 0.14	4-4 0.20	4-9 0.26	5-1 0.33	5-5 0.41	5-9 0.49	6-1 0.57	6-5 0.66	6-8 0.75	6-11 0.84
	13.7	2-7 0.05	3-1 0.09	3-7 0.13	4-0 0.19	4-5 0.25	4-9 0.31	5-1 0.38	5-5 0.46	5-8 0.53	6-0 0.61	6-3 0.70	6-6 0.79
	16.0	2-4 0.04	2-11 0.08	3-4 0.12	3-9 0.17	4-1 0.23	4-5 0.29	4-9 0.35	5-0 0.42	5-3 0.49	5-6 0.57	5-9 0.65	6-0 0.73
	19.2	2-2 0.04	2-8 0.07	3-1 0.11	3-5 0.16	3-9 0.21	4-0 0.26	4-4 0.32	4-7 0.38	4-10 0.45	5-1 0.52	5-3 0.59	5-6 0.67
	24.0	1-11 0.04	2-4 0.07	2-9 0.10	3-1 0.14	3-4 0.19	3-7 0.24	3-10 0.29	4-1 0.34	4-4 0.40	4-6 0.46	4-9 0.53	4-11 0.60
2x6	12.0	4-3 0.05	5-3 0.09	6-1 0.14	6-9 0.20	7-5 0.26	8-0 0.33	8-7 0.41	9-1 0.49	9-7 0.57	10-0 0.66	10-6 0.75	10-11 0.84
	13.7	4-0 0.05	4-11 0.09	5-8 0.13	6-4 0.19	6-11 0.25	7-6 0.31	8-0 0.38	8-6 0.46	8-11 0.53	9-5 0.61	9-10 0.70	10-3 0.79
	16.0	3-8 0.04	4-6 0.08	5-3 0.12	5-10 0.17	6-5 0.23	6-11 0.29	7-5 0.35	7-10 0.42	8-3 0.49	8-8 0.57	9-1 0.65	9-5 0.73
	19.2	3-5 0.04	4-2 0.07	4-9 0.11	5-4 0.16	5-10 0.21	6-4 0.26	6-9 0.32	7-2 0.38	7-7 0.45	7-11 0.52	8-3 0.59	8-8 0.67
	24.0	3-0 0.04	3-8 0.07	4-3 0.10	4-9 0.14	5-3 0.19	5-8 0.24	6-1 0.29	6-5 0.34	6-9 0.40	7-1 0.46	7-5 0.53	7-9 0.60
2x8	12.0	5-8 0.05	6-11 0.09	8-0 0.14	8-11 0.20	9-9 0.26	10-7 0.33	11-3 0.41	12-0 0.49	12-7 0.57	13-3 0.66	13-10 0.75	14-5 0.84
	13.7	5-3 0.05	6-6 0.09	7-6 0.13	8-4 0.19	9-2 0.25	9-11 0.31	10-7 0.28	11-2 0.46	11-10 0.53	12-5 0.61	12-11 0.70	13-6 0.79
	16.0	4-11 0.04	6-0 0.08	6-11 0.12	7-9 0.17	8-6 0.23	9-2 0.29	9-9 0.35	10-4 0.42	10-11 0.49	11-6 0.57	12-0 0.65	12-6 0.73
	19.2	4-6 0.04	5-6 0.07	6-4 0.11	7-1 0.16	7-9 0.21	8-4 0.26	8-11 0.32	9-6 0.38	10-0 0.45	10-6 0.52	10-11 0.59	11-5 0.67
	24.0	4-0 0.04	4-11 0.07	5-8 0.10	6-4 0.14	6-11 0.19	7-6 0.24	8-0 0.29	8-6 0.34	8-11 0.40	9-4 0.46	9-9 0.53	10-2 0.60
2x10	12.0	7-2 0.05	8-10 0.09	10-2 0.14	11-5 0.20	12-6 0.26	13-6 0.33	14-5 0.41	15-3 0.49	16-1 0.57	16-11 0.66	17-8 0.75	18-4 0.84
	13.7	6-9 0.05	8-3 0.09	9-6 0.13	10-8 0.19	11-8 0.25	12-7 0.31	13-6 0.38	14-3 0.46	15-1 0.53	15-10 0.61	16-6 0.70	17-2 0.79
	16.0	6-3 0.04	7-8 0.08	8-10 0.12	9-10 0.17	10-10 0.23	11-8 0.29	12-6 0.35	13-3 0.42	13-11 0.49	14-8 0.57	15-3 0.65	15-11 0.73
	19.2	5-8 0.04	7-0 0.07	8-1 0.11	9-0 0.16	9-10 0.21	10-8 0.26	11-5 0.32	12-1 0.38	12-9 0.45	13-4 0.52	13-11 0.59	14-6 0.67
	24.0	5-1 0.04	6-3 0.07	7-2 0.10	8-1 0.14	8-10 0.19	9-6 0.24	10-2 0.29	10-10 0.34	11-5 0.40	11-11 0.46	12-6 0.53	13-0 0.60

Note: The required modulus of elasticity, E, in 1,000,000 pounds per square inch is shown below each span.

RAFTERS: Spans are measured along the horizontal projection and loads are considered as applied on the horizontal projection.

Allowable Extreme Fiber Stress in Bending F_b (psi)												RAFTER	
1400	1500	1600	1700	1800	1900	2000	2100	2200	2400	2700	3000	SPACING (IN)	SIZE (IN)
7-3 0.94	7-6 1.05	7-8 1.15	7-11 1.26	8-2 1.38	8-5 1.49	8-7 1.61	8-10 1.73	9-0 1.86	9-5 2.12	10-0 2.53		12.0	2x4
6-9 0.88	7-0 0.98	7-3 1.08	7-5 1.18	7-8 1.29	7-10 1.40	8-1 1.51	8-3 1.62	8-5 1.74	8-10 1.98	9-4 2.36		13.7	
6-3 0.82	6-6 0.91	6-8 1.00	6-11 1.09	7-1 1.19	7-3 1.29	7-6 1.40	7-8 1.50	7-10 1.61	8-2 1.83	8-8 2.19	9-2 2.56	16.0	
5-8 0.75	5-11 0.83	6-1 0.91	6-3 1.00	6-6 1.09	6-8 1.18	6-10 1.27	7-0 1.37	7-2 1.47	7-6 1.67	7-11 2.00	8-4 2.34	19.2	
5-1 0.67	5-3 0.74	5-5 0.82	5-7 0.89	5-9 0.97	5-11 1.06	6-1 1.14	6-3 1.23	6-5 1.31	6-8 1.50	7-1 1.79	7-6 2.09	24.0	
11-4 0.94	11-9 1.05	12-1 1.15	12-6 1.26	12-10 1.38	13-2 1.49	13-6 1.61	13-10 1.73	14-2 1.86	14-10 2.12	15-9 2.53		12.0	2x6
10-7 0.88	11-0 0.98	11-4 1.08	11-8 1.18	12-0 1.29	12-4 1.40	12-8 1.51	13-0 1.62	13-3 1.74	13-10 1.98	14-9 2.36		13.7	
9-10 0.82	10-2 0.91	10-6 1.00	10-10 1.09	11-1 1.19	11-5 1.29	11-9 1.40	12-0 1.50	12-4 1.61	12-10 1.83	13-7 2.19	14-4 2.56	16.0	
8-11 0.75	9-3 0.83	9-7 0.91	9-10 1.00	10-2 1.09	10-5 1.18	10-8 1.27	11-0 1.37	11-3 1.47	11-9 1.67	12-5 2.00	13-1 2.34	19.2	
8-0 0.67	8-3 0.74	8-7 0.82	8-10 0.89	9-1 0.97	9-4 1.06	9-7 1.14	9-10 1.23	10-0 1.31	10-6 1.50	11-1 1.79	11-9 2.09	24.0	
14-11 0.94	15-5 1.05	16-0 1.15	16-5 1.26	16-11 1.38	17-5 1.49	17-10 1.61	18-3 1.73	18-9 1.86	19-7 2.12	20-9 2.53		12.0	2x8
14-0 0.88	14-6 0.98	14-11 1.08	15-5 1.18	15-10 1.29	16-3 1.40	16-8 1.51	17-1 1.62	17-6 1.74	18-3 1.98	19-5 2.36		13.7	
12-11 0.82	13-5 0.91	13-10 1.00	14-3 1.09	14-8 1.19	15-1 1.29	15-5 1.40	15-10 1.50	16-3 1.61	16-11 1.83	18-0 2.19	18-11 2.56	16.0	
11-10 0.75	12-3 0.83	12-7 0.91	13-0 1.00	13-5 1.09	13-9 1.18	14-1 1.27	14-6 1.37	14-10 1.47	15-5 1.67	16-5 2.00	17-3 2.34	19.2	
10-7 0.67	10-11 0.74	11-3 0.82	11-8 0.89	12-0 0.97	12-4 1.06	12-7 1.14	12-11 1.23	13-3 1.31	13-10 1.50	14-8 1.79	15-5 2.09	24.0	
19-1 0.94	19-9 1.05	20-4 1.15	21-0 1.26	21-7 1.38	22-2 1.49	22-9 1.61	23-4 1.73	23-11 1.86	24-11 2.12	26-6 2.53		12.0	2x10
17-10 0.88	18-5 0.98	19-1 1.08	19-8 1.18	20-2 1.29	20-9 1.40	21-4 1.51	21-10 1.62	22-4 1.74	23-4 1.98	24-9 2.36		13.7	
16-6 0.82	17-1 0.91	17-8 1.00	18-2 1.09	18-9 1.19	19-3 1.29	19-9 1.40	20-2 1.50	20-8 1.61	21-7 1.83	22-11 2.19	24.2 2.56	16.0	
15-1 0.75	15-7 0.83	16-1 0.91	16-7 1.00	17-1 1.09	17-7 1.18	18-0 1.27	18-5 1.37	18-11 1.47	19-9 1.67	20-11 2.00	22-1 2.34	19.2	
13-6 0.67	13-11 0.74	14-5 0.82	14-10 0.89	15-3 0.97	15-8 1.06	16-1 1.14	16-6 1.23	16-11 1.31	17-8 1.50	18-9 1.79	19-9 2.09	24.0	

Note: The required modulus of elasticity, E, in 1,000,000 pounds per square inch is shown below each span.

TABLE NO. 25-21-R-13—HIGH SLOPE RAFTERS
Slope Over 3 in 12—20 Pounds Per Square Foot Live Load (Light Roof Covering)

DESIGN CRITERIA:
Strength - 7 pounds per square foot dead load plus 20 pounds per square foot live load determines required fiber stress.
Deflection - For 20 pounds per square foot live load. Limited to span in inches divided by 180.

RAFTER SIZE (IN)	SPACING (IN)	Allowable Extreme Fiber Stress in Bending F_b (psi)											
		200	300	400	500	600	700	800	900	1000	1100	1200	1300
2x4	12.0	3-11 0.07	4-9 0.14	5-6 0.21	6-2 0.29	6-9 0.38	7-3 0.49	7-9 0.59	8-3 0.71	8-8 0.83	9-1 0.96	9-6 1.09	9-11 1.23
	13.7	3-8 0.07	4-5 0.13	5-2 0.20	5-9 0.27	6-4 0.36	6-10 0.45	7-3 0.55	7-9 0.66	8-2 0.77	8-6 0.89	8-11 1.02	9-3 1.15
	16.0	3-4 0.06	4-1 0.12	4-9 0.18	5-4 0.25	5-10 0.33	6-4 0.42	6-9 0.51	7-2 0.61	7-6 0.72	7-11 0.83	8-3 0.94	8-7 1.06
	19.2	3-1 0.06	3-9 0.11	4-4 0.17	4-10 0.23	5-4 0.30	5-9 0.38	6-2 0.47	6-6 0.56	6-10 0.65	7-3 0.76	7-6 0.86	7-10 0.97
	24.0	2-9 0.05	3-4 0.10	3-11 0.15	4-4 0.21	4-9 0.27	5-2 0.34	5-6 0.42	5-10 0.50	6-2 0.59	6-5 0.68	6-9 0.77	7-0 0.87
2x6	12.0	6-1 0.07	7-6 0.14	8-8 0.21	9-8 0.29	10-7 0.38	11-5 0.49	12-3 0.59	13-0 0.71	13-8 0.83	14-4 0.96	15-0 1.09	15-7 1.23
	13.7	5-9 0.07	7-0 0.13	8-1 0.20	9-0 0.27	9-11 0.36	10-8 0.45	11-5 0.55	12-2 0.66	12-9 0.77	13-5 0.89	14-0 1.02	14-7 1.15
	16.0	5-4 0.06	6-6 0.12	7-6 0.18	8-4 0.25	9-2 0.33	9-11 0.42	10-7 0.51	11-3 0.61	11-10 0.72	12-5 0.83	13-0 0.94	13-6 1.06
	19.2	4-10 0.06	5-11 0.11	6-10 0.17	7-8 0.23	8-4 0.30	9-0 0.38	9-8 0.47	10-3 0.56	10-10 0.65	11-4 0.76	11-10 0.86	12-4 0.97
	24.0	4-4 0.05	5-4 0.10	6-1 0.15	6-10 0.21	7-6 0.27	8-1 0.34	8-8 0.42	9-2 0.50	9-8 0.59	10-2 0.68	10-7 0.77	11-0 0.87
2x8	12.0	8-1 0.07	9-10 0.14	11-5 0.21	12-9 0.29	13-11 0.38	15-1 0.49	16-1 0.59	17-1 0.71	18-0 0.83	18-11 0.96	19-9 1.09	20-6 1.23
	13.7	7-6 0.07	9-3 0.13	10-8 0.20	11-11 0.27	13-1 0.36	14-1 0.45	15-1 0.55	16-0 0.66	16-10 0.77	17-8 0.89	18-5 1.02	19-3 1.15
	16.0	7-0 0.06	8-7 0.12	9-10 0.18	11-0 0.25	12-1 0.33	13-1 0.42	13-11 0.51	14-10 0.61	15-7 0.72	16-4 0.83	17-1 0.94	17-9 1.06
	19.2	6-4 0.06	7-10 0.11	9-0 0.17	10-1 0.23	11-0 0.30	11-11 0.38	12-9 0.47	13-6 0.56	14-3 0.65	14-11 0.76	15-7 0.86	16-3 0.97
	24.0	5-8 0.05	7-0 0.10	8-1 0.15	9-0 0.21	9-10 0.27	10-8 0.34	11-5 0.42	12-1 0.50	12-9 0.59	13-4 0.68	13-11 0.77	14-6 0.87
2x10	12.0	10-3 0.07	12-7 0.14	14-6 0.21	16-3 0.29	17-10 0.38	19-3 0.49	20-7 0.59	21-10 0.71	23-0 0.83	24-1 0.96	25-2 1.09	26-2 1.23
	13.7	9-7 0.07	11-9 0.13	13-7 0.20	15-2 0.27	16-8 0.36	18-0 0.45	19-3 0.55	20-5 0.66	21-6 0.77	22-7 0.89	23-7 1.02	24-6 1.15
	16.0	8-11 0.06	10-11 0.12	12-7 0.18	14-1 0.25	15-5 0.33	16-8 0.42	17-10 0.51	18-11 0.61	19-11 0.72	20-10 0.83	21-10 0.94	22-8 1.06
	19.2	8-2 0.06	9-11 0.11	11-6 0.17	12-10 0.23	14-1 0.30	15-2 0.38	16-3 0.47	17-3 0.56	18-2 0.65	19-1 0.76	19-11 0.86	20-9 0.97
	24.0	7-3 0.05	8-11 0.10	10-3 0.15	11-6 0.21	12-7 0.27	13-7 0.34	14-6 0.42	15-5 0.50	16-3 0.59	17-1 0.68	17-10 0.77	18-6 0.87

Note: The required modulus of elasticity, E, in 1,000,000 pounds per square inch is shown below each span.

RAFTERS: Spans are measured along the horizontal projection and loads are considered as applied on the horizontal projection.

Allowable Extreme Fiber Stress in Bending F_b (psi)											RAFTER	
1400	1500	1600	1700	1800	1900	2000	2100	2200	2400	2700	SPACING (IN)	SIZE (IN)
10-3 1.37	10-8 1.52	11-0 1.68	11-4 1.84	11-8 2.00	12-0 2.17	12-4 2.34	12-7 2.52				12.0	
9-7 1.28	10-0 1.42	10-3 1.57	10-7 1.72	10-11 1.87	11-3 2.03	11-6 2.19	11-9 2.36	12-1 2.53			13.7	
8-11 1.19	9-3 1.32	9-6 1.45	9-10 1.59	10-1 1.73	10-5 1.88	10-8 2.03	10-11 2.18	11-2 2.34			16.0	2x4
8-2 1.08	8-5 1.20	8-8 1.33	9-0 1.45	9-3 1.58	9-6 1.71	9-9 1.85	10-0 1.99	10-2 2.14	10-8 2.43		19.2	
7-3 0.97	7-6 1.08	7-9 1.19	8-0 1.30	8-3 1.41	8-6 1.53	8-8 1.66	8-11 1.78	9-1 1.91	9-6 2.18	10-1 2.60	24.0	
16-2 1.37	16-9 1.52	17-3 1.68	17-10 1.84	18-4 2.00	18-10 2.17	19-4 2.34	19-10 2.52				12.0	
15-1 1.28	15-8 1.42	16-2 1.57	16-8 1.72	17-2 1.87	17-7 2.03	18-1 2.19	18-6 2.36	19-0 2.53			13.7	
14-0 1.19	14-6 1.32	15-0 1.45	15-5 1.59	15-11 1.73	16-4 1.88	16-9 2.03	17-2 2.18	17-7 2.34			16.0	2x6
12-9 1.08	13-3 1.20	13-8 1.33	14-1 1.45	14-6 1.58	14-11 1.71	15-3 1.85	15-8 1.99	16-0 2.14	16-9 2.43		19.2	
11-5 0.97	11-10 1.08	12-3 1.19	12-7 1.30	13-0 1.41	13-4 1.53	13-8 1.66	14-0 1.78	14-4 1.91	15-0 2.18	15-11 2.60	24.0	
21-4 1.37	22-1 1.52	22-9 1.68	23-6 1.84	24-2 2.00	24-10 2.17	25-6 2.34	26-1 2.52				12.0	
19-11 1.28	20-8 1.42	21-4 1.57	22-0 1.72	22-7 1.87	23-3 2.03	23-10 2.19	24-5 2.36	25-0 2.53			13.7	
18-5 1.19	19-1 1.32	19-9 1.45	20-4 1.59	20-11 1.73	21-6 1.88	22-1 2.03	22-7 2.18	23-2 2.34			16.0	2x8
16-10 1.08	17-5 1.20	18-0 1.33	18-7 1.45	19-1 1.58	19-8 1.71	20-2 1.85	20-8 1.99	21-1 2.14	22-1 2.43		19.2	
15-1 0.97	15-7 1.08	16-1 1.19	16-7 1.30	17-1 1.41	17-7 1.53	18-0 1.66	18-5 1.78	18-11 1.91	19-9 2.18	20-11 2.60	24.0	
27-2 1.37	28-2 1.52	29-1 1.68	30-0 1.84	30-10 2.00	31-8 2.17	32-6 2.34	33-4 2.52				12.0	
25-5 1.28	26-4 1.42	27-2 1.57	28-0 1.72	28-10 1.87	29-8 2.03	30-5 2.19	31-2 2.36	31-11 2.53			13.7	
23-7 1.19	24-5 1.32	25-2 1.45	25-11 1.59	26-8 1.73	27-5 1.88	28-2 2.03	28-10 2.18	29-6 2.34			16.0	2x10
21-6 1.08	22-3 1.20	23-0 1.33	23-8 1.45	24-5 1.58	25-1 1.71	25-8 1.85	26-4 1.99	26-11 2.14	28-2 2.43		19.2	
19-3 0.97	19-11 1.08	20-7 1.19	21-2 1.30	21-10 1.41	22-5 1.53	23-0 1.66	23-7 1.78	24-1 1.91	25-2 2.18	26-8 2.60	24.0	

Note: The required modulus of elasticity, E, in 1,000,000 pounds per square inch is shown below each span.

TABLE NO. 25-21-R-14—HIGH SLOPE RAFTERS
Slope Over 3 in 12—30 Pounds Per Square Foot Live Load (Light Roof Covering)

DESIGN CRITERIA:

Strength—7 pounds per square foot dead load plus 30 pounds per square foot live load determines required fiber stress.

Deflection—For 30 pounds per square foot live load. Limited to span in inches divided by 180.

RAFTER SIZE (IN)	RAFTER SPACING (IN)	Allowable Extreme Fiber Stress in Bending F_b (psi)											
		200	300	400	500	600	700	800	900	1000	1100	1200	1300
2x4	12.0	3-4 0.07	4-1 0.13	4-8 0.20	5-3 0.27	5-9 0.36	6-3 0.45	6-8 0.55	7-1 0.66	7-5 0.77	7-9 0.89	8-2 1.02	8-6 1.15
	13.7	3-1 0.06	3-10 0.12	4-5 0.18	4-11 0.26	5-5 0.34	5-10 0.42	6-3 0.52	6-7 0.62	6-11 0.72	7-3 0.84	7-7 0.95	7-11 1.07
	16.0	2-11 0.06	3-6 0.11	4-1 0.17	4-7 0.24	5-0 0.31	5-5 0.39	5-9 0.48	6-1 0.57	6-5 0.67	6-9 0.77	7-1 0.88	7-4 0.99
	19.2	2-8 0.05	3-3 0.10	3-9 0.15	4-2 0.22	4-7 0.28	4-11 0.36	5-3 0.44	5-7 0.52	5-10 0.61	6-2 0.71	6-5 0.80	6-8 0.91
	24.0	2-4 0.05	2-11 0.09	3-4 0.14	3-9 0.19	4-1 0.25	4-5 0.32	4-8 0.39	5-0 0.47	5-3 0.55	5-6 0.63	5-9 0.72	6-0 0.81
2x6	12.0	5-3 0.07	6-5 0.13	7-5 0.20	8-3 0.27	9-1 0.36	9-9 0.45	10-5 0.55	11-1 0.66	11-8 0.77	12-3 0.89	12-9 1.02	13-4 1.15
	13.7	4-11 0.06	6-0 0.12	6-11 0.18	7-9 0.26	8-5 0.34	9-2 0.42	9-9 0.52	10-4 0.62	10-11 0.72	11-5 0.84	12-0 0.95	12-5 1.07
	16.0	4-6 0.06	5-6 0.11	6-5 0.17	7-2 0.24	7-10 0.31	8-5 0.39	9-1 0.48	9-7 0.57	10-1 0.67	10-7 0.77	11-1 0.88	11-6 0.99
	19.2	4-2 0.05	5-1 0.10	5-10 0.15	6-6 0.22	7-2 0.28	7-9 0.36	8-3 0.44	8-9 0.52	9-3 0.61	9-8 0.71	10-1 0.80	10-6 0.91
	24.0	3-8 0.05	4-6 0.09	5-3 0.14	5-10 0.19	6-5 0.25	6-11 0.32	7-5 0.39	7-10 0.47	8-3 0.55	8-8 0.63	9-1 0.72	9-5 0.81
2x8	12.0	6-11 0.07	8-5 0.13	9-9 0.20	10-11 0.27	11-11 0.36	12-10 0.45	13-9 0.55	14-7 0.66	15-5 0.77	16-2 0.89	16-10 1.02	17-7 1.15
	13.7	6-5 0.06	7-11 0.12	9-1 0.18	10-2 0.26	11-2 0.34	12-1 0.42	12-10 0.52	13-8 0.62	14-5 0.72	15-1 0.84	15-9 0.95	16-5 1.07
	16.0	6-0 0.06	7-4 0.11	8-5 0.17	9-5 0.24	10-4 0.31	11-2 0.39	11-11 0.48	12-8 0.57	13-4 0.67	14-0 0.77	14-7 0.88	15-2 0.99
	19.2	5-5 0.05	6-8 0.10	7-8 0.15	8-7 0.22	9-5 0.28	10-2 0.36	10-11 0.44	11-6 0.52	12-2 0.61	12-9 0.71	13-4 0.80	13-10 0.91
	24.0	4-10 0.05	6-0 0.09	6-11 0.14	7-8 0.19	8-5 0.25	9-1 0.32	9-9 0.39	10-4 0.47	10-11 0.55	11-5 0.63	11-11 0.72	12-5 0.81
2x10	12.0	8-9 0.07	10-9 0.13	12-5 0.20	13-11 0.27	15-2 0.36	16-5 0.45	17-7 0.55	18-7 0.66	19-8 0.77	20-7 0.89	21-6 1.02	22-5 1.15
	13.7	8-3 0.06	10-1 0.12	11-7 0.18	13-0 0.26	14-3 0.34	15-4 0.42	16-5 0.52	17-5 0.62	18-4 0.72	19-3 0.84	20-1 0.95	20-11 1.07
	16.0	7-7 0.07	9-4 0.12	10-9 0.19	12-0 0.26	13-2 0.34	14-3 0.43	15-2 0.53	16-2 0.63	17-0 0.74	17-10 0.85	18-7 0.97	19-5 1.09
	19.2	6-11 0.05	8-6 0.10	9-10 0.15	11-0 0.22	12-0 0.28	13-0 0.36	13-11 0.44	14-9 0.52	15-6 0.61	16-3 0.71	17-0 0.80	17-8 0.91
	24.0	6-2 0.05	7-7 0.09	8-9 0.14	9-10 0.19	10-9 0.25	11-7 0.32	12-5 0.39	13-2 0.47	13-11 0.55	14-7 0.63	15-2 0.72	15-10 0.81

Note: The required modulus of elasticity, E, in 1,000,000 pounds per square inch is shown below each span.

RAFTERS: Spans are measured along the horizontal projection and loads are considered as applied on the horizontal projection.

Allowable Extreme Fiber Stress in Bending F_b (psi)											RAFTER	
1400	1500	1600	1700	1800	1900	2000	2100	2200	2400	2700	SPACING (IN)	SIZE (IN)
8-9 1.28	9-1 1.42	9-5 1.57	9-8 1.72	10-0 1.87	10-3 2.03	10-6 2.19	10-9 2.36	11-0 2.53			12.0	2x4
8-3 1.20	8-6 1.33	8-9 1.47	9-1 1.61	9-4 1.75	9-7 1.90	9-10 2.05	10-1 2.20	10-4 2.36			13.7	
7-7 1.11	7-11 1.23	8-2 1.36	8-5 1.49	8-8 1.62	8-10 1.76	9-1 1.90	9-4 2.04	9-7 2.19	10-0 2.49		16.0	
6-11 1.01	7-2 1.12	7-5 1.24	7-8 1.36	7-11 1.48	8-1 1.60	8-4 1.73	8-6 1.86	8-9 2.00	9-1 2.28		19.2	
6-3 0.91	6-5 1.01	6-8 1.11	6-10 1.21	7-1 1.32	7-3 1.43	7-5 1.55	7-7 1.67	7-9 1.79	8-2 2.04	8-8 2.43	24.0	
13-10 1.28	14-4 1.42	14-9 1.57	15-3 1.72	15-8 1.87	16-1 2.03	16-6 2.19	16-11 2.36	17-4 2.53			12.0	2x6
12-11 1.20	13-4 1.33	13-10 1.47	14-3 1.61	14-8 1.75	15-1 1.90	15-5 2.05	15-10 2.20	16-2 2.36			13.7	
12-0 1.11	12-5 1.23	12-9 1.36	13-2 1.49	13-7 1.62	13-11 1.76	14-4 1.90	14-8 2.04	15-0 2.19	15-8 2.49		16.0	
10-11 1.01	11-4 1.12	11-8 1.24	12-0 1.36	12-5 1.48	12-9 1.60	13-1 1.73	13-4 1.86	13-8 2.00	14-4 2.28		19.2	
9-9 0.91	10-1 1.01	10-5 1.11	10-9 1.21	11-1 1.32	11-5 1.43	11-8 1.55	12-0 1.67	12-3 1.79	12-9 2.04	13-7 2.43	24.0	
18-2 1.28	18-10 1.42	19-6 1.57	20-1 1.72	20-8 1.87	21-3 2.03	21-9 2.19	22-4 2.36	22-10 2.53			12.0	2x8
17-0 1.20	17-8 1.33	18-2 1.47	18-9 1.61	19-4 1.75	19-10 1.90	20-4 2.05	20-10 2.20	21-4 2.36			13.7	
15-9 1.11	16-4 1.23	16-10 1.36	17-4 1.49	17-11 1.62	18-4 1.76	18-10 1.90	19-4 2.04	19-9 2.19	20-8 2.49		16.0	
14-5 1.01	14-11 1.12	15-5 1.24	15-10 1.36	16-4 1.48	16-9 1.60	17-2 1.73	17-8 1.86	18-1 2.00	18-10 2.28		19.2	
12-10 0.91	13-4 1.01	13-9 1.11	14-2 1.21	14-7 1.32	15-0 1.43	15-5 1.55	15-9 1.67	16-2 1.79	16-10 2.04	17-11 2.43	24.0	
23-3 1.28	24-1 1.42	24-10 1.57	25-7 1.72	26-4 1.87	27-1 2.03	27-9 2.19	28-5 2.36	29-1 2.53			12.0	2x10
21-9 1.20	22-6 1.33	23-3 1.47	23-11 1.61	24-8 1.75	25-4 1.90	26-0 2.05	26-7 2.20	27-3 2.36			13.7	
20-1 1.22	20-10 1.35	21-6 1.49	22-2 1.63	22-10 1.78	23-5 1.93	24-1 2.08	24-8 2.24	25-3 2.40			16.0	
18-4 1.01	19-0 1.12	19-8 1.24	20-3 1.36	20-10 1.48	21-5 1.60	21-11 1.73	22-6 1.86	23-0 2.00	24-1 2.28		19.2	
16-5 0.91	17-0 1.01	17-7 1.11	18-1 1.21	18-7 1.32	19-2 1.43	19-8 1.55	20-1 1.67	20-7 1.79	21-6 2.04	22-10 2.43	24.0	

Note: The required modulus of elasticity, E, in 1,000,000 pounds per square inch is shown below each span.

TABLE NO. 25-21-R-15—HIGH SLOPE RAFTERS
Slope Over 3 in 12—40 Pounds Per Square Foot Live Load (Light Roof Covering)

DESIGN CRITERIA:
Strength - 7 pounds per square foot dead load plus 40 pounds per square foot live load determines required fiber stress.
Deflection - For 40 pounds per square foot live load. Limited to span in inches divided by 180.

RAFTER SIZE (IN)	RAFTER SPACING (IN)	Allowable Extreme Fiber Stress in Bending F_b (psi)											
		200	300	400	500	600	700	800	900	1000	1100	1200	1300
2x4	12.0	2-11 0.06	3-7 0.12	4-2 0.18	4-8 0.25	5-1 0.34	5-6 0.42	5-11 0.52	6-3 0.62	6-7 0.72	6-11 0.83	7-3 0.95	7-6 1.07
	13.7	2-9 0.06	3-5 0.11	3-11 0.17	4-4 0.24	4-9 0.31	5-2 0.40	5-6 0.48	5-10 0.58	6-2 0.67	6-6 0.78	6-9 0.89	7-0 1.00
	16.0	2-7 0.06	3-2 0.10	3-7 0.16	4-0 0.22	4-5 0.29	4-9 0.37	5-1 0.45	5-5 0.53	5-8 0.62	6-0 0.72	6-3 0.82	6-6 0.93
	19.2	2-4 0.05	2-10 0.09	3-4 0.14	3-8 0.20	4-0 0.26	4-4 0.33	4-8 0.41	4-11 0.49	5-3 0.57	5-6 0.66	5-8 0.75	5-11 0.85
	24.0	2-1 0.05	2-7 0.08	2-11 0.13	3-4 0.18	3-7 0.24	3-11 0.30	4-2 0.36	4-5 0.44	4-8 0.51	4-11 0.59	5-1 0.67	5-4 0.76
2x6	12.0	4-8 0.06	5-8 0.12	6-7 0.18	7-4 0.25	8-0 0.34	8-8 0.42	9-3 0.52	9-10 0.62	10-4 0.72	10-10 0.83	11-4 0.95	11-10 1.07
	13.7	4-4 0.06	5-4 0.11	6-2 0.17	6-10 0.24	7-6 0.31	8-1 0.40	8-8 0.48	9-2 0.58	9-8 0.67	10-2 0.78	10-7 0.89	11-1 1.00
	16.0	4-0 0.06	4-11 0.10	5-8 0.16	6-4 0.22	6-11 0.29	7-6 0.37	8-0 0.45	8-6 0.53	9-0 0.62	9-5 0.72	9-10 0.82	10-3 0.93
	19.2	3-8 0.05	4-6 0.09	5-2 0.14	5-9 0.20	6-4 0.26	6-10 0.33	7-4 0.41	7-9 0.49	8-2 0.57	8-7 0.66	9-0 0.75	9-4 0.85
	24.0	3-3 0.05	4-0 0.08	4-8 0.13	5-2 0.18	5-8 0.24	6-2 0.30	6-7 0.36	6-11 0.44	7-4 0.51	7-8 0.59	8-0 0.67	8-4 0.76
2x8	12.0	6-1 0.06	7-6 0.12	8-8 0.18	9-8 0.25	10-7 0.34	11-5 0.42	12-3 0.52	12-11 0.62	13-8 0.72	14-4 0.83	14-11 0.95	15-7 1.07
	13.7	5-9 0.06	7-0 0.11	8-1 0.17	9-0 0.24	9-11 0.31	10-8 0.40	11-5 0.48	12-1 0.58	12-9 0.67	13-5 0.78	14-0 0.89	14-7 1.00
	16.0	5-3 0.06	6-6 0.10	7-6 0.16	8-4 0.22	9-2 0.29	9-11 0.37	10-7 0.45	11-3 0.53	11-10 0.62	12-5 0.72	12-11 0.82	13-6 0.93
	19.2	4-10 0.05	5-11 0.09	6-10 0.14	7-8 0.20	8-4 0.26	9-0 0.33	9-8 0.41	10-3 0.49	10-10 0.57	11-4 0.66	11-10 0.75	12-4 0.85
	24.0	4-4 0.05	5-3 0.08	6-1 0.13	6-10 0.18	7-6 0.24	8-1 0.30	8-8 0.36	9-2 0.44	9-8 0.51	10-2 0.59	10-7 0.67	11-0 0.76
2x10	12.0	7-9 0.06	9-6 0.12	11-0 0.18	12-4 0.25	13-6 0.34	14-7 0.42	15-7 0.52	16-6 0.62	17-5 0.72	18-3 0.83	19-1 0.95	19-10 1.07
	13.7	7-3 0.06	8-11 0.11	10-4 0.17	11-6 0.24	12-7 0.31	13-8 0.40	14-7 0.48	15-5 0.58	16-4 0.67	17-1 0.78	17-10 0.89	18-7 1.00
	16.0	6-9 0.06	8-3 0.10	9-6 0.16	10-8 0.22	11-8 0.29	12-7 0.37	13-6 0.45	14-4 0.53	15-1 0.62	15-10 0.72	16-6 0.82	17-2 0.93
	19.2	6-2 0.05	7-7 0.09	8-9 0.14	9-9 0.20	10-8 0.26	11-6 0.33	12-4 0.41	13-1 0.49	13-9 0.57	14-5 0.66	15-1 0.75	15-8 0.85
	24.0	5-6 0.05	6-9 0.08	7-9 0.13	8-9 0.18	9-6 0.24	10-4 0.30	11-0 0.36	11-8 0.44	12-4 0.51	12-11 0.59	13-6 0.67	14-1 0.76

Note: The required modulus of elasticity, E, in 1,000,000 pounds per square inch is shown below each span.

RAFTERS: Spans are measured along the horizontal projection and loads are considered as applied on the horizontal projection.

Allowable Extreme Fiber Stress in Bending F_b (psi)											RAFTER SPACING (IN)	SIZE (IN)
1400	1500	1600	1700	1800	1900	2000	2100	2200	2400	2700		
7-10 1.19	8-1 1.32	8-4 1.46	8-7 1.60	8-10 1.74	9-1 1.89	9-4 2.04	9-7 2.19	9-9 2.35			12.0	2x4
7-4 1.12	7-7 1.24	7-10 1.37	8-0 1.50	8-3 1.63	8-6 1.77	8-9 1.91	8-11 2.05	9-2 2.20	9-7 2.51		13.7	
6-9 1.03	7-0 1.15	7-3 1.26	7-5 1.38	7-8 1.51	7-10 1.64	8-1 1.77	8-3 1.90	8-6 2.04	8-10 2.32		16.0	
6-2 0.94	6-5 1.05	6-7 1.15	6-10 1.26	7-0 1.38	7-2 1.49	7-4 1.61	7-7 1.74	7-9 1.86	8-1 2.12	8-7 2.53	19.2	
5-6 0.84	5-8 0.94	5-11 1.03	6-1 1.13	6-3 1.23	6-5 1.34	6-7 1.44	6-9 1.55	6-11 1.66	7-3 1.90	7-8 2.26	24.0	
12-3 1.19	12-8 1.32	13-1 1.46	13-6 1.60	13-11 1.74	14-3 1.89	14-8 2.04	15-0 2.19	15-4 2.35			12.0	2x6
11-6 1.12	11-10 1.24	12-3 1.37	12-8 1.50	13-0 1.63	13-4 1.77	13-8 1.91	14-0 2.05	14-4 2.20	15-0 2.51		13.7	
10-7 1.03	11-0 1.15	11-4 1.26	11-8 1.38	12-0 1.51	12-4 1.64	12-8 1.77	13-0 1.90	13-4 2.04	13-11 2.32		16.0	
9-8 0.94	10-0 1.05	10-4 1.15	10-8 1.26	11-0 1.38	11-3 1.49	11-7 1.61	11-10 1.74	12-2 1.86	12-8 2.12	13-5 2.53	19.2	
8-8 0.84	9-0 0.94	9-3 1.03	9-7 1.13	9-10 1.23	10-1 1.34	10-4 1.44	10-7 1.55	10-10 1.66	11-4 1.90	12-0 2.26	24.0	
16-2 1.19	16-9 1.32	17-3 1.46	17-10 1.60	18-4 1.74	18-10 1.89	19-4 2.04	19-9 2.19	20-3 2.35			12.0	2x8
15-1 1.12	15-8 1.24	16-2 1.37	16-8 1.50	17-2 1.63	17-7 1.77	18-1 1.91	18-6 2.05	18-11 2.20	19-9 2.51		13.7	
14-0 1.03	14-6 1.15	14-11 1.26	15-5 1.38	15-10 1.51	16-4 1.64	16-9 1.77	17-2 1.90	17-6 2.04	18-4 2.32		16.0	
12-9 0.94	13-3 1.05	13-8 1.15	14-1 1.26	14-6 1.38	14-11 1.49	15-3 1.61	15-8 1.74	16-0 1.86	16-9 2.12	17-9 2.53	19.2	
11-5 0.84	11-10 0.94	12-3 1.03	12-7 1.13	12-11 1.23	13-4 1.34	13-8 1.44	14-0 1.55	14-4 1.66	14-11 1.90	15-10 2.26	24.0	
20-7 1.19	21-4 1.32	22-0 1.46	22-9 1.60	23-4 1.74	24-0 1.89	24-8 2.04	25-3 2.19	25-10 2.35			12.0	2x10
19-3 1.12	19-11 1.24	20-7 1.37	21-3 1.50	21-10 1.63	22-6 1.77	23-1 1.91	23-7 2.05	24-2 2.20	25-3 2.51		13.7	
17-10 1.03	18-6 1.15	19-1 1.26	19-8 1.38	20-3 1.51	20-10 1.64	21-4 1.77	21-10 1.90	22-4 2.04	23-4 2.32		16.0	
16-4 0.94	16-10 1.05	17-5 1.15	17-11 1.26	18-6 1.38	19-0 1.49	19-6 1.61	19-11 1.74	20-5 1.86	21-4 2.12	22-8 2.53	19.2	
14-7 0.84	15-1 0.94	15-7 1.03	16-1 1.13	16-6 1.23	17-0 1.34	17-5 1.44	17-10 1.55	18-3 1.66	19-1 1.90	20-3 2.26	24.0	

Note: The required modulus of elasticity, E, in 1,000,000 pounds per square inch is shown below each span.

UNIFORM BUILDING CODE STANDARD NO. 25-22

PLANK-AND-BEAM FRAMING

Based on Wood Construction Data No. 4 (1970) of the National Forest Products Association

See Section 2501 (a), Uniform Building Code

Scope

Sec. 25.2201. This standard covers plank-and-beam construction under the provisions of the Uniform Building Code, and is subject to the regulations of Chapter 25. Tables in this standard are for use where moderate uniform loads occur and are not applicable for concentrated loads such as partitions, bathtubs, refrigerators, etc. See also Uniform Building Code Table No. 25-U.

Definition

Sec. 25.2202. The plank-and-beam structural floor or roof system consists of a plank subfloor or roof decking with supporting beams spaced a maximum of 8 feet on center.

Design

Sec. 25.2203. The load strength and deflection requirements for 2-inch planks and beams are set forth in Tables No. 25-22-A, No. 25-22-B, No. 25-22-C and No. 25-22-D.

The allowable unit stress *f* appropriate for each grade and species of lumber is set forth in Table No. 25-A-1 of the Uniform Building Code.

TABLE NO. 25-22-A—2-INCH PLANK—REQUIRED MINIMUM f AND E LIVE LOAD: 20, 30 AND 40 POUNDS PER SQUARE FOOT WITHOUT PLASTERED CEILING BELOW

PLANK SPAN (IN FEET)	LIVE LOAD (Pounds Per Square Foot)	DEFLECTION LIMITATION	TYPE A		TYPE B		TYPE C		TYPE D	
			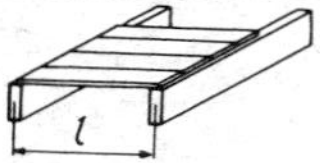		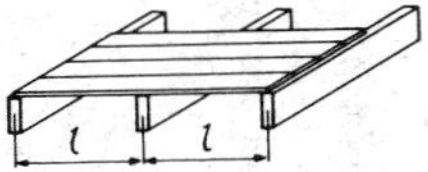		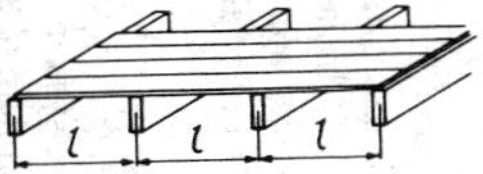		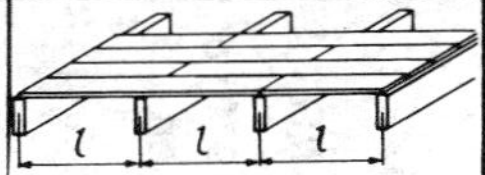	
			f psi	E psi	f psi	E psi	f psi	E psi	f psi	E psi
6′	20	$\frac{l}{240}$	360	576000	360	239000	288	305000	360	408000
		$\frac{l}{360}$	360	864000	360	359000	288	457000	360	611000
	30	$\frac{l}{240}$	480	864000	480	359000	384	457000	480	611000
		$\frac{l}{360}$	480	1296000	480	538000	384	685000	480	917000
	40	$\frac{l}{240}$	600	1152000	600	478000	480	609000	600	815000
		$\frac{l}{360}$	600	1728000	600	717000	480	914000	600	1223000

7′	20	$\frac{l}{240}$	490	915000	490	380000	392	484000	490	647000
		$\frac{l}{360}$	490	1372000	490	570000	392	726000	490	971000
	30	$\frac{l}{240}$	653	1372000	653	570000	522	726000	653	971000
		$\frac{l}{360}$	653	2058000	653	854000	522	1088000	653	1456000
	40	$\frac{l}{240}$	817	1829000	817	759000	653	968000	817	1294000
		$\frac{l}{360}$	817	2744000	817	1139000	653	1451000	817	1941000
8′	20	$\frac{l}{240}$	640	1365000	640	567000	512	722000	640	966000
		$\frac{l}{360}$	640	2048000	640	850000	512	1083000	640	1449000
	30	$\frac{l}{240}$	853	2048000	853	850000	682	1083000	853	1449000
		$\frac{l}{360}$	853	3072000	853	1275000	682	1625000	853	2174000
	40	$\frac{l}{240}$	1067	2731000	1067	1134000	853	1444000	1067	1932000
		$\frac{l}{360}$	1067	4096000	1067	1700000	853	2166000	1067	2898000

TABLE NO. 25-22-B—ROOF BEAMS—LIVE LOAD 20 POUNDS PER SQUARE FOOT—DEFLECTION LIMITATION L/240 (NOT FOR SUPPORT OF PLASTER)

SPAN OF BEAM	NOMINAL SIZE OF BEAM	MINIMUM f & E IN psi FOR BEAMS SPACED:					
		6′ - 0″		7′ - 0″		8′ - 0″	
		f	E	f	E	f	E
10′	2-3x6	1070	780000	1250	910000	1430	1040000
	1-3x8	1235	680000	1440	794000	1645	906000
	2-2x8	1030	570000	1200	665000	1370	760000
	1-4x8	880	485000	1030	566000	1175	646000
	3-2x8	685	380000	800	443000	915	506000
	2-3x8	615	340000	720	397000	820	453000
	2-2x10	630	273000	735	219000	840	364000
11′	2-3x6	1295	1037000	1510	121000	1730	1382000
	1-3x8	1490	905000	1740	1056000	1990	1206000
	2-2x8	1245	754000	1450	880000	1660	1005000
	1-4x8	1065	647000	1245	755000	1420	862000
	3-2x8	830	503000	970	587000	1105	670000
	2-3x8	745	453000	870	529000	995	604000
	2-2x10	765	363000	890	424000	1020	484000
12′	2-3x6	1545	1346000	1800	1571000	2060	1794000
	1-3x8	1775	1175000	2070	1371000	2370	1566000
	2-2x8	1480	980000	1725	1144000	1970	1306000
	1-4x8	1270	840000	1480	980000	1690	1120000
	3-2x8	985	653000	1150	762000	1315	870000
	2-3x8	890	588000	1035	686000	1185	784000
	1-6x8	755	483000	880	564000	1005	644000
	2-2x10	910	472000	1060	551000	1210	629000
	1-3x10	1090	566000	1275	660000	1455	754000
13′	2-3x6	1815	1711000	2110	1997000	2415	2281000
	1-3x8	2085	1494000	2430	1743000	2780	1991000
	2-2x8	1740	1245000	2025	1453000	2315	1660000
	1-4x8	1490	1067000	1735	1245000	1985	1422000
	3-2x8	1160	830000	1350	969000	1545	1106000
	2-3x8	1045	747000	1215	872000	1390	996000
	1-6x8	885	614000	1040	716000	1185	818000
	2-2x10	1070	600000	1245	700000	1420	800000
	1-3x10	1280	719000	1495	839000	1710	958000
14′	2-2x8	2015	1555000	2350	1815000	2685	2073000
	3-2x8	1340	1037000	1570	1210000	1790	1382000
	2-3x8	1210	933000	1410	1089000	1610	1244000
	1-6x8	1025	766000	1200	894000	1370	1021000
	1-3x10	1485	899000	1730	1049000	1980	1198000
	2-2x10	1235	749000	1445	874000	1650	998000
	1-4x10	1060	642000	1240	749000	1415	856000
	3-2x10	825	499000	965	582000	1100	665000
	2-3x10	740	449000	865	524000	990	598000
15′	3-2x8	1540	1275000	1800	1488000	2055	1699000
	2-3x8	1390	1148000	1620	1340000	1850	1530000
	1-6x8	1180	943000	1375	1100000	1570	1257000
	1-3x10	1705	1105000	1990	1289000	2270	1473000
	2-2x10	1420	921000	1660	1075000	1895	1228000
	1-4x10	1220	789000	1420	921000	1625	1052000
	3-2x10	950	614000	1105	717000	1265	818000
	2-3x10	850	553000	995	645000	1135	737000
	1-6x10	735	464000	855	541000	980	618000
	4-2x10	710	461000	830	538000	945	614000
	2-2x10	960	512000	1120	597000	1280	682000

TABLE NO. 25-22-C—ROOF BEAMS—LIVE LOAD 30 POUNDS PER SQUARE FOOT—DEFLECTION LIMITATION *L*/240 (NOT FOR SUPPORT OF PLASTER)

SPAN OF BEAM	NOMINAL SIZE OF BEAM	MINIMUM *f* & *E* IN psi FOR BEAMS SPACED:					
		6′ - 0″		7′ - 0″		8′ - 0″	
		f	*E*	*f*	*E*	*f*	*E*
10′	2-3x6	1430	1170000	1670	1365000	1905	1560000
	1-3x8	1645	1020000	1920	1190000	2195	1360000
	1-4x8	1175	727000	1370	848000	1565	969000
	3-2x8	915	570000	1070	665000	1220	760000
	2-3x8	820	510000	955	595000	1095	680000
	2-4x8	590	364000	690	425000	785	485000
	2-2x10	840	409000	980	477000	1120	545000
11′	2-3x6	1725	1555000	2015	1815000	2300	2073000
	1-3x8	1990	1357000	2320	1584000	2655	1809000
	1-4x8	1420	970000	1660	1132000	1895	1293000
	3-2x8	1105	754000	1290	880000	1475	1005000
	2-3x8	995	679000	1160	792000	1325	905000
	2-4x8	710	485000	830	566000	945	646000
	2-2x10	1020	544000	1190	635000	1360	725000
12′	1-4x8	1690	1260000	1970	1470000	2255	1679000
	3-2x8	1315	979000	1535	1142000	1755	1305000
	2-3x8	1185	882000	1385	1029000	1580	1176000
	2-4x8	845	630000	985	735000	1125	840000
	1-6x8	1005	724000	1175	845000	1340	965000
	2-2x10	1210	708000	1410	826000	1615	944000
	3-2x10	810	472000	945	551000	1080	629000
	2-3x10	725	424000	845	495000	965	565000
13′	1-4x8	1985	1600000	2315	1867000	2645	2133000
	3-2x8	1545	1245000	1805	1453000	2060	1659000
	2-3x8	1390	1120000	1620	1307000	1855	1493000
	2-4x8	990	801000	1155	935000	1320	1068000
	1-6x8	1180	921000	1375	1075000	1575	1228000
	2-2x10	1425	900000	1665	1050000	1900	1200000
	3-2x10	950	600000	1110	700000	1265	800000
	2-3x10	855	540000	1000	630000	1140	720000
	1-4x10	1220	923000	1425	1079000	1625	1230000
14′	3-2x8	1790	1555000	2090	1815000	2385	2073000
	2-3x8	1610	1400000	1880	1634000	2145	1866000
	2-4x8	1150	1000000	1340	1167000	1535	1333000
	1-6x8	1370	1149000	1600	1341000	1825	1532000
	2-2x10	1650	1123000	1925	1310000	2200	1497000
	3-2x10	1100	748000	1285	873000	1465	997000
	2-3x10	990	673000	1155	785000	1320	897000
	1-4x10	1415	963000	1650	1124000	1885	1283000
	1-6x10	915	943000	1070	1100000	1220	1257000
	2-4x10	705	481000	825	561000	940	641000
15′	2-4x8	1320	1230000	1540	1435000	1760	1640000
	1-6x8	1570	1414000	1830	1650000	2095	1885000
	2-2x10	1895	1381000	2210	1612000	2525	1841000
	3-2x10	1260	921000	1470	1075000	1680	1228000
	2-3x10	1135	829000	1325	967000	1515	1105000
	1-4x10	1620	1183000	1890	1380000	2160	1577000
	1-6x10	980	696000	1145	812000	1305	928000
	2-4x10	810	592000	945	691000	1080	789000
	4-2x10	945	691000	1105	806000	1260	921000
	1-8x10	720	510000	840	595000	960	680000
	2-2x12	1280	768000	1495	896000	1705	1024000
	1-4x12	1095	658000	1280	768000	1460	877000

TABLE NO. 25-22-D—ROOF AND FLOOR BEAMS—LIVE LOAD 40 POUNDS PER SQUARE FOOT—DEFLECTION LIMITATION L/360 (NOT FOR SUPPORT OF PLASTER)

SPAN OF BEAM	NOMINAL SIZE OF BEAM	MINIMUM f & E IN psi FOR BEAMS SPACED:					
		6′ - 0″		7′ - 0″		8′ - 0″	
		f	E	f	E	f	E
10′	1-3x8	2055	1700000	2400	1984000	2740	2266000
	2-2x8	1710	1417000	1995	1654000	2280	1889000
	1-4x8	1470	1211000	1715	1413000	1960	1614000
	1-6x8	875	697000	1020	813000	1165	929000
	2-2x10	1050	681000	1225	795000	1400	908000
	1-3x10	1260	819000	1470	956000	1680	1092000
	1-4x10	900	585000	1050	683000	1200	780000
11′	2-2x8	2070	1886000	2415	2201000	2760	2514000
	1-4x8	1775	1616000	2070	1886000	2365	2154000
	1-6x8	1055	929000	1230	1084000	1405	1238000
	2-2x10	1275	906000	1490	1057000	1700	1208000
	1-3x10	1575	1090000	1780	1272000	2030	1453000
	1-4x10	1090	779000	1270	909000	1455	1038000
	3-2x10	850	605000	990	706000	1135	806000
12′	1-6x8	1255	1206000	1465	1407000	1670	1607000
	3-2x8	1645	1631000	1920	1903000	2190	2174000
	2-2x10	1510	1180000	1760	1377000	2010	1573000
	1-3x10	1820	1415000	2125	1651000	2425	1886000
	1-4x10	1300	1010000	1515	1179000	1735	1346000
	3-2x10	1010	786000	1180	917000	1345	1048000
	2-3x10	905	706000	1055	824000	1205	941000
	1-6x10	785	594000	915	693000	1045	792000
	2-4x10	650	505000	760	589000	865	673000
13′	1-6x8	1475	1535000	1720	1791000	1965	2046000
	2-3x8	1735	1866000	2025	2178000	2315	2487000
	2-4x8	1235	1335000	1440	1558000	1645	1779000
	3-2x10	1185	1000000	1380	1167000	1580	1333000
	2-2x10	1780	1500000	2075	1750000	2370	2000000
	1-3x10	2130	1799000	2485	2099000	2840	2398000
	2-3x10	1070	900000	1250	1050000	1425	1200000
	1-4x10	1525	1537000	1780	1794000	2035	2049000
	2-4x10	760	642000	890	749000	1015	856000
14′	2-4x8	1435	1666000	1675	1944000	1915	2221000
	3-2x10	1375	1246000	1605	1454000	1830	1661000
	2-3x10	1235	1121000	1440	1308000	1645	1494000
	1-4x10	1770	1605000	2065	1873000	2360	2139000
	2-4x10	880	801000	1025	935000	1175	1068000
	3-3x10	825	749000	960	874000	1100	998000
	1-6x10	1145	1571000	1335	1833000	1525	2094000
	1-8x10	780	691000	910	806000	1040	921000
	4-2x10	1030	936000	1200	1092000	1375	1248000
	2-2x12	1395	1040000	1630	1214000	1860	1386000
15′	3-2x10	1575	1535000	1840	1791000	2100	2046000
	2-3x10	1420	1381000	1655	1612000	1890	1841000
	2-4x10	1010	986000	1175	1151000	1345	1314000
	3-3x10	945	921000	1100	1075000	1260	1228000
	1-6x10	1225	1160000	1430	1354000	1635	1546000
	1-8x10	900	850000	1050	992000	1200	1133000
	4-2x10	1180	1151000	1375	1343000	1575	1534000
	2-2x12	1600	1280000	1865	1494000	2130	1706000
	3-2x12	1065	854000	1240	997000	1420	1138000
	1-3x12	1920	1536000	2240	1792000	2560	2047000
	4-2x12	800	640000	935	747000	1065	853000
	2-3x12	960	767000	1120	895000	1280	1022000

UNIFORM BUILDING CODE STANDARD NO. 25-25

WOOD PARTICLEBOARD

Based on American National Standard for Wood Particleboard, ANSI A208.1-1989

See Sections 2501 (a), 2502 (a), 2516 (g) 5 and 2517 (f), Uniform Building Code

Scope

Sec. 25.2501. (a) **General.** The particleboards covered by this standard are made from particles of wood or combinations of wood particles and wood fibers bonded together with synthetic resins or other suitable bonding systems by a process in which the interparticle bond is created by the bonding system. Other materials may be added during manufacture to improve certain properties. This standard includes dimensional tolerances, physical and mechanical property requirements and maximum formaldehyde emissions for different grades of wood particleboard. Also included are test methods, inspection practices and methods of identification.

(b) **Property Values.** The property values in this standard are minimum or maximum values for each grade as the context requires and as determined by the specified test methods. It should be clearly recognized, however, that the strength values are not engineering design values.

Definitions

Sec. 25.2502. The following are definitions of some trade terms commonly used in the particleboard industry:

ADDITIVE is any material included in wood particleboard other than the primary components which are wood and bonding systems.

BINDER is an extraneous bonding agent, either organic or inorganic, used to bind wood particles together to produce a particleboard.

BONDING SYSTEM is any system used to bind wood particles together to produce particleboard.

FIBERS are the slender threadlike elements or groups of wood fibers resulting from chemical or mechanical defiberization, or both, and sometimes referred to as fiber bundles.

FLAKE is a wood particle of predetermined dimensions, specifically produced by specialized equipment of various types. Each flake is essentially flat, of uniform thickness, and has the grain of the wood running essentially in the plane of the flake.

FORMALDEHYDE TEST METHOD (FTM 2-1985) is a large chamber test method for determining formaldehyde emissions from wood products.

MAT-FORMED PARTICLEBOARD is a particleboard in which the coated particles are formed first into a mat having substantially the same length and width as the finished board before being flatplaten pressed.

PARTICLES are the aggregate component of a particleboard manufactured by mechanical means from wood, including all small subdivisions of wood such as flakes, shavings, slivers and wafers. Particle size may be measured by screen mesh that permits passage of particles and another screen upon which they are retained, or by measured dimensions as for flakes.

SHAVING is a thin slice or strip of wood pared off with a knife, planer or other cutting instrument in which the cut may be either across, parallel to, or at an angle to the axis of the fibers.

SLIVER is a particle of nearly square or rectangular cross section with a length parallel to the grain of the wood at least four times the thickness.

WAFER is a flake having a length in the direction of the grain of the wood which is at least $1^1/_4$ inches.

Requirements

Sec. 25.2503. (a) **General.** All particleboard represented as complying with any grade in this standard shall meet the requirements specified for that grade when tested in accordance with the provisions of this section.

All values obtained in accordance with such procedures shall be rounded off to the nearest unit in the last righthand place of figures used in expressing the limiting value.

(b) **Materials.** 1. **Wood.** The wood material shall be in the form of flakes, shavings, slivers, fibers and other types of particles that are produced from wood by cutting, hammermilling, grinding and similar processes.

2. **Bonding system.** The wood particles shall be bonded by one of the following systems:

Type 1—A system, e.g., urea-formaldehyde, which enables the products to meet all applicable requirements specified herein for the relevant Type 1 grade.

Type 2—A system, e.g., phenol-formaldehyde, which enables the products to meet all applicable requirements specified herein for the relevant Type 2 grade.

3. **Additives.** Additives that enhance dimensional stability, fire retardation, resistance to fungi and insects or impart other desired properties may be incorporated into the particleboard at the time of manufacture, or subsequently, provided that the products containing the additives meet all applicable requirements specified herein.

(c) **Dimensional Tolerances.** 1. **Width and length.** The trimmed width and length of the panels shall conform to specified dimensions tolerances as shown for each grade in Tables Nos. 25-25-A and 25-25-B. Width and length shall be determined by measuring the width of each end and at midlength and by measuring the length near each edge and at midwidth.

2. **Thickness.** Thickness of a panel and variance from a panel's average thickness shall conform to the thickness tolerance requirements of Table No. 25-25-A or 25-25-B. Thickness shall be determined by measuring the caliper (to the nearest 0.001 inch) one inch from the edge at each panel corner and one inch from the edge at the midlength of each panel edge. The average of these eight measurements shall

constitute the panel average thickness and shall be compared with the nominal thickness as stated by the manufacturer. Each individual measurement shall be compared to the panel average for variance.

3. **Squareness.** The two diagonal measurements of a trimmed panel shall not differ more than $^1/_{32}$ inch per foot of panel width when trimmed length and width satisfy tolerance requirements.

4. **Straightness.** Trimmed edges of panels 24 inches wide or wider shall not deviate more than $^1/_{64}$ inch per each 2 feet of panel length or width. Straightness shall be determined by measuring to the nearest $^1/_{64}$ inch the maximum deviation from a straight line extending from corner to corner on the same trimmed panel edge.

(d) **Physical and Mechanical Properties.** 1. **General.** Particleboard shall conform to the physical and mechanical requirements in Tables Nos. 25-25-A and 25-25-B and the applicable parts of this section for the respective grade. The values specified in Tables Nos. 25-25-A and 25-25-B and the other requirements of Section 25.2503 for physical and mechanical properties are averages obtained in testing five panels. In addition, no property of a single panel in any multipanel sample may be more than 20 percent out of compliance with the value shown for that particular grade in the tables.

2. **Moisture Content.** The average moisture content at the time of shipment from the manufacturer shall not be in excess of 10 percent (based on the overdry weight of the board) for grades listed in Tables Nos. 25-25-A and 25-25-B. Moisture specimens shall be cut from three different bending specimens in each panel tested. The moisture content of the panel shall be the average of the test results of the three specimens.

3. **Density tolerance.** The average density of the particleboard shall not be more than 10 percent below the nominal density as stated by the manufacturer. Panel density shall be determined by calculation based on the weight and the volume of the six modulus of elasticity specimens.

4. **Bonding system durability (Type 2 only).** The durability of the bonding system shall be determined by evaluating the modulus of rupture in static bending of specimens that have been subjected to the following "Six-Cycle Soak-Steam-Freeze-Dry" conditioning regimen:

A. Six cycles, each comprising the following steps:

(i) Immersion in water at 120°F. ± 3°F. for one hour.

(ii) Exposure to steam and water vapor at 200°F. ± 5°F. for three hours.

(iii) Freezing at 10°F. ± 5°F. for 20 hours.

(iv) Heating at 210°F. ± 3°F. for three hours.

(v) Exposure to steam and water vapor at 200°F. ± 5°F. for three hours.

(vi) Heating in dry air at 210°F. ± 3°F. for 18 hours.

B. After the six cycles, condition for at least 48 hours at 68°F. ± 6°F. and 65 plus 1 percent humidity.

The average modulus of rupture after accelerated aging shall not be less than 50 percent of the modulus of rupture listed for the particular grade in Table No.

25-25-B. The modulus of rupture shall be calculated based upon the thickness before the bonding system durability test.

5. **Exterior durability (Grade 2-M-W only).** The probable effect of adverse weather exposure shall be determined by evaluating the modulus of rupture and the modulus of elasticity in static bending of specimens that have been subjected to the following "Three-Cycle Soak" conditioning regimen:

A. Three cycles, each comprising the following steps:

(i) Immersion in water at 120°F. ± 3°F. for six hours.

(ii) Heating in dry air at 210°F. ± 3°F. for 18 hours.

B. After the three cycles, condition for at least 24 hours at 68°F. ± 6°F. and 65 plus 1 percent relative humidity.

The average modulus of rupture tested shall not be less than 1,700 psi and the average modulus of elasticity shall not be less than 342,000 psi. In all cases, the results shall be based upon the thickness before soaking.

6. **Modulus of rupture and modulus of elasticity.** The values for modulus of rupture and modulus of elasticity shall be determined by static bending tests with the specimens tested without soaking. In static bending tests, it is not necessary to obtain a full load-deflection curve; only two load values (and corresponding deflections) within the elastic range need to be recorded. The stiffness shall be calculated by the following formula:

$$E = P_1L^3/4bd^3Y_1$$

In this formula, P_1 (load at proportional limit) shall be the difference between the two recorded loads, and Y_1 (center deflection at proportional limit load) shall be the difference between the two corresponding recorded deflections. Three specimens shall be cut parallel to the length of each panel to be tested and a like number of specimens shall be cut perpendicular to the length of each panel. The average property values of the six specimens shall determine the modulus of rupture and modulus of elasticity values for one panel.

7. **Internal bond.** The internal bond shall be determined in accordance with procedures testing tensile strength perpendicular to the surface. Three specimens shall be cut from each panel to be tested. The average of the three specimen tests shall determine the internal bond of one panel.

8. **Linear expansion.** The linear expansion (between 50 and 90 percent relative humidity) shall be made to measure dimensional stability. One specimen shall be cut parallel to the length of each panel to be tested, and one shall be cut perpendicular to the length of the same panel. The average of the two specimen tests shall determine the value for the panel.

9. **Face screw-holding capacity.** The face screw-holding capacity shall be determined by direct screw withdrawal with the specimen in the dry condition. Either a 1-inch No. 10, Type A or Type AB sheet metal screw shall be used and the speed of testing shall be 0.6 inch per minute. If the boards are less than $^3/_4$ inch thick, the specimen shall be made up of 2 thicknesses bonded together with an adhesive. Boards less than $^3/_8$ inch thick (nominal) shall not be tested. Test specimens shall be at least 3 inches by 4 inches in size. A $^1/_8$-inch pilot hold $^1/_2$ inch deep shall be used.

Four tests shall be made on each panel to be tested. The results of the four tests shall be averaged to determine the screw-holding capacity of one panel.

10. **Edge screw-holding capacity.** The average edge screw-holding capacity shall be determined by direct screw withdrawal with the specimen in the dry condition. Either a 1-inch No. 10, Type A or Type AB sheet metal screw shall be used. The speed of testing shall be 0.6 inch per minute. Boards less than $^5/_8$ inch thick shall not be tested. The test specimens shall be 3 inches wide by any convenient length greater than 6 inches. A $^1/_8$-inch pilot hole $^1/_2$ inch deep shall be used. Four tests shall be made on each panel to be tested. The results of the four tests shall be averaged to determine the edge screw-holding capacity of one panel.

11. **Hardness.** The hardness shall be determined in accordance with the modified Janka ball test. Two specimens shall be cut from each panel to be tested. The results of all test penetrations shall be averaged to determine the hardness of the panel.

(e) **Formaldehyde Provisions.** 1. **Maximum emissions.** Emissions of formaldehyde from all Type 1 grades shall not exceed 0.30 parts per million when tested in accordance with the following sections.

2. **Testing method.** Formaldehyde emissions shall be determined in accordance with the Large Scale Test Method for Determining Formaldehyde Emissions from Wood Products, FTM 2-1985, except as otherwise provided in this section.

3. **Test conditions.** The following conditions shall prevail when testing for formaldehyde:

	GRADES 1-H, 1-M	GRADE 1-LD
Loading ratio:	0.13 ft.^{2}/ft..^{3}	0.04 ft.^{2}/ft.^{3}
Air change rate:	0.5/hour	0.5/hour
Test temperature:	77°F. ± 2°F.	77°F. ± 2°F.

Loading ratio is an expression of the total exposed surface area of the product in square feet divided by the test chamber volume in cubic feet. The surface area of the edges shall be included in the calculation of total exposed surface area only if it constitutes 5 percent or more of the total surface area. Air change rate is the ratio of hourly indoor air change and indoor space volume measured in identified volume units expressed in air changes per hour.

Conformance Testing

Sec. 25.2504. Produce test values of board for the most recent five panels tested in each panel grade and thickness shall be used as the sample for determining conformance with the property requirements in Table No. 25-25-A or 25-25-B and Section 25.2503 (d) and (e). At least one sample of product per 200,000 square feet ($^3/_4$-inch basis) shall be tested, except that the testing for conformance to Sections 25.2503 (d) 3 and 4, and 25.2503 (e) 1 shall be conducted once per year.

Identification

Sec. 25.2505. (a) **Explanation of Grades.** The particleboard grades in this standard have three parts: a first digit, a letter designation and a final digit or letter. The first digit indicates the type of bonding system used [see Section 25.2503 (b) 2]. The letters have the following meanings:

M Medium nominal density (40 to 50 lb./ft^3).

LD Lower nominal density (less than 40 lb./ft^3).

The final digit or letter indicates the grade identification within a particular description. For instance, 1-M-2 indicates Type 1 medium density particleboard, Grade 2.

(b) **Information to Be Provided.** All particleboard which is represented as conforming to this standard shall be identified with the following information:

1. Manufacturer's name or trademark.

2. Compliance with the requirements of this standard in accordance with Section 2505 of the Uniform Building Code.

3. The grade.

4. The lot number or date of production.

5. With respect only to particleboard intended for use as underlayment, the word "underlayment."

6. With respect only to Type 2 products intended for exterior application, the words "exterior glue."

(c) **Methods of Identification.** The information required by Section 25.2505 (b) shall be stamped on each panel of particleboard intended for use as underlayment.

With respect to all other grades, the information shall be provided by either stamping each panel or providing a written statement in a unit label, invoice or other commercial document.

TABLE NO. 25-25-A—REQUIREMENTS FOR GRADES OF TYPE 1 WOOD PARTICLEBOARD

GRADE	LENGTH AND WIDTH TOLERANCE (Inches)	THICKNESS TOLERANCE[1]		MODULUS OF RUPTURE (psi)	MODULUS OF ELASTICITY (psi)	INTERNAL BOND (psi)	HARDNESS (Pounds)	LINEAR EXPANSION MAX. AVG. (Percent)	SCREWHOLDING		FORMALDEHYDE[2,3]
		Panel Average from Nominal (Inches)	Variance from Panel Average (Inches)						Face (Pounds)	Edge (Pounds)	Maximum Emissions (ppm)
1-M-1	+0 −1/8	±0.015	±0.010	1,600	250,000	60	500	0.35	NS	NS	0.30
1-M-2	±1/16	±0.010	±0.005	2,100	325,000	60	500	0.35	225	200	0.30
1-M-3	±1/16	±0.010	±0.005	2,400	400,000	80	500	0.35	250	225	0.30
1-M-8	±1/16	±0.010	±0.005	1,800	275,000	60	500	0.45	200	175	0.30
1-LD-1	±1/16	+0.005 −0.015	±0.005	400	80,000	20	NS	0.35	90	NS	0.30
1-LD-2	±1/16	+0.005 −0.015	±0.005	800	150,000	20	NS	0.35	125	NS	0.30

[1]Thickness tolerance values are only for sanded panels as defined by the manufacturer. Unsanded panels shall be in accordance with the thickness tolerances specified by agreement between the manufacturer and the purchaser.

[2]Particleboard made with phenol formaldehyde based resins do not emit significant quantities of formaldehyde. Therefore, such products and other particleboard products made with resin not containing formaldehyde are not subject to the formaldehyde emission requirements.

[3]Product loading ratios used in formaldehyde testing typically reflect actual end use loading. For example, products 1-M loading ratios (0.13 ft.^{2}/ft.^{3}) simulate full floor coverage, while loading ratios for 1-LD (0.04 ft.^{2}/ft.^{3}) more closely reflect loading for use in interior door cores.

[4]NS—Not Specified.

TABLE NO. 25-25-B—REQUIREMENTS FOR GRADES OF TYPE 2 WOOD PARTICLEBOARD[1]

GRADE	LENGTH AND WIDTH TOLERANCE (Inches)	THICKNESS TOLERANCE[2]		MODULUS OF RUPTURE (psi)	MODULUS OF ELASTICITY (psi)	INTERNAL BOND (psi)	HARDNESS (Pounds)	LINEAR EXPANSION MAX. AVG. (Percent)	SCREWHOLDING	
		Panel Average from Nominal (Inches)	Variance from Panel Average (Inches)						Face (Pounds)	Edge (Pounds)
2-M-1	+0 −1/8	±0.015	±0.010	1,800	250,000	60	500	0.35	225	160
2-M-2	+0 −1/8	±0.015	±0.010	2,500	450,000	60	500	0.35	250	200
2-M-3	+0 −1/8	±0.015	±0.010	3,000	500,000	60	500	0.35	NS	NS
2-M-W[4]	+0 −1/8	+0.015	±0.010	2,500	450,000	50	500	0.20	NS	NS

[1]Particleboard made with phenol formaldehyde based resins do not emit significant quantities of formaldehyde. Therefore, such products and other particleboard products made with resins not containing formaldehyde are not subject to the formaldehyde emission requirements.

[2]Thickness tolerance values are only for sanded panels as defined by the manufacturer. Values for unsanded 2-M-W graded panels shall be ±0.030″ for panel average from nominal and ±0.030″ for variance from panel average.

[3]NS—Not Specified.

[4]"W" indicates that this product is made from wafers.

UNIFORM BUILDING CODE STANDARD NO. 25-27

TEMPERATURE EFFECTS

Based on National Design Specification for Wood Construction (1986), including the 1986 Supplement of the National Forest Products Association

See Sections 2501 (a) and 2504 (c) 9, Uniform Building Code

Scope

Sec. 25.2701. This standard covers adjustments to design values for wood structural members which are exposed by manufacturing and equipment processes to prolonged elevated temperatures up to 150°F. This standard does not apply to wood members exposed to the normal range of climatic temperatures ordinarily encountered in buildings.

Working Stress

Sec. 25.2702. Wood members heated to temperatures up to 150°F. for extended periods of time shall have the design values adjusted. The average factors given in Table No. 25-27-A shall be used in making such adjustments. Tabulated adjustments are for immediate temperature effects.

TABLE NO. 25-27-A—PERCENT DECREASE IN DESIGN VALUES FOR EACH 1°F. INCREASE IN TEMPERATURE[1]

PROPERTY	MOISTURE CONTENT OF MEMBER[2]	HEATING ABOVE 68°F. (Max. 150°F.)
Modulus of elasticity and tension parallel to grain	0% 12% 24%	−0.11% −0.13% −0.15%
Other properties	0% 12% 24%	−0.19% −0.38% −0.57%

[1]Linear interpolation may be used for other moisture contents.

[2]In service (equilibrium) moisture content at design temperature.

UNIFORM BUILDING CODE STANDARD NO. 25-28

FIRE-RETARDANT-TREATED WOOD TESTS ON DURABILITY AND HYGROSCOPIC PROPERTIES

Based on American Society for Testing and Materials Standard Test Methods ASTM D 2898-81 and D 3201-79. Extracted, with permission, from the Annual Book of ASTM Standards, copyright American Society for Testing and Materials, 1916 Race Street, Philadelphia, PA 19103, and American Wood Preservers Association Standards C 20-83 and C 27-83.

See Sections 401 (b), 407 and 2501 (a), Uniform Building Code

Scope

Sec. 25.2801. These methods cover the (1) durability of a fire-retardant treatment of wood and wood-base products under exposure to accelerated weathering, (2) measurement of the hygroscopic properties of fire-retardant-treated wood, and (3) identification classifications for material having qualified under these tests. The fire-retardant treatment for lumber and plywood is by pressure impregnation.

Accelerated Weathering

Sec. 25.2802. (a) **Scope.** This section describes the conditioning method for a test specimen prior to subjecting that specimen to an appropriate fire test. The condition simulates effects of leaching, drying and temperature such as might reasonably be anticipated on a wood element exposed to the weather over a long term.

(b) **Apparatus.** The test apparatus shall be capable of subjecting the specimen uniformly to the test conditions described in Subsection (d).

No special means of protecting the specimen back and edges are required, but water shall not impinge directly on those surfaces which are not exposed either to the weather in the assembled form, or to fire in the subsequent test. Water spray nozzles shall be provided and arranged so as to distribute water evenly over the exposed specimen surface.

Heating shall be thermostatically controlled. Forced-air movement shall be uniform across the specimen surface, with provisions made for adequate air changes to assure thorough drying.

(c) **Test Specimen.** The test specimen shall include all those essential parts of the corresponding fire test specimen that may be subjected to weather exposure in normal use.

Specimens may be mounted in sections which can be reassembled subsequently without trimming into the appropriate fire test specimen.

The specimen surface shall have a slope of 4 in 12.

(d) **Exposure Cycle.** Subject the specimens to an exposure cycle consisting of twelve one-week cycles. Each cycle is to consist of 96 hours of water exposure and 72 hours of drying.

Apply water in a moderately fine spray uniformly over the exposed specimen surfaces by spray nozzles that deliver an average of 0.7 inch of water per hour (0.0073 gallons per minute per square foot of specimen surface) at a temperature between 35° and 60°F. Do not recirculate the water.

Dry at a thermostatically controlled temperature of 135° to 140°F. in a room or cell. The controlling temperature shall be the air temperature measured 1 inch above the specimen surface. Accompany drying with the air movement directed across the face of the specimens at a rate of at least 25 feet per minute.

At the end of each cycle, change the position of each specimen within the apparatus so that each specimen or segment occupies approximately an equal number of cycles in each location used.

(e) **Conditioning.** Upon completion of the prescribed exposure, the specimen shall be conditioned to a moisture content specified by the applicable fire test standard.

Hygroscopic Properties of Fire-retardant Wood

Sec. 25.2803. (a) **Scope.** This section prescribes the method for determining the moisture content of fire-retardant-treated wood samples after exposure to a standard high relative humidity condition of 92 ± 2 percent at 27 ± 2°C.

(b) **Apparatus.** Conditioning room or chamber with air circulation and controlling instruments capable of being maintained at 27 ± 2°C. and a relative humidity of 92 ± 2 percent. Other suitable means of maintaining these conditions are also acceptable.

Oven, air-circulated and vented, capable of maintaining a temperature of 103 ± 2°C.

A weighing scale or balance that will weigh a specimen within an accuracy of ± 0.2 percent.

(c) **Test Specimens.** Specimens shall be selected that represent the lot. Unless otherwise specified, specimens shall be full cross sections, no less than 25.4 millimeters along the grain, but longer as needed to provide a minimum volume of 33 cubic centimeters.

The specimens shall be penetrated by the chemical to be representative for the treated product.

The specimens shall be in moisture equilibrium with a laboratory ambient condition of 30 to 65 percent relative humidity or shall be exposed for at least 7 days at such a condition prior to high-humidity exposure.

Untreated specimens, when available, of the same species or wood-base product and of the same size, shall be exposed to the preconditioning, high-humidity exposure, and drying along with the treated specimens.

(d) **Procedure.** Weigh each specimen to an accuracy of ± 0.2 percent.

Expose all specimens under constant humidity conditions of 92 ± 2 percent at 27 ± 2°C. for seven days. Specimens shall be suitably suspended so that all surfaces are exposed.

Weigh each specimen immediately to an accuracy of ±0.2 percent one at a time as they are removed from the conditioning chamber. Observe and record the general appearance of the specimens.

Dry each specimen in an oven at 103 ± 2°C. until approximately constant weight is attained, and reweigh. Constant weight can be assumed when two consecutive readings taken two hours apart agree within 0.2 percent. Avoid drying for periods longer than necessary to achieve constant weight, since thermal decomposition of chemical or wood might occur reflecting a higher than actual moisture content.

(e) **Calculations.** Calculate the "apparent" moisture content of each sample prior to high-humidity exposure as follows:

Moisture content: percent = $[(A - B)/B] \times 100$

WHERE:

A = weight prior to high-humidity exposure, and

B = oven-dry weight

Calculate the "apparent" moisture content of each sample after high-humidity exposure as follows:

Moisture content: percent = $[(C - B)/B] \times 100$

WHERE:

C = weight after high-humidity exposure, and

B = oven-dry weight

The change in the "apparent" moisture content of the specimens shall be calculated as the difference between the average moisture content for the treated and untreated specimens as calculated in this section.

(f) **Report.** The report shall include the following:

Complete identification of the fire-retardant product as to species of wood, wood product, and treatment.

Description of sampling procedure and number and dimensions of test specimens.

General description of humidity chamber and controls used for the test.

The average moisture content of the untreated specimens shall be reported.

The average "apparent" moisture content for the treated specimens, both before and after high-humidity exposure, including the basis of the computation; treated specimen (wood and chemical) or wood-only basis, shall be reported. The change in the average moisture content after high-humidity exposure compared to the moisture content of untreated specimens shall also be reported.

Report any change in the appearance of the specimen during exposure, including surface wetness, chemical exudation, or crystals on surface.

Classification

Sec. 25.2804. (a) **Scope.** This part establishes the classification of fire-retardant-treated wood that has been satisfactorily fire tested after exposure to conditions specified in Sections 25.2802 and 25.2803.

(b) **Classifications.** Material that has been subjected to conditioning tests specified in Sections 25.2802 and 25.2803 and then fire tested in accordance with Section 407 of the code to qualify as fire-retardant-treated wood shall be classified as follows:

1. **Interior Type A.** Material shall have an equilibrium moisture content of not over 28 percent when tested at 92 ± 2 percent relative humidity when conditioned as specified in Section 28.2803.
2. **Interior Type B.** Material that has not qualified as Interior Type A.
3. **Exterior Type.** Material that has been subjected to the weathering test of Section 25.2802.

UNIFORM BUILDING CODE STANDARD NO. 25-29

FIRE-RETARDANT-TREATED WOOD

Based on National Design Specification for Wood Construction Policy on Design Values for Fire-retardant-treated Lumber

See Sections 407, 2501 (a) and 2507 (c) 3, Uniform Building Code

Scope

Sec. 25.2901. This standard establishes the test protocol, acceptance criteria, and quality control procedure for assuring that fire-retardant treatments qualify for the design values assigned and that appropriate treating and redrying methods are used. Only lumber pressure impregnated with fire-retardant chemicals that is identified by the quality mark of an approved inspection agency shall be eligible for the design values specified in Section 2504 (c) 3.

Part I—Test Protocol

Sec. 25.2902. Type of Material. The effects of fire-retardant treatment shall be determined on the basis of tests on matched samples of clear, straight-grain material. This is consistent with procedures presently used to establish design values and modifications for condition of use for visually graded sawn lumber.

Sec. 25.2903. Number of Species. The effects of fire-retardant treatment may vary depending upon species. Because evaluation of such treatment for all species and properties is considered prohibitive, testing of three species representative of a range of wood density and treating characteristics is recommended. A specific treatment may be evaluated for only one of these species, but testing of three species representative of a range of wood density and treated characteristics is recommended.

Qualification may be obtained for any one species by evaluation of that species.

Sec. 25.2904. Identification. Each fire-retardant treatment shall be identified by the commercial name assigned by the developer of the treatment and each specimen shall be marked to identify the drying temperatures and relative humidity schedules used.

Sec. 25.2905. Strength Testing. Material to be subjected to strength testing shall be treated to the penetration and retention level required for that treatment and species to meet the definition of fire-retardant-treated wood given in Section 407.

To allow for variability in treatment, especially for species classified as moderate to difficult to treat, it may be necessary to treat up to twice the number of samples required for test. Equal numbers of samples of low and high treatability may be excluded from strength testing to ensure that material of average treatability is evaluated.

Following treatment, strength test material shall be dried at a maximum temperature of 160°F. with relative humidity schedules and air velocities that will simulate commercial conditions. A record of the operating conditions of the kiln shall be kept for the entire run and shall include humidity conditions and temperature in the hottest part of the kiln.

Sec. 25.2906. Sampling and Treatment. (a) **Species.** For each fire-retardant treatment to be evaluated for general qualification, strength test material shall be selected from each of the following species:

Southern pine (Pinus taeda or echinata)

Coast Douglas fir

White spruce (Picea glauca)

The southern pine material shall be all sapwood. Where a treatment is to be evaluated only for a particular species, strength test material shall be selected from each such species.

(b) **Number of Samples, Size and Quality.** For each species to be evaluated, 25 essentially clear, straight-grained 2 by 4s, 8 feet or longer shall be selected from the production of one or more mills. All pieces shall be identified as being Surfaced Dry and shall have an average specific gravity within ± 10 percent of the average specific gravity (green volume basis) of the species.

(c) **Sample Identification.** From each 2 by 4 member selected for sampling, two end-matched 4-foot blanks shall be cut for strength testing. One blank shall be designated for treatment and the other as control. All blanks shall be coded as to member number and treatment or control.

(d) **Pressure Treatment of Samples.** All blanks to be fire-retardant treated shall be processed in accordance with the specific procedures established for the treatment being evaluated. Blanks shall be pressure treated and dried to a maximum moisture content of 19 percent in 2 by 4 by 4-foot size. The same treatment and drying times, stickering practices, and other procedures to be employed in commercial charges shall be used.

(e) **Conditioning of Blanks.** After redrying to a maximum moisture content of 19 percent, treated blanks and untreated controls shall be conditioned at 68° ± 6°F. and 65 percent ± 1 percent relative humidity until approximate equilibrium weight is attained.

Sec. 25.2907. Strength Tests. (a) **Type and Number of Specimens.** One and one-half-inch by 1 1/2-inch by 23-inch static bending specimen, two-1-inch by 1/4-inch by 16-inch tension specimens, one 1 1/2-inch by 1 1/2-inch by 6-inch compression specimen, one 1 1/2-inch by 1 1/2-inch by 2 1/2-inch shear specimen, and 1 1/2-inch by 1 1/2-inch by 2-inch specific gravity specimen shall be cut from each treated and untreated blank. Bending and compression specimens from both treated and control blanks shall be cut such that three sides of the specimen represent the original surfaces or edge of the 2 by 4 member. Two sides of the shear and specific gravity specimens shall represent original surfaces. One of the 1-inch-wide faces of one of the tension specimens shall represent one original surface of the blank and one of the wide surfaces of the other specimen shall represent the opposite original blank surface.

One method of selecting specimens to obtain the required placement of original surfaces is shown in Figure No. 1. Any orientation of growth rings relative to the edge of the specimens shall be acceptable.

Tension specimens shall be further machined to the size and shape shown in Figure No. 2. Shear specimens shall be notched as shown in Figure No. 3.

(b) **Slope of Grain.** The slope of grain in all bending specimens and in the critical section of tension specimens shall be 1 in 20 or less. Compression and shear specimens shall have a slope of grain of 1 in 16 or less.

(c) **Identification and Conditioning.** The blank identification of each treated and control specimen shall be retained. After final machining, test specimens shall be reconditioned to constant weight before test.

Sec. 25.2908. Testing Procedure. (a) **General.** Testing procedures of an approved nationally recognized test standard shall be used. Load deformation curves shall be taken for static bending tests only. Maximum load shall be observed in all tests.

(b) **Order of Testing.** The treated specimen and the matching untreated control from each blank shall be tested consecutively.

(c) **Measurement.** The dimensions of the critical cross-sectional area, or in the case of the shear specimen, the area of the shear plane of each specimen shall be measured to an accuracy of at least 0.01 inch.

(d) **Static Bending.** Bending specimens shall be center loaded at span of 21 inches. A machine cross-head speed of 0.075 inch per minute shall be used. Bending specimens shall be positioned in the testing machine such that two opposite original surfaces represent the compression and tension faces of the beam.

(e) **Moisture Samples.** All moisture samples selected from each specimen after test shall be oven dried at 130° ± 2°C. until approximately constant weight of the untreated control is reached.

(f) **Specific Gravity.** Dimensions of the specific gravity samples shall be measured after final conditioning to determine volume at 65 percent relative humidity. Samples shall be dried at 103° ± 2°C. until approximate constant weight of the untreated control is reached.

Sec. 25.2909. Report. The treatment and redrying procedures shall be described in accordance with Section 25.2905.

The species evaluated and testing procedures followed shall be fully described.

Individual values of treated and control specimens shall be reported for specific gravity, moisture content, modulus of elasticity, modulus of rupture, maximum tensile stress, maximum compression stress, and maximum shear stress. Average values, standard deviations, average ratios of treated to control values, and median ratios of treated to control values shall be reported for each strength and stiffness property and each species.

Part II—Acceptance Criteria

Sec. 25.2910. Minimum Property Ratio. A fire-retardant treatment evaluated for a particular species under this standard shall qualify for the design value adjustments in Section 2504 (c) 3 if the median ratio of treated to untreated strength or stiffness for each of the following properties equals or exceeds the specified adjustment factor for that property:

Extreme fiber in bending

Modulus of elasticity

Maximum stress in tension parallel to grain

Maximum stress in compression parallel to grain

Maximum stress in horizontal shear

Qualification of the adjustment factor for compression perpendicular to grain shall be based on the median factor for maximum stress in compression parallel to grain. Qualification of the adjustment factor for fastener loads shall be based on the lower of the median ratio for maximum stress in compression parallel to grain and the median ratio for maximum stress in horizontal shear.

Sec. 25.2911. Resampling. Where marginal results occur for one property, a second 25-piece sample may be taken for that property and the combined results of the first and second samples be used to determine qualification.

Sec. 25.2912. General Qualification. A treatment meeting the requirements of Section 25.2910 for each of the three species identified in Section 25.2906 of this standard shall be considered qualifying for the design value adjustments in Section 2504 (c) 3 for all species.

Part III—Identification

Sec. 25.2913. Product Eligibility. Only lumber pressure impregnated with fire-retardant chemicals that is identified by the quality mark of an approved inspection agency shall be eligible for the design value adjustments given in Section 2504 (c) 3. Such agency shall maintain continuing supervision, testing and inspection over the quality of the treated product as necessary to (1) assure compliance with the fire performance requirements for fire-retardant-treated wood in Section 407 and (2) assure eligibility for strength classification under the provisions of this standard.

Sec. 25.2914. Qualification Compliance. The approved agency shall review and analyze the test data developed in accordance with Part I of this standard and shall attest to the following:

1. Competency of the personnel and the adequacy of the facilities of the testing laboratory.
2. Conformance of reported sampling and testing procedures to Part I of this standard.
3. Compliance of test results with acceptance criteria in Part II of this standard.

Sec. 25.2915. Quality Mark. The quality symbol shall indicate that the treated lumber bearing the mark has been treated and redried in conformance with the procedures established by the manufacturer of the treatment which were used in the evaluation and qualification of that treatment under Parts I and II of this standard.

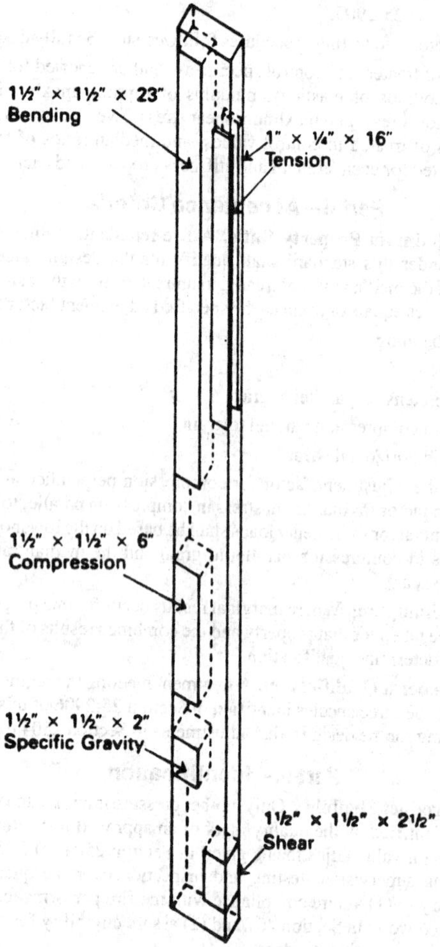
1½" × 1½" × 23"
Bending
1" × ¼" × 16"
Tension
1½" × 1½" × 6"
Compression
1½" × 1½" × 2"
Specific Gravity
1½" × 1½" × 2½"
Shear

FIGURE NO. 1. MATCHING DIAGRAM

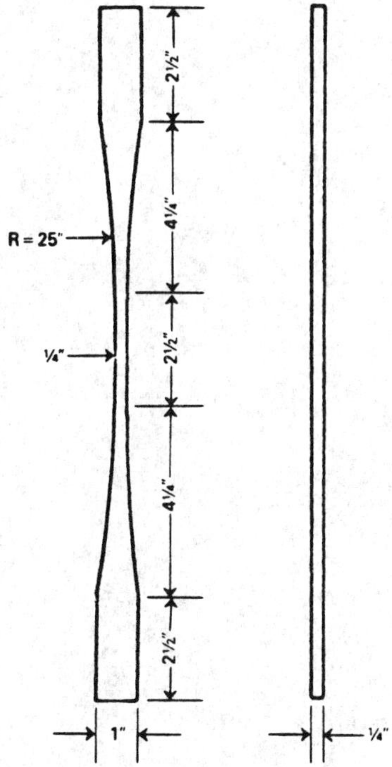
2½"
4¼"
R = 25"
¼"
2½"
4¼"
2½"
1"
¼"

FIGURE NO. 2. TENSION SPECIMEN

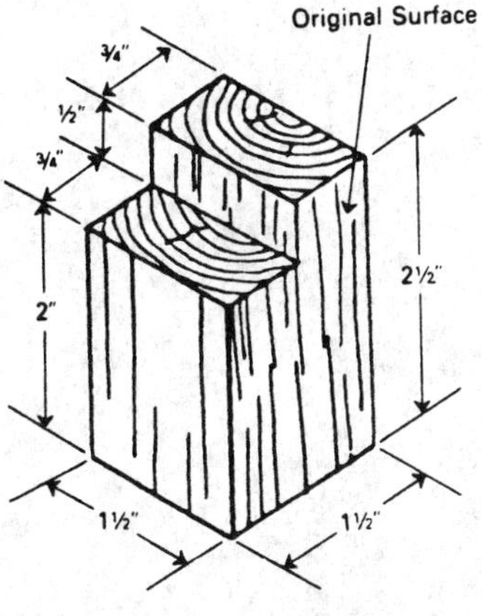
Original Surface
¾"
½"
¾"
2"
2½"
1½"
1½"

FIGURE NO. 3. SHEAR SPECIMEN

UNIFORM BUILDING CODE STANDARD NO. 25-30

DESIGN PROVISIONS FOR SAWN LUMBER

Based on the National Design Specification, 1986 Edition

See Sections 2501 (a), 2502 (b), 2504 (c), 2506 (d) and 2509, Uniform Building Code

Scope

Sec. 25.3001. This standard covers design practices of sawn lumber which are applicable to glued-laminated timber and similar solid-wood products. Design practices specified herein are acceptable under the requirements specified in Chapter 25 of the Building Code.

Bearing On End Grain

Sec. 25.3002. Allowable design values for end grain in bearing F_g are listed in Table No. 25-30-A. Values apply to the net area in bearing. Unit stresses in bearing on the end grain of wood, for parallel to grain, shall not exceed these design values.

When the stress in end-grain bearing exceeds 75 percent of the values provided in this table, the bearing shall be on a metal plate or strap or on other durable, rigid, homogeneous material of adequate strength.

The design values for end-grain bearing apply to end-to-end bearing of compression members, provided there is adequate lateral support and the end cuts are accurately squared and parallel. When a rigid insert is required, it shall be of not less than a 20-gauge metal, or equivalent, inserted with a snug fit between abutting ends.

Where the load at bearing is at an angle to grain, the maximum bearing value shall be determined by the Hankinson formula, using the design for end-grain bearing, parallel to grain in Table No. 25-30-A and design values in compression perpendicular to grain in Tables Nos. 25-A-1 and 25-A-2 in Chapter 25 of the Building Code.

Slenderness Factor and Flexural Stress

Sec. 25.3003. Where the depth of a bending member exceeds its breadth, lateral support shall be provided as specified in Section 2504 (c) 6 of the Building Code and the allowable design value modified in accordance with the following paragraphs.

(a) **Slenderness Factor.** The slenderness factor for a bending member shall be calculated by the following formula:

$$C_s = \sqrt{\frac{l_e d}{b2}}$$

For single span beam with concentrated load at center, $l_e = 1.37l_u + 3d$

For single span beam with uniformly distributed load, $l_e = 1.63l_u + 3d$

For single span beam with equal end moments, $l_e = 1.84l_u$

For cantilever beam with concentrated load at unsupported end, $l_3 = 1.44l_u + 3d$

For cantilever beam with uniformly distributed load, $l_e = 0.90l_u + 3d$

For single span or cantilever beam with any load, conservative value for $l_e = 1.84l_u$ if l_u/d is greater than 14.3 and $l_e = 1.63l_u + 3d$ if l_u/d is less than 14.3

When the compression edge of a bending member is supported throughout its length to prevent its lateral displacement and the ends at points of bearing have lateral support to prevent rotation, the unsupported length l_u may be taken as zero.

When lateral support is provided to prevent rotation at the points of end bearing but no other lateral support is provided throughout the length of the bending member, the unsupported length l_u is the distance between such points of end bearing or the length of a cantilever.

When a bending member is provided with lateral support to prevent rotational or lateral displacement at intermediate points as well as at the ends, the unsupported length l_u is the distance between such points of intermediate lateral support.

The slenderness factor C_s shall not exceed 50.

(b) **Allowable Stresses.** The design values for extreme fiber in bending, F'_b, and modulus of elasticity E used in the following formulae shall be modified in accordance with the provisions of Section 2504 (c), of the Building Code, except that the modification for size factor shall not apply to f_b for intermediate beams and long beams.

Design values for extreme fiber in bending adjusted for slenderness factor F'_b obtained from the following formulae are not subject to further modifications for moisture service conditions, duration of load, temperature, type of treatment or size.

1. **Short beams.** Where the slenderness factor C_s does not exceed 10, the full design value for extreme fiber in bending, $F_b' = F_b$, may be used.

2. **Intermediate beams.** Where the slenderness factor C_s is greater than 10 but does not exceed C_k, the design value for extreme fiber in bending F_b' shall be determined from the following formula:

$$F_b' = F_b\left[1 - \frac{1}{3}\left(\frac{C_s}{C_k}\right)^4\right]$$

In which

$$C_k = .811\sqrt{E/F_b}$$

3. **Long beams.** When the slenderness factor C_s is greater than C_k but less than or equal to 50, the design value for extreme fiber in bending F_b' shall be determined by the following formula:

$$F_b' = \frac{0.438E}{(C_s)2}$$

The design value for extreme fiber in bending F_b' determined in accordance with procedures for long and intermediate beams shall not exceed the full design value for extreme fiber in bending F_b modified in accordance with Section 2504 (c) of the Building Code, including the modification for size factor.

Horizontal Shear

Sec. 25.3004. Design shear in sawn lumber bending members shall be determined in accordance with Section 2506 (c) of the Building Code or by the following provisions:

> **EXCEPTION:** These provisions and the horizontal shear stress values therein do not apply when designing for horizontal shear in notched beams, joints, and beams supported by fastenings.

For continuous or cantilevered bending members of sawn lumber 2 to 4 inches (nominal) in thickness, the unit horizontal shear stress, f_v, at any cross section which is five times or more the depth (actual) from the member end shall not exceed two times the shear design values F_v given in Tables Nos. 25-A-1 and 25-A-2. For southern pine, this shear stress shall not exceed (2 × 85 psi) for lumber S-green, (2 × 90 psi) for lumber S-dry, or (2 × 95 psi) for lumber KD-15. For redwood and yellow poplar, this shear stress shall not exceed

(2 × 80 psi) and (2 × 75 psi), respectively. Shear design values F_v or equivalent values in this section are subject to modification in accordance with Section 2504 (c) of the Building Code, except for Footnote No. 8, Table No. 25-A-1.

In the stress grades of sawn lumber, allowances for checks, end splits and shakes have been included in the shear design values in Tables Nos. 25-A-1 and 25-A-2 of the Building Code. For such members, the procedures of Section 2506 (c) of the Building Code do not indicate the actual horizontal shear resistance because of the redistribution of shear stress that occurs in checked beams.

Thus, for a sawn lumber bending member which does not qualify under Item 5 below, the shear force V may be determined in accordance with Items 1 and 2 below, and the limiting design shear stress value in accordance with Items 3 and 4 below:

1. The design shear force is calculated as in Item 5, except that if there is a single moving load or one moving load that is considerably larger than any of the others, that load is placed at distances from each support equal to three times the depth of the bending member or at the quarter points, whichever is closer. Other loads are kept in their normal relation, and loads within a distance from supports equal to the depth of the bending member are neglected. The procedure in Item 2 shall be used when there are two or more moving loads of about equal weight and in proximity.

2. In lieu of the simplified procedure in Item 1 above, the design shear force may be determined by the following formulas:

For uniformly distributed load

$$V = \frac{W}{2}\left(1 - \frac{2d}{l_c}\right)C_v$$

For concentrated load

$$V = \frac{P(l_c - x)\,(x/d)^2}{l_c\,[2 + (x/d)^2]}$$

Where $C_v = 0.95 + \frac{\sqrt{l_c/d}}{250} - 1.32\,(d/l_c) + 11.5\,(d/l_c)^3$

The factor C_v shall not exceed one.

For a combination of concentrated loads, V is the sum $V1 + V2 + \ldots Vn$ resulting from each such load at its distance $x1, x2, \ldots xn$ from the reaction. The load combination should be placed in that position which provides the maximum value for V.

3. The methods set forth in Items 1 and 2 for determining design shear force V shall not result in horizontal shear stress f_v when calculated as in Section 2506 (c) of the Building Code, that exceeds the shear design values F_v published in Tables Nos. 25-A-1 and 25-A-2 and modified in accordance with Section 2504 (c) of the Building Code, and such other sections as may apply (but excepting Footnote No. 8 of Table No. 25-A-1). For southern pine, the design value in shear shall not exceed 85 psi for lumber S-green, 90 psi for lumber S-dry, or 95 psi for lumber KD-15. For California redwood and yellow poplar the design value in shear shall not exceed 80 psi and 75 psi, respectively.

4. The provisions of Items 1, 2 and 3 shall not permit allowable loads which induce horizontal shear stresses f_v when calculated as in Section 2506 (c) of the Building Code, and Item 5 that exceed two times the shear design values F_v given in Tables Nos. 25-A-1 and

25-A-2. For southern pine, induced horizontal shear stress f_v calculated as in Section 2506 (c) and Item 5 shall not exceed (2 × 85 psi) for lumber S-green, (2 × 90 psi) for lumber S-dry, or (2 × 95 psi) for lumber KD-15. For California redwood and yellow poplar, induced horizontal shear stress f_v calculated as in Section 2506 (c) and Item 5 shall not exceed (2 × 80 psi) and (2 × 75 psi), respectively. Shear design values, F_v, or equivalent values in the foregoing provisions are subject to modification in accordance with Section 2504 (c) and such other sections as may apply (but excepting Footnote No. 8 of Table No. 25-A-1) before application of the 2.0 factor.

5. **Calculation of design shear.** When calculating the shear force V in bending members:

A. All loads within a distance from supports equal to the depth of the bending member may be neglected for beams supported by full bearing on one surface and loads applied to the opposite surface (see Figure No. 1).

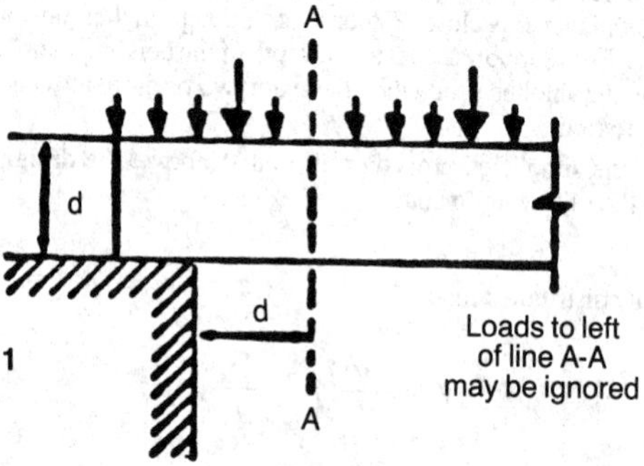
A
d
d
Loads to left
of line A-A
may be ignored
A

Figure No. 1

B. With a single moving load, or one moving load that is considerably larger than any of the others, the load shall be placed at distances from each support equal to the depth of the bending member, keeping others in their normal relation. With two or more moving loads of about equal weight and in proximity, loads shall be placed in the position that produces the highest shear force V neglecting any load within a distance from a support equal to the depth of the bending member.

TABLE NO. 25-30-A—DESIGN VALUES FOR END-GRAIN BEARING PARALLEL TO GRAIN ON A RIGID SURFACE F_g IN POUNDS PER SQUARE INCH

SPECIES	WET SERVICE CONDITIONS[1]	DRY SERVICE CONDITIONS[1]		
		SAWN LUMBER[2]		
		MORE THAN 4″ THICK	NOT MORE THAN 4″ THICK[3]	GLUED-LAMINATED TIMBER
Ash, Commercial White	1370	1510	2060	2400
Aspen	740	820	1110	1300
Balsam Fir	1140	1250	1710	1990
Beech	1190	1310	1780	2080
Birch, Sweet and Yellow	1150	1260	1720	2010
Black Cottonwood	620	690	930	1090
California Redwood	1560	1720	2270	2620
California Redwood, Open Grain	1150	1270	1670	1940
Coast Sitka Spruce	950	1040	1420	1660
Coast Species	950	1040	1420	1660
Cottonwood, Eastern	760	840	1150	1340
Douglas Fir—Larch (Dense)[4]	1570	1730	2360	2750
Douglas Fir—Larch[4]	1340	1480	2020	2350
Douglas Fir South	1220	1340	1820	2130
Eastern Hemlock—Tamarack[4]	1150	1270	1730	2020
Eastern Hemlock	1140	1260	1710	2000
Eastern Softwoods	890	980	1340	1560
Eastern Spruce	890	980	1340	1560
Eastern White Pine[4]	900	1000	1360	1580
Eastern Woods	740	820	1110	1300
Engelmann Spruce—Alpine Fir	810	890	1220	1420
Hem—Fir[4]	1110	1220	1670	1940
Hickory and Pecan	1370	1510	2050	2400
Idaho White Pine	930	1020	1390	1630
Lodgepole Pine	970	1060	1450	1690

(Continued)

TABLE NO. 25-30-A—DESIGN VALUES FOR END-GRAIN BEARING PARALLEL TO GRAIN ON A RIGID SURFACE F_g IN POUNDS PER SQUARE INCH—(Continued)

Maple, Black and Sugar	1140	1260	1710	2000
Mountain Hemlock	1070	1170	1600	1870
Mountain Hemlock—Hem-Fir	1070	1170	1600	1870
Northern Aspen	740	810	1110	1290
Northern Pine	1040	1150	1570	1830
Northern Species	880	970	1320	1540
Northern White Cedar	740	810	1110	1290
Oak, Red and White	1060	1160	1590	1850
Ponderosa Pine—Sugar Pine	910	1000	1370	1600
Red Pine	880	970	1320	1540
Sitka Spruce	990	1090	1480	1730
Southern Cypress	1330	1460	1990	2320
Southern Pine (Dense)	1540	1690	2310	2690
Southern Pine	1320	1450	1970	2300
Spruce—Pine—Fir	940	1040	1410	1650
Sweetgum and Tupelo	1020	1120	1530	1780
Virginia Pine—Pond Pine	1270	1390	1800	2220
Western Cedars[4]	1040	1140	1820	1750
Western Hemlock	1240	1360	1860	2170
Western White Pine	930	1030	1400	1630
White Woods (Western Woods)	810	890	1220	1420
West Coast Woods (Mixed Species)	810	890	1220	1420
Yellow Poplar	890	980	1340	1560

[1]Wet and dry service conditions are defined for sawn lumber and for glued-laminated timber [Section 2504 (c)].

[2]Applies to sawn lumber members which are at a moisture content of 19 percent or less when full design load is applied, regardless of moisture content at time of manufacture.

[3]When 4-inch or thinner sawn lumber is surfaced at a moisture content of 15 percent or less and is used under dry service conditions, the values listed for glued-laminated timber may be applied.

[4]Values also apply when species name includes the designation "North."

UNIFORM BUILDING CODE STANDARD NO. 26-1

PORTLAND CEMENT AND BLENDED HYDRAULIC CEMENTS

Based on Standard Specifications C 150-85a and C 595-86 of the American Society for Testing and Materials. Extracted, with permission, from the Annual Book of ASTM Standards, copyright American Society for Testing and Materials, 1916 Race Street, Philadelphia, PA 19103.

See Sections 2603 (b) and 2605 (e), Uniform Building Code

Part I—Portland Cement

Scope

Sec. 26.101. This part of the standard covers eight types of portland cement as follows:

Type I—For use in general concrete construction when the special properties specified for Types II, III, IV and V are not required.

Type I A. Same use as Type I where air entrainment is required.

Type II—For use in general concrete construction exposed to moderate sulfate action, or where moderate heat of hydration is required.

Type II A. Same use as Type II where air entrainment is required.

Type III—For use when high early strength is required.

Type III A. Same use as Type III where air entrainment is required.

Type IV—For use when a low heat of hydration is required.

Type V—For use when high sulfate resistance is required.

Definition

Sec. 26.102. Portland cement is a hydraulic cement produced by pulverizing clinker consisting essentially of hydraulic calcium silicates, usually containing one or more of the forms of calcium sulfate as an interground addition.

Air-entrained portland cement is a hydraulic cement produced by pulverizing clinker consisting essentially of hydraulic calcium silicates, usually containing one or more of the forms of calcium sulfate as an interground addition, and with which there has been an interground air-entrained addition.

The cement shall contain no addition, except that water or calcium sulfate, or both, may be added in amounts such that the limits shown in Table No. 26-1-A for sulfur trioxide, and loss-on-ignition shall not be exceeded. Processing additions may be used in the manufacture of the cement, provided such materials in the amounts used have been shown to not be harmful by nationally recognized tests carried out or reviewed by an approved laboratory.

Chemical Requirements

Sec. 26.103. Portland cement of each of the eight types shown in Section 26.101 shall conform to the respective chemical requirements prescribed in Table No. 26-1-A. In addition, optional chemical requirements are shown in Table No. 26-1-D.

Physical Requirements

Sec. 26.104. Portland cement of each of the eight types shown in Section 26.101 shall conform to the respective physical requirements prescribed in Table No. 26-1-B.

TABLE NO. 26-1-A—CHEMICAL REQUIREMENTS FOR CEMENT

STANDARD REQUIREMENTS	PORTLAND CEMENT TYPES				
	I and IA	II and IIA	III and IIIA	IV	V
Silicon dioxide (SiO_2), min., %	—	20.0	—	—	—
Aluminum oxide (Al_2O_3), max., %	—	6.0	—	—	—
Ferric oxide (Fe_2O_3), max., %	—	6.0	—	6.5	—
Magnesium oxide (MgO), max., %	6.0	6.0	6.0	6.0	6.0
Sulfur trioxide (SO_3),[1] max., %					
When (C_3A)[2] is 8% or less	3.0	3.0	3.5	2.3	2.3
When (C_3A)[2] is more than 8%	3.5	NA[3]	4.5	NA[3]	NA[3]
Loss on ignition, max., %	3.0	3.0	3.0	2.5	3.0
Insoluble residue, max., %	0.75	0.75	0.75	0.75	0.75
Tricalcium silicate (C_3S),[2] max., %	—	—	—	35[4]	—
Dicalcium silicate (C_2S),[2] min., %	—	—	—	40[4]	—
Tricalcium aluminate (C_3A),[2] max., %	—	8	15	7[4]	5[5]
Tetracalcium aluminoferrite plus twice the tricalcium aluminate[2] [$C_4AF + 2(C_3A)$], or solid solution ($C_4AF + C_2F$), as applicable, max., %	—	—	—	—	20[5]
OPTIONAL REQUIREMENTS[6]					
Tricalcium aluminate (C_3A),[2] max., %	—	—	8[7]	—	—
Tricalcium aluminate (C_3A),[2] max., %	—	—	5[4]	—	—
Sum of tricalcium silicate and tricalcium aluminate,[2] max., %[8]	—	58[9]	—	—	—
Alkalies ($Na_2O + 0.658K_2O$), max., %[10]	0.60[11]	0.60[11]	0.60[11]	0.60[11]	0.60[11]

(Continued)

FOOTNOTES FOR TABLE NO. 26-1-A

[1]There are cases where optimum SO for a particular cement is close to or exceeds the limit in this standard. Where it has been demonstrated that this condition exists, an additional amount of SO_3 is permissible, provided that when the cement with the additional calcium sulfate is tested in accordance with nationally recognized standards, the calcium sulfate in the hydrated mortar at $24 \pm {}^1/_4$ hour expressed as SO_3 does not exceed 0.50 gram/liter. The supporting data shall be submitted to the building official upon request.

[2]The expressing of chemical limitations by means of calculated assumed compounds does not necessarily mean that the oxides are actually or entirely present as such compounds.

When expressing compounds, C = CaO, S = SiO_2, A = $A1_2O_3$, F = Fe_2O_3. For example, C_3A = 3CaO x $A1_2O_3$.

Titanium dioxide and phosphorus pentoxide (TiO_2 and P_2O_5) shall be included with the $A1_2O_3$ content. The value historically and traditionally used for $A1_2O_3$ in calculating potential compounds for specification purposes is the ammonium hydroxide group minus ferric oxide (R_2O_2-Fe_2O_3) as obtained by classical wet chemical methods. This procedure includes as $A1_2O_3$ the $TiO_2P_2O_5$ and other trace oxides which precipitate with the ammonium hydroxide group in the classical wet chemical methods. Many modern instrumental methods of cement analysis determine aluminum or aluminum oxide directly without the minor and trace oxides included by the classical method. Consequently, for consistency and to provide comparability with historic data and among various analytical methods, when calculating potential compounds for specification purposes, those using methods which determine A1 or $A1_2O_3$ directly should add to the determined $A1_2O_3$ weight quantities of P_2O_5, TiO_2 and any other oxide except Fe_2O_3 which would precipitate with the ammonium hydroxide group when analyzed by the classical method and which is present in an amount of 0.05 weight percent or greater. The weight percent of minor trace oxides to be added to $A1_2O_3$ by those using direct methods may be obtained by actual analysis of those oxides in the sample being tested or estimated from historical data on those oxides on cements from the same source, provided that the estimated values are identified as such.

When the ratio of percentages of aluminum oxide to ferric oxide is 0.64 or more, the percentages of tricalcium silicate, dicalcium silicate, tricalcium aluminate, and tetracalcium aluminoferrite shall be calculated from the chemical analysis as follows:

Tricalcium silicate = (4.071 x % CaO) – (7.600 x % SiO_2) – (6.718 x % $A1_2O_3$) – (1.430 x % Fe_2O_3) – (2.852 x % SO_3)

Dicalcium silicate = (2.867 x % SiO_2) – (0.7544 x % C_3S)

Tricalcium aluminate = (2.650 x % $A1_2O_3$) – (1.692 x % Fe_2O_3)

Tetracalcium aluminoferrite = 3.043 x % Fe_2O_3

When the alumina-ferric oxide ratio is less than 0.64, a calcium aluminoferrite solid solution [expressed as ss(C_4AF + C_2F)] is formed. Contents of this solid solution and of tricalcium silicate shall be calculated by the following formulas:

ss(C_4AF + C_2F) = (2.100 x % $A1_2O_3$) + (1.702 x % Fe_2O_3)

Tricalcium silicate = (4.071 x % CaO) – (7.600 x % SiO_2) – (4.479 x % $A1_2O_3$) – (2.859 x % Fe_2O_3) – (2.852 x % SO_3)

No tricalcium aluminate will be present in cements of this composition. Dicalcium silicate shall be calculated as previously shown.

In the calculation of all of C_3A, the values of Al_2O_3 and Fe_2O_3 determined to the nearest 0.01 percent shall be used. In the calculation of other compounds, the oxides determined to the nearest 0.1 percent shall be used.

All values calculated as described in this note shall be reported to the nearest 1 percent.

[3]NA—Not applicable.

[4]For high sulfate resistance.

[5]Does not apply when the sulfate expansion limit in the "Optional Requirements" section of this table is specified.

[6]These optional requirements apply only when specifically requested.

[7]For moderate sulfate resistance.

[8]For moderate heat of hydration.

[9]This limit does not apply when the heat of hydration limit in the "Optional Requirements" section of this table is specified.

[10]For low-alkali cement.

[11]This limit may be specified when the cement is to be used on concrete with aggregates that may be deleteriously reactive.

TABLE NO. 26-1-B—PHYSICAL REQUIREMENTS

STANDARD REQUIREMENTS	PORTLAND CEMENT TYPES							
	I	IA	II	IIA	III	IIIA	IV[8]	V
Air content of mortar,[1] volume percent:								
max.	12	22	12	22	12	22	12	12
min.	—	16	—	16	—	16	—	—
Fineness,[2] specific surface, m^2/kg (alternative methods:								
Turbidimeter test, min.	160	160	160	160	—	—	160	160
Air permeability test, min.	280	280	280	280	—	—	280	280
Autoclave expansion, max., percent	0.80	0.80	0.80	0.80	0.80	0.80	0.80	0.80
Strength, not less than the values shown for the ages indicated below[3]								
Compressive strength, psi:								
1 day	—	—	—	—	1800	1450	—	—
3 days	1800	1450	1500	1200	3500	2800	—	1200
	—	—	1000[4]	800[4]	—	—	—	—
7 days	2800	2250	2500	2000	—	—	1000	2200
	—	—	1700[4]	1350[4]	—	—	—	—
28 days	—	—	—	—	—	—	2500	3000
Time of setting (alternative methods):								
Gillmore test:								
Initial set, min., not less than	60	60	60	60	60	60	60	60
Final set, h., not more than	10	10	10	10	10	10	10	10
Vicat test:								
Initial set, min., not less than	45	45	45	45	45	45	45	45
Final set, h., not more than	8	8	8	8	8	8	8	8

OPTIONAL REQUIREMENTS[5]	PORTLAND CEMENT TYPES							
	I	IA	II	IIA	III	IIIA	IV[8]	V
False set, final penetration, min., percent	50	50	50	50	50	50	50	50
Heat of hydration:								
7 days, max., cal/g	—	—	70[6]	70[6]	—	—	60	—
28 days, max., cal/g	—	—	80[6]	80[6]	—	—	70	—
Strength, not less than the values shown:								
Compressive strength, psi (MPa)								
28 days	4000	3200	4000	3200	—	—	—	—
	—	—	3200[6]	2560[6]	—	—	—	—
Sulfate expansion,[7] 14 days, max., percent	—	—	—	—	—	—	—	0.040

[1]Compliance with the requirements of this specification does not necessarily ensure that the desired air content will be obtained in concrete.

[2]Either of the two alternative fineness methods may be used at the option of the testing laboratory. However, when the sample fails to meet the requirements of the air-permeability test, the turbidimeter test shall be used, and the requirements in this table for the turbidimetric method shall govern.

[3]The strength at any specified test age shall not be less than that attained at any previous specified test age.

[4]When the optional heat of hydration or the chemical limit on the sum of tricalcium silicate and tricalcium aluminate requirements are requested.

[5]These optional requirements apply only when specifically requested.

[6]The optional limit for the sum of the tricalcium silicate and tricalcium aluminate in Table No. 26-1-B shall not be requested when this optional limit is requested. These strength requirements apply when either heat of hydration or the sum of tricalcium silicate and tricalcium aluminate requirements are specified.

[7]When the sulfate expansion is specified, it shall be instead of the limits of C_3A and $C_4AF + 2C_3A$ listed in Table No. 26-1-A.

[8]When the heat of hydration limit is specified, it shall be used instead of the limits of C_3S, C_2S and C_3A listed in Table No. 26-1-A.

Part II—Blended Hydraulic Cement

Scope

Sec. 26.105. This part of the standard covers five classes of blended hydraulic cements using slag or pozzolan, or both, with portland cement or portland cement clinker or slag with lime.

The types of blended cement covered by this specification are as follows:

Portland Blast-furnace Slag Cement—One type with three optional provisions is covered as follows:

Type IS—Portland blast-furnace slag cement for use in general concrete construction.

Moderate sulfate resistance, air entrainment or moderate heat of hydration, or any combination, may be specified by adding the suffixes (MS), (A) or (MH).

Portland-pozzolan Cement—Two types, each with three optional provisions are covered as follows:

Type IP—Portland-pozzolan cement for use in general concrete construction.

Moderate sulfate resistance, air entrainment or moderate heat of hydration, or any combination, may be specified by adding the suffixes (MS), (A) or (MH).

Type P—Portland-pozzolan cement for use in concrete construction where high strengths at early ages are not required.

Moderate sulfate resistance, air entrainment or low heat of hydration, or any combination, may be specified by adding the suffixes (MS), (A) or (LH).

Slag Cement—One type is covered as follows:

Type S—Slag cement for use in combination with portland cement in making concrete and in combination with hydrated lime in making masonry mortar.

Air entraining can be specified by adding the suffix (A).

Pozzolan-modified Portland Cement—One type is covered as follows:

Type I (PM)—Pozzolan-modified portland cement for use in general concrete construction.

Moderate sulfate resistance, air entraining or moderate heat of hydration, or any combination, may be specified by adding the suffixes (MS), (A) or (MH).

Pozzolan-modified portland cement should not be used when special characteristics attributable to the larger quantities of pozzolan in portland-pozzolan cement are desired.

Slag-modified Portland Cement—One type is covered as follows:

Type I (SM)—Slag-modified portland cement for use in general construction.

Moderate sulfate resistance, air entraining or moderate heat of hydration, or any combination, may be specified by adding the suffixes (MS), (A) or (MH).

Definitions

Sec. 26.106. Certain words and terms used in this standard are defined as follows:

PORTLAND BLAST-FURNACE SLAG CEMENT, TYPE IS, is a hydraulic cement consisting of an intimate and uniform blend of portland cement and fine granulated blast-furnace slag produced either by intergrinding portland cement clinker and granulated blast-furnace slag or by blending portland cement and finely ground granulated blast-furnace slag, in which the slag constituent is between 25 and 70 percent of the weight of portland blast-furnace slag cement.

AIR-ENTRAINING PORTLAND BLAST-FURNACE SLAG CEMENT, TYPE IS-A, is portland blast-furnace slag cement as defined, except that sufficient air-entraining addition, as specified in Section 26.107, has been used so that the resulting product complies with the air content of mortar requirements given in Table No. 26-1-C.

SLAG-MODIFIED PORTLAND CEMENT, TYPE I (SM), is an intimate and uniform blend of portland cement and granulated blast-furnace slag produced either by intergrinding portland cement clinker and granulated blast-furnace slag, by blending portland cement and finely ground granulated blast-furnace slag, or a combination of intergrinding and blending in which the slag constituent is less than 25 percent of the weight of the slag-modified portland cement.

AIR-ENTRAINING SLAG-MODIFIED PORTLAND CEMENT, TYPE I (SM)-A, is Type I (SM) slag-modified portland cement, except that sufficient air-entraining addition, as specified in Section 26.107, has been used so that the resulting product complies with the air content of mortar requirements given in Table No. 26-1-C.

BLAST-FURNACE SLAG is the nonmetallic product consisting essentially of silicates and aluminosilicates of calcium and of other bases that is developed in a molten condition simultaneously with iron in a blast furnace.

GRANULATED BLAST-FURNACE SLAG is the glassy granular material formed when molten blast-furnace slag is rapidly chilled, as by immersion in water.

Granulation may be achieved by quenching blast-furnace slag from its original molten state or by quenching air-cooled blast-furnace slag after remelting. Small percentages of silica and alumina may be added while the slag is molten to enhance desired characteristics.

PORTLAND CEMENT is the product obtained by pulverizing clinker consisting essentially of hydraulic calcium silicates meeting the requirements of Part I of this standard. Portland cement or other hydraulic materials, or both, containing high free lime may be used as long as the autoclave test limits for the blended cement are met.

PORTLAND CEMENT CLINKER is partially fused clinker consisting primarily of hydraulic calcium silicates.

PORTLAND-POZZOLAN CEMENT, TYPE IP, is a hydraulic cement consisting of an intimate and uniform blend of portland cement or portland blast-furnace slag cement and fine pozzolan produced either by intergrinding portland cement clinker and pozzolan, by blending portland cement or portland blast-furnace slag cement and finely divided pozzolan, or a combination of intergrinding and blending, in which the pozzolan constituent is between 15 and 40 weight percent of the portland-pozzolan cement.

AIR-ENTRAINING PORTLAND-POZZOLAN CEMENT, TYPE IP-A, is portland-pozzolan cement, except that sufficient air-entraining addition, as specified in Section 26.107, has been used so that the resulting product complies with the air content of mortar requirements given in Table No. 26-1-C.

POZZOLAN-MODIFIED PORTLAND CEMENT, TYPE I (PM), is an intimate and uniform blend of portland cement or portland blast-furnace slag cement and fine pozzolan produced either by intergrinding portland cement clinker and pozzolan, by blending portland cement or portland blast-furnace slag cement and finely divided pozzolan, or a combination of intergrinding and blending, in which the pozzolan constituent is less than 15 weight percent of the pozzolan-modified portland cement.

AIR-ENTRAINING POZZOLAN-MODIFIED PORTLAND CEMENT TYPE I (PM)-A, is air-entraining pozzolan portland cement Type IP-A, except that sufficient air-entraining addition, as specified in Section 26.107, has been used so that the resulting product complies with the air content of mortar requirements given in Table No. 26-1-C.

POZZOLAN is a siliceous or siliceous and aluminous material, which in itself possesses little or no cementitious value but will, in finely divided form and in the presence of moisture, chemically react with calcium hydroxide at ordinary temperatures to form compounds possessing cementitious properties.

SLAG CEMENT, TYPE S, is a blended hydraulic cement consisting mostly of an intimate and uniform blend of granulated blast-furnace slag and portland cement, or hydrated lime, or both, in which the slag constituent is at least 70 percent of the weight of the slag cement.

AIR-ENTRAINING SLAG CEMENTS, TYPE SA, is slag cement Type S, except that sufficient air-entraining addition, as specified in Section 26.107, has been used so that the resulting product complies with the air content of mortar requirements given in Table No. 26-1-C.

HYDRATED LIME is the product described as Type N of U.B.C. Standard No. 24-18,except that it must meet the chemical composition requirements of Type S of the same standard.

Additions

Sec. 26.107. (a) **Air-entraining Addition.** When air-entraining cement is specified, an addition meeting the requirements of nationally recognized standards shall be used.

(b) **Processing Additions.** At the option of the manufacturer, processing additions may be used in the manufacture of cement, provided such materials in the amounts used have been shown to meet the requirement of nationally recognized standards.

(c) **Other Additions.** The cement covered by this standard shall contain no additions except as provided for above except that water or calcium sulfate, or both, may be added in amounts so that the limits shown in Table No. 26-1-A for sulfate reported as SO_3 and loss on ignition are not exceeded.

Chemical Requirements

Sec. 26.108. (a) **General.** Cement of the type specified shall conform to the chemical requirements prescribed in Table No. 26-1-C.

(b) **Moderate Sulfate Resistance.** When moderate sulfate resistance (MS) is specified, the tricalcium aluminate ($3CaO \bullet Al_2O_3$) content of the portland cement calculated as in Part I shall not exceed 8.0 percent and the sum of the amounts of silicon dioxide (SiO_2), aluminum oxide (Al_2O_3), and iron oxide (Fe_2O_3) in the pozzolan used in portland-pozzolan cement shall not be less than 70 percent.

Physical Properties

Sec. 26.109. (a) **Blended Cement.** Blended cement of the type specified shall conform to the applicable physical requirements prescribed in Table No. 26-1-D.

(b) **Pozzolan or Slag.** Pozzolan or slag that is to be blended with cement shall be tested in the same state of subdivision as that in which it is to be blended. Pozzolan shall conform to the fineness requirement and the pozzolanic activity requirement of Table No. 26-1-E. Slag that is to be used for slag-modified portland cements shall conform to the slag activity requirement of Table No. 26-1-E. Such pozzolan or slag that is to be interground with portland cement clinker shall, before testing for conformance with requirements of Table No. 26-1-E, be ground in the laboratory to a fineness at which it is believed to be present in the finished cement.

Pozzolan for use in the manufacture of pozzolan-modified portland cement, Types I (PM) and I (PM)-A, shall meet the requirements of Table No. 26-1-E when tested for mortar expansion of pozzolan. If the alkali content of the clinker to be used for the production lots changes by more than 0.2 percent total as equivalent Na_2O, calculated as $Na_2O + 0.658\ K_2O_2$ from that of the clinker with which the acceptance tests were carried out, the pozzolan shall be retested to show compliance with the requirements of Table No. 26-1-E.

Testing Local Supply

Sec. 26.110. Every 90 days, each lime producer shall retain an approved agency to obtain a random sample of bagged cement from a local point of supply in the market area served by the producer.

The agency shall test the cement for compliance with the provisions of this standard.

Upon request of the building official, the producer shall furnish (at no cost) test results to the building official, architect, structural engineer, general contractor and masonry contractor.

TABLE NO. 26-1-C—CHEMICAL REQUIREMENTS

CHEMICAL	CEMENT TYPE			
	I(SM), I(SM)-A, IS, IS-A (Max. Percent)	S, SA (Max. Percent)	I(PM), I(PM)-A (Max. Percent)	P, PA, IP, IP-A (Max. Percent)
Magnesium oxide (MgO)	—	—	5.0	5.0
Sulfur reported as sulfate (SO_3)	3.0	4.0	4.0	4.0
Sulfide sulfur (S)	1.0	2.0	—	—
Insoluble residue	1.0	1.0	—	—
Loss on ignition	3.0	4.0	5.0	5.0
Water-soluble alkali	—	0.03[1]	—	—

[1]Applicable only when the cement is specified to be nonstaining to limestone. The amount and nature of the staining material in limestone may vary with the stone. The alkali in any cement may, therefore, induce markedly different staining on different stone, even though the stone may have come apparently from the same source. The amount of alkali permitted by the specification should not cause stain unless stone high in staining material has been used or unless insufficient means have been used to prevent infiltration of water into the masonry.

[2]When it has been demonstrated by test that the optimum SO_3 exceeds a value 0.5 percent less than the specification limit, an additional amount of SO_3 is permissible, provided that when the cement with the additional calcium sulfate is tested, the calcium sulfate in the hydrated mortar at 24 $\pm$ $^1/_4$ *h*, expressed as SO_3, does not exceed 0.50 *g/L*. When the manufacturer supplies cement under this provision, the manufacturer will, upon re-quest, supply support data to the purchaser.

TABLE NO. 26-1-D—PHYSICAL REQUIREMENTS

STANDARD REQUIREMENTS	CEMENT TYPE											
	I(SM), IS	I(SM)-A, IS-A	IS(MS)	IS-A(MS)	S	SA	I(PM), IP	I(PM)-A, IP-A	P	PA	IP(MS)	IP-A(MS)
Autoclave expansion, max. percent[1]	0.50	0.50	0.50	0.50	0.50	0.50	0.50	0.50	0.50	0.50	0.50	0.50
Autoclave contraction, max. percent[1]	0.20	0.20	0.20	0.20	0.20	0.20	0.20	0.20	0.20	0.20	0.20	0.20
Time of setting, Vicat test:												
Set, minutes, not less than	45	45	45	45	45	45	45	45	45	45	45	45
Set, hours, not more than	7	7	7	7	7	7	7	7	7	7	7	7
Air content of mortar volume, percent	12 max	19 ± 3	12 max	19 ± 3	12 max	19 ± 3	12 max	19 ± 3	12 max	19 ± 3	12 max	19 ± 3
Compressive strength, min., psi												
3 days	1800	1400	1500	1200	—	—	1800	1450	—	—	1500	1200
7 days	2800	2250	2500	2000	600	500	2800	2250	1500	1250	2500	2000
28 days	3500	2800	3500	2800	1500	1250	3500	2800	3000	2500	3500	2800
Heat of hydration[2]												
7 days, max., cal/g	70	70	70	70	—	—	70	70	60	60	70	70
28 days, max., cal/g	80	80	80	80	—	—	80	80	70	70	80	80
Water requirement, max. weight percent of cement	—	—	—	—	—	—	—	—	—	64	56	—
Drying shrinkage, max., percent	—	—	—	—	—	—	—	—	—	0.15	0.15	—
Mortar expansion[3]												
At age of 14 days, max., percent	0.020	0.020	0.020	0.020	0.020	0.020	0.020	0.020	0.020	0.020	0.020	0.020
At age of 8 weeks, max., percent	0.060	0.060	0.060	0.060	0.060	0.060	0.060	0.060	0.060	0.060	0.060	0.060

[1]The specimens shall remain firm and hard and show no signs of distortion, cracking, checking, pitting or disintegration when subject to the autoclave expansion test.

[2]Applicable only when moderate (MH) or low (LH) heat of hydration is specified, in which case the strength requirements shall be 80 percent of the values shown in the table.

[3]The test for mortar expansion is an optional requirement unless the cement will be used with alkali-reactive aggregate.

TABLE NO. 26-1-E PHYSICAL REQUIREMENTS FOR POZZOLAN FOR USE IN BLENDED CEMENTS AND FOR SLAG FOR USE IN SLAG-MODIFIED PORTLAND CEMENTS

Fineness:	
Amount retained when wet sieved on 45 micron (No. 325) sieve, maximum, percent	20.0
Alkali reactivity of pozzolan for use in Types 1 (PM) and 1 (PM)-A, cements, six tests, mortar bar expansion at 91 days, maximum, percent	0.05
Slag or pozzolan activity index:	
With portland cement, at 28 days, minimum, percent	75

Note: A pozzolan has acceptable pozzolanic activity under this specification if it meets either of the two alternative limits. All activity tests shall be conducted in accordance with nationally recognized tests and may be subject to the approval of the building official.

UNIFORM BUILDING CODE STANDARD NO. 26-8

WELDING REINFORCING STEEL, METAL INSERTS AND CONNECTIONS IN REINFORCED CONCRETE CONSTRUCTION

See Sections 2603 (b) 4, 2603 (c), 2612 (o) 3, and 2625 (c) 6, Uniform Building Code

Adoption of AWS Code

Sec. 26.801. Except for the limitations, deletions, modifications or amendments set forth in Section 26.802 of this standard, the welding of concrete reinforcing steel for splices (prestressing steel excepted), steel connection devices, inserts, anchors and anchorage details, as well as any other welding required in reinforced concrete construction, shall be in accordance with the Structural Welding Code—Reinforcing Steel, AWS D1.4-79, published by the American Welding Society, Inc., Copyright 1979, 550 North LeJeune Road, Miami, Florida 33126, as if set out at length herein.

Deletions and Amendments

Sec. 26.802. (a) **General.** The American Welding Society, Inc., code adopted by Section 26.801 applies to the materials, processes, design, workmanship and testing of welding performed as a part of reinforced concrete construction, except as set forth in this section.

(b) **Deletions.** The following sections and chapters are deleted.

Section 1.5

Section 1.6

Section 3.8

Section 5.6.4

Chapter 7

(c) **Amendments**

1. **Sec. 1.1.1** is amended by changing the last sentence to read as follows:

   When welding reinforcing steel to primary structural members, the provisions of U.B.C. Standard No. 27-6 shall be fully satisfied.

2. **Sec. 1.1.3** is amended to read as follows:

   1.1.3 All references to the need for approval shall be interpreted to mean approval by the building official. Hereinafter, when the term "engineer" is used, it is to be construed to mean the building official.

3. **Sec. 1.2.3** is amended to read as follows:

   1.2.3 Material other than those listed above shall be one of the structural steels listed in U.B.C. Standard No. 27-6.

4. **Sec. 1.4** is amended to read as follows:

   1.4 Definitions

   The welding terms used in this code shall be interpreted in accordance with the definitions given in Appendix B of this code.

5. **Sec. 2.2.1** is amended to read as follows:

   2.2.1 The permissible stresses for bevel-, V-groove and Thermit direct butt splices in tension or compression shall be the same as the corresponding allowable unit stresses for the base metal in the Building Code for reinforced concrete construction, provided the filler metal used has a strength classification at least equal to the tensile strength of the material being welded. (See Table No. 2.2.)

UNIFORM BUILDING CODE STANDARD NO. 26-13

READY-MIXED CONCRETE

Based on Standard Specification C 94-86a of the American Society for Testing and Materials. Extracted, with permission, from the Annual Book of ASTM Standards, copyright American Society for Testing and Materials, 1916 Race Street, Philadelphia, PA 19103.

See Sections 301 (c); 305 (e), Item 1; 2603 (b) 6; and 2605 (i), Uniform Building Code

Scope

Sec. 26.1301. This standard covers requirements for ready-mixed concrete. Requirements for quality of materials and for proportions and quality of concrete shall conform to the Uniform Building Code and U.B.C. Standard No. 26-1. Where the requirements are in conflict with this standard, the requirements of the Uniform Building Code shall govern.

For the purpose of these specifications, ready-mixed concrete is portland cement concrete, manufactured for delivery to a purchaser in a plastic and unhardened state and delivered as hereinafter specified.

Quality of Concrete

Sec. 26.1302. 1. **General.** The quality of ready-mixed concrete and the material used to make the concrete shall conform to the requirements of Chapter 26 of the Uniform Building Code and this standard.

2. **Water.** Water shall be clear and apparently clean. If it contains quantities of substances which discolor it or make it smell or taste unusual or objectionable or cause suspicion, it shall not be used unless service records of concrete made with it or other information indicates that it is not injurious to the quality of the concrete. Water of questionable quality shall be subject to the acceptance criteria of Table No. 26-13-A.

Wash water from mixer washout operations may be used for mixing concrete, provided tests of wash water comply with the physical tests mentioned in this item. Wash water shall be tested at a weekly interval for approximately four weeks and thereafter at a monthly interval, provided no single test exceeds the applicable limit. Optional chemical tests in Table No. 26-13-B may be specified by the purchaser, using the same testing frequency of chemical limits. When recycled wash water is used, attention shall be given to effects on the dosage rate and batch sequence of air-entraining and other chemical admixtures, and a uniform amount shall be used in consecutive batches.

3. **Admixtures.** Admixtures shall conform to applicable specifications acceptable to the building official.

Tolerances in Slump

Sec. 26.1303. Unless other tolerances are included in the project specifications, the following shall apply.

1. When the project specifications for slump are written as a "maximum" or "not to exceed" requirement:

	SPECIFIED SLUMP:	
	If 3 inches or less	If more than 3 inches
Plus tolerance:	0	0
Minus tolerance:	$1^1/_2$ inches	$2^1/_2$ inches

This option is to be used if one addition of water is permitted on the job provided such addition does not increase the water-cement ratio above the maximum permitted by the specifications.

2. When the project specifications for slump are not written as a "maximum" or "not to exceed" requirement:

TOLERANCES FOR NOMINAL SLUMPS

For Specified Slump of:	Tolerance
2 inches and less	$\pm\ ^1/_2$ inch
More than 2 through 4 inches	$\pm$ 1 inch
More than 4 inches	$\pm\ 1^1/_2$ inches

Concrete shall be available, within the permissible range of slump, for a period of 30 minutes starting either on arrival at the job site or after the initial slump adjustment permitted in Section 26.1309 (f), third paragraph, whichever is later. The first and last $^1/_4$ cubic yard discharged are exempt from this requirement. If the user is unprepared for discharge of the concretes from the vehicle, the producer shall not be responsible for the limitation of minimum slump after 30 minutes have elapsed, starting either on arrival of the vehicle at the prescribed destination or at the requested delivery time, whichever is later.

Air-entrained Concrete

Sec. 26.1304. When air-entrained concrete is used, the total air content shall be in accordance with Section 26.1406 of U.B.C. Standard No. 26-14.

Manufacturer's Statement

Sec. 26.1305. Prior to the actual delivery of the concrete, the manufacturer shall furnish a statement available to the building official giving the properties of the materials and the proportions by weight (dry) of cement and of fine and coarse aggregates that are proposed to be used in the manufacture of each class of concrete, the water content, the type and amount of admixture, and the maximum and minimum limits of air content ordered for the job.

Measuring Materials

Sec. 26.1306. Except as otherwise specifically permitted, cement shall be measured by weight. When fly ash or other pozzolans are specified in the mix design, they may be weighed cumulatively with cement. Cement and pozzolan shall be weighed on a scale and in a weigh hopper which is separate and distinct from those used for other materials. Cement shall be weighed before pozzolan. When the quantity of cement in a batch of concrete exceeds 30 percent of the full capacity of the scale, the quantity of cement, and the cumulative quantity of cement plus pozzolan, shall be within ± 1 percent of the required weight. For smaller batches to a minimum of 1 cubic yard, the quantity of cement and the quantity of cement plus pozzolan used shall not be less than the required amount nor more than 4 percent in excess. Under special circumstances, cement may be measured in bags of standard weight. No fraction of a bag of cement shall be used unless weighed.

Aggregate shall be measured by weight. Batch weights shall be based on dry materials and shall be the required weights of dry materials plus the total weight of moisture (both absorbed and surface) contained in the aggregate. The quantity of aggregate used in any batch of concrete as indicated by the scale shall be within ± 2 percent of the required weight when weighed in individual aggregate weigh batchers. In a cumulative aggregate weigh batcher, the cumulative weight after each successive weighing shall be within ± 1 percent of the required cumulative amount when the scale is used in excess of 30 percent of its capacity. For cumulative weights for less than 30 percent of scale capacity, the tolerance shall be ± 0.3 percent of scale capacity or ± 3 percent of the required cumulative weight, whichever is less.

Mixing water shall consist of water added to the batch, ice added to the batch, water occurring as surface moisture on the aggregates, and water introduced in the form of admixtures. The added water shall be measured by weight or volume to an accuracy of 1 percent of the required total mixing water. Added ice shall be measured by weight. In the case of truck mixers, any wash water retained in the drum for use in the next batch of concrete shall be accurately measured; if this proves impractical or impossible the wash water shall be discharged prior to loading the next batch of concrete. Total water (including any wash water) shall be measured or weighed to an accuracy of ± 3 percent of the specified total amount.

Powdered admixtures shall be measured by weight, and paste or liquid admixtures by weight or volume. Accuracy of weighing admixtures shall be within ± 3 percent of the required weight. Volumetric measurement shall be within an accuracy of ± 3 percent of the total amount required or plus or minus the volume of dose required for one sack of cement, whichever is greater.

Batching Plant

Sec. 26.1307. Bins with adequate separate compartments for fine aggregates and for each required size of coarse aggregate shall be provided in the batching plant. Each bin compartment shall be designed and operated so as to discharge efficiently and freely, with minimum segregation, into the weighing hopper. Means of control shall be provided so that, as the quantity desired in the weighing hopper is approached, the material may be shut off with precision. Weighing hoppers shall be constructed so as to eliminate accumulations of tare materials and to discharge fully.

Scales for batching concrete ingredients may be either beam or springless dial scales. All weighing and indicating devices shall be in full view and near enough to be read accurately by the operator while charging the hopper, and the operator shall have convenient access to all controls.

Scales in use shall be accurate when static load tested to ±0.4 percent of the total capacity of the scale.

Methods for weighing (electric, hydraulic, load cells, etc.) other than beam or springless dial scales which meet the above weighing tolerances are also acceptable.

Adequate standard test weights shall be available for checking accuracy. All exposed fulcrums, clevises and similar working parts of scales shall be kept clean. Beam-type scales shall be equipped with a balance indicator sensitive enough to show movement when a weight equal to 0.1 percent of the nominal capacity of the scale is placed in the batch hopper. Pointer travel shall be a minimum of 5 percent of the net rated capacity of the largest weigh beam for underweight and 4 percent for overweight.

The device for the measurement of the added water shall be capable of delivering to the batch the quantity required within the accuracy required in Section 26.1306, paragraph three. The device shall be so arranged that the measurements will not be affected by variable pressures in the water supply line. Measuring tanks shall be equipped with outside taps and valves to provide for checking their calibration unless other means are provided for readily and accurately determining the amount of water in the tank.

Mixers and Agitators

Sec. 26.1308. Mixers may be stationary mixers or truck mixers. Agitators may be truck mixers or truck agitators.

1. Stationary mixers shall be equipped with a metal plate or plates on which are plainly marked the mixing speed of the drum or paddles and the maximum capacity in terms of the volume of mixed concrete. When used for the complete mixing of concrete, stationary mixers shall be equipped with an acceptable timing device that will not permit the batch to be discharged until the specified mixing time has elapsed.

2. Each truck mixer or agitator shall have attached thereto in a prominent place a metal plate or plates on which are plainly marked the gross volume of the drum, the capacity of the drum or container in terms of the volume of mixed concrete and the minimum and maximum mixing speeds of rotation of the drum, blades or paddles. When the concrete is truck mixed or shrink mixed, the volume of mixed concrete shall not exceed 63 percent of the total volume of the drum or container. When the concrete is central mixed as described in Section 26.1309 (c), the volume of concrete in the truck mixer or agitator shall not exceed 80 percent of the total volume of the drum or container. Truck mixers and agitators shall be equipped with means by which the number of revolutions of the drum, blades or paddles may be readily verified.

All stationary and truck mixers shall be capable of combining the ingredients of the concrete within the specified time or the number of revolutions specified in Section 26.1309 (e) into a thoroughly mixed and uniform mass.

The agitator shall be capable of maintaining the mixed concrete in a thoroughly mixed and uniform mass and of discharging the concrete with a satisfactory degree of uniformity.

Slump tests of individual samples taken after discharge of approximately 15 percent and 85 percent of the load may be made for a quick check of the probable degree of uniformity. In order to provide samples that are representative of widely separated portions, but not the beginning and end of the load, no samples should be taken before 10 percent or after 90 percent of the batch has been discharged. These two samples shall be obtained within an elapsed time of not more than 15 minutes. If these slumps differ more than that specified, the mixer or agitator shall not be used unless the condition is corrected.

Use of the equipment may be permitted when operation with a longer mixing time, a smaller load or a more efficient charging sequence will permit meeting specified requirements.

Mixers and agitators shall be examined or weighed routinely as frequently as necessary to detect changes in condition due to accumulations of hardened concrete or mortar and examined to detect wear of blades. When such changes are extensive enough to affect the mixer performance, proof tests shall be performed to show whether the correction of the deficiencies is required.

Mixing and Delivery

Sec. 26.1309. (a) **General.** Ready-mixed concrete shall be mixed and delivered by means of one of the following combinations of operations:

1. Central-mixed concrete.
2. Shrink-mixed concrete.
3. Truck-mixed concrete.

(b) **Operation.** Mixers and agitators shall be operated within the limits of capacity and speed of rotation designated by the manufacturer of the equipment.

(c) **Central-mixed Concrete.** Concrete that is mixed completely in a stationary mixer and transported to the point of delivery either in a truck agitator or a truck mixer operating at agitating speed, or in nonagitating equipment meeting the requirements of Section 26.1310, shall conform to the following: The mixing time shall be counted from the time all the solid materials are in the drum. The batch shall be so charged into the mixer that some water will enter in advance of the cement and aggregate, and all water shall be in the drum by the end of the first one fourth of the specified mixing time.

1. Where no mixer performance tests are made, the acceptable mixing time for mixers having capacities of 1 cubic yard or less shall be not less than one minute. For mixers of greater capacity, this minimum shall be increased 15 seconds for each cubic yard or fraction thereof of additional capacity.

2. Where mixer performance tests have been made on given concrete mixtures in accordance with the testing program set forth in the following paragraphs, and the mixers have been charged to their rated capacity, the acceptable mixing time may be reduced for those particular circumstances to a point at which satisfactory

mixing defined in paragraph 3 below shall have been accomplished. When the mixing time is so reduced, the maximum time of mixing shall not exceed this reduced time by more than 60 seconds for air-entrained concrete.

3. Samples of concrete for comparative purposes shall be obtained immediately after arbitrarily designated mixing times, in accordance with one of the following procedures:

Alternative procedure 1. The mixer shall be stopped, and the required samples removed by any suitable means from the concrete at approximately equal distances from the front and back of the drum, or

Alternative procedure 2. As the mixer is being emptied, individual samples shall be taken after discharge of approximately 15 percent and 85 percent of the load. Any appropriate method of sampling may be used, provided the samples are representative of widely separated portions, but not the very ends of the batch.

4. The samples of concrete shall be tested in accordance with nationally recognized tests. Mixer performance tests shall be repeated whenever the appearance of the concrete or the coarse aggregate content of samples selected as outlined in this section indicates that adequate mixing has not been accomplished.

(d) **Shrink-mixed Concrete.** Concrete that is first partially mixed in a stationary mixer, and then mixed completely in a truck mixer, shall conform to the following: The time of mixing shall be minimum required to intermingle the ingredients. After transfer to a truck mixer the amount of mixing at the designated mixing speed will be that necessary to meet the requirements for uniformity of concrete. Tests to confirm such performance may be made in accordance with Section 26.1309 (c) 3 and 4. Additional turning of the mixer, if any, shall be at a designated agitation speed.

(e) **Truck-mixed Concrete.** Concrete is completely mixed in a truck mixer, 70 to 100 revolutions at the mixing speed designated by the manufacturer to produce the specified uniformity of concrete. Concrete uniformity tests may be made in accordance with Section 26.1309 (f) below and if requirements for uniformity of concrete are not met with 100 revolutions of mixing, after all ingredients, including water, are in the drum, that mixer shall not be used until the condition is corrected, except as provided in Section 26.1308, seventh paragraph. When satisfactory performance is found in one truck mixer, the performance of mixers of substantially the same design and condition of blades may be regarded as satisfactory. Additional revolutions of the mixer beyond the number found to produce the required uniformity of concrete shall be at a designated agitating speed.

(f) **Sampling for uniformity of concrete produced in truck mixers.** The concrete shall be discharged at the normal operating rate for the mixer being tested, with care being exercised not to obstruct or retard the discharge by an incompletely opened gate or seal. A minimum of two samples, each consisting of approximately 2 cubic feet, shall be taken after discharge of approximately 15 percent and 85 percent of the load. These samples shall be obtained within an elapsed time of not more than 15 minutes. The samples shall be secured, but shall be kept separate to represent specific points in the batch rather than combined to form a composite sample. Between samples, where necessary to maintain slump, the mixer may be turned in mixing direction at agitating speed. During sampling the receptacle shall receive the full discharge of the chute. Additional samples may be taken at other points in the load, if desired. Regardless of the number of samples, sufficient personnel must be available to perform the required tests promptly. Segregation during sampling and handling must be avoided. Each sample shall be remixed the minimum amount to ensure uniformity before specimens are molded for a particular test.

When a truck mixer or truck agitator is used for transporting concrete that has been completely mixed in a stationary mixer, any turning during transportation shall be at the speed designated by the manufacturer of the equipment as agitating speed.

When a truck mixer or agitator is approved for mixing or delivery of concrete, no water from the truck water system or elsewhere shall be added after the initial introduction of the mixing water for the batch except when on arrival at the job site the slump of the concrete is less than that specified. Such additional water to bring the slump within required limits shall be injected into the mixer under such pressure and direction of flow that the requirements for uniformity are met. The drum or blades shall be turned an additional 30 revolutions or more if necessary, at mixing speed, until the uniformity of the concrete is within these limits. Water shall not be added to the batch at any later time. Discharge of the concrete shall be completed within one and one-half hours or before the drum has revolved 300 revolutions, whichever comes first, after the introduction of the mixing water to the cement and aggregates or the introduction of the cement to the aggregates. These limitations may be waived if the concrete is of such slump after the one and one half-hour time or 300-revolution limit has been reached that it can be placed, without the addition of water, to the batch. In hot weather, or under conditions contributing to quick stiffening of the concrete, a time less than one and one-half hours may be required.

Concrete delivered in cold weather shall have the applicable minimum temperature indicated in the following table.

	MINIMUM CONCRETE TEMPERATURE (°F.)	
Air Temperature (°F.)	Thin Sections and Uniform Slabs	Heavy Sections and Mass Concrete
30 to 45	60	50
0 to 30	65	55
Below 0	70	60

The maximum temperature of concrete produced with heated aggregates, heated water, or both, shall at no time during its production or transportation exceed 90°F.

Every effort should be made to maintain the temperature of the concrete produced during hot weather as low as practicable. In some situations difficulty may be encountered when concrete temperatures approach 90°F.

Use of Nonagitating Equipment

Sec. 26.1310. Central-mixed concrete may be transported in suitable nonagitating equipment. The proportions of the concrete shall be approved and the following limitations shall apply:

1. Bodies of nonagitating equipment shall be smooth, watertight, metal containers equipped with gates that will permit control of the discharge of the concrete. Covers shall be provided for protection against the weather.

2. The concrete shall be delivered to the site of the work in a thoroughly mixed and uniform mass and discharged with a satisfactory degree of uniformity.

3. Slump tests of individual samples taken after discharge of approximately 15 percent and 85 percent of the load may be made for a quick check of the probable degree of uniformity. These two samples shall be obtained within an elapsed time of not more than 15 minutes. If these slumps differ more than that specified, the nonagitating equipment shall not be used unless the conditions are corrected. Use of the equipment may be permitted when operated using shorter hauls, longer mixing times, or combinations thereof that will result in meeting the specified requirements.

Inspection

Sec. 26.1311. (a) **Manufacturer's Site.** Proper facilities shall be provided to inspect ingredients and processes used in the manufacture and delivery of the concrete. The manufacturer shall afford the inspector all reasonable access, without charge, for making necessary checks of the production facilities and for securing necessary samples to determine if the concrete is being produced in accordance with this standard. All tests and inspections shall be so conducted as not to interfere unnecessarily with the manufacture and delivery of the concrete.

(b) **Construction Site.** Slump and air-content tests shall be made at the time of placement at the option of the inspector as often as is necessary for control checks and acceptance purposes, and always when strength specimens are made.

If the measured slump or air content falls outside the specified limits, a check test shall be made immediately on another portion of the same sample. In the event of a second failure, the concrete shall be considered to have failed the requirements of the specification.

Certification

Sec. 26.1312. (a) **Delivery Ticket.** The manufacturer of the concrete shall furnish to the purchaser with each batch of concrete before unloading at the site, a delivery ticket on which is printed, stamped or written information concerning said concrete as follows:

1. Name of ready-mix batch plant,
2. Serial number of ticket,
3. Date and truck number,
4. Name of contractor,
5. Specific designation of job (name and location),

6. Specific class or designation of concrete in conformance with that employed in job specifications,

7. Amount of concrete (cubic yards),

8. Time loaded or of first mixing of cement and aggregates, and

9. Water added by receiver of concrete and the receiver's initials.

(b) **Additional Information.** Additional information designated and required by the job specifications shall be furnished also upon request, such information may include:

1. Reading of revolution counter at first addition of water,

2. Signature or initials of ready-mix representative,

3. Type and brand of cement,

4. Amount of cement,

5. Information necessary to calculate the total mixing water added by the producer. Total mixing water includes free water on the aggregates, water, and ice batched at the plant and water added by the truck operator from the mixer tank.

6. Admixtures and amount of same,

7. Maximum size of aggregate,

8. Weights of fine and coarse aggregate, and

9. Ingredients certified as being previously approved.

Strength

Sec. 26.1313. When strength is used as a basis for acceptance of concrete, standard specimens shall be made. The specimens shall be cured under standard moisture and temperature conditions. Strength tests shall be made frequently and, in general, not less frequently than one strength test as well as slump and air content tests as stated in Chapter 26 of the Uniform Building Code.

For a strength test, two standard test specimens shall be made from a composite sample. The test result shall be the average of the strengths of the two specimens except that, if one specimen in a test shows definite evidence of improper sampling, handling, curing, molding or testing, it shall be discarded and the remaining cylinder shall be considered the test result.

Additional tests may be made at other ages to obtain information on the adequacy of the strength development or to check the adequacy of curing and protection of the concrete. Specimens made to check the adequacy of curing and protection should be properly cured.

The delivery ticket number for the concrete and the exact location in the work at which each load represented by a strength test is deposited shall be recorded.

To conform to the requirements of this standard, the average of all the strength tests representing each class of concrete shall be sufficient to ensure that the following requirements are met:

1. For concrete in structures designed by the working stress method and all construction other than that covered below, not more than 20 percent of the strength tests shall have values less than the specified strength, f'_c, and the average of any

six consecutive strength tests shall be equal to or greater than the specified strength.

2. For concrete in structures designed by the ultimate strength method and in prestressed structures, not more than 10 percent of the strength tests shall have values less than the specified strength, f'_c, and the average of any three consecutive strength tests shall be equal to or greater than the specified strength.

3. Due to variations in materials, operations and testing, the average strength necessary to meet these requirements will be substantially higher than the specified strength. The amount increases as these variations increase and decreases as they are reduced. This is a function of the coefficient of variation and other factors of control. Pertinent data are found in Table No. 26-13-C.

When the number of tests made of any class of concrete total six or less, the average of all the tests shall be equal to or greater than the specified strength divided by the appropriate value shown in the following table:

REQUIRED AVERAGE STRENGTH OF CONSECUTIVE TESTS, f'_c		
No. of Tests	Sec. 26.1313 Item 1	Sec. 26.1313 Item 2
1	0.79	0.86
2	0.90	0.97
3	0.94	1.02
4	0.97	1.05
5	0.99	1.07
6	1.00	1.08

TABLE NO. 26-13-A— ACCEPTANCE CRITERIA FOR QUESTIONABLE WATER SUPPLIES[1]

	LIMITS
Compressive strength, min. % control at 7 days	90
Time of set, deviation from control, h: min.	from 1:00 early to 1:30 later

[1]Comparisons shall be based on fixed proportions and the same volume of test water compared to control mix using city water or distilled water and following nationally recognized test procedures.

TABLE NO. 26-13-B— CHEMICAL LIMITATIONS FOR WASH WATER[1]

	LIMITS
Chemical requirements, maximum concentration in mixing water, ppm[2]	
Chloride as Cl, ppm:	
Prestressed concrete or in bridge decks	500[3]
Other reinforced concrete in moist environments or containing aluminum embedments or dissimilar metals or with stay-in-place galvanized metal forms	1,000[3]
Sulfate as SO_4, ppm	3,000
Alkalies as (Na_2O + 0.658 K_2O), ppm	600
Total solids, ppm	50,000

[1]Testing shall follow nationally recognized test procedures.

[2]Wash water reused as mixing water in concrete may exceed the listed concentrations of chloride and sulfate if it can be shown that the concentration calculated in the total mixing water, including mixing water on the aggregates and other sources does not exceed the stated limits.

[3]For conditions allowing use of $CaCl_2$ accelerator as an admixture, the chloride limitation may be waived by the purchaser.

TABLE NO. 26-13-C—STRENGTH REQUIREMENTS

Average Strength Requirements for Limiting Probability of Tests Falling Below the Specified Strength, f'_c, to One Out of Every Ten Tests					
Coefficient of Variation	5	10	15	20	25
Required Overdesign Factor	1.07	1.15	1.24	1.34	1.47
Design Strength	Required Average Strength[1]				
2,000 psi	2,140	2,300	2,480	2,680	2,940
2,500 psi	2,675	2,875	3,100	3,350	3,675
3,000 psi	3,210	3,450	3,720	4,030	4,420
3,500 psi	3,745	4,025	4,340	4,690	5,145
4,000 psi	4,270	4,590	4,960	5,380	5,890
4,500 psi	4,815	5,175	5,580	6,030	6,615
5,000 psi	5,340	5,740	6,200	6,720	7,360
Average Strength Requirements for Limiting Probability of Tests Falling Below the Specified Strength, f'_c, to One Out of Every Five Tests					
Coefficient of Variation	5	10	15	20	25
Required Overdesign Factor	1.04	1.09	1.14	1.20	1.27
Design Strength	Required Average Strength[1]				
2,000 psi	2,080	2,180	2,280	2,400	2,450
2,500 psi	2,600	2,725	2,850	3,000	3,180
3,000 psi	3,120	3,270	3,420	3,600	3,810
3,500 psi	3,640	3,820	3,990	4,200	4,450
4,000 psi	4,160	4,360	4,560	4,800	5,080
4,500 psi	4,680	4,910	5,130	5,400	5,720
5,000 psi	5,200	5,450	5,700	6,000	6,350

[1]In the absence of statistical experience, a coefficient of variation of 20 percent shall be assumed.

UNIFORM BUILDING CODE STANDARD NO. 26-14

CONCRETE MADE BY VOLUMETRIC BATCHING AND CONTINUOUS MIXING

Based on Standard Specification C 685-86 of the American Society for Testing and Materials. Extracted, with permission, from the Annual Book of ASTM Standards, copyright American Society for Testing and Materials, 1916 Race Street, Philadelphia, PA 19103.

See Sections 2603 (b) 6 and 2605 (i), Uniform Building Code

Scope

Sec. 26.1401. This standard covers concrete made from materials continuously batched by volume, mixed in a continuous mixer, and delivered in a freshly mixed and unhardened state.

Materials

Sec. 26.1402. (a) **General.** The materials used to make concrete by the volumetric batching and continuous mixing process shall comply with the requirements of Chapter 26 of the Uniform Building Code and this standard.

(b) **Water.** The mixing water shall be clear and apparently clean. If it contains quantities of substances that discolor it or make it smell or taste unusual or objectionable, or cause suspicion, it shall not be used unless service records of concrete made with it indicate that it is not injurious to the quality of the concrete.

Water of questionable quality shall be subject to the acceptance criteria of Table No. 26-13-A of U.B.C. Standard No. 26-13. Wash water from mixer washout operation may be used for mixing concrete, provided it meets the requirements of Section 26.1302 of U.B.C. Standard No. 26-13.

(c) **Admixtures.** Admixtures shall conform to applicable specifications acceptable to the building official.

Measuring Materials

Sec. 26.1403. (a) **General.** Cement, fine and coarse aggregates, water, and admixtures may be measured by weight or by volume. If volume proportioning is employed, devices such as counters, calibrated gate openings, or flowmeters shall be available for controlling and determining the quantities of the ingredients discharged. In operation, the entire measuring and dispensing mechanism shall produce the specified proportions of each ingredient.

The recommendations of the equipment manufacturer in the operation of the equipment and in calibrating and using the various gages, revolution counters, speed indicators, or other control devices shall be followed.

Indicating devices that bear on the accuracy of proportioning and mixing of concrete shall be in full view and near enough to be read by the operator while concrete is being produced. The operator shall have convenient access to controls.

Proportioning and indicating devices shall be individually checked by following the equipment manufacturer's recommendations as related to each individual concrete batching and mixing unit. Adequate standard volume measures, scales, and weights shall be available for the checking accuracy of the proportioning mechanism. The device for the measurement of the added water shall be capable of delivering to the batch the required quantity within the accuracy of ±1 percent; the device shall be so arranged that the measurements will not be affected by variable pressures in the water supply line.

(b) **Yield Check.** The volume of concrete discharged from the mixer is checked by first weighing the amount of concrete discharged during some number of revolutions, or as determined by another output indicator; this is then followed immediately by a determination of the weight of concrete per cubic foot. The weight of concrete discharged divided by the weight per cubic foot is equal to the number of cubic feet mixed and discharged during the chosen interval. The accuracy of the output indicator is thus checked.

About 2.5 to 3.0 cubic feet shall be discharged for this purpose; this amount of concrete will weigh from 350 to 500 lb. and can be discharged into and contained in a 35- or 55-gallon drum or other suitable container which in turn can be placed on a weighing scale of adequate capacity. The output of a batcher-mixer unit may be indicated by the number of revolutions, travel of a belt, or changes in gage readings; if so, these figures may be used as a measure of output.

(c) **Proportioning Check.** Whenever the sources or characteristics of the ingredients are changed, or the characteristics of the mixture have changed, a check of the fine aggregate content and the coarse aggregate content by use of the washout test shall be performed. In the washout test, 1 cubic foot of concrete is washed through a No. 4 sieve and through a No. 100 sieve; that retained on the No. 4 sieve is coarse aggregate whereas that passing the No. 4 and retained on the No. 100 sieve is fine aggregate.

Corrections to the quantity of aggregates per cubic foot of concrete can be made if the original sieve analysis of each aggregate is available.

The rate of water supplied a continuous mixer shall be measured by a calibrated flowmeter coordinated with the cement and aggregate feeding mechanism, and with the mixer. The rate shall be capable of being adjusted in order to control slump at the desired levels and to determine that the water-cement ratios are bring met.

Liquid admixtures shall be dispensed through a controlled flowmeter.

Tolerances in proportioning the various ingredients shall be as follows:

Cement, weight percent	0 to + 4
Fine Aggregate, weight percent	±2
Coarse Aggregate, weight percent	±2
Admixtures, weight or volume percent	±3
Water, weight or volume percent	±1

The tolerances shall be based on a volume/weight relationship established by calibration of the measuring devices furnished as an integral part of the whole equipment.

Mixing Mechanisms

Sec. 26.1404. General. The continuous mixer shall be an auger-type mixer or other type suitable for mixing concrete to meet the required consistency and uniformity requirements.

Each batching or mixing unit, or both, shall carry in a prominent place a metal plate or plates on which are plainly marked the gross volume of the unit in terms of mixed concrete, discharge speed, and the weight-calibrated constant of the machine in terms of a revolution counter or other output indicator. The mixer shall produce a thoroughly mixed and uniform concrete.

Slump and air content tests of samples shall be made for a quick check of the probable degree of uniformity.

Mixing and Delivery

Sec. 26.1405. (a) **General.** The batch-mixer unit shall contain in separate compartments all the necessary ingredients needed for the manufacture of concrete. The unit shall be equipped with calibrated proportioning devices to vary the mix proportions and it shall produce concrete as required by this standard and specifications for the project.

(b) **Cold Weather Concrete.** Concrete delivered in cold weather shall have the applicable minimum temperature indicated in the following table.

AIR TEMPERATURE °F	MINIMUM CONCRETE TEMPERATURE: THIN SECTIONS AND UNFORMED SLABS °F	MINIMUM CONCRETE TEMPERATURE: HEAVY SECTIONS AND MASS CONCRETE °F
30 to 45	60	50
0 to 30	65	55
Below 0	70	60

The maximum temperature of concrete produced with heated aggregates, heated water, or both, shall at no time during its production or transportation exceed 90°F. The temperature of the concrete produced during hot weather shall be as low as practicable.

Slump and Air Content

Sec. 26.1406. (a) **General.** Slump and air-content tests shall be made at the time of placement as often as is necessary for control checks and acceptance purposes, and always when strength specimens are made.

If the measured slump or air content falls outside the specified limits, a check test shall be made immediately on another portion of the same sample. In the event of a second failure, the concrete shall be considered to have failed the requirements of the specification.

(b) **Tolerances in Slump.** Unless other tolerances are included in the project specifications, the following shall apply:

When the project specifications for slump are written as a "maximum" or "not to exceed" requirement:

SPECIFIED SLUMP	TOLERANCE, IN.
3 in. or less	+ 0 − 1 1/2
More than 3 in.	+ 0 − 2 1/2

This option may be used only if one addition of water is permitted on the job, provided such addition does not increase the water-cement ratio above the maximum permitted by the project specifications.

When the project specifications for slump are *not* written as a "maximum" or "not to exceed" requirement:

SPECIFIED SLUMP	TOLERANCE, IN.
2 in. and less	± 1/2
More than 2 in. through 4 in.	± 1
More than 4 in.	± 1 1/2

Except when project specifications provide otherwise, air content shall comply with Table No. 26-14-A.

The air content of air-entrained concrete when sampled from the transportation unit at the point of discharge shall be within a tolerance of ±1.5 of the specified value.

Strength

Sec. 26.1407. (a) **General.** When strength is used as a basis for acceptance of the concrete, standard specimens shall be made and cured under standard moisture and temperature conditions.

One strength test set of two cylinders and the accompanying slump and air content tests shall be made for each 25 cubic yards of concrete or fraction thereof, or whenever significant changes have been made in the proportioning controls. There shall be at least one strength test made for each class of concrete placed in one day.

For each strength test, two standard-size cylinders shall be made. The test result shall be the average of the strength of the two specimens except that, if any specimen shows definite evidence other than low strength, of improper sampling, molding, handling, curing, or testing, it shall be discarded and the strength of the remaining cylinder shall then be considered the test result.

The delivery ticket number for the concrete and the exact location in the work where the concrete represented by each strength test was deposited shall be recorded.

(b) **Specifications.** To conform to the requirements of this standard, the average of all of the strength tests representing each class of concrete shall be sufficient to ensure that the following requirements are met.

1. For concrete in structures designed by the working stress method and all construction other than that covered in item 2 following, not more than 20 percent of the strength tests shall have values less than the specified strength, f'_c, and the average of any six consecutive strength tests shall be equal to or greater than the specified strength.
2. For concrete in structures designed by the ultimate strength method and in prestressed structures not more than 10 percent of the strength tests shall have values less than the specified strength, f'_c, and the average of any three consecutive strength tests shall be equal to or greater than the specified strength.
3. Table No. 26-14-B shall be used to determine the average strength necessary to assure that the design strength is achieved with a high degree of assurance.

When the number of tests made of any class of concrete totals six or less, the average of all the tests shall be equal to or greater than the following:

NO. OF TESTS	REQUIRED AVERAGE STRENGTH OF CONSECUTIVE TEST, f'_c WORKING STRESS METHOD	ULTIMATE STRENGTH METHOD
1	0.79	0.86
2	0.90	0.97
3	0.94	1.02
4	0.97	1.05
5	0.99	1.07
6	1.00	1.08

Test Methods

Sec. 26.1408. Cure concrete in accordance with a method approved by the building official.

Inspection

Sec. 26.1409. (a) **Materials, Batching Facilities and Mixing Facilities.** The manufacturer shall afford the inspector reasonable access without charge for obtaining necessary samples of materials used in the concrete, and for making necessary checks of the batching and mixing facilities to determine if the concrete is being produced in accordance with this standard. All tests and inspection shall be conducted so as not to interfere with the batching, mixing and discharge of the concrete.

(b) **Fresh Concrete.** The inspector shall be accorded reasonable access without charge for the procurement of samples of fresh concrete at the time of placement so as to determine conformance of the concrete to this standard.

At any time after at least 2 cubic feet of concrete have been discharged, one sample of concrete shall be taken for the slump test, the air content test, if required, and the strength test. The sample shall be at least 2 cubic feet in volume. Two cylinders for each age of test shall be made. Tests for slump or air content or both shall be started within 5 minutes of sampling; these tests should then be completed expeditiously. Molding of specimens for strength tests shall be started within 15 minutes of sampling.

Samples for determining the uniformity of mixing shall be taken at arbitarily designated times. After at least 2 cubic feet have been discharged, a sample of at least 4 cubic feet shall be taken followed by another sample being taken no sooner than after 4 minutes of continuous discharge or 1 cubic yard whichever is smaller. These samples shall be checked for conformance to the criteria set forth in Section 26.1410.

Concrete Uniformity Requirements

Sec. 26.1410. (a) **Variation.** The variation within a batch as provided in Table No. 26-14-C shall be determined for each property listed as the difference between the highest value and the lowest value obtained from the different portions of the same batch. For this standard the comparison will be between two samples, representing the first and last portions of the batch being tested. Test results conforming to the limits of five of the six tests listed in Table No. 26-14-C shall indicate uniform concrete within the limits of this specification.

(b) **Coarse Aggregate Content.** Coarse aggregate content using the washout test, shall be computed from the following relations:

$$P = (c/b) \times 100$$

WHERE:

P = weight % of coarse aggregate in concrete.

c = saturated surface-dry weight, lb. of aggregate retained on the No. 4 sieve, resulting from washing all material finer than this sieve from the fresh concrete, and

b = weight of sample of fresh concrete in unit weight container, lb.

(c) **Unit Weight of Air-free Mortar.** Shall be calculated as follows:
Inch-pound units:

$$M = \frac{b-c}{V-\left(\dfrac{V \times A}{100} + \dfrac{c}{G \times 62.4}\right)}$$

WHERE:

M = unit weight of air-free mortar, lb./ft.^{3}

b = weight of concrete sample in unit weight container, lb.

c = saturated surface-dry weight of aggregate retained on No. 4 sieve, lb.

V = volume of unit weight container, ft.^{3}

A = air content of concrete, %.

G = specific gravity of coarse aggregate (saturated surface dry).

Batch Ticket Information

Sec. 26.1411. (a) **General.** The producer of the concrete shall furnish with each increment of discharged concrete, a delivery ticket or a statement of particulars on which is shown the following:

1. Name of concrete producer,
2. Serial number of the delivery ticket or statement,
3. Date, starting time, and finishing time,
4. Identification number of batching or mixing equipment, or both,

5. Name of the consignee,
6. Specific designation of the job (name and location),
7. Specific class or designation of the concrete in conformance with that employed in the job specification,
8. Amount of concrete in cubic yards and reading of the revolution counter or other device that indicates quantity of concrete.

(b) **Additional Information.** Additional information designated by the consignee and required by the job specifications shall be furnished when requested. Such information may include the following:

1. Type, brand, and amount of cement,
2. Type, name, and amount of each admixture,
3. Information necessary to calculate total mixing water added by the producer. Total mixing water includes free water on the aggregates and water batched by the producer from the mixing equipment or other sources,
4. Maximum size of aggregate,
5. Weights or volumes of fine and coarse aggregate,
6. Notation of calibrated settings for flow control of fine and coarse aggregate, added water, and admixtures,
7. Ingredients certified as being previously approved, and
8. Signature or initials of the person operating the batching or mixing apparatus.

TABLE NO. 26-14-A
TOTAL AIR CONTENT FOR AIR-ENTRAINED CONCRETE

	Total Air Content, %						
Exposure Condition	Nominal Max Sizes of Aggregate, in. 3/8	1/2	3/4	1	1 1/2	2	3
Negligible	4.5	4.0	3.5	3.0	2.5	2.0	1.5
Moderate	6.0	5.5	5.0	4.5	4.5	4.0	3.5
Severe	7.5	7.0	6.0	6.0	5.5	5.0	4.5

TABLE NO. 26-14-B—STRENGTH REQUIREMENTS

Average Strength Requirements for Limiting Probability of Tests Falling Below the Specified Strength f_c', to One Out of Every Ten Tests

Coefficient of Variation	5	10	15	20	25
Required Overdesign Factor	1.07	1.15	1.24	1.34	1.47
Design Strength, psi	Required Average Strength, psi[1]				
2000	2140	2300	2480	2680	2940
2500	2675	2875	3100	3350	3675
3000	3210	3450	3720	4030	4420
3500	3745	4025	4340	4690	5145
4000	4270	4590	4960	5380	5890
4500	4815	5175	5580	6030	6615
5000	5340	5740	6200	6720	7300

Average Strength Requirements for Limiting Probability of Tests Falling Below the Specified Strength f_c', to One Out of Every Five Tests

Coefficient of Variation	5	10	15	20	25
Required Overdesign Factor	1.04	1.09	1.14	1.20	1.27
Design Strength, psi	Required Average Strength, psi[1]				
2000	2080	2180	2280	2400	2540
2500	2600	2725	2850	3000	3180
3000	3120	3270	3420	3600	3810
3500	3640	3820	3990	4200	4450
4000	4160	4360	4560	4800	5080
4500	4680	4910	5130	5400	5720
5000	5200	5450	5700	6000	6350

[1]Computed from Eq. 4.1 and values of "*t*" for more than 30 samples from Table 4.1 (ACI 214-77). In the absence of statistical experience, a coefficient of variation of 20% shall be assumed.

TABLE NO. 26-14-C
REQUIREMENTS FOR UNIFORMITY OF CONCRETE

Test	Requirement Expressed as Maximum Permissible Difference in Results of Tests of Samples Taken from Two Locations in the Concrete Batch
Weight per cubic foot calculated to an air-free basis, $lb./ft.^3$	1.0
Air content, volume % of concrete	1.0
Slump:	
If average slump is 4 in. or less, in.	1.0
If average slump is 4 to 6 in.	1.5
Coarse aggregate content, portion by weight of each sample retained on No. 4 sieve, %	6.0
Unit weight of air-free mortar[1] based on average for all comparative samples tested, %	1.6
Average compressive strength at 7 days for each sample[2], based on average strength of all comparative test specimens, %	7.5[3]

[1]"Test for Variability of Constituents in Concrete," Designation 26, Bureau of Reclamation *Concrete Manual,* 7th Ed. Available from Superintendent of Documents, U.S. Government Printing Office, Washington, DC 20402.

[2]Not less than 3 cylinders will be molded and tested from each of the samples.

[3]Tentative approval of the mixer may be granted pending results of the 7-day compressive strength tests.

UNIFORM BUILDING CODE STANDARD NO. 26-15

MILL-MIXED GYPSUM CONCRETE AND POURED GYPSUM ROOF DIAPHRAGMS

Based on Reports of Test Programs by S. B. Barnes and Associates dated February, 1955; November, 1956; January, 1958; and February, 1962 and Standard Specification C 317-70 of the American Society for Testing and Materials. Extracted, with permission, from the Annual Book of ASTM Standards, copyright American Society for Testing and Materials, 1916 Race Street, Philadelphia, PA 19103.

See Sections 2603 (b) and 2627 (c), Uniform Building Code

Part I

Scope

Sec. 26.1501. This part covers mill-mixed gypsum concrete. Gypsum concrete supplied under this standard shall be mill-mixed gypsum concrete, consisting essentially of calcined gypsum and suitable aggregate, requiring the addition of water only at the job. Gypsum concrete is intended for use in construction of poured-in-place roof decks or slabs. Two classes, based on the compressive strength and density, are covered.

Composition

Sec. 26.1502. Gypsum concrete shall consist essentially of calcined gypsum and wood chips or wood shavings, proportioned to meet the applicable requirements of this standard. Calcined gypsum used in the mill mixed gypsum concrete shall conform to the requirements of U.B.C. Standard No. 47-9. Wood chips or wood shavings shall be of dry wood, uniform and clean in appearance, shall pass a 1-inch sieve, and shall be not more than 1/16 inch in thickness.

Time of Setting

Sec. 26.1503. Gypsum concrete shall set in not less than 20 minutes nor more than 90 minutes.

Compressive Strength and Density

Sec. 26.1504. Gypsum concrete shall have the following compressive strength and density for the respective classes:

	COMPRESSIVE STRENGTH MINIMUM psi	DENSITY POUNDS PER CUBIC FOOT
Class A.................	500	60
Class B.................	1000	—

Methods of Testing

Sec. 26.1505. The physical properties of gypsum concrete shall be determined in accordance with approved methods.

Part II

Scope

Sec. 26.1506. This part covers the design of poured-in-place reinforced gypsum concrete roof decks when used as a horizontal diaphragm.

Design

Sec. 26.1507. (a) **General.** The gypsum roof diaphragm shall consist of subpurlins welded transversely to primary purlins. Formboard is then placed on the flanges of the subpurlins. Wire mesh reinforcement is then placed over the subpurlins and formboard and lapped at least 4 inches or one mesh on ends and edges, whichever is greater. Gypsum concrete meeting the requirements of Part I of this standard is then placed to a minimum thickness of 2 inches over the formboard and 5/8 inch over the subpurlins and doweling elements. The bulb section or top flange of the subpurlin shall be fully embedded in the gypsum concrete.

(b) **Diaphragm Shear.** Shear in poured gypsum concrete diaphragms shall be determined by the formula:

$$Q = .16 f_g \, t \, C_l + 1000 \, (k_1 \, d_1 + k_2 \, d_2)$$

WHERE:

Q = Allowable shear on diaphragm in pounds per linear foot, which includes a one-third increase for short-time loading.

f_g = Oven-dry compressive strength of gypsum in pounds per square inch as determined by tests conforming to this standard.

C_l = 1.0 for Class A gypsum; 1.5 for Class B gypsum.

t = Thickness of gypsum concrete between subpurlins, in inches. For the purpose of computing diaphragm shear values, *t* shall not exceed 4 inches.

k_1 = Number of mesh wires per foot passing over subpurlins.

d_1 = Diameter of mesh wires passing over subpurlins, in inches, except hexagonal mesh.

k_2 = Number of mesh wires per foot parallel to subpurlins or .7 times the number of hexagonal wires. Note: k_2 = 8.5 for 2-inch hexagonal mesh woven of No. 19 gage galvanized wire with additional longitudinal No. 16 gage galvanized wires spaced every 3 inches across the width of the mesh.

d_2 = Diameter, in inches, of mesh wires parallel to subpurlins or of hexagonal wires.

The solution of the above equation for commonly used thickness and mesh types for each class of gypsum would give the values set forth in Table No. 26-15-A.

(c) **Shear Transfer.** Bolts, dowels or other approved elements may be used to transfer diaphragm shears to perimeter or other structural members. Allowable bolt and dowel stresses shall comply with Table No. 26-K and Section 2303 of the Uniform Building Code.

TABLE NO. 26-15-A—ALLOWABLE SHEAR VALUES IN POUNDS PER FOOT USING BULB TEE SUBPURLINS[1]

CLASS OF GYPSUM CONCRETE	CONCRETE THICKNESS (In Inches)	MESH TYPE[2]		
		4″ x 8″ No. 12-No. 14 (Galvanized)	6″ x 6″ No. 10-No. 10	Hexagonal[3] (Galvanized)
A (500 psi)	2 2½	600 640	700 740	760 800
B (1000 psi)	2 2½	920 1040	1020 1140	1080 1200

[1]The tabulated shear values are for short-time loads due to wind or earthquake forces and are not permitted a one-third increase for duration of load.

[2]Mesh shall be lapped at least 4 inches or one mesh on ends and edges, whichever is greater.

[3]Two-inch hexagonal mesh woven of No. 19 gage galvanized wire with additional longitudinal No. 16 gage galvanized wires spaced every 3 inches across the width of the mesh.

UNIFORM BUILDING CODE STANDARD NO. 26-16

GROUND-IRON BLAST-FURNACE SLAG FOR USE IN CONCRETE AND MORTARS

Based on Standard Specifications C 989-84 of the American Society for Testing and Materials

See Section 2603 (b), Uniform Building Code

Scope

Sec. 26.1601. This specification covers three strength grades of finely ground granulated iron blast-furnace slag for use as a cementitious material in concrete and mortar.

The material described in this specification may be used for blending with portland cement to produce a cement meeting the requirements of U.B.C. Standard No. 26-1 for mortar mixtures.

Definitions

Sec. 26.1602. IRON BLAST-FURNACE SLAG is a nonmetallic product consisting essentially of silicates and aluminosilicates of calcium and of other bases that is developed in a molten condition simultaneously with iron in a blast furnace.

GRANULATED IRON BLAST-FURNACE SLAG is the glassy granular material formed when molten blast-furnace slag is rapidly chilled. Compositional adjustments may be made while the slag is molten.

Classification

Sec. 26.1603. Finely ground iron blast-furnace slag is classified by performance in the slag activity test in three grades: Grade 80, Grade 100 and Grade 120 (see Table No. 26-16-B).

Additions

Sec. 26.1604. The ground slag covered by this specification shall contain no additions except as follows:

Calcium sulfate may be added in amounts such that the limits in Table No. 26-16-A for sulfur trioxide are not exceeded.

Processing additions may be used in the manufacture of the ground slag, provided such materials in the amounts used have been shown to meet the requirements of U.B.C. Standard No. 26-1 when tested using a 50-50 blend by weight with portland cement.

Chemical Composition

Sec. 26.1605. Ground granulated blast-furnace slag shall conform to the chemical requirements prescribed in Table No. 26-16-A.

Physical Requirements

Sec. 26.1606. Ground granulated blast-furnace slag shall conform to the fineness and air-content requirements in Table No. 26-16-B. A slag shall be assigned to the lowest activity grade realized based on the minimum activity index values in Table No. 26-16-B. The limits for individual samples shall govern until tests of five samples become available, after which time both limits shall apply.

Sampling and Test Methods

Sec. 26.1607. Sampling and test methods shall be in accordance with approved standards.

Table No. 26-16-A—Chemical Requirements

Sulfide sulfur (S), max., %	2.5
Sulfate ion reported as SO_3, max., %	4.0

Table No. 26-16-B—Physical Requirements

Item	
Fineness:	
Amount retained when wet screened on No. 325 (45-μm) sieve, max., %	20
Specific surface by air permeability shall be determined and reported although no limits are required.	—
Air content of slag mortar, max., %	12
Slag activity index, min., %	

	Average of Last Five Consecutive Samples	Any Individual Sample
7-Day Index		
Grade 80	—	—
Grade 100	75	70
Grade 120	95	90
28-Day Index		
Grade 80	75	70
Grade 100	95	90
Grade 120	115	110

UNIFORM BUILDING CODE STANDARD NO. 27-1

MATERIAL SPECIFICATIONS FOR STRUCTURAL STEEL

Based on Standard Specifications A 27, A 36, A 48, A 53, A 148 A 242, A 252, A 283, A 307, A 325, A 366, A 441, A 446, A 449, A 490, A 500, A 501, A 514, A 529, A 563, A 569, A 570, A 572, A 588, A 606, A 607, A 611, A 618, A 666, A 690 and A 715 of the American Society for Testing and Materials. Extracted, with permission, from the Annual Book of ASTM Standards, copyright American Society for Testing and Materials, 1916 Race Street, Philadelphia, PA 19103.

See Sections 2603 (f) 5, 2721 (b), 2909 (f) 1 and 2909 (g) 1, Uniform Building Code, and Section 402 (b), Uniform Sign Code

Scope

Sec. 27.101. This standard covers steel and iron shapes, plates, sheet, strip, connectors and bars for use in the construction of buildings and for general structural purposes.

Material Requirements

Sec. 27.102. The material shall conform to the requirements as to the tensile properties set forth in Table No. 27-1-A.

TABLE NO. 27-1-A—TENSILE REQUIREMENTS

MATERIAL	GRADE	SPECIFICATION TITLE	SIZE & PRODUCT LIMITATIONS	TENSILE STRENGTH (ksi)	YIELD POINT (ksi)	REFERENCED IN OTHER U.B.C. STANDARD
A27-81a	60-30	Mild- to Medium-strength Carbon Steel Castings		60	30	
	65-35			65	35	
	70-36			70	36	
	70-40			70	40	
A36-81a		Structural Steel		58-80	36	27-4 27-9
A48-76	**Class No.**	Gray Iron Castings				
	20 A, B, C & S			20	—	
	25 "			25	—	
	30 "			30	—	
	35 "			35	—	
	40 "			40	—	
	45 "			45	—	
	50 "			50	—	
	55 "			55	—	
	60 "			60	—	
A53-82	Type F	Steel Pipe, Black and Hot Dipped, Zinc Coated; Welded and Seamless	Furnace—Butt Welded	45	25	U.M.C. 15-1
	A (Type E & S)		Electric—Resistance Welded and Seamless	48	30	
	B (Type E & S)		Electric—Resistance Welded and Seamless	60	35	
A148-81	80- 40	High-strength Steel Casting for Structural Purposes		80	40	
	80- 50			80	50	
	90- 60			90	60	
	105- 85			105	85	
	120- 95			120	95	
	150-125			150	125	
	175-145			175	145	

MATERIAL	GRADE	SPECIFICATION TITLE	SIZE & PRODUCT LIMITATIONS	TENSILE STRENGTH (ksi)	YIELD POINT (ksi)	REFERENCED IN OTHER U.B.C. STANDARD
A242-81		High-strength Low-alloy Structural Steel	3/4″ thick and under Over 3/4″ to 1 1/2″, inclusive Over 1 1/2″ to 4″ thick	70 67 63	50 46 42	27-4 27-9
A252-82	1 2 3	Welded and Seamless Steel Pipe Piles		50 60 66	30 35 45	
A283-81	A B C D	Low and Intermediate Strength Carbon Steel Plates Shapes and Bars		45-55 50-60 55-65 60-72	24 27 30 33	
A307-82a	A & B B	Bolts Bolts with Cast-iron Flanges		60 (min) 100 (max)	—	
A325-83c		High-strength Bolts for Structural Steel Joints	1/2″ to 1″ diameter, inclusive 1 1/8″ to 1 1/2″ diameter, inclusive	105 120	92 81	27-7
A366-72 (79)		Carbon Steel Cold-rolled Sheet, Commercial Quality		—	—	
A441-81		High-strength Low-alloy Structural Manganese Vanadium Steel	**Plates & Bars** 3/4″ thick and under Over 3/4″ to 1 1/2″ thick Over 1 1/2″ to 4″ thick Over 4″ to 8″ thick **Structural Shapes** Groups 1 and 2 Group 3 Groups 4 and 5	 70 67 63 60 70 67 63	 50 46 42 40 50 46 42	27-4 27-9

(Continued)

TABLE NO. 27-1-A—TENSILE REQUIREMENTS—(Continued)

MATERIAL	GRADE	SPECIFICATION TITLE	SIZE & PRODUCT LIMITATIONS	TENSILE STRENGTH (ksi)	YIELD POINT (ksi)	REFERENCED IN OTHER U.B.C. STANDARD
A446-76 (81)	A B C D E F	Steel Sheet Zinc Coated (Galvanized) by Hot-dip Process Structural Quality		45 52 55 65 82 70	33 37 40 50 80 50	27-9
A449-83a		Quenched and Tempered Steel Bolts and Studs	1/4″ to 1″, inclusive Over 1″ to 1 1/2″, inclusive Over 1 1/2″ to 3″, inclusive	120 105 90	92 81 58	
A490-83a		Quenched and Tempered Alloy Steel Bolts for Structural Steel Connections	1/2″ to 1 1/2″, inclusive	150 (min) 170 (max)	130	27-7
A500-82a	A B C A B C	Cold-formed Welded and Seamless Carbon Steel Structural Tubing in Rounds and Shapes	Rounds Shapes	45 58 62 45 58 62	33 42 46 39 46 50	
A501-83		Hot-formed Welded and Seamless Carbon Steel Structural Tubing		58	36	
A514-82a		High-yield Strength Quenched and Tempered Allow Steel Plate	2 1/2″ Over 2 1/2″ to 6″, inclusive	110-130 100-130	100 90	
A529-82		Structural Steel with 42,000 psi Minimum Yield Point	1/2″ maximum thickness	60-85	42	27-9

MATERIAL	GRADE	SPECIFICATION TITLE	SIZE & PRODUCT LIMITATIONS	TENSILE STRENGTH (ksi)	YIELD POINT (ksi)	REFERENCED IN OTHER U.B.C. STANDARD
A563-88a	O A B C D DH	Carbon and Alloy Steel Nuts				27-15
A569-72 (79)		Steel, Carbon Hot-rolled Sheet and Strip, Commercial Quality		—	—	
A570-79	30 33 36 40 45 50	Hot-rolled Carbon Steel Sheets and Strip, Structural Quality	Maximum thickness of 0.2299″	49 52 53 55 60 65	30 33 36 40 45 50	27-4 27-9
A572-82	42 50 60 65	High-strength Low-alloy Columbium-Vanadium Steel, Structural Quality	Shapes, plates, piling and bars	60 65 75 80	42 50 60 65	27-4 27-9
A588-82		High-strength Low-alloy Structural Steel with a 50 ksi Minimum Yield Point to 4 Inches Thick	Plate and bars to 4″, inclusive Over 4″ to 5″, inclusive Over 5″ to 8″, inclusive Structural shapes—all grades	70 67 63 70	50 46 42 50	27-4 27-9
A606-75		Steel Sheet and Strip Hot-rolled and Cold-rolled High-strength Low-alloy Improved Atmospheric Corrosion Resistance	Hot-rolled cut lengths Hot-rolled coils, Annealed or normalized cut lengths and coils	70 65 65	50 45 45	27-4 27-9

(Continued)

TABLE NO. 27-1-A—TENSILE REQUIREMENTS—(Continued)

MATERIAL	GRADE	SPECIFICATION TITLE	SIZE & PRODUCT LIMITATIONS	TENSILE STRENGTH (ksi)	YIELD POINT (ksi)	REFERENCED IN OTHER U.B.C. STANDARD
A607-75 (81)	45 50 55 60 65 70	Steel Sheet and Strip Hot-rolled and Cold-rolled High-strength Low-alloy Columbium and/or Vanadium	Cut lengths or coils	60 65 70 75 80 85	45 50 55 60 65 70	27-4 27-9
A611-82	A B C D E	Type I and II Cold-rolled Sheet Carbon Steel, Structural		42 45 48 52 82	25 30 33 40 80	27-4 27-9
A618-81	Ia, Ib, II Ia, Ib, II III	Hot-formed Welded and Seamless High-strength Low-alloy Structural Tubing	Walls $^3/_4''$ and under Walls over $^3/_4''$ to $1^1/_2''$, inclusive Walls over $^3/_4''$ to $1^1/_2''$, inclusive	70 67 65	50 46 50	27-9
A666-82	A B C D	Austenitic Stainless Steel, Sheet Strip, Plate and Flat Bar for Structural Applications		75 75-95 115-125 125-150	30 40-4 75 100-11 0	27-10

MATERIAL	GRADE	SPECIFICATION TITLE	SIZE & PRODUCT LIMITATIONS	TENSILE STRENGTH (ksi)	YIELD POINT (ksi)	REFERENCED IN OTHER U.B.C. STANDARD
A668-85a	A	Steel Forgings, Carbon and Alloy for General Industrial Use		47	—	27-15
	B			60	30	
	C			66	33	
	D			75	37	
	E			85-83	44-43	
	F			90-82	55-48	
	G			80	50	
	H			90	60-58	
	J			95-105	65-80	
	K			105-100	80-75	
	L			125-110	105-85	
	M			145-135	120-110	
	N			170-160	140-130	
A690-81a		Sheet Piling for Marine Environment		70	50	
A715-81	50	Steel Sheet and Strip Hot-rolled High-strength Low-alloy		60	50	27-9
	60			70	60	
	70			80	70	
	80			90	80	
A792-85	33	Steel Sheet, Aluminum-Zinc Alloy Coated by the Hot-dip Process	Coils and lengths	45	33	
	37			52	37	
	40			55	40	
	50B			65	50	
	50A			—	50	
A852-88a		Quenched and Tempered Low-alloy Structural Steel Plate with 70 ksi Minimum Yield Strength	Maximum 4″ thick	90-110	70	27-15

UNIFORM BUILDING CODE STANDARD NO. 27-3

STRESS VARIATION OR STRESS REVERSAL DESIGN

Based on Specifications of the American Institute of Steel Construction, Inc. (November 1,1978)

See Section 2701 (a) 2, Uniform Building Code

Scope

Sec. 27.301. This standard covers the design of structural steel members subject to repeated variation of stress.

Definitions

Sec. 27.302. For the purpose of this standard, certain terms are defined as follows:

FATIGUE is the damage that may result in fracture after a sufficient number of fluctuations of stress.

STRESS RANGE is the magnitude of fatigue fluctuations.

Stress Range Computation

Sec. 27.303. In the case of a stress reversal, stress range shall be computed as the numerical sum of maximum repeated tensile and compressive stresses or the sum of maximum shearing stresses of opposite direction at a given point resulting from differing arrangements of live load.

Design for Fatigue

Sec. 27.304. Members and their connections subject to fatigue loading shall be proportioned to satisfy the stress range limitations as provided in this standard.

In the design of members and connections subject to repeated variation of live load stress, consideration shall be given to the number of stress cycles, the expected range of stress and type and location of member or detail.

Loading conditions shall be classified as shown in Table No. 27-3-A.

The type and location of material shall be categorized as shown in Table No. 27-3-B.

The maximum stress shall not exceed the basic allowable stress provided in the Uniform Building Code, and the maximum range of stress shall not exceed that given in Table No. 27-3-C.

Provisions for Mechanical Fasteners

Sec. 27.305. Range in stress in properly tightened A325 and A490 bolts need not be considered, but the maximum computed stress, including prying action, shall not exceed the values given in U.B.C. Standard No. 27-15, subject to the following stipulations:

1. Connections subject to more than 20,000 cycles but not more than 500,000 cycles of direct tension may be designed for the stress produced by the sum of

applied and prying loads if the prying load does not exceed 10 percent of the externally applied load. If the prying force exceeds 10 percent, the allowable tensile stress given in U.B.C. Standard No. 27-15 shall be reduced 40 percent, applicable to the external load alone.

2. Connections subject to more than 500,000 cycles of direct tension may be designed for the stress produced by the sum of applied and prying loads if the prying load does not exceed 5 percent of the externally applied load. If the prying force exceeds 5 percent, the allowable tensile stress given in U.B.C. Standard No. 27-15 shall be reduced 50 percent, applicable to the external load alone.

The use of other bolts and threaded parts subjected to tensile fatigue loading is not recommended.

Rivets, bolts and threaded parts subjected to cyclic loading in shear may be designed for the bearing-type shear stresses given in U.B.C. Standard No. 27-15 insofar as the fatigue strength of the fasteners themselves is concerned.

TABLE NO. 27-3-A

Loading Condition	Number of Loading Cycles	
	From	To
1	20,000[1]	100,000[2]
2	100,000	500,000[3]
3	500,000	2,000,000[4]
4	Over 2,000,000	

[1]Approximately equivalent to two applications every day for 25 years.
[2]Approximately equivalent to 10 applications every day for 25 years.
[3]Approximately equivalent to 50 applications every day for 25 years.
[4]Approximately equivalent to 200 applications every day for 25 years.

TABLE NO. 27-3-B

GENERAL CONDITION	SITUATION	KIND OF STRESS[1]	STRESS CATEGORY (See Table No. 27-3-C)
Plain material	Base metal with rolled or cleaned surfaces.	T or Rev.	A
Built-up members	Base metal and weld metal in members, without attachments, built up of plates or shapes connected by continuous full or partial-penetration groove welds and continuous fillet welds parallel to the direction of applied stress.	T or Rev.	B
	Calculated flexural stress, f_b, at toe of welds on girder webs or flanges adjacent to welded transverse stiffeners.	T or Rev.	C
	Base metal at end of partial length welded cover plates having square or tapered ends, with or without welds across the ends.	T or Rev.	E
Mechanically fastened connections	Base metal at gross section of high-strength-bolted slip-resistant connections, except bearing-type connections subject to stress reversal and axially loaded joints which induce out-of-plane bending in connected material.	T or Rev.	B
	Base metal at net section of high-strength-bolted bearing-type connections.	T or Rev.	B
	Base metal at net section of riveted and other mechanically fastened joints.	T or Rev.	D

(Continued)

TABLE NO. 27-3-B—(Continued)

GENERAL CONDITION	SITUATION	KIND OF STRESS [1]	STRESS CATEGORY (See Table No. 27-3-C)
Groove welds	Base metal and weld metal at full-penetration groove-welded splices of parts of similar cross section ground flush, with grinding in the direction of applied stress and with weld soundness established by radiographic or ultrasonic inspection.	T or Rev.	B
	Base metal and weld metal in or adjacent to full-penetration groove-welded splices at transitions in width or thickness, with welds ground to provide slopes no steeper than 1 to 2½, with grinding in the direction of applied stress and with weld soundness established by radiographic or ultrasonic inspection.	T or Rev.	B
	Base metal and weld metal in or adjacent to full-penetration groove-welded splices, with or without transitions having slopes no greater than 1 to 2½, when reinforcement is not removed and weld soundness is established by radiographic or ultrasonic inspection in accordance with the requirements of U.B.C. Standard No. 27-6.	T or Rev.	C
	Weld metal or partial-penetration transverse groove welds, based on effective throat area of the weld or welds.	T or Rev.	F

GENERAL CONDITION	SITUATION	KIND OF STRESS[1]	STRESS CATEGORY (See Table No. 27-3-C)
Attachments	Base metal at detail of any length attached by groove welds subject to transverse and/or longitudinal loading when the detail embodies a radiused transition with the weld termination ground smooth. $R \geq 24$ inches 24 inches $> R \geq 6$ inches 6 inches $> R \geq 2$ inches	T or Rev. T or Rev. T or Rev.	B C D
	Base metal at detail of limited length attached by groove weld subject to longitudinal loading with detail length, L, and with no transition or with transition radius less than 2 inches. 2 inches $< L \leq 12t$ or 4 inches $L > 12t$ or 4 inches where t is plate thickness.	T or Rev. T or Rev.	D E
Attachments (cont'd)	Base metal adjacent to a detail of any length in the direction parallel to the stress attached by fillet weld or partial-penetration groove welds when the details embody a radiused transition ≥ 2 inches with weld termination ground smooth. $R > 24$ inches 24 inches $> R \geq 6$ inches 6 inches $> R \geq 2$ inches	T or Rev. T or Rev. T or Rev.	B C D
	Base metal adjacent to a detail of limited length, L, in the direction parallel to the stress attached by fillet weld or partial-penetration groove weld with no transition or with transition radius less than 2 inches. 2 inches $< L \leq 12t$ or 4 inches $L > 12t$ or 4 inches.	T or Rev. R or Rev.	D E
Fillet-welded Connections	Base metal at intermittent fillet welds.	T or Rev.	E

(Continued)

TABLE NO. 27-3-B—(Continued)

GENERAL CONDITION	SITUATION	KIND OF STRESS[1]	STRESS CATEGORY (See Table No. 27-3-C)
Fillet-welded connections (cont'd)	Base metal at junction of axially loaded members with fillet welded end connections. Welds shall be disposed about the axis of the member so as to balance weld stresses.	T or Rev.	E
	Continuous or intermittent longitudinal or transverse fillet welds.	S	F
Miscellaneous details	Base metal at plug or slot welds.	T or Rev.	E
	Shear stress on nominal area of stud-type shear connectors.	S	F
	Shear on plug or slot welds.	S	F
	Base metal at a stud-type shear connector attached by fillet weld.	T or Rev.	C

[1]"T" signifies range in tensile stress only; "Rev." signifies a range involving reversal of tensile or compressive stress; "S" signifies range in shear including shear stress reversal.

TABLE NO. 27-3-C

CATEGORY (FROM TABLE NO. 27-3-B)	ALLOWABLE RANGE OF STRESS, F_{sr} (ksi)			
	Loading Condition 1 F_{sr1}	Loading Condition 2 F_{sr2}	Loading Condition 3 F_{sr3}	Loading Condition 4 F_{sr4}
A[1]	60	36	24	24
B	45	27.5	18	16
C	32	19	13	10[1]
D	27	16	10	7
E	21	12.5	8	5
F	15	12	9	8

[1]Flexural stress range of 12 ksi is permitted at toe of stiffener welds on girder webs or flanges.

UNIFORM BUILDING CODE STANDARD NO. 27-4

OPEN WEB STEEL JOISTS

Based on Standard Specifications of the Steel Joist Institute for Open Web Steel Joists, H Series; K Series; Longspan Steel Joists, LH Series; Deep Longspan Steel Joists, DLH Series; and Joist Girders, 1978 (Including 1986 revisions)

See Sections 2701 (b) and 2715 (a), Uniform Building Code

Part I—H Series

Scope

Sec. 27.401. This part covers the design, manufacture and use of open web steel joists, H Series.

Definition

Sec. 27.402. OPEN WEB STEEL JOISTS, H SERIES, are open web parallel chord load-carrying members suitable for the direct support of floors and roof decks in buildings, utilizing hot-rolled or cold-formed steel, including cold-formed steel whose yield strength has been attained by cold working. They shall be designed in accordance with this part to develop the resisting moments and maximum end reactions shown in Table No. 27-4-A.

The design of chord sections for H-Series joists shall be based on a yield strength of 50,000 psi. The design of web sections for H-Series joists shall be based on a yield strength of either 36,000 psi or 50,000 psi. Steel used for H-Series joist chord or web sections shall have a minimum yield strength determined in accordance with one of the procedures specified in Section 27.403 (b), which is equal to the yield strength assumed in the design.

Materials

Sec. 27.403. (a) **Steel.** The steel used in the manufacture of chord and web sections shall conform to U.B.C. Standard No. 27-1 and be of one of the following: A36; A242; A441; A570; A572, Grade 50; A588, A606, A607, Grade 50; and A611, Grade D, or shall be of suitable quality ordered or produced to other than the listed specifications, provided that such material in the state used for final assembly and fabrication is weldable and is proved by tests performed by the producer or fabricator to have the properties specified in Section 27.403 (b).

(b) **Mechanical Properties.** The yield strength used as a basis for the design stresses prescribed in Section 27.404 shall be either 36,000 psi or 50,000 psi. Evidence that the steel furnished meets or exceeds the design yield strength shall be provided in the form of witnessed or certified test reports.

For material used without consideration of increase in yield strength resulting from cold forming, the specimens shall be taken from as-rolled material. In the case of material, the mechanical properties of which conform to the requirements of one of the listed specifications, test specimens and procedure shall conform to approved standards. In the case of material, the mechanical properties of which do not conform to the requirements of one of the listed specifications, the test specimens and procedure shall conform to the applicable requirements of approved standards and the specimens shall exhibit a yield strength equal to or exceeding the design yield strength and an elongation of not less than: (1) 20 percent in 2 inches for sheet and strip or (2) 18 percent in 8 inches for plates, shapes and bars with adjustments for thickness for plates, shapes and bars as prescribed for A36, A242, A441, A572 and A588, whichever specification is applicable on the basis of design yield strength. The number of tests shall be the same as prescribed in ASTM A6 for plates, shapes and bars; and A570, A606, A607 and A611 for sheet and strip.

If as-formed strength is utilized, the test reports shall show the results of tests performed on full section specimens in accordance with approved standards or the provisions of U.B.C. Standard No. 27-9 and shall indicate compliance with these provisions and with the following additional requirements:

(1) The yield strength measured in the tests shall equal or exceed the design yield strength.

(2) Where tension tests are made for acceptance and control purposes, the tensile strength shall be at least 6 percent greater than the test yield strength of the section.

(3) Where compression tests are used for acceptance and control purposes, the specimen shall withstand a gross shortening of 2 percent of its original length without cracking. The length of specimen shall be not greater than 20 times its least radius of gyration.

(4) If any test specimen fails to pass the requirements of subparagraphs (1), (2) or (3) above, as applicable, two retests shall be made of specimens from the same lot. Failure of one of the retest specimens to meet such requirements shall be the cause for rejection of the lot represented by the specimens.

(c) **Paint.** The standard shop paint shall conform to an approved standard for red oxide paint, or a paint which meets the minimum requirements of such standard.

Design and Manufacture

Sec. 27.404. (a) **Method.** Joists shall be designed in accordance with this part as simply supported uniformly loaded trusses supporting a floor or roof deck so constructed as to brace the top chord of the joists against lateral buckling. Where any applicable design feature is not specifically covered herein, the design shall be in accordance with the requirements of the Uniform Building Code or U.B.C. Standard No. 27-9. Where the requirements in the Uniform Building Code are more restrictive, such requirements shall govern.

(b) **Unit Stresses.** Joists shall have their components so proportioned that the unit stresses in pounds per square inch shall not exceed the following, where F_y is the yield strength defined in Section 27.403 (b).

1. **Tension:**

Chord and web members having a minimum yield strength of 50,000 psi. 30,000

Web members having a minimum yield strength of 36,000 psi 22,000

2. **Compression:**

For members with l/r less than C_c:

$$\frac{\left[1 - \frac{(l/r)^2}{2C_c^2}\right] F_y Q}{\frac{5}{3} + \frac{3}{8}\left(\frac{l/r}{C_c}\right) - \frac{1}{8}\left(\frac{l/r}{C_c}\right)^3} \text{ where } C_c = \sqrt{\frac{2\pi^2 E}{QF_y}} \textit{ and}$$

where Q is a form factor equal to unity except when the width-thickness ratio of one or more elements of the profile exceeds the limits specified in Chapter 27 of the Uniform Building Code for hot-rolled or cold-formed sections.

For members with l/r greater than C_c:

$$\frac{12\pi^2 E}{23\ (l/r)^2}$$

In the above formulas l is taken as the distance between panel points for the chord members and the unbraced length clear of attachments for web members, and r is the corresponding least radius of gyration of the member or any component thereof. E is equal to 29,000,000 psi.

3. **Bending:**

For chords and for web members other than solid rounds having yield strength of

50,000 psi. . . . . 30,000 psi
36,000 psi . . . . 22,000 psi

For web members of solid round cross section having yield strength of

50,000 psi. . . . . 45,000 psi
36,000 psi. . . . . 32,500 psi

For bearing plates having yield strength of

50,000 psi. . . . . 37,500 psi
36,000 psi . . . . 27,000 psi

(c) **Maximum Slenderness Ratios.** The slenderness ratio l/r, where l is as used in Section 27.404 (b) 2 and r is the corresponding least radius of gyration shall not exceed the following:

Top chord interior panels. 90
Top chord end panels. 120
Compression members other than top chord. 200
Tension members. 240

(d) **Members.** 1. **Chords.** The bottom chord shall be designed as an axially loaded tension member.

The top chord shall be designed for only axial compressive stress when the panel length, l, does not exceed 24 inches. When the panel length exceeds 24 inches, the top chord shall be designed as a continuous member subject to combined axial and bending stresses and shall be so proportioned that when fully loaded the quantity

$$\frac{f_a}{0.6F_y} + \frac{f_b}{F_b}$$

does not exceed unity at the panel point and the quantity

$$\frac{f_a}{F_a} + \frac{C_m f_b}{\left(1 - \frac{f_a}{F'_e}\right) F_b Q}$$

does not exceed unity at midpanel; in which

C_m = $1 - 0.3 f_a/F'_e$ for end panels.

C_m = $1 - 0.4 f_a/F'_e$ for interior panels.

f_a = Computed axial unit compressive stress.

f_b = Computed bending unit compressive stress at the point under consideration.

F_a = Permissible axial unit compressive stress based on l/r as defined in Section 27.404 (b) 2.

F_b = Permissible bending unit stress.

F_y = Specified minimum yield strength.

F'_e = $\dfrac{12\pi^2 E}{23\,(l/r_x)^2}$ where l is the panel length as defined in Section 27.404 (b) 2 and r_x is the radius of gyration about the axis of bending.

Q = Form factor as defined in Section 27.404 (b) 2.

The top chord shall be considered as stayed laterally by the floor slab or roof deck when attachments are in accordance with the requirements of Section 27.405 (h) 5.

Lateral stability during erection shall be provided by bridging and the chord properties shall be such that $F_a \geq 10{,}000$ psi, when

$$F_a = \frac{14.15 \times 10^6 C_1 C_2}{hS^2 A_t} \sqrt{(I_t + I_b)(J_t + J_b)S^2 + 25.6 I_t I_b h^2}$$

WHERE:

S = spacing of bridging, inches.

h = effective joist depth, inches.

A_t = area of top chord, square inches.

I_t = moment of inertia of top chord about the vertical axis, inches ^{4}.

I_b = moment of inertia of bottom chord about vertical axis, inches ^{4}.

J_t, J_b = torsion constant of top and bottom chord respectively, inches ^{4}.

The torsion constant of angles or hat-shaped sections is determined by the formula

$$J = \frac{At^2}{3}$$

where A is the cross-sectional area of the member being considered and t is its thickness.

The coefficient $C_1 = 0.85$ for two-piece chord joists and $C_1 = 1.0$ for one-piece chord joists. The coefficient C_2 is given in the following tabulation:

Number of Rows of Bridging	C_2
1	4.00
2	3.00
3	4.00
4	3.33
5	4.00

2. **Web.** The vertical shears to be used in the design of the web members shall be determined from full uniform loading, but such vertical shear shall be not less than 50 percent of the maximum end reaction. Due consideration shall be given to the effect of eccentricity. The effect of combined axial compression and bending may be investigated using the provisions of Section 27.404 (d) 1 letting $C_m = 0.4$ when bending due to eccentricity produces reversed curvature.

3. **Bearings.** The bearing area shall be proportioned so that unit bearing pressure in pounds per square inch does not exceed the following values:

On masonry laid in cement mortar. . . . . 250 psi
On structural concrete. . . . . 750 psi

4. **Extended ends.** Extended ends shall be designed as cantilever beams with their reactions carried back at least to the first interior panel point of the joist.

(e) **Connections.** 1. **Method.** Joint connections and splices shall be made by attaching the members to one another by arc or resistance welding or other approved methods.

2. **Strength.** Joint connections shall be capable of withstanding the forces due to an ultimate load equal to at least two times the design load shown in Table No. 27-4-A.

3. **Splices.** Splices may occur at any point in chord or web members. Members containing a butt weld splice shall develop an ultimate tensile force of at least 57,000 psi times the full design area of the chord or web. The term "member" shall be defined as all component parts comprising the chord or web at the point of the splice.

4. **Eccentricity.** Members connected at a joint shall have their centroidal axes meet at a point, if practical. Otherwise, due consideration shall be given to the effect of eccentricity. In no case shall eccentricity of any web member at a joint exceed three fourths of the overall dimension, measured in the plane of the web, of the largest member connected. Such eccentricity shall be the perpendicular distance from a point at the centroid of the joint located on the centrodal axis of the chord to the centroidal axis of the web member.

Ends of joists shall be proportioned to resist bending produced by eccentricity at the support.

(f) **Design Verification Tests.** 1. **Chord and web members.** Each manufacturer shall, at the time of design review, verify by tests that his design, in accordance with Section 27.404 (a) through (e) of this standard, will provide a minimum factor of safety of 1.65 on the theoretical design capacity of critical members. Such tests shall be evaluated considering the actual yield strength of the members of the test joists.

Material tests for determining mechanical properties of component members may be conducted on full sections.

2. **Joints and connections.** Each manufacturer shall verify by shear tests on representative joints of typical joists that connections will meet the provisions of Section 27.404 (e) 2. Chord and web members may be reinforced for such tests.

(g) **Camber.** Camber is optional with the manufacturer but, when provided, recommended approximate camber is as follows:

TOP CHORD LENGTH	APPROXIMATE CAMBER
20 feet	¼ inch
30 feet	⅜ inch
40 feet	⅝ inch
50 feet	1 inch
60 feet	1½ inches

In no case shall joists be manufactured with negative camber.

(h) **Shop Paint.** Joists and accessories shall receive at least one shop coat of approved paint.

Application

Sec. 27.405. (a) **Usage.** These specifications shall apply to any type of structure where floors and roofs are to be supported directly by steel joists installed as hereinafter specified. Where joists are used other than on simple spans under uniformly distributed loading as specified in Section 27.404 (a), they shall be investigated and modified if necessary to limit the unit stresses to those listed in Section 27.404 (b).

(b) **Span.** The clear span of a joist shall not exceed 24 times its depth.

(c) **End Supports.** 1. **Steel.** Due consideration of the end reactions shall be taken in the design of supporting steel. The ends of joists shall extend a distance of not less than 2½ inches on steel supports. Where it is deemed necessary to butt opposite joists over a narrow steel support with bearing less than noted above, special ends must be specified, and such ends shall have positive attachment to the support, either by bolting or welding.

2. **Masonry and concrete.** The following minimum bearing lengths, parallel to the

length of joists, shall be provided for bearing on masonry and concrete:

MINIMUM BEARING LENGTH

CHORD SIZE	JOIST DEPTH	ON MASONRY	ON CONCRETE
No. 3 through No. 8	8 in. through 24 in.	4 in.	4 in.
No. 8	26 in. through 30 in.	5 in.	4 in.
No. 9	18 in. through 30 in.	5 in.	4 in.
No. 10 and No. 11	18 in. through 30 in.	6 in.	4 in.

(d) **Bridging.** Bridging is required and shall consist of one of the following types:

1. **Horizontal.** Horizontal bridging shall consist of two continuous horizontal steel members, one attached to the top chord and the other attached to the bottom chord. Each attachment to the joists shall be made by welding or mechanical means and shall be capable of resisting a horizontal force of not less than 700 pounds.

The ratio of unbraced length to least radius of gyration (l/r) of the bridging member shall not exceed 300, where l is the distance in inches between attachments and r is the least radius of gyration of the bridging member. If the bridging member is a round bar, the diameter shall be at least ½ inch.

2. **Diagonal.** Diagonal bridging shall consist of cross bracing with l/r ratio of not more than 200, where l is the distance in inches between connections and r is the least radius of gyration of the bracing member. Where cross bracing members are connected at their point of intersection, the l distance shall be taken as the distance in inches between connections at the point of intersection of the bracing members and the connections to the chord of the joists. Connections to chords of steel joists shall be made by positive mechanical means or by welding.

3. **Quantity.** In no case shall the number of rows of bridging be less than shown in the following table. Spaces between rows shall be approximately uniform.

NUMBER OF ROWS OF BRIDGING

CHORD SIZE[1]	ONE ROW	TWO ROWS	THREE ROWS	FOUR ROWS	FIVE ROWS[2]
#3	Up to 13′	13′ to 17′	17′ to 28′		
#4	Up to 16′	16′ to 21′	21′ to 32′		
#5	Up to 16′	16′ to 21′	21′ to 33′	33′ to 38′	38′ to 40′
#6	Up to 18′	18′ to 22′	22′ to 36′	36′ to 40′	40′ to 48′
#7	Up to 20′	20′ to 25′	25′ to 41′	41′ to 46′	46′ to 48′
#8	Up to 21′	21′ to 27′	27′ to 43′	43′ to 48′	48′ to 60′
#9	Up to 23′	23′ to 30′	30′ to 46′	46′ to 52′	52′ to 60′
#10	Up to 24′	24′ to 30′	30′ to 47′	47′ to 53′	53′ to 60′
#11	Up to 24′	24′ to 31′	31′ to 48′	48′ to 55′	55′ to 60′

[1]Last digit of joist designation shown in load table.

[2]Where five rows of bridging are required and spans are over 40 feet, the middle row shall be diagonal bridging with bolted connections at chords and intersection.

(e) **Installation of Bridging.** All bridging and bridging anchors shall be completely installed before construction loads are placed on the joists.

Bridging shall support the top chords against lateral movement during the construction period and shall hold the steel joists in the approximate position as shown on the plans.

The ends of all bridging lines terminating at walls or beams shall be anchored thereto at top and bottom chords.

(f) **End Anchorage.** 1. **Masonry supports.** Joists resting on masonry supports shall be bedded in mortar and anchored thereto with an anchor equivalent to a ⅜-inch round steel bar not less than 8 inches long. Every third joist in floors and every joist in roofs shall be anchored. In roofs where parapet walls are not present, two ½-inch anchor bolts or other equal means shall be used in lieu of the steel bar.

2. **Steel supports.** Ends of joists resting on steel supports shall be connected thereto with the equivalent of two ⅛-inch fillet welds 1 inch long or a ½-inch bolt. In steel framing, where columns are not framed in at least two directions with structural steel members, joists at column lines shall be field bolted at the columns to add lateral stability.

3. **Uplift.** Where uplift forces are a design consideration, roof joists shall be anchored to resist such forces.

(g) **Joist Spacing.** Joists shall be spaced so that the loading on each joist does not exceed the allowable load for the particular joist design.

(h) **Floors and Roof Decks.** 1. **Material.** Floors and roof decks may consist of cast-in-place or precast concrete or gypsum, formed steel, wood or other suitable material capable of supporting the required load at the specified joist spacing.

2. **Thickness.** Cast-in-place slabs shall be not less than 2 inches thick.

3. **Centering.** Centering for cast-in-place slabs may be ribbed metal lath, corrugated steel sheets, paperbacked welded wire fabric, removable centering or any other suitable material capable of supporting the slab at the designated joist spacing. Centering shall not cause lateral displacement or damage to the top chord of joists during installation or removal of the centering or placing of the concrete.

4. **Bearing.** Slabs or decks shall bear uniformly along the top chords of the joists.

5. **Attachments.** Each attachment for slab or deck to top chords of joists shall be capable of resisting a lateral force of not less than 300 pounds and not less than that required by Chapter 23 of the Uniform Building Code. The spacing shall not exceed 36 inches along the top chord.

6. **Wood nailers.** Where wood nailers are used, such nailers in conjunction with deck or slab shall be attached to the top chords of the joists in conformance with Section 27.405 (h) 5.

(i) **Deflection.** The deflection due to the design live load shall not exceed the following:

Floors:	1/360 of span
Roofs:	1/360 of span where a plaster ceiling is attached or suspended
	1/240 of span for all other cases

(j) **Ponding.** Unless a roof surface is provided with sufficient slope toward points of free drainage or adequate individual drains to prevent the accumulation of rain water, the roof system shall be investigated to assure stability under ponding conditions in accordance with the Uniform Building Code and U.B.C. Standard No. 25-15 or 27-14.

(k) **Inspection.** Joists shall be inspected by the manufacturer before shipment to ensure compliance of materials and workmanship with the requirements of this standard.

(l) **Uplift.** Where uplift forces due to wind are a design requirement, these forces shall be indicated on the contract drawings in terms of net uplift in pounds per square foot. When these forces are specified, they shall be considered in the design of joists and bridging or both.

Handling and Erection

Sec. 27.406. Care shall be exercised at all times to avoid damage through careless handling during unloading, storing and erecting.

As soon as joists are erected, all bridging shall be completely installed and the joists permanently fastened into place before the application of any loads except the weight of the erectors. Many joists exhibit some degree of lateral instability under the weight of an erector until bridging is installed. Therefore, where three or more rows of bridging are required by Section 27.405 (d) 3, caution shall be exercised by the erector until all bridging is completely and properly installed.

Where five rows of bridging are required in spans of over 40 feet, each joist shall be adequately braced laterally before the next joist is erected and before any loads are applied. Hoisting cables shall not be released until support has been provided by the center row of diagonal bridging and the bridging line has been anchored to prevent lateral movement and, where joists are bottom bearing, their ends have been restrained laterally.

During the construction period means for adequate distribution of concentrated loads shall be provided so that the carrying capacity of any joist is not exceeded.

Field welding shall not damage the joists. The total length of weld at any one point on cold-formed members whose yield strength has been attained by cold working and whose as-formed strength is used in the design shall not exceed 50 percent of the overall developed width of the cold-formed section.

Part II—K Series

Scope

Sec. 27.420. These specifications cover the design, manufacture and use of Open Web Steel Joists, K Series.

Definition

Sec. 27.421. The term "Open Web Steel Joists K Series," as used herein, refers to open-web, parallel-chord, load-carrying members suitable for the direct support of floors and roof decks in buildings, utilizing hot-rolled or cold-formed steel, including cold-formed steel whose yield strength has been attained by cold working. They shall be designed in accordance with this part to support the uniformly distributed loads shown in Table No. 27-4-B.

The design of chord sections for K-Series joists shall be based on a yield strength of 50,000 psi. The design of web sections for K-Series joists shall be based on a yield strength of either 36,000 psi or 50,000 psi. Steel used for K-Series joist chord or web sections shall have a minimum yield strength determined in accordance with one of the procedures specified in Section 27.422 (b), which is equal to the yield strength assumed in the design.

Materials

Sec. 27.422. (a) **Steel.** The steel used in the manufacture of chord and web sections shall conform to one of the following: A 36; A 242; A 441; A 570; A 572, Grade 50; A 588; A 606; A 607, Grade 50; and A 611, Grade D, or shall be of suitable quality ordered or produced to other than the listed specifications, provided that such material in the state used for final assembly and fabrication is weldable and is proved by tests performed by the producer or fabricator to have the properties specified in Section 27.422 (b).

(b) **Mechanical Properties.** The yield strength used as a basis for the design stresses prescribed in Section 27.410 shall be either 36,000 psi or 50,000 psi. Evidence that the steel furnished meets or exceeds the design yield strength shall, if requested, be provided in the form of an affidavit or by witnessed or certified test reports.

For material used without consideration of increase in yield strength resulting from cold forming, the specimens shall be taken from as-rolled material. In the case of material the mechanical properties of which conform to the requirements of one of the listed specifications, test specimens and procedures shall conform to approved standards. In the case of material the mechanical properties of which do not conform to the requirements of one of the listed specifications, the test specimens and procedures shall conform to the applicable requirements of approved standards, and the specimens shall exhibit a yield strength equal to or exceeding the design yield strength and an elongation of not less than (a) 20 percent in 2 inches for sheet and strip, or (b) 18 percent in 8 inches for plates, shapes and bars with adjustments for thickness for plates, shapes and bars as prescribed for A 36, A 242, A 441, A 572 and A 588, whichever specification is applicable on the basis of design yield strength.

If as-formed strength is utilized, the test reports shall show the results of tests performed on full-section specimens in accordance with the provisions of U.B.C. Standard No. 27-9 and shall indicate compliance with these provisions and with the following additional requirements:

1. The yield strength measured in the tests shall equal or exceed the design yield strength.
2. Where tension tests are made for acceptance and control purposes, the tensile strength shall be at least 6 percent greater than the yield strength of the section.
3. Where compression tests are used for acceptance and control purposes, the specimen shall withstand a gross shortening of 2 percent of its original length without cracking. The length of the specimen shall not be greater than 20 times its least radius of gyration.
4. If any test specimen fails to pass the requirements of the Items 1, 2 or 3 above, as applicable, two retests shall be made of specimens from the same lot. Failure of one of the retest specimens to meet such requirements shall be the cause for rejection of the lot represented by the specimens.

(c) **Paint.** The standard shop paint shall conform to an approved standard for red oxide paint, or paint which meets the minimum performance requirements of such standard.

Design and Manufacture

Sec. 27.423. (a) **Method.** Joists shall be designed in accordance with this part as simply supported, uniformly loaded trusses supporting a floor or roof deck so constructed as to brace the top chord of the joists against lateral buckling. Where any applicable design feature is not specifically covered herein, the design shall be in accordance with the requirements of the Uniform Building Code or U.B.C. Standard No. 27-9. Where the requirements in the Uniform Building Code are more restrictive, such requirements shall govern.

(b) **Unit Stresses.** Joists shall have their components so proportioned that the unit stresses in pounds per square inch shall not exceed the following where F_y is the yield strength defined in section 27.422 (b).

1. **Tension:**

Chords

F_y = 50,000 psi . . . . F_t = 30,000 psi

Webs

F_y = 50,000 psi . . . . F_t = 30,000 psi

F_y = 36,000 psi . . . . F_t = 22,000 psi

2. **Compression:**

For members with l/r less than C_c:

$$F_a = \frac{\left[1 - \frac{(l/r)^2}{2C_c^2}\right] QF_y}{\frac{5}{3} + \frac{3}{8}\left(\frac{l/r}{C_c}\right) - \frac{1}{8}\left(\frac{l/r}{C_c}\right)^3} \quad \text{where } C_c = \sqrt{\frac{2\pi^2 E}{QF_y}} \text{ and}$$

where Q is a form factor equal to unity except when the width-thickness ratio of one or more elements of the profile exceeds the limits specified in Chapter 27 of the Uniform Building Code for hot-rolled sections or cold-formed sections.

For members with l/r greater than C_c:

$$F_a = \frac{12\pi^2 E}{23\ (l/r)^2}$$

In the above formulas, l is taken as the distance between panel points for the chord members and the unbraced length clear of attachments for web members, and r is the corresponding least radius of gyration of the member or any component thereof. E is equal to 29,000,000 ksi.

3. **Bending:**

For chords

F_y = 50,000 psi .... F_b = 30,000 psi

For web members other than solid rounds

F_y = 50,000 psi .... F_b = 30,000 psi

F_y = 36,000 psi .... F_b = 22,000 psi

For web members of solid round cross section

F_y = 50,000 psi .... F_b = 45,000 psi

F_y = 36,000 psi .... F_b = 32,500 psi

For bearing plates

F_y = 50,000 psi .... F_b = 37,500 psi

F_y = 36,000 psi .... F_b = 27,000 psi

(c) **Maximum Slenderness Ratios.** The slenderness ratio, l/r where l is as used in Section 27.423 (b) 1 and r is the corresponding least radius of gyration, shall not exceed the following:

Top chord interior panels 90

Top chord end panels 120

Compression members other than top chord 200

Tension members 240

(d) **Members.** 1. **Chords.** The bottom chord shall be designed as an axially loaded tension member.

The top chord shall be designed for only axial compressive stress when the panel length, l, does not exceed 24 inches. When the panel length exceeds 24 inches, the top chord shall be designed as a continuous member subject to combined axial and bending stresses and shall be so proportioned that:

$$f_a + f_b \leq 0.6\,F_y, \text{ at the panel point; and}$$

$$\frac{f_a}{F_a} + \frac{C_m f_b}{\left(1 - \frac{f_a}{F'_e}\right) Q F_b} \leq 1.0, \text{ at mid-panel; in which}$$

C_m = $1\text{-}0.3 f_a / F'_e$ for end panels

C_m = $1\text{-}0.4 f_a / F'_e$ for interior panels

f_a = computed axial unit compressive stress

f_b = computed bending unit compressive stress at the point under consideration

F_a = permissible axial unit compressive stress based on l/r as defined in Section 27.423 (b) 2

F_b = permissible bending unit stress

F_y = specified minimum yield strength

$F'_e = \dfrac{12\pi^2 E}{23\,(l/r_x)^2}$ where l is the panel length as defined in Section 27.423 (b) 2 and r_x is the radius of gyration about the axis of bending.

Q = form factor as defined in Section 27.423 (b) 2

In order to ensure lateral stability during erection, the radius of gyration of the top chord about its vertical axis shall be not less than $l/145$ where l is the spacing in inches between lines of bridging as specified in Section 27.424 (d) 3.

The top chord shall be considered as stayed laterally by the floor slab or roof deck when attachments are in accordance with the requirements of Section 27.424 (h) 5.

2. **Web.** The vertical shears to be used in the design of the web members shall be determined from full uniform loading, but such vertical shears shall not be less than 25 percent of the end reaction. Due consideration shall be given to the effect of eccentricity. The effect of combined axial compression and bending may be investigated using the provisions of Section 27.423 (d) 1, letting $C_m = 0.4$ when bending due to eccentricity produces reversed curvature.

Interior vertical web members used in modified Warren-type web systems shall be designed to resist the gravity loads supported by the members plus one half of 1.0 percent of the top chord axial force.

3. **Extended ends.** Extended top chords or full-depth cantilever ends require the special attention of the specifying engineer or architect.

The magnitude and location of the design loads to be supported, the deflection requirements and the proper bracing shall be clearly indicated on the structural drawings.

(e) **Connections.** 1. **Methods.** Joint connections and splices shall be made by attaching the members to one another by arc or resistance welding or other approved method.

2. **Welding connections.** A. Selected welds shall be inspected visually by the manufacturer. Prior to this inspection, weld slag shall be removed.

B. Cracks are not acceptable and shall be repaired.

C. Thorough fusion shall exist between weld and base metal for the required design length of the weld; such fusion shall be verified by visual inspection.

D. Unfilled weld craters shall not be included in the design length of the weld.

E. Undercut shall not exceed $^{1}/_{16}$ inch provided it is oriented parallel to the principle stress.

F. The sum of surface (piping) porosity diameters shall not exceed $^{1}/_{16}$ inch in any 1 inch of design weld length.

G. Weld spatter that does not interfere with paint coverage is acceptable.

3. **Welding program.** Manufacturers shall have a program for establishing weld procedures and operator qualification, and for weld sampling and testing.

4. **Strength.** Joint connections shall be capable of withstanding forces due to an ultimate load equal to at least two times the design load shown in the applicable Standard Load Table.

5. **Splices.** Splices may occur at any point in chord or web members. Members containing a butt weld splice shall develop an ultimate tensile force of at least 57,000 psi times the full design area of the chord or web. The term "member" shall be defined as all component parts comprising the chord or web, at the point of splice.

6. **Eccentricity.** Members connected at a joint shall have their centroidal axes meet at a point if practical. Otherwise, due consideration shall be given to the effect of eccentricity. In no case shall eccentricity of any web member at a joint exceed three fourths of the overall dimension, measured in the plane of the web of the largest member connected. The eccentricity of any web member shall be the perpendicular distance from the centroidal axis of that web member to the point on the centroidal axis of the chord which is vertically above or below the intersection of the centroidal axes of the web members forming the joint. Ends of joists shall be proportioned to resist bending produced by eccentricity at the support.

(f) **Design Verification Tests.** 1. **Chord and web members.** Each manufacturer shall, at the time of design review, verify by tests that the design, in accordance with Section 24.423 (a) through (e) of this standard, will provide a minimum factor of safety of 1.65 on the theoretical design capacity of critical members. Such tests shall be evaluated considering the actual yield strength of the members of the test joists.

Material tests for determining mechanical properties of component members shall be conducted on full sections.

2. **Joints and connections.** Each manufacturer shall verify by shear tests on representative joints of typical joists that connections will meet the provision of Section 27.423 (e). Chord and web members may be reinforced for such tests.

(g) **Camber.** Unless specified by the engineer, camber is as follows;

TOP CHORD LENGTH	APPROXIMATE CAMBER
20 feet	$^1/_4$ inch
30 feet	$^3/_8$ inch
40 feet	$^5/_8$ inch
50 feet	1 inch
60 feet	$1^1/_2$ inches

In no case will joists be manufactured with negative camber.

(h) **Shop Paint**. Joists and accessories shall receive one shop coat of paint in accordance with Section 27.422 (c).

Application

Sec. 27.424. (a) **Usage.** This section shall apply to any type of structure where floors and roofs are to be supported directly by steel joists installed as hereinafter specified. Where joists are used other than on simple spans under uniformly distributed loading as prescribed in Section 27.423 (a), they shall be investigated and modified if necessary to limit the unit stresses to those listed in Section 27.423 (b).

(b) **Span.** The span of a joist shall not exceed 24 times its depth.

(c) **End Supports.** 1. **Masonry and concrete.** Due consideration of the end reactions and all other vertical and lateral forces shall be taken in the design of any masonry or concrete support. The ends of K-Series joists should extend a distance of not less than 4 inches over masonry or concrete supports and be attached to a steel bearing plate. This plate is to be located not more than 1/2 inch from the face of the wall and is to be not less than 6 inches wide perpendicular to the length of the joists. It is to be designed by the specifying engineer or architect in compliance with the allowable unit bending stresses in Section 27.423 (b) and the allowable unit bearing pressure in accordance with Chapter 27 of the Uniform Building Code.

2. **Steel.** Due consideration of the end reactions on all other vertical and lateral forces shall be taken in the design of the steel support. The ends of K-Series joists shall extend a distance of not less than 21/2 inches over the steel supports. Where it is deemed necessary to butt opposite joists over a narrow steel support with bearing less than that noted above, special ends must be specified, and such ends shall have positive attachment to the support, either by bolting or welding.

(d) **Bridging.** Bridging is required and shall consist of one of the following types:

1. **Horizontal.** Horizontal bridging shall consist of two continuous horizontal steel

members, one attached to the top chord and the other attached to the bottom chord. Each attachment to the joists shall be made by welding or mechanical means and shall be capable of resisting a horizontal force of not less than 700 pounds.

The ratio of unbraced length to least radius of gyration (l/r) of the bridging member shall not exceed 300, where l is the distance in inches between attachments and r is the least radius of gyration of the bridging member. If the bridging member is a round bar, the diameter shall be at least 1/2 inch.

2. **Diagonal.** Diagonal bridging shall consist of cross bracing with l/r ratio of not more than 200, where l is the distance in inches between connections and r is the least radius of gyration of the bracing member. Where cross-bracing members are connected at their point of intersection, the l distance shall be taken as the distance in inches between connections at the point of intersection of the bracing members and the connections to the chord of the joists. Connections to the chords of steel joists shall be made by positive mechanical means or by welding.

3. **Quantity.** In no case shall the number of rows of bridging be less than shown in the following table.

NUMBER OF ROWS OF BRIDGING
Distances are Span Lengths[1]
(See "Definition of Span" in front of load table)

SECTION NUMBER[2]	ONE ROW	TWO ROWS	THREE ROWS	FOUR ROWS[2]	FIVE ROWS[3]
1	Up through 16′	Over 16′ through 24′	Over 24′ through 28′		
2	Up through 17′	Over 17′ through 25′	Over 25′ through 32′		
3	Up through 18′	Over 18′ through 28′	Over 28′ through 38′	Over 38′ through 40′	
4	Up through 19′	Over 19′ through 28′	Over 28′ through 38′	Over 38′ through 48′	
5	Up through 19′	Over 19′ through 29′	Over 29′ through 39′	Over 39′ through 50′	Over 50′ through 52′
6	Up through 19′	Over 19′ through 29′	Over 29′ through 39′	Over 39′ through 51′	Over 51′ through 56′
7	Up through 20′	Over 20′ through 33′	Over 33′ through 45′	Over 45′ through 58′	Over 58′ through 60′
8	Up through 20′	Over 20′ through 33′	Over 33′ through 45′	Over 45′ through 58′	Over 58′ through 60′
9	Up through 20′	Over 20′ through 33′	Over 33′ through 46′	Over 46′ through 59′	Over 59′ through 60′
10	Up through 20′	Over 20′ through 37′	Over 37′ through 51′	Over 51′ through 60′	
11	Up through 20′	Over 20′ through 38′	Over 38′ through 53′	Over 53′ through 60′	
12	Up through 20′	Over 20′ through 39′	Over 39′ through 53′	Over 53′ through 60′	

[1]Span length:

a) Center line to center line of beams (or girders) when joist is supported by steel members.

b) Clear span plus 8 inches when joist is supported by masonry.

c) Center line of beam (or girder) to face of masonry support plus 4 inches when joist is supported by steel members on one end and by masonry on the other end.

[2]Where four or five rows of bridging are required, a row nearest the midspan of the joist shall be diagonal bridging with bolted connections at chords and intersection.

[3]Last digit of joist designation shown in load tables.

Spaces between rows shall be approximately uniform. See Section 27.424 (k) for bridging required for uplift forces.

(e) **Installation of Bridging.** All bridging and bridging anchors shall be completely installed before construction loads are placed on the joists.

Bridging shall support the top chords against lateral movement during the construction period and shall hold the steel joists in the approximate position as shown on the plans.

The ends of all bridging lines terminating at walls or beams shall be anchored thereto.

(f) **End Anchorage.** 1. **Masonry and concrete.** Ends of K-Series joists resting on steel bearing plates on masonry or structural concrete shall be attached thereto with a minimum of two $^1/_8$-inch fillet welds 1 inch long, or with a $^1/_2$-inch bolt.

2. **Steel.** Ends of K-Series joists resting on steel supports shall be attached thereto with a minimum of two $^1/_8$-inch fillet welds 1 inch long, or with a $^1/_2$-inch bolt. In steel frames, where columns are not framed in at least two directions with structural steel members, joists at column lines shall be field bolted at the columns to provide lateral stability during construction.

3. **Uplift.** Where uplift forces are a design consideration, roof joists shall be anchored to resist such forces.

(g) **Joist Spacing.** Joists shall be spaced so that the loading on each joist does not exceed the allowable load for the particular joist design.

(h) **Floor and Roof Decks.** 1. **Material.** Floors and roof decks may consist of cast-in-place or precast concrete or gypsum, formed steel, wood or other suitable material capable of supporting the required load at the specified joist spacing.

2. **Thickness.** Cast-in-place slabs shall be not less than 2 inches thick.

3. **Centering.** Centering for cast-in-place slabs may be ribbed metal lath, corrugated steel sheets, paperbacked welded wire fabric, removable centering or any other suitable material capable of supporting the slab at the designated joist spacing. Centering shall not cause lateral displacement or damage to the top chord of joists during installation or removal of the centering or placing of the concrete.

4. **Bearing.** Slabs or decks shall bear uniformly along the top chords of the joists.

5. **Attachments.** Each attachment for slab or deck to top chords of joists shall be capable of resisting a lateral force of not less than 300 pounds. The spacing shall not exceed 36 inches along the top chord.

6. **Wood nailers.** Where wood nailers are used, such nailers in conjunction with deck or slab shall be attached to the top chords of the joists in conformance with Section 27.424 (h) 5.

(i) **Deflection.** The deflection due to the design live load shall not exceed the following:

Floors: $^1/_{360}$ span.

Roofs: $^1/_{360}$ of span where a plaster ceiling is attached or suspended.

$^1/_{240}$ of span for all other cases.

(j) **Ponding.** Unless a roof surface is provided with sufficient slope toward points of free drainage or adequate individual drains to prevent the accumulation of rain water, the roof system shall be investigated to assure stability under ponding conditions in accordance with the Uniform Building Code and U.B.C. Standard No. 27-14 or 27-15.

(k) **Uplift.** Where uplift forces due to wind are a design requirement, these forces must be indicated on the contract drawings in terms of net uplift in pounds per square foot. When these forces are specified, they must be considered in the design of joists and/or bridging. A single line of bottom chord bridging must be provided near the first bottom chord panel points whenever uplift due to wind forces is a design consideration.

(l) **Inspection.** Joists shall be inspected by the manufacturer before shipment to ensure compliance of materials and workmanship with the requirements of this standard.

(m) **Handling and Erection.** Care shall be exercised at all times to avoid damage through careless handling during unloading, storing and erecting.

As soon as joists are erected, all bridging shall be completely installed and the joists permanently fastened into place before the application of any loads except the weight of the erectors. When three or more rows of bridging are required by the table in Section 27.424 (d) 3, caution shall be exercised by the erectors until all bridging is completely and properly installed.

Where four or five rows of bridging are required, each joist shall be adequately braced laterally before the next joist is erected and before any loads are applied. Hoisting cables shall not be released until support has been provided by a row of diagonal bridging nearest the mid-span of the joist, and the bridging line has been anchored to prevent lateral movement; where joists are bottom bearing, their ends shall be restrained laterally.

During the construction period, the contractor shall provide means for adequate distribution of concentrated loads so that the carrying capacity of any joist is not exceeded.

Field welding shall not damage the joists. The total length of weld at any one point on cold-formed members which yield strength has been attained by cold working, and whose as-formed strength is used in the design, shall not exceed 50 percent of the overall developed width of the cold-formed section.

Part III—Longspan Steel Joists, LH Series, and Deep Longspan Steel Joists, DLH Series

Scope

Sec. 27.430. This part covers the design, manufacture and use of longspan steel joists, LH Series, and deep longspan steel joists, DLH Series.

Definition

Sec. 27.431. LONGSPAN STEEL JOISTS, LH SERIES, AND DEEP LONGSPAN STEEL JOISTS, DLH SERIES, are open-web load-carrying members utilizing hot-rolled or cold-formed steel, including cold-formed steel whose yield strength has been attained by cold working. LH Series are suitable for the direct support of floors and roof decks in buildings and DLH Series are suitable for the direct support of roof decks in buildings.

The design of LH- and DLH-Series joist chord or web sections shall be based on a yield strength of at least 36,000 psi but not greater than 50,000 psi. Steel used for LH- and DLH-Series joist chord or web sections shall have a minimum yield strength determined in accordance with one of the procedures specified in the Uniform Building Code, which is equal to the yield strength assumed in the design. LH- and DLH-Series joists shall be designed in accordance with this part to support the loads given in Table No. 27-4-C and Table No. 27-4-D.

Materials

Sec. 27.432. (a) **Steel.** The steel used in the manufacture of chord and web sections shall conform to U.B.C. Standard No. 27-1 and be of one of the following: A36; A242; A441; A570; A572, Grades 42, 45 and 50; A588; A606; A607, Grades 45 and 50; or A611, Grade D, or shall be of suitable quality ordered or produced to other than the listed specifications, provided that such material in the state used for final assembly and fabrication is weldable and is proved by tests performed by the producer or fabricator to have the properties specified in Section 27.432 (b).

(b) **Mechanical Properties.** Mechanical properties shall be as specified in Section 27.403 (b).

(c) **Welding Electrodes.** The following electrodes shall be used for arc welding:

1. For connected members both having a specified minimum yield strength greater than 36,000 psi:

   AWS A5.1 or A5.5, E70XX

   AWS A5.17, F7X-EXXX flux-electrode combination

   AWS A5.18, E70S-X or E70U-1

   AWS A5.20, E70T-X

2. For connected members both having a specified minimum yield strength of 36,000 psi, or one having a specified minimum yield strength of 36,000 psi and the other having a specified minimum yield strength greater than 36,000 psi:

   AWS A5.1, E60XX

   AWS A5.17, F6X-EXXX flux-electrode combination

   AWS A5.20, 60T-X

   or any of those listed in Item 1 above.

Other welding methods, providing equivalent strength as demonstrated by tests, may be used.

(d) **Paint.** The standard shop paint shall conform to an approved standard for red oxide paint or a paint which meets the minimum requirements of such standard.

Design and Manufacture

Sec. 27.433. (a) **Method.** Joists shall be designed as specified in Section 27.404 (a) except as provided in this section.

(b) **Unit Stresses.** Joists shall have their components so proportioned that the unit stresses in pounds per square inch shall not exceed the following where F_y is the yield strength defined in Section 27.403 (b).

1. **Tension:** All members. . . . . $0.6\ F_y$
2. **Compression:**

For members with Kl/r less than C_c:

$$\frac{\left[1-\frac{(Kl/r)^2}{2C_c^{\,2}}\right]F_yQ}{\frac{5}{3}+\frac{3\,(Kl/r)}{8C_c}-\frac{(Kl/r)^3}{8C_c^{\,3}}} \quad \text{where } C_c=\sqrt{\frac{2\pi^2E}{QF_y}} \text{ and}$$

where Q is a form factor equal to unity except when the width-thickness ratio of one or more elements of the profile exceeds the limits specified in Chapter 27 of the Uniform Building Code for hot-rolled or cold-formed sections, and where K is a length factor used to determine the effective slenderness ratio as shown in Table No. 27-4-E.

For members with Kl/r greater than C_c:

$$\frac{12\pi^2E}{23(Kl/r)^2}$$

In the above formulas Kl/r is the appropriate effective slenderness ratio as determined from Section 27.433 (c).

3. **Bending:**

For chords, and for web members other than solid rounds . . . . $0.6F_y$

For web members of solid round cross section . . . . $0.9F_y$

For bearing plates . . . . $0.75F_y$

4. **Weld stresses:**

Shear at throat of fillet welds:

Made with E70 series electrodes or F7X-EXXX flux-electrode combinations . . . . 21,000 psi

Made with E60 series electrodes or F6X-EXXX flux-electrode combinations . . . . 18,000 psi

Tension or compression on groove or butt welds shall be the same as those specified for the connected material.

(c) **Maximum Slenderness Ratios.** The slenderness ratios, $1.0\ l/r$ and $1.0\ l_s/r$, of members as a whole or any component part shall not exceed the values given in Table No. 27-4-E, Part A.

The effective slenderness ratio, Kl/r, to be used in calculating the allowable stresses F_a and F'_e is the largest value as determined from Table No. 27-4-E, Parts B and C.

In compression members when fillers or ties are used, they shall be spaced so that the l_s/r_z ratio of each component does not exceed the governing l/r ratio of the member as a whole. The terms are defined as follows:

l = length center-to-center of panel points, except l = 36 inches for calculating l/r_y of top chord member.

l_s = maximum length center-to-center between panel point and filler (tie), or between adjacent fillers (ties).

r_x = member radius of gyration in the plane of the joist.

r_y = member radius of gyration out of the plane of the joist.

r_z = least radius of gyration of a member component.

(d) **Members.** 1. **Chords.** The bottom chord shall be designed as an axially loaded tension member.

The top chord shall be designed as a continuous member subject to combined axial and bending stresses and shall be so proportioned that when fully loaded the quantity

$$f_a + f_b$$

does not exceed $0.6F_y$ at the panel point, and the quantity

$$\frac{f_a}{F_a} + \frac{C_m f_b}{\left(1 - \frac{f_a}{F'_e}\right) F_b Q}$$

does not exceed unity at midpanel; in which

$C_m = 1 - 0.3f_a/F'_e$ for end panels.

$C_m = 1 - 0.4f_a/F'_e$ for interior panels.

f_a = computed axial unit compressive stress.
f_b = computed bending unit compressive stress at the point under consideration.
F_a = permissible axial unit compressive stress based on Kl/r.
F_b = permissible bending unit stress; $0.6F_y$.

$$F'_e = \frac{12\pi^2 E}{23\,(Kl/r_x)^2}$$

r_x = radius of gyration about the axis of bending.
Q = form factor as defined in Section 27.433 (b) 2.

The radius of gyration of the top chord about its vertical axis shall be not less than $l/170$ where l is the spacing in inches between lines of bridging as specified in Section 27.434 (e) 2.

The top chord shall be considered as stayed laterally by the floor or roof deck, provided the requirements of Section 27.434 (i) of this standard are met.

2. **Web.** The vertical shears to be used in the design of the web members shall be determined from full uniform loading but such vertical shear shall be not less than 25 percent of the end reaction. Interior vertical web members used in modified Warren-type web systems shall be designed to resist the gravity loads supported by the member plus 0.5 percent of the top chord axial force.

3. **Depth.** Joists may have either parallel chords or a top chord slope of 1/8 inch per foot. The depth, for the purpose of design, in all cases shall be the depth at midspan.

4. **Eccentricity.** Members connected at a joint shall have their center of gravity lines meet at a point, if practical. Eccentricity on either side of the neutral axis of chord members may be neglected when it does not exceed the distance between the neutral axis and the back of the chord. Otherwise, provision shall be made for the stresses due to eccentricity. Ends of joists shall be proportioned to resist bending produced by eccentricity at the support.

In those cases where a single angle compression member is attached to the outside of the stem of a tee or double-angle chord, due consideration shall be given to eccentricity.

5. The magnitude and location of the design loads to be supported, the deflection requirements and the proper bracing shall be clearly indicated on the structural drawings.

(e) **Connections.** 1. **Method.** Joint connections and splices shall be made by attaching the members to one another by arc or resistance welding, bolting or other approved method.

2. **Strength.** Joint connections shall develop the maximum force due to any of the design loads, but not less than 50 percent of the allowable strength of the member in tension or compression, whichever is the controlling factor in the selection of the member.

3. **Shop splices.** Shop splices may occur at any point in chord or web members. Splice shall be designed for the member force but not less than 50 percent of the allowable member strength. Members containing a butt weld splice shall develop an ultimate tensile force of at least 57,000 psi times the full design area of the chord or web. The term "member" shall be defined as all component parts, comprising the chord or web, at the point of splice.

4. **Field splices.** Field splices shall be designed by the manufacturer and may be either bolted or welded. Splices shall develop the design stress but not less than 50 percent of the allowable strength of the member.

(f) **Camber.** Joists shall have approximate cambers in accordance with the following:

TOP CHORD LENGTH	APPROXIMATE CAMBER	TOP CHORD LENGTH	APPROXIMATE CAMBER
20′-0″	1/4″	90′-0″	3 1/2″
30′-0″	3/8″	100′-0″	4 1/4″
40′-0″	5/8″	110′-0″	5″
50′-0″	1″	120′-0″	6″
60′-0″	1 1/2″	130′-0″	7″
70′-0″	2″	140′-0″	8″
80′-0″	2 3/4″	144′-0″	8 1/2″

(g) **Shop Painting.** Joists and accessories shall receive at least one shop coat of approved protective paint.

Application

Sec. 27.434. (a) **Usage.** This section shall apply to any type of structure where floors and roof decks are to be supported directly by steel joists installed as hereinafter specified. Where joists are used other than on simple spans under uniformly distributed loading, as specified in Section 27.433 (a), they shall be investigated and modified if necessary to limit the unit stresses to those listed in Section 27.433 (b). If a rigid connection of the bottom chord is to be made to the column or other support, it shall be made only after the application of the dead loads. The joist system must be investigated for continuous frame action by the specifying engineer or architect.

(b) **Span.** The clear span of joists shall not exceed 24 times their nominal depth.

(c) **Depth.** The nominal depth of sloping chord joists shall be the depth at midspan. The standard slope of the top chord shall be 1/8 inch per foot.

(d) **End Supports.** 1. **Masonry and concrete.** Due consideration of the end reactions and all other vertical and lateral forces shall be taken by the specifying engineer or architect in the design of any masonry or concrete support. The ends of LH- or DLH-Series joists should extend a distance of not less than 6 inches over masonry or concrete supports and be attached to a steel bearing plate. This plate is to be located not more than 1/2 inch from the face of the wall and is to be not less than 9 inches wide perpendicular to the length of the joists. It shall be designed in compliance with the allowable unit bending stresses in Section 27.433 (b) and the allowable unit bearing pressures in Chapter 27.

2. **Steel.** Due consideration of the end reactions an all other vertical and lateral forces shall be taken in the design of the steel support. The ends of LH- or DLH-Series joists shall extend a distance of not less than 4 inches over the steel supports. Where it is deemed necessary to butt opposite joists over a narrow steel support with bearing less than that noted above, special ends must be specified, and such ends shall have positive attachment to the support, either by bolting or welding.

(e) **Bridging.** 1. **General.** Bridging shall be provided and shall consist of one of the types specified in Subsection 2 or 3 in this section.

2. **Horizontal.** Horizontal bridging shall consist of two continuous horizontal steel members, one attached to the top chord and the other attached to the bottom chord. Horizontal bridging members shall be properly anchored.

The ratio of unbraced length to least radius of gyration (l/r) of the bridging member shall not exceed 300, where l is the distance in inches between attachments and r is the least radius of gyration of the bridging member.

3. **Diagonal.** Diagonal bridging shall consist of cross bracing with *l/r* ratio of not more than 200, where *l* is the distance in inches between connections and *r* is the least radius of gyration of the bracing member. Where cross-bracing members are connected at their point of intersection, the *l* distance shall be taken as the distance in inches between connections at the point of intersection of the bracing members and the connections to the chords of the joists. Connections to chords of steel joists shall be made by positive mechanical means or by welding.

4. **Bridging lines.** For spans up to 40 feet, welded horizontal bridging may be used. For spans over 40 feet to 60 feet, welded horizontal bridging may be used except that one row nearest midspan shall be bolted diagonal bridging.

For spans over 60 feet, bolted diagonal bridging shall be used.

5. **Spacing.** The maximum spacing of lines of bridging shall not exceed the values in the following table:

LH SECTION NUMBER[1]	MAXIMUM SPACING OF LINES OF BRIDGING	HORIZONTAL BRACING FORCES[2]
02 to 09, inclusive	11′-0″	1100 lbs.
10 to 12, inclusive	16′-0″	1100 lbs.
13 to 14, inclusive	16′-0″	1400 lbs.
15 to 17, inclusive	21′-0″	2700 lbs.

DLH SECTION NUMBER[1]	MAXIMUM SPACING OF LINES OF BRIDGING	HORIZONTAL BRACING FORCES[2]
10	14′-0″	1100 lbs.
11 to 12, inclusive	16′-0″	1100 lbs.
13 to 14, inclusive	16′-0″	1400 lbs.
15 to 17, inclusive	21′-0″	2700 lbs.
18 to 19, inclusive	26′-0″	3400 lbs.

Numbers of lines of bridging are based on joist clear span dimensions.

[1]Last two digits of joist designation shown in load table.

[2]Each connection to the chord shall resist one half of this force.

6. **Connections.** Connections to the chords of the steel joists shall be made by positive mechanical means or by welding, and capable of resisting a horizontal force not less than that specified in above table.

(f) **Installation of Bridging.** All bridging and bridging anchors shall be completely installed before construction loads are placed on the joists.

Bridging shall support the top and bottom chords against lateral movement during the construction period and shall hold the steel joists in the approximate position as shown on the plans.

The ends of all bridging lines terminating at walls or beams shall be anchored thereto at top and bottom chords.

(g) **End Anchorage.** 1. **Masonry supports.** Ends of LH- or DLH-Series joists resting on steel bearing plates on masonry or structural concrete shall be attached thereto with a minimum of two 1/4-inch fillet welds 2 inches long, or with two 3/4-inch bolts.

2. **Steel supports.** Ends of joists resting on steel supports shall be connected thereto with the equivalent of two $^1/_4$-inch fillet welds 2 inches long, or with two $^3/_4$-inch bolts.

In steel frames, where columns are not framed in at least two directions with structural steel members, joists at column lines shall be field bolted at the columns to provide lateral stability during construction.

3. **Uplift.** Where uplift forces are a design consideration, roof joists shall be anchored to resist such forces.

(h) **Joist Spacing.** Joists shall be spaced so that the loading on each joist does not exceed the allowable load for the particular joist design.

(i) **Floors and Roof Decks.** Floors and roof decks shall comply with Section 27.405 (h), except that attachments of the slab or deck to the top chords of the joists shall be capable of resisting the following forces:

SECTION NUMBER	EQUIVALENT FORCE REQUIRED
02 to 04, inclusive	120 lbs./ft.
05 to 09, inclusive	150 lbs./ft.
10 to 17, inclusive	200 lbs./ft.
18 and 19, inclusive	250 lbs./ft.

(j) **Deflection.** The deflection due to the design live load shall not exceed the following:

Floors: 1/360 of span

Roofs: 1/360 of span where a plaster ceiling is attached or suspended

1/240 of span for all other cases

(k) **Ponding.** Unless a roof surface is provided with sufficient slope toward points of free drainage or adequate individual drains to prevent the accumulation of rain water, the roof system shall be investigated to assure stability under ponding conditions in accordance with the Uniform Building Code and U.B.C. Standard No. 27-14 or 27-15.

(l) **Inspection.** Joists shall be inspected by the manufacturer before shipment to ensure compliance of materials and workmanship with the requirements of this standard.

(m) **Uplift.** Where uplift forces due to wind are a design requirement, these forces shall be indicated on the contract drawings in terms of net uplift in pounds per square foot. When these forces are specified, they shall be considered in the design of joists and/or bridging. A single line of bottom chord bridging must be provided near the first bottom chord panel points whenever uplift due to wind forces is a design consideration.

Handling and Erection

Sec. 27.435. Particular attention should be paid to the erection of longspan and deep longspan steel joists.

Care shall be exercised at all times to avoid damage through careless handling during unloading, storing and erecting. Dropping of joists shall not be permitted.

Each joist shall be adequately braced laterally before the next joist is erected and before any loads are applied. If lateral support is provided by bridging, the bridging lines as defined below must be anchored to prevent lateral movement.

Hoisting cables shall not be released until one line of bolted bridging nearest midspan for spans up to 60 feet, and two lines of bolted bridging nearest the third points of the span for spans up to 100 feet, and all bridging lines for spans over 100 feet, are installed, and, where joists are bottom bearing, their ends have been restrained laterally. For ease of alignment, anchorage of joist ends in accordance with Section 27.434 (g) shall follow the installation of bridging. During the construction period, means for the adequate distribution of concentrated loads shall be provided so that the carrying capacity of any joist is not exceeded.

Field welding shall not damage the joists. The total length of weld at any one cross section on cold-formed members whose yield strength has been attained by cold working and whose as-formed stength is used in the design shall not exceed 50 percent of the overall developed width of the cold-formed section.

Part IV—Joist Girders

Scope

Sec. 27.441. This part covers the design, manufacture and use of joist girders.

Definition

Sec. 27.442. JOIST GIRDERS are open-web, load-carrying members utilizing hot-rolled or cold-formed steel, including cold-formed steel whose yield strength has been attained by cold working.

The design of joist girder chord or web sections shall be based on a yield strength of at least 36,000 psi but not greater than 50,000 psi. Steel used for joist girder chord or web sections shall have a minimum yield strength determined in accordance with one of the procedures specified in Section 27.443 (b), which is equal to the yield strength assumed in the design. Joist girders shall be designed in accordance with this part to support panel point loadings.

Materials

Sec. 27.443. (a) **Steel.** The steel used in the manufacture of chord and web sections shall conform to U.B.C. Standard No. 27-1 and be one of the following: A36; A242; A441; A570; A572, Grades 42, 45 and 50; A588; A606; A607, Grades 45 and 50; and ASTM 611, Grade D, or shall be of suitable quality ordered or produced to other than the listed specifications, provided that such material in the state used for final assembly and fabrication is weldable and is proved by tests performed by the producer or fabricator to have the properties specified in Section 27.443 (b).

(b) **Mechanical Properties.** Mechanical properties shall be as specified in Section 27.403 (b).

(c) **Welding Electrodes.** Welding electrodes shall be as specified in Section 27.432 (c).

(d) **Paint.** The standard shop paint shall conform to an approved standard for red oxide paint or asphaltic coating.

Design and Manufacture

Sec. 27.444. (a) **Method.** Joist girders shall be designed in accordance with this part as simply supported primary members. All loads will be applied through steel joists equal in magnitude and evenly spaced along joist girder top chord. Where any applicable design feature is not specifically covered herein, the design shall be in accordance with the requirements of the Uniform Building Code or U.B.C. Standard No. 27-9. Where the requirements of the Uniform Building Code are more restrictive, such requirements shall govern.

Joist girders are designed by listing the depth in inches, number of joist spaces and the load in kips on each panel point.

(b) **Unit Stresses.** Joist girders shall have their components so proportioned that the unit stresses in pounds per square inch shall not exceed the following where F_y is the yield strength defined in Section 27.403 (b):

1. **Tension:**

   All members .... $F_t = 0.6F_y$

2. **Compression:**

For members with l/r less than C_c:

$$\frac{\left[1-\frac{(l/r)^2}{2C_c^2}\right]QF_y}{\frac{5}{3}+\frac{3}{8}\left(\frac{l/r}{C_c}\right)-\frac{1}{8}\left(\frac{l/r}{C_c}\right)^3} \quad \text{where } C_c=\sqrt{\frac{2\pi^2E}{QF_y}} \text{ and}$$

where Q is a form factor equal to unity except when the width-thickness ratio of one or more elements of the profile exceeds the limits specified in Chapter 27 of the Uniform Building Code for hot-rolled sections or cold-formed sections. For members with l/r greater than C_c:

$$F_a = \frac{12\pi^2 E}{23\ (l/r)^2}$$

In the above formula, l is the length center-to-center of panel points, and r is the corresponding least radius of gyration of the member or any component thereof, both in inches, and E is equal to 29,000,000 psi.

3. **Bending:**

For chords and for web members other than solid rounds . . . . 0.6 F_y
For web members of solid round cross section . . . . 0.9 F_y
For outstanding legs of top chord angles at points of loading . . . . 0.75 F_y
For bearing plates . . . . 0.75 F_y

4. **Weld stresses:**

Shear at throat of fillet welds:
Made with E70 series electrodes or F7X-EXXX
flux-electrode combinations . . . . 21,000 psi
Made with E60 series electrodes or F6X-EXXX
flux-electrode combinations . . . . 18,000 psi
Tension or compression on groove or butt welds shall be the same as those specified for the connected material.

(c) **Maximum Slenderness Ratios.** The slenderness ratio, l/r, where l is the length center-to-center of support points and r is the corresponding least radius of gyration, shall not exceed the following:

Top chord interior panels 90
Top chord end panels 120
Compression members other than top chord 200
Tension members 240

(d) **Members.** 1. **Chords.** The bottom chord shall be designed as an axially loaded tension member. The radius of gyration of the bottom chord about its vertical axis shall not exceed $l/240$ where l is the distance between lines of bracing.

The top chord shall be designed as an axially loaded compression member. The radius of gyration of the top chord about the vertical axis shall be not less than Span/575.

The top chord shall be considered as stayed laterally by the steel joists, provided positive attachment is made.

2. **Web.** The vertical shears to be used in the design of the web members shall be determined from full loading but such vertical shear shall be not less than 25 percent of the end reaction.

Interior vertical web members used in modified Warren-type web systems that do not support the direct loads through steel joists shall be designed to resist 2 percent of the top chord axial force.

Tension members shall be designed to resist at least 25 percent of its axial force in compression.

3. **Fillers and ties.** Chord and web members in compression, composed of two components, shall have fillers, ties or welds spaced so that the *l/r* ratio for each component shall not exceed the *l/r* ratio of the whole member. Chord and web members in tension, composed of two components, shall have fillers, ties or welds spaced so that the *l/r* ratio of each component shall not exceed 240. The least *r* shall be used in computing the *l/r* ratio of a component.

4. **Eccentricity.** Members connected at a joint shall have their center-of-gravity lines meet at a point, if practical. Eccentricity on either side of the neutral axis of chord members may be neglected when it does not exceed the distance between the neutral axis and the back of the chord. Otherwise provision shall be made for the stresses due to eccentricity. Ends of joist girders shall be proportioned to resist bending produced by eccentricity at the support. In those cases where a single angle compression member is attached to the outside of the stem of a tee or double angle chord, due consideration shall be given to eccentricity.

5. The magnitude and location of the design loads to be supported, the deflection requirements and the proper bracing shall be clearly indicated on the structural drawings.

(e) **Connections.** 1. **Method.** Joint connections and splices shall be made by attaching the members to one another by arc or resistance welding, bolting or other approved method.

2. **Strength.** Joint connections shall develop the maximum force due to any of the design loads but not less than 50 percent of allowable strength of the member in tension or compression, whichever force is the controlling factor in the selection of the member.

3. **Shop splices.** Shop splices may occur at any point in the chord or web members. Splices shall be designed for the member force but not less than 50 percent of the allowable member strength. Members containing a butt weld splice shall develop an ultimate tensile force of at least 57,000 psi times the full design area of the chord or web. The term "member" shall be defined as all component parts, comprising the chord or web, at the point of splice.

4. **Field splices.** Field splices shall be designed by the manufacturer and may be either bolted or welded. Splices shall develop the design stress but not less than 50 percent of the allowable strength of the member.

(f) **Camber.** Joist girders, when used in roof construction, shall have approximate cambers in accordance with the following:

TOP CHORD LENGTH	APPROXIMATE CAMBER
20′ 0″	1/4″
30′ 0″	3/8″
40′ 0″	5/8″
50′ 0″	1″
60′ 0″	11/2″

(g) **Shop Painting.** Joist girders and accessories shall receive one shop coat of approved protective paint.

Application

Sec. 27.445. (a) **Usage.** This section shall apply to any type of structure where steel joists are to be supported directly by joist girders installed as hereinafter specified. Where joist girders are used other than on simple spans under equal concentrated gravity loading, as prescribed in Section 27.444 (a), they shall be investigated and modified if necessary to limit the unit stresses to those listed in Section 27.444 (b). The magnitude and location of all loads and forces, other than equal concentrated gravity loadings, shall be provided on the contract documents. The specifying engineer or architect shall design the supporting structure including the design of columns and connections. This design shall account for the stresses caused by lateral forces and the stresses due to connecting the bottom chord to the column or other support.

(b) **Depth.** The nominal depth of sloping chord joist girders shall be the depth at mid-span.

(c) **End Supports.** 1. **Masonry and concrete.** The ends of joist girders should extend a distance of not less than 6 inches over masonry or concrete supports and be attached to a steel bearing plate. This plate is to be located not more than 1/2 inch from the face of the wall and is to be not less than 9 inches wide perpendicular to the length of the joist girder. It is to be designed in compliance with the allowable unit bending stresses in Section 27.419 (b) and the allowable unit bearing pressures in Chapter 27 of the Uniform Building Code.

2. **Steel.** Due consideration of the end reactions and all other vertical and lateral forces shall be taken in the design of the steel support. The ends of joist girders shall extend a distance of not less than 4 inches over the steel supports and shall have positive attachment to the support, either by bolting or welding.

(d) **Bracing.** Joist girders shall be proportioned such that they can be erected without bridging. Therefore, the following requirements must be met:

1. The strutted ends of the bottom chord are restrained from lateral movement to brace the girder from overturning.
2. No other loads shall be placed on the joist girder until the steel joists bearing on the girder are in place and welded to the girder.

(e) **End Anchorage.** 1. **Masonry and concrete supports.** Ends of joist girders resting on steel bearing plates on masonry or structural concrete shall be attached thereto with a minimum of two 1/4-inch fillet welds 2 inches long, or with two 3/4-inch bolts.

2. **Steel supports.** Ends of joist girders resting on steel supports shall be connected thereto with a minimum of two 1/4-inch fillet welds 2 inches long, or with two 3/4-inch bolts. In steel frames, joist girders at column lines shall be field bolted to the columns to provide lateral stability during construction.

3. **Uplift.** Where uplift forces are a design consideration, roof joist girders shall be anchored to resist such forces.

(f) **Deflection.** The maximum deflection due to the design live load shall not exceed 1/360 of span where a plaster ceiling is attached or suspended; and 1/240 of span for all other cases.

(g) **Ponding.** Unless a roof surface is provided with sufficient slope toward points of free drainage or adequate individual drains to prevent the accumulation of rain water, the roof system shall be investigated to assure stability under ponding conditions in accordance with the Uniform Building Code and U.B.C. Standard No. 27-14 or 27-15.

(h) **Inspection.** Joist girders shall be inspected by the manufacturer before shipment to ensure compliance of materials and workmanship with the requirements of this standard.

(i) **Uplift.** Where uplift forces due to wind are a design requirement, these forces must be indicated on the structural drawings in terms of net uplift in pounds per square foot. When these forces are specified, they must be considered in the design of the joist girders or bracing. If the ends of the bottom chord are not strutted, bracing must be provided near the first bottom chord panel points whenever uplift due to wind forces is a design consideration.

Handling and Erection

Sec. 27.446. Particular attention should be paid to the erection of joist girders.

Care shall be exercised at all times to avoid damage through careless handling during unloading, storing and erecting. Dropping of joist girders shall not be permitted.

During the construction period, means shall be provided for the adequate distribution of concentrated loads so that the carrying capacity of any joist girder is not exceeded.

Field welding shall not damage the joist girder. The total length of weld at any one cross-section or cold-formed member whose yield strength has been attained by cold working and whose as-formed strength as used in the design shall not exceed 50 percent of the overall developed width of the cold-formed section.

(Tables appear on the following pages.)

TABLE NO. 27-4-A
STANDARD LOAD TABLE—OPEN WEB STEEL JOISTS, H-SERIES
(Based on a Maximum Allowable Tensile Stress of 30,000 psi)[1]

The figures in the following table give the total safe uniformly distributed load-carrying capacities, in pounds per linear foot, of H-Series steel joists. The weight of dead loads, including the joists, must be deducted to determine the live load-carrying capacities of the joists. The load table may be used for parallel chord joists installed to a maximum slope of ½ inch per foot.

Where two figures are shown in this load table, the lower figures are the live loads per linear foot of joist which will produce an approximate deflection of 1/360 of the span. Live loads which will produce a deflection of 1/240 of the span may be obtained by multiplying the lower figures by 1.5. In no case shall the total load capacity of the joists be exceeded.

The Standard Load Tables are applicable for concentrated top chord loadings (such as are developed in bulb-tee roof construction) when the sum of the equal concentrated top chord loadings does not exceed the allowable uniform loading for the joist type and span and the loads are placed at spacings not exceeding 33 inches along the top chord.

NOTE: Loads above the heavy lines are governed by shear.

Joist Designation	8H3	10H3	10H4	12H3	12H4	12H5	12H6	14H3	14H4	14H5	14H6	14H7	16H4	16H5	16H6	16H7	16H8
Nominal Depth (in.)	8	10	10	12	12	12	12	14	14	14	14	14	16	16	16	16	16
Resist. Moment (in.-lbs.)	91,000	116,000	148,000	140,000	180,000	222,000	260,000	165,000	212,000	259,000	307,000	369,000	221,000	289,000	344,000	413,000	478,000
Max. End React. (lbs.)	2400	2500	2800	2800	3200	3600	3900	3200	3500	3800	4200	4600	3800	4300	4600	4900	5200
Approx. Wt.[2] (lbs./ft.)	5.0	5.0	6.1	5.2	6.2	7.1	8.2	5.5	6.5	7.4	8.6	10.0	6.6	7.8	8.6	10.3	11.4
Clear Span in Feet 8 or Less	600	500	560	467	533	600	650	457	500	543	600	657	475	538	575	613	650
9	533	500	560	467	533	600	650	457	500	543	600	657	475	538	575	613	650
10	480 460	500	560	467	533	600	650	457	500	543	600	657	475	538	575	613	650
11	436 345	455	509	467	533	600	650	457	500	543	600	657	475	538	575	613	650

12	400 266	417	467	467	533	600	650	457	500	543	600	657	475	538	575	613	650
13	359 209	385 337	431 417	431	492	554	600	457	500	543	600	657	475	538	575	613	650
14	310 167	357 270	400 334	400 393	457	514	557	457	500	543	600	657	475	538	575	613	650
15	270 136	333 219	373 271	373 320	427 418	480	520	427	467	507	560	613	475	538	575	613	650
16	232 112	302 181	350 223	350 264	400 345	450 404	488 480	400 366	438	475	525	575	475	538	575	613	650
17		268 151	329 186	323 220	376 287	424 337	459 400	376 305	412 398	447	494	541	447	506	541	576	612
18		239 127	305 157	288 185	356 242	400 284	433 337	340 257	389 336	422 393	467	511	422 413	478	511	544	578
19		214 108	273 133	259 157	332 206	379 241	411 286	305 218	368 285	400 334	442 399	484 470	400 351	453 432	484	516	547
20		193 92	247 114	233 135	300 177	360 207	390 246	275 187	350 245	380 287	420 342	460 403	368 301	430 370	460 437	490	520
21				212 117	272 152	336 179	371 212	249 162	320 212	362 248	400 295	438 348	334 260	410 320	438 377	467 454	495
22				193 101	248 133	306 155	355 185	227 141	292 184	345 215	382 257	418 302	304 226	391 278	418 328	445 395	473 454

(Continued)

TABLE NO. 27-4-A—(Continued)
STANDARD LOAD TABLE—OPEN WEB STEEL JOISTS, H-SERIES
(Based on a Maximum Allowable Tensile Stress of 30,000 psi)[1]
NOTE: Loads Above the Heavy Lines are Governed by Shear

Joist Designation	8H3	10H3	10H4	12H3	12H4	12H5	12H6	14H3	14H4	14H5	14H6	14H7	16H4	16H5	16H6	16H7	16H8
23				176 89	227 116	280 136	328 162	208 123	267 161	326 189	365 225	400 265	279 198	364 243	400 287	426 346	452 398
24				162 78	208 102	257 120	301 142	191 108	245 142	300 166	350 198	383 233	256 174	334 214	383 253	408 304	433 350
25								176 96	226 125	276 147	327 175	368 206	236 154	308 190	367 224	392 269	416 310
26								163 85	209 111	255 131	303 156	354 183	218 137	285 169	339 199	377 239	400 275
27								151 76	194 99	237 117	281 139	337 164	202 122	264 151	315 177	363 214	385 246
28								140 68	180 89	220 104	261 125	314 147	188 110	246 135	293 159	350 192	371 220
29													175 99	229 121	273 143	327 172	359 198
30													164 89	214 110	255 129	306 156	347 179
31													153 81	200 99	239 117	287 141	332 162
32													144 74	188 90	224 107	269 128	311 148

Joist Designation	18H5	18H6	18H7	18H8	18H9	18H10	18H11	20H5	20H6	20H7	20H8	20H9	20H10	20H11	22H6	22H7	22H8	22H9	22H10	22H11
Nominal Depth (in.)	18	18	18	18	18	18	18	20	20	20	20	20	20	20	22	22	22	22	22	22
Resist. Moment (in.-lbs.)	325,000	383,000	466,000	540,000	627,000	705,000	814,000	365,000	406,000	499,000	602,000	701,000	789,000	912,000	422,000	526,000	653,000	776,000	873,000	1,009,000
Max. End React. (lbs.)	4500	4800	5200	5400	5900	6600	7600	4800	5100	5400	5600	6400	7000	7900	5400	5600	5800	6700	7200	8100
Approx. Wt.[2] (lbs./ft.)	8.0	9.2	10.4	11.6	12.6	14.0	15.8	8.4	9.6	10.7	12.2	13.2	14.6	16.4	9.7	10.7	12.0	13.8	15.2	16.9
Clear Span in Feet 18 or Less	500	533	578	600	621	629	633	480	510	540	560	640	636	632	491	509	527	609	626	648
19	474	505	547	568	621	629	633	480	510	540	560	640	636	632	491	509	527	609	626	648
20	450	480	520	540	590	629	633	480	510	540	560	640	636	632	491	509	527	609	626	648
21	429 409	457	495	514	562	629	633	457	486	514	533	610	636	632	491	509	527	609	626	648
22	409 356	436 420	473	491	536	600	633	436	464	491	509	582	636	632	491	509	527	609	626	648

(Continued)

TABLE NO. 27-4-A—(Continued)
STANDARD LOAD TABLE—OPEN WEB STEEL JOISTS, H-SERIES
(Based on a Maximum Allowable Tensile Stress of 30,000 psi)[1]
NOTE: Loads above the heavy lines are governed by shear.

Joist Designation	18H5	18H6	18H7	18H8	18H9	18H10	18H11	20H5	20H6	20H7	20H8	20H9	20H10	20H11	22H6	22H7	22H8	22H9	22H10	22H11
23	391 312	417 368	452 441	470	513	574	633	417 380	443 434	470	487	557	609	632	470	487	504	583	626	648
24	375 274	400 324	433 388	450 444	492 484	550 546	633 619	400 335	425 382	450	467	533	583	632	450 446	467	483	558	600	648
25	347 243	384 286	416 343	432 393	472 428	528 483	608 548	384 296	408 338	432 411	448	512	560	632	432 395	448	464	536	576	648
26	321 216	369 255	400 305	415 349	454 380	508 429	585 487	360 263	392 300	415 365	431	492 476	538	608	415 351	431 426	446	515	554	623
27	297 193	350 227	385 272	400 312	437 340	489 383	563 435	334 235	371 268	400 326	415 392	474 425	519 480	585 545	386 313	415 380	430	496	533	600
28	276 173	326 204	371 244	386 280	421 305	471 344	543 390	310 211	345 240	386 292	400 352	457 381	500 431	564 488	359 281	400 341	414	479 468	514	579
29	258 155	304 184	359 220	372 252	407 274	455 309	524 351	289 190	322 216	372 263	386 317	441 343	483 388	545 440	335 253	386 307	400 379	462 421	497 473	559 539
30	241 140	284 166	345 199	360 227	393 248	440 280	507 317	270 171	301 195	360 238	373 286	427 310	467 350	527 397	313 228	373 277	387 343	447 381	480 428	540 487
31	225 127	266 150	323 180	348 206	381 224	426 253	490 287	253 155	282 177	346 215	361 259	413 281	452 317	510 360	293 207	361 251	374 311	432 345	465 387	523 441
32	212 116	249 137	303 164	338 187	369 204	413 230	475 261	238 141	264 161	325 196	350 236	400 255	438 288	494 327	275 188	342 228	363 282	419 314	450 352	506 401

33	199 106	234 125	285 149	327 171	358 186	400 210	461 238	223 129	249 147	305 178	339 215	388 233	424 263	479 298	258 172	322 208	352 257	406 286	436 321	491 366
34	187 96	221 114	269 136	311 156	347 170	388 192	447 218	210 118	234 134	288 163	329 196	376 213	412 240	465 273	243 157	303 190	341 235	394 261	424 294	476 335
35	177 88	208 104	254 125	294 143	337 156	377 176	434 200	199 108	221 123	272 150	320 180	366 195	400 220	451 250	230 144	286 175	331 216	383 240	411 269	463 307
36	167 81	197 96	240 115	278 132	323 143	363 162	419 183	188 99	209 113	257 137	310 166	356 179	389 203	439 230	217 132	271 160	322 198	372 220	400 247	450 282
37								178 91	198 104	243 127	293 152	341 165	378 187	427 212	206 122	256 148	314 183	362 203	389 228	438 260
38								169 84	187 96	230 117	278 141	324 153	364 172	416 195	195 112	243 136	301 169	353 187	379 210	426 240
39								160 78	178 89	219 108	264 130	307 141	346 159	400 181	185 104	231 126	286 156	340 173	369 195	415 222
40								152 72	169 82	208 100	251 121	292 131	329 148	380 168	176 96	219 117	272 145	323 161	360 180	405 205
41															167 89	209 109	259 134	308 149	346 167	395 191
42															159 83	199 101	247 125	293 139	330 156	381 177
43															152 78	190 94	235 116	280 129	315 145	364 165
44															145 72	181 88	225 109	267 121	301 136	347 154

(Continued)

TABLE NO. 27-4-A—(Continued)
STANDARD LOAD TABLE—OPEN WEB STEEL JOISTS, H-SERIES
(Based on a Maximum Allowable Tensile Stress of 30,000 psi)[1]

NOTE: Loads above the heavy lines are governed by shear.

Joist Designation	24H6	24H7	24H8	24H9	24H10	24H11	26H8	26H9	26H10	26H11	28H8	28H9	28H10	28H11	30H8	30H9	30H10	30H11
Nominal Depth (in.)	24	24	24	24	24	24	26	26	26	26	28	28	28	28	30	30	30	30
Resist. Moment (in.-lbs.)	462,000	576,000	716,000	851,000	957,000	1,106,000	784,000	925,000	1,040,000	1,203,000	846,000	1,000,000	1,124,000	1,300,000	909,000	1,075,000	1,207,000	1,397,000
Max. End React. (lbs.)	5600	5800	6000	7000	7500	8200	6700	7200	7600	8300	6700	7200	7700	8400	6800	7500	8100	8700
Approx. Wt.[2] (lbs./ft.)	10.3	11.5	12.7	14.0	15.5	17.5	12.8	14.8	16.2	17.9	13.5	15.2	16.8	18.3	14.2	15.4	17.3	18.8
Clear Span in Feet 24 or Less	467	483	500	583	625	631	515	554	585	638	479	514	550	600	453	500	540	580
25	448	464	480	560	600	631	515	554	585	638	479	514	550	600	453	500	540	580
26	431	446	462	538	577	631	515	554	585	638	479	514	550	600	453	500	540	580
27	415 375	430	444	519	556	607	496	533	563	615	479	514	550	600	453	500	540	580
28	393 336	414 406	429	500	536	586	479	514	543	593	479	514	550	600	453	500	540	580
29	366 303	400 365	414	483	517	566	462	497	524	572	462	497	531	579	453	500	540	580
30	342 273	387 330	400	467 457	500	547	447	480	507	553	447	480	513	560	453	500	540	580
31	320 248	374 299	387 373	452 414	484 465	529	432 418	465	490	535	432	465	497	542	439	484	523	561

32	301 225	363 272	375 339	438 376	469 423	513 482	419 380	450 445	475	519	419	450	481	525	425	469	506	544
33	283 205	352 248	364 309	424 343	455 386	497 440	406 346	436 405	461 456	503	406 404	436	467	509	412	455	491	527
34	266 188	332 227	353 283	412 314	441 353	482 402	394 317	424 371	447 417	488 476	394 370	424	453	494	400	441	476	512
35	251 172	313 208	343 259	400 288	429 323	469 369	383 290	411 340	434 383	474 437	383 339	411 396	440	480	389	429	463	497
36	238 158	296 191	333 238	389 264	417 297	456 339	372 267	400 312	422 352	461 401	372 311	400 364	428 410	467	378 359	417	450	483
37	225 146	280 176	324 219	378 243	405 274	443 312	362 246	389 288	411 324	449 370	362 287	389 336	416 378	454 432	368 330	405 387	438 436	470
38	213 135	266 162	316 202	368 225	395 253	432 288	353 227	379 266	400 299	437 341	353 265	379 310	405 349	442 399	358 305	395 357	426 402	458
39	202 124	252 150	308 187	359 208	385 234	421 266	344 210	369 246	390 276	426 316	344 245	369 287	395 322	431 369	349 282	385 331	415 372	446 426
40	193 115	240 139	298 174	350 193	375 217	410 247	327 194	360 228	380 256	415 292	335 227	360 266	385 299	420 342	340 262	375 306	405 345	435 395
41	183 107	228 129	284 161	337 179	366 201	400 229	311 181	351 211	371 238	405 272	327 211	351 247	376 278	410 318	332 243	366 285	395 320	424 367
42	175 100	218 120	271 150	322 166	357 187	390 213	296 168	343 197	362 221	395 253	319 196	343 229	367 258	400 295	324 226	357 265	386 298	414 341
43	167 93	208 112	258 140	307 155	345 174	381 199	283 156	334 183	353 206	386 235	305 183	335 214	358 241	391 275	316 211	349 247	377 278	405 318
44	159 87	198 105	247 130	293 145	330 163	373 186	270 146	319 171	345 193	377 220	291 171	327 200	350 225	382 257	309 196	341 230	368 259	395 297

(Continued)

TABLE NO. 27-4-A—(Continued)
STANDARD LOAD TABLE—OPEN WEB STEEL JOISTS, H-SERIES
(Based on a Maximum Allowable Tensile Stress of 30,000 psi)[1]
NOTE: Loads above the heavy lines are governed by shear.

Joist Designation	24H6	24H7	24H8	24H9	24H10	24H11	26H8	26H9	26H10	26H11	28H8	28H9	28H10	28H11	30H8	30H9	30H10	30H11
45	152 81	190 98	236 122	280 135	315 152	364 173	258 137	305 160	338 180	369 205	279 159	320 187	342 210	373 240	299 184	333 215	360 242	387 278
46	146 76	181 92	226 114	268 127	302 142	348 162	247 128	291 150	328 168	361 192	267 149	313 175	335 197	365 225	286 172	326 202	352 227	378 260
47	139 71	174 86	216 107	257 119	289 133	334 152	237 120	279 140	314 158	353 180	255 140	302 164	328 184	357 211	274 161	319 189	345 213	370 244
48	134 67	167 81	207 100	246 111	277 125	320 143	227 112	268 132	301 148	346 169	245 131	289 154	321 173	350 198	263 151	311 177	338 200	363 229
49							218 106	257 124	289 139	334 159	235 124	278 144	312 163	343 186	252 142	298 167	331 188	355 215
50							209 100	247 117	277 131	321 150	226 116	267 136	300 153	336 175	242 134	287 157	322 177	348 202
51							201 94	237 110	267 124	308 141	217 110	256 128	288 144	329 165	233 126	276 148	309 166	341 191
52							193 88	228 104	256 117	297 133	209 103	247 121	277 136	321 156	224 119	265 139	298 157	335 180
53											201 98	237 114	267 128	309 147	216 112	255 132	286 148	328 170
54											193 92	229 108	257 121	297 139	208 106	246 125	276 140	319 161
55											186 87	220 102	248 115	287 132	200 101	237 118	266 133	308 152

56											180 83	213 97	239 109	276 125	193 95	229 112	257 126	297 144
57															187 90	221 106	248 119	287 137
58															180 86	213 101	239 113	277 130
59															174 81	206 95	231 108	268 123
60															168 77	199 91	224 102	259 117

[1]For an approximate total load-carrying capacity at a maximum allowable tensile stress of 22,000 psi, the total load-carrying capacity shown in the load table should be multiplied by the ratio 22/30.

[2]Approximate weights per linear foot of steel joists only. Accessories and nailer strip not included.

TABLE NO. 27-4-B—STANDARD LOAD TABLE—OPEN WEB STEEL JOISTS, K-SERIES (Based on a Maximum Allowable Tensile Stress of 30,000 psi)

The upper figures in the following table give the total safe uniformly distributed load-carrying capacities, in pounds per linear foot, of K-Series Steel Joists. The weight of dead loads, including the joists, must be deducted to determine the live load-carrying capacities of the joists. The load table may be used for parallel chord joists installed to a maximum slope of 1/2 inch per foot.

The lower figures in this load table are the live loads per linear foot of joist which will produce an approximate deflection of 1/360 of the span. Live loads which will produce a deflection of 1/240 of the span may be obtained by multiplying the figures by 1.5. In no case shall the total load capacity of the joists be exceeded.

Joist Designation	8K1	10K1	12K1	12K3	12K5	14K1	14K3	14K4	14K6	16K2	16K3	16K4	16K5	16K6	16K7	16K9
Depth (In.)	8	10	12	12	12	14	14	14	14	16	16	16	16	16	16	16
Approx. Wt. (lbs./ft.)	5.1	5.0	5.0	5.7	7.1	5.2	6.0	6.7	7.7	5.5	6.3	7.0	7.5	8.1	8.6	10.0
*Span (ft.) ↓																
8	550 550															
9	550 550															
10	550 480	550 550														
11	532 377	550 542														
12	444 288	550 455	550 550	550 550	550 550											
13	377 225	479 363	550 510	550 510	550 510											
14	324 179	412 289	500 425	550 463	550 463	550 550	550 550	550 550	550 550							
15	281 145	358 234	434 344	543 428	550 434	511 475	550 507	550 507	550 507							
16	246 119	313 192	380 282	476 351	550 396	448 390	550 467	550 467	550 467	550 550	550 550	550 550	550 550	550 550	550 550	550 550

17		277 159	336 234	420 291	550 366	395 324	495 404	550 443	550 443	512 488	550 526	550 526	550 526	550 526	550 526	550 526
18		246 134	299 197	374 245	507 317	352 272	441 339	530 397	550 408	456 409	508 456	550 490	550 490	550 490	550 490	550 490
19		221 113	268 167	335 207	454 269	315 230	395 287	475 336	550 383	408 347	455 386	547 452	550 455	550 455	550 455	550 455
20		199 97	241 142	302 177	409 230	284 197	356 246	428 287	525 347	368 297	410 330	493 386	550 426	550 426	550 426	550 426
21			218 123	273 153	370 198	257 170	322 212	388 248	475 299	333 255	371 285	447 333	503 373	548 405	550 406	550 406
22			199 106	249 132	337 172	234 147	293 184	353 215	432 259	303 222	337 247	406 289	458 323	498 351	550 385	550 385
23			181 93	227 116	308 150	214 128	268 160	322 188	395 226	277 194	308 216	371 252	418 282	455 307	507 339	550 363
24			166 81	208 101	282 132	196 113	245 141	295 165	362 199	254 170	283 189	340 221	384 248	418 269	465 298	550 346
25						180 100	226 124	272 145	334 175	234 150	260 167	313 195	353 219	384 238	428 263	514 311
26						166 88	209 110	251 129	308 156	216 133	240 148	289 173	326 194	355 211	395 233	474 276
27						154 79	193 98	233 115	285 139	200 119	223 132	268 155	302 173	329 188	366 208	439 246
28						143 70	180 88	216 103	265 124	186 106	207 118	249 138	281 155	306 168	340 186	408 220
29										173 95	193 106	232 124	261 139	285 151	317 167	380 198
30										161 86	180 96	216 112	244 126	266 137	296 151	355 178
31										151 78	168 87	203 101	228 114	249 124	277 137	332 161
32										142 71	158 79	190 92	214 103	233 112	259 124	311 147

(Continued)

TABLE NO. 27-4-B—STANDARD LOAD TABLE—OPEN WEB STEEL JOISTS, K-SERIES—(Continued)
(Based on a Maximum Allowable Tensile Stress of 30,000 psi)

Joist Designation	18K3	18K4	18K5	18K6	18K7	18K9	18K10	20K3	20K4	20K5	20K6	20K7	20K9	20K10	22K4	22K5	22K6	22K7	22K9	22K10	22K11
Depth (In.)	18	18	18	18	18	18	18	20	20	20	20	20	20	20	22	22	22	22	22	22	22
Approx. Wt. (lbs./ft.)	6.6	7.2	7.7	8.5	9.0	10.2	11.7	6.7	7.6	8.2	8.9	9.3	10.8	12.2	8.0	8.8	9.2	9.7	11.3	12.6	13.8
*Span (ft.) ↓																					
18	550 550	550 550	550 550	550 550	550 550	550 550	550 550														
19	514 494	550 523	550 523	550 523	550 523	550 523	550 523														
20	463 423	550 490	550 490	550 490	550 490	550 490	550 490	517 517	550 550	550 550	550 550	550 550	550 550	550 550							
21	420 364	506 426	550 460	550 460	550 460	550 460	550 460	468 453	550 520	550 520	550 520	550 520	550 520	550 520							
22	382 316	460 370	518 414	550 438	550 438	550 438	550 438	426 393	514 461	550 490	550 490	550 490	550 490	550 490	550 548	550 548	550 548	550 548	550 548	550 548	550 548
23	349 276	420 323	473 362	516 393	550 418	550 418	550 418	389 344	469 402	529 451	550 468	550 468	550 468	550 468	518 491	550 518	550 518	550 518	550 518	550 518	550 518
24	320 242	385 284	434 318	473 345	526 382	550 396	550 396	357 302	430 353	485 396	528 430	550 448	550 448	550 448	475 431	536 483	550 495	550 495	550 495	550 495	550 495
25	294 214	355 250	400 281	435 305	485 337	550 377	550 377	329 266	396 312	446 350	486 380	541 421	550 426	550 426	438 381	493 427	537 464	550 474	550 474	550 474	550 474
26	272 190	328 222	369 249	402 271	448 299	538 354	550 361	304 236	366 277	412 310	449 337	500 373	550 405	550 405	404 338	455 379	496 411	550 454	550 454	550 454	550 454
27	252 169	303 198	342 222	372 241	415 267	498 315	550 347	281 211	339 247	382 277	416 301	463 333	550 389	550 389	374 301	422 337	459 367	512 406	550 432	550 432	550 432
28	234 151	282 177	318 199	346 216	385 239	463 282	548 331	261 189	315 221	355 248	386 269	430 298	517 353	550 375	348 270	392 302	427 328	475 364	550 413	550 413	550 413

29	218 136	263 159	296 179	322 194	359 215	431 254	511 298	243 170	293 199	330 223	360 242	401 268	482 317	550 359	324 242	365 272	398 295	443 327	532 387	550 399	550 399
30	203 123	245 144	276 161	301 175	335 194	402 229	477 269	227 153	274 179	308 201	336 218	374 242	450 286	533 336	302 219	341 245	371 266	413 295	497 349	550 385	550 385
31	190 111	229 130	258 146	281 158	313 175	376 207	446 243	212 138	256 162	289 182	314 198	350 219	421 259	499 304	283 198	319 222	347 241	387 267	465 316	550 369	550 369
32	178 101	215 118	242 132	264 144	294 159	353 188	418 221	199 126	240 147	271 165	295 179	328 199	395 235	468 276	265 180	299 201	326 219	363 242	436 287	517 337	549 355
33	168 92	202 108	228 121	248 131	276 145	332 171	393 201	187 114	226 134	254 150	277 163	309 181	371 214	440 251	249 164	281 183	306 199	341 221	410 261	486 307	532 334
34	158 84	190 98	214 110	233 120	260 132	312 156	370 184	176 105	212 122	239 137	261 149	290 165	349 195	414 229	235 149	265 167	288 182	321 202	386 239	458 280	516 314
35	149 77	179 90	202 101	220 110	245 121	294 143	349 168	166 96	200 112	226 126	246 137	274 151	329 179	390 210	221 137	249 153	272 167	303 185	364 219	432 257	494 292
36	141 70	169 82	191 92	208 101	232 111	278 132	330 154	157 88	189 103	213 115	232 125	259 139	311 164	369 193	209 126	236 141	257 153	286 169	344 201	408 236	467 269
37								148 81	179 95	202 106	220 115	245 128	294 151	349 178	198 116	223 130	243 141	271 156	325 185	386 217	442 247
38								141 74	170 87	191 98	208 106	232 118	279 139	331 164	187 107	211 119	230 130	256 144	308 170	366 200	419 228
39								133 69	161 81	181 90	198 98	220 109	265 129	314 151	178 98	200 110	218 120	243 133	292 157	347 185	397 211
40								127 64	153 75	172 84	188 91	209 101	251 119	298 140	169 91	190 102	207 111	231 123	278 146	330 171	377 195
41															161 85	181 95	197 103	220 114	264 135	314 159	359 181
42															153 79	173 83	188 96	209 106	252 126	299 148	342 168
43															146 73	165 82	179 89	200 99	240 117	285 138	326 157
44															139 68	157 76	171 83	191 92	229 109	272 128	311 146

(Continued)

TABLE NO. 27-4-B—STANDARD LOAD TABLE—OPEN WEB STEEL JOISTS, K-SERIES—(Continued)
(Based on a Maximum Allowable Tensile Stress of 30,000 psi)

Joist Designation	24K4	24K5	24K6	24K7	24K8	24K9	24K10	24K12	26K5	26K6	26K7	26K8	26K9	26K10	26K12	28K6	28K7	28K8	28K9	28K10	28K12
Depth (In.)	24	24	24	24	24	24	24	24	26	26	26	26	26	26	26	28	28	28	28	28	28
Approx. Wt. (lbs./ft.)	8.4	9.3	9.7	10.1	11.5	12.0	13.1	16.0	9.8	10.6	10.9	12.1	12.2	13.8	16.6	11.4	11.8	12.7	13.0	14.3	17.1
*Span (ft.) ↓																					
24	520 516	550 544	550 544	550 544	550 544	550 544	550 544	550 544													
25	479 456	540 511	550 520	550 520	550 520	550 520	550 520	550 520													
26	442 405	499 453	543 493	550 499	550 499	550 499	550 499	550 499	542 535	550 541	550 541	550 541	550 541	550 541	550 541						
27	410 361	462 404	503 439	550 479	550 479	550 479	550 479	550 479	502 477	547 519	550 522	550 522	550 522	550 522	550 522						
28	381 323	429 362	467 393	521 436	550 456	550 456	550 456	550 456	466 427	508 464	550 501	550 501	550 501	550 501	550 501	548 541	550 543	550 543	550 543	550 543	550 543
29	354 290	400 325	435 354	485 392	536 429	550 436	550 436	550 436	434 384	473 417	527 463	550 479	550 479	550 479	550 479	511 486	550 522	550 522	550 522	550 522	550 522
30	331 262	373 293	406 319	453 353	500 387	544 419	550 422	550 422	405 346	441 377	492 417	544 457	550 459	550 459	550 459	477 439	531 486	550 500	550 500	550 500	550 500
31	310 237	349 266	380 289	424 320	468 350	510 379	550 410	550 410	379 314	413 341	460 378	509 413	550 444	550 444	550 444	446 397	497 440	550 480	550 480	550 480	550 480
32	290 215	327 241	357 262	397 290	439 318	478 344	549 393	549 393	356 285	387 309	432 343	477 375	519 407	549 431	549 431	418 361	466 400	515 438	549 463	549 463	549 463
33	273 196	308 220	335 239	373 265	413 289	449 313	532 368	532 368	334 259	364 282	406 312	448 342	488 370	532 404	532 404	393 329	438 364	484 399	527 432	532 435	532 435
34	257 179	290 201	315 218	351 242	388 264	423 286	502 337	516 344	315 237	343 257	382 285	422 312	459 338	516 378	516 378	370 300	412 333	456 364	496 395	516 410	516 410
35	242 164	273 184	297 200	331 221	366 242	399 262	473 308	501 324	297 217	323 236	360 261	398 286	433 310	501 356	501 356	349 275	389 305	430 333	468 361	501 389	501 389
36	229 150	258 169	281 183	313 203	346 222	377 241	447 283	487 306	280 199	305 216	340 240	376 263	409 284	486 334	487 334	330 252	367 280	406 306	442 332	487 366	487 366
37	216 138	244 155	266 169	296 187	327 205	356 222	423 260	474 290	265 183	289 199	322 221	356 242	387 262	460 308	474 315	312 232	348 257	384 282	418 305	474 344	474 344

38	205 128	231 143	252 156	281 172	310 189	338 204	401 240	461 275	251 169	274 184	305 204	337 223	367 241	436 284	461 299	296 214	329 237	364 260	396 282	461 325	461 325
39	195 118	219 132	239 144	266 159	294 174	320 189	380 222	449 261	238 156	260 170	289 188	320 206	348 223	413 262	449 283	280 198	313 219	346 240	376 260	447 306	449 308
40	185 109	208 122	227 133	253 148	280 161	304 175	361 206	438 247	227 145	247 157	275 174	304 191	331 207	393 243	438 269	266 183	297 203	328 222	357 241	424 284	438 291
41	176 101	198 114	216 124	241 137	266 150	290 162	344 191	427 235	215 134	235 146	262 162	289 177	315 192	374 225	427 256	253 170	283 189	312 206	340 224	404 263	427 277
42	168 94	189 106	206 115	229 127	253 139	276 151	327 177	417 224	205 125	224 136	249 150	275 164	300 178	356 210	417 244	241 158	269 175	297 192	324 208	384 245	417 264
43	160 88	180 98	196 107	219 118	242 130	263 140	312 165	406 213	196 116	213 126	238 140	263 153	286 166	339 195	407 232	230 147	257 163	284 179	309 194	367 228	407 252
44	153 82	172 92	187 100	209 110	231 121	251 131	298 154	387 199	187 108	204 118	227 131	251 143	273 155	324 182	398 222	220 137	245 152	271 167	295 181	350 212	398 240
45	146 76	164 86	179 93	199 103	220 113	240 122	285 144	370 185	179 101	194 110	217 122	240 133	261 145	310 170	389 212	210 128	234 142	259 156	282 169	334 198	389 229
46	139 71	157 80	171 87	191 97	211 106	230 114	272 135	354 174	171 95	186 103	207 114	229 125	250 135	296 159	380 203	201 120	224 133	248 146	270 158	320 186	380 219
47	133 67	150 75	164 82	183 90	202 99	220 107	261 126	339 163	164 89	178 96	199 107	219 117	239 127	284 149	369 192	192 112	214 125	237 136	258 148	306 174	372 210
48	128 63	144 70	157 77	175 85	194 93	211 101	250 118	325 153	157 83	171 90	190 100	210 110	229 119	272 140	353 180	184 105	206 117	227 128	247 139	294 163	365 201
49									150 78	164 85	183 94	202 103	220 112	261 131	339 169	177 99	197 110	218 120	237 130	282 153	357 193
50									144 73	157 80	175 89	194 97	211 105	250 124	325 159	170 93	189 103	209 113	228 123	270 144	350 185
51									139 69	151 75	168 83	186 91	203 99	241 116	313 150	163 88	182 97	201 106	219 115	260 136	338 175
52									133 65	145 71	162 79	179 86	195 93	231 110	301 142	157 83	175 92	193 100	210 109	250 128	325 165
53																151 78	168 87	186 95	203 103	240 121	313 156
54																145 74	162 82	179 89	195 97	232 114	301 147
55																140 70	156 77	173 85	188 92	223 108	290 139
56																135 66	151 73	166 80	181 87	215 102	280 132

(Continued)

TABLE NO. 27-4-B—STANDARD LOAD TABLE—OPEN WEB STEEL JOISTS, K-SERIES—(Continued)
(Based on a Maximum Allowable Tensile Stress of 30,000 psi)

Joist Designation	30K7	30K8	30K9	30K10	30K11	30K12
Depth (In.)	30	30	30	30	30	30
Approx. Wt. (lbs./ft.)	12.3	13.2	13.4	15.0	16.4	17.6
*Span (ft.) ↓						
30	550 543	550 543	550 543	550 543	550 543	550 543
31	534 508	550 520	550 520	550 520	550 520	550 520
32	501 461	549 500	549 500	549 500	549 500	549 500
33	471 420	520 460	532 468	532 468	532 468	532 468
34	443 384	490 420	516 441	516 441	516 441	516 441
35	418 351	462 384	501 415	501 415	501 415	501 415
36	395 323	436 353	475 383	487 392	487 392	487 392
37	373 297	413 325	449 352	474 374	474 374	474 374
38	354 274	391 300	426 325	461 353	461 353	461 353
39	336 253	371 277	404 300	449 333	449 333	449 333
40	319 234	353 256	384 278	438 315	438 315	438 315
41	303 217	335 238	365 258	427 300	427 300	427 300
42	289 202	320 221	348 240	413 282	417 284	417 284

43	276 188	305 206	332 223	394 263	407 270	407 270
44	263 176	291 192	317 208	376 245	398 258	398 258
45	251 164	278 179	303 195	359 229	389 246	389 246
46	241 153	266 168	290 182	344 214	380 236	380 236
47	230 144	255 157	277 171	329 201	372 226	372 226
48	221 135	244 148	266 160	315 188	362 215	365 216
49	212 127	234 139	255 150	303 177	347 202	357 207
50	203 119	225 130	245 141	291 166	333 190	350 199
51	195 112	216 123	235 133	279 157	320 179	343 192
52	188 106	208 116	226 126	268 148	308 169	336 184
53	181 100	200 109	218 119	258 140	296 159	330 177
54	174 94	192 103	209 112	249 132	285 150	324 170
55	168 89	185 98	202 106	240 125	275 142	312 161
56	162 84	179 92	195 100	231 118	265 135	301 153
57	156 80	173 88	188 95	223 112	256 128	290 145
58	151 76	167 83	181 90	215 106	247 121	280 137
59	146 72	161 79	175 86	208 101	239 115	271 130
60	141 69	156 75	169 81	201 96	231 109	262 124

*Span is (a) center line to center line of beams (or girders), when joist is supported by steel members; (b) clear span plus 8 inches, when joist is supported by masonry; or (c) center line of beam (or girder) to face of masonry support plus 4 inches, when joist is supported by steel members on one end and by masonry on the other end.

TABLE NO. 27-4-C—STANDARD LOAD TABLE—LONGSPAN STEEL JOISTS, LH SERIES (Based on a Maximum Allowable Tensile Stress of 30,000 psi[1])

The upper figures in the following table give the total safe uniformly distributed load-carrying capacities, in pounds per linear foot, of LH-Series joists. The weight of **dead** loads, including the joists, must in all cases be deducted to determine the **live** load-carrying capacities of the joists. The approximate **dead** load of the joists may be determined from the weights per linear foot shown in the tables.

The lower figures in this load table are the **live** loads per linear foot of joist which will produce an approximate deflection of 1/360 of the span. **Live** loads which will produce a deflection of 1/240 of the span may be obtained by multiplying the lower figures by 1.5. (**Note:** The tabulated loads corresponding to these deflection limitations have been computed on the basis of 30,000 psi allowable stress provisions. For joists designed to a lower working stress these loads may be increased in the ratio of 30,000 psi to the design stress used, in order to meet the same deflection limitations.) In no case shall the total load capacity of the joists be exceeded.

This load table applies to joists with either parallel chords or standard pitched top chords. When top chords are pitched, the carrying capacities are determined by the nominal depth of the joists at center of the span. Standard top chord pitch is $1/8$ inch per foot. If pitch exceeds this standard, the load table **does not** apply. The load table may be used for parallel chord joists installed to a maximum slope of $1/2$ inch per foot.

When holes are required in top or bottom chords, the carrying capacities must be reduced in proportion to reduction of chord areas.

The top chords are considered as being stayed laterally by floor slab or roof deck.

The approximate joist weights per linear foot shown in these tables do not include accessories.

JOIST DESIG-NATION	APPROX. WT. IN LBS. PER LINEAR FT.	NOMINAL DEPTH IN INCHES	SAFE LOAD[2] IN LBS. BETWEEN	CLEAR OPENING OR NET SPAN IN FEET														
			21-24	25	26	27	28	29	30	31	32	33	34	35	36			
18LH02	10	18	12,000	468	442	418	391	367	345	324	306	289	273	259	245			
				313	284	259	234	212	193	175	160	147	135	124	114			
18LH03	11	18	13,300	521	493	467	438	409	382	359	337	317	299	283	267			
				348	317	289	262	236	213	194	177	161	148	136	124			
18LH04	12	18	15,500	604	571	535	500	469	440	413	388	365	344	325	308			
				403	367	329	296	266	242	219	200	182	167	153	141			
18LH05	15	18	17,500	684	648	614	581	543	508	476	448	421	397	375	355			
				454	414	378	345	311	282	256	233	212	195	179	164			

18LH06	15	18	20,700	809	749	696	648	605	566	531	499	470	443	418	396				
				526	469	419	377	340	307	280	254	232	212	195	180				
18LH07	17	18	21,500	840	809	780	726	678	635	595	559	526	496	469	444				
				553	513	476	428	386	349	317	288	264	241	222	204				
18LH08	19	18	22,400	876	843	812	784	758	717	680	641	604	571	540	512				
				577	534	496	462	427	387	351	320	292	267	246	226				
18LH09	21	18	24,000	936	901	868	838	810	783	759	713	671	633	598	566				
				616	571	527	491	458	418	380	346	316	289	266	245				
			22-24	**25**	**26**	**27**	**28**	**29**	**30**	**31**	**32**	**33**	**34**	**35**	**36**	**37**	**38**	**39**	**40**
20LH02	10	20	11,300	442	437	431	410	388	365	344	325	307	291	275	262	249	237	225	215
				306	303	298	274	250	228	208	190	174	160	147	136	126	117	108	101
20LH03	11	20	12,000	469	463	458	452	434	414	395	372	352	333	316	299	283	269	255	243
				337	333	317	302	280	258	238	218	200	184	169	156	143	133	123	114
20LH04	12	20	14,700	574	566	558	528	496	467	440	416	393	372	353	335	318	303	289	275
				428	406	386	352	320	291	265	243	223	205	189	174	161	149	139	129
20LH05	14	20	15,800	616	609	602	595	571	544	513	484	458	434	411	390	371	353	336	321
				459	437	416	395	366	337	308	281	258	238	219	202	187	173	161	150
20LH06	15	20	21,100	822	791	763	723	679	635	596	560	527	497	469	444	421	399	379	361
				606	561	521	477	427	386	351	320	292	267	246	226	209	192	178	165
20LH07	17	20	22,500	878	845	814	786	760	711	667	627	590	556	526	497	471	447	425	404
				647	599	556	518	484	438	398	362	331	303	278	256	236	218	202	187
20LH08	19	20	23,200	908	873	842	813	785	760	722	687	654	621	588	558	530	503	479	457
				669	619	575	536	500	468	428	395	365	336	309	285	262	242	225	209
20LH09	21	20	25,400	990	953	918	886	856	828	802	778	755	712	673	636	603	572	544	517
				729	675	626	581	542	507	475	437	399	366	336	309	285	264	244	227
20LH10	23	20	27,400	1068	1028	991	956	924	894	865	839	814	791	748	707	670	636	604	575
				786	724	673	626	585	545	510	479	448	411	377	346	320	296	274	254

(Continued)

TABLE NO. 27-4-C—STANDARD LOAD TABLE—LONGSPAN STEEL JOISTS, LH SERIES—(Continued)
(Based on a Maximum Allowable Tensile Stress of 30,000 psi[1])

JOIST DESIG-NATION	APPROX. WT. IN LBS. PER LINEAR FT.	NOMINAL DEPTH IN INCHES	SAFE LOAD[2] IN LBS. BETWEEN	CLEAR OPENING OR NET SPAN IN FEET															
			28-32	33	34	35	36	37	38	39	40	41	42	43	44	45	46	47	48
24LH03	11	24	11,500	342	339	336	323	307	293	279	267	255	244	234	224	215	207	199	191
				235	226	218	204	188	175	162	152	141	132	124	116	109	102	96	90
24LH04	12	24	14,100	419	398	379	360	343	327	312	298	285	273	262	251	241	231	222	214
				288	265	246	227	210	195	182	169	158	148	138	130	122	114	107	101
24LH05	13	24	15,100	449	446	440	419	399	380	363	347	331	317	304	291	280	269	258	248
				308	297	285	264	244	226	210	196	182	171	160	150	141	132	124	117
24LH06	16	24	20,300	604	579	555	530	504	480	457	437	417	399	381	364	348	334	320	307
				411	382	356	331	306	284	263	245	228	211	197	184	172	161	152	142
24LH07	17	24	22,300	665	638	613	588	565	541	516	491	468	446	426	407	389	373	357	343
				452	421	393	367	343	320	297	276	257	239	223	208	195	182	171	161
24LH08	18	24	23,800	707	677	649	622	597	572	545	520	497	475	455	435	417	400	384	369
				480	447	416	388	362	338	314	292	272	254	238	222	208	196	184	173
24LH09	21	24	28,000	832	808	785	764	731	696	663	632	602	574	548	524	501	480	460	441
				562	530	501	460	424	393	363	337	313	292	272	254	238	223	209	196
24LH10	23	24	29,600	882	856	832	809	788	768	737	702	668	637	608	582	556	533	511	490
				596	559	528	500	474	439	406	378	251	326	304	285	266	249	234	220
24LH11	25	24	31,200	927	900	875	851	829	807	787	768	734	701	671	642	616	590	567	544
				624	588	555	525	498	472	449	418	388	361	337	315	294	276	259	243
			33-40	41	42	43	44	45	46	47	48	49	50	51	52	53	54	55	56
28LH05	13	28	14,000	337	323	310	297	286	275	265	255	245	237	228	220	213	206	199	193
				219	205	192	180	169	159	150	142	133	126	119	113	107	102	97	92
28LH06	16	28	18,600	448	429	412	395	379	364	350	337	324	313	301	291	281	271	262	253
				289	270	253	238	223	209	197	186	175	166	156	148	140	133	126	120
28LH07	17	28	21,000	505	484	464	445	427	410	394	379	365	352	339	327	316	305	295	285
				326	305	285	267	251	236	222	209	197	186	176	166	158	150	142	135

28LH08	18	28	22,500	540	517	496	475	456	438	420	403	387	371	357	344	331	319	308	297
				348	325	305	285	268	252	236	222	209	196	185	175	165	156	148	140
28LH09	21	28	27,700	667	639	612	586	563	540	519	499	481	463	446	430	415	401	387	374
				428	400	375	351	329	309	291	274	258	243	228	216	204	193	183	173
28LH10	27	23	30,300	729	704	679	651	625	600	576	554	533	513	495	477	460	444	429	415
				466	439	414	388	364	342	322	303	285	269	255	241	228	215	204	193
28LH11	25	28	32,500	780	762	736	711	682	655	629	605	582	561	540	521	502	485	468	453
				498	475	448	423	397	373	351	331	312	294	278	263	249	236	223	212
28LH12	27	28	35,700	857	837	818	800	782	766	737	709	682	656	632	609	587	566	546	527
				545	520	496	476	454	435	408	383	361	340	321	303	285	270	256	243
28LH13	30	28	37,200	895	874	854	835	816	799	782	766	751	722	694	668	643	620	598	577
				569	543	518	495	472	452	433	415	396	373	352	332	314	297	281	266
			38-48	**49**	**50**	**51**	**52**	**53**	**54**	**55**	**56**	**57**	**58**	**59**	**60**	**61**	**62**	**63**	**64**
32LH06	14	32	16,700	338	326	315	304	294	284	275	266	257	249	242	234	227	220	214	208
				211	199	189	179	169	161	153	145	138	131	125	119	114	108	104	99
32LH07	16	32	18,800	379	366	353	341	329	318	308	298	288	279	271	262	254	247	240	233
				235	223	211	200	189	179	170	162	154	146	140	133	127	121	116	111
32LH08	17	32	20,400	411	397	383	369	357	345	333	322	312	302	393	284	275	267	259	252
				255	242	229	216	205	194	184	175	167	159	151	144	137	131	125	120
32LH09	21	32	25,600	516	498	480	463	447	432	418	404	391	379	367	356	345	335	325	315
				319	302	285	270	256	243	230	219	208	198	189	180	172	164	157	149
32LH10	21	32	28,300	571	550	531	512	495	478	462	445	430	416	402	389	376	364	353	342
				352	332	315	297	282	267	254	240	228	217	206	196	186	178	169	162
32LH11	24	32	31,000	625	602	580	560	541	522	505	488	473	458	443	429	416	403	390	378
				385	363	343	325	308	292	277	263	251	239	227	216	206	196	187	179
32LH12	27	32	36,400	734	712	688	664	641	619	598	578	559	541	524	508	492	477	463	449
				450	428	406	384	364	345	327	311	295	281	267	255	243	232	221	211
32LH13	30	32	40,600	817	801	785	771	742	715	690	666	643	621	600	581	562	544	527	511
				500	480	461	444	420	397	376	354	336	319	304	288	275	262	249	238
32LH14	33	32	41,800	843	826	810	795	780	766	738	713	688	665	643	622	602	583	564	547
				515	495	476	458	440	417	395	374	355	337	321	304	290	276	264	251
32LH15	35	32	43,200	870	853	837	821	805	791	776	763	750	725	701	678	656	635	616	597
				532	511	492	473	454	438	422	407	393	374	355	338	322	306	292	279

(Continued)

TABLE NO. 27-4-C—STANDARD LOAD TABLE—LONGSPAN STEEL JOISTS, LH SERIES—(Continued)
(Based on a Maximum Allowable Tensile Stress of 30,000 psi[1])

JOIST DESIG-NATION	APPROX. WT. IN LBS. PER LINEAR FT.	NOMINAL DEPTH IN INCHES	SAFE LOAD[2] IN LBS. BETWEEN	CLEAR OPENING OR NET SPAN IN FEET															
			42-56	57	58	59	60	61	62	63	64	65	66	67	68	69	70	71	72
36LH07	16	36	16,800	292	283	274	266	258	251	244	237	230	224	218	212	207	201	196	191
				177	168	160	153	146	140	134	128	122	117	112	107	103	99	95	91
36LH08	18	36	18,500	321	311	302	293	284	276	268	260	253	246	239	233	227	221	215	209
				194	185	176	168	160	153	146	140	134	128	123	118	113	109	104	100
36LH09	21	36	23,700	411	398	386	374	363	352	342	333	323	314	306	297	289	282	275	267
				247	235	224	214	204	195	186	179	171	163	157	150	144	138	133	127
36LH10	21	36	26,100	454	440	426	413	401	389	378	367	357	347	338	328	320	311	303	295
				273	260	248	236	225	215	206	197	188	180	173	165	159	152	146	140
36LH11	23	36	28,500	495	480	465	451	438	425	412	401	389	378	368	358	348	339	330	322
				297	283	269	257	246	234	224	214	205	196	188	180	173	166	159	153
36LH12	25	36	34,100	593	575	557	540	523	508	493	478	464	450	437	424	412	400	389	378
				354	338	322	307	292	279	267	255	243	232	222	213	204	195	187	179
36LH13	30	36	40,100	697	675	654	634	615	596	579	562	546	531	516	502	488	475	463	451
				415	395	376	359	342	327	312	298	285	273	262	251	240	231	222	213
36LH14	36	36	44,200	768	755	729	706	683	661	641	621	602	584	567	551	535	520	505	492
				456	434	412	392	373	356	339	323	309	295	283	270	259	247	237	228
36LH15	36	36	46,600	809	795	781	769	744	721	698	677	656	637	618	600	583	567	551	536
				480	464	448	434	413	394	375	358	342	327	312	299	286	274	263	252
			47-64	65	66	67	68	69	70	71	72	73	74	75	76	77	78	79	80
40LH08	16	40	16,600	254	247	241	234	228	222	217	211	206	201	196	192	187	183	178	174
				150	144	138	132	127	122	117	112	109	104	100	97	93	90	86	83
40LH09	21	40	21,800	332	323	315	306	298	291	283	276	269	263	256	250	244	239	233	228
				196	188	180	173	166	160	153	147	141	136	131	126	122	118	113	109
40LH10	21	40	24,000	367	357	347	338	329	321	313	305	297	290	283	276	269	262	255	249
				216	207	198	190	183	176	169	162	156	150	144	139	134	129	124	119

40LH11	22	40	26,200	399	388	378	368	358	349	340	332	323	315	308	300	293	286	279	273
				234	224	215	207	198	190	183	176	169	163	157	151	145	140	135	130
40LH12	25	40	31,900	486	472	459	447	435	424	413	402	392	382	373	364	355	346	338	330
				285	273	261	251	241	231	222	213	205	197	189	182	176	169	163	157
40LH13	30	40	37,600	573	557	542	528	514	500	487	475	463	451	440	429	419	409	399	390
				334	320	307	295	283	271	260	250	241	231	223	214	207	199	192	185
40LH14	35	40	43,000	656	638	620	603	587	571	556	542	528	515	502	490	478	466	455	444
				383	367	351	336	323	309	297	285	273	263	252	243	233	225	216	209
40LH15	36	40	48,100	734	712	691	671	652	633	616	599	583	567	552	538	524	511	498	486
				427	408	390	373	357	342	328	315	302	290	279	268	258	248	239	230
40LH16	42	40	53,000	808	796	784	772	761	751	730	710	691	673	655	638	622	606	591	576
				469	455	441	428	416	404	387	371	356	342	329	316	304	292	282	271
			52-72	**73**	**74**	**75**	**76**	**77**	**78**	**79**	**80**	**81**	**82**	**83**	**84**	**85**	**86**	**87**	**88**
44LH09	19	44	20,000	272	265	259	253	247	242	236	231	226	221	216	211	207	202	198	194
				158	152	146	141	136	131	127	122	118	114	110	106	103	99	96	93
44LH10	21	44	22,100	300	293	286	279	272	266	260	254	249	243	238	233	228	223	218	214
				174	168	162	155	150	144	139	134	130	125	121	117	113	110	106	103
44LH11	22	44	23,900	325	317	310	302	295	289	282	276	269	264	258	252	247	242	236	232
				188	181	175	168	162	157	151	146	140	136	131	127	123	119	115	111
44LH12	25	44	29,600	402	393	383	374	365	356	347	339	331	323	315	308	300	293	287	280
				232	224	215	207	200	192	185	179	172	166	160	155	149	144	139	134
44LH13	30	44	35,100	477	466	454	444	433	423	413	404	395	386	377	369	361	353	346	338
				275	265	254	246	236	228	220	212	205	198	191	185	179	173	167	161
44LH14	31	44	40,400	549	534	520	506	493	481	469	457	446	436	425	415	406	396	387	379
				315	302	291	279	268	259	249	240	231	223	215	207	200	193	187	181
44LH15	36	44	47,000	639	623	608	593	579	565	551	537	524	512	500	488	476	466	455	445
				366	352	339	326	314	303	292	281	271	261	252	243	234	227	219	211
44LH16	42	44	54,200	737	719	701	684	668	652	637	622	608	594	580	568	555	543	531	520
				421	405	390	375	362	348	336	324	313	302	291	282	272	263	255	246
44LH17	47	44	58,200	790	780	769	759	750	732	715	699	683	667	652	638	624	610	597	584
				450	438	426	415	405	390	376	363	351	338	327	316	305	295	285	276

(Continued)

TABLE NO. 27-4-C—STANDARD LOAD TABLE—LONGSPAN STEEL JOISTS, LH SERIES—(Continued)
(Based on a Maximum Allowable Tensile Stress of 30,000 psi[1])

JOIST DESIG-NATION	APPROX. WT. IN LBS. PER LINEAR FT.	NOMINAL DEPTH IN INCHES	SAFE LOAD[2] IN LBS. BETWEEN	CLEAR OPENING OR NET SPAN IN FEET															
			56-80	81	82	83	84	85	86	87	88	89	90	91	92	93	94	95	96
48LH10	21	48	20,000	246	241	236	231	226	221	217	212	208	204	200	196	192	188	185	181
				141	136	132	127	123	119	116	112	108	105	102	99	96	93	90	87
48LH11	22	48	21,700	266	260	255	249	244	239	234	229	225	220	216	212	208	204	200	196
				152	147	142	137	133	129	125	120	117	113	110	106	103	100	97	94
48LH12	25	48	27,400	336	329	322	315	308	301	295	289	283	277	272	266	261	256	251	246
				191	185	179	173	167	161	156	151	147	142	138	133	129	126	122	118
48LH13	29	48	32,800	402	393	384	376	368	360	353	345	338	332	325	318	312	306	300	294
				228	221	213	206	199	193	187	180	175	170	164	159	154	150	145	141
48LH14	32	48	38,700	475	464	454	444	434	425	416	407	399	390	383	375	367	360	353	346
				269	260	251	243	234	227	220	212	206	199	193	187	181	176	171	165
48LH15	36	48	44,500	545	533	521	510	499	488	478	468	458	448	439	430	422	413	405	397
				308	298	287	278	269	260	252	244	236	228	221	214	208	201	195	189
48LH16	42	48	51,300	629	615	601	588	576	563	551	540	528	518	507	497	487	477	468	459
				355	343	331	320	310	299	289	280	271	263	255	247	239	232	225	218
48LH17	47	48	57,600	706	690	675	660	646	632	619	606	593	581	569	558	547	536	525	515
				397	383	371	358	346	335	324	314	304	294	285	276	268	260	252	245

[1]For an approximate load-carrying capacity at a maximum allowable tensile stress of 22,000 psi, the total load-carrying capacity shown in the load table should be multiplied by the ratio 22/30.

[2]To solve for safe uniform load between spans shown, divide the safe load in pounds by net span in feet plus .67 feet. (The added .67 feet, eight inches, is necessary to obtain the proper span for which the load tables were developed.)

In no case shall the safe uniform load exceed the uniform load calculated for the minimum span listed.

To solve for live load between spans shown, multiply the live load of the shortest net span shown in the load table by the (shortest net span plus .67 feet)2, and divide by the (actual net span plus .67 feet)2. The live load shall not exceed the safe uniform load.

TABLE NO. 27-4-D—STANDARD LOAD TABLE FOR DEEP LONGSPAN STEEL JOISTS, DLH SERIES (Based on a Maximum Allowable Tensile Stress of 30,000 psi[1])

All loads shown are for roof construction only. The weight of **dead** loads, including weight of joists, must in all cases be deducted to determine the **live** load-carrying capacity of the joists. Approximate weights per linear foot of joist do not include accessories.

The lower figures are the **live** loads per linear foot of joist which will produce an approximate deflection of 1/360 of the span. Loads which will produce an approximate deflection of 1/240 of the span may be obtained by multiplying the lower figures by 1.5. (**Note:** The tabulated loads corresponding to these deflection limitations have been computed on the basis of 30,000 psi allowable stress provisions. For joists designed to a lower working stress, these loads may be increased in the ratio of 30,000 psi to the design stress used, in order to meet the same deflection limitations.) In no case shall the total capacity of the joists be exceeded.

When holes are required in the top or bottom chords, the carrying capacities must be reduced in proportion to reduction of chord areas.

The top chords are considered as being stayed laterally by the roof deck.

The load table applies to joists with either parallel chords or standard pitched chords. When top chords are pitched, the carrying capacities are determined by the nominal depth of the joist at the center of the span. Standard top chord pitch is 1/8 inch per foot. If pitch exceeds this standard, the load table **does not** apply.

The load table may be used for parallel chord joists installed to a maximum slope of 1/2 inch per foot.

JOIST DESIG-NATION	APPROX. WT. IN LBS. PER LINEAR FT.	NOMINAL DEPTH IN INCHES	SAFE LOAD[2] IN LBS. BETWEEN	CLEAR OPENING OR NET SPAN IN FEET															
			61-88	89	90	91	92	93	94	95	96	97	98	99	100	101	102	103	104
52DLH10	25	52	26,700	298	291	285	279	273	267	261	256	251	246	241	236	231	227	223	218
				171	165	159	154	150	145	140	136	132	128	124	120	116	114	110	107
52DLH11	26	52	29,300	327	320	313	306	299	293	287	281	275	270	264	259	254	249	244	240
				187	181	174	169	164	158	153	149	144	140	135	132	128	124	120	117
52DLH12	29	52	32,700	365	357	349	342	334	327	320	314	307	301	295	289	284	278	273	268
				204	197	191	185	179	173	168	163	158	153	149	144	140	135	132	128

(Continued)

TABLE NO. 27-4-D—STANDARD LOAD TABLE FOR DEEP LONGSPAN STEEL JOISTS, DLH SERIES—(Continued)
(Based on a Maximum Allowable Tensile Stress of 30,000 psi[1])

JOIST DESIGNATION	APPROX. WT. IN LBS. PER LINEAR FT.	NOMINAL DEPTH IN INCHES	SAFE LOAD[2] IN LBS. BETWEEN	CLEAR OPENING OR NET SPAN IN FEET															
			61-88	89	90	91	92	93	94	95	96	97	98	99	100	101	102	103	104
52DLH13	34	52	39,700	443	433	424	414	406	397	389	381	373	366	358	351	344	338	331	325
				247	239	231	224	216	209	203	197	191	185	180	174	170	164	159	155
52DLH14	39	52	45,400	507	497	486	476	466	457	447	438	430	421	413	405	397	390	382	375
				276	266	258	249	242	234	227	220	213	207	201	194	189	184	178	173
52DLH15	42	52	51,000	569	557	545	533	522	511	500	490	480	470	461	451	443	434	426	418
				311	301	291	282	272	264	256	247	240	233	226	219	213	207	201	195
52DLH16	45	52	55,000	614	601	588	575	563	551	540	528	518	507	497	487	478	468	459	451
				346	335	324	314	304	294	285	276	267	260	252	245	237	230	224	217
52DLH17	52	52	63,300	706	691	676	661	647	634	620	608	595	583	572	560	549	539	528	518
				395	381	369	357	346	335	324	315	304	296	286	279	270	263	255	247
			66-96	97	98	99	100	101	102	103	104	105	106	107	108	109	110	111	112
56DLH11	26	56	28,100	288	283	277	272	267	262	257	253	248	244	239	235	231	227	223	219
				169	163	158	153	149	145	140	136	133	129	125	122	118	115	113	110
56DLH12	30	56	32,300	331	324	318	312	306	300	295	289	284	278	273	268	263	259	254	249
				184	178	173	168	163	158	153	150	145	141	137	133	130	126	123	119
56DLH13	34	56	39,100	401	394	386	379	372	365	358	351	344	338	331	325	319	314	308	303
				223	216	209	204	197	191	186	181	175	171	166	161	157	152	149	145
56DLH14	39	56	44,200	453	444	435	427	419	411	403	396	388	381	375	368	361	355	349	343
				249	242	234	228	221	214	209	202	196	190	186	181	175	171	167	162
56DLH15	42	56	50,500	518	508	498	488	478	469	460	451	443	434	426	419	411	403	396	389
				281	272	264	256	248	242	234	228	221	215	209	204	198	192	188	182
56DLH16	46	56	54,500	559	548	537	526	516	506	496	487	478	469	460	452	444	436	428	420
				313	304	294	285	277	269	262	254	247	240	233	227	221	214	209	204
56DLH17	51	56	62,800	643	630	618	605	594	582	571	560	549	539	529	520	510	501	492	483
				356	345	335	325	316	306	298	289	281	273	266	258	251	245	238	231

			70-104	105	106	107	108	109	110	111	112	113	114	115	116	117	118	119	120
60DLH12	29	60	31,100	295	289	284	279	274	270	265	261	256	252	248	244	240	236	232	228
				168	163	158	154	150	146	142	138	134	131	128	124	121	118	115	113
60DLH13	35	60	37,800	358	351	345	339	333	327	322	316	311	306	301	296	291	286	282	277
				203	197	191	187	181	176	171	167	163	158	154	151	147	143	139	135
60DLH14	40	60	42,000	398	391	383	376	370	363	356	350	344	338	332	327	321	316	310	305
				216	210	205	199	193	189	183	178	173	170	165	161	156	152	149	145
60DLH15	43	60	49,300	467	458	450	442	434	427	419	412	405	398	392	385	379	373	367	361
				255	248	242	235	228	223	216	210	205	200	194	190	185	180	175	171
60DLH16	46	60	54,200	513	504	494	485	476	468	460	451	444	436	428	421	414	407	400	393
				285	277	269	262	255	247	241	235	228	223	217	211	206	201	196	190
60DLH17	52	60	62,300	590	579	569	558	548	538	529	519	510	501	493	484	476	468	460	453
				324	315	306	298	290	283	275	267	261	254	247	241	235	228	223	217
60DLH18	59	60	71,900	681	668	656	644	632	621	610	599	589	578	568	559	549	540	531	522
				366	357	346	337	327	319	310	303	294	286	279	272	266	259	252	246
			75-112	**113**	**114**	**115**	**116**	**117**	**118**	**119**	**120**	**121**	**122**	**123**	**124**	**125**	**126**	**127**	**128**
64DLH12	31	64	30,000	264	259	255	251	247	243	239	235	231	228	224	221	218	214	211	208
				153	150	146	142	138	135	132	129	125	122	119	116	114	111	109	106
64DLH13	34	64	36,400	321	315	310	305	300	295	291	286	281	277	273	269	264	260	257	253
				186	181	176	171	168	163	159	155	152	148	144	141	137	134	131	128
64DLH14	40	64	41,700	367	360	354	349	343	337	332	326	321	316	311	306	301	296	292	287
				199	193	189	184	179	174	171	166	162	158	154	151	147	143	140	136
64DLH15	43	64	47,800	421	414	407	400	394	387	381	375	369	363	358	352	347	341	336	331
				234	228	223	217	211	206	201	196	191	187	182	177	173	170	165	161
64DLH16	46	64	53,800	474	466	458	450	443	435	428	421	414	407	401	394	388	382	376	370
				262	254	248	242	235	229	224	218	213	208	203	198	193	189	184	180
64DLH17	52	64	62,000	546	536	527	518	509	501	492	484	476	468	461	454	446	439	432	426
				298	290	283	275	268	262	255	248	243	237	231	226	220	215	210	205
64DLH18	59	64	71,600	630	619	608	598	587	578	568	559	549	540	532	523	515	507	499	491
				337	328	320	311	304	296	288	282	274	267	261	255	249	243	237	232

(Continued)

TABLE NO. 27-4-D—STANDARD LOAD TABLE FOR DEEP LONGSPAN STEEL JOISTS, DLH SERIES—(Continued)
(Based on a Maximum Allowable Tensile Stress of 30,000 psi[1])

JOIST DESIG-NATION	APPROX. WT. IN LBS. PER LINEAR FT.	NOMINAL DEPTH IN INCHES	SAFE LOAD[2] IN LBS. BETWEEN	CLEAR OPENING OR NET SPAN IN FEET															
			80-120	121	122	123	124	125	126	127	128	129	130	131	132	133	134	135	136
68DLH13	37	68	35,000	288	284	279	275	271	267	263	259	255	252	248	244	241	237	234	231
				171	168	164	159	155	152	149	145	142	138	135	133	130	127	124	121
68DLH14	40	68	40,300	332	327	322	317	312	308	303	299	294	290	286	281	277	273	269	266
				184	179	175	171	167	163	159	155	152	148	145	141	138	135	133	130
68DLH15	40	68	45,200	372	365	360	354	348	343	337	332	327	322	317	312	308	303	299	294
				206	201	196	191	187	182	178	174	170	166	162	158	155	152	148	145
68DLH16	49	68	53,600	441	433	427	420	413	407	400	394	388	382	376	371	365	360	354	349
				242	236	230	225	219	214	209	204	199	195	190	186	182	178	174	171
68DLH17	55	68	60,400	497	489	481	474	467	460	453	446	439	433	427	420	414	408	403	397
				275	268	262	256	249	244	238	232	228	222	217	212	208	203	198	194
68DLH18	61	68	69,900	575	566	557	549	540	532	524	516	508	501	493	486	479	472	465	459
				311	304	297	289	283	276	269	263	257	251	246	240	234	230	225	219
68DLH19	67	68	80,500	662	651	641	631	621	611	601	592	583	574	565	557	548	540	532	525
				353	344	336	328	320	313	305	298	291	285	278	272	266	260	254	248

			84-128	129	130	131	132	133	134	135	136	137	138	139	140	141	142	143	144
72DLH14	41	72	39,200	303	298	294	290	285	281	277	274	270	266	262	259	255	252	248	245
				171	167	163	159	155	152	149	146	143	139	136	133	131	128	125	123
72DLH15	44	72	44,900	347	342	336	331	326	322	317	312	308	303	299	295	291	286	282	279
				191	187	183	178	174	171	167	163	160	156	152	150	147	143	140	137
72DLH16	50	72	51,900	401	395	390	384	378	373	368	363	358	353	348	343	338	334	329	325
				225	219	214	209	205	200	196	191	188	183	179	175	171	169	165	161
72DLH17	56	72	58,400	451	445	438	432	426	420	414	408	402	397	391	386	381	376	371	366
				256	250	245	239	233	228	224	218	213	209	205	200	196	191	188	184
72DLH18	59	72	68,400	528	520	512	505	497	490	483	479	470	463	457	450	444	438	432	426
				289	283	276	270	265	258	252	247	242	236	231	227	222	217	212	209
72DLH19	70	72	80,200	619	609	600	591	582	573	565	557	549	541	533	526	518	511	504	497
				328	321	313	306	300	293	286	280	274	268	263	257	251	247	241	236

[1]For an approximate load-carrying capacity at a maximum allowable tensile stress of 22,000 psi, the total load-carrying capacity shown in the load table should be multiplied by the ratio 22/30.

[2]To solve for safe uniform load between spans shown, divide the safe load in pounds by net span in feet plus .67 feet. (The added .67 feet, 8 inches, is necessary to obtain the proper span for which the load tables were developed.)

In no case shall the safe uniform load exceed the uniform load calculated for the minimum span listed.

To solve for live load between spans shown, multiply the live load of the shortest net span shown in the load table by the (shortest net span plus .67 feet)2, and divide by the (actual net span plus .67 feet)2. The live load shall not exceed the safe uniform load.

TABLE NO. 27-4-E
MAXIMUM AND EFFECTIVE SLENDERNESS RATIOS

I. Top Chord Interior Panel				
A. The slenderness ratios, $1.0l/r$ and $1.0l_s/r$, of members as a whole or any component part shall not exceed 90.				
B. The effective slenderness ratio to determine "F_a"				
1. With fillers or ties	$0.75l/r_x$	$1.0l/r_y$		$1.0l_s/r_z$
2. Without fillers or ties			$0.75l/r_z$	
3. Single-component members	$0.75l/r_x$	$1.0l/r_y$		
C. The effective slenderness ratio to determine "F'_e"				
1. With fillers or ties	$0.75l/r_x$			
2. Without fillers or ties	$0.75l/r_x$			
3. Single-component members	$0.75l/r_x$			
II. Top Chord End Panel				
A. The slenderness ratios, $1.0l/r$ and $1.0l_s/r$, of members as a whole or any component part shall not exceed 120.				
B. The effective slenderness ratio to determine "F_a"				
1. With fillers or ties	$1.0l/r_x$	$1.0l/r_y$		$1.0l_s/r_z$
2. Without fillers or ties			$1.0l/r_z$	
3. Single-component members	$1.0l/r_x$	$1.0l/r_y$		
C. The effective slenderness ratio to determine "F'_e"				
1. With fillers or ties	$1.0l/r_x$			
2. Without fillers or ties	$1.0l/r_x$			
3. Single-component members	$1.0l/r_x$			
III. Tension Members—Chords and Webs				
A. The slenderness ratios, $1.0l/r$ and $1.0l_s/r$, of members as a whole or any component part shall not exceed 240.				
IV. Compression Web Members				
A. The slenderness ratios, $1.0l/r$ and $1.0l_s/r$, of members as a whole or any component part shall not exceed 200.				
B. The effective slenderness ratio to determine "F_a"				
1. With fillers or ties	$0.75l/r_x$	$1.0l/r_y$		$1.0l_s/r_z$
2. Without fillers or ties			$1.0l/r_z$	
3. Single-component members	$0.75l/r_x$[1]	$1.0l/r_y$		

[1]If moment-resistant weld groups are not used at the ends of a crimped, first primary compression web member, then $1.2l/r_x$ must be used.

UNIFORM BUILDING CODE STANDARD NO. 27-6

STRUCTURAL WELDING

See Sections 2702 (e), 2714 (a), 2722 (a) and (f) and Table No. 27-B, Uniform Building Code

Adoption of AWS Code

Sec. 27.601. Except for the limitations, deletions, modifications or amendments set forth in Section 27.602 of this standard, the welding of structural steel shall be in accordance with the "Structural Welding Code—Steel," ANSI/AWS D1.1-90, published by the American Welding Society, Inc., copyright 1990, 550 North LeJeune Road, Miami, Florida 33126, as if set out at length herein.

Amendments

Sec. 27.602. (a) **General.** The American Welding Society, Inc., standard adopted by Section 27.601 applies to the materials, processes design, workmanship, testing and inspection of structural welding of buildings and structures except as set forth in this section or U.B.C. Standard No. 27-14 or 27-15.

(b) **Deletions.** The following sections and chapters are deleted.

Section 1.2.1

Section 1.6

Section 1.7

Sections 6.1 through and including 6.6

Chapter 9

Chapter 11

(c) **Amendments.**

1. **Sec. 1.1.1** is amended to read as follows:

   1.1.1 This code covers welding requirements applicable to any type of welded structure. It is to be used in conjunction with the Uniform Building Code for the design and construction of steel structures. It is not intended to apply to pressure vessels or pressure piping.

2. **Sec. 1.2.3** is amended by replacing references to AWS D1.3 with U.B.C. Standard 27-13.

3. **Sec. 1.5** is amended to read as follows:

   1.5 Definitions

   The welding terms used in this code shall be interpreted in accordance with the definitions given in Appendix I of this code.

4. **Sec. 2.2** is amended to read as follows:

   2.2 Basic Unit Stresses

   Allowable unit stresses for base metals and for effective areas of weld metal for application to buildings and structures shall be as shown in the Uniform Building Code or U.B.C. Standard No. 27-14 or 27-15.

UNIFORM BUILDING CODE STANDARD NO. 27-7

HIGH-STRENGTH BOLTS

Based on the Allowable Stress Design Specification for Structural Joints Using ASTM A 325 or A 490 Bolts

Approved by the Research Council on Structural Connections of the Engineering Foundation, November 18,1985, and endorsed by American Institute of Steel Construction and by Industrial Fasteners Institute

See Sections 2701 (a) and 2708, Uniform Building Code

Scope

Sec. 27.701. This standard relates to the allowable stress design for strength and slip resistance of structural joints using A 325 high-strength bolts, A 490 heat-treated high-strength bolts or equivalent fasteners, and for the installation of such bolts in connections of structural steel members. The standard relates only to those aspects of the connected materials that bear upon the performance of the fasteners.

Construction shall conform to applicable requirements of the Uniform Building Code except as otherwise provided herein.

Bolts, Nuts Washers and Paint

Sec. 27.702. (a) **Bolt Specifications.** Bolts shall conform to the requirements of U.B.C. Standard No. 27-1 except as provided in Section 27.702 (d). The designer shall specify the type of bolts to be used.

(b) **Bolt Geometry.** Bolt dimensions shall conform to Table No. 27-7-F, except as provided in Section 27.702 (d). The length of bolts shall be such that the end of the bolt will be flush with or outside the face of the nut.

(c) **Nut Specifications.** Nuts shall conform to the chemical and mechanical requirements of Tables Nos. 27-7-G, 27-7-H and 27-7-I. The grade and surface finish of nuts for each bolt type shall be as follows:

A 325 Bolt Type	Nut Specifications, Grade and Finish
1 and 2, plain (uncoated)	C, C3, D, DH and DH3 or 2 and 2H; plain
1 and 2, galvanized	DH or 2H; galvanized
3 plain	C3 and DH3

A 490 Bolt Type	Nut Specification, Grade and Finish
1 and 2, plain	DH and DH3 or 2H; plain
3 plain	DH3

Nut dimensions shall conform to the requirements of Table No. 27-7-J except as provided in Section 27.702 (d).

(d) **Alternate Fastener Designs.** Other fasteners or fastener assemblies which meet the materials, manufacturing, chemical composition and mechanical property requirements of A 325 or A 490 high-strength bolts and which have a body diameter and bearing areas under the head and nut not less than those provided by a bolt and nut of the same nominal dimensions prescribed by Section 27.702 (b) and (c), may be used. Such alternate fasteners may differ in other dimensions from those of the specified bolts and nuts. Their installation procedure and inspection may differ from procedures specified for regular high-strength bolts in Sections 27.708 and 27.709. When a different installation procedure or inspection is used, it shall be detailed in a supplemental specification applying to the alternate fastener and that specification must be approved by the engineer responsible for the design of the structure.

(e) **Washers.** Flat circular washers and square or rectangular beveled washers shall conform to the requirements of Tables Nos. 27-7-K, 27-7-L, 27-7-M and 27-7-N.

(f) **Load-indicating Devices.** Load-indicating devices may be used in conjunction with bolts, nuts and washers specified in Subsections 27.702 (a) through (c), provided they satisfy the requirements of Section 27.708 (d) (4). Their installation procedure and inspection shall be detailed in supplemental specifications provided by the manufacturer and subject to the approval of the engineer responsible for the design of the structure.

(g) **Faying Surface Coatings.** Paint, if used on faying surfaces of connections which are not specified to be slip critical, may be of any formulation. Paint, used on the faying surfaces of connections specified to be slip critical, shall be qualified by approved test methods to determine the slip coefficient for coatings used in bolted joints.

Bolted Parts

Sec. 27.703. (a) **Connected Material.** All material within the grip of the bolt shall be steel. There shall be no compressible material such as gaskets or insulation within the grip. Bolted steel parts shall fit solidly together after the bolts are tightened and may be coated or noncoated. The slope of the surfaces of parts in contact with the bolt head or nut shall not exceed 1:20 with respect to a plane normal to the bolt axis.

(b) **Surface Conditions.** When assembled, all joint surfaces, including surfaces adjacent to the bolt head and nut, shall be free of scale, except tight mill scale, and shall be free of dirt or other foreign material. Burrs that would prevent solid seating of the connected parts in the snug tight condition shall be removed.

Paint is permitted on the faying surfaces unconditionally in connections, except in slip-critical connections as defined in Section 27.705 (a).

The faying surfaces of slip-critical connections shall meet the requirements of the following paragraphs, as applicable.

1. In noncoated joints, paint, including any inadvertent overspray, shall be excluded from areas closer than one bolt diameter but not less than 1 inch from the edge of any hole and all areas within bolt pattern.

2. Joints specified to have painted faying surfaces shall be blast cleaned and coated with a paint which has been qualified as Class A or B in accordance with the requirements of Section 27.702 (g), except as provided in Subsection 27.703 (b) (3).

3. Subject to the approval of the building official, coatings providing a slip coefficient less than 0.33 may be used, provided the mean slip coefficient is established by test in accordance with the requirements of Section 27.702 (g) and the allowable slip load per unit area established. The allowable slip load per unit shall be taken as equal to the allowable slip load per unit area from Table No. 27-7-C for Class A coatings as appropriate for the hole type and bolt type times the slip coefficient determined by test divided by 0.33.

4. Coated joints shall not be assembled before the coatings have cured for the minimum time used in the qualifying test.

5. Galvanized faying surfaces shall be hot dip galvanized in accordance with Table No. 27-7-0 and shall be roughened by means of hand wire brushing. Power wire brushing is not permitted.

(c) **Hole Types.** Hole types recognized under this specification are standard holes, oversize holes, short slotted holes and long slotted holes. The nominal dimensions for each type hole shall be not greater than those shown in Table No. 27-7-A. Holes shall not be more than 1/32 inch larger in diameter than the true decimal equivalent of the nominal diameter. The slightly conical hole that naturally results from punching operations is considered acceptable. The width of slotted holes which are produced by flame cutting or a combination of drilling or punching and flame cutting shall generally be not more than 1/32 inch greater than the nominal width, except that gouges not more than 1/16 inch deep shall be permitted. For statically loaded connections, the flame-cut surface need not be ground. For dynamically loaded connections, the flame-cut surface shall be ground smooth.

Design for Strength of Bolted Connections

Sec. 27.704. (a) **Allowable Strength.** The allowable working stress in shear and bearing, independent of the method of tightening, for A 325 and A 490 bolts shall be as set forth in Table No. 27-7-B. The allowable working stress in axial tension for A 325 and A 490 bolts which are tightened to the minimum fastener tension shall be in accordance with Table No. 27-7-D. The allowable working stresses in Table No. 27-7-B are to be used in conjunction with the cross-sectional area of the bolt corresponding to the nominal diameter.

(b) **Bearing Force.** The computed bearing force shall be assumed to be distributed over an area equal to the nominal bolt diameter times the thickness of the connected part.

A value of allowable bearing pressure on the connected material at a bolt greater than permitted by Table No. 27-7-B may be justified, provided deformation around the bolt hole is not a design consideration and adequate pitch and end distance L is provided according to:

$$F_p = LF_u/2d \leq 1.5F_u$$

WHERE:

d = bolt diameter

F_p = allowable bearing pressure at a bolt

F_u = specified minimum tensile strength of connected part

(c) **Prying Action.** The force in bolts required to support loads by means of direct tension shall be calculated considering the effects of the external load and any tension resulting from prying action produced by deformation of the connected parts.

(d) **Tensile Fatigue.** When subject to tensile fatigue loading, the tensile stress in the bolt due to the combined applied load and prying forces shall not exceed the following values, depending upon the bolt grade and number of cycles, and the prying force shall not exceed 60 percent of the externally applied load.

Number of Cycles	A 325	A 490
Not more than 20,000	44	54
From 20,000 to 500,000	40	49
More than 500,000	31	38

Bolts shall be tensioned to requirements of Table No. 27-7-D

Design Check for Slip Resistance.

Sec. 27.705. (a) **Slip-critical Joints.** Slip-critical joints are defined as joints in which slip would be detrimental to the serviceability of the structure. They include:

1. Joints subject to fatigue loading.

2. Joints with bolts installed in oversized holes.

3. Except where the engineer intends otherwise and so indicates in the plans or specifications, joints with bolts installed in slotted holes where the force on the joint is in a direction other than normal (between approximately 80 and 100 degrees) to the axis of the slot.

4. Joints subject to significant load reversal.

5. Joints in which welds and bolts are in transmitting load at a common faying surface.

6. Joints in which any slip would be critical to the performance of the joint or the structure and so designated on the contract plans and specifications.

(b) **Allowable Slip Load.** In addition to the requirements of Section 27.704, the force on a slip-critical joint shall not exceed the allowable resistance P_s of the connection according to:

$$P_s = F_s A_b N_b N_s$$

WHERE:

F_s = allowable slip load per unit area of bolt from Table No. 27-7-C
A_b = area corresponding to the nominal body area of the bolt
N_b = number of bolts in the joint
N_s = number of slip planes

Class A, B or C surface conditions of the bolted parts as defined in Table No. 27-7-C shall be used in joints designated as slip-critical except as permitted in Section 27.703 (b) 3.

Increase in Allowable Stresses

Sec. 27.706. When an increase in working stress for loads in combination with wind or seismic forces is permitted, increases in working stresses may be applied with wind or seismic forces. The increases in working stresses may be applied to the allowable stresses in Sections 27.704 and 27.705. When the effect of loads in combination with wind or seismic forces are accounted for by reduction in the load factors, the allowable stresses in Section 27.704 and 27.705 shall not be increased.

Design Details of Bolted Connections

Sec. 27.707. (a) **Standard Holes.** In the absence of approval by the engineer for use of other hole types, standard holes shall be used in high-strength bolted connections.

(b) **Oversize and Slotted Holes.** When approved by the building official, oversize, short-slotted holes or long-slotted holes may be used, subject to the following joint detail requirements:

1. Oversize holes may be used in all plies of connections in which the allowable slip resistance of the connection is greater than the applied load.

2. Short-slotted holes may be used in any or all plies of connections designed on the basis of allowable stress on the fasteners in Table No. 27-7-B, provided the load is applied approximately normal (between 80 and 100 degrees) to the axis of the slot. Short-slotted holes may be used without regard for the direction of applied load in any or all plies of connections in which the allowable slip resistance is greater than the applied force.

3. Long-slotted holes may be used in one of the connected parts at any individual faying surface in connections designed on the basis of allowable stress on the fasteners in Table No. 27-7-B, provided the load is applied approximately normal (between 80 and 100 degrees) to the axis of the slot. Long-slotted holes may be used in one of the connected parts at any individual faying surface without regard for the direction of applied load on connections in which the allowable slip resistance is greater than the applied force.

4. Fully inserted finger shims between the faying surfaces of load transmitting elements of connections are not to be considered a long-slot element of a connection.

(c) **Washer Requirements.** Design details shall provide for washers in high strength bolted connections as follows:

1. Where outer face of the bolted parts has a slope greater than 1:20 with respect to a plane normal to the bolt axis, a hardened beveled washer shall be used to compensate for the lack of parallelism.

2. Hardened washers are not required for connections using A 325 and A 490 bolts except as required in Subsections 27.707 (c) 3 through 7 for slip-critical connections and connections subject to direct tension or as required by Section 27.708 (c) for shear/bearing connections.

3. Hardened washers shall be used under the element turned in tightening when the tightening is to be performed by calibrated wrench method.

4. Irrespective of the tightening method, hardened washers shall be used under both the head and the nut when A 490 bolts are to be installed and tightened to the tension specified in Table No. 27-7-D in material having a specified yield point less than 40 ksi.

5. Where A 325 of any diameter or A 490 bolts equal to or less than 1 inch in diameter are to be installed and tightened in an oversize or short-slotted hole in an outer ply, a hardened washer conforming to Section 27.702 (e) shall be used.

6. When A 490 bolts over 1 inch in diameter are to be installed and tightened in an oversize or short slotted hole in an outer ply, hardened washers conforming to Section 27.702 (e) except with 5/16-inch minimum thickness shall be used under both the head and the nut in lieu of standard thickness hardened washers. Multiple hardened washers with combined thickness equal to or greater than 5/16 inch do not satisfy this requirement.

7. Where A 325 bolts of any diameter or A 490 bolts equal to or less than 1 inch in diameter are to be installed and tightened in a long-slotted hole in an outer ply, a plate washer or continuous bar of at least 5/16-inch thickness with standard holes shall be provided. These washers or bars shall have a size sufficient to completely cover the slot after installation and shall be of structural grade material, but need not be hardened except as follows: When A 490 bolts over 1 inch in diameter are to be used in long-slotted holes in external plies, a single hardened washer conforming to Section 27.702 (e) but with 5/16-inch minimum thickness shall be used in lieu of washers or bars of structural grade material. Multiple hardened washers with combined thickness equal to or greater than 5/16 inch do not satisfy this requirement.

8. Alternate design fasteners meeting the requirements of Section 27.702 (d) with a geometry which provides a bearing circle on the head or nut with a diameter equal to or greater than the diameter of hardened washers meeting the requirements of Section 27.702 (e) satisfy the requirements for washers specified in Subsections 27.707 (c) 4 and (c) 5.

Installation and Tightening

Sec. 27.708. (a) **Handling and Storage of Fasteners.** Fasteners shall be protected from dirt and moisture at the jobsite. Only as may fasteners as are anticipated to be installed and tightened during a work shift shall be taken from protected storage. Fasteners not used shall be returned to protected storage at the end of the shift. Fasteners shall not be cleaned of lubricant that is present in as delivered condition. Fasteners for slip-critical connections which must be cleaned of accumulated rust or dirt resulting from on-site conditions shall be cleaned and relubricated prior to installation.

(b) **Tension Calibrator.** A tension measuring device shall be provided at jobsites where bolts in slip-critical joints or connections subject to direct tension are being installed and tightened. The tension-measuring device shall be used to confirm: (1) the suitability to satisfy the requirements of Table No. 27-7-D of the complete fastener assembly, including lubrication if required to be used in the work, (2) calibration of wrenches, if applicable, and (3) the understanding and proper use by the bolting crew of the method to be used. The frequency of confirmation testing, the number of tests to be performed and the test procedure shall be as specified in Section 27.708 (d), as applicable. The accuracy of the tension measuring device shall be confirmed through calibration by an approved testing agency at least annually.

(c) **Joint Assembly and Tightening of Shear/Bearing Connections.** Bolts in connections not requiring full pretension shall be installed in properly aligned holes, but need only be tightened to the snug-tight condition. The snug-tight condition is defined as the tightness that exists when all plies in a joint are in firm contact. This may be attained by a few impacts of an impact wrench or the full effort of a man using an ordinary spud wrench. If a slotted hole occurs in an outer ply, a flat hardened washer or common plate washer shall be installed over the slot. Bolts which may be tightened only to a snug-tight condition shall be clearly identified on the drawings.

(d) **Joint Assembly and Tightening of Connections Requiring Full Pretension.** 1. **General:** In connections requiring full pretension, fasteners, together with washers of size and quality specified, located as required by Section 27.707 (c) shall be installed in properly aligned holes and tightened by one of the methods described in Subsections 27.708 (d) 2 through 5 to at least the minimum tension specified in Table No. 27-7-D when all the fasteners are tight. Tightening may be done by turning the bolt while the nut is prevented from rotating when it is impractical to turn the nut. Impact wrenches, if used, shall be of adequate capacity and sufficiently supplied with air to perform the required tightening of each bolt in approximately 10 seconds.

2. **Turn-of-nut tightening.** When turn-of-nut tightening is used, hardened washers are not required except as may be specified in Section 27.707 (c).

A representative sample of not less than three bolts and nuts of each diameter, length and grade to be used in the work shall be checked at the start of work in a device capable of indicating bolt tension. The test shall demonstrate that the method of estimating the snug-tight condition and controlling turns from snug tight to be used by the bolting crews develops a tension not less than 5 percent greater than the tension required by Table No. 27-7-D.

Bolts shall be installed in all holes of the connection and brought to a snug-tight condition. "Snug tight" is defined as the tightness that exist when the plies of the joint are in firm contact. This may be attained by a few impacts of an impact wrench or the full effort of a man using an ordinary spud wrench. Snug tightening shall progress systematically from the most rigid part of the connection to the free edges, and then the bolts of the connection shall be retightened in a similar systematic manner as necessary until all bolts are simultaneously snug tight and the connection shall be tightened further by the applicable amount of rotation specified in Table No. 27-7-E. During the tightening operation there shall be no rotation of the part not turned by the wrench. Tightening shall progress systematically from the most rigid part of the joint to its free edges.

3. **Calibrated wrench tightening.** Calibrated wrench tightening may be used only when installation procedures are calibrated on a daily basis and when a hardened washer is used under the element turned in tightening. This specification does not recognize standard torques determined from tables or from formulas which are assumed to relate torque to tension.

When calibrated wrenches are used for installation, they shall be set to provide a tension not less than 5 percent in excess of the minimum tension specified in Table No. 27-7-D. The installation procedures shall be calibrated at least once each working day for each bolt diameter, length and grade using fastener assemblies that are being installed in the work. Calibration shall be accomplished in a device capable of indicating actual bolt tension by tightening three typical bolts of each diameter, length and grade from the bolts being installed and with a hardened washer from the washers being used in the work under the element turned in tightening. Wrenches shall be recalibrated when significant difference is noted in the surface condition of the bolts threads, nuts or washers. It shall be verified during actual installation in the assembled steel work that the wrench adjustment selected by the calibration does not produce a nut or bolt head rotation from snug tight greater than that permitted in Table No. 27-7-E. If manual torque wrenches are used, nuts shall be turned in the tightening direction when torque is measured.

When calibrated wrenches are used to install and tension bolts in a connection, bolts shall be installed with hardened washers under the element turned in tightening bolts in all holes of the connection and brought to a snug-tight condition. Following this initial tightening operation, the connection shall be tightened using the calibrated wrench. Tightening shall progress systematically from the most rigid part of the joint to its free edges. The wrench shall be returned to "touch up" previously tightened bolts which may have been relaxed as a result of the subsequent tightening of adjacent bolts until all bolts are tightened to the prescribed amount.

4. **Installation of alternate design bolts.** When fasteners which incorporate a design feature intended to indirectly indicate the bolt tension or to automatically provide the tension required by Table No. 27-7-D and which have been qualified under Section 27.702 (d) are to be installed, a representative sample of not less than three bolts of each diameter, length and grade shall be checked at the jobsite in a device capable of indicating bolt tension. The test assembly shall include flat hardened washers, if required in the actual connection, arranged as in the actual connections to be tensioned. The calibration test shall demonstrate that each bolt develops a tension not less than 5 percent greater than the tension required by Table No. 27-7-D. Manufacturer's installation procedure as required by Section 27.702 (d) shall be followed for installation of bolts in the calibration device and in all connections.

When alternate design features of the fasteners involve an irreversible mechanism such as yield or twist-off of an element, bolts shall be installed in all holes of the connection and initially brought to a snug-tight condition. All fasteners shall then be tightened, progressing systematically from the most rigid part of the connection of the free edges in a manner that will minimize relaxation of previously tightened fasteners prior to final twist-off or yielding of the control or indicator element of the individual fasteners. In some cases, proper tensioning of the bolts may require more than a single cycle of systematic tightening.

5. **Direct-tension indicator tightening.** Tightening of bolts using direct-tension-indicator devices is permitted, provided the suitability of the device can be demonstrated by testing a representative sample of not less than three devices for each diameter and grade of fastener in a calibration device capable of indicating bolt tension. The test assembly shall include flat hardened washers, if required in the actual connection, arranged as those in the actual connections to be tensioned. The calibration test shall demonstrate that the device indicates a tension not less than 5 percent greater than that required by Table No. 27-7-D. Manufacturer's installation procedure as required by Section 27.702 (d) shall be followed for installation of bolts in the calibration device and in all connections. Special attention shall be given to proper installation of flat hardened washers when load indicating devices are used with bolts installed in oversize or slotted holes and when the load indicating devices are used under the turned elements.

When the direct tension involves an irreversible mechanism such as yielding or fracture of an element, bolts shall be installed in all holes of the connection and brought to snug-tight conditions. All fasteners shall then be tightened, progressing systematically from the most rigid part of the connection to the free edges in a manner that will minimize relaxation of previously tightened fasteners prior to final twist-off or yielding of the control or indicator element of the individual devices. In some cases, proper tensioning of the bolts may require more than a single cycle of systematic tightening.

(e) **Reuse of bolts.** A 490 and galvanized A 325 bolts shall not be reused. Other A 325 bolts may be reused if approved by the building official. Touching up or retightening previously tightened bolts which may have been loosened by the tightening of adjacent bolts shall not be considered as reuse provided the snugging up continues from the initial position and does not require greater rotation, including the tolerance, than that required by Table No. 27-7-E.

Inspection

Sec. 27.709. (a) **Inspector Responsibility.** While the work is in progress, the special inspector shall determine that the requirements of Sections 27.702, 27.703 and 27.708 are met. The special inspector shall observe the calibration procedures when such procedures are required by the plans or specifications and shall monitor the installation of bolts to determine that all plies of connected material have been drawn together and that the selected procedure is properly used to tighten all bolts.

In addition, all connections specified to be slip critical or subject to axial tension, the special inspector shall assure that the specified procedure was followed to achieve the pretension specified in Table No. 27-7-D. Bolts installed by procedures in Section 27.708 (d) may reach tensions substantially greater than values given in Table No. 27-7-D, but this shall not be cause for rejection.

Bolts in connections identified as not being slip critical nor subject to direct tension need not be inspected for bolt tension other than to ensure that the plies of the connected elements have been brought into snug contact.

(b) **Arbitration Inspection.** When high strength bolts in slip-critical connections and connections subject to direct tension have been installed by any of the tightening methods in Section 27.708 (d) and inspected in accordance with Section 27.709 (a) and a disagreement exists as to the minimum tension of the installed bolts, the following arbitration procedure may be used. Other methods for arbitration inspection may be used if approved by the building official.

1. The special inspector shall use a manual torque wrench which indicates torque by means of a dial or which may be adjusted to give an indication that the job inspecting torque has been reached.

2. This standard does not recognize standard torques determined from tables or from formulas which are assumed to relate torque to tension. Testing using such standard torques shall not be considered valid.

3. A representative sample of five bolts from the diameter, length and grade of the bolts used in the work shall be tightened in the tension measuring device by a convenient means to an initial condition equal to approximately 15 percent of the required fastener tension and then to be minimum tension specified in Table No. 27-7-D. Tightening beyond the initial condition must not produce greater nut rotation than one and one-half times that permitted in Table No. 27-7-E. The job inspecting torque shall be taken as the average of three values thus determined after reflecting the high and low values. The inspecting wrench shall then be applied to the tightened bolts in the work and the torque necessary to turn the nut or head 5 degrees (approximately 1 inch at 12 inch radius) in the tightening direction shall be determined.

4. Bolts represented by the sample in the foregoing paragraph which have been tightened in the structure shall be inspected by applying, in the tightening direction, the inspecting wrench and its job torque to 10 percent of the bolts, but not less than two bolts, selected at random in each connection in question. If no nut or bolt head is turned by application of the job inspecting torque, the connection shall be accepted as properly tightened. If any nut or bolt is turned by the application of the job inspecting torque, all bolts in the connection shall be tested, and all bolts whose nut or head is turned by the job inspecting torque shall be tightened and reinspected. Alternatively, the fabricator or erector, at his option, may retighten all of the bolts in the connection and then resubmit the connection for the specified inspection.

(c) **Delayed Verification Inspection.** The procedure specified in Subsections 27.709 (a) and (b) are intended for inspection of bolted connections and verification of pretension at the time of tensioning the joint. If verification of bolt tension is required after a passage of a period of time and exposure of the completed joints, the procedures of Section 27.709 (b) will provide indication of bolt tension which is of questionable accuracy. Procedures appropriate to the specific situation should be used for verification of bolt tension. This might involve use of the arbitration inspection procedure contained herein, or might require the development and use of alternate procedures.

TABLE NO. 27-7-A—NOMINAL HOLE DIMENSIONS

	HOLE DIMENSIONS			
BOLT DIA.	Standard (Dia.)	Oversize (Dia.)	Short Slot (Width × Length)	Long Slot (Width × Length)
1/2	9/16	5/8	9/16 × 11/16	9/16 × 1 1/4
5/8	11/16	13/16	11/15 × 7/8	11/16 × 1 9/16
3/4	13/16	15/16	13/16 × 1	13/16 × 1 7/8
7/8	15/16	1 1/16	15/16 × 1 1/8	15/16 × 2 3/16
1	1 1/16	1 1/4	1 1/16 × 1 5/16	1 1/16 × 2 1/2
$\geq$ 1 1/8	d + 1/16	d + 5/16	(d + 1/16) × (d + 3/8)	(d + 1/16) × (2.5 × d)

TABLE NO. 27-7-B—ALLOWABLE WORKING STRESS[1] ON FASTENERS OR CONNECTED MATERIAL (ksi)

LOAD CONDITION	A 325	A 490
Applied static tension[2, 3]	44	54
Shear on bolt with threads in shear plane.	21[4]	28[4]
Shear on bolt without threads in shear plane.	30[4]	40[4]
Bearing on connected material with single bolt in line of force in a standard or short-slotted hole.	$1.0F_u$[5]	
Bearing on connected material with 2 or more bolts in line of force in standard or short-slotted holes.	$1.2F_u$[5]	
Bearing on connected material in long-slotted holes.	$1.0F_u$[5]	

[1]Ultimate failure load divided by factor of safety.

[2]Bolts must be tensioned to requirements of Table No. 27-7-D.

[3]See Section 27.704 (d) for bolts subject to tensile fatigue.

[4]In connections transmitting axial force whose length between extreme fasteners measured parallel to the line of force exceeds 50 inches, tabulated values shall be reduced 20 percent.

[5]F_u = specified minimum tensile strength of connected part.

Connections using high-strength bolts in slotted holes with the load applied in a direction other than approximately normal (between 80 and 100 degrees) to the axis of the hole and connections with bolts in oversize holes shall be designated for resistance against slip at working load in accordance with Section 27.705.

Tabulated values apply when the distance L parallel to the line of force from the center of the bolt to the edge of the connected part is not less than $1^1/_2 d$ and the distance from the center of a bolt to the center of an adjacent bolt is not less than 3 (d). When either of these conditions is not satisfied, the distance L requirement of Section 27.704 (b) determines allowable bearing stress.

Except as may be justified under provisions of Section 27.704 (b).

TABLE NO. 27-7-C—ALLOWABLE LOAD FOR SLIP-CRITICAL CONNECTIONS (Slip Load per Unit of Bolt Area, ksi)

CONTACT SURFACE OF BOLTED PARTS	HOLE TYPE AND DIRECTION OF LOAD APPLICATION							
	Any Direction				Transverse		Parallel	
	Standard		Oversize & Short Slot		Long Slots		Long Slots	
	A 325	A 490	A 325	A 490	A 325	A 490	A 325	A 490
Class A (Slip Coefficient 0.33) Clean mill scale and blast-cleaned surfaces with Class A coatings[1]	17	21	15	18	12	15	10	13
Class B (Slip Coefficient 0.50) Blast-cleaned surfaces and blast-cleaned surfaces with Class B coatings[1]	28	34	24	29	20	24	17	20
Class C (Slip Coefficient 0.40) Hot dip glavanized and rough-ened surfaces	22	27	19	23	16	19	14	16

[1]Coatings classified as Class A or Class B includes those coatings which provide a mean slip coefficent not less than 0.33 or 0.50, respectively, as determined by approved methods.

TABLE NO. 27-7-D—FASTENER TENSION REQUIRED FOR SLIP-CRITICAL CONNECTIONS AND CONNECTIONS SUBJECT TO DIRECT TENSION

NOMINAL BOLT SIZE, INCHES	MINIMUM TENSION[1] IN 1000's OF POUNDS (kips)	
	A 325 Bolts	A 490 Bolts
1/2	12	15
5/8	19	24
3/4	28	35
7/8	39	49
1	51	64
1 1/8	56	80
1 1/4	71	102
1 3/8	85	121
1 1/2	103	148

[1]Equal to 70 percent of specified minimum tensile strength of bolts (as specified for tests of full-size A 325 and A 490 bolts with UNC threads loaded in axial tension) rounded to the nearest kip.

TABLE NO. 27-7-E—NUT ROTATION FROM SNUG-TIGHT CONDITION[1 2]

BOLT LENGTH (Underside of head to end of bolt)	DISPOSITION OF OUTER FACE OF BOLTED PARTS		
	Both faces normal to bolt axis	One face normal to bolt axis and other sloped not more than 1:20 (beveled washer not used)	Both faces sloped not more than 1:20 from normal to the bolt axis (beveled washer not used)
Up to and including 4 diameters	1/3 turn	1/2 turn	2/3 turn
Over 4 diameters but not exceeding 8 diameters	1/2 turn	2/3 turn	5/6 turn
Over 8 diameters but not exceeding 12 diameters[3]	2/3 turn	5/6 turn	1 turn

[1]For bolts installed by 1/2 turn and less, the tolerance shall be plus or minus 30 degrees; for bolts installed by 2/3 turn and more, the tolerance shall be plus or minus 45 degrees.

[2]Applicable only to connections in which all material within the grip of the bolt is steel.

[3]The rotation shall be determined by actual test in a suitable tension measuring device which simulates conditions of solidly fitted steel.

TABLE NO. 27-7-F—DIMENSIONS OF HEAVY HEX STRUCTURAL BOLTS[1]

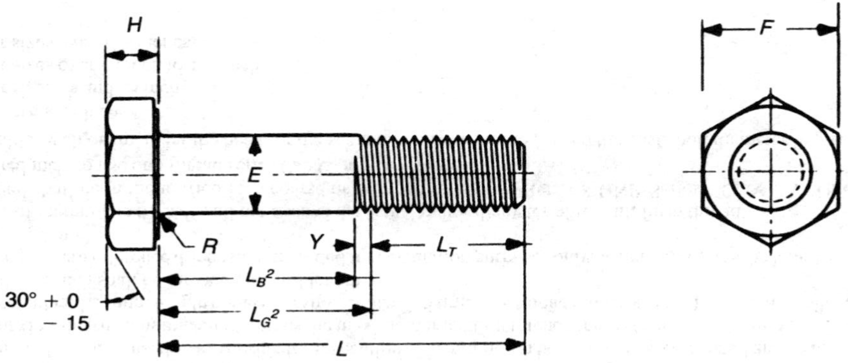
H
E
R
Y
L_T
L_B^2
L_G^2
L
30° + 0
− 15
F

NOMINAL SIZE	E		F		H	R		L_T	Y	RUNOUT OF BEARING SURFACE FIM[7]
	BODY DIAMETER[3, 4]		WIDTH ACROSS FLATS[5, 6]		HEIGHT	RADIUS OF FILLET		THREAD LENGTH[2]	TRANSITION THREAD LENGTH[2]	
	MAX.	MIN.	BASIC/MAX.	MIN.	MIN.	MAX.	MIN.	BASIC	MAX.	MAX.
1/2	0.515	0.482	0.875	0.850	0.302	0.031	0.009	1.00	0.19	0.016
5/8	0.642	0.605	1.062	1.031	0.378	0.062	0.021	1.25	0.22	0.019
3/4	0.768	0.729	1.250	1.212	0.455	0.062	0.021	1.38	0.25	0.022
7/8	0.895	0.852	1.438	1.394	0.531	0.062	0.031	1.50	0.28	0.025
1	1.022	0.976	1.625	1.575	0.591	0.093	0.062	1.75	0.31	0.028
1 1/8	1.149	1.098	1.812	1.756	0.658	0.093	0.062	2.00	0.34	0.032
1 1/4	1.277	1.223	2.000	1.938	0.749	0.093	0.062	2.00	0.38	0.035
1 3/8	1.404	1.345	2.188	2.119	0.810	0.093	0.062	2.25	0.44	0.038
1 1/2	1.531	1.470	2.375	2.300	0.902	0.093	0.062	2.25	0.44	0.041

(Continued)

(Continued)

[1]**Identification Symbols.** Identification marking symbols on the tops of heads for bolt sizes 5/8 inch and smaller shall project not less than 0.005 inch above the surface nor more than 0.015 inch over the specified maximum head height. Bolt sizes larger than 5/8 inch shall project not less than the equivalent in inches of 0.0075 times the basic bolt diameter above the surface nor more than 0.030 inch over the specified maximum head height.

[2]The length of thread on bolts shall be controlled by the grip gauging length L_G max. and body length L_B min. as set forth in the following:

Grip gauging length L_G max. is the distance measured parallel to the axis of bolt from the underhead bearing surface to the face of a noncounterbored or noncountersunk standard GO thread ring gauge assembled by hand as far as the thread will permit. It shall be used as the criterion for inspection. The maximum grip gauging length, as calculated and rounded to two decimal places for any bolt not threaded full length, shall be equal to the nominal bolt length minus the basic thread length (L_G max. $= L$ nom $- L_T$). For bolts which are threaded full length, L_B max. defines the unthreaded length under the head and shall not exceed the length of 2.5 times the thread pitch for sizes up to and including 1 inch, and 3.5 times the thread pitch for sizes larger than 1 inch. L_G max. represents the minimum design grip length of the bolt and shall be used for determining thread availability when selecting bolt lengths even though usable threads may extend beyond this point.

Basic thread length L_T is a reference dimension, intended for calculation purposes only, which represents the distance from the extreme end of the bolt to the last complete (full form) thread.

Body length L_B min. is the distance measured parallel to the axis of bolt from the underhead bearing surface to the last scratch of thread or to the top of the extrusion angle. It shall be used as a criterion for inspection. The minimum body length as calculated and rounded to two decimal places shall be equal to the maximum grip gauging length minus the maximum transition thread length (L_B min. $= L_G$ max. $- Y$ max.). Bolts of nominal lengths which have a calculated L_B min. length equal to or shorter than 2.5 times the thread pitch for sizes 1 inch and smaller and 3.5 times the thread pitch for sizes larger than 1 inch shall be threaded for full length.

Transition thread length Y is a reference dimension, intended for calculation purposes only, which represents the length of incomplete threads and tolerance on grip gauging length.

The major diameter of incomplete thread shall not exceed the actual major diameter of the full form thread.

Threads, when rolled shall be in the unified inch coarse or 8 thread series (UNRC or 8 UNR Series), Class 2A. Threads produced by other methods may be unified inch coarse or 8 thread series (UNC or 8 UN Series), Class 2A.

[3]There may be a reasonable swell or fin under the head, or die seam on the body not to exceed the basic bolt diameter by the following:

0.030 inch for sizes 1/2 inch
0.050 inch for sizes 5/8 and 3/4 inch
0.060 inch for sizes over 3/4 inch to 1 1/4 inch
0.090 inch for sizes over 1 1/4 inches

[4]Shanks of bolts shall be straight within the following limits: for bolts with nominal lengths to and including 12 inches the maximum camber shall be 0.006 inch per inch of bolt length, and for bolts with nominal lengths over 12 inches to and including 24 inches the maximum camber shall be 0.008 inch per inch of length.

[5]Maximum width across flats shall not be exceeded. No transverse section through the head between 25 and 75 percent of actual head height as measured from the bearing surface shall be less than the minimum width across flats.

[6]The axis of the head shall be located at true position with respect to the axis of the body (determined over a distance under the head equal to one diameter) within a tolerance zone having a diameter equivalent to six percent of the maximum width across flats, regardless of feature size.

[7]Bearing surface shall be flat and washer faced. Diameter of bearing surface shall be equal to the maximum width across flats within a tolerance of minus 10 percent.

Thickness of the washer face shall be not less than 0.015 inch nor greater than 0.025 inch for bolt sizes 3/4 inch and smaller and not less than 0.015 inch nor greater than 0.035 inch for sizes larger than 3/4 inch.

The plane of the bearing surface shall be perpendicular to the axis of the body within the full indicator movement (FIM) limits specified. Measurement of FIM shall be made as close to the periphery of the bearing surface as possible while the bolt is being held in a collet or other gripping device at a distance of one bolt diameter from the underside of the head.

TABLE NO. 27-7-G—CHEMICAL REQUIREMENTS FOR GRADES O, A, B, C, D, DH AND 2, 2H NUTS

GRADE OF NUT	COMPOSITION, percent				
	Analysis	Carbon	Manganese, min.	Phosphorus, max.	Suflur, max.
O, A, B, C	heat	0.55 max	. . .	0.12	0.15[1]
	product	0.58 max	. . .	0.13[2]	. . .
D[3]	heat	0.55 max	0.30	0.04	0.05
	product	0.58 max	0.27	0.048	0.058
DH[3]	heat	0.20–0.55	0.60	0.04	0.05
	product	0.18–0.58	0.57	0.48	0.08
2 and 2H	—	0.40 min.	—	0.040	0.05

[1]Sulfur content may be 0.23 max. for Grade O, A and B nuts if agreed between the manufacturer and the purchaser.

[2]Acid bessemer steel only.

[3]For D and DH nuts, sulfur content may be 0.05 to 0.15 percent in which case manganese must be a minimum of 1.35 percent.

ELEMENT	COMPOSITION, percent							
	Classes for Grade C3 Nuts[1]							GRADE DH3 NUTS
	N	A	B	C	D	E	F	
Carbon:								
Heat analysis	. . .	0.33–0.40	0.38–0.48	0.15–0.25	0.14–0.25	0.20–0.25	0.20–0.25	0.20–0.53
Product analysis	. . .	0.31–0.42	0.36–0.50	0.14-0.26	0.14–0.26	0.18–0.27	0.19–0.26	0.19–0.55
Manganese:								
Heat analysis	. . .	0.90–1.20	0.70–0.90	0.80–1.35	0.40–1.20	0.60–1.00	0.90–1.20	0.40 max
Product analysis	. . .	0.86–1.24	0.67–0.93	0.76–1.39	0.36–1.24	0.56–1.04	0.86–1.24	0.37 min
Phosphorus:								
Heat analysis	0.07–0.15	0.040 max	0.06–0.12	0.035 max	0.040 max	0.040 max	0.040 max	0.046 max
Product analysis	0.07–0.155	0.045 max	0.06–1.25	0.040 max	0.045 max	0.045 max	0.045 max	0.052 max
Sulfur:								
Heat analysis	0.050 max	0.050 max	0.050 max	0.040 max	0.050 max	0.040 max	0.040 max	0.050 max
Product analysis	0.055 max	0.055 max	0.055 max	0.045 max	0.055 max	0.045 max	0.045 max	0.055 max
Silicon:								
Heat analysis	0.20–0.90	0.15–0.35	0.30–0.50	0.15–0.35	0.25–0.50	0.15–0.35	0.15–0.35	. . .
Product analysis	0.15–0.95	0.13–0.37	0.25–0.55	0.13–0.37	0.20–0.55	0.13–0.37	0.13–0.37	. . .
Copper:								
Heat analysis	0.25–0.55	0.25–0.45	0.20–0.40	0.20–0.50	0.30–0.50	0.30–0.60	0.20–0.40	0.20 min[2]
Product analysis	0.22–0.58	0.22–0.48	0.17–0.43	0.17–0.53	0.27–0.53	0.27–0.63	0.17–0.43	0.17 min
Nickel:								
Heat analysis	1.00 max	0.25–0.45	0.50–0.80	0.25–0.50	0.50–0.80	0.30–0.60	0.20–0.40	0.20 min
Product analysis	1.03 max	0.22–0.48	0.47–0.83	0.22–0.53	0.47–0.83	0.27–0.63	0.17–0.43	0.17 min
Chromium:								
Heat analysis	0.30–1.25	0.45–0.65	0.50–0.75	0.30–0.50	0.50–1.00	0.60–0.90	0.45–0.65	0.45 min
Product analysis	0.25–1.30	0.42–0.68	0.47–0.83	0.27–0.53	0.45–1.05	0.55–0.95	0.42–0.68	0.42 min
Vanadium:								
Heat analysis	. . .	. . .	. . .	0.20 min	. . .	. . .	. . .	. . .
Product analysis	. . .	. . .	. . .	0.10 min	. . .	. . .	. . .	. . .
Molybdenum:								
Heat analysis	. . .	. . .	0.06 max	. . .	0.10 max	. . .	. . .	0.15 min[2]
Product analysis	. . .	. . .	0.07 max	. . .	0.11 max	. . .	. . .	0.14 min
Titanium:								
Heat analysis	. . .	. . .	. . .	. . .	0.05 max	. . .	. . .	. . .
Product analysis	. . .	. . .	. . .	. . .	. . .	. . .	. . .	. . .

[1]C3 nuts may be made of any of the above-listed material classes. Selection of the class shall be at the option of the manufacturer.

[2]Nickel or molybdenum may be used.

TABLE NO. 27-7-I—MECHANICAL REQUIREMENTS
Nuts with UNC, 8 UN, 6 UN and Coarser Pitch Threads

GRADE OF NUT	NOMINAL NUT SIZE, In.	STYLE OF NUT	PROOF LOAD STRESS, ksi[1]		HARDNESS			
			Non-zinc-coated Nuts[2]	Zinc-coated Nuts[2]	Brinell		Rockwell	
					min.	max.	min.	max.
O	1/4 to 1 1/2	square	69	52	103	302	B55	C32
A	1/4 to 1 1/2	square	90	68	116	302	B68	C32
O	1/4 to 1 1/2	hex	69	52	103	302	B55	C32
A	1/4 to 1 1/2	hex	90	68	116	302	B68	C32
B	1/4 to 1	hex	120	90	121	302	B69	C32
B	1 1/8 to 1 1/2	hex	105	79	121	302	B69	C32
D[3]	1/4 to 1 1/2	hex	135	135	159	352	B84	C38
DH[4]	1/4 to 1 1/2	hex	150	150	248	352	C24	C38
A	1/4 to 4	heavy hex	100	75	116	302	B68	C32
B	1/4 to 1	heavy hex	133	100	121	302	B69	C32
B	1 1/8 to1 1/2	heavy hex	116	87	121	302	B69	C32
C[3]	1/4 to 4	heavy hex	144	144	143	352	B78	C38
C3	1/4 to 4	heavy hex	144	144	143	352	B78	C38
D[3]	1/4 to 4	heavy hex	150	150	159	352	B84	C38
DH[4]	1/4 to 4	heavy hex	175	175	248	352	C24	C38
DH3	1/4 to 4	heavy hex	175	175	248	352	C24	C38
A	1/4 to 1 1/2	hex thick	100	75	116	302	B68	C32
B	1/4 to 1	hex thick	133	100	121	302	B69	C32
B	1 1/8 to 1 1/2	hex thick	116	87	121	302	B69	C32
D[3]	1/4 to 1 1/2	hex thick	150	150	159	352	B84	C38
DH[4]	1/4 to 1 1/2	hex thick	175	175	248	352	C24	C38

Nuts with UNF, 12 UN and Finer Pitch Threads								
O	1/4 to 1 1/2	hex	65	49	103	302	B55	C32
A	1/4 to 1 1/2	hex	80	60	116	302	B68	C32
B	1/4 to 1	hex	109	82	121	302	B69	C32
B	1 1/8 to 1 1/2	hex	94	70	121	302	B69	C32
D[3]	1/4 to 1 1/2	hex	135	135	159	352	B84	C38
DH[4]	1/4 to 1 1/2	hex	150	150	248	352	C24	C38
A	1/4 to 4	heavy hex	90	68	116	302	B68	C32
B	1/4 to 1	heavy hex	120	90	121	302	B69	C32
B	1 1/8 to 1 1/2	heavy hex	105	79	121	302	B69	C32
D[3]	1/4 to 4	heavy hex	150	150	159	352	B84	C38
DH[4]	1/4 to 4	heavy hex	175	175	248	352	C24	C38
A	1/4 to 1 1/2	hex thick	90	68	116	302	B68	C32
B	1/4 to 1	hex thick	120	90	121	302	B69	C32
B	1 1/8 to 1 1/2	hex thick	105	79	121	302	B69	C32
D[3]	1/4 to 1 1/2	hex thick	150	150	159	352	B84	C38
DH[4]	1/4 to 1 1/2	hex thick	175	175	248	352	C24	C38

[1]To determine nut proof load in pounds, multiply the appropriate nut proof load stress by the tensile stress area of the thread.

[2]Nonzinc-coated nuts are nuts intended for use with externally threaded fasteners which have a plain (nonplated or noncoated) finish or have a plating or coating of insufficient thickness to necessitate overtapping the nut thread to provide assemblability. Zinc-coated nuts are nuts intended for use with externally threaded fasteners which are hot-dip zinc-coated, mechanically zinc-coated, or have a plating or coating of sufficient thickness to necessitate overtapping the nut thread to provide assemblability.

[3]Nuts made in accordance to the requirements of Grade 2 or 2H, and marked with their grade symbol are acceptable equivalents for Grades C and D nuts.

[4]Nuts made in accordance with the requirements of Grade 2H, and marked with its grade symbol are an acceptable equivalent for Grade DH nuts.

GRADE AND TYPE	COMPLETED NUTS			SAMPLE NUT AFTER TREATMENT	
	Brinell Hardness	Rockwell Hardness C Scale	Rockwell Hardness B Scale	Brinell Hardness, min.	Rockwell Hardness B Scale, min.
2	159 to 352	. . .	84 min.	159	84
2H	248 to 352	24 to 38	. . .	179	89

TABLE NO. 27-7-J—DIMENSIONS OF HEAVY HEX NUTS[1,2,3,4]

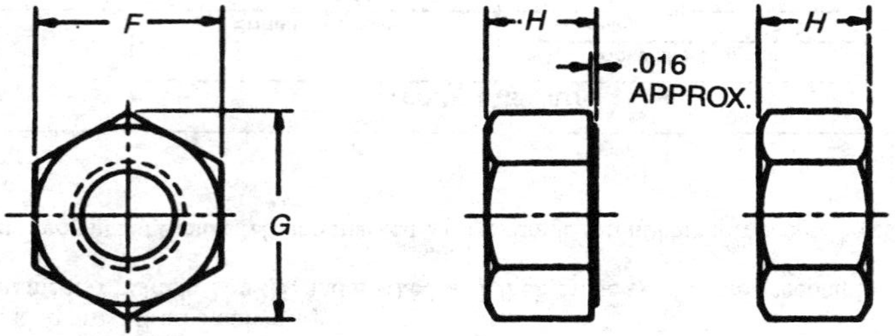
F
G
H
H
.016
APPROX.

NOMINAL SIZE	F WIDTH ACROSS FLATS[6]		G WIDTH ACROSS CORNERS[7]		H THICKNESS HEAVY HEX NUTS	HEAVY HEX NUTS SPECIFIED PROOF LOAD[5] UP TO 150,000 psi	HEAVY HEX NUTS SPECIFIED PROOF LOAD[5] 150,000 psi AND GREATER
	BASIC/MAX.	MIN.	MAX.	MIN.	MIN.	RUNOUT OF BEARING FACE, FIR MAX.	
1/4	0.500	0.488	0.577	0.556	0.218	0.017	0.011
5/16	0.562	0.546	0.650	0.622	0.280	0.020	0.012
3/8	0.688	0.669	0.794	0.763	0.341	0.021	0.014
7/16	0.750	0.728	0.866	0.830	0.403	0.022	0.015
1/2	**0.875**	**0.850**	**1.010**	**0.969**	**0.464**	0.023	0.016
9/16	0.938	0.909	1.083	1.037	0.526	0.024	0.017
5/8	**1.062**	**1.031**	**1.227**	**1.175**	**0.587**	0.025	0.018
3/4	**1.250**	**1.212**	**1.443**	**1.382**	**0.710**	0.027	0.020
7/8	**1.438**	**1.394**	**1.660**	**1.589**	**0.833**	0.029	0.022
1	**1.625**	**1.575**	**1.876**	**1.796**	**0.956**	0.031	0.024
1 1/8	**1.812**	**1.756**	**2.093**	**2.002**	**1.079**	0.033	0.027
1 1/4	**2.000**	**1.938**	**2.309**	**2.209**	**1.187**	0.035	0.030
1 3/8	**2.188**	**2.119**	**2.526**	**2.416**	**1.310**	0.038	0.033

1 1/2	**2.375**	**2.300**	**2.742**	**2.622**	**1.433**	0.041	0.036
1 5/8	2.562	2.481	2.959	2.828	1.556	0.044	0.038
1 3/4	**2.750**	**2.662**	**3.175**	**3.035**	**1.679**	0.048	0.041
1 7/8	2.938	2.844	3.392	3.242	1.802	0.051	0.044
2	**3.125**	**3.025**	**3.606**	**3.449**	**1.925**	0.055	0.047
2 1/4	3.500	3.388	4.041	3.862	2.155	0.061	0.052
2 1/2	3.875	3.750	4.474	4.275	2.401	0.068	0.058
2 3/4	4.250	4.112	4.907	4.688	2.647	0.074	0.064
3	4.625	4.475	5.340	5.102	2.893	0.081	0.070
3 1/4	5.000	4.838	5.774	5.515	3.124	0.087	0.075
3 1/2	5.375	5.200	6.207	5.928	3.370	0.094	0.081
3 3/4	5.750	5.562	6.640	6.341	3.616	0.100	0.087
4	6.125	5.925	7.073	6.755	3.862	0.107	0.093

[1]Unification: Bold type indicates products unified dimensionally with British and Canadian standards. Unification of fine thread products is limited to sizes 1 inch and under.

[2]Concentricity of tapped hole: Axis of tapped hole shall be concentric with axis of nut body within a tolerance equal to 3 percent (6 percent FIR) of the maximum width across flats.

[3]Countersink: Tapped hole shall be countersunk on the bearing face or faces. The maximum countersink diameter shall be the thread basic (nominal) major diameter plus 0.030 inch for 3/8 inch nominal size nuts and smaller and 1.08 times the basic major diameter for nuts larger than 3/8 inch. No part of the threaded portion shall project beyond the bearing surface.

[4]Threads: Threads shall be unified coarse, fine or 8 thread series (UNC, UNF or 8 UN series), Class 2B.

[5]Tops and bearing surfaces of nuts: Nuts in sizes 7/16 inch nominal size and smaller shall be double chamfered. Larger size nuts shall be double chamfered or have washer faced bearing surface and chamfered top.

The diameter of chamfer circle on double chamfered nuts and diameter of washer face shall be within the limits of the maximum width across flats and 95 percent of the minimum width across flats.

The tops of washer faced nuts shall be flat and the diameter of chamfer circle shall be equal to the maximum width across flats within a tolerance of minus 15 percent. The length of chamfer at hex corners shall be from 5 to 15 percent of the basic thread diameter. The surface of chamfer may be slightly convex or rounded.

(Continued)

(Continued)

Bearing surfaces shall be flat and perpendicular to the axis of the threaded hole within the FIR limits specified for the respective nut type and strength level.

[6]Width across flats: Maximum width across flats shall not be exceeded. No transverse section through the nut between 25 and 75 percent of the actual nut thickness as measured from the bearing surface shall be less than the minimum width across flats.

[7]Corner fill: A rounding or lack of fill at junction of hex corners with chamfer shall be permissible provided the width across corners is within specified limits at and beyond a distance equal to 17.5 percent of the basic thread diameter from the chamfered faces.

TABLE NO. 27-7-K—CHEMICAL REQUIREMENTS

ELEMENT	COMPOSITION, percent	
	Carbon Steel Washers	Weathering Steel Washers
Phosphorus, max.		
Heat analysis	0.040	0.040
Product analysis	0.050	0.045
Sulfur, max.		
Heat analysis	0.050	0.050
Product analysis	0.060	0.055
Silicon		
Heat analysis	. . .	0.15–0.35
Product analysis	. . .	0.13–0.37
Chromium		
Heat analysis	. . .	0.45–0.65
Product analysis	. . .	0.42–0.68
Nickel		
Heat analysis	. . .	0.25–0.45
Product analysis	. . .	0.22–0.48
Copper		
Heat analysis	. . .	0.25–0.45
Product analysis	. . .	0.22–0.48

TABLE NO. 27-7-L—HARDENED CIRCULAR AND CLIPPED CIRCULAR WASHERS[1]

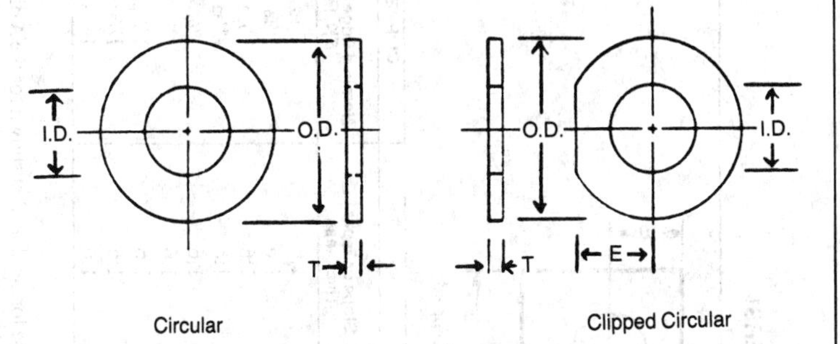
I.D.
O.D.
T
O.D.
I.D.
T
E
Circular
Clipped Circular

BOLT SIZE	CIRCULAR AND CLIPPED CIRCULAR				CLIPPED
	Nominal Outside Diameter (O.D.) In.	Normal Inside Diameter (I.D.) In.	Thickness (*T*), In. min.	Thickness (*T*), In. max.	Minimum Edge Distance (*E*)[2], In.
1/4	5/8	9/32	0.051	0.080	7/32
5/16	11/16	11/32	0.051	0.080	9/32
3/8	13/16	13/32	0.051	0.080	11/32
7/16	59/64	15/32	0.051	0.080	13/32
1/2	1 1/16	17/32	0.097	0.177	7/16
5/8	1 5/16	11/16	0.122	0.177	9/16
3/4	1 15/32	13/16	0.122	0.177	21/32
7/8	1 3/4	15/16	0.136	0.177	25/32
1	2	1 1/8	0.136	0.177	7/8
1 1/8	2 1/4	1 1/4	0.136	0.177	1
1 1/4	2 1/2	1 3/8	0.136	0.177	1 3/32
1 3/8	2 3/4	1 1/2	0.136	0.177	1 7/32
1 1/2	3	1 5/8	0.136	0.177	1 5/16
1 3/4	3 3/8	1 7/8	0.178[3]	0.28[3]	1 17/32
2	3 3/4	2 1/8	0.178[3]	0.28[3]	1 3/4
2 1/4	4	2 3/8	0.24[4]	0.34[4]	2
2 1/2	4 1/2	2 5/8	0.24[4]	0.34[4]	2 3/16
2 3/4	5	2 7/8	0.24[4]	0.34[4]	2 13/32
3	5 1/2	3 1/8	0.24[4]	0.34[4]	2 5/8
3 1/4	6	3 3/8	0.24[4]	0.34[4]	2 7/8
3 1/2	6 1/2	3 5/8	0.24[4]	0.34[4]	3 1/16
3 3/4	7	3 7/8	0.24[4]	0.34[4]	3 5/16
4	7 1/2	4 1/8	0.24[4]	0.34[4]	3 1/2

[1] Tolerances are as noted in Table No. 27-7-N.
[2] Clipped edge *E* shall be not closer than 7/8 of the bolt diameter from the center of the washer.
[3] 3/16 in. nominal.
[4] 1/4 in. nominal.

TABLE NO. 27-7-M—HARDENED BEVELED WASHERS[1]

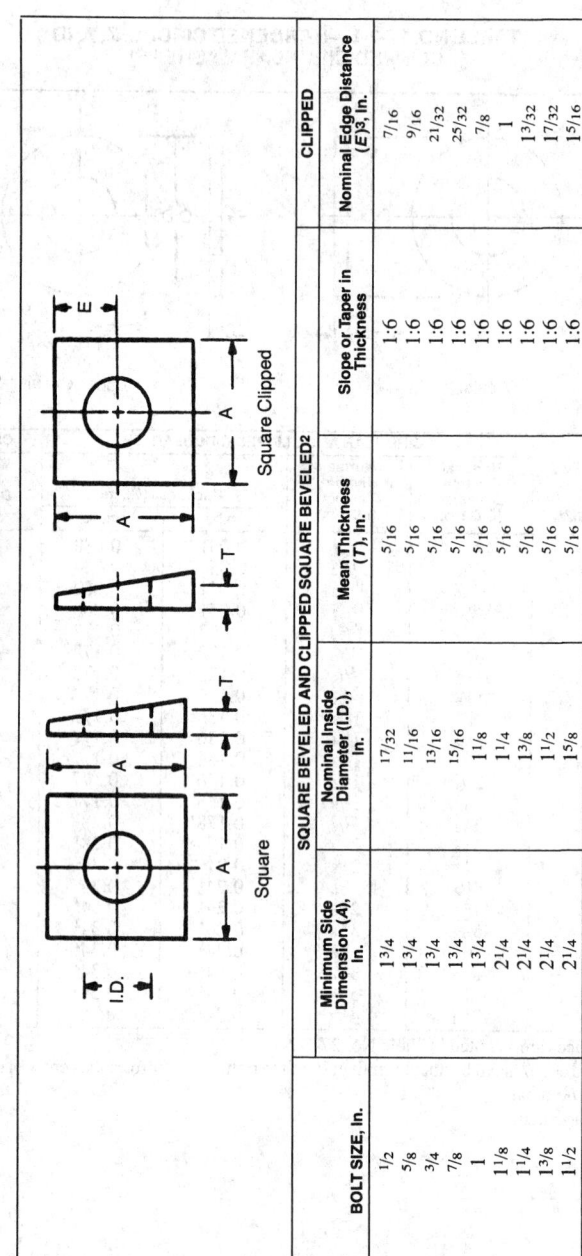

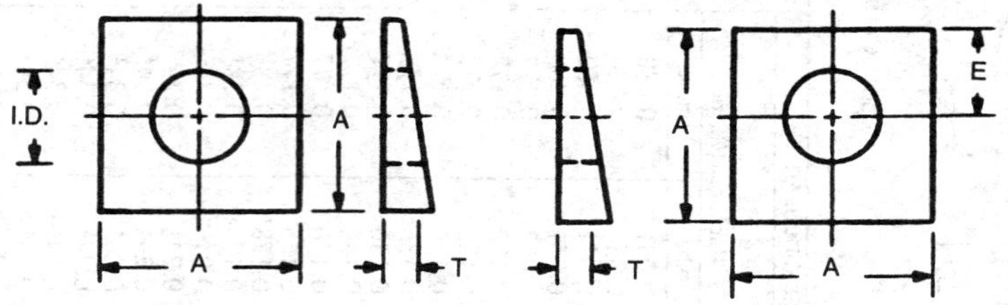
I.D.
A
A
T
T
A
A
E
Square   Square Clipped

BOLT SIZE, In.	SQUARE BEVELED AND CLIPPED SQUARE BEVELED[2]				CLIPPED
	Minimum Side Dimension (*A*), In.	Nominal Inside Diameter (I.D.), In.	Mean Thickness (*T*), In.	Slope or Taper in Thickness	Nominal Edge Distance (*E*)[3], In.
1/2	1 3/4	17/32	5/16	1:6	7/16
5/8	1 3/4	11/16	5/16	1:6	9/16
3/4	1 3/4	13/16	5/16	1:6	21/32
7/8	1 3/4	15/16	5/16	1:6	25/32
1	1 3/4	1 1/8	5/16	1:6	7/8
1 1/8	2 1/4	1 1/4	5/16	1:6	1
1 1/4	2 1/4	1 3/8	5/16	1:6	1 3/32
1 3/8	2 1/4	1 1/2	5/16	1:6	1 7/32
1 1/2	2 1/4	1 5/8	5/16	1:6	1 5/16

[1]Tolerances are as noted in Table No. 27-7-N.

[2]Rectangular beveled washers shall conform to the dimensions shown above, except that one side may be longer than that shown for the *A* dimension.

[3]Clipped edge *E* shall not be closer than 7/8 of the bolt diameter from the center of the washer.

TABLE NO. 27-7-N—WASHER DIMENSION TOLERANCES

	TO 1 1/2 IN. NOMINAL BOLT SIZE, INCL.	OVER 1 1/2 IN. NOMINAL BOLT SIZE, INCL.	OVER 3 TO 4 IN. NOMINAL BOLT SIZE, INCL.
Nominal diameter of hole, in.	–0, + 1/32	–0, + 1/16	–0, + 1/8
Nominal outside diameter, in.	± 1/32	± 1/16	± 1/8
Flatness: max. deviation from straightedge placed on cut side shall not exceed (in.)	0.010	0.015	0.032
Concentricity, in.: center of hole to outside diameter	0.030 FIR[1]	0.090 FIR[1]	0.250 FIR[1]
Burr shall not project above immediately adjacent washer surface more than (in.)	0.010	0.015	0.025

[1]Full indicator runout.

TABLE NO. 27-7-O—WEIGHT OF ZINC COATING FOR VARIOUS THICKNESSES OF BASE METAL

SPECIFIED BASE METAL THICKNESS, In.	MINIMUM WEIGHT OF ZINC COATING oz./ft.^{2} OF SURFACE		EQUIVALENT THICKNESS OF ZINC COATING, mils[1]	
	Average of Specimen Tested	Any Individual Specimen or Computed Value[2]	Average of Specimen Tested	Any Individual Specimen or Computed Value[2]
22 gauge (0.0299) to under 1/16	1.10	0.85	1.87	1.45
1/16 to under 1/8	1.50	1.25	2.55	2.13
1/8 to under 1/4	2.00	1.80	3.40	3.06
1/4 or over	2.30	2.00	3.91	3.40
For wire in assemblies (diameters):				
Under 3/16	1.00	0.75	1.70	1.28
3/16 to under 1/4	1.50	1.25	2.55	2.13
1/4 or over	2.00	1.80	3.40	3.06

[1]Equivalent thickness of zinc coating is based upon mathematical calculations and does not take into consideration the iron content of the coating.

[2]Computed average of at least 5 spot measurements.

UNIFORM BUILDING CODE STANDARD NO. 27-9

SPECIFICATION FOR THE DESIGN OF COLD-FORMED STEEL STRUCTURAL MEMBERS

Based on Specifications for the Design of Cold-formed Steel Structural Members of the American Iron and Steel Institute (1986)

See Sections 2701 (a) and (b), 2703 and 3208 (b) 6, Uniform Building Code

Part I of this standard contains the exceptions to the referenced specification. Part II of this standard, "Specification for the Design of Cold-formed Steel Structural Members," is reproduced with permission of the publisher.

Part I

Scope

Sec. 27.901. Except for the limitations, deletions, modifications or amendments set forth in this section, buildings or structures may be designed in accordance with Part II of this standard. When other codes, standards or specifications are referred to in this standard, they are to be considered as only an indication of an acceptable method or material that can be used with the approval of the building official. Part II of this standard is amended as follows:

Sec. A6 is amended by substituting "U.B.C. Standard No. 27-13" for "American Welding Society Standard D1.3."

Sec. A6 is amended further by substituting "U.B.C. Standard No. 27-15" for AISC "Specification for the Design, Fabrication and Erection of Structural Steel Buildings."

Sec. A6 is amended further by substituting "U.B.C. Standard No. 27-7" for "Research Council for Structural Connections 'Specifications for Structural Joints Using ASTM A 325 of A 490 Bolts.'"

Sec. A6 is amended further by substituting "U.B.C. Standard No. 27-4" for Steel Joist Institute "Standard Specifications Load Tables and Weight Tables for Steel Joists and Joist Girders."

Sec. A6 is amended further by substituting "U.B.C. Standard No. 27-10" for AISI "Stainless Steel Cold-formed Structural Design Manual."

Part II

 The following standard is not necessarily the latest version used by AISI. If the reader desires to compare with that version, the same is available from AISI.

TABLE OF CONTENTS

SPECIFICATION FOR THE DESIGN OF COLD-FORMED STEEL STRUCTURAL MEMBERS

Sec. 27.905. C. MEMBERS

Sec. 27.906. D. STRUCTURAL ASSEMBLIES

Sec. 27.902. SYMBOLS AND DEFINITIONS

Symbol	Definition	Section
A	Full unreduced cross-sectional area of the member	C3.1.1, C3.1.2, C4, C6.2, D4.1
A	Contact area	E5.1
A_b	$b_1t + A_s$, for transverse stiffeners at interior support and under concentrated load, and $b_2t + A_s$, for transverse stiffeners at end support	B6.1, E3.4
A_c	$18t^2 + A_s$, for transverse stiffeners at interior support and under concentrated load, and $10t^2 + A_s$, for transverse stiffeners at end support	B6.1
A_e	Effective area at the stress F_n	C4, C6.2, D4.1
A_n	Net area of cross section	C2, E3.2
A_s	Cross-sectional area of transverse stiffeners	B4, B4.1, B4.2, B6.1
A'_s	Effective area of stiffener	B4, B4.1, B4.2
A_{st}	Gross area of shear stiffener	B6.2
A_{wn}	Net web area	E4
A_1	Bearing area	E5.1
A_2	Full cross-sectional area of concrete support	E5.1
a	Shear panel length of the unreinforced web element. For a reinforced web element, the distance between transverse stiffeners	B6.2, C3.2, D3.2
a	Lateral deflection of the compression flange at assumed load, q	C3.1.3
a	Length of bracing interval	D3.2
B	Stud spacing	D4.1
B_c	Term for determining the tensile yield point of corners	A5.2.2
b	Effective design width of compression element	B2.1, B2.2, B2.3, B3.1, B3.2, B4.1, B4.2, B5
b	Overall width of compression flange, C or Z	D3.2.1
b_d	Effective widths for deflection calculations	B2.1, B2.2
b_e	Effective design width of sub-element or element	A1.2, B2.3, B5
b_o	See Figure B4.1	B4, B4.1, B5
C	For flexural members, ratio of the total corner cross-sectional area of the controlling flange to the full cross-sectional area of the controlling flange	A5.2.2
C_b	Bending coefficient dependent on moment gradient	C3.1.1
C_m	End moment coefficient in interaction formula	C5
C_{ms}	Coefficient for lateral bracing of C-and Z-section	D3.2.1
C_{mx}, C_{my}	End moment coefficient in interaction formula	C5
C_s	Coefficient for lateral torsional buckling	C3.1.1
C_{TF}	End moment coefficient in interaction formula	C3.1.1

C_{th}, C_{tr}	Coefficient for lateral bracing of C- and Z-sections	D3.2.1.
C_v	Shear stiffener coefficient	B6.2
C_w	Torsional warping constant of the cross-section	C3.1.1
C_y	Compression strain factor	C3.1.1
C_o	Initial column imperfection	D4.1
C_1	Term used to compute shear strain in wall board	B4, B4.1, D4.2
C_2	Coefficient as defined in Figure B4-2	B4, B4.2
c	Distance from the neutral axis to the extreme fiber of untwisted section	C3.1.3
c_f	Amount of curling	B1.1b
D	Outside diameter of cylindrical tube	C6.1, C6.2, D4.2
D	Dead load, includes weight of the test specimen	F1
D	Overall depth of lip	B1.1, B4, D1.1
D	Shear stiffener coefficient	B6.2
D_o	Initial column imperfection	D4.1
d	Depth of section	B1.1b, B4, C3.1.1, C3.1.3, D1.1, D3.2.1, D4.1, E3.4
d	Width of arc seam weld	E2.3
d	Visible diameter of outer surface of arc spot weld	E2.2
d	Diameter of bolt	E3, E3.1, E3.2
d_a	Average diameter of the arc spot weld at mid-thickness of t	E2.2
d_a	Average width of seam weld	E2.3
d_e	Effective diameter of fused area	E2.2
d_e	Effective width of arc seam weld at fused surfaces	E2, E2.3
d_h	Diameter of standard hole	B2.2, E3.1, E4
d_s	Reduced effective width of stiffener	B4, B4.2
d'_s	Actual effective width of stiffener	B4, B4.2
d_{wc}	Coped web depth	E4
E	Modulus of elasticity of steel (29,500 ksi)	B1.1b, B2.1, B6.1, C3.1.1, C3.1.3, C3.2, C3.5.2, C4, C4.1, C5, C6.1, D1.2, D4.1, D4.2 , E2.2
E_o	Initial column imperfection; a measure of the initial twist of the stud from the initial, ideal, unbuckled location	D4.1
E_1	Term used to compute shear strain in wallboard	D4.1
E′	Inelastic modulus of elasticity	D4.1
e_{min}	Minimum allowable distance measured in the line of force from the centerline of a weld to the nearest edge of an adjacent weld or to the end of the connected part which the force is directed	E2.2
e_{min}	The distance e measured in the line of force from the center of a standard hole to the nearest edge of an adjacent hole or to the end of the connected part toward which the force is directed	E3.1
e_y	Yield strain = F_y/E	C3.1.1
F_D	Dead load factor	F1

F_e	Elastic buckling stress	C4, C4.1, C4.2, C4.3, C6.2, D4.1
F_L	Live load factor	F1
F_n	Nominal buckling stress	C4, C6.2, D4.2
F_p	Allowable bearing stress	E3.3, E5.1
F_{sy}	Yield point as specified in Sections A3.1 or A3.2	A3.3.2, E2.2, E3.1, E3.2
F_t	Nominal tension stress limit on net section	E3.2, E3.4
F'_t	Allowable tension stress for bolts subject to combination of shear and tension	E3.4
F_u	Tensile strength as specified in Sections A3.1 or A3.2, or as reduced for low ductility steel	A3.3, A3.3.2, E2.2, E2.3, E2.4, E2.5, E3.1, E3.2, E3.3, E4
F_{uv}	Ultimate tensile strength of virgin steel specified by Section A3 or established in accordance with Section F3.3	A5.2.2, E2.2
F_v	Allowable shear stress on the gross area of a bolt	E3.4
F_{wy}	Yield point for design of transverse stiffeners	B6.1
F_{xx}	Strength level designation in AWS electrode classification	E2.2, E2.3, E2.4, E2.5
F_y	Yield point used for design, not to exceed the specified yield point as established in accordance with Section F3, or as increased for cold work of forming in Section A5.5.2, or as reduced for low-ductility steels in Section A3.2.2	A1.2, A3.3, A5.2.1, A5.2.2, B2.1, B5, B6.1, C2, C3.1, C3.1.3, C3.2, C3.5.2, C4, C6.1, C6.2, D1.2, D4.2, E2
F_{ya}	Average yield point of section	A5.2.2
F_{yc}	Tensile yield point of corners	A5.2.2
F_{yf}	Weighted average tensile yield point of the flat portions	F3.2, A5.2.2
F_{ys}	Yield point of stiffener steel	B6.1
F_{yv}	Tensile yield point of virgin steel specified by Section A3 or established in accordance with Section F3.3	A5.2.2
f	Stress in the compression element computed on the basis of the effective design width	B2.1, B2.2, B3.2, B4, B4.1
f_{av}	Average computed stress in the full, unreduced flange width	B1.1b
f_b	Maximum bending stress equal to the bending moment divided by appropriate section modulus of member	C3.1.3
f_c	Computed stress at design load in the cover plate or sheet	D1.2
f'_c	Specified compression stress of concrete	E5.1
f_d	Computed compressive stress in the element being considered. Calculations	B2.1, B2.2, B3.1, B4.1,

	are based on the effective section at the load for which deflections are determined	B4.2
f_{d1}, f_{d2}	Computed stresses f_1 and f_2 as shown in Figure B2.3-1. Calculations are based on the effective section at the load for which deflections are determined	B2.3
f_{d3}	Computed stress f_3 in edge stiffener, as shown in Figure B4-2. Calculations are based on the effective section at the load for which deflections are determined	B3.2
f_t	The computed maximum compressive stress due to twisting and lateral bending	C3.1.3
f_v	Computed shear stress on a bolt	E4
f_1, f_2	Web stresses defined by Figure B2.3-1	B2.3
f_3	Edge stiffener stress defined by Figure B4.2	B3.2
G	Shear modulus for steel = 11,300 ksi	C3.1.1, D4.1
G′	Inelastic shear modulus	D4.1
g	Vertical distance between two rows of connections nearest to the top and bottom flanges	D1.1
h	Depth of flat portion of web measured along the plane of web	B1.2, B6.2, C3.2, C3.4, C3.5.2
I_a	Adequate moment of inertia of stiffener so that each component will behave as a stiffened element	B1.1, B4, B4.1, B4.2
I_b	Moment of inertia of the full unreduced section about the bending axis	C5
I_o	Moment of inertia of effective section about its major axis	C3.1.3
I_s	Actual moment of inertia of the full stiffener about its own centroidal axis parallel to the element to be stiffened	B1.1, B4, B4.1, B4.2, B5
I_{sf}	Moment of inertia of the full area of the multiple stiffened element, including the intermediate stiffeners, about its own centroidal axis parallel to the element to be stiffened	B5
I_{yc}	Moment of inertia of the compression portion of a section about the gravity axis of the entire section about the y-axis	D3.1.1
I_x, I_y	Moment of inertia of full section about principal axis	D3.2.2, D1.1
I_{xy}	Product of inertia of full section about major and minor centroidal axes	D3.2.2, D4.1
J	St. Venant torsion constant	C3.1.1
j	Section property for torsional-flexural buckling	C3.1.1
K	Effective length factor	C3.1.3, C4, C4.1, C5
K′	A constant	D3.2.2
K_b	Effective length factor in the plane of bending	C5
K_t	Effective length factor for torsion	C3.1.2

K_x	Effective length factor for bending about x-axis	C3.1.2
K_y	Effective length factor for bending about y-axis	C3.1.2
k	Plate buckling coefficient	B2.1, B2.3, B3.1, B3.2, B4 B4.1, B4.2
k_v	Shear buckling coefficient	B6.2, C3.2
L	Full span for simple beams, distance between inflection points for continuous beams, twice the length of cantilever beams	B1.1c, D3.2.1
L	Length of seam weld not including the circular ends	E2.3
L	Length of fillet weld	E2.4, E2.5
L	Unbraced length of member	C3.1.2, C3.1.3, C4.1, D1.1
L	Live load	F1
L_a	Length of the portion of the span between supports where the flange that is not connected to the sheathing is in compression	C3.1.3
L_{st}	Length of transverse stiffener	B6.1
L_t	Unbraced length of compression member for torsion	C3.1.1
L_x	Unbraced length of compression member for bending about x-axis	C3.1.1
L_y	Unbraced length of compression member for bending about y-axis	C3.1.1
M	Applied bending moment	C3.3, C3.5.1, C3.5.2
M_a	Allowable bending moment permitted if bending stress only exists	C3.1, C3.3, C3.5.1, C3.5.2, C6.1
M_{ax}, M_{ay}	Allowable moments about the centroidal axes determined in accordance with Section C3	C5
M_{axo}, M_{ayo}	Allowable moments about the centroidal axes determined in accordance with Section C3.1 excluding the provisions of Section C3.1.2	C5, D4.2
M_c	Critical moment	C3.1.2
M_e	Elastic critical moment	C3.1.2
M_n	Nominal moment strength	C3.1, C3.1.1, C3.1.2, C6.1
M_x, M_y	Applied moments about the centroidal axes determined in accordance with Section C3	C5
M_y	Moment causing a maximum strain of e_y	B2.1, C3.1
M_1	Smaller end moment	C3.1.1, C5
M_2	Larger end moment	C3.1.1, C5
m	Distance from the shear center of one channel to the mid-plane of its web	D3.2.2, D1.1
m	$0.192 (F_{uv}/F_{yv}) - 0.068$	A5.2.2
N	Actual length of bearing	D3.6
n	Number of holes	E4
n_p	Number of parallel purlin lines	D3.2.1
P	Concentrated load or reaction	C3.5
P	Applied axial load	C5, D4.1

P	Force transmitted by bolt	E3, E3.1
P	Force transmitted by weld	E2, E2.2
P_a	Allowable concentrated load or reaction for one transverse stiffener	B6.1
P_{ao}	Allowable axial load determined in accordance with Section C4 for $L = 0$	C5
P_L	Force to be resisted by intermediate beam brace	B3.2.2
P_n	Nominal axial strength of member	C4, C6.2
P_n	Nominal strength of connection component	E2, E2.2, E2.3, E2.4, E2.5
$\overline{Q}$	Design shear rigidity for sheathing on both sides of the wall assembly	D4.1
q	Uniformly distributed load in the plane of the web	C3.1.3, D1.1
q_w	Allowable uniform load	C3.1.3
$\overline{q}$	Design shear rigidity for sheathing per inch of stud spacing	D4.1
$\overline{q}_o$	Factor used to determine design shear rigidity	D4.1
q_u	Maximum uniformly distributed load in the plane of the web	C3.1.3
R	Required load-carrying capacity	F1
R	Coefficient	C4, C6.2
R	Inside bend radius	A5.2.2, C3.4
r	Radius of gyration of full unreduced cross section	C3.1.1, C4, C4.1
r	Force transmitted by the bolt or bolts at the section considered, divided by the tension force in member at that section	E3.2
r_{cy}	Radius of gyration of one channel about its centroidal axis parallel to web	D1.1
r_o	Polar radius of gyration of cross section about the shear center	C3.1.1, C4.2, D4.1
r_x, r_y	Radius of gyration of cross section about centroidal principal axes	C3.1.1
r_I	Radius of gyration of I-section about the axis perpendicular to the direction in which buckling would occur for the given conditions of end support and intermediate bracing	D1.1
S	$1.28\sqrt{E/f}$	B4, B4.1
S_c	Elastic section modulus of the effective section calculated at a stress M_c/S_f in the extreme compression fiber	C3.1.1, C3.1.2, C4
S_e	Elastic section modulus of the effective section calculated with extreme compression or tension fiber at F_y	C3.1.1
S_f	Elastic section modulus of full unreduced section for the extreme compression fiber	C3.1.1, C3.1.2, C6.1

s_{max}	Maximum permissible longitudinal spacing of welds or other connectors joining two channels to form an I-section	D1.1
s	Fastener spacing	D1.2, D4.1
s	Spacing in line of stress of welds, rivets, or bolts connecting a compression coverplate or sheet to a non-integral stiffener or other element	E3.2
s	Weld spacing	D1.1
T_a	Allowable tensile strength	C2
T_n	Nominal tensile strength	C2
T_s	Strength of connection in tension	D1.1
t	Base steel thickness of any element or section	A1.2, A3.4, A5.2.1, B1.1, B1.1b, B1.2, B2.1, B4, B4.1, B4.2, B5, B6.1, C3.1.1, C3.1.3, C3.2, C3.4, C3.5.2, C4, C6.1, C6.2, D1.2, E2.4, E2.5
t	Total thickness of the two welded sheets	E2.2
t	Thickness of thinnest connected part	E2.2, E3.1, E4
t_s	Equivalent thickness of a multiple-stiffened element	B5, B6.1
t_w	Effective throat of weld	E2.4, E2.5
V	Actual shear force	C3.3
V_a	Allowable shear force	B6.2, C3.2, C3.3
W	Total load supported by the purlin lines between adjacent supports, lbs.	D3.2.1.
w	Flat width of element exclusive of radii	A1.2, B1.1, B2.1, B2.2, B3.1, B4, B4.1, B4.2, B5, C3.1.1., C3.1.3, C4, D1.2
w	Flat width of the beam flange which contacts the bearing plate	C3.5
w_f	Width of flange projection beyond the web or half the distance between webs for box- or U-type sections	B1.1
w_f	Projection of flanges from inside face of web	D1.1
w_1, w_2	Leg on weld	E2.4
x	Distance from concentrated load to brace	D3.2
x_o	Distance from shear center to centroid along the principal x-axis	C3.1.1, C4.2, D4.1
Y	Yield point of web steel divided by yield point of stiffener steel	B6.2
$1/\alpha_x$, $1/\alpha_y$	Magnification factors	C5
β	Coefficient	C4.2, D4.1
γ	Actual shear strain in the sheathing	D4.1
$\bar{\gamma}$	Permissible shear strain of the sheathing	D4.1
θ	Angle between web and bearing surface > 45° but not more than 90°	C3.4

θ	Angle between the vertical and the plane of the web of the Z-section, degrees	D3.2.1
σ	Stress related to shear strain in sheathing	D4.1
σ_{CR}	Theoretical elastic buckling stress	D4.1
σ_t	Torsional buckling stress	C3.1.1, C4.2, D4.1
ρ	Reduction factor	B2.1
λ, λ_c	Slenderness factors	B2.1, C3.5.2
ψ	f_2/f_1	B2.3
Ω_b	Factor of safety for bearing	E3.3
Ω_c	Factor of safety for axial compression	B6.1, C4, C5, C6.2, D4.1
Ω_e	Factor of safety for sheet tearing	E2.2, E3.1
Ω_f	Factor of safety for flexure	C3.1, C6.1
Ω_{st}	Factor of safety for end crushing of transverse stiffener	B6.1
Ω_t	Factor of safety for tension on net section	C2, E3.2
Ω_w	Factor of safety for welded connections	E2

A. GENERAL PROVISIONS

Sec. 27.903. A1 Limits of Applicability and Terms. A1.1. Scope and Limits of Applicability. This Specification shall apply to the design of structural members cold-formed to shape from carbon or low-alloy steel sheet, strip, plate or bar not more than one inch in thickness and used for load-carrying purposes in buildings. It may also be used for structures other than buildings provided appropriate allowances are made for dynamic effects. Appendices to this Specification shall be considered as integral parts of the Specification.

A1.2 Terms. Where the following terms appear in this Specification they shall have the meaning herein indicated:

(a) *Stiffened or Partially Stiffened Compression Elements.* A stiffened or partially stiffened compression element is a flat compression element (i.e., a plane compression flange of a flexural member or a plane web or flange of a compression member) of which both edges parallel to the direction of stress are stiffened by a web, flange, stiffening lip, intermediate stiffener, or the like.

(b) *Unstiffened Compression Elements.* An unstiffened compression element is a flat compression element which is stiffened at only one edge parallel to the direction of stress.

(c) *Multiple-Stiffened Elements.* A multiple-stiffened element is an element that is stiffened between webs, or between a web and a stiffened edge, by means of intermediate stiffeners which are parallel to the direction of stress. A *sub-element* is the portion between adjacent stiffeners or between web and intermediate stiffener or between edge and intermediate stiffener.

(d) *Flat-Width-to-Thickness Ratio.* The flat width of an element measured along its plane, divided by its thickness.

(e) *Effective Design Width.* Where the flat width of an element is reduced for design purposes, the reduced design width is termed the effective width or effective design width.

(f) *Thickness.* The thickness, t, of any element or section shall be the base steel thickness, exclusive of coatings.

(g) *Torsional-Flexural Buckling.* Torsional-flexural buckling is a mode of buckling in which compression members can bend and twist simultaneously.

(h) *Point-Symmetric Section.* A point-symmetric section is a section symmetrical about a point (centroid) such as a Z-section having equal flanges.

(i) *Yield Point.* Yield point, F_y or F_{sy}, as used in this Specification shall mean yield point or yield strength.

(j) *Stress.* Stress as used in this Specification means force per unit area.

(k) *Confirmatory Test.* A confirmatory test is a test made, when desired, on members, connections, and assemblies designed according to the provisions of Sections A through E of this Specification or its specific references, in order to compare actual versus calculated performance.

(l) *Performance Test.* A performance test is a test made on structural members, connections and assemblies, whose performance cannot be determined by the provisions of Sections A through E of this Specification or its specific references.

(m) *Virgin Steel.* Virgin steel refers to steel as received from the steel producer or warehouse before being cold worked as a result of fabricating operations.

(n) *Virgin Steel Properties.* Virgin steel properties refer to mechanical properties of virgin steel such as yield point, tensile strength, and elongation.

(o) *Specified Minimum Yield Point.* The specified minimum yield point is the lower limit of yield point which must be equaled or exceeded in a specification test to qualify a lot of steel for use in a cold-formed steel structural member designed at that yield point.

(p) *Cold-Formed Steel Structural Members.* Cold-formed steel structural members are shapes which are manufactured by press-braking blanks sheared from sheets, cut lengths of coils or plates, or by roll forming cold- or hot-rolled coils or sheets; both forming operations being performed at ambient room temperature, that is, without manifest addition of heat such as would be required for hot forming.

A1.3 Units of Symbols and Terms. The Specification is written so that any compatible system of units may be used except where explicitly stated otherwise in the text of these provisions.

A2 Non-Conforming Shapes and Construction. The provisions of the Specification are not intended to prevent the use of alternate shapes or constructions not specifically prescribed herein. Such alternates shall meet the provisions of Section F of the Specification and be approved by the appropriate building code authority.

A3 Material. A3.1 Applicable Steels. This Specification requires the use of steel of structural quality as defined in general by the provisions of the following specifications of the American Society for Testing and Materials: A36/A36M,

A242/A242M, A441M, A446/A446M, A500, A529/A529M, A570/A570M, A572/A572M, A588/A588M, A606, A607, A611, A715 and A792.

A3.2 Other Steels. The listing in Section A3.1 does not exclude the use of steel up to and including one inch in thickness ordered or produced to other than the listed specifications, provided such steel conforms to the chemical and mechanical requirements of one of the listed specifications or other published specification which establishes its properties and suitability, and provided it is subjected by either the producer or the purchaser to analyses, tests and other controls to the extent and in the manner prescribed by one of the listed specifications and Section A3.3.

A3.3 Ductility. Steels not listed in Section A3.1 and used for structural members and connections shall comply with one of the following ductility requirements:

A3.3.1 The ratio of tensile strength to yield point shall not be less than 1.08, and the total elongation shall not be less than 10 percent for a two-inch gage length or 7 percent for an eight-inch gage length standard specimen tested in accordance with ASTM A370. The provisions of Chapters B through E of this Specification are limited to steels conforming to these requirements.

A3.3.2 Steels conforming to A446 Grade E and A611 Grade E and other steels which do not meet the provisions of Section A3.3.1 may be used for particular configurations provided (1) the yield strength, F_y, used for design in Chapters B, C and D is taken as 75 percent of the specified minimum yield point or 60 ksi, whichever is less and (2) the tensile strength, F_u, used for design in Chapter E is taken as 75 percent of the specified minimum tensile stress or 62 ksi, whichever is less. Alternatively, the suitability of such steels for the configuration shall be demonstrated by load tests in accordance with Section F1. Allowable loads based on these tests shall not exceed the loads calculated according to Chapters B through E, using the specified minimum yield point, F_{sy}, for F_y and the specified minimum tensile strength, F_u.

Allowable loads based on existing use shall not exceed the loads calculated according to Chapters B through E, using the specified minimum yield point, F_{sy}, for F_y and the specified minimum tensile strength, F_u.

A3.4 Delivered Minimum Thickness. The uncoated minimum steel thickness of the cold-formed product as delivered to the job site shall not at any location be less than 95 percent of the thickness, t, used in its design; however, thicknesses may be less at bends, such as corners, due to cold-forming effects.

A4 Loads. A4.1 Dead Load. The dead load to be assumed in design shall consist of the weight of steelwork and all material permanently fastened thereto or supported thereby.

A4.2 Live Load. The live load shall be that stipulated by the applicable code or specification under which the structure is being designed or that dictated by the conditions involved.

A4.3 Impact Load. For structures carrying live load which induce impact, the assumed live load shall be increased sufficiently to provide for impact.

A4.4 Wind or Earthquake Loads. Where load combinations specified by the applicable building code include wind or earthquake loads, the resulting forces may be multiplied by 0.75.

A4.5 Ponding. Unless a roof surface is provided with sufficient slope toward points of free drainage or adequate individual drains to prevent the accumulation of rainwater, the roof system shall be investigated by rational analysis to assure stability under ponding conditions.

A5 Structural Analysis and Design. A5.1 Design Basis. This Specification is based upon the allowable stress concept presented in terms of allowable moments and loads. The allowable moments and loads are determined by dividing the corresponding nominal capacities by an accepted factor of safety.

A5.2 Yield Point and Strength Increase from Cold Work of Forming. A5.2.1 Yield Point. The yield point used in design, F_y, shall not exceed the specified minimum yield point, or as established in accordance with Chapter F, or as increased for cold work of forming in Section A5.2.2, or as reduced for low ductility steels in Section A3.3.2.

A5.2.2 Strength Increase from Cold Work of Forming. Provisions for the strength increase from cold work of forming are given in Appendix A5.2.2.

A5.3 Serviceability and Durability. A structure shall be designed to perform its required functions during its expected life, including serviceability and durability considerations.

A6 Reference Documents. See Part I for modifications to this section. This Specification recognizes other published and latest approved specifications and manuals for designs contemplated herein, as follows:

1. American National Standards Institute, ANSI A58.1-1982, "Minimum Design Loads in Buildings and Other Structures," American National Standards Institute, Inc., (ANSI), 1430 Broadway, New York, New York 10018
2. Applicable standards of the American Society for Testing and Materials, (ASTM), 1916 Race Street, Philadelphia, Pennsylvania 19013
3. American Institute of Steel Construction, "Specification for the Design, Fabrication and Erection of Structural Steel for Buildings," American Institute of Steel Construction, (AISC), 400 North Michigan Avenue, Chicago, Illinois 60601, November 1, 1978
4. U.B.C. Standard No. 27-13, "Structural Welding Code—Sheet Steel," American Welding Society, (AWS), 550 N.W. LeJeune Road, Miami, Florida 33126
5. U.B.C. Standard No. 27-7, "Specification for Structural Joints Using ASTM A 325 or A 490 Bolts," Research Council on Structural Connections, (RCSC), American Institute of Steel Construction, (AISC), 400 North Michigan Avenue, Chicago, Illinois 60611, November 13, 1985
6. Metal Building Manufacturers Association, *Low Rise Building Systems Manual*, Metal Building Manufacturers Association, (MBMA), 1230 Keith Building, Cleveland, Ohio 44115

7. Steel Deck Institute, "Design Manual for Composite Decks, Formed Decks, and Roof Decks," Steel Deck Institute, Inc., P.O. Box 9506, Canton, Ohio 44711, 1984
8. U.B.C. Standard No. 27-4, Steel Joist Institute, (SJI), Suite A, 1205 48th Avenue North, Myrtle Beach, South Carolina 29577, 1986
9. Rack Manufacturers Institute, "Specification for the Design, Testing and Utilization of Industrial Steel Storage Racks," Rack Manufacturers Institute, (RMI), 8720 Red Oak Boulevard, Suite 201, Charlotte, North Carolina 28210, 1985
10. U.B.C. Standard No. 27-10, American Iron and Steel Institute, (AISI), 1000 16th Street, N.W., Washington, D.C. 20036
11. American Society of Civil Engineers, "ASCE Standard, Specification for the Design and Construction of Composite Slabs, "American Society of Civil Engineers, (ASCE), 345 East 47th Street, New York, New York 10017, October, 1984
12. American Iron and Steel Institute, "Tentative Criteria for Structural Applications of Steel Tubing and Pipe," American Iron and Steel Institute, (AISI), 1000 16th Street, N.W., Washington, D.C. 20036, August, 1976

B. ELEMENTS

Sec. 27.904. B1 Dimensional Limits and Considerations. B1.1 Flange Flat-Width-to-Thickness Considerations. (a) *Maximum Flat-Width-to-Thickness Ratios.* Maximum allowable overall flat-width-to-thickness ratios, w/t, disregarding intermediate stiffeners and taking as t the actual thickness of the element, shall be as follows:

(1) Stiffened compression element having *one* longitudinal edge connected to a web or flange element, the other stiffened by:

Simple lip	60
Any other kind of stiffener having $I_s > I_a$ and $D/w < 0.8$ according to Section B4.2	90

(2) Stiffened compression element with *both* longitudinal edges connected to other stiffened elements — 500

(3) Unstiffened compression element and elements with an edge stiffener having $I_s < I_a$ and $D/w \leq 0.8$ according to Section B4.2 — 60

Note: Unstiffened compression elements that have w/t ratios exceeding approximately 30 and stiffened compression elements that have w/t ratios exceeding approximately 250 are likely to develop noticeable deformation at the full allowable load, without affecting the ability of the member to carry design loads.

Stiffened elements having w/t ratios larger than 500 may be used with safety to support loads, but substantial deformation of such elements under load may occur and may render inapplicable the design formulas of this Specification.

(b) *Flange Curling*. Provisions for limiting the amount of curling or the deflection of a tension or compression flange are given in Appendix B1.1 (b).

(c) *Shear Lag Effects—Unusually Short Spans Supporting Concentrated Loads*. The effective design width of tension and compression flanges of beams supporting concentrated loads and having short spans shall be limited in accordance with Appendix B1.1 (c).

B1.2 Maximum Web Depth-to-Thickness Ratio. The ratio, h/t, of the webs of flexural members shall not exceed the following limitations:

(a) For unreinforced webs: $(h/t)_{max} = 200$

(b) For webs which are provided with transverse stiffeners satisfying the requirements of Section B6.1:

(1) When using bearing stiffeners only, $(h/t)_{max} = 260$

(2) When using bearing stiffeners and intermediate stiffeners, $(h/t)_{max} = 300$

In the above,

h = Depth of flat portion of web measured along the plane of web

t = Web thickness

Where a web consists of two or more sheets, the h/t ratio shall be computed for the individual sheets.

B2 Effective Widths of Stiffened Elements. B2.1 Uniformly Compressed Stiffened Elements. (a) *Load Capacity Determination*. The effective widths, b, of uniformly compressed elements shall be determined from the following formulas:

$b = w$ when $\lambda \leq 0.673$ (*Eq*. B2.1-1)

$b = \rho w$ when $\lambda > 0.673$ (*Eq*. B2.1-2)

where

w = Flat width as shown in Figure B2.1

$\rho = (1-0.22/\lambda)/\lambda$ (*Eq*. B2.1-3)

λ is a slenderness factor determined as follows:

$$\lambda = \frac{1.052}{\sqrt{k}}\left(\frac{w}{t}\right)\sqrt{\frac{f}{E}}$$ (*Eq*. B2.1-4)

where

f for load capacity determination is as follows:

For flexural members:

(1) If Procedure I of Section C3.1.1 is used, $f = F_y$ if the initial yielding is in compression in the element considered.

If the initial yielding is not in compression in the element considered, then the stress f shall be determined for the element considered on the basis of the effective section at M_y (moment causing initial yield).

(2) If Procedure II of Section C3.1.1 is used, then f is the stress in the element considered at M_n determined on the basis of the effective section.

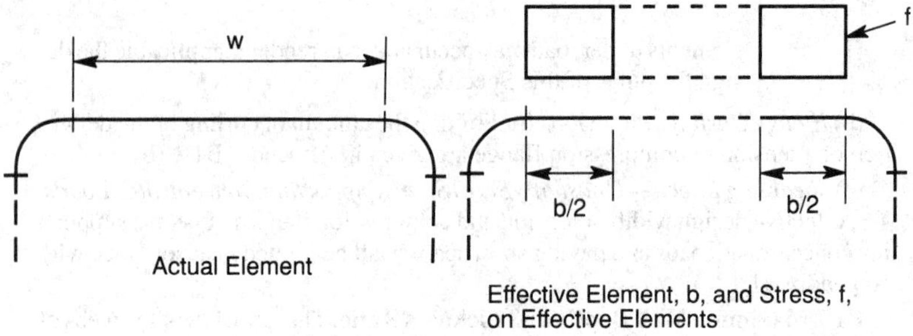
w
Actual Element
f
b/2
b/2
Effective Element, b, and Stress, f, on Effective Elements

Figure B2.1–1 Stiffened Elements

(3) If Section C3.1.2. is used, then $f = \frac{M_c}{S_f}$ as described in that Section in determining S_c.

For compression members f is taken equal to F_n as determined in Section C4 or D4 as applicable.

E = Modulus of elasticity

k = Plate buckling coefficient

= 4 for stiffened elements supported by a web on each longitudinal edge. Values for different types of elements are given in the applicable sections.

(b) *Deflection Determination.* The effective widths, b_d, used in computing deflections shall be determined from the following formulas:

$b_d = w$ when $\lambda \leq 0.673$ (*Eq.* B2.1-5)

$b_d = \rho w$ when $\lambda > 0.673$ (*Eq.* B2.1-6)

where

w = Flat width

ρ = Reduction factor determined by either of the following two procedures:

(1) Procedure I.

A low estimate of the effective width may be obtained from Eqs. B2.1-3 and B2.1-4 where f_d is substituted for f where f_d is the computed compressive stress in the element being considered.

(2) Procedure II.

For stiffened elements supported by a web on each longitudinal edge an improved estimate of the effective width can be obtained by calculating ρ as follows:

$\rho = 1$ when $\lambda \leq 0.673$ (*Eq.* B2.1-7)

$\rho = (1.358 - 0.461/\lambda)/\lambda$ when $0.673 < \lambda < \lambda_c$ (*Eq.* B2.1-8)

$\rho = (0.41 + 0.59\sqrt{F_y/f_d} - 0.22/\lambda)/\lambda$ when $\lambda \geq \lambda_c$ (*Eq.* B2.1-9)

where

$\lambda_c = 0.256 + 0.328\,(w/t)\sqrt{F_y/E}$ (*Eq.* B2.1-10) and λ is as defined by Eq. B2.1-4 except that f_d is substituted for f.

B2.2 Uniformly Compressed Stiffened Elements with Circular Holes. (a) *Load Capacity Determination.* The effective width, b, of stiffened elements with uniform compression having circular holes shall be determined as follows:

for $0.50 \geq \frac{d_h}{w} \geq 0$, and $\frac{w}{t} \leq 70$

center-to-center spacing of holes > 0.50w, and $3d_h$,

$b = w - d_h$ when $\lambda \leq 0.673$ (*Eq.* B2.2-1)

$$b = \frac{w\left[1 - \frac{(0.22)}{\lambda} - \frac{(0.8d_h)}{w}\right]}{\lambda} \text{ when } \lambda > 0.673$$ (*Eq.* B2.2-2)

where

w = Flat width

d_h = Diameter of holes

λ is as defined in Section B2.1.

(b) *Deflection Determination.* The effective width, b_d, used in deflection calculations shall be equal to b determined in accordance with Procedure I of Section B2.2a except that f_d is substituted for f, where f_d is the computed compressive stress in the element being considered.

B2.3 Effective Width of Webs and Stiffened Elements with Stress Gradient. (a) *Load Capacity Determination.* The effective widths, b_1 and b_2, as shown in Figure B2.3-1 shall be determined from the following formulas:

$b_1 = b_e/(3 - \psi)$ (*Eq.* B2.3-1)

For $\psi \leq -0.236$

$b_2 = b_e/2$ (*Eq.* B2.3-2)

$b_1 + b_2$ shall not exceed the compression portion of the web calculated on the basis of effective section

For $\psi > -0.236$

$b_2 = b_e - b_1$ (*Eq.* B2.3-3)

where

b_e = Effective width b determined in accordance with Section B2.1 with f_1 substituted for f and with k determined as follows:

$k = 4 + 2(1 - \psi)^3 + 2(1 - \psi)$ (*Eq.* B2.3-4)

$\psi = f_2/f_1$

f_1, f_2 = Stresses shown in Figure B2.3-1 calculated on the basis of effective section. f_1 is compression (+) and f_2 can be either tension (–) or compression. In case f_1 and f_2 are both compression, $f_1 \geq f_2$

(b) *Deflection Determination.* The effective widths in computing deflections at a given load shall be determined in accordance with Section B2.3a except that f_{d1} and f_{d2} are substituted for f_1 and f_2, where f_{d1}, f_{d2} = Computed stresses f_1 and f_2 as shown in Figure B2.3-1. Calculations are based on the effective section at the load for which deflections are determined.

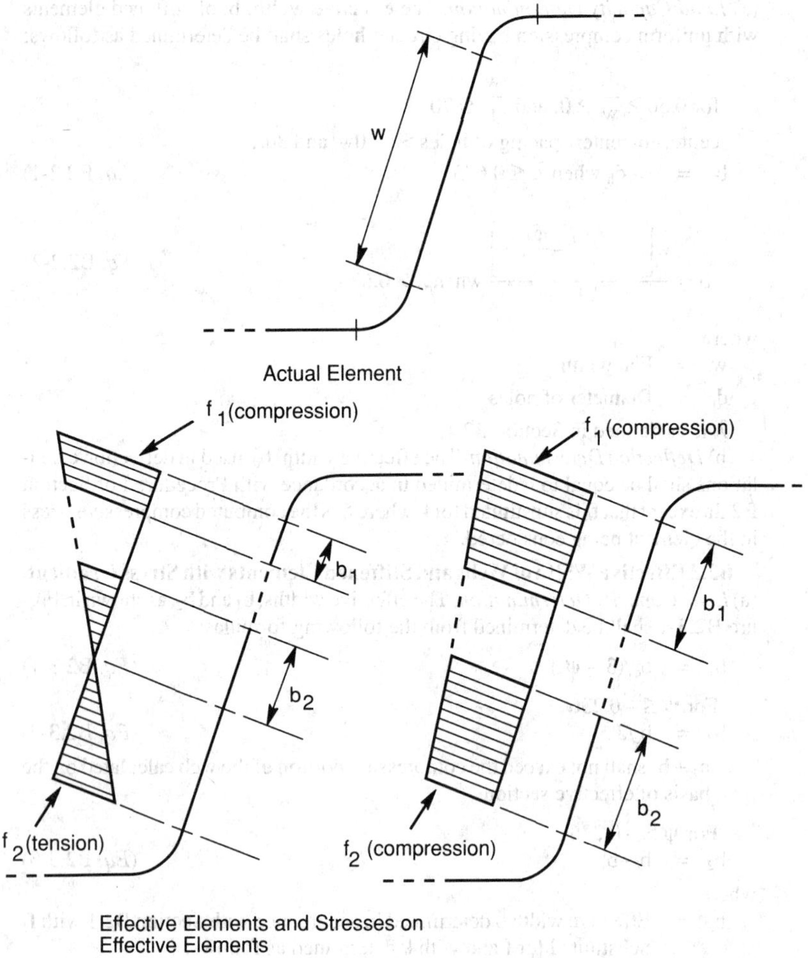
w
Actual Element
f_1(compression)
f_1(compression)
b_1
b_2
b_1
b_2
f_2(tension)
f_2 (compression)
Effective Elements and Stresses on
Effective Elements

Figure B2.3–1 Stiffened Elements with Stress Gradient and Webs

B3 Effective Widths of Unstiffened Elements. B3.1 Uniformly Compressed Unstiffened Elements. (a) *Load Capacity Determination.* Effective widths, b, of unstiffened compression elements with uniform compression shall be determined in accordance with Section B2.1a with the exception that k shall be taken as 0.43 and w as defined in Figure B3.1-1.

(b) *Deflection Determination.* The effective widths used in computing deflections shall be determined in accordance with Procedure I of Section B2.1b except that f_d is substituted for f and k = 0.43.

B3.2 Unstiffened Elements and Edge Stiffeners with Stress Gradient. (a) *Load Capacity Determination.* Effective widths, b, of unstiffened compression elements and edge stiffeners with stress gradient shall be determined in accordance with Section B2.1a with $f = f_3$ as in Figure B4-2 in the element and k = 0.43.

(b) *Deflection Determination.* Effective widths, b, of unstiffened compression elements and edge stiffeners with stress gradient shall be determined in accordance with Procedure I Section B2.1b except that f_{d3} is substituted for f and k = 0.43.

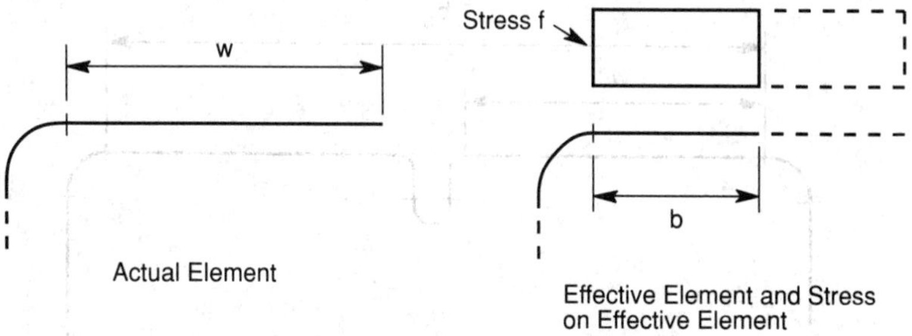
Stress f
w
b
Actual Element
Effective Element and Stress on Effective Element

Figure B3.1–1 Unstiffened Element with Uniform Compression

B4 Effective Widths of Elements with an Edge Stiffener or One Intermediate Stiffener. The following notations are used in this section.

S	=	$1.28\sqrt{E/f}$
k	=	Buckling coefficient
b_o	=	Dimension defined in Figure B4-1
d, w, D	=	Dimensions defined in Figure B4-2
d_s	=	Reduced effective width of the stiffener as specified in this section. d_s, calculated according to Section B4.2, is to be used in computing the overall effective section properties (see Figure B4-2)
d'_s	=	Effective width of the stiffener calculated according to Section B3.1 (see Figure B4-2)
C_1, C_2	=	Coefficients defined in Figures B4-1 and B4-2
A_s	=	Reduced area of the stiffener as specified in this section. A_s is to be used in computing the overall effective section properties. The centroid of the stiffener is to be considered located at the centroid of the full area of the stiffener, and the moment of inertia of the stiffener about its own centroidal axis shall be that of the full section of the stiffener.

I_a = Adequate moment of inertia of stiffener, so that each component element will behave as a stiffened element.

I_s, A'_s = Moment of inertia of the full stiffener about its own centroidal axis parallel to the element to be stiffened and the effective area of the stiffener, respectively. For edge stiffeners the round corner between the stiffener and the element to be stiffened shall not be considered as a part of the stiffener.

For the stiffener shown in Figure B4-2,

$$I_s = (d^3 t \sin^2 \theta)/12 \qquad (Eq.\ B4\text{-}2)$$

$$A'_s = d'_s t \qquad (Eq.\ B4\text{-}3)$$

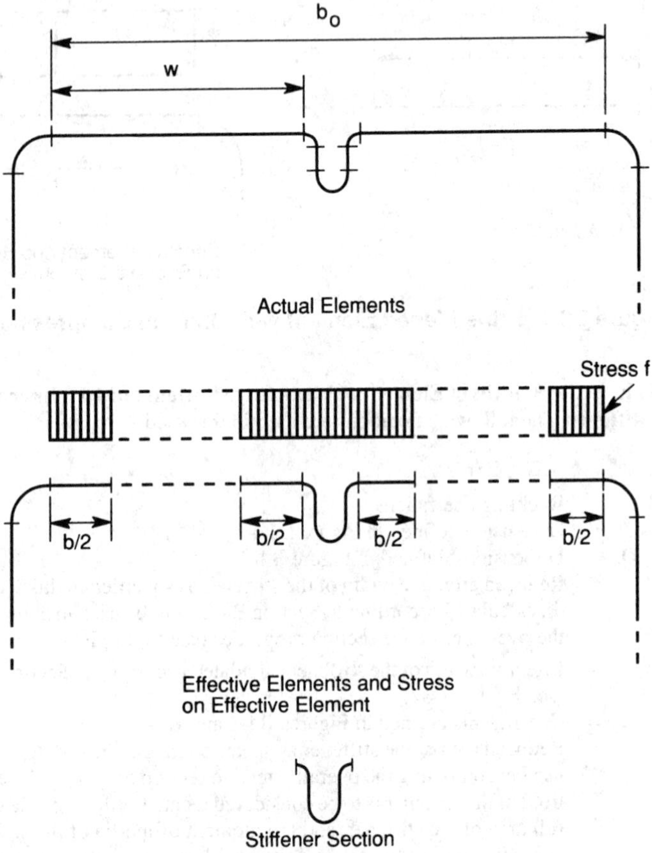

b_o
w
Actual Elements
Stress f
b/2
b/2
b/2
b/2
Effective Elements and Stress on Effective Element
Stiffener Section

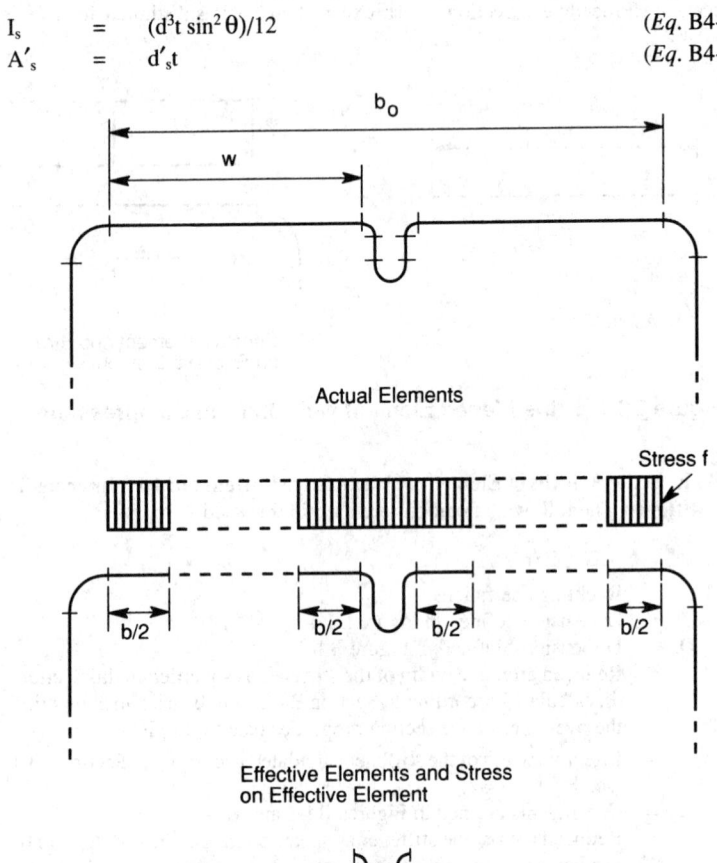

Figure B4-1 Elements with Intermediate Stiffener

B4.1 Uniformly Compressed Elements with an Intermediate Stiffener. (a) *Load Capacity Determination.*

Case I: $b_o/t \le S$ (*Eq.* B4.1-1)

$I_a = 0$ (no intermediate stiffener needed) (*Eq.* B4.1-2)

$b = w$ (*Eq.* B4.1-3)

$A_s = A'_s$ (*Eq.* B4.1-4)

Case II: $S < b_o/t < 3S$ (*Eq.* B4.1-5)

$I_a/t^4 = [50(b_o/t)/S]-50$ (*Eq.* B4.1-6)

b and A_s shall be calculated according to Section B2.1a where

$k = 3(I_s/I_a)^{1/2} + 1 \le 4$ (*Eq.* B4.1-7)

$A_s = A'_s(I_s/I_a) \le A'_s$ (*Eq.* B4.1-8)

Case III: $b_o/t \ge 3S$

$I_a/t^4 = [128(b_o/t)/S]-285$ (*Eq.* B4.1-9)

b and A_s are calculated according to Section B2.1a where

$k = 3(I_s/I_a)^{1/3} + 1 \le 4$ (*Eq.* B4.1-10)

$A_s = A'_s (I_s/I_a) \le A'_s$ (*Eq.* B4.1-11)

(b) *Deflection Determination.* Effective widths shall be determined as in Section B4.1a except that f_d is substituted for f.

B4.2 Uniformly Compressed Elements with an Edge Stiffener. (a) *Load Capacity Determination.*

Case I: $w/t \le S/3$ (*Eq.* B4.2-1)

$I_a = 0$ (no edge stiffener needed) (*Eq.* B4.2-2)

$b = w$ (*Eq.* B4.2-3)

$d_s = d'_s$ for simple lip stiffener (*Eq.* B4.2-4)

$A_s = A'_s$ for other stiffener shapes (*Eq.* B4.2-5)

Case II: $S/3 < w/t < S$

$I_a/t^4 = 399\{[(w/t)/S]-0.33\}^3$ (*Eq.* B4.2-6)

$n = 1/2$

$C_2 = I_s/I_a \le 1$ (*Eq.* B4.2-7)

$C_1 = 2 - C_2$ (*Eq.* B4.2-8)

b shall be calculated according to Section B2.1 where

$k = [4.82-5(D/w)](I_s/I_a)^n + 0.43 \le 5.25-5(D/w)$ (*Eq.* B4.2-9)

for $0.8 \ge D/w > 0.25$

$k = 3.57(I_s/I_a)^n + 0.43 \le 4.0$ (*Eq.* B4.2-10)

for $(D/w) \le 0.25$

$d_s = d'_s (I_s/I_a) \le d'_s$ (*Eq.* B4.2-11)

for simple lip stiffener

$A_s = A'_s (I_s/I_a) \le A'_s$ (*Eq.* B4.2-12)

for other stiffener shape

Case III: $w/t \geq S$

$$I_a/t^4 = [115\,(w/t)/S] + 5 \qquad (Eq.\ B4.2\text{-}13)$$

C_1, C_2, b, k, d_s, A_s are calculated per Case II with n = 1/3.

(b) *Deflection Determination.* Effective widths shall be determined as in Section B4.2a except that f_d is substituted for f.

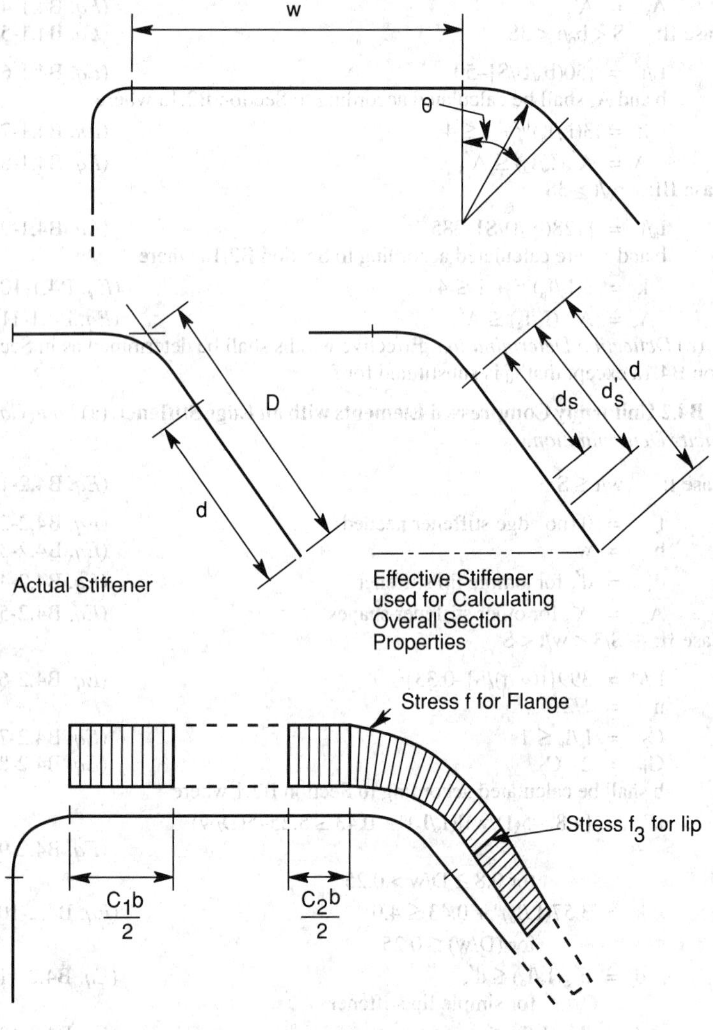
w
θ
D
d
Actual Stiffener
d
d_s
d'_s
Effective Stiffener used for Calculating Overall Section Properties
Stress f for Flange
Stress f_3 for lip
$\frac{C_1 b}{2}$
$\frac{C_2 b}{2}$

Effective Element and Stress on Effective Element

Figure B4-2 Elements with Edge Stiffener

B5 Effective Widths of Edge Stiffened Elements with Intermediate Stiffeners or Stiffened Elements with More Than One Intermediate Stiffener. For the determination of the effective width, the intermediate stiffener of an edge stiffened element or the stiffeners of a stiffened element with more than one stiffener shall be disregarded unless each intermediate stiffener has the minimum I_s as follows:

$$I_{min} = [3.66\sqrt{(w/t)^2 - (0.136E)/F_y}]t^4 \quad \text{but not less than } 18.4\, t^4 \qquad (Eq.\ B5\text{–}1)$$

where

w/t = Width-thickness ratio of the larger stiffened sub-element

I_s = Moment of inertia of the full stiffener about its own centroid axis parallel to the element to be stiffened

(a) If the spacing of intermediate stiffeners between two webs is such that for the sub-element between stiffeners $b < w$ as determined in Section B2.1, only two intermediate stiffeners (those nearest each web) shall be considered effective.

(b) If the spacing of intermediate stiffeners between a web and an edge stiffener is such that for the sub-element between stiffeners $b < w$ as determined in Section B2.1, only one intermediate stiffener, that nearest the web, shall be considered effective.

(c) If intermediate stiffeners are spaced so closely that for the elements between stiffeners $b = w$ as determined in Section B2.1, all the stiffeners may be considered effective. In computing the flat-width-to-thickness ratio of the entire multiple-stiffened element, such element shall be considered as replaced by an "equivalent element" without intermediate stiffeners whose width, b_o, is the full width between webs or from web to edge stiffener, and whose equivalent thickness, t_s, is determined as follows:

$$t_s = \sqrt[3]{12I_{sf}/b_o} \qquad (Eq.\ B5\text{–}2)$$

where

I_{sf} = Moment of inertia of the full area of the multiple-stiffened element, including the intermediate stiffeners, about its own centroidal axis. The moment of inertia of the entire section shall be calculated assuming the "equivalent element" to be located at the centroidal axis of the multiple stiffened element, including the intermediate stiffener. The actual extreme fiber distance shall be used in computing the section modulus.

(d) If $w/t > 60$, the effective width, b_e, of the sub-element or element shall be determined from the following formula:

$$\frac{b_e}{t} = \frac{b}{t} - 0.10\left[\frac{w}{t} - 60\right] \qquad (Eq.\ B5\text{–}3)$$

where:

w/t = flat-width ratio of sub-element or element

b = effective design width determined in accordance with the provisions of Section B2.1, in.

b_e = effective design width of sub-element or element to be used in design computations, in.

For computing the effective structural properties of a member having compression sub-elements or element subject to the above reduction in effective width, the area of stiffeners (edge stiffener or intermediate stiffeners) shall be considered reduced to an effective area as follows:

For $60 < w/t < 90$:

$A_{ef} = \alpha A_{st}$ (*Eq.* B5-4)

where

$$\alpha = (3 - 2b_e/w) - \frac{1}{30}\left[1 - \frac{b_e}{w}\right]\left[\frac{w}{t}\right] \quad (Eq.\ B5\text{–}5)$$

For $w/t \geq 90$:

$A_{ef} = (b_e/w)\, A_{st}$ (*Eq.* B5-6)

In the above expressions, A_{ef} and A_{st} refer only to the area of the stiffener section, exclusive of any portion of adjacent elements.

The centroid of the stiffener is to be considered located at the centroid of the full area of the stiffener, and the moment of inertia of the stiffener about its own centroidal axis shall be that of the full section of the stiffener.

B6 Stiffeners. B6.1 Transverse Stiffeners. Transverse stiffeners attached to beam webs at points of concentrated loads or reactions, shall be designed as compression members. Concentrated loads or reactions shall be applied directly into the stiffeners, or each stiffener shall be fitted accurately to the flat portion of the flange to provide direct load bearing into the end of the stiffener. Means for shear transfer between the stiffener and the web shall be provided according to Chapter E. The concentrated loads or reactions shall not exceed the smaller of the allowable loads, P_a, given by (a) and (b) as follows:

(a) $P_a = P_n/\Omega_{st}$ (*Eq.* B6.1-1)

where

$P_n = F_{wy}A_c$ (*Eq.*B6.1-2)

$\Omega_{st} = 2.00$

$A_c = 18t^2 + A_s$, for transverse stiffeners at interior support and under concentrated load (*Eq.* B6.1-3)

$A_c = 10t^2 + A_s$, for transverse stiffeners at end support (*Eq.* B6.1-4)

F_{wy}= Lower value of beam web, F_y or stiffener section, F_{ys}

(b) $P_a = P_n/\Omega_c$ (*Eq.* B6.1-5)

where

P_n = Nominal axial load evaluated according to Section C4(a) with A_e replaced by A_b

Ω_c = Factor of safety for axial compression evaluated according to Section C4(a)

$A_b = b_1t + A_s$, for transverse stiffeners at interior support and under concentrated load (*Eq.* B6.1-6)

A_b = $b_2t + A_s$, for transverse stiffeners at end support (*Eq.* B6.1-7)

A_s = Cross sectional area of transverse stiffeners

b_1 = $25t\,[0.0024(L_{st}/t) + 0.72] \le 25t$ (*Eq.* B6.1-8)

b_2 = $12t\,[0.0044(L_{st}/t) + 0.83] \le 12t$ (*Eq.* B6.1-9)

L_{st} = Length of transverse stiffener

t = Base thickness of beam web

The w/t_s ratio for the stiffened and unstiffened elements of cold-formed steel transverse stiffeners shall not exceed $1.28\sqrt{(E/F_{ys})}$ and $0.37\sqrt{(E/F_{ys})}$ respectively, where F_{ys} is the yield stress, F_y, and t_s the thickness of the stiffener steel.

B6.2 Shear Stiffeners. Where shear stiffeners are required, the spacing shall be such that the web shear force shall not exceed the allowable shear force, V_a, permitted by Section C3.2, and the ratio a/h shall not exceed $[260/(h/t)]^2$ nor 3.0.

The actual moment of inertia, I_s, of a pair of attached shear stiffeners, or of a single shear stiffener, with reference to an axis in the plane of the web, shall have a minimum value of

$$I_{smin} = 5ht^3[h/a - 0.7(a/h)] \ge (h/50)^4 \qquad (Eq.\ B6.2\text{-}1)$$

The gross area of shear stiffeners shall be not less than

$$A_{st} = \frac{1 - C_v}{2}\left[\frac{a}{h} - \frac{(a/h)^2}{(a/h) + \sqrt{1 + (a/h)^2}}\right]YDht \qquad (Eq.\ B6.2\text{–}2)$$

where

$$C_v = \frac{45{,}000k_v}{F_y(h/t)^2} \text{ when } C_v \le 0.8 \qquad (Eq.\ B6.2\text{–}3)$$

$$C_v = \frac{190}{h/t}\left(\sqrt{\frac{k_v}{F_y}}\right) \text{ when } C_v > 0.8 \qquad (Eq.\ B6.2\text{–}4)$$

$$k_v = 4.00 + \frac{5.34}{(a/h)^2} \text{ when } a/h \le 1.0 \qquad (Eq.\ B6.2\text{–}5)$$

$$k_v = 5.34 + \frac{4.00}{(a/h)^2} \text{ when } a/h > 1.0 \qquad (Eq.\ B6.2\text{–}6)$$

a = Distance between transverse stiffeners

$$Y = \frac{\text{Yield point of web steel}}{\text{Yield point of stiffener steel}}$$

D = 1.0 for stiffeners furnished in pairs

D = 1.8 for single-angle stiffeners

D = 2.4 for single-plate stiffeners

t and h are as defined in Section B1.2

B6.3 Nonconforming Stiffeners. The allowable load carrying capacity of members with transverse stiffeners that do not meet the requirements of Sections B6.1 or B6.2, such as stamped or rolled-in transverse stiffeners shall be determined by tests in accordance with Chapter F of this Specification.

C. MEMBERS

Sec. 27.905. C1 Properties of Sections. Properties of sections (cross-sectional area, moment of inertia, section modulus, radius of gyration, etc.) shall be determined in accordance with conventional methods of structural design. Properties shall be based on the full cross section of the members (or net sections where the use of net sections is applicable) except where the use of a reduced cross section, or effective design width, is required.

C2 Tension Members. For axially loaded tension members, the applied tensile force shall not exceed T_a determined as follows:

$$T_a = T_n/\Omega_t \qquad (Eq.\ C2\text{-}1)$$

where

T_n = Strength of member when loaded in tension

$= A_nF_y$ *(Eq.* C2-2)

Ω_t = Factor of safety for tension

= 1.67

A_n = Net area of the cross section

F_y = Design yield stress

C3 Flexural Members. C3.1 Strength for Bending Only. In flexural members, the applied moment uncoupled from axial load, shear, and local concentrated forces or reactions shall not exceed the allowable M_a calculated as follows:

$$M_a = M_n/\Omega_f \qquad (Eq.\ C3.1\text{-}1)$$

where

M_n = Smaller of the nominal moment strengths calculated according to Sections C3.1.1 and C3.1.2

Ω_f = Factor of safety for bending

= 1.67

C3.1.1 Nominal Section Strength. Section strength shall be calculated either on the basis of initiation of yielding in the effective section (Procedure I) or on the basis of the inelastic reserve capacity (Procedure II) as applicable.

(a) Procedure I—Based on Initiation of Yielding. Effective yield moment based on section strength, M_n, shall be determined as follows:

$$M_n = S_eF_y \qquad (Eq.\ C3.1.1\text{-}1)$$

where

F_y = Design yield stress as determined in Section A5.2.1

S_e = Elastic section modulus of the effective section calculated with the extreme compression or tension fiber at F_y

(b) Procedure II—Based on Inelastic Reserve Capacity. The inelastic flexural reserve capacity may be used when the following conditions are met:

(1) The member is not subject to twisting or to lateral, torsional, or torsional-flexural buckling.

(2) The effect of cold forming is not included in determining the yield point F_y.

(3) The ratio of the depth of the compressed portion of the web to its thickness does not exceed λ_1.

(4) The shear force does not exceed $0.35F_y$ times the web area, $h \times t$.

(5) The angle between any web and the vertical does not exceed 30 degrees.

The nominal moment strength, M_n, shall not exceed either $1.25\ S_eF_y$ determined according to Procedure I or that causing a maximum compression strain of C_ye_y (no limit is placed on the maximum tensile strain).

where

e_y = Yield strain = F_y/E

E = Modulus of elasticity

C_y = Compression strain factor determined as follows:

(a) Stiffened compression elements without intermediate stiffeners

$C_y = 3$ for $w/t \leq \lambda_1$

$$C_y = 3 - 2\left(\frac{w/t - \lambda_1}{\lambda_2 - \lambda_1}\right) \text{ for } \lambda_1 < \frac{w}{t}\lambda_2$$

$C_y = 1$ for $w/t \geq \lambda_2$

where

$$\lambda_1 = \frac{1.11}{\sqrt{F_y/E}} \qquad (Eq.\ C3.1.1\text{-}2)$$

$$\lambda_2 = \frac{1.28}{\sqrt{F_y/E}} \qquad (Eq.\ C3.1.1\text{-}3)$$

(b) Unstiffened compression elements

$C_y = 1$

(c) Multiple-stiffened compression elements and compression elements with edge stiffeners

$C_y = 1$

When applicable, effective design widths defined in Section B3.1 shall be used in calculating section properties. M_n shall be calculated considering equilibrium of stresses, assuming an ideally elastic-plastic stress-strain curve which is the same in tension as in compression, assuming small deformation and assuming that plane sections remain plane during bending. Combined bending and web crippling shall be checked by provisions of Section C3.4.

C3.1.2 Lateral Buckling Strength. The provisions of this section apply to I-, Z-, C- and other singly-symmetric section flexural members (not including multiple-web deck, U- and closed box-type members, and curved or arch members). The provisions of this section do not apply to laterally unbraced compression flanges of otherwise laterally stable sections. Refer to C3.1.3 for C- and Z-purlins in which the tension flange is attached to sheathing. For the laterally unbraced segments of doubly or singly symmetric sections subject to lateral buckling, M_n shall be determined as follows:

$$M_n = S_c \frac{M_c}{S_f} \qquad (Eq.\ C3.1.2\text{-}1)$$

where

S_f = Elastic section modulus of the full unreduced section for the extreme compression fiber

S_c = Elastic section modulus of the effective section calculated at a stress M_c/S_f in the extreme compression fiber

M_c = Critical moment calculated according to (a) or (b) below:

(a) For I- or Z-sections bent about the centroidal axis perpendicular to the web (x-axis):

For $M_e \geq 2.78M_y$

$$M_c = M_y \qquad (Eq.\ C3.1.2\text{-}2)$$

For $2.78M_y > M_e > 0.56M_y$

$$M_c = \frac{10}{9} M_y \left(1 - \frac{10M_y}{36M_e}\right) \qquad (Eq.\ C3.1.2\text{-}3)$$

For $M_e \leq 0.56M_y$

$$M_c = M_e \qquad (Eq.\ C3.1.2\text{-}4)$$

where

M_y = Moment causing initial yield at the extreme compression fiber of the full section

= S_fF_y

M_e = Elastic critical moment determined either as defined in (a) below or as follows:

$$= \pi^2 EC_b \frac{dI_{yc}}{L^2} \text{ for doubly–symmetric I-sections} \qquad (Eq.\ C3.1.2\text{-}6)$$

$$= \frac{\pi^2 EC_b dI_{yc}}{2L^2} \text{ for point–symmetric Z-sections} \qquad (Eq.\ C3.1.2\text{-}7)$$

L = Unbraced length of the member

I_{yc} = Moment of inertia of the compression portion of a section about the gravity axis of the entire section parallel to the web, using the full unreduced section

Other terms are defined in (b) below.

(b) For singly-symmetric sections (x-axis is assumed to be the axis of symmetry):

For $M_e > 0.5M_y$

$$M_c = M_y\left(1 - \frac{M_y}{4M_e}\right) \qquad (Eq.\ C3.1.2\text{-}8)$$

For $M_e \leq 0.5M_y$

$$M_c = M_e \qquad (Eq.\ C3.1.2\text{-}9)$$

where

M_y = Is as defined in (a) above

M_e = Elastic critical moment

= $C_b r_o A \sqrt{\sigma_{ey}\sigma_t}$ for bending about the symmetry axis (x-axis is the axis of symmetry oriented such that the shear center has a negative x-coordinate). (*Eq.* C3.1.2-5)

Alternatively, M_e can be calculated using the formula for doubly-symmetric I-sections or point-symmetric sections given in (b) below

= $C_s A \sigma_{ex}[j + C_s \sqrt{j^2 + r_o^2(\sigma_t/\sigma_{ex})}]/C_{TF}$ for bending (*Eq.* C3.1.2-11)

centroidal axis perpendicular to the symmetry axis

C_s = +1 for moment causing compression on the shear center side of the centroid

C_s = −1 for moment causing tension on the shear center side of the centroid

$$\sigma_{ex} = \frac{\pi_2 E}{(K_x L_x/r_x)^2} \qquad (Eq.\ C3.1.2\text{-}12)$$

$$\sigma_{ey} = \frac{\pi_2 E}{(K_y L_y/r_y)^2} \qquad (Eq.\ C3.1.2\text{-}12)$$

$$\sigma_t = \frac{1}{Ar_o^2}\left[GJ + \frac{\pi^2 EC_w}{(K_t L_t)^2}\right] \qquad (Eq.\ C3.1.2\text{-}14)$$

A = Full cross-sectional area

C_b = Bending coefficient which can conservatively be taken as unity, or calculated from

C_b = $1.75 + 1.05[(M_1/M_2)] + 0.3\ [(M_1/M_2)]^2 \leq 2.3$

where

M_1 is the smaller and M_2 the larger bending moment at the ends of the unbraced length, taken about the strong axis of the member, and where M_1/M_2, the ratio of end moments, is positive when M_1 and M_2 have the same sign (reverse curvature bending) and negative when they are of opposite sign (single curvature bending). When the bending moment at any point within an unbraced length is larger than that at both ends of this length, and for members subject to combined axial load and bending moment (Section C5), C_b shall be taken as unity.

C_{TF} = $0.6 - 0.4\ (M_1/M_2)$

where

M_1 is the smaller and M_2 the larger bending moment at the ends of the unbraced length, and where M_1/M_2, the ratio of end moments, is positive when M_1 and M_2 have the same sign (reverse curvature bending) and negative when they are of opposite sign (single curvature bending). When the bending moment at any point within an unbraced length is larger than that at both ends of this length, and for members subject to combined axial load and bending moment (Section C5), C_b shall be taken as unity.

r_o = Polar radius of gyration of the cross section about the shear center

$$= \sqrt{r_x^2 + r_y^2 + x_o^2} \qquad (Eq.\ C3.1.2\text{-}15)$$

r_x, r_y = Radii of gyration of the cross section about the centroidal principal axes

E = Modulus of elasticity

G = Shear modulus

K_x, K_y, K_t = Effective length factors for bending about the x- and y-axes, and for twisting

L_x, L_y, L_t = Unbraced length of compression member for bending about the x- and y-axes, and for twisting

x_o = Distance from the shear center to the centroid along the principal x-axis, taken as negative

J = St. Venant torsion constant of the cross section

C_w = Torsional warping constant of the cross section

$$j = \frac{1}{2I_y}\left[\int_A x^3 dA + \int_A xy^2 dA\right] - x_o \qquad (Eq.\ C3.1.2\text{-}16)$$

C3.1.3 Beams with One Flange Attached to Deck or Sheathing. C- and Z-sections with the tension flange attached to deck or sheathing and with the compression flange laterally unbraced shall be designed using a rational method of analysis; alternatively, full scale testing in accordance with Section F1 may be used.

C3.2 Strength for Shear Only. The shear force at any section shall not exceed the allowable shear, V_a, calculated as follows:

(a) For $h/t \leq 1.38\sqrt{Ek_v/F_y}$

$$V_a = 0.38t^2\sqrt{k_vF_yE} \leq 0.4F_yht \qquad (Eq.\ C3.2\text{-}1)$$

(b) For $h/t > 1.38\sqrt{Ek_v/F_y}$

$$V_a = 0.53Ek_vt^3/h \qquad (Eq.\ C3.2\text{-}2)$$

where

t = Web thickness

h = Depth of the flat portion of the web measured along the plane of the web

k_v = Shear buckling coefficient determined as follows:

1. For unreinforced webs, $k_v = 5.34$
2. For beam webs with transverse stiffeners satisfying the requirements of Section B6

when $a/h \leq 1.0$

$$k_v = 4.00 + \frac{5.34}{(a/h)^2} \qquad (Eq.\ C3.2\text{-}3)$$

when $a/h > 1.0$

$$k_v = 5.34 + \frac{4.00}{(a/h)^2} \qquad (Eq.\ C3.2\text{-}4)$$

where

a = the shear panel length for unreinforced web element
= distance between transverse stiffeners for web elements.

For a web consisting of two or more sheets, each sheet shall be considered as a separate element carrying its share of the shear force.

C3.3 Strength for Combined Bending and Shear. For beams with unreinforced webs, the moment, M, and shear, V, shall satisfy the following interaction equation:

$$(M/M_a)^2 + (V/V_a)^2 \leq 1.0 \qquad (Eq.\ C3.3\text{-}1)$$

For beams with transverse web stiffeners, the moment, M, and shear, V, shall not exceed M_a and V_a, respectively. When $M/M_a > 0.5$ and $V/V_a > 0.7$, then M and V shall satisfy the following interaction equation:

$$0.6\,(M/M_a) + (V/V_a) \leq 1.3 \qquad (Eq.\ C3.3\text{-}2)$$

In the above equations:

M_a = Allowable moment when bending alone exists
V_a = Allowable shear force when shear alone exists

C3.4 Web Crippling Strength. These provisions are applicable to webs of flexural members subject to concentrated loads or reactions, or the components thereof, acting perpendicular to the longitudinal axis of the member, acting in the plane of the web under consideration, and causing compressive stresses in the web.

To avoid crippling of unreinforced flat webs of flexural members having a flat width ratio, h/t, equal to or less than 200, concentrated loads and reactions shall not exceed the values of P_a given in Table C3.4-1. Webs of flexural members for which h/t is greater than 200 shall be provided with adequate means of transmitting concentrated loads and/or reactions directly into the webs.

The formulas in Table C3.4-1 apply to beams when $R/t \leq 6$ and to deck when $R/t \leq 7$, $N/t \leq 210$ and $N/h \leq 3.5$.

P_a represents the concentrated load or reaction for one solid web connecting top and bottom flanges. For two or more webs, P_a shall be computed for each individual web and the results added to obtain the allowable load or reaction for the multiple web.

For built-up I-sections, or similar sections, the distance between the web connector and beam flange shall be kept as small as practical.

TABLE C3.4-1
P_a

		Shapes Having Single Webs		Shapes Having Multiple $Webs_{(1)}$
		Stiffened Flanges	Unstiffened Flanges	Stiffened and Unstiffened Flanges
Opposing Loads Spaced > $1.5h_{(2)}$	End $Reaction_{(3)}$	*Eq.* C3.4-1	*Eq.* C3.4-2	*Eq.* C3.4-3
	Interior $Reaction_{(4)}$	*Eq.* C3.4-4	*Eq.* C3.4-4	*Eq.* C3.4-5
Opposing Loads Spaced ≤ $1.5h_{(5)}$	End $Reaction_{(3)}$	*Eq.* C3.4-6	*Eq.* C3.4-6	*Eq.* C3.4-7
	Interior $Reaction_{(4)}$	*Eq.* C3.4-8	*Eq.* C3.4-8	*Eq.* C3.4-9

Footnotes and Equation References to Table C3.4-1:

(1) I-sections made of two channels connected back to back or similar sections which provide a high degree of restraint against rotation of the web (such as I-sections made by welding two angles to a channel).

(2) At locations of one concentrated load or reaction acting either on the top or bottom flange, when the clear distance between the bearing edges of this and adjacent opposite concentrated loads or reactions is greater than 1.5h.

(3) For end reactions of beams or concentrated loads on the end of cantilevers when the distance from the edge of the bearing to the end of the beam is less than 1.5h.

(4) For reactions and concentrated loads when the distance from the edge of bearing to the end of the beam is equal to or greater than 1.5h.

(5) At locations of two opposite concentrated loads or of a concentrated load and an opposite reaction acting simultaneously on the top and bottom flanges, when the clear distance between their adjacent bearing edges is equal to or less than 1.5h.

Equations for Table C3.4-1:

$$t^2 kC_3C_4C\theta[179 - 0.33(h/t)]\,[1 + 0.01(N/t)] \qquad (Eq.\ C3.4\text{-}1)$$

$$t^2 kC_3C_4C\theta\,[117 - 0.15(h/t)]\,[1 + 0.01(N/t)] \qquad (Eq.\ C3.4\text{-}2)$$

When $N/t > 60$, the factor $[1 + 0.01(N/t)]$ may be increased to $[0.71 + 0.015(N/t)]$

$$t^2F_yC_6(5.0 + 0.63\sqrt{N/t}) \qquad (Eq.\ C3.4\text{-}3)$$

$$t^2kC_1C_2C\theta[291 - 0.40(h/t)]\,[1 + 0.007(N/t)] \qquad (Eq.\ C3.4\text{-}4)$$

When $N/t > 60$, the factor $[1 + 0.007(N/t)]$ may be increased to $[0.75 + 0.011(N/t)]$

$$t^2F_yC_5(0.88 + 0.12m)(7.50 + 1.63\sqrt{N/t}) \qquad (Eq.\ C3.4\text{-}5)$$

$$t^2kC_3C_4C\theta[132 - 0.31(h/t)]\,[1 + 0.01(N/t)] \qquad (Eq.\ C3.4\text{-}6)$$

$t^2F_yC_8(0.64 + 0.31m)(5.0 + 0.63\sqrt{N/t})$ (*Eq.* C3.4-7)

$t^2 kC_1C_2C\theta[417 - 1.22(h/t)] [1 + 0.0013(N/t)]$ (*Eq.* C3.4-8)

$t^2F_yC_7(0.82 + 0.15m)(7.50 + 1.63\sqrt{N/t})$ (*Eq.* C3.4-9)

In the above-referenced formulas,

P_a = Allowable concentrated load or reaction per web, kips

$C_1 = (1.22 - 0.22k)$ (*Eq.* C3.4-10)

$C_2 = (1.06 - 0.06R/t) \leq 1.0$ (*Eq.* C3.4-11)

$C_3 = (1.33 - 0.33k)$ (*Eq.* C3.4-12)

$C_4 = 0.50 < (1.15 - 0.15R/t) \leq 1.0$ (*Eq.* C3.4-13)

$C_5 = (1.49 - 0.53k) \geq 0.6$ (*Eq.* C3.4-14)

$C_6 = 1 + \left(\frac{h/t}{750}\right)$ when $h/t \leq 150$ (*Eq.* C3.4-15)

$= 1.20$, when $h/t > 150$ (*Eq.* C3.4-16)

$C_7 = 1/k$, when $h/t \leq 66.5$ (*Eq.* C3.4-17)

$= \left[1.10 - \frac{h/t}{665}\right]\frac{1}{k}$, when $h/t > 66.5$ (*Eq.* C3.4-18)

$C_8 = \left[0.98 - \frac{h/t}{865}\right]\frac{1}{k}$ (*Eq.* C3.4-19)

$C\theta = 0.7 + 0.3 (\theta /90)^2$ (*Eq.* C3.4-20)

F_y = Design yield stress of the web, ksi

h = Depth of the flat portion of the web measured along the plane of the web

k $= F_y/33$ (*Eq.* C3.4-21)

m = $t/0.075$ (*Eq.* C3.4-22)

t = Web thickness, inches

N = Actual length of bearing, inches. For the case of two equal and opposite concentrated loads distributed over unequal bearing lengths, the smaller value of N shall be taken

R = Inside bend radius

θ = Angle between the plane of the web and the plane of the bearing surface $\geq 45°$, but not more than 90°

C3.5 Combined Bending and Web Crippling Strength. Unreinforced flat webs of shapes subjected to a combination of bending and concentrated load or reaction shall be designed to meet the following requirements:

For shapes having single unreinforced webs:

$1.2 (P/P_a) + (M/M_a) \leq 1.5$ (*Eq.* C3.5-1)

Exception: At the interior supports of continuous spans, the above formula is not applicable to deck or beams with two or more single webs, provided the compression edges of adjacent webs are laterally supported in the negative moment region by continuous or intermittently connected flange elements, rigid cladding, or lateral bracing, and the spacing between adjacent webs does not exceed 10 inches.

For shapes having multiple unreinforced webs such as I-sections made of two channels connected back-to-back, or similar sections which provide a high degree of restraint against rotation of the web (such as I-sections made by welding two angles to a channel);

$$1.1\,(P/P_a) + (M/M_a) \leq 1.5 \qquad (Eq.\ C3.5\text{-}2)$$

Exception: When $h/t \leq 2.33/\sqrt{F_y/E}$ and $\lambda \leq 0.673$, the allowable concentrated load or reaction may be determined by Section C3.4.

In the above formulas:

P = Concentrated load or reaction in the presence of bending moment

P_a = Allowable concentrated load or reaction in the absence of bending moment determined in accordance with Section C3.4

M = Applied bending moment at, or immediately adjacent to, the point of application of the concentrated load or reaction

M_a = Allowable bending moment if bending alone exists

w = Flat width of the beam flange which contacts the bearing plate

t = Thickness of the web or flange

λ = Slenderness factor given by Section B2.1

C4 Concentrically Loaded Compression Members. This section applies to members in which the resultant of all loads acting on the member is an axial load passing through the centroid of the effective section calculated at the stress, F_n, defined in this section.

(a) The axial load shall not exceed P_a calculated as follows:

$$P_a = P_n/\Omega_c \qquad (Eq.\ C4\text{-}1)$$

where

$$P_n = A_eF_n \qquad (Eq.\ C4\text{-}2)$$

A_e = Effective area at the stress F_n. For sections with circular holes, A_e shall be determined according to Section B2.2a, subject to the limitations of that section. If the number of holes in the effective length region times the hole diameter divided by the effective length does not exceed 0.015, A_e can be determined ignoring the holes.

F_n is determined as follows:

For $F_e > F_y/2$ $\quad F_n = F_y\,(1 - F_y/4F_e)$ $\quad$ (*Eq.* C4-3)

For $F_e \leq F_y/2$ $\quad F_n = F_e$ $\quad$ (*Eq.* C4-4)

F_e is the least of the elastic flexural, torsional and torsional-flexural buckling stress determined according to Sections C4.1 through C4.3.

Ω_c = Factor of safety for axial compression

= 1.92, except when F_e is determined according to Section C4.1 for fully effective sections having wall thicknesses greater than or equal to 0.09 inches and $F_e > F_y/2$. In this case,

$$\Omega_c = \frac{5}{3} + \frac{3}{8}R - \frac{1}{8}R^3$$

where

$$R = \sqrt{F_y/2F_e}$$

(b) For C- and Z-shapes, and single-angle sections with unstiffened flanges, P_n shall be taken as the smaller of P_n calculated above and P_n calculated as follows:

$$P_n = \frac{A\pi^2 E}{25.7(w/t)^2} \qquad (Eq.\ C4\text{-}5)$$

where

A = Area of the full, unreduced cross section
w = Flat width of the unstiffened element
t = Thickness of the unstiffened element

(c) Angle sections shall be designed for the applied axial load, P, acting simultaneously with a moment equal to PL/1000 applied about the minor principal axis causing compression in the tips of the angle legs.

(d) The slenderness ratio, KL/r, of all compression members preferably should not exceed 200, except that during construction only, KL/r preferably should not exceed 300.

C4.1 Sections Not Subject to Torsional or Torsional-Flexural Buckling. For doubly-symmetric sections, closed cross sections and any other sections which can be shown not to be subject to torsional or torsional-flexural buckling, the elastic flexural buckling stress, F_e, shall be determined as follows:

$$F_e = \frac{\pi^2 E}{(KL/r)^2} \qquad (Eq.\ C4.1\text{-}1)$$

where

E = Modulus of elasticity
K = Effective length factor. (In frames where lateral stability is provided by diagonal bracing, shear walls, attachment to an adjacent structure having adequate lateral stability, or floor slabs or roof decks secured horizontally by walls or bracing systems parallel to the plane of the frame, and in trusses, the effective length factor, K, for compression members which do not depend upon their own bending stiffness of lateral stability of the frame or truss, shall be taken as unity, unless analysis shows that a smaller value may be used. In a frame which depends upon its own bending stiffness for lateral stability, the effective length, KL, of the compression members shall be determined by a rational method and shall not be less than the actual unbraced length.)
L = Unbraced length of member
r = Radius of gyration of the full, unreduced cross section

C4.2 Doubly- or Singly-Symmetric Sections Subject to Torsional or Torsional-Flexural Buckling. For sections subject to torsional or torsional-flexural buckling, F_e shall be taken as the smaller of F_e calculated according to Section C4.1 and F_e calculated as follows:

$$F_e = \frac{1}{2\beta}\left[(\sigma_{ex}+\sigma_t) - \sqrt{(\sigma_{ex}+\sigma_t)^2 - 4\beta\sigma_{ex}\sigma_t}\right] \qquad (Eq.\ C4.2\text{-}1)$$

Alternatively, a conservative estimate of F_e can be obtained using the following equation:

$$F_e = \frac{\sigma_t\sigma_{ex}}{\sigma_t + \sigma_{ex}} \qquad (Eq.\ C4.2\text{-}2)$$

where σ_t and σ_{ex} are as defined in C3.1.2(b)

$$\beta = 1 - (x_o/r_o)^2 \qquad (Eq.\ C4.2\text{-}3)$$

For singly-symmetric sections, the x-axis is assumed to be the axis of symmetry.

C4.3 Nonsymmetric Sections. For shapes whose cross sections do not have any symmetry, either about an axis or about a point, F_e shall be determined by rational analysis. Alternatively, compression members composed of such shapes may be tested in accordance with Chapter F.

C5 Combined Axial Load and Bending. The axial force and bending moments shall satisfy the following interaction equations:

$$\frac{P}{P_a} + \frac{C_{mx}M_x}{M_{ax}\alpha_x} + \frac{C_{my}M_y}{M_{ay}\alpha_y} \le 1.0 \qquad (Eq.\ C5\text{-}1)$$

$$\frac{P}{P_{ao}} + \frac{M_x}{M_{axo}} + \frac{M_y}{M_{ayo}} \le 1.0 \qquad (Eq.\ C5\text{-}2)$$

When $P/P_a \le 0.15$, the following formula may be used in lieu of the above two formulas:

$$\frac{P}{P_a} + \frac{M_x}{M_{ax}} + \frac{M_y}{M_{ay}} \le 1.0 \qquad (Eq.\ C5\text{-}3)$$

where

P = Applied axial load

M_x and M_y = Applied moments with respect to the centroidal axes of the effective section determined for the axial load alone. For angle sections, M_y shall be taken either as the applied moment or the applied moment plus PL/1000, whichever results in a lower value of P_a.

P_a = Allowable axial load determined in accordance with Section C4

P_{ao} = Allowable axial load determined in accordance with Section C4, with $F_n = F_y$

M_{ax} and M_{ay} = Allowable moments about the centroidal axes determined in accordance with Section C3

M_{axo} and M_{ayo} = Allowable moments about the centroidal axes determined in accordance with Section C3.1, excluding the provisions of Section C3.12 (lateral buckling)

$1/\alpha_x$, $1/\alpha_y$ = Magnification factors

$= 1/[1-(\Omega_c P/P_{cr})]$ (*Eq.* C5-4)

Ω_c = Factor of safety used in determining P_a

$$P_{cr} = \frac{\pi^2 EI_b}{(K_bL_b)^2} \qquad (Eq.\ C5\text{-}5)$$

I_b = Moment of inertia of the full, unreduced cross section about the axis of bending

L_b = Actual unbraced length in the plane of bending

K_b = Effective length factor in the plane of bending

C_{mx}, C_{my} = Coefficients whose value shall be taken as follows:

1. For compression members in frames subject to joint translation (sidesway)

   $C_m = 0.85$

2. For restrained compression members in frames braced against joint translation and not subject to transverse loading between their supports in the plane of bending

   $$C_m = 0.6 - 0.4\,(M_1/M_2) \qquad (Eq.\ C5\text{-}6)$$

   where

   M_1/M_2 is the ratio of the smaller to the larger moment at the ends of that portion of the member under consideration which is unbraced in the plane of bending. M_1/M_2 is positive when the member is bent in reverse curvature and negative when it is bent in single curvature.

3. For compression members in frames braced against joint translation in the plane of loading and subject to transverse loading between their supports, the value of C_m may be determined by rational analysis. However, in lieu of such analysis, the following values may be used:

   (a) for members whose ends are restrained, $C_m = 0.85$,

   (b) for members whose ends are unrestrained, $C_m = 1.0$.

C6 Cylindrical Tubular Members. The requirements of this Section apply to cylindrical tubular members having a ratio of outside diameter to wall thickness, D/t, not greater than $0.441\ E/F_y$.

C6.1 Bending. For flexural members, the actual moment uncoupled from axial load, shear, and local concentrated forces or reactions shall not exceed M_a calculated as follows:

$$M_a = M_n/\Omega_f \qquad (Eq.\ C6.1\text{-}1)$$

where

M_n = Nominal moment

Ω_f = Factor of safety for bending

= 1.67

For $D/t \leq 0.070\ E/F_y$

$$M_n = 1.25\ F_yS_f \qquad (Eq.\ C6.1\text{-}2)$$

For $0.070\ E/Fy < D/t \leq 0.319\ E/F_y$

$$M_n = \left[0.970 + 0.020\frac{E/F_y}{D/t}\right]F_yS_f \qquad (Eq.\ C6.1\text{-}3)$$

For $0.319\ E/F_y < D/t \leq 0.441\ E/F_y$

$M_n = [0.328E/(D/t)]S_f$ (*Eq.* C6.1-4)

where

S_f = Elastic section modulus of the full, unreduced cross section

C6.2 Compression. The requirements of this Section apply to members in which the resultant of all loads and moments acting on the member is equivalent to a single force in the direction of the member axis passing through the centroid of the section.

The axial load shall not exceed P_a calculated as follows:

$P_a = P_n/\Omega_c$ (*Eq.* C6.2-1)

where

$P_n = F_n A_e$ (*Eq.* C6.2-2)

For F_e greater than $F_y/2$

F_n = Flexural buckling stress

$= F_y [1 - F_y/4F_e]$ (*Eq.* C6.2-3)

F_e = The elastic flexural buckling stress determined according to Section C4.1

Ω_c = Factor of safety for axial compression

$$= \frac{5}{3} + \frac{3}{8}R - \frac{1}{8}R^3$$ (*Eq.* C6.2-4)

$$R = \sqrt{F_y/2F_e}$$ (*Eq.* C6.2-5)

$$A_e = [1 - (1 - R^2)(1 - A_o/A)]A$$ (*Eq.* C6.2-6)

$$A_o = \left[\frac{0.037}{\frac{DF_y}{tE}} + 0.667\right]A \le A \text{ for } \frac{D}{t} \le 0.441\frac{E}{F_y}$$ (*Eq.* C6.2-7)

A = Area of the unreduced cross section

For $F_e \le F_y/2$

$F_n = F_e$

Ω_c = Factor of safety for axial compression

= 1.92

$A_e = A$

C6.3 Combined Bending and Compression. Combined bending and compression shall satisfy the provisions of Section C5.

D. STRUCTURAL ASSEMBLIES

Sec. 27.906. D1 Built-Up Sections. D1.1 I-Sections Composed of Two Channels. The maximum permissible longitudinal spacing of welds or other connectors s_{max}, joining two channels to form an I-section shall be

(a) For compression members:

$$s_{max} = \frac{Lr_{cy}}{2r_1}$$ (*Eq.* D1.1-1)

where

L = Unbraced length of compression member

r_I = Radius of gyration of the I-section about the axis perpendicular to the direction in which buckling would occur for the given conditions of end support and intermediate bracing

r_{cy} = Radius of gyration of one channel about its centroidal axis parallel to the web

(b) For flexural members:

$$s_{max} = L/6 \qquad (Eq.\ D1.1\text{-}2)$$

In no case shall the spacing exceed the value

$$s_{max} = \frac{2gT_s}{mq} \qquad (Eq.\ D1.1\text{-}3)$$

where

L = Span of beam

T_s = Strength of connection in tension

g = Vertical distance between the two rows of connections nearest to the top and bottom flanges

q = Intensity of load on the beam (For methods of determination, see below)

m = Distance from the shear center of one channel to the mid-plane of its web. For simple channels without stiffening lips at the outer edges,

$$m = \frac{w_f^2}{2w_f + d/3} \qquad (Eq.\ D1.1\text{-}4)$$

For channels with stiffening lips at the outer edges,

$$m = \frac{w_f dt}{4I_x}\left[w_f d + 2D\left(d - \frac{4D^2}{3d}\right)\right] \qquad (Eq.\ D1.1\text{-}5)$$

w_f = Projection of flanges from the inside face of the web (For channels with flanges of unequal width, w_f shall be taken as the width of the wider flange)

d = Depth of channel or beam

D = Overall depth of lip

I_x = Moment of inertia of one channel about its centroidal axis normal to the web

The intensity of load, q, is obtained by dividing the magnitude of concentrated loads or reactions by the length of bearing. For beams designed for a uniformly distributed load, q shall be taken equal to three times the intensity of the uniformly distributed design load. If the length of bearing of a concentrated load or reaction is smaller than the weld spacing, s, the required strength of the welds or connections closest to the load or reaction is

$$T_s = Pm/2g \qquad (Eq.\ D1.1\text{-}6)$$

The required maximum spacing of connections, s_{max}, depends upon the intensity of the load directly at the connection. Therefore, if uniform spacing of connections is used over the whole length of the beam, it shall be determined at the point of maximum local load intensity. In cases where this procedure would result in uneconomically close spacing, either one of the following methods may be adopted: (a) the connection spacing may be varied along the beam according to the variation of the load intensity; or (b) reinforcing cover plates may be welded to the flanges at points where concentrated loads occur. The shear strength of the connections joining these plates to the flanges shall then be used for T_s, and g shall be taken as the depth of the beam.

D1.2 Spacing of Connections in Compression Elements. The spacing, s, in the line of stress, of welds, rivets, or bolts connecting a compression cover plate or sheet to a non-integral stiffener or other element shall not exceed

(a) that which is required to transmit the shear between the connected parts on the basis of the design strength per connection specified elsewhere herein; nor

(b) $1.16t\sqrt{(E/f_c)}$, where t is the thickness of the cover plate or sheet, and f_c is the stress at design load in the cover plate or sheet; nor

(c) three times the flat width, w, of the narrowest unstiffened compression element tributary to the connections, but need not be less than $1.11t\sqrt{(E/f_y)}$ if $w/t < 0.50\sqrt{(E/f_y)}$, or $1.33t\sqrt{(E/f_y)}$ if $w/t \geq 0.50\sqrt{(E/f_y)}$, unless closer spacing is required by (a) or (b) above.

In the case of intermittent fillet welds parallel to the direction of stress, the spacing shall be taken as the clear distance between welds, plus one-half inch. In all other cases, the spacing shall be taken as the center-to-center distance between connections.

Exception: The requirements of this Section do not apply to cover sheets which act only as sheathing material and are not considered as load-carrying elements.

D2 Mixed Systems. The design of members in mixed systems using cold-formed steel components in conjunction with other materials shall conform to this Specification and the applicable Specification of the other material.

D3 Lateral Bracing. Braces shall be designed to restrain lateral bending or twisting of a loaded beam or column, and to avoid local crippling at the points of attachment.

D3.1 Symmetrical Beams and Columns. Braces and bracing systems, including connections, shall be designed considering strength and stiffness requirements.

D3.2 Channel-Section and Z-Section Beams. The following provisions for bracing to restrain twisting of channels and Z-sections used as beams loaded in the plane of the web, apply only when (a) the top flange is connected to deck or sheathing material in such a manner as to effectively restrain lateral deflection of the connected flange, or (b) neither flange is so connected. When both flanges are so connected, no further bracing is required.

D3.2.1 Anchorage of Bracing for Roof Systems under Gravity Load with Top Flange Connected to Sheathing. For channels and Z-sections designed according to Section C3.1.1, and having deck or sheathing fastened directly to the top flanges in such a manner shown to effectively inhibit relative movement between the deck or sheathing and the purlin flange, provisions shall be made to restrain the flanges so that the maximum top flange lateral displacements with respect to the purlin reaction points do not exceed the span length divided by 360. If the top flanges of all purlins face in the same direction, anchorage of the restraint system must be capable of satisfying the requirements of Sections D3.2.1(a) and D3.2.1(b). If the top flanges of adjacent lines of purlins face in opposite directions, the provisions of Section D3.2.1(a) and (b) do not apply.

Anchored braces may be connected to only one line of purlins in each purlin bay of each roof slope if provision is made to transmit forces from other purlin lines through the roof deck and its fastening system. Anchored braces shall be as close as possible to the flange which is connected to the deck or sheathing. Anchored braces shall be provided for each purlin bay.

For bracing arrangements other than those covered in Section D3.2.1(a) and (b), tests in accordance with Chapter F shall be performed so that the type and/or spacing of braces selected are such that the test strength of the braced Z-section assembly is equal to or greater than $^5/_3$ times its flexural design strength, instead of that required by Chapter F.

(a) Channel Sections

For roof systems using channel sections for purlins with all compression flanges facing in the same direction, a restraint system capable of resisting 0.05W, in addition to other loading, shall be provided where W is the load supported by all purlin lines being restrained. Where more than one brace is used at a purlin line, the restraint force 0.05W shall be divided equally between all braces.

(b) Z-Sections

For roof systems having a diaphragm stiffness of at least 2,000 lb/in., having four to twenty Z-purlin lines with all top flanges facing in the direction of the upward roof slope, and with restraint braces at the purlin supports, midspan or one-third points, each brace shall be designed to resist a force determined as follows:

(1) Single-Span System with Restraints at the Supports:

$$P_L = 0.5\left[\frac{0.220b^{1.50}}{n_p^{0.72}d^{0.90}t^{0.60}} - \tan\theta\right]W \qquad (Eq.\ D3.2.1\text{-}1)$$

(2) Single-Span System with Third-Point Restraints:

$$P_L = 0.5\left[\frac{0.474b^{1.22}}{n_p^{0.57}d^{0.89}t^{0.33}} - \tan\theta\right]W \qquad (Eq.\ D3.2.1\text{-}2)$$

(3) Single-Span System with Midspan Restraint:

$$P_L = \left[\frac{0.224b^{1.32}}{n_p^{0.65}d^{0.83}t^{0.50}} - \tan\theta\right]W \qquad (Eq.\ D3.2.1\text{-}3)$$

(4) Multiple-Span System with Restraints at the Supports:

$$P_L = C_{tr}\left[\frac{0.053b^{1.88}L^{0.13}}{n_p^{0.95}d^{1.07}t^{0.94}} - \sin\theta\right]W \qquad (Eq.\ D3.2.1\text{-}4)$$

with

C_{tr} = 0.63 for braces at end supports of multiple-span systems
C_{tr} = 0.87 for braces at the first interior supports
C_{tr} = 0.81 for all other braces

(5) Multiple-Span System with Third-Point Restraints:

$$P_L = C_{th}\left[\frac{0.181 b^{1.15} L^{0.25}}{n_p^{0.54} d^{1.11} t^{0.29}} - \sin\theta\right] W \qquad (Eq.\ D3.2.1\text{-}5)$$

with

C_{th} = 0.57 for outer braces in exterior spans
C_{th} = 0.48 for all other braces

(6) Multiple-Span System with Midspan Restraints:

$$P_L = C_{ms}\left[\frac{0.116\ b^{1.32} L^{0.18}}{n_p^{0.70} d^{1.00} t^{0.50}} - \tan\theta\right] W \qquad (Eq.\ D3.2.1\text{-}6)$$

with

C_{ms} = 1.05 for braces in exterior spans
C_{ms} = 0.90 for all other braces

where

b = Flange width, in.
d = Depth of section, in.
t = Thickness, in.
L = Span length, in.
θ = Angle between the vertical and the plane of the web of the Z-section, degrees
n_p = Number of parallel purlin lines
W = Total load supported by the purlin lines between adjacent supports, pounds

The force, P_L, is positive when restraint is required to prevent movement of the purlin flanges in the upward roof slope direction.

For systems having less than four purlin lines, the brace force can be determined by taking 1.1 times the force found from Equations D3.2.1-1 through D3.2.1-6, with $n_p = 4$. For systems having more than twenty purlin lines, the brace force can be determined from Equations D3.2.1-1 through D3.2.1-6, with $n_p = 20$.

D3.2.2 Neither Flange Connected to Sheathing. Each intermediate brace, at the top and bottom flange, shall be designed to resist a lateral force, P_L, determined as follows:

(a) For uniform loads, $P_L = 1.5K'$ times the load within a distance 0.5a each side of the brace.

(b) For concentrated loads, $P_L = 1.0K'$ times each concentrated load within a distance 0.3a each side of the brace, plus $1.4K'[1 - (x/a)]$ times each concentrated load located farther than 0.3a but not farther than 1.0a from the brace.

In the above formulas:

For channels and Z-sections:

x = Distance from the concentrated load to the brace

a = Distance between center line of braces

For channels:

$$K' = m/d \qquad (Eq.\ D3.2.2\text{-}1)$$

where

m = Distance from the shear center to the mid-plane of the web, as specified in Section D1.1

d = Depth of channel

For Z-sections:

$$K' = I_{xy}/I_x \qquad (Eq.\ D3.2.2\text{-}2)$$

where

I_{xy} = Product of inertia of the full section about centroidal axes parallel and perpendicular to the web

I_x = Moment of inertia of the full section about the centroidal axis perpendicular to the web

Braces shall be designed to avoid local crippling at the points of attachment to the member.

Braces shall be attached both to the top and bottom flanges of the sections, at the ends and at intervals not greater than one-quarter of the span length, in such a manner as to prevent tipping at the ends and lateral deflection of either flange in either direction at intermediate braces. If one-third or more of the total load on the beam is concentrated over a length of one-twelfth or less of the span of the beam, an additional brace shall be placed at or near the center of this loaded length.

Exception: When all loads and reactions on a beam are transmitted through members which frame into the section in such a manner as to effectively restrain the section against rotation and lateral displacement, no other braces will be required.

D3.3 Laterally Unbraced Box Beams. For closed box-type sections used as beams subject to bending about the major axis, the ratio of the laterally unsupported length to the distance between the webs of the section shall not exceed $0.086\ E/F_y$.

D4 Wall Studs and Wall Stud Assemblies. The safe load-carrying capacity of a stud may be computed on the basis that sheathing (attached to one or both sides of the stud) furnishes adequate lateral and rotational support to the stud in the plane of the wall, provided that the stud, sheathing, and attachments comply with the following requirements:

Both ends of the stud shall be braced to restrain rotation about the longitudinal stud axis and horizontal displacement perpendicular to the stud axis; however, the ends may or may not be free to rotate about both axes perpendicular to the stud axis. The sheathing shall be connected to the top and bottom members of the wall assembly to enhance the restraint provided to the stud and stabilize the overall assembly.

D4.1 Wall Studs in Compression. For studs having identical sheathing attached to both flanges, and neglecting any rotational restraint provided by the sheathing* , the applied axial load, P, shall not exceed P_a calculated as follows:

$$P_a = A_e F_n / \Omega_c \qquad (Eq.\ D4.1\text{-}1)$$

where

A_e = Effective area determined at F_n

Ω_c = Factor of safety for axial compression, i.e., in accordance with Section C4(a) when either Sections D4.1(a) or D4.1(b) govern or 1.92 when Section D4.1(c) governs

F_n = The lowest value determined by the following three conditions:

(a) To prevent column buckling between fasteners in the plane of the wall, F_n shall be calculated according to Section C4 with KL equal to two times the distance between fasteners.

(b) To prevent flexural and/or torsional overall column buckling, F_n shall be calculated in accordance with Section C4 with F_e taken as the smaller of the two σ_{CR} values specified for the following section types, where σ_{CR} is the theoretical elastic buckling stress under concentric loading.

(1) Singly-symmetric channels and C-Sections

$$\sigma_{CR} = \sigma_{ey} + \overline{Q}_a \qquad (Eq.\ D4.1\text{-}2)$$

$$\sigma_{CR} = \frac{1}{2\beta}\left[(\sigma_{ex} + \sigma_{tQ}) - \sqrt{(\sigma_{ex} + \sigma_{tQ})^2 - (4\beta\sigma_{ex}\sigma_{tQ})}\right] \qquad (Eq.\ D4.1\text{-}3)$$

(2) Z-Sections

$$\sigma_{CR} = \sigma_t + \overline{Q}_t \qquad (Eq.\ D4.1\text{-}4)$$

$$\sigma_{CR} = \frac{1}{2}\{(\sigma_{ex} + \sigma_{ey} + \overline{Q}_a) - [(\sigma_{ex} + \sigma_{ey} + \overline{Q}_a)^2 - 4(\sigma_{ex}\sigma_{ey} + \sigma_{ex}\overline{Q}_a - \sigma_{exy}^2)]^{1/2}\} \qquad (Eq.\ D4.1\text{-}5)$$

(3) I-Sections (doubly-symmetric)

$$\sigma_{CR} = \sigma_{ey} + \overline{Q}_a \qquad (Eq.\ D4.1\text{-}6)$$

$$\sigma_{CR} = \sigma_{ex} \qquad (Eq.\ D4.1\text{-}7)$$

In the above formulas:

$$\sigma_{ex} = \frac{\pi^2 E}{(K_x L_x / r_x)^2} \qquad (Eq.\ D4.1\text{-}8)$$

$$\sigma_{exy} = (\pi^2 E I_{xy}) / (AL^2) \qquad (Eq.\ D4.1\text{-}9)$$

$$\sigma_{ey} = \frac{\pi^2 E}{(K_y L_y / r_y)^2} \qquad (Eq.\ D4.1\text{-}10)$$

*Studs with sheathing on one flange only, or with unidentical sheathing on both flanges, or having rotational restraint that is not neglected, or having any combination of the above, shall be designed in accordance with the same basic analysis principles used in deriving the provisions of this Section.

$$\sigma_t = \frac{1}{Ar_o^2}\left[GJ + \frac{\pi^2 EC_w}{(K_t L_t)^2}\right] \qquad (Eq.\ D4.1\text{-}11)$$

$\sigma_{tQ} = \sigma_t + \overline{Q}_t$ (*Eq.* D4.1-12)

$\overline{Q}$ = $\overline{q}\,B$ = Design shear rigidity for sheathing on both sides of wall assembly

$\overline{q}$ = Design shear rigidity for sheathing per inch of stud spacing (see Table D4)

B = Stud spacing

$\overline{Q}_a = \overline{Q} / A$ (*Eq.* D4.1-13)

A = Area of full unreduced cross section

L = Length of stud

$\overline{Q}_t = (\overline{Q}d^2) / (4Ar_o^2)$ (*Eq.* D4.1-14)

d = Depth of section

I_{xy} = Product of inertia

(c) To prevent shear failure of the sheathing, a value of F_n shall be used in the following equations so that the shear strain of the sheathing, γ, does not exceed the permissible shear strain, $\overline{\gamma}$. The shear strain, γ, shall be determined as follows:

$\gamma = (\pi / L)\,[C_1 + (E_1\, d/2)]$ (*Eq.* D4.1-15)

where

C_1 and E_1 are the absolute values of C_1 and E_1 specified below for each section type:

(1) Singly-Symmetric Channels

$C_1 = (F_n C_o) / (\sigma_{ey} - F_n + \overline{Q}_a)$ (*Eq.* D4.1-16)

$$E_1 = \frac{F_n[(\sigma_{ex} - F_n)(r_o^2 E_o - x_o D_o) - F_n x_o(D_o - x_o E_o)]}{(\sigma_{ex} - F_n) r_o^2 (\sigma_{tQ} - F_n) - (F_n x_o)^2} \qquad (Eq.\ D4.1\text{-}17)$$

(2) Z-Sections

$$C_1 = \frac{F_n[C_o(\sigma_{ex} - F_n) - D_o \sigma_{exy}]}{(\sigma_{ey} - F_n + \overline{Q}_a)(\sigma_{ex} - F_n) - \sigma^2_{exy}} \qquad (Eq.\ D4.1\text{-}18)$$

$E_1 = (F_n E_o) / (\sigma_{tQ} - F_n)$ (*Eq.*D4.1-19)

(3) I-Sections

$C_1 = (F_n C_o) / (\sigma_{ey} - F_n + \overline{Q}_a)$ (*Eq.* D4.1-20)

$E_1 = 0$

where

x_o = distance from shear center to centroid along principal x-axis, in. (absolute value)

C_o, E_o, and D_o are initial column imperfections which shall be assumed to be at least

C_o = L/350 in a direction parallel to the wall (*Eq.* D4.1-21)

D_o = L/700 in a direction perpendicular to the wall (*Eq.* D4.1-22)

E_o = $L/(d \times 10{,}000)$, rad., a measure of the initial twist of the stud from the initial, ideal, unbuckled shape (*Eq.* D4.1-23)

If $F_n > 0.5\,F_y$, then in the definitions for σ_{ey}, σ_{ex}, σ_{exy} and σ_{tQ}, the parameters E and G shall be replaced by E′ and G′, respectively, as defined below:

$E' = 4EF_n(F_y - F_n)/F_y^2$ (*Eq.* D4.1-24)

$G' = G(E'/E)$ (*Eq.* D4.1-25)

Sheathing parameters $\bar{q}_o$ and $\bar{\gamma}$ may be determined from representative full-scale tests, conducted and evaluated as described by published documented methods or from the small-scale-test values given in Table D4.

D4.2 Wall Studs in Bending. For studs having identical sheathing attached to both flanges, and neglecting any rotational restraint provided by the sheathing, the allowable moments are M_{axo} and M_{ayo}

where

M_{axo} and M_{ayo} = Allowable moments about the centroidal axes determined in accordance with Section C3.1, excluding the provisions of Section C3.1.2 (lateral buckling)

Studs with sheathing on one flange only, or with unidentical sheathing on both flanges, or having rotational restraint that is not neglected, or having any combination of the above, shall be designed in accordance with the same basic analysis principles used in deriving the provisions of this Section.

D4.3 Wall Studs with Combined Axial Load and Bending. The axial load and bending moments shall satisfy the interaction equations of Section C5 with the following redefined terms:

P_a = Allowable axial load determined according to Section D4.1

M_{ax} and M_{ay} in Equations C5-1 and C5-3 shall be replaced by allowable moments, M_{axo} and M_{ayo}, respectively.

TABLE D4
Sheathing Parameters(1)

Sheathing(2)	$\bar{q}_o$(3) k/in.	$\bar{\gamma}$ in./in.
3/8 to 5/8 in. thick gypsum	2.0	0.008
Lignocellulosic board	1.0	0.009
Fiberboard (regular or impregnated)	0.6	0.007
Fiberboard (heavy impregnated)	1.2	0.010

(1) The values given are subject to the following limitations:
All values are for sheathing on both sides of the wall assembly.
All fasteners are No. 6, type S-12, self-drilling drywall screws with pan or bugle head, or equivalent, at 6- to 12-inch spacing.

(2) All sheathing is 1/2-inch thick except as noted.

(3) $\bar{q} = \bar{q}_o(2 - s/12)$ (*Eq.* D4.1-26)
where s = fastener spacing, in.

For other types of sheathing, $\bar{q}_o$ and $\bar{\gamma}$ may be determined conservatively from representative small-specimen tests as described by published documented methods (see Commentary).

E. CONNECTIONS AND JOINTS

Sec. 27.907. E1 General Provisions. Connections shall be designed to transmit the maximum load in the connected member. Proper regard shall be given to eccentricity.

E2 Welded Connections. Arc welds on steel where each connected part is over 0.18 inch in thickness shall be made in accordance with AISC Specification (Reference 3 of Section A6).

Except as modified herein, arc welds on steel where at least one of the connected parts is 0.18 inch or less in thickness shall be made in accordance with the AWS D-1.3 (Reference 4 of Section A6). Welders and welding procedures shall be qualified as specified in AWS D1.3. These provisions are intended to cover the welding positions as shown in Table E2.

The load on each weld shall not exceed P_a, calculated as follows:

$$P_a = P_n/\Omega_w \qquad (Eq.\ E2\text{-}1)$$

where

Ω_w = Factor of safety for arc welded connections
= 2.50

P_n = Nominal strength of welds determined according to Sections E2.1 through E2.5.

Allowable loads, P_a, for resistance welds made in conformance with the procedures given in AWS C1.1, "Recommended Practices for Resistance Welding" or AWS C1.3, "Recommended Practice for Resistance Welding Coated Low Carbon Steels" are given in Section E2.6.

TABLE E2

Connection	Welding Position					
	Square Groove Butt Weld	Arc Spot Weld	Arc Seam Weld	Fillet Weld, Lap or T	Flare-Bevel Groove	Flare-V Groove Weld
Sheet to Sheet	F H V OH	— — — —	F H — —	F H V OH	F H V OH	F H V OH
Sheet to Supporting Member	— — — —	F — — —	F — — —	F H V OH	F H V OH	— — — —

(F = flat, H = horizontal, V = vertical, OH = overhead)

E2.1 Groove Welds in Butt Joints. The maximum load for a groove weld in a butt joint, welded from one or both sides, shall be determined on the basis of the lower strength base steel in the connection, provided that an effective throat equal to or greater than the thickness of the material is consistently obtained.

E2.2 Arc Spot Welds. Arc spot welds permitted by this Specification are for welding sheet steel to thicker supporting members in the flat position. Arc spot welds (puddle welds) shall not be made on steel where the thinnest connected part is over 0.15 inch thick, nor through a combination of steel sheets having a total thickness over 0.15 inch.

Weld washers, Figures E2.2(A) and E2.2(B), shall be used when the thickness of the sheet is less than 0.028 inch. Weld washers shall have a thickness between 0.05 and 0.08 inch with a minimum prepunched hole of $^3/_8$-inch diameter.

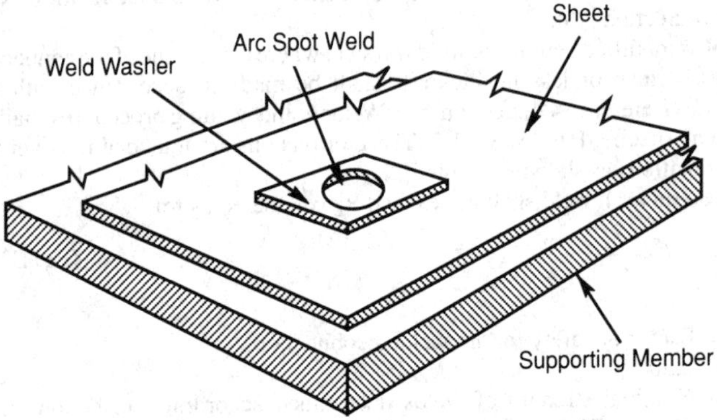
Sheet
Arc Spot Weld
Weld Washer
Supporting Member

Figure E2.2A Typical Weld Washer

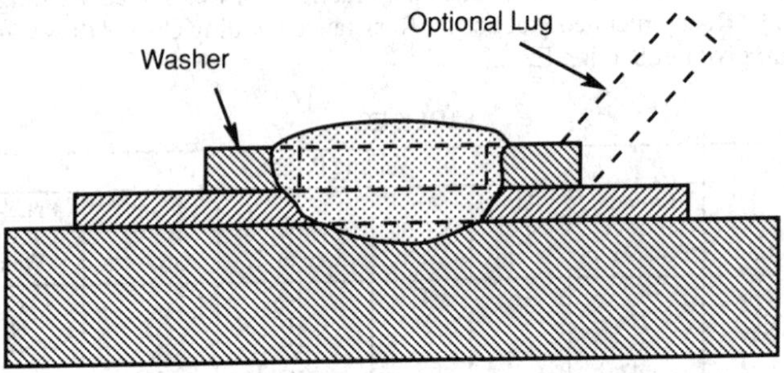
Optional Lug
Washer

Figure E2.2B Arc Spot Weld Using Washer

Arc spot welds shall be specified by minimum effective diameter of fused area, d_e. Minimum allowable effective diameter is $^3/_8$ inch.

The nominal shear load, P_n, on each arc spot weld between sheet or sheets and supporting member shall not exceed the smaller of either

$$P_n = 0.625\, d_e^2\, F_{xx} \text{ ; or} \qquad (Eq.\ E2.2\text{-}1)$$

For $(d_a/t) \leq 0.815\sqrt{(E/F_u)}$:

$$P_n = 2.20\, t\, d_a\, F_u\, ; \qquad (Eq.\ E2.2\text{-}2)$$

For $0.815\sqrt{(E/F_u)} < (d_a/t) < 1.397\sqrt{(E/F_u)}$:

$$P_n = 0.280\left[1 + \frac{5.59t\sqrt{E}}{d_a\sqrt{F_u}}\right] t d_a F_u; \qquad (Eq.\ E2.2\text{-}3)$$

For $(d_a/t) \geq 1.397\sqrt{(E/F_u)}$:

$$P_n = 1.40\, t\, d_a\, F_u \qquad (Eq.\ E2.2\text{-}4)$$

where

d = Visible diameter of outer surface of arc spot weld

d_a = Average diameter of the arc spot weld at mid-thickness of t [where $d_a = (d-t)$ for a single sheet, and $(d - 2t)$ for multiple sheets (not more than four lapped sheets over a supporting member)]

d_e = Effective diameter of fused area

d_e = $0.7d-1.5t$ but $\leq 0.55d$ (*Eq.* E2.2-5)

t = Total combined base steel thickness (exclusive of coatings) of sheets involved in shear transfer

F_{xx} = Stress level designation in AWS electrode classification

F_{sy} = Yield point as specified in Section A3.1 or A3.2.

F_u = Tensile strength as specified in Section A3.1 or A3.2 or as reduced for low-ductility steel.

Note: See Figures E2.2(C) and E2.2(D) for diameter definitions.

The distance measured in the line of force from the centerline of a weld to the nearest edge of an adjacent weld or to the end of the connected part toward which the force is directed shall not be less than the value of e_{min} as given below:

$$e_{min} = e\,\Omega_e \qquad (Eq.\ E2.2\text{-}6)$$

where

$$e = \frac{P}{F_u t} \qquad (Eq.\ E2.2\text{-}7)$$

Ω_e = Factor of safety for sheet tearing

= 2.0 when $F_u/F_{sy} \geq 1.15$

= 2.22 when $F_u/F_{sy} < 1.15$

P = Force transmitted by weld

t = Thickness of thinnest connected sheet

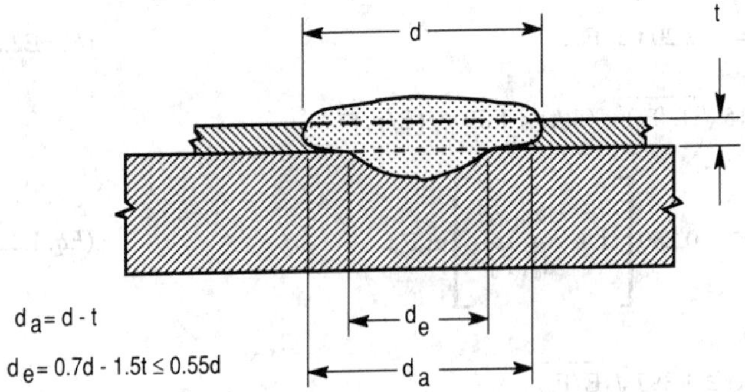
d
t
$d_a = d - t$
$d_e = 0.7d - 1.5t \leq 0.55d$
d_e
d_a

(C) Arc Spot Weld-Single Thickness of Sheet

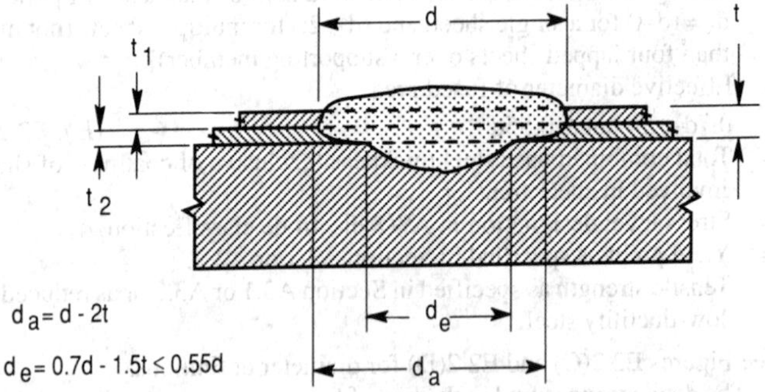
d
t
t_1
t_2
$d_a = d - 2t$
$d_e = 0.7d - 1.5t \leq 0.55d$
d_e
d_a

(D) Arc Spot Weld-Double Thickness of Sheet

Figure E2.2 C, D Arc Spot Welds

Note: See Figures E2.2(E) and E2.2(F) for edge distances of arc welds.

In addition, the distance from the centerline of any weld to the end or boundary of the connected member shall not be less than 1.5d. In no case shall the clear distance between welds and the end of member be less than 1.0d.

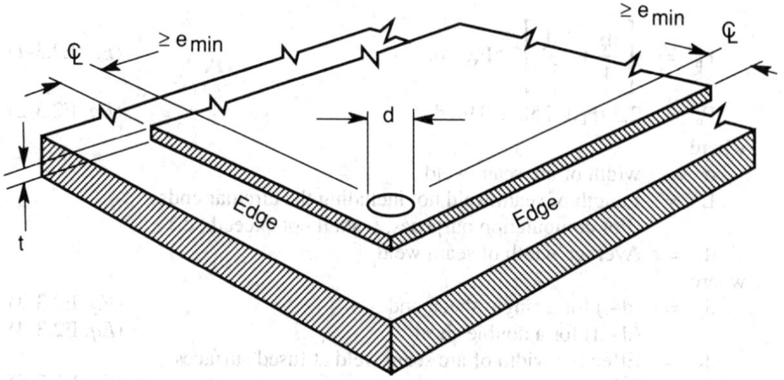
≥ e min
≥ e min
℄
℄
d
t
Edge
Edge

(E) Single Sheet

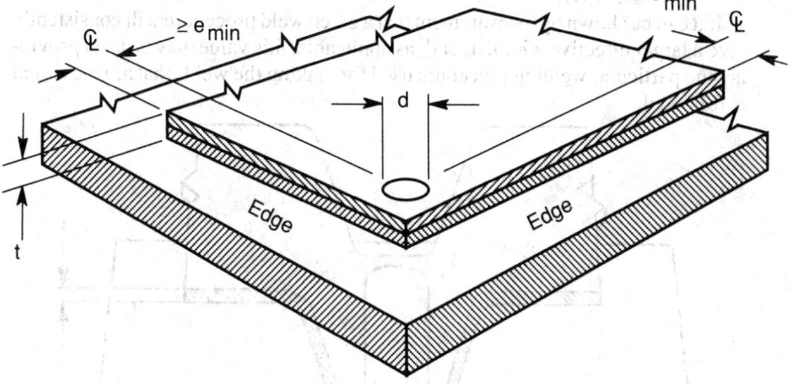
≥ e min
≥ e min
℄
℄
d
t
Edge
Edge

(F) Double Sheet

Figure E2.2 E, F Edge Distances for Arc Spot Welds

If it can be shown by measurement that a given weld procedure will consistently give a larger effective diameter, d_e, or average diameter, d_a, as applicable, this larger diameter may be used providing the particular welding procedure used for making those welds is followed.

E2.3 Arc Seam Welds. Arc seam welds [Figure E2.3(A)] covered by this Specification apply only to the following joints:

(a) Sheet to thicker supporting member in the flat position.

(b) Sheet to sheet in the horizontal or flat position.

The shear load, P_n, on each arc seam weld shall not exceed either

$$P_n = \left[\frac{d_e^2}{4} + \frac{Ld_e}{3}\right] 2.5F_{xx} \text{ ; or} \qquad (Eq.\ E2.3\text{-}1)$$

$$P_n = 2.5\, tF_u(0.25L + 0.96\, d_a) \qquad (Eq.\ E2.3\text{-}2)$$

where

d = width of arc seam weld

L = Length of seam weld not including the circular ends (For computation purposes, L shall not exceed 3d.)

d_a = Average width of seam weld

where

d_a = (d–t) for a single sheet, and (*Eq.* E2.3-3)

(d–2t) for a double sheet (*Eq.* E2.3-4)

d_e = Effective width of arc seam weld at fused surfaces

d_e = 0.7d–1.5t (*Eq.* E2.3-5)

and F_u and F_{xx} are defined in Section E2.2. The minimum edge distance shall be as determined for the arc spot weld, Section E2.2 [see Figure E2.3(B)].

If it can be shown by measurement that a given weld procedure will consistently give a larger effective width, d_e or d_a as applicable, this value may be used providing the particular welding procedure used for making the welds that are measured is followed.

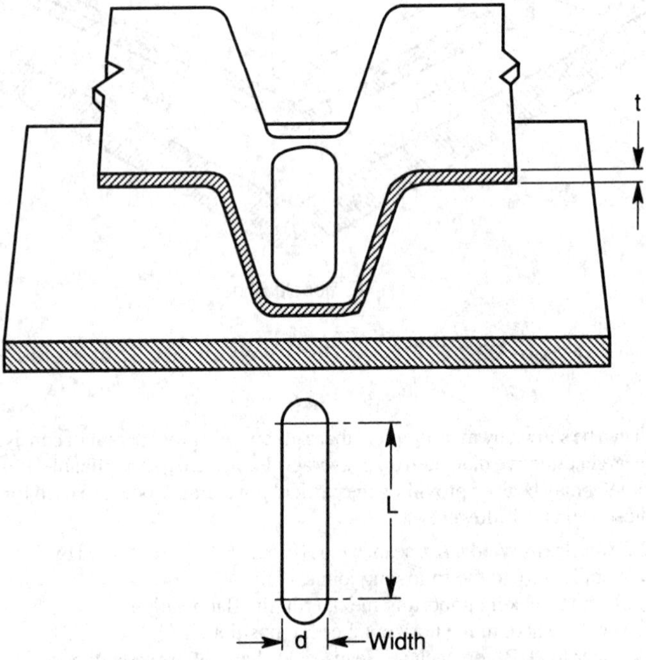
t
L
d
Width

Figure E2.3A Arc Seam Welds—Sheet to Supporting Member in Flat Position

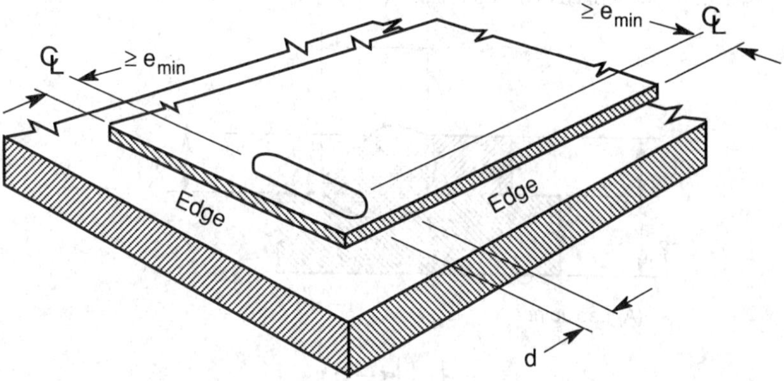
≥ e_{min}
℄
≥ e_{min}
℄
Edge
Edge
d

Figure E2.3B Edge Distances for Arc Seam Welds

E2.4 Fillet Welds. Fillet welds covered by this Specification apply to the welding of joints in any position, either

(a) Sheet to sheet, or

(b) Sheet to thicker steel member.

The shear load, P_n, on a fillet weld in lap and T-joints shall not exceed the following:

For longitudinal loading:

For L/t < 25 :

$$P_n = \left(1 - \frac{0.01L}{t}\right) tLF_u \qquad (Eq.\ E2.4\text{-}1)$$

For L/t ≥ 25:

$$P_n = 0.75\ tLF_u \qquad (Eq.\ E2.4\text{-}2)$$

For transverse loading:

$$P_n = tLF_u \qquad (Eq.\ E2.4\text{-}3)$$

where

t = Least value of t_1 or t_2, Figure E2.4

In addition, for t > 0.150 inch, the allowable load for a fillet weld in lap and T-joints shall not exceed:

$$P_n = 0.75\ t_wLF_{xx} \qquad (Eq.\ E2.4\text{-}4)$$

where

L = Length of fillet weld

t_w = Effective throat = 0.707 w_1 or 0.707 w_2, whichever is smaller. A larger effective throat may be taken if it can be shown by measurement that a given welding procedure will consistently give a larger value providing the particular welding procedure used for making the welds that are measured is followed.

w_1 and w_2 = leg on weld (see Figure E2.4).

F_u and F_{xx} are defined in Section E2.2.

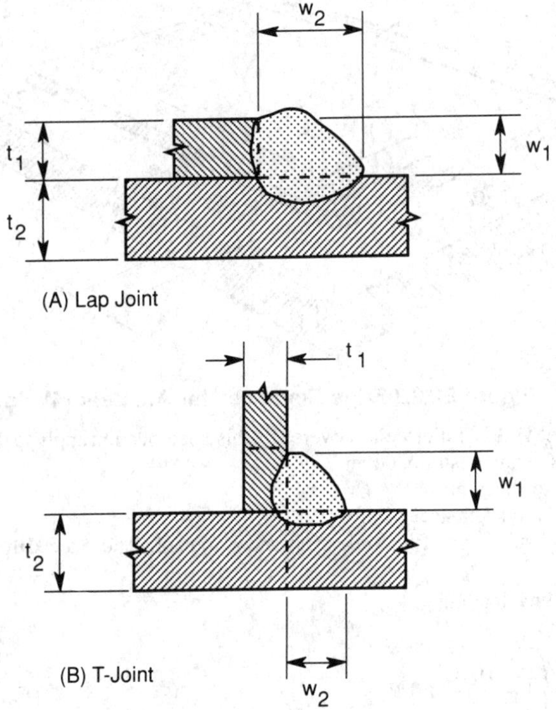
w2
t1
w1
t2
(A) Lap Joint
t1
w1
t2
(B) T-Joint
w2

Figure E2.4 Fillet Welds

E2.5 Flare Groove Welds. Flare groove welds covered by this Specification apply to welding of joints in any position, either:

(a) Sheet to sheet for flare-V groove welds, or

(b) Sheet to sheet for flare-bevel groove welds, or

(c) Sheet to thicker steel member for flare-bevel groove welds.

The shear load, P_n, on a weld shall be governed by the thickness, t, of the sheet steel adjacent to the weld. The load shall not exceed:

For flare-bevel groove welds, transverse loading [see Figure E2.5(A)]:

$$P_n = 0.833tLF_u \qquad (Eq.\ E2.5\text{-}1)$$

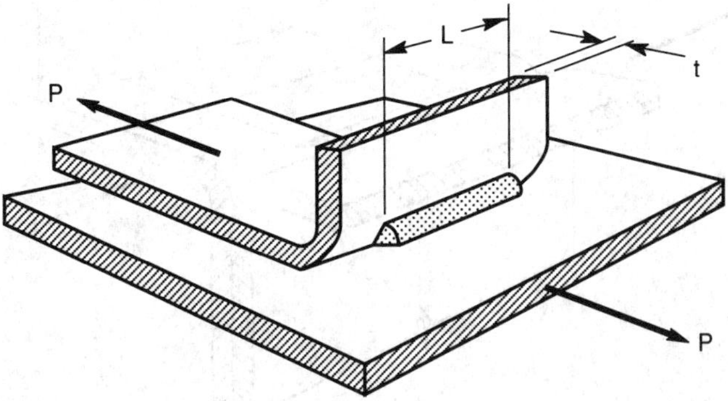
L
t
P
P

Figure E2.5A Flare-Bevel Groove Weld

For flare groove welds, longitudinal loading [see Figures E2.5(B), E2.5(C), and E2.5(D)]:

If the effective throat, t_w, is equal to or greater than t but less than 2t or if the lip height is less than weld length, L, then:

$$P_n = 0.75tLF_u \quad (Eq.\ E2.5\text{-}2)$$

If t_w is equal to or greater than 2t and the lip height is equal to or greater than L, then:

$$P_n = 1.50tLF_u \quad (Eq.\ E2.5\text{-}3)$$

In addition, if $t > 0.15$ inch, then:

$$P_n = 0.75t_wLF_{xx} \quad (Eq.\ E2.5\text{-}4)$$

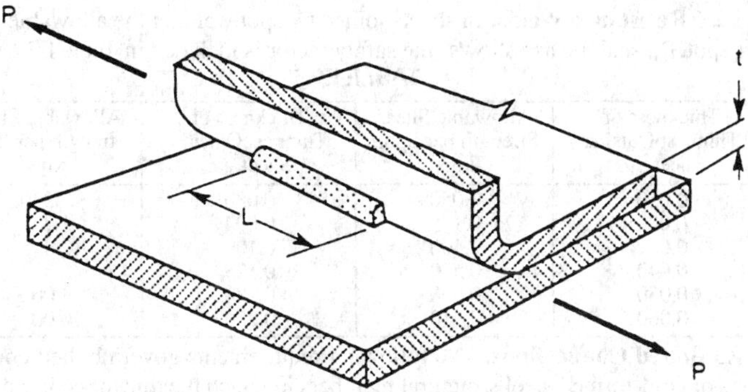
P
t
L
P

Figure E2.5 B, C, D Shear in Flare Groove Welds

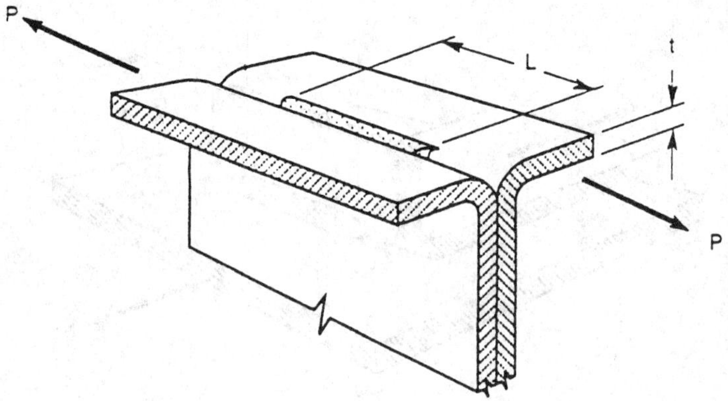
P
L
t
P

(C) Flare V-Groove

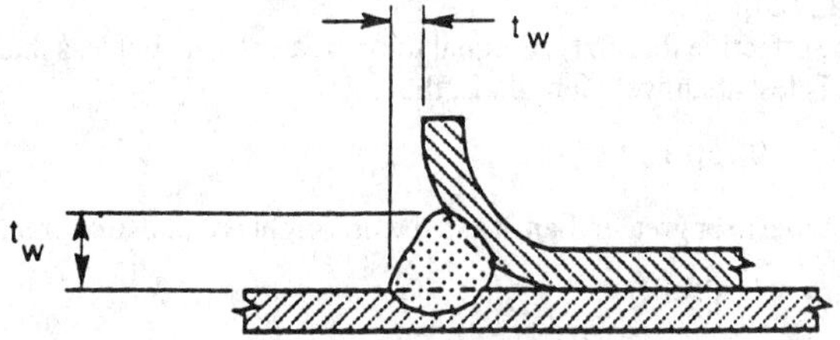
t_w
t_w

(D) Throat

Figure E.25 B, C, D Shear in Flare Grove Welds (continued)

E2.6 Resistance Welds. In sheets joined by spot welding the allowable shear per spot, P_a, shall be as follows (the safety factor is included in Table E2.6):

TABLE E2.6

Thickness of Thinnest Outside Sheet, in.	Allowable Shear Strength per Spot, kips	Thickness of Thinnest Outside Sheet, in.	Allowable Shear Strength per Spot, kips
0.010	0.050	0.080	1.330
0.020	0.175	0.094	1.725
0.030	0.400	0.109	2.395
0.040	0.570	0.125	2.88
0.050	0.660	0.188	4.00
0.060	0.910	0.250	6.00

E3 Bolted Connections. The following requirements govern bolted connections of cold-formed steel structural members in which the thickness of the thinnest connected part is less than $^3/_{16}$ inch and there are no gaps between connected parts. For bolted connections in which the thinnest connected part is equal to or greater than $^3/_{16}$ inch, refer to AISC Specification (Reference 3 of Section A6).

Bolts, nuts and washers shall generally conform to one of the following specifications:

A 307 (Type A), A 325, A 354 (Grade BD), A 449 and A 490.

When other than the above are used, drawings shall indicate clearly the type and size of fasteners to be employed and the allowable force assumed in design.

Bolts shall be installed and tightened to achieve satisfactory performance of the connections involved under usual service conditions.

The holes for bolts shall not exceed the sizes specified in Table E3, except that larger holes may be used in column base details or structural systems connected to concrete walls.

TABLE E3
Maximum Size of Bolt Holes, Inches

Nominal Bolt Diameter, d, in.	Standard Hole Diameter, d, in.	Oversized Hole Diameter, d, in.	Short-Slotted Hole Dimensions, in.	Long-Slotted Hole Dimensions, in.
$^1/_2$	$d + {}^1/_{32}$	$d + {}^1/_{16}$	$(d + {}^1/_{32})$ by $(d + {}^1/_4)$	$(d + {}^1/_{32})$ by $(2^1/_2\, d)$
$\geq {}^1/_2$	$d + {}^1/_{16}$	$d + {}^1/_8$	$(d + {}^1/_{16})$ by $(d + {}^1/_4)$	$(d + {}^1/_{16})$ by $(2^1/_2\, d)$

Standard holes shall be used in bolted connections, except that oversized and slotted holes may be used as approved by the designer. The length of slotted holes shall be normal to the direction of the shear load. Washers or backup plates shall be installed over oversized or short-slotted holes in an outer ply unless suitable performance is demonstrated by load tests in accordance with Section F.

E3.1 Spacing and Edge Distance. The distance, e, measured in the line of force from the center of a standard hole to the nearest edge of an adjacent hole or to the end of the connected part toward which the force is directed shall not be less than the value of e_{min} determined as follows:

$$e_{min} = e\,\Omega_e \qquad (Eq.\ E3.1\text{-}1)$$

where

$$e = \frac{P}{F_u t} \qquad (Eq.\ E3.1\text{-}2)$$

(a) When $F_u/F_{sy} \geq 1.15$:

Ω_e = Factor of safety for sheet tearing
= 2.0

(b) When $F_u/F_{sy} < 1.15$:

Ω_e = Factor of safety for sheet tearing
= 2.22

where

P = Force transmitted by bolt
t = Thickness of thinnest connected part
F_u = Tensile strength of the connected part as specified in Section A3.1 or A3.2
F_{sy} = Yield point of the connected part as specified in Section A3.1 or A3.2

In addition, the minimum distance between centers of bolt holes shall provide sufficient clearance for bolt heads, nuts, washers and the wrench but shall not be less than 3 times the nominal bolt diameter, d. Also, the distance from the center of any standard hole to the end or other boundary of the connecting member shall not be less than $1^1/_2$ d.

For oversized and slotted holes, the distance between edges of two adjacent holes and the distance measured from the edge of the hole to the end or other boundary of the connecting member in the line of stress shall not be less than the value of $[e_{min} - (d_h/2)]$, in which e_{min} is the required distance computed from the applicable equation given above, and d_h is the diameter of a standard hole defined in Table E3. In no case shall the clear distance between edges of two adjacent holes be less than 2d and the distance between the edge of the hole and the end of the member be less than d.

E3.2 Tension in Connected Part. The tension force on the net section of a bolted connection shall not exceed T_a from Section C2 or P_a calculated as follows:

$$P_a = P_n/\Omega_t \qquad (Eq.\ E3.2\text{-}1)$$

where

$P_n = A_nF_t$

A_n = Net section area

F_t and Ω_t are determined as follows:

(a) When $t \geq {}^3/_{16}$ in.:

See AISC Specification (Reference 3 of Section A6)

(b) When $t < {}^3/_{16}$ inch and washers are provided under both the bolt head and the nut

$$F_t = (1.0 - 0.9r + 3rd/s)\ F_u \leq F_u \qquad (Eq.\ E3.2\text{-}2)$$

Ω_t = Factor of safety for tension on the net section

= 2.0 for double shear

= 2.22 for single shear

(c) When $t < {}^3/_{16}$ inch and either washers are not provided under the bolt head and nut, or only one washer is provided under either the bolt head or nut

$$F_t = (1.0 - r + 2.5rd/s)\ F_u \leq F_u \qquad (Eq.\ E3.2\text{-}3)$$

Ω_t = Factor of safety for tension on the net section

= 2.22

where

r = Force transmitted by the bolt or bolts at the section considered, divided by the tension force in the member at that section. If r is less than 0.2, it may be taken equal to zero.

s = Spacing of bolts perpendicular to line of stress.
In the case of a single bolt,

s = Width of sheet

F_t = Nominal tension stress limit on net section

F_u = Tensile strength of the connected part as specified in Sections A3.1 or A3.2

d and t are defined in Section E3.1.

E3.3 Bearing. The bearing force shall not exceed P_a calculated as follows:

$$P_a = P_n/\Omega_b \qquad (Eq.\ E3.3\text{-}1)$$

where

$$P_n = F_p dt \qquad (Eq.\ E3.3\text{-}2)$$

Ω_b = Safety factor for bearing
= 2.22

F_p = Nominal bearing stress as given in Tables E3.3-1 and E3.3-2

For conditions not shown, forces shall be determined on the basis of test data using a factor of safety of 2.22.

TABLE E3.3-1
Nominal Bearing Stress for Bolted Connections with Washers under Both Bolt Head and Nut

Thickness of connected part, in.	Type of joint	F_u/F_{sy} ratio of connected part	Nominal bearing stress, F_p
≥ 0.024 but $< {}^{3}/_{16}$	Inside sheet of double shear connection	≥ 1.15	$3.33\ F_u$
		< 1.15	$3.00\ F_u$
	Single shear and outside sheets of double shear connection	No limit	$3.00\ F_u$
$\geq {}^{3}/_{16}$	See AISC Specification (Reference 3 of Section A6)		

TABLE NO. 3.3-2
Nominal Bearing Stress for Bolted Connections Without Washers under Both Bolt Head and Nut, or with Only One Washer

Thickness of connected part, in.	Type of joint	F_u/F_{sy} ratio of connected part	Nominal bearing stress, F_p
≥ 0.036 but $< {}^{3}/_{16}$	Inside sheet of double shear connection	≥ 1.15	$3.00\ F_u$
	Single shear and outside sheets of double shear connection	≥ 1.15	$2.22\ F_u$
$\geq {}^{3}/_{16}$	See AISC Specification (Reference 3 of Section A6)		

E3.4 Shear and Tension in Bolts. The bolt force resulting from shear, tension or combination of shear and tension shall not exceed allowable bolt force, P_a, calculated as follows (the factor of safety is included in Tables E3.4-1 and E3.4-2):

$$P_a = A_b F \qquad (Eq.\ E3.4\text{-}1)$$

where

A_b = Gross cross-sectional area of bolt

F is given by F_v, F_t or F'_t in Tables E3.4-1 and E3.4-2.

TABLE E3.4-1

Description of Bolts	Allowable Shear Stress*, F_v, ksi		Allowable Tension Stress, F_t, ksi
	Threads Not Excluded from Shear Plane	Threads Excluded from Shear Plane	
A325 Bolts	21	30	44
A354 Grade B Bolts ($^1/_4$ in. $\le d < {}^1/_2$ in.)	24	40	49
A449 Bolts ($^1/_4$ in. $\le d < {}^1/_2$ in.)	18	30	40
A490 Bolts	28	40	54
A307 Bolts, Grade A ($^1/_4$ in. $\le d < {}^1/_2$ in.)	9		18
A307 Bolts, Grade A ($^1/_4$ in. $\le d < {}^1/_2$ in.)	10		20

*Applies to bolts in holes as limited by Table E3. Washers or back-up plates shall be installed over long-slotted holes and the capacity of connections using long-slotted holes shall be determined by load tests in accordance with Section F.

The pullover strength of the connected sheet at the bolt head, nut or washer should be considered where bolt tension is involved. See Section E5.2.

When bolts are subject to a combination of shear and tension, the tension force shall not exceed the allowable force, P_a, based on F'_t, given in Table E3.4-2, where f_v, the shear stress produced by the same forces, shall not exceed the allowable value F_v given above.

TABLE E3.4-2
Allowable Tension Stress, F'_t, for Bolts Subject to the Combustion of Shear and Tension

Description of Bolts	Threads Not Excluded from Shear Planes	Threads Excluded from Shear Planes
A325 Bolts	$55 - 1.8 f_v \le 44$	$55 - 1.4 f_v \le 44$
A354 Grade BD Bolts	$61 - 1.8 f_v \le 49$	$61 - 1.4 f_v \le 49$
A449 Bolts	$50 - 1.8 f_v \le 40$	$50 - 1.4 f_v \le 40$
A490 Bolts	$68 - 1.8 f_v \le 54$	$68 - 1.4 f_v \le 54$
A307 Bolts, Grade A		
When $^1/_4$ in. $\le d < {}^1/_2$ in.	$23 - 1.8 f_v \le 18$	
When $d \ge {}^1/_2$ in.	$26 - 1.8 f_v \le 20$	

E4 Shear Rupture. At beam-end connections, where one or more flanges are coped and failure might occur along a plane through the fasteners, the shear force shall not exceed the allowable shear force V_a, calculated as follows:

$$V_a = V_n/\Omega_v \qquad (Eq.\ E4\text{-}1)$$

where

$$V_n = 0.6 F_u A_{wn} \qquad (Eq.\ E4\text{-}2)$$

$$A_{wn} = (d_{wc} - n d_h)t \qquad (Eq.\ E4\text{-}3)$$

d_{wc} = Coped web depth
n = Number of holes in the critical plane
d_h = Hole diameter
F_u = Tensile strength as specified in Sections A3.1 or A3.2
t = Thickness of coped web

Ω_v = Factor of safety for shear rupture
= 2.00

E5 Connections to Other Materials. E5.1 Bearing. Proper provisions shall be made to transfer bearing forces resulting from axial loads and moments from steel components covered by the Specification to adjacent structural components made of other materials. The bearing force in the contact area shall not exceed the allowable bearing force P_a calculated as follows:

$$P_a = F_p A$$

where

A = Contact area

F_p = Allowable bearing stress (The factor of safety is included in values for F_p)

In the absence of code regulations for other materials, the following allowable stresses may be used:

F_p = 0.40 ksi on sandstone and limestone

F_p = 0.25 ksi on brick in cement mortar

F_p = $0.35 f'_c$ on the full area of a concrete support

F_p = $0.35 f'_c \sqrt{(A_2/A_1)} \leq 0.7 f'_c$ on less than the full area of a concrete support

where

f'_c = Specified compression strength of concrete

A_1 = Bearing area

A_2 = Full cross-sectional area of concrete support

E5.2 Tension. The pull-over shear/tension forces in the steel sheet around the head of the fastener should be considered as well as the pull-out force resulting from axial loads and bending moments transmitted onto the fastener from various adjacent structural components in the assembly.

The allowable tensile strength of the fastener and the allowable imbedment strength of the adjacent structural component shall be determined by applicable product code approvals, or product specifications and/or product literature.

E5.3 Shear. Proper provisions shall be made to transfer shearing forces from steel components covered by this Specification to adjacent structural components made of other materials. The allowable shear and/or bearing forces on the steel components shall not exceed that allowed by this Specification. The allowable shear force on the fasteners and other material shall not be exceeded. Imbedment requirements are to be met. Proper provision shall also be made for shearing forces in combination with other forces.

F. TESTS FOR SPECIAL CASES

Sec. 27.908. (a) Tests shall be made by an independent testing laboratory or by a testing laboratory of a manufacturer.

(b) The provisions of Chapter F do not apply to cold-formed steel diaphragms.

F1 Tests for Determining Structural Performance. Where the composition or configuration of elements, assemblies, connections, or details of cold-formed steel structural members are such that calculation of their safe load-carrying capacity or deflection cannot be made in accordance with the provisions of this Specification, their structural performance shall be established from tests and evaluated in accordance with the following procedure.

(a) Where practicable, evaluation of tests results shall be made on the basis of the mean values resulting from tests of not fewer than three identical specimens, provided the deviation of any individual test result from the mean value obtained from all tests does not exceed ±10 percent. If such deviation from the mean exceeds 10 percent, at least three more tests of the same kind shall be made. The average of the three lowest values of all tests made shall then be regarded as the result of the series of tests.

(b) The required load-carrying capacity shall be:

$$R = D F_D + L F_L \qquad (Eq.\ F1\text{-}1)$$

where D and L are the dead and live loads, respectively, D shall include the weight of the test specimen. F_D and F_L are the dead and live load factors specified below. R shall be taken as the largest applicable value determined as follows:

(1) The minimum load-carrying capacity, R, shall be calculated from the formula

$$R \geq 1.5D + 2L \qquad (Eq.\ F1\text{-}2)$$

R shall be multiplied by 1.25 for steels not listed in Section A3.1

R may be divided by $1^1/_3$ when the loading consists of wind or earthquake loads alone, or in combination with dead, live, or snow loads, but shall not be less than R calculated for the combination of dead and live loads only, without wind or earthquake loads.

(2) The load at which distortions interfere with the proper functioning of the specimen in actual use shall not be less than:

$$R \geq D + 1.5L \qquad (Eq.\ F1\text{-}3)$$

(3) The load carrying capacity when limited by connection failure shall not be less than:

$$R \geq 2.5D + 2.5L \qquad (Eq.\ F1\text{-}4)$$

(c) If the yield point of the steel from which the tested sections are formed is larger than the specified value, the test results shall be adjusted down to the specified minimum yield point of the steel which the manufacturer intends to use. The test results shall not be adjusted upward if the yield point of the test specimen is less than the minimum specified yield point. Similar adjustments shall be made on the basis of tensile strength instead of yield point where tensile strength is the critical factor.

Consideration must also be given to any variation or differences which may exist between the design thickness and the thickness of the specimens used in the tests.

F2 Tests for Confirming Structural Performance. The procedures and formulas specified in Section F1 are not applicable to confirmation tests on specimens whose capacities can be computed according to this Specification or its specific references. A successful confirmatory test shall demonstrate a safety factor not less than that implied in the Specification for the type of behavior involved.

F3 Tests for Determining Mechanical Properties. F3.1 Full Section. Tests for determination of mechanical properties of full sections to be used in Section A5.2.2 shall be made as specified below:

(a) Tensile testing procedures shall agree with Standard Methods and Definitions for Mechanical Testing of Steel Products, ASTM A370.
Compressive yield point determinations shall be made by means of compression tests of short specimens of the section.

(b) The comprehensive yield stress shall be taken as the smaller value of either the maximum compressive strength of the sections divided by the cross section area or the stress defined by one of the following methods:

(1) For sharp yielding steel, the yield point shall be determined by the autographic diagram method or by the total strain under load method.

(2) For gradual yielding steel, the yield point shall be determined by the strain under load method or by the 0.2 percent offset method.
When the total strain under load method is used, there shall be evidence that the yield point so determined agrees within 5 percent with the yield point which would be determined by the 0.2 percent offset method.

(c) Where the principal effect of the loading to which the member will be subjected in service will be to produce bending stresses, the yield point shall be determined for the flanges only. In determining such yield points, each specimen shall consist of one complete flange plus a portion of the web of such flat width ratio that the value of ρ for the specimen is unity.

(d) For acceptance and control purposes, two full section tests shall be made from each lot of not more than 50 tons nor less than 30 tons of each section, or one test from each lot of less than 30 tons of each section. For this purpose, a lot may be defined as that tonnage of one section that is formed in a single production run of material from one heat.

(e) At the option of the manufacturer, either tension or compression tests may be used for routine acceptance and control purposes, provided the manufacturer demonstrates that such tests reliably indicate the yield point of the section when subjected to the kind of stress under which the member is to be used.

F3.2 Flat Elements of Formed Sections. Tests for determining mechanical properties of flat elements of formed sections and representative mechanical properties of virgin steel to be used in Section A5.2.2 shall be made in accordance with the following provisions:

The yield point of flats, F_{yf}, shall be established by means of a weighted average of the yield points of standard tensile coupons taken longitudinally from the flat portions of a representative cold-formed member. The weighted average shall be the sum of the products of the average yield point for each flat portion times its cross sectional area, divided by the total area of flats in the cross section. The exact number of such coupons will depend on the shape of the member, i.e.,on the number of flats in the cross section. At least one tensile coupon shall be taken from the middle of each flat. If the actual virgin yield point exceeds the specified minimum yield point, the yield point of the flats, F_{yf}, shall be adjusted by multiplying the test values by the ratio of the specified minimum yield point to the actual virgin yield point.

F3.3 Virgin Steel. The following provisions apply to steel produced to other than the ASTM Specifications listed in Section A3.1 when used in sections for which the increased yield point of the steel after cold forming shall be computed from the virgin steel properties according to Section A5.2.2. For acceptance and control purposes, at least four tensile specimens shall be taken from each lot as defined in Section F3.1(d) for the establishment of the representative values of the virgin tensile yield point and ultimate strength. Specimens shall be taken longitudinally from the quarter points of the width near the outer end of the coil.

APPENDICES

Sec. 27.909. Appendix A5.2.2 Strength Increase from Cold Work of Forming. Strength increase from cold work of forming may be obtained by substituting F_{ya} for F_y, where F_{ya} is the average yield point of the full section. Such increase shall be limited to Sections C3.1 (excluding Section C3.1.1(b)), C4, C5, C6 and D4. The limitations and methods for determining F_{ya} are as follows:

(a) For axially loaded compression members and flexural members whose proportions are such that the quantity ρ is unity as determined according to Section B2 for each of the component elements of the section, the design yield stress, F_{ya}, of the steel shall be determined on the basis of one of the following methods:

(1) full section tensile tests [see paragraph (a) of Section F3.1]

(2) stub column tests [see paragraph (b) of Section F3.1]

(3) computed as follows:

$$F_{ya} = CF_{yc} + (1 - C)\,F_{yf} \qquad (Eq.\ A5.2.1\text{-}1)$$

where

F_{ya} = Average tensile yield point of the steel in the full flange sections of flexural members

C = For compression members, ratio of the total corner cross-sectional area to the total cross-sectional area of the full section; for flexural members, ratio of the total corner cross-sectional area of the controlling flange to the full cross-sectional area of the controlling flange

F_{yf} = Weighted average tensile yield point of the flat portions established in accordance with Section F3.2 or virgin yield point if tests are not made

F_{yc} = $B_cF_{yv}/(R/t)^m$, tensile yield point of corners (*Eq.* A5.2.1-2)

when

$F_{uv}/F_{yv} \geq 1.2$, $R/t \leq 7$, minimum included angle $\leq 120°$

$$B_c = 3.69\,(F_{uv}/F_{yv}) - 0.819\,(F_{uv}/F_{yv})^2 - 1.79 \qquad (Eq.\ A5.2.1\text{-}3)$$

$$m = 0.192\,(F_{uv}/F_{yv}) - 0.068 \qquad (Eq.\ A5.2.1\text{-}4)$$

R = Inside bend radius

F_{yv} = Tensile yield point of virgin steel* specified by Section A3 or established in accordance with Section F3.3

F_{uv} = Ultimate tensile strength of virgin steel* specified by Section A3 or established in accordance with Section F3.3

(b) For axially loaded tension members, the yield point of the steel shall be determined by either method (1) or method (3) prescribed in paragraph (a) of this Section.

(c) The effect of any welding on mechanical properties of a member shall be determined on the basis of tests of full section specimens containing within the gage length, such welding as the manufacturer intends to use. Any necessary allowance for such effect shall be made in the structural use of the member.

Appendix B1.1(b) Flange Curling. Where the flange of a flexural member is unusually wide and it is desired to limit the maximum amount of curling or movement of the flange toward the neutral axis, the following formula applies to compression and tension flanges, either stiffened or unstiffened:

$$w_f = \sqrt{0.061tdE/f_{av}} - \sqrt{(100c_f/d)} \qquad (Eq.\ B1.1b\text{-}1)$$

where

w_f = Width of flange projecting beyond the web; or half of the distance between webs for box- or U-type beams

t = Flange thickness

d = Depth of beam

c_f = Amount of curling

f_{av} = Average stress in the full, unreduced flange width. (Where members are designed by the effective design width procedure, the average stress equals the maximum stress multiplied by the ratio of the effective design width to the actual width.)

Appendix B1.1 (c) Shear Lag Effects. Where the span of the beam is less than $30w_f$ (w_f as defined below) and it carries one concentrated load, or several loads spaced farther apart than $2w_f$, the effective design width of any flange, whether in tension or compression, shall be limited to the following:

APPENDIX TABLE B1.1 (c)
SHORT, WIDE FLANGES
MAXIMUM ALLOWABLE RATIO OF EFFECTIVE DESIGN WIDTH TO ACTUAL WIDTH

L/w_f	Ratio	L/w_f	Ratio
30	1.00	14	0.82
25	0.96	12	0.78
20	0.91	10	0.73
18	0.89	8	0.67
16	0.86	6	0.55

* Virgin steel refers to the condition (i.e., coiled or straight) of the steel prior to the cold-forming operation.

where

L = Full span for simple beams; or the distance between inflection points for continuous beams; or twice the length of cantilever beams

w_f = Width of flange projection beyond the web for I-beam and similar sections or half the distance between webs of box- or U-type sections

For flanges of I-beams and similar sections stiffened by lips at the outer edges, w_f shall be taken as the sum of the flange projection beyond the web plus the depth of the lip.

UNIFORM BUILDING CODE STANDARD NO. 27-10

SPECIFICATION FOR THE DESIGN OF COLD-FORMED STAINLESS STEEL STRUCTURAL MEMBERS

Based on Specification Manual (1974) of the American Iron and Steel Institute

See Sections 2701 (a) and (b), 2704 and 2710 (k), Uniform Building Code

General

Scope

Sec. 27.1001. This standard shall apply to the design of structural members cold formed to shape from sheet, strip, plate or flat bar stainless steels, annealed and cold rolled, when used for load-carrying purposes in buildings and other statically loaded structures. It may also be used for other structures subjected to dynamic loads, provided appropriate allowances are made for dynamic effects.

Nothing herein is intended to conflict with U.B.C. Standard No. 27-9.

Material

Sec. 27.1002. This standard applies to the use of sheet, strip, plate and flat bar stainless steel conforming to ASTM Standard Specification A666, "Austenitic Stainless Steel, Sheet, Strip, Plate and Flat Bar for Structural Applications," in U.B.C. Standard No. 27-1.

Design Procedure

Procedure

Sec. 27.1003. All computations such as those for safe load, stress and deflection shall be in accordance with conventional methods of structural design except as otherwise provided herein.

Definitions

Sec. 27.1004. Where the following terms appear in this specification they shall have the meanings here given:

STIFFENED COMPRESSION ELEMENT is a flat compression element (e.g., plane compression flanges of flexural members and plane webs and flanges of compression members) of which both edges parallel to the direction of stress are stiffened by connection to a stiffening element (e.g., web, flange, stiffening lip, intermediate stiffener or the like) conforming to the requirements of Section 27.1005 (c).

UNSTIFFENED COMPRESSION ELEMENT is any flat element which is stiffened at only one edge parallel to the direction of stress.

MULTIPLE-STIFFENED ELEMENT is an element that is stiffened between webs or between a web and an edge, by means of intermediate stiffeners which are parallel to the direction of stress and which conform to the requirements of Section 27.1005 (c) 2.

SUBELEMENT is the portion of a multiple-stiffened element between adjacent stiffeners or between web and intermediate stiffener or between edge and intermediate stiffener.

WIDTH, *w,* in the case of section such as I-, T-, channel- and Z-shaped sections, the width of the flat projection of flange from web exclusive of fillets and of any stiffening lip that may be at the outer edge of the flange. In the case of multiple-web sections such as hat, U- or box-shaped sections, the width, *w,* is the flat width of flange between adjacent webs exclusive of fillets.

FLAT-WIDTH RATIO, *w/t,* is the ratio of the flat width, *w,* exclusive of edge fillets, of a single flat element to the thickness, *t,* of such element.

EFFECTIVE DESIGN WIDTH, *b,* is the flat width of an element, as reduced for design purposes in accordance with Section 27.1005 (b) and (f), referred to as an "effective width."

STRESS is the force per unit area expressed in kips per square inch (ksi).

Properties of Sections

Sec. 27.1005. (a) **General.** Properties of sections (cross-sectional area, moment of inertia, section modulus, radius of gyration, etc.) shall be determined in accordance with conventional methods used in structural design. Properties shall be based on the full cross section of the members (or net section where the use of a net section is permissible) except where the use of a reduced cross section or "effective design width" is required by the provisions of Section 27.1005 (b) and (f).

(b) **Properties of Compression Elements.** 1. **Effective design width.** In computing properties of sections of flexural members and values of Q [Section 27.1012 (a)] for compression members, the flat width, *w,* of any stiffened compression element having a flat-width ratio larger than the limiting w/t ratio, as hereinafter defined, shall be reduced for design purposes to an effective design width, b or b_e, as determined in accordance with the provisions of Section 27.1005 (b) 2 or 27.1005 (b) 3, whichever is applicable, and subject to the limitations of Section 27.1005 (f), if applicable. That portion of the total width which is disregarded in determining the effective design width shall be located symmetrically about the center line of the element.

2. **Stiffened elements without intermediate stiffeners.** The effective design widths of compression elements which are not subject to the provisions of Section 27.1005 (b) 3 shall be determined from the following formulas:

For load determination:

Flanges are fully effective ($b = w$) up to

$$(w/t)_{lim} = \frac{155}{\sqrt{f}}$$

For flanges with w/t larger than $(w/t)_{lim}$

$$\frac{b}{t} = \frac{230}{\sqrt{f}}\left[1 - \frac{50.5}{(w/t)\sqrt{f}}\right] \qquad (27\text{-}10\text{-}1)$$

For deflection determination:

Flanges are fully effective ($b = w$) up to

$$(w/t)_{lim} = \frac{210}{\sqrt{f}}$$

For flanges with w/t larger than $(w/t)_{lim}$

$$\frac{b}{t} = \frac{312}{\sqrt{f}}\left[1 - \frac{68.7}{(w/t)\sqrt{f}}\right] \qquad (27\text{-}10\text{-}2)$$

In the above,
w/t = flat-width ratio.
b = effective design width, inches.
f = actual unit stress in the compression element computed on the basis of the effective design width, ksi.
t = thickness of element, inches.

3. **Multiple-stiffened elements and wide stiffened element with edge stiffeners.** Where the flat-width ratio, (w/t), of a sub-element of a multiple-stiffened compression element or of a stiffened compression element which does not have intermediate stiffeners and which has only one longitudinal edge connected to a web does not exceed 60, the effective design width, b, of such sub-element or element shall be determined in accordance with the provisions of Section 27.1005 (b). Where such flat-width ratio exceeds 60, the effective design width, b_c, of the sub-element or element shall be determined from the following formula:

$$\frac{b_e}{t} = \frac{b}{t} - 0.10\left[\frac{w}{t} - 60\right] \qquad \text{(27-10-3)}$$

[See Section 27.1005 (d) 1 for limitations on the allowable flat-width ratio of a compression element stiffened at one edge by other than a simple lip.]

WHERE:
w/t = flat-width ratio of sub-element or element.
b = effective design width determined in accordance with the provisions of Item No. 2 above, inches.
b_e = effective design width of subelement or element to be used in design computations, inches.

For computing the effective structural properties of a member having a compression element or subelements subject to the above reduction in effective width, the area of stiffeners (edge stiffener or intermediate stiffeners) shall be considered reduced to an effective area as follows:

For w/t between 60 and 90:

$$A_{ef} = \alpha A_{st} \qquad \text{(27-10-4)}$$

WHERE:

$$\alpha = (3 - 2b_e/w) - \frac{1}{30}\left[1 - \frac{b_e}{w}\right]\left(\frac{w}{t}\right) \qquad \text{(27-10-5)}$$

[See Section 27.1005 (c) 2 for limitations on number of intermediate stiffeners which may be considered effective and their minimum moment of inertia.]

For w/t greater than 90:

$$A_{ef} = (b_e/w)A_{st}$$

In the above expressions, A_{ef} and A_{st} refer only to the area of the stiffener section, exclusive of any portion of adjacent elements.

The centroid of the stiffener shall be considered located at the centroid of the full area of the stiffener and the moment of inertia of the stiffener about its own centroidal axis shall be that of the full section of the stiffener.

(c) **Stiffeners for Compression Elements.** 1. **Edge stiffeners.** For a flat compression element to be considered as a "stiffened compression element" it shall be stiffened along each longitudinal edge parallel to the direction of stress by a web, lip or other stiffening element having the following minimum moment of inertia:

$$I_{min} = 1.83t^4 \sqrt{\left(\frac{w}{t}\right)^2 - \frac{3320}{F_y}} \qquad (27\text{-}10\text{-}6)$$

but not less than $9.2t^4$, inches^4.

WHERE:

w/t = flat-width ratio of stiffened element, and

I_{min} = minimum allowable moment of inertia of stiffener (of any shape) about its own centroidal axis parallel to the stiffened element.

Where the stiffener consists of a simple lip bent at right angles to the stiffened element, the required overall depth, d_{min}, of such lip may be determined as follows:

$$d_{min} = 2.8t \sqrt[6]{\left(\frac{w}{t}\right)^2 - \frac{3320}{F_y}} \qquad (27\text{-}10\text{-}7)$$

but not less than $4.8t$, inches.

A simple lip shall not be used as an edge stiffener for any element having a flat-width ratio greater than 50.

2. **Intermediate stiffeners.** For a flat compression element to be considered as a "multiple-stiffened element," it shall be stiffened between webs or between a web and an edge by means of intermediate stiffeners parallel to the direction of stress, and the moment of inertia of each such intermediate stiffener shall be not less than twice the minimum allowable moment of inertia specified for edge stiffeners in Section 27.1005 (c). The following limitations also shall apply:

A. If the spacing of stiffeners between two webs is such that the flat-width ratio of the sub-element between stiffeners is larger than $(w/t)_{lim}$ [Section 27.1005 (b)] only two intermediate stiffeners (those nearest each web) shall be considered effective.

B. If the spacing of stiffeners between a web and edge stiffener is such that flat-width ratio of the sub-element between stiffeners is larger than $(w/t)_{lim}$ [Section 27.1005 (b)] only one intermediate stiffener shall be considered effective.

C. If intermediate stiffeners are spaced so closely that the flat-width ratio between stiffeners does not exceed $(w/t)_{lim}$ [Section 27.1005 (b)], all the stiffeners may be considered effective. In computing the flat-width ratio of the entire multiple-stiffened element, such element shall be considered as replaced by an element without intermediate stiffeners whose width w_s is the whole width between webs or from web to edge stiffener and whose equivalent thickness t_s is determined as follows:

$$t_s = \sqrt[3]{\frac{12I_s}{w_s}}, \text{ inches} \qquad (27\text{-}10\text{-}8)$$

WHERE:

I_s = moment of inertia of the full area of the multiple-stiffened element, including the intermediate stiffeners, about its own centroidal axis.

(d) **Maximum Allowable Flat-width ratios.** Maximum allowable overall flat-width ratios, w/t, disregarding intermediate stiffeners and taking t as the actual thickness of the element, shall be as follows:

1. Stiffened compression element having one longitudinal edge connected to a web or flange element, the other stiffened by:
   Simple lip. 50
   Any other kind of stiffener 90
2. Stiffened compression element with both longitudinal edges connected to a web or flange element (U-type or box-type sections). 400
3. Unstiffened compression element 50

   NOTE: Unstiffened compression elements with w/t ratios larger than approximately 30 may develop noticeable out-of-plane distortions without impairment of load- carrying capacity. For w/t ratios between 30 and 50, two allowable stresses for unstiffened elements are specified in Section 27.1008 (a), one to be used when distortions (waving) cannot be tolerated, the other when slight distortions are permissible.

   Stiffened compression elements with w/t ratios in excess of approximately 75 may develop noticeable out-of-plane distortions if loaded to the basic design stress (Section 27.1007). These distortions do not impair the load-carrying capacity of the element; however, when it is necessary to minimize or prevent visible distortions for elements with large w/t ratios the allowable stress should be determined as specified in Section 27.1008 (b).

   Stiffened elements having flat-width ratios larger than 400 may be used with safety to support loads, but substantial deformation of such elements under load may occur and may render inapplicable the design formulas of this specification.
4. Unusually wide flanges: Where a flange of a flexural member is unusually wide and it is desired to limit the maximum amount of curling or movement of the flange toward the neutral axis, the following formula shall apply to compression and tension flanges, either stiffened or unstiffened:

$$w_f = \sqrt{\frac{1700td}{f_{av}}} \times \sqrt[4]{\frac{100c_f}{d}}, \text{ inches} \quad \ldots\ldots\ (27\text{-}10\text{-}9)$$

WHERE:

w_f = the width in inches of the flange projection beyond the web or half of the distance between webs for box- or U-type beams.

t = thickness of flange, inches.

d = depth of beam, inches.

c_f = the amount of curling, inches.

f_{av} = the average stress in the full, unreduced flange width, ksi. Where members are designed by the effective design width procedure, the average stress equals the maximum stress times the ratio of the effective design width to the actual width.

(e) **Maximum Allowable Depth of Plane Unstiffened Webs.** The ratio h/t of the webs of flexural members shall not exceed the following limitations:

1. For members with unstiffened webs:

$$(h/t)_{max} = 150$$

2. For members which are provided with adequate means of transmitting concentrated loads and/or reactions into the web:

$$(h/t)_{max} = 200$$

WHERE:

h = clear distance between flanges, inches.

t = thickness of web, inches.

Where a web consists of two or more sheets, the h/t ratio shall be computed for individual sheets.

(f) Unusually Short Spans Supporting Concentrated Loads. Where the span of the beam is less than 30 w_f (w_f as defined below) and it carries one concentrated load, or several loads spaced farther apart than 2 w_f, the effective design width of any flange whether in tension or compression shall be limited to the following:

TABLE NO. 27-10-A—SHORT, WIDE FLANGES MAXIMUM ALLOWABLE RATIO OF EFFECTIVE DESIGN WIDTH TO ACTUAL WIDTH

L/w_f	RATIO	L/w_f	RATIO
30	1.00	14	0.82
25	0.96	12	0.78
20	0.91	10	0.73
18	0.89	8	0.67
16	0.86	6	0.55

In Table No. 27-10-A:

L = full span for simple beams or the distance between inflection points for continuous beams, or twice the length of cantilever beams, inches.

w_f = width of flange projection beyond the web for I-beam and similar sections or half the distance between webs of box or U-type sections, inches.

For flanges of I-beams and similar sections stiffened by lips at the outer edges, w_f shall be taken as the sum of the flange projection beyond the web plus the depth of the lip.

Flexural Member Design

Sec. 27.1006. (a) Load Determination. The permissible load which a flexural member can sustain shall be determined by conventional methods of elastic design subject to the following provisions, as applicable:

1. For members having stiffened compression flanges, the effective design width of compression flanges shall be determined in accordance with Formula (27-10-1) or (27-10-3) of Section 27.1005 (b). When the member is used for unusually short spans to support concentrated loads the allowable load shall also be determined by the reduced section, for which the effective width of both compression and tension flanges shall be determined in accordance with Section 27.1005 (f).
2. For members having unstiffened compression flanges the sectional properties used for determining the allowable load shall be based on the full section. For unusually short spans supporting concentrated loads the allowable load shall also be determined by the reduced cross section, for which the effective

widths of the compression and tension flanges shall be determined in accordance with Section 27.1005 (f).

3. The allowable stresses shall be determined by the applicable provisions of Sections 27.1007 through 27.1015.

(b) **Deflection Determination.** Deflections under loading shall be determined by conventional methods of elastic design, subject to the following modifications:

1. The effective moment of inertia, I_{eff}, shall be used for those members which have stiffened compression flanges. I_{eff} shall be calculated using effective width of these stiffened flanges determined in accordance with Formula (27-10-2) or (27-10-3) of Section 27.1005 (b), subject to the provisions of Section 27.1005 (f) for unusually short spans supporting concentrated loads.
2. The reduced modulus of elasticity as determined below shall be used for stresses in the inelastic range.

$$E_r = \frac{E_{ts} + E_{cs}}{2}\text{, ksi} \quad \text{. . . . . (27-10-10)}$$

WHERE:

E_r = reduced modulus of elasticity.

E_{ts} = secant modulus corresponding to the stress in the tension flange.

E_{cs} = secant modulus corresponding to the stress in the compression flange.

Values of the secant moduli shall be obtained from Table No. 27-10-B.

Allowable Design Stresses

Basic Design Stress

Sec. 27.1007. (a) **General.** Stress on the net section of tension members and tension and compression on the extreme fibers of flexural members shall not exceed the value F specified below except as otherwise specifically provided herein.

$$F = 0.541\, F_y \quad \text{. . . . . (27-10-11)}$$

where F_y is the specified yield strength.

Values of the basic design stresses for tension and compression, F, and for shear, F_{vb}, shall be as shown in Tables No. 27-10-D and No. 27-10-E, respectively, for the yield strengths listed in Table No. 27-10-C.

If the orientation of the member with respect to the rolling direction is not known the minimum stress value shall be used in all cases.

When the increase in steel strength resulting from cold work of forming is utilized in accordance with Section 27.1007 (b), the basic design stress for tension and compression shall not exceed the value F specified below except as otherwise specifically provided herein.

$$F = 0.541\, F_{ya}$$

where F_{ya} is the average yield strength of the full section.

(b) **Utilization of Cold Work of Forming.** Except as permitted by this section, allowable stresses shall be based upon the specified properties of the flat unformed material. Utilization, for design purposes, of any increase in material strength that results from a cold forming operation is permissible, provided that the increase in strength obtained is for the kind of stress (tension or compression, transverse or longitudinal) that is to be imposed on the final product in service and under the limitations prescribed in Section 27.1007 (b) 1 and 27.1007 (b) 2.

TABLE NO. 27-10-B SECANT MODULI FOR DEFLECTION CALCULATIONS

STRESS ksi	SECANT MODULUS, ksi x 10^3											
	LONGITUDINAL COMPRESSION			TRANSVERSE COMPRESSION			LONGITUDINAL TENSION			TRANSVERSE TENSION		
	GRADE			GRADE			GRADE			GRADE		
	A & B	C	D	A & B	C	D	A & B	C	D	A & B	C	D
0	28.0	27.0	27.0	28.0	28.0	28.0	28.0	27.0	27.0	28.0	28.0	28.0
4	28.0	27.0	27.0	28.0	28.0	28.0	28.0	27.0	27.0	28.0	28.0	28.0
8	28.0	27.0	27.0	28.0	28.0	28.0	28.0	27.0	27.0	28.0	28.0	28.0
12	28.0	27.0	27.0	28.0	28.0	28.0	28.0	27.0	27.0	28.0	28.0	28.0
16	24.8	27.0	27.0	28.0	28.0	28.0	28.0	27.0	27.0	28.0	28.0	28.0
20	21.3	27.0	27.0	28.0	28.0	28.0	28.0	27.0	27.0	28.0	28.0	28.0
24	18.5	26.2	26.7	27.7	28.0	28.0	27.1	27.0	27.0	25.6	28.0	28.0
28		24.0	25.4		28.0	28.0		27.0	27.0		28.0	28.0
32		21.3	24.2		28.0	28.0		26.8	27.0		28.0	28.0
36		18.8	23.0		27.9	28.0		26.1	27.0		27.9	28.0
40		16.9	21.8		27.8	28.0		25.4	27.0		27.4	28.0
44		15.3	20.6		27.4	28.0		24.6	26.8		26.8	28.0
48		13.9	19.4		27.0	28.0		23.8	26.6		25.9	28.0
52		12.5	18.2		26.4	27.9		22.9	26.4		25.0	27.9
56			17.1			27.6			26.1			27.6
60			16.0			27.2			25.7			27.2
64			15.0			26.8			25.3			26.7
68			14.0			26.4			24.9			26.2

TABLE NO. 27-10-C
YIELD STRENGTH, F_y, ksi

TYPE OF STRESS	A 666 GRADE			
	A	B	C	D
Longitudinal Tension	30	40[1] 45	75	110[1] 110
Transverse Tension	30	40[1] 45	75	100[1] 110
Transverse Compression	30	40[1] 45	90	120[1] 120
Longitudinal Compression	28	36[1] 41	50	65[1] 65
Shear	17	23[1] 25	42	56[1] 56

[1]Flat bars.

TABLE NO. 27-10-D
BASIC DESIGN STRESSES FOR TENSION AND COMPRESSION, F, ksi

TYPE OF STRESS	GRADE			
	A	B	C	D
Longitudinal Tension	16	22 24	41[1]	59[1] 59[1]
Transverse Tension	16	22 24	41	54 59
Transverse Compression	16	22 24	49[1]	65[1] 65[1]
Longitudinal Compression	15[1]	19[1] 22[1]	27[1]	35[1] 35[1]

[1]For this type of stress, the basic design stress is larger than the effective proportional limit.

TABLE NO. 27-10-E
BASIC DESIGN STRESSES FOR SHEAR, F_{vb}, ksi

TYPE OF STRESS	GRADE			
	A	B	C	D
Shear	10	13 15	26[1]	34[1] 34[1]

[1]For this type of stress, the basic design stress is larger than the effective proportional limit.

1. **Type of sections.** The provisions of Section 27.1007 (b) shall apply only to the following, regardless of whether the stress to be imposed on the member in service is in tension or compression:

A. Axially loaded members and flanges of flexural members whose proportions are such that when treated as compression members the quantity Q [Section 27.1012 (a)] is unity. This includes tubular members composed of flat elements.

B. Cylindrical tubular members in which the ratio D/t of mean diameter-to-wall thickness does not exceed $3140/F_y$.

2. **Limitations.** Application of the provisions of Section 27.1007 (b) shall be on the following basis:

A. Mechanical properties shall be determined on the basis of approved tests.

B. Provisions shall apply only to the following sections of the standard:

27.1007 (a)—Basic Design Stress
27.1007 (c)—Wind, Earthquake and Combined Forces
27.1008 (a)—Unstiffened Compression Elements, paragraphs (a) 1 and (a) 2 A, only
27.1009—Laterally Unbraced Single Web Beams
27.1012—Axially Loaded Compression Members
27.1013—Combined Axial and Bending Stresses
27.1014—Cylindrical Tubular Members in Compression or Bending

Application of all other provisions of this standard shall be based upon the properties of the flat unformed material.

C. The effect on mechanical properties of any welding or other applied process with potentially deleterious effect on the member shall be determined on the basis of tests of full-section specimens containing, within the gage length, such welding or other intended process. Any necessary allowance for such effect shall be made in the structural design of the member.

(c) **Wind, Earthquake and Combined Forces.** 1. **Wind or earthquake only.** Members and assemblies subject only to stresses produced by wind or earthquake forces may be proportioned for unit stresses 33⅓ percent greater than those specified for dead and live load stresses. A corresponding increase may be applied also to the allowable unit stresses in connections and details.

2. **Combined forces.** Members and assemblies subject to stresses produced by a combination of wind or earthquake and other loads may be proportioned for unit stresses 33⅓ percent greater than those specified for dead and live load stresses, provided the section thus required is not less than that required for the combination of dead and live load. A corresponding increase may be applied also to the allowable unit stresses in connections and details.

Allowable Stresses for Compression Elements

Sec. 27.1008. (a) **Unstiffened Compression Elements.** Compression stress, f_c, in kips per square inch on flat unstiffened elements shall not exceed the following:

1. For angle struts:

$$F_c = \frac{0.244\,E_o}{(w/t)^2}\left(\frac{E_s}{E_o}\right), \text{ ksi with a maximum of } F \ldots\ldots (27\text{-}10\text{-}12)$$

WHERE:

$\frac{E_s}{E_o}$ = plasticity reduction factor corresponding to $1.85f_c$.

E_o = initial modulus of elasticity, ksi (Table No. 27-10-F).

TABLE NO. 27-10-F
INITIAL MODULI OF ELASTICITY AND INITIAL SHEAR MODULI

	GRADE		
	A & B	C & D	
	LONGITUDINAL AND TRANSVERSE TENSION AND COMPRESSION	LONGITUDINAL COMPRESSION AND TENSION	TRANSVERSE COMPRESSION AND TENSION
Initial Modulus of Elasticity ksi x 10^{-3}	28.0	27.0	28.0
Initial Shear Modulus ksi x 10^{-3}	10.8	10.5	10.5

Values of the plasticity reduction factor shall be obtained from Table No. 27-10-J.

2. For all other sections:

A. For w/t less than or equal to

$$(w/t)_{lim} = \frac{57.6}{\sqrt{F_y}}$$

$$F_c = 0.541F_y, \text{ ksi} \quad \text{(27-10-13)}$$

B. For $(w/t)_{lim} \leq w/t \leq 175/\sqrt{F_y}$

$$F_c = F_y \left[0.541 - \frac{(0.541 - 11.05E_o \times 10^{-6})\left(\frac{w}{t} - \frac{57.6}{F_y}\right)}{\frac{117.4}{\sqrt{F_y}}} \right] \quad \text{(27-10-14)}$$

C. For $175/\sqrt{F_y} \leq w/t \leq 50$

(i) if no waving at design loads is permissible:

$$F_c = \frac{0.339E_o}{(w/t)^2}, \text{ ksi} \quad \text{(27-10-15)}$$

(ii) if some slight waving at design loads is permissible:

$$F_c = 11.05E_oF_y \times 10^{-6} - \frac{(1105E_oF_y \times 10^{-6} - 5.73)}{(50 - \frac{175}{\sqrt{F_y}})} \left[\frac{w}{t} - \frac{175}{F_y}\right] \quad \ldots\ldots\ldots\ldots (27\text{-}10\text{-}16)$$

Note: In the range of $\frac{175}{F_y} \leq w/t \leq 50$,

the allowable stress for no permissible waving is to be used for important exposed unstiffened elements. The allowable stress for slight permissible waving at design loads is to be used for unstiffened elements which are concealed or for which waving of a depth approximately equal to the sheet thickness can be tolerated. Such waving will not be detrimental to the load-carrying capacity of the member.

(b) **Buckling Stresses for Stiffened Elements.** For members in which local distortions at service loads must be limited to small, barely perceptible amounts, the stress in stiffened compression elements shall be limited to $1.2F_{cr}$. For members in which local distortions caused by service loads are not permissible, the stress in stiffened compression elements shall be limited to $0.9F_{cr}$. (This standard does not contain provisions to prevent distortions caused by thermal buckling.) In no case shall the allowable stress exceed as the basic design stress, F.

Where application of the above provision is necessary, the critical stress F_{cr} shall be determined as follows:

$$F_{cr} = \frac{3.62\ E_o}{(w/t)^2} \sqrt{\frac{E_t}{E_o}}\text{, ksi} \quad \ldots\ldots\ldots (27\text{-}10\text{-}17)$$

where $\sqrt{E_t/E_o}$ = plasticity reduction factor. Values of the plasticity reduction factor shall be obtained from Table No. 27-10-G.

Laterally Unbraced Single Web Beams

Sec. 27.1009. To prevent lateral buckling, the maximum compression stress f_c in ksi, on extreme fibers of compression flanges of laterally unsupported straight I-, Z- or channel-shaped flexural members (not including multiple-web deck, U- and closed box-type members and curved or arch members) shall not exceed the allowable stress as specified in Section 27.1007 or 27.1008, or the following maximum stress:

1. When bending is about the centroidal axis perpendicular to the web for either I-shaped sections symmetrical about an axis in the plane of the web or symmetrical channel-shaped sections:

$$F_b = 0.541\pi^2E_oC_b(E_t/E_o)\frac{dI_{yc}}{L^2S_{xc}} \quad \ldots . (27\text{-}10\text{-}18)$$

with a maximum of $0.541\ F_y$.

2. For point-symmetrical Z-shaped sections bent about the centroidal axis perpendicular to the web:

$$F_b = 0.27\pi^2E_oC_b(E_t/E_o)\frac{dI_{yc}}{L^2S_{xc}} \quad \ldots\ldots . (27\text{-}10\text{-}19)$$

with a maximum of $0.541\ F_y$.

TABLE NO. 27-10-G PLASTICITY REDUCTION FACTORS FOR STIFFENED ELEMENTS

STRESS $1.85 f_c$ ksi	$\sqrt{E_t/E_o}$					
	LONGITUDINAL COMPRESSION			TRANSVERSE COMPRESSION		
	Grade			Grade		
	A & B	C	D	A & B	C	D
0	1.00	1.00	1.00	1.00	1.00	1.00
4	1.00	1.00	1.00	1.00	1.00	1.00
8	1.00	1.00	1.00	1.00	1.00	1.00
12	1.00	1.00	1.00	1.00	1.00	1.00
16	0.77	1.00	1.00	1.00	1.00	1.00
20	0.67	1.00	1.00	1.00	1.00	1.00
24	0.58	0.79	0.98	0.81	1.00	1.00
28	0.50	0.71	0.86	0.62	1.00	1.00
32		0.65	0.80		1.00	1.00
36		0.60	0.75		1.00	1.00
40		0.56	0.71		0.99	1.00
44		0.52	0.68		0.93	1.00
48		0.48	0.64		0.88	1.00
52		0.45	0.60		0.84	1.00
56			0.57		0.80	0.97
60			0.53		0.77	0.94
64			0.50		0.73	0.91
68			0.47		0.70	0.87

In the above,

L = the unbraced length of the member, inches.

I_{yc} = the moment of inertia of the compression portion of a section about the gravity axis of the entire section parallel to the web, inches^4.

S_{xc} = compression section modulus of entire section about major axis I_x divided by distance to extreme compression fiber, inches^3.

C_b = bending coefficient which can conservatively be taken as unity or calculated from

$$C_b = 1.75 + 1.05\left(\frac{M_1}{M_2}\right) + 0.3\left(\frac{M_1}{M_2}\right)^2$$

but not more than 2.3.

Where M_1 is the smaller and M_2 the larger bending moment at the ends of the unbraced length, taken about the strong axis of the member, and where M_1/M_2, the ratio of end moments, is positive when M_1 and M_2 have the same sign (reverse curvature bending) and negative when they are of opposite sign (single curvature bending). When the bending moment at any point within an unbraced length is larger than that at both ends of this length, C_b shall be taken as unity. For members subject to combined axial and bending stress, C_b shall be 1.

E_o = initial modulus of elasticity, ksi (Table No. 27-10-F).

d = depth of section, inches.

E_t/E_o = plasticity reduction factors corresponding to 1.85 f_c. (Table No. 27-10-H).

F_y = yield strength of steel, ksi.

TABLE NO. 27-10-H PLASTICITY REDUCTION FACTORS FOR DESIGN OF LATERALLY UNBRACED SINGLE WEB BEAMS

STRESS ksi	E_t/E_o					
	LONGITUDINAL COMPRESSION			TRANSVERSE COMPRESSION		
	GRADE			GRADE		
	A & B	C	D	A & B	C	D
0	1.00	1.00	1.00	1.00	1.00	1.00
4	1.00	1.00	1.00	1.00	1.00	1.00
8	1.00	1.00	1.00	1.00	1.00	1.00
12	1.00	1.00	1.00	1.00	1.00	1.00
16	0.60	1.00	1.00	1.00	1.00	1.00
20	0.45	1.00	1.00	1.00	1.00	1.00
24	0.34	0.63	0.96	0.66	1.00	1.00
28	0.25	0.50	0.74	0.38	1.00	1.00
32	0.16	0.42	0.64	0.21	1.00	1.00
36	0.10	0.36	0.56	0.09	1.00	1.00
40	0.05	0.31	0.51	0.04	0.98	1.00
44	0.01	0.27	0.46	0.02	0.86	1.00
48		0.23	0.41		0.78	1.00
52		0.20	0.36		0.71	1.00
56		0.18	0.33		0.65	0.94
60		0.15	0.29		0.59	0.88
64		0.13	0.25		0.54	0.82
68		0.11	0.22		0.49	0.77
72		0.10	0.19		0.44	0.73
76			0.17		0.39	0.68
80			0.16		0.34	0.64
84			0.14		0.29	0.60
88			0.13		0.25	0.56
92			0.12		0.20	0.53
96			0.11		0.16	0.49
100			0.11		0.13	0.46
104					0.10	0.43
108					0.07	0.39
112						0.36
116						0.32
120						0.29
124						0.26
128						0.23
132						0.20
136						0.16
140						0.13
144						0.10
148						0.07

Allowable Stresses in Webs of Beams

Sec. 27.1010. (a) **Shear Stresses in Webs.** The maximum average shear stress, f_v, in kips per square inch on the gross area of a flat web shall not exceed the basic allowable shear stress specified in Section 27.1007, nor

$$F_v = \frac{2.61\,E_o}{(h/t)^2}\left(\frac{G_s}{G_o}\right),\ \text{ksi} \qquad \text{(27-10-20)}$$

WHERE:

h = clear distance between flanges, inches.
t = web thickness, inches.
E_o = initial modulus of elasticity, ksi (Table No. 27-10-F).
G_s/G_o = plasticity reduction factor corresponding to a shear stress equal to $1.85 f_v$, Table No. 27-10-I.

Where the web consists of two or more sheets, each sheet shall be considered as a separate member carrying its share of the shear.

TABLE NO. 27-10-I
Plasticity Reduction Factors for Shear Stresses in Webs

SHEAR STRESS $1.85 f_v$ ksi	G_s/G_o		
	GRADE		
	A & B	C	D
0	1.00	1.00	1.00
4	1.00	1.00	1.00
8	0.98	1.00	1.00
12	0.84	1.00	1.00
16	0.58	0.98	1.00
20	0.24	0.95	0.99
24	0.03	0.90	0.97
28		0.85	0.95
32		0.78	0.93
36		0.70	0.89
40		0.61	0.85
44		0.51	0.81
48			0.77
52			0.71
56			0.65

(b) **Bending Stresses in Webs.** The compressive stress, f_{bw}, in kips per square inch in the flat web of a beam, due to bending in its plane, shall not exceed F nor shall it exceed:

$$F_{bw} = \frac{15.5\,E_o}{(h/t)^2}\left(\frac{E_s}{E_o}\right),\ \text{ksi} \qquad \text{(27-10-21)}$$

WHERE:

h = clear distance between flanges, inches.
t = web thickness, inches.
$\frac{E_s}{E_o}$ = plasticity reduction factor corresponding to a stress equal to $1.4 f_{bw}$, Table No. 27-10-J.
E_o = initial modulus of elasticity, ksi (Table No. 27-10-F).

TABLE NO. 27-10-J
Plasticity Reduction Factors for Compression on Unstiffened Elements and Bending Stresses in Webs

STRESS $1.4\, f_{bw}$ or $1.85\, f_c$ ksi	E_s/E_o					
	LONGITUDINAL COMPRESSION			TRANSVERSE COMPRESSION		
	GRADE			GRADE		
	A & B	C	D	A & B	C	D
0	1.00	1.00	1.00	1.00	1.00	1.00
4	1.00	1.00	1.00	1.00	1.00	1.00
8	1.00	1.00	1.00	1.00	1.00	1.00
12	1.00	1.00	1.00	1.00	1.00	1.00
16	0.89	1.00	1.00	1.00	1.00	1.00
20	0.76	1.00	1.00	1.00	1.00	1.00
24	0.66	0.97	0.99	0.99	1.00	1.00
28	0.57	0.89	0.94	0.86	1.00	1.00
32	0.46	0.79	0.90	0.70	1.00	1.00
36	0.35	0.70	0.85	0.49	1.00	1.00
40	0.23	0.63	0.81	0.28	0.99	1.00
44	0.12	0.57	0.76	0.08	0.98	1.00
48		0.51	0.72		0.96	1.00
52		0.46	0.67		0.94	0.99
56			0.63		0.92	0.98
60			0.59		0.89	0.97
64			0.56		0.86	0.96
68			0.52		0.83	0.94
72					0.80	0.92
76					0.76	0.91
80					0.72	0.89
84					0.68	0.87
88					0.64	0.86
92					0.59	0.84
96						0.82
100						0.80
104						0.78
108						0.76
112						0.74
116						0.71
120						0.68

(c) **Combined Bending and Shear Stresses in Webs.** For webs subject to both bending and shear stresses, the member shall be proportioned so that such stresses do not exceed the allowable values specified in Section 27.1010 (a) and (b) and the quantity

$$\left(\frac{f_{bw}}{F_{bw}}\right)^2 + \left(\frac{f_v}{F_v}\right)^2 \leq 1 \quad \text{(27-10-22)}$$

In the above,

f_{bw} = actual compressive stress at junction of flange and web, ksi.

$$F_{bw} = \frac{15.5\, E_o}{(h/t)^2}\left(\frac{E_s}{E_o}\right), \text{ksi}$$

$$F_v = \frac{2.61\,E_o}{(h/t)^2}\left(\frac{G_s}{G_o}\right), \text{ ksi}$$

f_v = actual average shear stress; i.e., shear force per web divided by web area, ksi.

Web Crippling of Beams

Sec. 27.1011. To avoid crippling of flat webs of beams, concentrated loads and reactions shall not exceed the values of P_{max} given below:

1. Beams having single unreinforced webs with inside corner radii equal to or less than the thickness of the sheet:

A. For end reactions or for concentrated loads on the outer ends of cantilevers

$$P_{max} = (F_y/33)\,[1.33 - 0.33\,(F_y/33)] \times t^2\,[98 + 4.20\,(N/t) - 0.022\,(N/t)\,(h/t) - 0.011\,(h/t)], \text{ kips} \quad (27\text{-}10\text{-}23)$$

For webs having other corner radii up to $4t$, the value P_{max} given by the above formula is to be multiplied by

$$(1.15 - 0.15\,R/t)$$

B. For reactions of interior supports or for concentrated loads located anywhere on the span

$$P_{max} = (F_y/33)\,[1.22 - 0.22\,(F_y/33)] \times t^2\,[305 + 2.30\,(N/t) - 0.009\,(N/t)\,(h/t) - 0.5\,(h/t)], \text{ kips} \quad (27\text{-}10\text{-}24)$$

For webs having other corner radii up to $4t$, the value P_{max} given by the above formula is to be multiplied by

$$(1.06 - 0.06\,R/t)$$

C. For corner radii larger than $4t$, tests shall be made in accordance with Sections 27.1024 and 27.1025.

2. For I-beams made up of two channels connected back to back or for similar sections which provide a high degree of restraint against rotation of the web, such as I-sections made by welding two angles to a channel:

A. For end reactions or for concentrated loads on the outer ends of cantilevers

$$P_{max} = t^2F_y\,(4.44 + 0.558\,\sqrt{N/t}), \text{ kips} \quad (27\text{-}10\text{-}25)$$

B. For reactions of interior supports or for concentrated loads located anywhere on the span

$$P_{max} = t^2F_y\,(6.66 + 1.446\,\sqrt{N/t}), \text{ kips} \quad (27\text{-}10\text{-}26)$$

In all of the above, P_{max} represents the load or reaction for one solid web sheet connecting top and bottom flanges. For webs consisting of two or more such sheets

P_{max} shall be computed for each individual sheet and the results added to obtain the allowable load or reaction for the composite web.

For loads located close to the ends of beams, provisions 1 B and 2 B shall apply, provided that for cantilevers the distance from the free end to the nearest edge of bearing, and for a load close to an end support of simple and continuous beams, the clear distance from edge of end bearing to nearest edge of load bearing is larger than 1.5 *h*. Otherwise, provisions 1 A and 2 A apply.

In the above formulas,

P_{max} = allowable concentrated load or reaction, kips.
t = web thickness, inches.
N = actual length of bearing, in inches, except that in the above formulas the value of N shall not be taken greater than h.
h = clear distance between flanges measured along the plane of web, inches.
F_y = longitudinal compressive yield strength, ksi.
R = inside bend radius, inches.

Axially Loaded Compression Members

Sec. 27.1012. (a) Unit Stresses. 1. Shapes not subject to torsional-flexural buckling. For doubly symmetric shapes, closed cross-section shapes or cylindrical sections, and any other shapes which can be shown not to be subject to torsional-flexural buckling and for members braced against twisting, the average axial stress P/A in compression members shall not exceed the values of F_a or F'_a determined as follows:

A. **Fully effective sections.** For fully effective sections (form factor Q as defined in this section equals unity):

$$F_a = 4.60 \frac{E_t}{(KL/r)^2}$$

with a maximum of $F_y/2.15$, ksi. . . . . (27-10-27)

B. **Partially effective sections.** For partially effective sections, (form factor Q as defined in this section is less than unity):

$$F'_a = \frac{(2 - Q) F_a}{1 + \dfrac{4.30}{F_y}\left[\dfrac{1}{Q} - 1\right] F_a}$$

with a maximum of F_a, ksi. . . . . (27-10-28)

In the above formulas,

P = total column load, kips.
A = full cross-sectional area of the member, inches^2.
F_a = maximum allowable average axial stress in compression determined in accordance with Section 27.1012 (a) 1 A, ksi.
F'_a = maximum allowable average axial stress in compression for partially effective sections, ksi.
E_t = tangent modulus in compression corresponding to 2.15 f_a, Table No. 27-10-K.
K = effective length factor. In frames where lateral stability is provided by diagonal bracing or attachment to an adjacent structure having adequate lateral stability, the effective length factor, K, for the compression members shall be taken as unity, unless analysis shows that a smaller

TABLE NO. 27-10-K—TANGENT MODULI FOR DESIGN OF COLUMNS

STRESS ksi $2.15 f_a$	TANGENT MODULUS, ksi x 10^3					
	Longitudinal Compression			Transverse Compression		
	Grade			Grade		
	A&B	C	D	A&B	C	D
0	28.0	27.0	27.0	28.0	28.0	28.0
4	28.0	27.0	27.0	28.0	28.0	28.0
8	28.0	27.0	27.0	28.0	28.0	28.0
12	28.0	27.0	27.0	28.0	28.0	28.0
16	16.7	27.0	27.0	28.0	28.0	28.0
20	12.5	27.0	27.0	28.0	28.0	28.0
24	9.5	17.0	26.0	18.5	28.0	28.0
28	7.0	13.5	20.0	10.7	28.0	28.0
32	4.6	11.3	17.2	5.9	28.0	28.0
36	2.7	9.7	15.2	2.5	28.0	28.0
40	1.4	8.4	13.7	1.2	27.3	28.0
44	0.4	7.2	12.4	0.6	24.0	28.0
48		6.3	11.0		21.7	28.0
52		5.5	9.8		19.9	28.0
56			8.8		18.1	26.4
60			7.7		16.6	24.5
64			6.8		15.1	23.0
68			6.0		13.7	21.5
72					12.3	20.4
76					10.9	19.1
80					9.5	18.0
84					8.2	16.9
88					6.9	15.8
92					5.7	14.8
96						13.8
100						12.8
104						11.9
108						10.9
112						10.0
116						9.0
120						8.1

value may be used. The effective length *KL* of compression members in a frame which depends on its own bending stiffness for lateral stability shall be determined by a rational method and shall be not less than the actual unbraced length.

L = unbraced length of the compression member, inches.

r = radius of gyration of the full cross section, inches.

F_y = yield strength in compression in the direction parallel to the applied load, ksi.

Q = a factor determined as follows:

(i) For members composed entirely of stiffened elements, Q is the ratio of the effective design area, as determined from the effective design widths of such elements, and the full or gross area of the cross section. The effective design area used in determining Q shall be based upon the basic design stress F as defined in Section 27.1007.

(ii) For members composed entirely of unstiffened elements, Q is the ratio between the allowable compression stress F_c for the weakest element of the cross section (the element having the largest width-thickness ratio) and the basic design stress F, where F_c is as defined in Section 27.1008 and F is as defined in Section 27.1007.

(iii) For members composed of both unstiffened and stiffened elements the factor Q is the product of a stress factor Q_s computed as outlined in paragraph (ii) above and an area factor Q_a computed as outlined in paragraph (i) above, except that the stress upon which Q_a is to be based shall be the value of the unit stress F_c which is used in computing Q_s, and the effective area to be used in computing Q_a shall include the full area of all unstiffened elements.

2. **Shapes potentially subject to torsional-flexural buckling.** For singly symmetric or nonsymmetric shapes of open cross section which may be subject to torsional-flexural buckling and which are not braced against twisting, the allowable average compression stress shall be determined by a rational method or by tests in accordance with Sections 27.1024 and 27.1025.

(b) Maximum Slenderness Ratio, *KL/r*. The maximum allowable ratio of effective length KL to radius of gyration r of compression members shall not exceed 200, except that during construction only KL/r shall not exceed 300.

Combined Axial and Bending Stresses

Sec. 27.1013. Members subject to both axial compression and bending stresses shall be proportioned to meet the requirements of both of the following formulas as applicable:

$$\frac{f_a}{F_a} + \frac{C_{mx} f_{bx}}{\left(1 - \frac{f_a}{F'_{ex}}\right) F_{bx}} + \frac{C_{my} f_{by}}{\left(1 - \frac{f_a}{F'_{ey}}\right) F_{by}} \leqq 1.0 \qquad \text{(27-10-29)}$$

$$\frac{f_a}{0.465QF_y} + \frac{f_{bx}}{F_{blx}} + \frac{f_{by}}{F_{bly}} \leqq 1.0 \qquad \text{(27-10-30)}$$

when $\frac{f_a}{F_a} \leqq 0.15$, the following formula may be used in lieu of the above two formulas:

$$\frac{f_a}{F_a} + \frac{f_{bx}}{F_{bx}} + \frac{f_{by}}{F_{by}} \leqq 1.0 \qquad \text{(27-10-31)}$$

The subscripts x and y in the above formulas indicate the axis of bending about which a particular stress or design property applies.

In Formulas (27-10-29), (27-10-30) and (27-10-31),

F_a = maximum unit axial stress in compression that is permitted by this standard where axial stress only exists [Section 27.1012 (a)]. For sections governed by Section 27.1012 (a) 1 B, F_a shall be replaced by F'_a, ksi.

F_b = maximum bending unit stress in compression that is permitted by this specification where bending stress only exists (Sections 27.1007, 27.1008 and 27.1009), ksi.

F_{bl} = maximum bending stress in compression permitted where bending stress only exists and the possibility of lateral buckling is excluded [Sections 27.1007 and 27.1008 (a)], ksi.

$$F'_e = \frac{\pi^2 E_o}{2.15\,(KL_b/r_b)^2}$$

[may be increased one-third in accordance with Section 27.1007 (c)], ksi.

f_a = axial unit stress = axial load divided by full cross-sectional area of member, P/A, ksi.

f_b = bending unit stress = bending moment divided by section modulus of member, M/S, noting that for members having stiffened compression elements the section modulus shall be based on the effective design widths of such elements, ksi.

K = effective length factor in the plane of bending.

L_b = actual unbraced length in the plane of bending, inches.

r_b = radius of gyration about axis of bending, inches.

C_m = a coefficient whose value shall be taken as follows:

1. For compression members in frames subject to joint translation (sidesway) $C_m = 0.85$.

2. For restrained compression members in frames braced against joint translation and not subject to transverse loading between their supports in the plane of bending,

$$C_m = 0.6 - 0.4\,\frac{M_1}{M_2}\text{, but not less than } 0.4$$

where M_1/M_2 is the ratio of the smaller to larger moments at the ends of that portion of the member unbraced in the plane of bending under consideration. M_1/M_2 is positive when the member is bent in reverse curvature and negative when it is bent in single curvature.

3. For compression members in frames braced against joint translation in the plane of loading and subject to transverse loading between their supports, the value of C_m may be determined by rational analysis. However, in lieu of such analysis the following values may be used:

A. for members whose ends are restrained, $C_m = 0.85$,

B. for members whose ends are unrestrained, $C_m = 1.0$.

Cylindrical Tubular Members in Compression or Bending

Sec. 27.1014. For cylindrical tubular members with a ratio of mean diameter to wall thickness, D/t, not greater than $3140/F_y$ the compression stress shall not exceed the basic design stress F.

For cylindrical tubular members with a ratio of mean diameter to wall thickness, D/t, larger than $3140/F_y$ but not greater than $24{,}670/F_y$ the compression stress shall not exceed

$$F_r = 0.154F_y + \frac{1214}{D/t} \qquad \text{(27-10-32)}$$

For compression members the allowable stress, P/A, under axial load also shall not exceed F_a as prescribed by Section 27.1012 (a) 1 for $Q = 1$.

Arc-and-tangent Corrugated Sheets

Sec. 27.1015. When arc-and-tangent corrugated sheets are used for roofing, siding and curtain wall the allowable design stress for bending may be taken as 0.60 F_y or as F_r calculated from Formula (27-10-32), whichever is smaller.

The allowable load-carrying capacity of arc-and-tangent corrugated sheets may be established in accordance with Section 27.1025 (b).

Connections

General

Sec. 27.1016. Connections shall be designed to transmit the maximum stress in the connected member with proper regard for eccentricity. In the case of members subject to reversal of stress, except that caused by wind or earthquake loads, the connection shall be proportioned for the sum of the stresses.

Welds

Sec. 27.1017. (a) Fusion Welds. Fusion welds shall be proportioned so that the unit stresses in shear on the throat of fillet or plug welds do not exceed 24 percent of the tensile strength of the weld metal (Table No. 27-10-L), or 30 percent of the tensile strength of the annealed base metal (Table No. 27-10-M).

The allowable unit stress in tension or compression on butt welds shall not exceed the applicable basic design stress (Section 27.1007), or 45 percent of the tensile strength of the annealed base metal (Table No. 27-10-M), or 40 percent of the tensile strength of the weld metal (Table No. 27-10-L), provided that the weld penetrates 100 percent of the section. Stresses due to eccentricity of loading, if any, shall be combined with the primary stresses, and the combined unit stresses shall not exceed the values given above.

TABLE NO. 27-10-L
Tensile Strength of Weld Metal

AWS Classification	Minimum Tensile Strength ksi
E308	80
E308L	75
E309	80
E309Cb	80
E309Mo	80
E310	80
E310Cb	80
E310Mo	80
E312	95
E16-8-2	80
E316	75
E316L	70
E317	80
E318	80
E320	80
E330	75
E347	80
E349	100
E410	70
E430	70
E502	60
E505	60
E7Cr	60

TABLE NO. 27-10-M
Tensile Strength of Annealed Base Metal

Type	Product	Minimum Tensile Strength ksi
201	Plate, Sheet, Strip Flat Bar	95 75
202	Plate, Sheet, Strip Flat Bar	90 75
301, 302, 304, 316	Plate, Sheet, Strip Flat Bar	75 75

TABLE NO. 27-10-N
ALLOWABLE SHEAR STRENGTH—SPOT WELDING

Thickness of Thinnest Outside Sheet, in.	Allowable Shear Strength[1] per Spot, kips		
	ASTM 666, Grade		
	A, B	C	D
.006	0.024	0.028	0.034
.008	0.040	0.052	0.058
.010	0.060	0.068	0.084
.012	0.074	0.084	0.100
.014	0.096	0.100	0.128
.016	0.112	0.120	0.152
.018	0.128	0.144	0.188
.021	0.148	0.188	0.200
.025	0.200	0.240	0.272
.031	0.272	0.320	0.372
.034	0.320	0.368	0.440
.040	0.400	0.508	0.560
.044	0.480	0.580	0.680
.050	0.580	0.680	0.800
.056	0.680	0.800	0.980
.062	0.780	0.960	1.160
.070	0.960	1.120	1.420
.078	1.080	1.360	1.600
.094	1.420	1.680	2.120
.109	1.680	2.000	2.560
.125	2.000	2.400	3.040

[1]The allowable tensile strength per spot may conservatively be taken as 25 percent of the allowable shear strength.

Stresses in a fillet weld or in a partial penetration weld shall be considered as shear on the throat for any direction of the applied stress. Neither plug nor slot welds shall be assigned any value in resistance to any stresses other than shear unless tests have been performed in accordance with Section 27.1025 (b).

All fusion welding shall comply with the provisions of U.B.C. Standard No. 27-6 except as otherwise specified herein and excepting such provisions of that standard as are clearly not applicable to material of the type and thickness to which this standard applies.

Filler metal shall be corrosion-resisting chromium and chromium-nickel steel covered welding electrodes and/or corrosion-resisting chromium and chromium-nickel steel welding rods and bare electrodes.

(b) **Resistance Welds.** When Type 301, 302, 304 or 316 sheets are joined by spot welding the allowable shear per spot shall be as set forth in Table No. 27-10-N.

When Type 301, 302, 304 or 316 sheets are joined by pulsation welding, the allowable shear per spot shall be as set forth in Table No. 27-10-O.

TABLE NO. 27-10-O
ALLOWABLE SHEAR STRENGTH—PULSATION WELDING

Thickness of Thinnest Outside Sheet, in.	Allowable Shear Strength per Spot, kips
	For Grades C and D of Stainless Steels, A 666
.156	3.040
.187	3.900
.203	4.240
.250	5.400

Values for intermediate thicknesses may be obtained by straightline interpolation. The values above may also be applied conservatively for Types 201 and 202. In all cases, welding shall be performed in accordance with nationally recommended practices for resistance welding.

Connecting Two Channels to Form an I-Section

Sec. 27.1018. The maximum permissible longitudinal spacing of welds or other connectors, S_{max}, joining two channels to form an I-section shall be

1. For compression members:

$$S_{max} = \frac{Lr_{cy}}{2r_I}\text{, inches} \quad \text{(27-10-33)}$$

WHERE:

S_{max} = longitudinal spacing of connections, inches.

L = unbraced length of compression member, inches.

r_I = radius of gyration of the I-section about the axis perpendicular to the direction in which buckling would occur for the given conditions of end support and intermediate bracing, if any, inches.

r_{cy} = radius of gyration of one channel about centroidal axis parallel to web, inches.

2. For flexural members:

$$S_{max} = L/6\text{, inches} \quad \text{(27-10-34)}$$

In no case shall the spacing exceed the value

$$S_{lim} = \frac{2gT_s}{mq}\text{, inches} \quad \text{(27-10-35)}$$

WHERE:

S_{lim} = limiting longitudinal spacing of connections, inches.
L = span of beam, inches.
T_s = strength of connection in tension, kips.
g = vertical distance between the two rows of connections near or at the top and bottom flanges, inches.
q = intensity of load on beam, kips per linear inch. (For methods of determination see below.)
m = distance of shear center of channel from mid-plane of the web, inches.

$$m = \frac{bt}{12I_x} [6d_1 (d)^2 + 3(b)(d)^2 - 8(d_1)^3] \quad \text{(27-10-36)}$$

$b = B - [t/2 + \alpha t/2]$
$d = d - t$
$d_1 = \alpha [d_1 - t/2]$
B = flange width, inches.
d = depth of channel or beam, inches.
d_1 = depth of stiffening lip, inches.
t = thickness of channel section, inches.
α = coefficient, for sections with stiffening lips, $\alpha = 1.0$; for sections without stiffening lips, $\alpha = 0$.
I_x = moment of inertia of one channel about its centroidal axis normal to the web, inches^4.

The intensity of load, q, is obtained by dividing the concentrated loads or reactions (kips) by the length of bearing (inches). For beams designed for uniformly distributed load the intensity, q, shall be taken equal to three times the intensity of the uniformly distributed design load. If the length of bearing of a concentrated load or reaction is smaller than the weld spacing, s, the required strength of the welds or connections closest to the load or reaction, P, is

$$T_s = Pm/2g, \text{ kips} \quad \text{(27-10-37)}$$

The maximum spacing of connections S_{lim} shall depend upon the intensity of the load directly at the connection. If uniform spacing of connections is used over the whole length of the beam it shall be determined at the point of maximum local load intensity. In cases where this procedure would result in uneconomically close spacing either one of the following methods may be adopted: (i) the connection spacing may be varied along the beam according to the variation of load intensity; or (ii) reinforcing cover plates may be welded to the flanges at points where concentrated loads occur. The strength in shear of the connections joining these plates to the flanges shall then be used for T_s, and g shall represent the depth of the beam.

Spacing of Connections in Compression Elements

Sec. 27.1019. The spacing, in line of stress, of welds, rivets or bolts connecting a compression cover plate or sheet to a nonintegral stiffener or other element shall not exceed:

1. that which is required to transmit the shear between the connected parts on the basis of the design strength per connection specified elsewhere herein, or

2. $$s = 1.11t \sqrt{\frac{E_t}{f}}, \text{ inches} \quad \text{(27-10-38)}$$

WHERE:

s = spacing of connections, inches.
t = thickness of the cover plate or sheet, inches.
f = design stress in the cover plate or sheet, ksi.
E_t = tangent modulus in compression corresponding to 1.85F (shall be obtained from Table No. 27-10-K), ksi;

nor:

3. three times the flat width, w, of the narrowest unstiffened compression element tributary to the connections, but need not be less than $30t$ unless closer spacing is required by paragraph 1 or 2 of this section.

In the case of intermittent fillet welds parallel to the direction of stress the spacing shall be taken as the clear distance between welds plus ½ inch. In all other cases the spacing shall be taken as the center-to-center distance between connections.

EXCEPTION: The requirements of Section 27.1019 do not apply to cover sheets which act only as sheathing material and are not considered as load-carrying elements.

Bolted Connections

Sec. 27.1020. (a) Minimum Spacing and Edge Distance in Line of Stress. The clear distance between bolts which are arranged in rows parallel to the direction of force and the distance from the center of any bolt to that end or other boundary of the connecting member towards which the pressure of the bolt is directed, shall be not less than $1\frac{1}{2}\,d$ or $P/[0.50\,(F_y)_{av}t]$.

WHERE:

d = diameter of bolt, inches.
P = force transmitted by bolt, kips.
t = thickness of thinnest connected sheet, inches.
$(F_y)_{av}$ = average of the four yield strengths for tension and compression in longitudinal and transverse directions, ksi.

(b) **Tension Stress on Net Section.** The tension stress on the net section of a bolted connection shall not exceed F_t nor shall it exceed

$$(1.0 - 0.9r + 3rd/s)F_T \text{ ksi} \quad \text{(27-10-39)}$$

WHERE:

r = the force transmitted by the bolt or bolts at the section considered divided by the tension force in the member at that section. If r is less than 0.2, it may be taken equal to zero.
s = spacing of bolts perpendicular to line of stress, inches. In the case of a single bolt, s = width of sheet.
d = diameter of bolt, inches.
F_T = basic design stress based on the yield strength for tension in line of stress, ksi.

(c) **Bearing Stress in Bolted Connections.** The bearing stress on the area $(d \times t)$ shall not exceed $1.4\,(F_y)_{av}$.

(d) **Shear Stress on Bolts.** Shear stress on the gross cross-sectional area of stainless steel bolts under dead and live load shall not exceed the values given in Table No. 27-10-P.

For the bolts not listed in Table No. 27-10-P, the permissible shear stress shall be determined from approved values or shall be determined by approved test procedures. When based upon approved tests, the ultimate shear strength shall be taken as 60 percent of the ultimate tensile strength and a safety factor 3.0 shall be applied to the ultimate shear strength to determine the allowable shear stress for design of bolted connections when threading is excluded from the shear plane. When the threading is included in the shear planes, 70 percent of the above determined allowable shear strength shall be used.

Bracing Requirements

General

Sec. 27.1021. Structural members and assemblies of light gage stainless steel construction shall be adequately braced in accordance with good engineering practice. The following provisions cover certain special cases and conditions.

Channel and Z-sections Used as Beams

Sec. 27.1022. (a) **General.** The following provisions for the bracing, against twist, of channel and Z-sections used as beams apply only when (1) neither flange is connected to deck, stringers or sheathing material in such a manner as to effectively restrain lateral deflection and rotation of the connected flange and (2) such members are loaded in the plane of the web.*

(b) **Spacing of Braces.** Braces shall be attached both to the top and bottom flanges of the sections at their ends, and at intervals not greater than one fourth of the span length, in such a manner as to prevent tipping at the ends and lateral deflection of either flange in either direction at intermediate braces. If one third or more of the total load on the beams is concentrated over a length of one twelfth or less of the span of the beam, an additional brace shall be placed at or near the center of this loaded length.

(c) **Design of Braces.** Each intermediate brace, at top and bottom flange, shall be designed to resist a lateral force P_L determined as follows:

1. For a uniformly loaded beam, $P_L = 1.5K'$ times the load within a distance $0.5a$ each side of the brace.
2. For concentrated loads, $P_L = 1.0K'$ times the concentrated load P within a distance $0.3a$ each side of the brace, plus a force F determined from the following formula, for each such concentrated load P located farther than $0.3a$, but not farther than a from the brace:

$$F = \frac{1.0}{0.7}\left(1 - \frac{x}{a}\right)PK', \text{ kips} \qquad (27\text{-}10\text{-}40)$$

In the above formulas:

For channels:

$K' = m/d$

WHERE:

m = distance from shear center to midplane of the web as specified in Section 27.1018, inches

d = depth of channel, inches

For Z-sections:

$K' = I_{xy}/I_x$

*When only one flange is connected to a deck or sheathing material to effectively restrain lateral deflection of the connected flange, bracing may or may not be needed to prevent twisting of the member, depending upon the dimensions of the member and span and upon whether the unconnected flange is in compression or tension.

TABLE NO. 27-10-P
ALLOWABLE SHEAR STRESS FOR STAINLESS STEEL BOLTS

TYPE	FINISH	CONDITION AND SPECIFICATION	DIAMETER d (IN.)	MINIMUM TENSILE REQUIREMENTS			
				0.2% YIELD STRENGTH (ksi)	TENSILE STRENGTH (ksi)	NO THREADS IN SHEAR PLANE	THREADS IN SHEAR PLANE
302[2] 304 316	Hot Finished	Condition A (Annealed) in A276 Class 1 (solution treated) in A193	all	30.0	75.0	15.0	10.5
302 304 316	Cold Finished	Condition A (Annealed) in A276	$\leqq \frac{1}{2}$	45.0	90.0	18.0	12.6
302[2] 304 316	Cold Finished	Condition B (cold-worked) in A276 Class 2 (solution treated and strain hardened) in A193[1]	$\leqq \frac{3}{4}$	100.0	125.0	25.0	17.5

[1]For Class 2: B8M in A193, the allowable shear stress is 22.0 ksi when threads are excluded from the shear plane, or 15.0 ksi when threads are in the shear plane.
[2]A276-71 only.

WHERE:

I_{xy} = product of inertia of full section about centroidal axes parallel and perpendicular to web, $inches^4$.

I_x = moment of inertia of full section about centroidal axis perpendicular to web, $inches^4$.

For channels and Z sections:

x = distance from concentrated load P to brace, inches.

a = length of bracing interval, inches.

End braces shall be designed for half of the above forces.

Braces shall be designed to avoid local crippling at the points of attachment to the member.

(d) **Allowable Stresses.** For channel and Z-beams intermediately braced according to the requirements of Section 27.1022 (b) and (c) the maximum compression stress shall be that specified in Section 27.1009 except that the length of the bracing interval, a, shall be used instead of the length L in the formulas of that Section.

Laterally Unbraced Box Beams

Sec. 27.1023. For closed box-type sections used as beams the ratio of the laterally unsupported length, L, to the distance between the webs of the section shall not exceed $2500/F_y$.

Tests

Determination of Stress-strain Relationship

Sec. 27.1024. For stainless steels produced to other than the stress-strain relationship and mechanical properties used for the purposes of design may be established on the basis of approved tests.

Statistical studies shall be made to insure that the mechanical properties so determined shall be those for which there is a 90 percent probability that they will be equalled or exceeded in a random selection of the material lot under consideration.

Tests for Special Cases

Sec. 27.1025. (a) **General.** 1. Where the composition or configuration of elements, assemblies or details of structural members formed from sheet or strip steel are such that calculation of their safe load-carrying capacity or deflection cannot be made in accordance with the provisions of Sections 27.1003 through 27.1023 of this standard, their structural performance shall be established from test procedure as specified in Section 27.1025 (b).

2. Tests for determination of mechanical properties of formed sections to be used in accordance with the provisions of Section 27.1007 (b) shall be made in accordance with provisions of Section 27.1025 (c).

3. Tests shall be made by an independent testing laboratory or by a manufacturer's testing laboratory witnessed by a qualified professional engineer.

(b) **Tests for Determining Structural Performance.** Where tests are necessary for the purpose defined in paragraph 1 of Section 27.1025 (a) they may be conducted in accordance with the following procedures. These test procedures and test factors are not applicable to confirmatory tests of members and assemblies whose properties can be calculated according to Sections 27.1003 through 27.1023, where the standard provides generally a safety factor of 1.85 except in the case of arc-and-tangent corrugated sheets used for roofing, siding and curtain walls, for which Section 27.1015 permits either calculation with a safety factor of 1/0.6 or tests.

1. Where practicable, reported test results shall represent the mean values resulting from tests of not fewer than three identical specimens, provided the deviation of any individual test result from the mean value obtained from all tests does not exceed ± 10 percent. If such deviation from the mean exceeds 10 percent, at least three more tests of the same kind shall be made. The average of the three lowest values of all tests made shall then be regarded as the result of the series of tests.
2. Determinations of allowable load-carrying capacity may be made on the following bases:
   A. The member, assembly or connection shall be capable of sustaining during the test, without failure, a total load, including the weight of the test specimen, equal to twice the live load plus twice the dead load.
   B. Harmful local distortions or overall deflections shall not develop during the test of a total load, including the weight of the test specimen, equal to the dead load plus one and one-half times the live load.
   C. For members and assemblies subjected to wind or earthquake loads, or combined forces, the foregoing load factors shall be divided by $\frac{4}{3}$ in accordance with Section 27.1007 (c).
3. In evaluating test results, due consideration shall be given to any differences existing between the mechanical properties and dimensions of the material from which the tested sections are formed and the mechanical properties and dimensions specified for the material intended for use. Consideration shall also be given to any variation or differences between the design thickness and the thickness of the specimens used in the tests.

(c) **Tests for Determining Mechanical Properties of Full Sections.** Tests to determine mechanical properties defined in paragraph 2 of Section 27.1025 (a) shall be conducted on full formed sections as follows:

1. Tensile yield strength determinations shall be made in accordance with nationally recognized test procedures.
2. Compressive yield strength determinations shall be made by means of compression tests of short stud column specimens of the section, and shall be taken as either the maximum compressive strength of the section or the stress determined by the 0.2 percent offset method, whichever is reached first in the test.
3. Where the principal effect of the loading to which the member will be subjected in service will be to produce bending stresses, the yield strength to be used shall be the lower of the yield strengths determined in tension and in compression. In determining such yield strengths in flanged sections, tension and compression tests shall be made on specimens cut from the section. Each such specimen shall consist of one complete flange plus a portion of the web of such flat width ratio that the value of Q for the specimen is unity.
4. For acceptance and control purposes two tests shall be made from each lot of not more than 50 tons nor less than 30 tons of each section, or one test from each lot of less than 30 tons of each section. For this purpose a lot may be defined as that tonnage of one section that is formed in a single production run of material from one heat or blow.

UNIFORM BUILDING CODE STANDARD NO. 27-11

STEEL STORAGE RACKS

Based on the Specification for the Design, Testing and Utilization of Industrial Steel Storage Racks, 1990 Edition, by the Rack Manufacturers Institute

See Table No. 23-P and Sections 2701 (a) and 2706, Uniform Building Code

General Provisions

Sec. 27.1101. (a) **Scope.** This standard shall apply to pallet racks, movable shelf racks and stacker-racks made of cold-formed or hot-rolled steel structural members. It shall not apply to other types of racks, such as cantilever racks, drive-in and drive-through racks and rack buildings.

The design of racks not covered by this standard shall be in accordance with the provisions of Section 2336 using the loads as defined in this standard.

> **EXCEPTION:** The building official may waive the design requirements for storage racks less than or equal to 8 feet in height.

(b) **Definitions.** For the purpose of this standard, certain terms are defined as follows:

FRAMES are the rigid-connection frames composed of posts and pallet beams in pallet racks, and the upright (trussed) frames.

MOVABLE-SHELF RACKS are a type of rack where the shelves are removable and replaceable in multiple locations in the section opening.

PALLET is a portable platform on which goods are placed for storage or transportation.

PALLET GUIDE is a device to prevent a pallet from sliding off its support beam or rail.

PALLET RACK (also **Standard Pallet Rack**) is a rack which utilizes horizontal beams connected to prefabricated upright frames to provide independent, multiple-level storage (usually on either side of an aisle). The horizontal beams support pallets.

PALLET RACK BEAMS (also **Shelf Beams**) are horizontal structural members used to support pallets in a rack.

STACKER RACKS (also **Stacker Crane Racks**) are a rack arrangement, usually higher than other types of racks, where floor-running storage and retrieval machines are used to shuttle loads. These machines are generally rail mounted and often fully automated and computer controlled.

STACKER-RACK BEAMS are horizontal structural members used to support pallets in a stacker rack.

STEEL STORAGE RACK is a single or multilevel storage system in single or multibays consisting of vertical columns or posts and horizontal beams. Diagonal and horizontal trussed bracing is often used to resist horizontal loads. The beams generally support pallets, and the system may be one of a number of different types (Standard Pallet Rack, Stacker Rack, etc.); see definitions of each type.

UNIT LOAD is a standardized load, meaning, for example, pallet load if pallets are used. Also refers to other standardized loads such as barrels which may be stored without pallets.

(c) **Materials.** This standard contemplates the use of steel of structural quality as listed in the Uniform Building Code, Chapter 27.

Steels not listed in the above provisions are not excluded, provided they conform to the chemical and mechanical requirements of one of the listed specifications or other published specifications which establish their properties and structural suitability; and provided they are subjected by either the producer or the purchaser to analyses, tests and other controls to the extent and in the manner prescribed by one of the two listed specifications, as applicable.

(d) **Applicable Design Specifications.** Except as either modified or supplemented herein the Uniform Building Code, Chapter 27, shall apply to the design of steel storage racks.

(e) **Integrity of Rack Installations.** Individual rack components and assemblies thereof shall comply with this standard.

All rack installations and racks manufactured in conformity with this standard shall display in one or more conspicuous locations a permanent plaque each not less than 50 square inches in area and showing the maximum permissible unit load in clear legible print.

> **EXCEPTION:** The building official may waive plaque installation for racks not exceeding 12 feet in height to top shelf, covering a floor area less than 300 square feet, with a unit load not exceeding 2,500 pounds, and without double stacking on top level.

Load application and rack configuration drawings shall be furnished with each rack installation. The drawings shall present the permissible configurations or limitations as to the maximum number of shelves or rails, the maximum distance between them, and the maximum distance from the floor to the bottom shelf or rail.

The bottom of all posts shall be furnished with bearing plates, according to Section 27.1106 (b). Drive-in, drive-through and stacker racks shall be anchored to the floor by anchor bolts capable of resisting the horizontal shear forces caused by the horizontal and vertical loads on the rack.

The stability of movable-shelf racks shall not be dependent upon movable shelves. Those components which provide stability, such as permanently bolted or welded top shelves and the longitudinal and transverse diagonal bracing, shall be clearly identified on the rack configuration drawings. In specific movable-shelf rack installations where rack height requires it, a conspicuous warning is to be placed in the owner's utilization instruction manual of any restrictions on shelf placement or shelf removal. Such restrictions also are to be permanently posted in locations clearly visible to forklift operators.

Lower portions of posts exposed to damage by forklift trucks or other moving equipment shall have protective devices. If not so protected the rack structure may, at the option of the building official: (1) be designed to maintain its full design load capacity at allowable stresses with the exposed post capacity reduced by one-half, or (2) be designed to maintain its full design load capacity at 50 percent increased allowable stresses with the exposed post assumed to have no carrying capacity.

Where racks are braced against the building structure, the building structure shall be designed for the horizontal and vertical forces listed in Section 27.1105 (a) imposed on the building structure.

Racks shall be installed with a maximum tolerance from the vertical of 1 inch in 10 feet of height. Special conditions may require more restrictive tolerances.

Support of racks by foundations, concrete floor slabs or other means shall be in conformance with Chapter 29 of the Uniform Building Code.

Design Procedures and Dimensional Limitations

Sec. 27.1102. (a) **General.** All computations for allowable loads, stresses and deflections shall be in accordance with conventional methods of structural design, and as specified in Section 27.1101 (d), except where modified or supplemented herein. Where adequate methods of design calculations are not available, justification by a testing program acceptable to the building official may be used.

(b) **Dimensional Limitations.** The limitations on flat-width ratios and slenderness ratios in U.B.C. Standard No. 27-9 and Uniform Building Code Chapter 27 shall apply except for the following conditions:

1. Slenderness limitations shall not be imposed on tension members which do not resist compression forces under any loading condition.

2. The unbraced length of compression or tension members shall be the length between connections to other structural members disposed in the direction of the pertinent radius of gyration, or from such a connection to the nearest attachment to an external fixed structure, such as a floor.

Allowable Stresses and Effective Widths

Sec. 27.1103. (a) **General.** Allowable stresses and effective design width shall be as specified in U.B.C. Standard No. 27-9 and Uniform Building Code Chapter 27 except as provided herein. Allowable stresses for working stress design may be increased one third when considering wind or earthquake forces either acting alone or when combined with vertical loads.

(b) **Perforated Compression Members.** The effect of perforations on the carrying capacity of compression members shall be recognized by modification of the Q-factor. Q-values for perforated compression members shall be determined by stub column tests acceptable to the building official. These members shall be designed in an approved manner. The effects of perforations on the capacity of members may be considered by using the section properties based on the minimum net area.

(c) **Torsional-flexural Buckling.** Sections subject to torsional-flexural buckling shall be designed according to U.B.C. Standard No. 27-9.

Pallet and Stacker-rack Beams

Sec. 27.1104. (a) **Allowable Loads.** Where the shape of the cross section permits, allowable loads of pallet-carrying beams shall be determined in accordance with U.B.C. Standard No. 27-9 or Uniform Building Code Chapter 27.

(b) **Deflections.** At working load the deflections, including possible deformations in the end connections, shall not exceed 1/180 of the span measured with respect to the beam ends.

(c) **Determination by Test.** Where the configuration of the cross section precludes calculation of allowable loads and deflections, determination may be made with a testing program acceptable to the building official.

Frame Design

Sec. 27.1105. (a) **General.** Frames shall be designed for the critical combinations of vertical loads in the most unfavorable positions, horizontal loads as specified in Section 27.1107 (c), and the additional effects of horizontal sway caused by looseness, if any, of the top tie beam to post connections.

(b) **Effective Lengths.** Effective lengths based on valid engineering principles shall be used in the design of posts and upright frames.

Connections and Bearing Plates

Sec. 27.1106. (a) **Connections.** Adequate strength of connections to withstand calculated resultant forces and moments, and adequate rigidity where such is required, shall be demonstrated by calculation or by testing in an approved manner.

Beams shall have support connections capable of withstanding an upward force of 1,000 pounds per connection within allowable design values of the Uniform Building Code.

For movable-shelf racks, the top shelf and other fixed shelves are to include support connections capable of withstanding an upward force of 1,000 pounds per connection within the allowable design values of the Uniform Building Code.

The movable shelves are generally constructed of a set of front and rear longitudinal beams connected to each other rigidly by transverse members. The movable shelves are to be connected in such a way to prevent forward displacement when lifting out the front beam of the shelf.

(b) **Bearing Plates.** Provision shall be made to transfer post loads and moments into the floor. Said forces and moments shall be consistent in magnitude, sense and direction with the rack analysis. Allowable bearing stresses on the bottom of base plates shall be determined in accordance with Uniform Building Code Chapter 26.

Loads

Sec. 27.1107. (a) **Gravity Loads.** Racks shall be designed for dead loads, live loads and unit loads as posted on the rack installation under Section 27.1101 (e).

(b) **Vertical Impact.** Unit load-carrying beams, supporting arms, if any, and end connections shall be designed for an additional vertical impact load of 25 percent of one unit load located to produce maximum moments and shears. Impact stresses shall not exceed stresses referenced in Section 27.1103, nor shall they cause detrimental permanent deformations in connections. When allowable loads are determined by tests due allowance shall be made for the additional impact load. Impact loads may be omitted when checking beam deflections and designing upright frames, posts and other vertical components.

(c) **Horizontal Loads.** 1. **General.** All racks shall be designed for the horizontal forces and allowable stresses specified in this standard. These forces shall not cause permanent distortions of connections when subject to test, nor permanent residual sway deflections (of the entire rack when subject to full-scale rack tests) larger than 20 percent of the sway deflections measured under the simultaneous action of horizontal and vertical loads.

2. **Horizontal stability.** Horizontal stability shall be determined by applying horizontal forces simultaneously at all beam-to-post connections equal to 1.5 percent of the maximum live load plus dead load at the connection. The forces shall be applied separately in each of the two principal directions of the rack and in conjunction with full dead and live loads.

3. **Stacker racks or racks wholly or partially supporting moving equipment.** Racks shall be designed for maximum forces and their locations, transmitted from moving equipment to racks, and applicable longitudinal and transverse impact factors due to moving equipment.

Devices acting as bumpers to stop moving equipment shall be considered in the design.

Forces described in this subsection need not act concurrently with those described in Section 27.1107 (c) 2 and (e) 1.

(d) **Wind Loads.** Outdoor racks exposed to wind shall be designed for the wind loads prescribed by Chapter 23 of the Uniform Building Code acting on the horizontal projection of rack plus contents. For stability, consideration shall be given to loading conditions which produce large wind forces combined with small stabilizing gravity forces, such as racks fully loaded, but the unit loads of much smaller weight than the maximum posted unit load.

Forces described in Section 27.1107 (c) 2 and (e) 1 need not act concurrently with wind loads. Forces described in Section 27.1107 (c) 3 shall act concurrently with wind forces for design purposes.

(e) **Earthquake Loads.** 1. **General.** Steel storage racks which are not connected to buildings or other structures shall be designed to resist seismic forces in conformance with this standard.

2. **Minimum earthquake forces.** The total minimum lateral force shall be determined by the following formula:

$$V = (ZIC/R_w)\,W$$

WHERE:

V = total lateral seismic force assumed to act nonconcurrently in the direction of each of the main axes of the rack. For racks having more than two storage levels, the total lateral force, V, shall be distributed over the height of the rack in accordance with

$$F_i = \frac{V W_i h_i}{\sum_{i=1}^{n} W_i h_i}$$

in which F_i is the lateral force applied at level i; W_i is the portion of the total weight, W, which is assigned to level i; h_i is the height of level i above the base of the rack; and n is the total number of storage levels. The lateral force, V, shall be distributed in proportion to the total weight, W.

Z = numerical coefficient dependent upon the zone as determined by Figure No. 2 in Chapter 23, Uniform Building Code. For locations in Seismic Zone No. 1, $Z = 0.075$. For locations in Seismic Zone No. 2A, $Z = 0.150$. For locations in Seismic Zone No. 2B, $Z = 0.200$. For locations in Seismic Zone No. 3, $Z = 0.300$. For locations in Seismic Zone No. 4, $Z = 0.400$.

I = occupancy importance factor as specified in Uniform Building Code Table No. 23-L.

C = $1.25\,S/T^{2/3}$. The value of C need not exceed 2.75 and may be used for any structure without regard to soil type or structure period. T is the fundamental period of vibration of the rack in seconds in the direction under consideration. Properly substantiated calculations or test data for establishing the period, T, shall be submitted. The minimum value of C/R_w shall be 0.075.

R_w = 6.0 for racks or portions thereof where lateral stability is dependent upon diagonal or x-bracing. Connection for the bracing members shall be capable of developing the required strength of the members.

R_w = 8.0 for racks where the lateral stability is wholly dependent on moment-resistant frame action.

S = the site soil coefficient for soil characteristics given in Table No. 23-J.

W = weight of rack structure plus contents. Where a number of storage rack units are interconnected so there are a minimum of four columns in any direction on each column line designed to resist horizontal forces, W may be equal to the total dead load plus 50 percent of the rack-rated capacity.

Other R_w values may be considered based on submission of substantiating data.

(f) **Storage Racks in Buildings.** Storage racks located in buildings at levels above the ground level, rack buildings or racks which depend upon attachments to buildings or other structures at other than the floor level for their lateral stability, shall be designed to resist earthquake forces that consider the responses of the building and storage rack to earthquake ground motions as specified in Uniform Building Code Chapter 23, Part III.

(g) **Other Considerations.** 1. **Overturning.** In determining overturning moments, the total weight shall be assumed to act at a height equal to 1.15 times the distance from the floor to the actual center of gravity of all the horizontal forces.

Equal safety against an overturning moment shall be provided when only the top level of the rack is loaded, in which case it is to be assumed that the force acts through the center of gravity of the top load. The safety factor against overturning of the rack by earthquake loads shall be no less than 1.5.

2. **Torsional forces.** Torsional forces shall be considered based on the critical combination of loaded and unloaded storage spaces.

3. **Concurrent forces.** Forces described in Section 27.1107 (c) 2, (c) 3, and (d), need not be assumed to act concurrently with earthquake loads.

Special Rack Design Provisions

Sec. 27.1108. (a) **Stability of Truss-braced Upright Frames.** The maximum allowable compression stress in the posts of truss-braced upright frames shall be determined from U.B.C. Standard No. 27-9 or Chapter 27 of the Uniform Building Code.

(b) **Overturning and Height-to-Depth Ratio.** The safety factor against overturning of the entire rack shall be no less than 1.5. Overturning shall be based on the critical combination of vertical and horizontal loads. Stabilizing forces provided by anchor bolts to the floor shall not be considered to resist overturning unless the anchors are specifically designed and installed to resist the uplift forces. Section 27.1107 (d) and (g) shall be considered in the design.

The height-to-depth ratio of a storage rack shall not exceed 6 to 1 measuring to the top of the topmost load unless the rack is anchored or braced externally.

(c) **Connections to Buildings.** Connections of racks to buildings, if any, shall be designed and installed to prevent reactions or displacements of the buildings or racks from damaging one another. Section 27.1101 (e) shall be considered.

UNIFORM BUILDING CODE STANDARD NO. 27-12

STRUCTURAL APPLICATIONS OF STEEL CABLES FOR BUILDINGS

Based on the Criteria for Structural Applications of Steel Cables for Buildings, 1973 Edition, and Standard Specifications A 586-68 (1976), A 603-70 (1974) and B 6-70 of the American Society for Testing and Materials. Extracted, with permission, from the Annual Book of ASTM Standards, copyright American Society for Testing and Materials, 1916 Race Street, Philadelphia, PA 19103.

See Sections 2701 (a) and 2708, Uniform Building Code

Scope

Sec. 27.1201. This standard is intended to provide for the design, fabrication and erection of cables used as load-carrying members in building structures or parts thereof.

Material

Sec. 27.1202. (a) **Cables.** Cable shall be either zinc-coated steel structural strand, zinc-coated steel structural wire rope or equivalent.

(b) **Poured Zinc Fittings.** Zinc used for attaching fittings shall be at least equal to the grade designated as "high grade."

Load Combinations for Selection of Cables

Sec. 27.1203. The effective design breaking strength of the cable shall be equal to or greater than the largest value produced by the following cable tension conditions:

(a) $2.2\ T_1$
(b) $1.6\ T_1 + 2.7\ T_2$
(c) $2.2\ T_3$
(d) $2.0\ T_4$
(e) $2.0\ T_5$
(f) $2.0\ T_6$

WHERE:

T_1 = Net tension in cable due to dead load and prestress.

T_2 = Change in cable tension due to the application of live load.

T_3 = Net tension in cable due to dead load, prestress and live load.

T_4 = Net tension in cable due to dead load, prestress, live load and wind or earthquake.

T_5 = Net tension in cable during erection of the structure.

T_6 = Net tension in cable due to dead load, prestress and wind.

Design Considerations

Sec. 27.1204. The design and analysis shall be based on the following considerations, in addition to those mentioned elsewhere in this standard.

(a) The effective design breaking strength shall be equal to the specified minimum breaking strength, except that when saddles are used the effective design breaking strength shall be reduced as follows:

RATIO OF SADDLE RADIUS TO STRAND DIAMETER	RATIO OF SADDLE RADIUS TO WIRE ROPE DIAMETER	EFFECTIVE DESIGN BREAKING STRENGTH AS PERCENT OF SPECIFIED MINIMUM BREAKING STRENGTH
20 and over	15 and over	100
19	14	95
18	13	90
17	12	85
16	11	80
15 minimum	10 minimum	75

(b) Cables shall be assumed to have no resistance to bending.

(c) Elastic stretch of the cables and deformation of the supporting structure shall be taken into account in the design.

(d) Displacement resulting from changes in magnitude and position of the load and its effects on cable stresses shall be considered.

Deflections

Sec. 27.1205. Cables supporting floors and roofs shall be proportioned with due regard to the deflection produced by the design loads.

Cables supporting floors and roofs shall be so proportioned that the maximum deflection under the combined action of applied loads and cable stretch will not damage the supported structure of finishes.

End Fittings, Saddles and Clamps

Sec. 27.1206. (a) **End Fittings.** In general, end fittings for anchored cables shall be designed and attached to develop the breaking strength of the cables.

End fittings shall be so positioned that visual inspection of the fittings and wire rope near the fittings can be accomplished. Such an arrangement shall not provide a collection point for dirt, moisture or other corrosive agents.

(b) **Saddles.** Saddles shall be designed with due consideration of bearing pressures, bend radii and groove diameters. All surfaces in contact with cables shall be smooth. The ends of grooves shall be contoured to avoid excessive bending and/or chafing of the cable.

(c) **Clamps.** Clamps shall be designed with due consideration of bearing pressures, deflection angles, holding power and groove diameters. All surfaces in contact with cables shall be smooth. All edges that contact the cable shall be sufficiently rounded to suit all conditions of design and erection.

Protective Coatings

Sec. 27.1207. Unless environmental conditions warrant the use of coating with other types of materials, or leaving the cables uncoated, cables shall have protection at least equivalent to Class A zinc coating on all wires as specified in Section 27.1202 (a).

Fabrication

Sec. 27.1208. (a) **General.** Cables for building structures shall be fabricated in accordance with the best current practice.

(b) **Splices.** Splicing of finished cables between end fittings shall not be permitted.

(c) **Prestretching.** Cables shall be fabricated to achieve the minimum values for the modulus of elasticity specified by the designer.

(d) **Cable Length Measurements.** Length measurements shall be made under loadings specified by the designer.

(e) **Striping.** Cables shall be longitudinally striped while under the specified loadings established for length measurement.

Erection

Sec. 27.1209. (a) **Bracing.** Temporary bracing shall be introduced wherever necessary to accommodate all loads to which the structure may be subjected during construction, including erection equipment and the operation of same. Such bracing shall be left in place as long as may be required for safety.

(b) **Adequacy of Temporary Connections.** As erection progresses, temporary connections shall be adequate for the most severe combinations of loads that may be encountered.

(c) **Cable Installation.** Care shall be exercised during erection to avoid damaging the cables and their coatings.

Each cable shall be positioned such that the relative turns from one end socket to the other end socket (external turns) are a maximum of 10 degrees. This will establish the theoretical position of the longitudinal stripe line as the line from striped end socket to striped end socket. At any cross section between sockets, the maximum turns of a point on the actual stripe line relative to a point on the theoretical position of the stripe line shall be ± 90 degrees (internal turns).

Fittings fastened to intermediate points along the cable shall be fastened to the cable in a position within a 10-degree turn from the actual stripe line. A positive twist may be induced in the cable as the fitting is positioned to the structure.

(d) **Intermediate Fittings.** Intermediate fittings shall be designed and attached in a manner to prevent damage to the cable.

(e) **Permanent Fittings Attached in the Field.** When permanent fittings are attached to cables in the field, the work shall be performed in accordance with the suggestions of the cable manufacturer.

Each cable shall be positioned [illegible].

UNIFORM BUILDING CODE STANDARD NO. 27-13
WELDING SHEET STEEL

See Sections 2701 (a) and 2708, Uniform Building Code, and Uniform Building Code Standard No. 27-6

Adoption of AWS Code

Sec. 27.1301. Except for the limitations, deletions, modifications or amendments set forth in Section 27.1302 of this standard, the arc welding of sheet steels or strip steels, or both, including cold-formed members 0.180 inch or less in thickness shall be in accordance with the Structural Welding Code—Sheet Steel, ANSI/AWS D1.3-81, published by the American Welding Society, Inc., copyright 1982, 550 North LeJeune Road, Miami, Florida 33126, as if set out at length herein.

Deletion and Amendments

Sec. 27.1302. (a) **General.** The American Welding Society, Inc., Code adopted by Section 27.1301 applies to the materials, processes, design, workmanship and testing of arc welding of sheet steels or strip steels, or both, including cold formed members, 0.180 inch or less in thickness, except as set forth in this section.

(b) **Deletions.** The following sections and chapters are deleted:

Section 1.5
Section 1.6
Section
Section 4.1.2
Chapter 7

(c) **Amendments**

1. **Sec. 1.1.1.** is amended to read as follows:

   1.1.1 This standard is applicable to the arc welding of sheet steels or strip steels, or both, including cold-formed members, 0.180 inch or less in thickness. Such welding may involve connections of sheet steel or strip steel, or both, to thicker supporting structural members. When sheet steel is welded to primary structural members, the provisions of U.B.C. Standard No. 27-6 shall also apply (e.g., adequate preheat, low-hydrogen electrodes, etc.)

2. **Sec. 1.1.6** is amended to read as follows:

   1.1.6 All references to the need for approval shall be interpreted to mean approval by the building official. Hereinafter, the term "engineer" will be used, and it is to be construed to mean the building official.

3. **Sec. 1.2.1** is amended by changing the reference to the Structual Welding Code, AWS D1.1. in the last sentence to U.B.C. Standard No. 27-6.

4. **Sec. 1.3.2** is amended by changing the reference to the Structural Welding Code, AWS D1.1 to U.B.C. Standard No. 27-6.

5. **Sec. 1.4** is amended to read as follows:

   1.4 Definitions The welding terms used in this specification shall be interpreted in accordance with definitions given in Appendix C of this specification.

6. **Sec. 2.1** is amended to read as follows:

   2.1 Base Metal Stresses. The allowable base metal stresses shall be those specified in U.B.C. Standard No. 27-9.

7. **Sec. 5.5** is amended by changing the reference to the Structual Welding Code, AWS D1.1 to U.B.C. Standard No. 27-6.

8. **Sec. 6.4** is amended by changing the reference to the Structural Welding Code, AWS D1.1 to U.B.C. Standard No. 27-6.
9. **Sec. 6.7.6** is amended by changing the reference to the Structural Welding Code, AWS D1.1 to U.B.C. Standard No. 27-6.

UNIFORM BUILDING CODE STANDARD NO. 27-14

LOAD AND RESISTANCE FACTOR DESIGN FOR STRUCTURAL STEEL BUILDINGS

Based on Load and Resistance Factor Design Specification for Structural Steel Buildings of the American Institute of Steel Construction, Inc.

(September 1, 1986, with Supplement No. 1, January 1, 1989)

See Sections 2701 (a) and 2702, Uniform Building Code

Part I of this standard contains the exceptions to the referenced specification. Part II of this standard is "Load and Resistance Factor Design Specification for Structural Steel Buildings" and Supplement No. 1 reproduced with permission of the publisher.

Part I

Scope

Sec. 27.1401. The American Institute of Steel Construction specification adopted by this standard applies to the design, fabrication, erection and quality control of structural steel except as modified by this part. Where other codes, standards or specifications are referred to in this standard, they are to be considered as only an indication of an acceptable method or material that can be used with the approval of the building official.

1. Appendices. Appendices Sections B5 Local Buckling, E3 Columns and Other Compression Members, F1 Design for Flexure, F4 Web-tapered Members, G Plate Girders, H3 Members under Torsion and Combined Forces, K2 Ponding and K4 Fatigue are specifically adopted and made a part of this standard.

2. Sec. A1 is amended as follows:

This standard is intended as an alternative to U.B.C. Standard No. 27-15.

3. Sec. A2.1 is amended by changing the last sentence as follows:

For the design of cold-formed steel structural members, which profiles contain rounded corners and slender flat elements, the provisions of U.B.C. Standards Nos. 27-9 and 27-16 shall apply. (**Note:** If the proposed U.B.C. Standard No. 27-16, based on AISI "Load and Resistance Factor Design for Cold-formed Steel Structural Members," is adopted, this cross-reference should be added.)

4. Sec. A4 is amended as follows:

The nominal loads shall be the minimum design loads required by the code, and the load combinations shall be as specified in Section A4.1.

5. Sec. A6 is amended further by substituting "U.B.C. Standard No. 27-6" for "American Welding Society Standard D1.1."

Sec. A6 is amended further by substituting "U.B.C. Standard No. 27- 7" for Research Council for Structural Connections "Specifications for Structural Joints Using ASTM A 325 or A 490 Bolts."

TABLE OF CONTENTS

B7. Limiting Slenderness Ratios

Sec. 27.1403C. FRAME AND OTHER STRUCTURES

C1. Second Order Effects

C2. Frame Stability

1. Braced Frames
2. Unbraced Frames

Sec. 27.1403D. TENSION MEMBERS

D1. Design Tensile Strength

D2. Built-up Members

D3. Eyebars and Pin-connected Members

Sec. 27.1403E. COLUMNS AND OTHER COMPRESSION MEMBERS

E1. Effective Length and Slenderness Limitations

1. Effective Length
2. Plastic Analysis

E2. Design Compressive Strength

E3. Flexural-torsional Buckling

E4. Built-up Members

E5. Pin-connected Compression Members

Sec. 27.1403F. BEAMS AND OTHER FLEXURAL MEMBERS

F1. Design for Flexure

1. Unbraced Length for Plastic Analysis
2. Flexural Design Strength
3. Compact Section Members with $L_b \leq L_r$
4. Compact Section Members with $L_b > L_r$
5. Tees and Double-angle Beams
6. Noncompact Plate Grinders
7. Nominal Flexural Strength of Other Sections

F2. Design for Shear

1. Web Area Determination
2. Design Shear Strength

F3. Transverse Stiffeners

F4. Web-tapered Members (see Appendix F4)

Sec. 27.1403G. PLATE GIRDERS

Sec. 27.1403H. MEMBERS UNDER TORSION AND COMBINED FORCES

H1. Symmetric Members Subject to Bending and Axial Force

1. Doubly and Singly Symmetric Members in Flexure and Tension
2. Doubly and Singly Symmetric Members in Flexure and Compression

5. Sidesway Web Buckling
6. Compression Buckling of the Web
7. Compression Members with Web Panels Subject to High Shear
8. Stiffener Requirements for Concentrated Loads

K2. Ponding

K3. Torsion

K4. Fatigue

Sec. 27.1403L. SERVICEABILITY DESIGN CONSIDERATIONS

L1. Camber

L2. Expansion and Contraction

L3. Deflections, Vibration and Drift

1. Deflections
2. Vibration
3. Drift

L4. Connection Slip (see Section J3.5)

L5. Corrosion

Sec. 27.1403M. FABRICATION, ERECTION AND QUALITY CONTROL

M1. Shop Drawings

M2. Fabrication

1. Cambering, Curving and Straightening
2. Thermal Cutting
3. Planning of Edges
4. Welded Construction
5. Bolted Construction
6. Compression Joints
7. Dimensional Tolerances
8. Finishing of Column Bases

M3. Shop Painting

1. General Requirements
2. Inaccessible Surfaces
3. Contact Surfaces
4. Finished Surfaces
5. Surfaces Adjacent to Field Welds

M4. Erection

1. Alignment of Column Bases
2. Bracing
3. Alignment
4. Fit of Column Compression Joints
5. Field Welding
6. Field Painting
7. Field Connections

NOMENCLATURE

Sec. 27.1402. The section number in parentheses after the definition of a symbol refers to the section where the symbol is first defined.

A	Cross-sectional area, in.^{2} (F1.3)
A_B	Loaded area of concrete, in.^{2} (I2.4)
A_b	Nominal body area of a fastener, in. (J3.4)
A_b	Area of an upset rod based on the major diameter of its threads (J3.3)
A_c	Area of concrete, in. (I2.2)
A_c	Area of concrete slab within effective width (I5.2)
A_e	Effective net area, in.^{2} (I2.2)
A_f	Area of flange, in. (Appendix F4)
A_g	Gross area, in.^{2} (B1)
A_n	Net area, in.^{2} (B2)
A_{ns}	Net area subject to shear, in.^{2} (J4)
A_{pb}	Projected bearing area, in.^{2} (D3, J8.1)
A_r	Area of reinforcing bars, in.^{2} (I2.2)
A_s	Area of steel cross section, in.^{2} (I2.2, I5.2)
A_{sc}	Cross-sectional area of stud shear connector, in.^{2} (I5.3)
A_{sf}	Shear area on the failure path, in.^{2} (D3)
A_w	Web area, in.^{2} (F2.1)
A_1	Area of steel bearing concentrically on a concrete support, in.^{2} (J9)
A_2	Total cross-sectional area of a concrete support, in.^{2} (J9)
B	Factor for bending stress in web-tapered members, in., defined by Formulas A-F4-7 through A-F4-10 (Appendix F4)
B_1,B_2	Factors used in determining M_u for combined bending and axial forces when first order analysis is employed (H1)
C_b	Bending coefficient dependent on moment gradient (F1.3)
C_m	Coefficient applied to bending term in interaction formula for prismatic members and dependent on column curvature caused by applied moments (H1)
C'_m	Coefficient applied to bending term in interaction formula for tapered members and dependent on axial stress at the small end of the member (Appendix F4)
C_p	Ponding flexibility coefficient for primary member in a flat roof (K2)
C_{PG}	Plate girder coefficient (Appendix G2)
C_s	Ponding flexibility coefficient for secondary member in a flat roof (K2)
C_v	Ratio of "critical" web stress, according to linear buckling theory, to the shear yield stress of web material (Appendix G4)
C_w	Warping constant, in.^{6} (F1.3)
D	Outside diameter of circular hollow section, in. (Appendix B5.3)

D	Dead load due to the self-weight of the structural and permanent elements on the structure (A4.1)
D	Factor used in Formula A-G4-2, dependent on the type of transverse stiffeners used in a plate girder (Appendix G4)
E	Modulus of elasticity of steel (29,000 ksi) (E2)
E	Earthquake load (A4.1)
E_c	Modulus of elasticity of concrete, ksi (I2.2)
E_m	Modified modulus of elasticity, ksi (I2.2)
F_{BM}	Nominal strength of the base material to be welded, ksi (J2.4)
F_{EXX}	Classification strength of weld metal, ksi (A3.5 and J2.4)
F_a	Axial design strength, ksi (A5.1)
F_b	Flexural stress for tapered members defined by Formulas A-F4-4 and A-F4-5 (Appendix F4)
F_{cr}	Critical stress, ksi (E2)
F_e	Elastic buckling stress, ksi (Appendix E3)
F_{ex}	Elastic flexural buckling stress about the major axis, ksi (Appendix E3)
F_{ey}	Elastic flexural buckling stress about the minor axis, ksi (Appendix E3)
F_{ez}	Elastic torsional buckling stress about the major axis, ksi (Appendix E3)
F_{my}	Modified yield stress for composite columns, ksi (I2.2)
F_n	Nominal shear rupture strength, ksi (J4)
F_r	Compressive residual stress in flange, ksi (F1.3)
$F_{s\gamma}$	Stress for tapered members defined by Formula A-F4-4 (Appendix F4)
F_u	Specified minimum tensile strength of the type of steel being used, ksi (D1)
F_w	Nominal strength of the weld electrode material, ksi (J2.4)
$F_{w\gamma}$	Stress for tapered members defined by Formula A-F4-7, ksi (J2.4)
F_y	Specified minimum yield stress of the type of steel being used, ksi. As used in this specification, "yield stress" denotes either the specified minimum yield point (for those steels that have a yield point) or specified yield strength (for those steels that do not have a yield point)
F_{yf}	Specified minimum yield stress of the flange, ksi (B5.1)
F_{ym}	Yield stress obtained from mill test reports or from physical tests, ksi (N2)
F_{yr}	Specified minimum yield stress of reinforcing bars, ksi (I2.2)
F_{ys}	Static yield stress, ksi (N2)
F_{yst}	Specified minimum yield stress of the stiffener material, ksi (Appendix G4)
F_{yw}	Specified minimum yield stress of the web, ksi (F2.2)
G	Shear modulus of elasticity of steel, ksi (G = 11,200) (F1.3)
H	Horizontal force, kips (H1.2)

H_s	Length of stud connector after welding, in. (I3.5)
I	Moment of inertia, in.4
I_d	Moment of inertia of the steel deck supported on secondary members, in.^{4} (K2)
I_p	Moment of inertia of primary members, in.^{4} (K2)
I_s	Moment of inertia of secondary members, in.^{4} (K2)
I_{st}	Moment of inertia of a transverse stiffener, in.^{4} (Appendix G4)
J	Torsional constant for a section, in.^{4} (F1.3)
K	Effective length factor for prismatic member (C2)
K_s	Slip coefficient (J3)
K_z	Effective length factor for torsional buckling (Appendix E3)
$K\gamma$	Effective length factor for a tapered member (Appendix F4.3)
L	Unbraced length of member measured between the center of gravity of the bracing members, in. (E2)
L	Story height, in. (H1.2)
L	Distance in line of force from center of a standard or oversized hole or from the center of the end of a slotted hole to an edge of a connected part, in. (J3.6)
L	Live load due to occupancy (A4.1)
L_b	Laterally unbraced length; length between points which are either braced against lateral displacement of compression flange or braced against twist of the cross section, in. (F1.1)
L_c	Length of channel shear connector, in. (I5.4)
L_p	Limiting laterally unbraced length for full plastic bending capacity, uniform moment case (C_b = 1.0), in. (F1.3)
L_p	Column spacing in direction of girder, in. (K2)
L_{pd}	Limiting laterally unbraced length for plastic analysis, in. (F1.1)
L_r	Limiting laterally unbraced length for inelastic lateral-torsional buckling, in. (F1.3)
L_r	Roof live load (A4.1)
L_s	Column spacing perpendicular to direction of girder, in. (K2)
M_1	Smaller moment at end of unbraced length of beam or beam-column, kip-in. (F1.1)
M_2	Larger moment at end of unbraced length of beam or beam-column, kip-in. (F1.3)
M_{cr}	Elastic buckling moment, kip-in. (F1.4)
M_{lt}	Required flexural strength in member due to lateral frame translation, kip-in. (H1)
M_n	Nominal flexural strength, kip-in. (F1.2)
M'_{nx}, M_{ny}	Flexural strength defined in Formulas A-H3-7 and A-H3-8 for use in alternate interaction equations for combined bending and axial force, kip-in. (Appendix H3)

M_{nt}	Required flexural strength in member assuming there is no lateral translation of the frame, kip-in. (H1)
M_p	Plastic bending moment, kip-in. (F1.1)
M'_p	Moment defined in Formulas A-H3-5 and A-H3-6, for use in alternate interaction equations for combined bending and axial force, kip-in. (Appendix H3)
M_r	Limiting buckling moment, M_{cr}, when $\lambda = \lambda_r$ and $C_b = 1.0$, kip-in. (F1.3)
M_u	Required flexural strength, kip-in. (H1)
N	Length of bearing, in. (K1.3)
N_r	Number of stud connectors in one rib at a beam intersection (I3.5)
P	Force transmitted by one fastener to the critical connected part, kips (J3.9)
P_e	Euler buckling strength, kips (H1)
P_e	Elastic buckling load, kips (I4)
P_n	Nominal axial strength (tension or compression), kips (D1)
P_p	Bearing load on concrete, kips (J9)
P_u	Required axial strength (tension or compression), kips (H1)
P_y	Yield strength, kips (B5.1)
Q	Full reduction factor for slender compression elements (Appendix E3)
Q_a	Reduction factor for slender stiffened compression elements (Appendix B5)
Q_n	Nominal strength of one stud shear connector, kips (I5)
Q_s	Reduction factor for slender unstiffened compression elements (Appendix B5.3)
R	Nominal load due to initial rainwater or ice exclusive of the ponding contribution (A4.1)
R_{PG}	Plate girder bending strength-reduction factor (Appendix G)
R_e	Hybrid girder factor (Appendix F1.7)
R_n	Nominal resistance (A5.3)
R_v	Web shear strength, kips (K1.7)
S	Elastic section modulus, in.^{3}
S	Spacing of secondary members, in. (K2)
S	Snow load (A4.1)
S'_x	Elastic section modulus of larger end of tapered member about its major axis, in.^{3} (Appendix F4)
$(Sx)_{eff}$	Effective section modulus about major axis, in.^{3} (Appendix F1.7)
S_{xt},S_{xc}	Elastic section modulus referred to tension and compression flanges, respectively, in.^{3} (Appendix G2)
T	Required tension force, kips (J3.5)

T	Factored applied tension force per bolt, kips (J3.5)
T_b	Specified pretension load in high-strength bolt, kips (J3.5)
U	Reduction coefficient, used in calculating effective net area (B3)
V	Shear force, kips (J10.2)
V_n	Nominal shear strength, kips (F2.2)
V_u	Required shear strength, kips (Appendix G4)
W	Wind load (A4.1)
X_1	Beam buckling factor defined by Formula F1-8 (F1.3)
X_2	Beam buckling factor defined by Formula F1-9 (F1.3)
Z	Plastic section modulus, in.^{3}
a	Clear distance between transverse stiffeners, in. (F2.2)
a	Distance between connectors in a built-up member, in. (E4)
a	Shortest distance from edge of pin hole to edge of member measured parallel to direction of force, in. (D3)
a_r	Ratio of web area to compression flange area (Appendix G2)
b	Compression element width (Table B5.1)
b_e	Reduced effective width for slender compression elements, in. (Appendix B5.3)
b_{eff}	Effective edge distance, in. (D3)
b_f	Flange width, in. (K1.5)
c_1,c_2,c_3	Numerical coefficients (I2.2)
d	Nominal fastener diameter, in. (J3.6)
d	Overall depth of member, in. (F2.1)
d	Pin diameter, in. (D3)
d	Roller diameter, in. (J8.2)
d_L	Depth at larger end of unbraced tapered segment, in. (Appendix F4)
d_c	Web depth clear of fillets, in. (K1.5)
d_h	Diameter of a standard size hole, in. (J3.9)
d_o	Depth at smaller end of unbraced tapered segment, in. (Appendix F4)
e	Base of natural logarithm = 2.71828. . .
f	Computed compressive stress in the stiffened element, ksi (Appendix B5.3)
f_a	Computed axial stress in column, ksi (A5.1)
f_{b1}	Smallest computed bending stress at one end of a tapered segment, ksi (Appendix F4)
f_{b2}	Largest computed bending stress at one end of a tapered segment, ksi (Appendix F4)
f'_c	Specified compressive strength of concrete, ksi (I2.2)
f_o	Stress due to $1.2D + 1.2R$, ksi (Appendix K2)
f_t	Computed tension stress in bolts or rivets, ksi (J3.4)

f_{un}	Required normal stress, ksi (H2)
f_{uv}	Required shear stress, ksi (H2)
f_v	Computed shear stress in bolts or rivets, ksi (J3.4)
g	Transverse center-to-center spacing (gage) between fastener gage lines, in. (B2)
g	Acceleration due to gravity = 32.2 ft./sec.^{2} (A4.3)
h	Clear distance between flanges less the fillet or corner radius for rolled shapes; and for built-up sections, the distance between adjacent lines of fasteners or the clear distance between flanges when welds are used, in. (B5.1)
h_c	Assumed web depth for stability, in. (B5.1)
h_r	Nominal rib height, in. (I3.5)
h_s	Factor used in Formula A-F4-6 for web-tapered members (Appendix F4.3)
h_w	Factor used in Formula A-F4-7 for web-tapered members (Appendix F4.3)
j	Factor defined by Formula F3-1 for minimum moment of inertia for a transverse stiffener (F3)
k	Web plate buckling coefficient (F2.2)
k	Distance from outer face of flange to web toe of fillet, in. (K1.3)
l	Largest laterally unbraced length along either flange at the point of load, in. (K1.5)
l	Length of bearing, in. (J8.2)
m	Ratio of web to flange yield stress or critical stress in hybrid beams (Appendix G2)
r	Governing radius of gyration, in. (E2)
r_i	Minimum radius of gyration of individual component in a built-up member, in. (E4)
r_T	Radius of gyration of compression flange plus one third of the compression portion of the web taken about an axis in the plane of the web, in. (Appendix F1.7)
r_{To}	Radius of gyration, r_T, for the smaller end of a tapered member, in. (Appendix F4.3)
r_m	Radius of gyration of the steel shape, pipe or tubing in composite columns. For steel shapes it may not be less than 0.3 times the overall thickness of the composite section, in. (I2)
$\bar{r}_o$	Polar radius of gyration about the shear center, in. (Appendix E3)
r_{ox}, r_{oy}	Radius of gyration about x and y axes at the smaller end of a tapered member, respectively, in. (Appendix F4.3)
r_x, r_y	Radius of gyration about x and y axes, respectively, in. (F1.1, E3)
s	Longitudinal center-to-center spacing (pitch) of any two consecutive holes, in. (B2)

t	Thickness of connected part, in. (J3.6)
t	Thickness of the critical part, in. (J3.9)
t_f	Flange thickness, in. (B5.1)
t_f	Flange thickness of channel shear connector, in. (I5.4)
t_w	Web thickness of channel shear connector, in. (I5.4)
t_w	Web thickness, in. (F2.1)
w	Plate width; distance between welds, in. (B3)
w	Unit weight of concrete, lbs./cu. ft. (I2)
w_r	Average width of concrete rib or haunch, in. (I3.5)
x	Subscript relating symbol to strong axis bending
x_o, y_o	Coordinates of the shear center with respect to the centroid, in. (Appendix E3)
y	Subscript relating symbol to weak axis bending
z	Distance from the smaller end of tapered member used in Formula A-F4-1 for the variation in depth, in. (Appendix F4)
Δ_{oh}	Translation deflection of the story under consideration, in. (H1)
γ	Depth tapering ratio (Appendix F4) Subscript for tapered members (Appendix F4)
ζ	Exponent for alternate beam-column interaction equation (Appendix H3)
η	Exponent for alternate beam-column interaction equation (Appendix H3)
λ_c	Column slenderness parameter (E2)
λ_e	Equivalent slenderness parameter (Appendix E3)
λ_{eff}	Effective slenderness ratio defined by Formula A-F4-2 (Appendix F4)
λ_p	Limiting slenderness parameter for compact element (B5.1)
λ_r	Limiting slenderness parameter for noncompact element (B5.1)
μ	Coefficient of friction (J10.2)
ϕ	Resistance factor (A5.3)
ϕ_b	Resistance factor for flexure (B1)
ϕ_c	Resistance factor for compression (E2)
ϕ_c	Resistance factor for axially loaded composite columns (I2.2)
ϕ_{sf}	Resistance factor for shear on the failure path (D3)
ϕ_t	Resistance factor for tension (D1)
ϕ_v	Resistance factor for shear (F2.2)

CHAPTER A

GENERAL PROVISIONS

Sec. 27.1403A.

A1. SCOPE

Modified per Part I.

This standard is intended as an alternative to U.B.C. Standard No. 27-15.

A2. LIMITS OF APPLICABILITY

1. Structural Steel Defined. Modified per Part I.

As used in this Specification, the term *structural steel* refers to the steel elements of the structural steel frame essential to the support of the design loads. Such elements are generally enumerated in Section 2.1 of the AISC *Code of Standard Practice for Steel Buildings and Bridges,* 1986. For the design of cold-formed steel structural members, which profiles contain rounded corners and slender flat elements, the provisions of U.B.C. Standard No. 27-9 shall apply.

2. Types of Construction. Two basic types of construction and associated design assumptions are permissible under the conditions stated herein, and each will govern in a specific manner the size of members and the types and strength of their connections. Both types must comply with the stability requirements of Section B4.

Type FR (fully restrained), commonly designated as "rigid-frame" (continuous frame), assumes that beam-to-column connections have sufficient rigidity to hold the original angles between intersecting members virtually unchanged.

Type PR (partially restrained) assumes that the connections of beams and girders possess an insufficient rigidity to hold the original angles between intersecting members virtually unchanged.

The design of all connections shall be consistent with assumptions as to type of construction called for on the design drawings.

The FR construction is permitted under the LRFD Specification.

The use of Type PR construction under this Specification depends on the evidence of predictable proportion of full end restraint. Where the connection restraint is ignored, commonly designated "simple framing," it is assumed that under gravity loads the ends of the beams and girders are connected for shear only and are free to rotate. For "simple framing" the following requirements apply:

a. The connections and connected members must be adequate to carry the factored gravity loads as "simple beams."

b. The connections and connected members shall be adequate to resist the factored lateral loads.

c. The connections shall have sufficient inelastic rotation capacity to avoid overload of fasteners or welds under combined factored gravity and lateral loading.

When the rotational restraint of the connections is used in the design of the connected members or for the stability of the structure as a whole, the capacity of the connection for such restraint shall be established by analytical or empirical means.

Type PR construction may necessitate some inelastic, but self-limiting, deformation of a structural steel part.

A3. MATERIAL

1. Structural Steel. Material conforming to one of the following standard specifications is approved for use under this Specification:

A36, A53 Grade B, A242, A441, A500, A501, A514, A529, A570 Grades 40, 45 and 50, A572, A588, A606, A607 and A618.

Certified mill test reports or certified reports of tests made by the fabricator or a testing laboratory in accordance with ASTM A6 or A568, as applicable, shall constitute sufficient evidence of conformity with one of the above ASTM standards. If requested, the fabricator shall provide an affidavit stating that the structural steel furnished meets the requirements of the grade specified.

Unidentified steel, if surface conditions are acceptable according to criteria contained in ASTM A6, may be used for unimportant members or details, where the precise physical properties and weldability of the steel would not affect the strength of the structure.

For A6 Group 4 and 5 rolled shapes to be used as members subject to primary tensile stresses due to tension or flexure, toughness need not be specified if splices are made by bolting. If such members are spliced using full penetration welds, the steel shall be specified in the contract document to be supplied with Charpy V-Notch testing in accordance with ASTM A6, Supplementary Requirement S5. The impact test shall meet a minimum average value of 20 ft-lbs. absorbed energy at + 70°F.

The above supplementary toughness requirements shall also be considered for welded full-penetration joints other than splices in heavy rolled and built-up members subject to primary tensile stresses.

Additional requirements for joints in heavy rolled and built-up members are given in Sections J1.10, J1.11, J2.7, J2.8 and M2.2.

2. Steel Castings and Forgings. Cast steel shall conform to one of the following standard specifications:

A27 Grade 65-25 and A148 Grade 80-50.

Steel forgings shall conform to the following standard specification:

A668.

Certified test reports shall constitute sufficient evidence of conformity with the standards.

3. Bolts. Steel bolts shall conform to one of the following standard specifications:

A307, A325, A449, A490, A563 and F436.

A449 bolts may be used only in connections requiring bolt diameters greater than $1^1/_2$ inches and shall not be used in slip-critical connections. A449 material is acceptable for high-strength anchor bolts and threaded rods of any diameter.

Manufacturer's certification shall constitute sufficient evidence of conformity with the standards.

4. Anchor Bolts and Threaded Rods. Anchor bolt and threaded rod steel shall conform to one of the following standard specifications:

A36, A354, A588, A687 and ANSI B18.1-72, Grade 2A tolerance.

Steel bolts conforming to other provisions of Section A3 may be used as anchor bolts.

Manufacturer's certification shall constitute sufficient evidence of conformity with the standards.

5. Filler Metal and Flux for Welding. Welding electrodes and fluxes shall conform to one of the following specifications of the American Welding Society.*

A5.1, A5.5, A5.17, A5.18, A5.20, A5.23, A5.28 and A5.29.

Manufacturer's certification shall constitute sufficient evidence of conformity with the standards.

6. Stud Shear Connectors. Steel stud shear connectors shall conform to the requirements of U.B.C. Standard No. 27-6.

Manufacturer's certification shall constitute sufficient evidence of conformity with the code.

A4. LOADS AND LOAD COMBINATIONS

Modified per Part I.

The nominal loads shall be the minimum design loads required by the code and the load combinations shall be as specified in Section A4.1.

1. Loads, Load Factors and Load Combinations. The following nominal loads are to be considered:

D = dead load due to the weight of the structural elements and the permanent features on the structure

L = live load due to occupancy and moveable equipment

L_r = roof live load

W = wind load

S = snow load

E = earthquake load

R = load due to initial rainwater or ice exclusive of the ponding contribution

The required strength of the structure and its elements must be determined from the appropriate critical combination of factored loads. The most critical effect may occur when one or more loads are not acting. The following load combinations and the corresponding load factors shall be investigated:

$$1.4D \quad \text{(A4-1)}$$

$$1.2D + 1.6L + 0.5(L_r \text{ or } S \text{ or } R) \quad \text{(A4-2)}$$

---

*Approval of these welding electrode specifications is given without regard to weld metal notch toughness requirements, which are generally not critical for building construction.

$$1.2D + 1.6(L_r \text{ or } S \text{ or } R) + (0.5L \text{ or } 0.8W) \quad \text{(A4-3)}$$

$$1.2D + 1.3W + 0.5L + 0.5(L \text{ or } S \text{ or } R) \quad \text{(A4-4)}$$

$$1.2D + 1.5E + (0.5L \text{ or } 0.2S) \quad \text{(A4-5)}$$

$$0.9D - (1.3W \text{ or } 1.5E) \quad \text{(A4-6)}$$

EXCEPTION: The load factor on L in combinations A4-3, A4-4 and A4-5 shall equal 1.0 for garages, areas occupied as places of public assembly and all areas where the live load is greater than 100 psf.

2. Impact. For structures carrying live loads which induce impact, the assumed nominal live load shall be increased to provide for this impact in Formulas (A4- 2) and A4-3.

If not otherwise specified, the increase shall be:

For supports of elevators and elevator machinery	100%
For supports of light machinery, shaft or motor driven, not less than	20%
For supports of reciprocating machinery or power driven units, not less than	50%
For hangers supporting floors and balconies	33%
For cab-operated traveling crane support girders and their connections	25%
For pendant-operated traveling crane support girders and their connections	10%

3. Crane Runway Horizontal Forces. The nominal lateral force on crane runways to provide for the effect of moving crane trolleys shall be a minimum of 20 percent of the sum of weights of the lifted load and of the crane trolley, but exclusive of other parts of the crane. The force shall be assumed to be applied at the top of the rails, acting in either direction normal to the runway rails, and shall be distributed with due regard for lateral stiffness of the structure supporting the rails.

The longitudinal force shall be a minimum of 10 percent of the maximum wheel loads of the crane applied at the top of the rail, unless otherwise specified.

A5. DESIGN BASIS

1. Required Strength at Factored Loads. The required strength of structural members and connections shall be determined by structural analysis for the appropriate factored load combinations given in Section A4.

Design by either elastic or plastic analysis is permitted, except that plastic analysis is permitted only for steels with yield stress not exceeding 65 ksi and is subject to provisions of Sections B5.2, C2, E1.2, F1.1, H1 and I1.

Except for hybrid girders and members of A514 steel, beams and girders (including members designed on the basis of composite action) which meet the requirements of the above, and are continuous over supports or are rigidly framed to columns by means of rivets, high-strength bolts, or welds, may be proportioned for $^9/_{10}$ of the negative moments produced by gravity loading which are maximum at points of support, provided that, for such members, the maximum positive moment shall be increased by $^1/_{10}$ of the average negative moments. This reduction shall not apply to moments produced by loading on cantilevers. If the negative moment is resisted by a column rigidly framed to the beam or girder, the $^1/_{10}$ reduction may be used in proportioning the column for the combined axial and bending loading, provided that the stress, f_a, due to any concurrent axial load on the member, does not exceed $0.15F_a$.

2. Limit States. LRFD is a method of proportioning structures so that no applicable limit state shall be exceeded when the structure is subjected to all appropriate factored load combinations.

Strength limit states are related to safety and concern maximum load carrying capacity. Serviceability limit states are related to performance under normal service conditions. The term "resistance" includes both strength limit states and serviceability limit states.

3. Design for Strength. The design strength of each structural component or assemblage shall equal or exceed the required strength based on the factored nominal loads. The design strength ϕR_n is calculated for each applicable limit state as the nominal strength R_n multiplied by a resistance factor ϕ. The required strength is determined for each applicable load combination as stipulated in Section A4.

Nominal strength R_n and resistance factors ϕ are given in the appropriate chapters. Additional strength considerations are given in Chapter K.

4. Design for Serviceability and Other Considerations. The overall structure and the individual members, connections and connectors should be checked for serviceability. Provisions for design for serviceability are given in Chapter L.

A6. REFERENCED CODES AND STANDARDS

Modified per Part I.

American National Standards Institute

B18.1-72

A58.1-82

American Society for Testing and Materials

A6-84c	A27-84	A36-84a
A53-84a	A148-84	A242-84
A307-84	A325-84	A354-84b
A441-84	A449-84a	A490-84
A500-84	A501-84	A514-84a
A529-84	A563-84	A570-84a
A572-84	A588-84a	A606-84
A607-84a	A618-84	A668-83
A687-84	C33-85	C330-85
F436-84		

American Welding Society

A5.1-81	A5.5-81	A5.17-80
A5.18-79	A5.20-79	A5.23-80
A5.28-79	A5.29-80	

International Conference of Building Officials
U.B.C. Standard No. 27-6
U.B.C. Standard No. 27-7

A7. DESIGN DOCUMENTS

1. Plans. The design plans shall show a complete design with sizes, sections and relative locations of the various members. Floor levels, column centers and offsets shall be dimensioned. Drawings shall be drawn to a scale large enough to show the information clearly.

Design documents shall indicate the type or types of construction as defined in Section A2.2 and include the nominal loads and design strengths if necessary for preparation of shop drawings.

Where joints are to be assembled with high-strength bolts, the design documents shall indicate the connection type (slip-critical, tension or bearing).

Camber of trusses, beams and girders, if required, shall be called for in the design documents. The requirements for stiffeners and bracing shall be shown on the design documents.

2. Standard Symbols and Nomenclature. Welding and inspection symbols used on plans and shop drawings shall preferably be the American Welding Society symbols. Other adequate welding symbols may be used, provided a complete explanation thereof is shown in the design documents.

3. Notation for Welding. Notes shall be made in the design documents and on the shop drawings of those joints or groups of joints in which the welding sequence and technique of welding should be carefully controlled to minimize distortion.

Weld lengths called for in the design documents and on the shop drawings shall be the net effective lengths.

CHAPTER B

DESIGN REQUIREMENTS

Sec. 27.1403B. This chapter contains provisions which are common to the Specification as a whole.

B1. GROSS AREA

The gross area A_g of a member at any point is the sum of the products of the thickness and the gross width of each element measured normal to the axis of the member. For angles, the gross width is the sum of the widths of the legs less the thickness.

Plate girders, coverplated beams and rolled or welded beams shall be proportioned on the basis of the gross section. No deduction shall be made for shop or field bolt holes in either flange, unless the reduction of the area of either flange by such holes calculated in accordance with the provisions of Section B2 exceeds 15 percent of the gross flange area, in which case the area in excess of 15 percent shall be deducted.

Hybrid girders may be proportioned on the basis of their gross section, provided that they are not required to resist an axial force greater than ϕ_b times $0.15 A_g F_{yf}$. No limit is placed on the flexural stress in the web.

Flanges of welded plate girders may be varied in thickness or width by splicing plates or by using cover plates.

B2. NET AREA

The net area A_n of a member is the sum of the products of the thickness and the net width of each element computed as follows:

In computing net area for tension, the width of a bolt hole shall be taken as $^1/_{16}$-inch greater than the nominal dimension of the hole normal to the direction of applied stress. For shear, the width shall be taken as the nominal dimension of the hole.

For a chain of holes extending across a part in any diagonal or zigzag line, the net width of the part shall be obtained by deducting from the gross width the sum of the diameters or slot dimensions as provided in Section J3.7 of all holes in the chain, and adding, for each gage space in the chain, the quantity $s^2/4_g$

WHERE:

s = longitudinal center-to-center spacing (pitch) of any two consecutive holes, in.

g = transverse center-to-center spacing (gage) between fastener gage lines, in.

For angles, the gage for holes in opposite adjacent legs shall be the sum of the gages from the back of the angles less the thickness.

The critical net area A_n of the part is obtained from that chain which gives the least net width.

In determining the net area across plug or slot welds, the weld metal shall not be considered as adding to the net area.

B3. EFFECTIVE NET AREA

When the load is transmitted directly to each of the cross-sectional elements by connectors, the effective net area A_e is equal to the net area A_n.

When the load is transmitted by bolts or rivets through some, but not all, of the cross-sectional elements of the member, the effective net area A_e shall be computed as:

$$A_e = U A_n \quad \text{(B3-1)}$$

WHERE:

A_n = net area of the member, in.^{2}

U = reduction coefficient

When the load is transmitted by welds through some, but not all, of the cross-sectional elements of the member, the effective net area A_e shall be computed as:

$$A_e = U A_g \quad \text{(B3-2)}$$

WHERE:

A_g = gross area of member, in.^{2}

Unless a larger coefficient can be justified by tests or other rational criteria, the following values of U shall be used:

a. W, M or S shapes with flange widths not less than two thirds the depth, and structural tees cut from these shapes, provided the connection is to the flanges. Bolted or riveted connections shall have no fewer than three fasteners per line in the direction of stress . . . . $U = 0.90$

b. W, M or S shapes not meeting the conditions of Subparagraph a, structural tees cut from these shapes and all other shapes, including built-up cross sections. Bolted or riveted connections shall have no fewer than three fasteners per line in the direction of stress . . . . $U = 0.85$

c. All members with bolted or riveted connections having only two fasteners per line in the direction of stress . . . . $U = 0.75$

When load is transmitted by transverse welds to some, but not all, of the cross-sectional elements of W, M or S shapes and structural tees cut from these shapes, A_e shall be taken as the area of the directly connected elements.

When the load is transmitted to a plate by longitudinal welds along both edges at the end of the plate, the length of the welds shall not be less than the width of the plate. The effective net area A_e shall be computed as:

$$A_e = U A_g \tag{B3-2}$$

Unless a larger coefficient can be justified by tests or other rational criteria, the following values of U shall be used:

a. When $l > 2w$ . . . . $U = 1.0$

b. When $2w > l > 1.5w$ . . . . $U = 0.87$

c. When $1.5w > lw$ . . . . $U = 0.75$

WHERE:

l = weld length, in.

w = plate width (distance between welds), in.

B4. STABILITY

General stability shall be provided for the structure as a whole and for each compression element.

Consideration shall be given to significant load effects resulting from the deflected shape of the structure or of individual elements of the lateral load resisting system.

B5. LOCAL BUCKLING

1. Classification of Steel Sections. Steel sections are classified as compact, noncompact and slender element sections. For a section to qualify as compact, its flanges shall be continuously connected to the web or webs and the width-thickness ratios of its compression elements must not exceed the limiting width-thickness ratios λ_p from Table B5.1. If the width-thickness ratio of one or more compression elements exceeds λ_p, but does not exceed λ_r, the section is noncompact. If the width-thickness ratio exceeds λ_r from Table B5.1, the element is referred to as a slender compression element.

For unstiffened elements which are supported along only one edge, parallel to the direction of the compression force, the width shall be taken as follows:

a. For flanges of I-shaped members and tees, the width b is half the full nominal width.

b. For legs of angles and flanges of channels and tees, the width b is the full nominal dimension.

c. For plates, the width b is the distance from the free edge to the first row of fasteners or line of welds.

d. For stems of tees, d is taken as the full nominal depth.

For stiffened elements, i.e., supported along two edges parallel to the direction of the compression force, the width shall be taken as follows:

a. For webs of rolled or formed sections, h is the clear distance between flanges less the fillet or corner radius at each flange; h_c is twice the distance from the neutral axis to the inside face of the compression flange less the fillet or corner radius.

b. For webs of built-up sections, h is the distance between adjacent lines of fasteners or the clear distance between flanges when welds are used, and h_c is twice the distance from the neutral axis to the nearest line of fasteners at the compression flange or the inside face of the compression flange when welds are used.

c. For flange or diaphragm plates in built-up sections, the width b is the distance between adjacent lines of fasteners or lines of welds.

d. For flanges of rectangular hollow structural sections, the width b is the clear distance between webs less the inside corner radius on each side. If the corner radius is not known, the flat width may be taken as the total section width minus three times the thickness.

For tapered flanges of rolled sections, the thickness is the nominal value halfway between the free edge and the corresponding face of the web.

TABLE B5.1
Limiting Width-Thickness Ratios for Compression Elements

Description of Element	Width-Thickness Ratio	Limiting Width-Thickness Ratios λ_p	Limiting Width-Thickness Ratios λ_r
Flanges of I-shaped rolled beams and channels in flexure	b/t	$65/\sqrt{F_y}$ [c]	$141/\sqrt{F_y - 10}$
Flanges of I-shaped hybrid or welded beams in flexure	b/t	$65/\sqrt{F_{yf}}$ [c]	$\frac{106}{\sqrt{F_{yw} - 16.5}}$
Flanges of I-shaped sections in pure compression, plates projecting from compression elements; outstanding legs of pairs of angles in continuous contact; flanges of channels in pure compression	b/t	NA	$95/\sqrt{F_y}$
Flanges of square and rectangular box and hollow structural sections of uniform thickness subject to bending or compression; flange cover plates and diaphragm plates between lines of fasteners or welds	b/t	$190/\sqrt{F_y}$	$238/\sqrt{F_y - F_r}$ [e]
Unsupported width of cover plates perforated with a succession of access holes[b]	b/t	NA	$317/\sqrt{F_y - F_r}$ [e]
Legs of single angle struts; legs of double angle struts with separators; unstiffened elements, i.e., supported along one edge	b/t	NA	$76/\sqrt{F_y}$
Stems of tees	d/t	NA	$127/\sqrt{F_y}$
All other uniformly compressed stiffened elements, i.e., supported along two edges	b/t h_c/t_w	NA	$253/\sqrt{F_y}$
Webs in flexural compression[a]	h_c/t_w	$640/\sqrt{F_y}$ [c]	$970/\sqrt{F_y}$
Webs in combined flexural and axial compression	h_c/t_w	for $P_u/\phi_b P_y \le 0.125$ $\frac{640}{\sqrt{F_y}}\left(1 - \frac{2.75P_u}{\phi_b P_y}\right)$ [c] for $P_u/\phi_b P_y > 0.125$ $\frac{191}{\sqrt{F_y}}\left(2.33 - \frac{P_u}{\phi_b P_y}\right) \ge \frac{253}{\sqrt{F_y}}$ [c]	$970/\sqrt{F_y}$
Circular hollow sections In axial compression In flexure	D/t	 $2{,}070/F_y$ [d] $2{,}070/F_y$ [d]	 $3{,}300/F_y$ $8{,}970/F_y$

[a]For hybrid beams, use the yield strength of the flange F_{yf} instead of F_y.
[b]Assumes net area of plate at widest hole.
[c]Assumes an inelastic rotation capacity of 3. For structures in zones of high seismicity, a greater rotation capacity may be required. See Table C-B5.1.
[d]For plastic design use $1{,}300/F_y$.
[e]F_r = compressive residual stress in flange
= 10 ksi for rolled shapes
= 16.5 ksi for welded shapes.

2. Sections for Plastic Analysis. Plastic analysis is permitted when flanges subject to compression involving hinge rotation and all webs have a width-thickness ratio less than or equal to the limiting λ_p from Table B5.1. For circular hollow sections, see Footnote d of Table B5.1.

Plastic analysis shall be subject to the limitations as outlined in Section A5.1.

3. Slender Compression Elements. For the flexural design of I-shaped sections, channels and rectangular or circular sections with slender compression elements, see Appendix F1.7. For other shapes in flexure or members in axial compression that have slender compression elements, see Appendix B5.3. For plate girders with $h_c/t_w > 970/\sqrt{F_{yf}}$, see Appendix G.

B6. BRACING AT SUPPORTS

At points of support for beams, girders and trusses, restraint against rotation about their longitudinal axis shall be provided unless restraint against rotation is otherwise assured.

B7. LIMITING SLENDERNESS RATIOS

For members whose design is based on compressive force, the slenderness ratio Kl/r preferably should not exceed 200.

For members whose design is based on tensile force, the slenderness ratio L/r preferably should not exceed 300. The above limitation does not apply to rods in tension. Such tension members may be subject to compressive force not exceeding 50 percent of the design compressive strength when such compressive force is due to wind or earthquake.

CHAPTER C

FRAMES AND OTHER STRUCTURES

Sec. 27.1403C. This chapter specifies general requirements to assure stability of the structure as a whole.

C1. SECOND ORDER EFFECTS

Second order ($P\Delta$) effects shall be considered in the design of frames.

C2. FRAME STABILITY

1. Braced Frames. In trusses and frames where lateral stability is provided by diagonal bracing, shear walls or equivalent means, the effective length factor K for compression members shall be taken as unity, unless structural analysis shows that a smaller value may be used.

The vertical bracing system for a braced multistory frame shall be adequate, as determined by structural analysis, to prevent buckling of the structure and maintain the lateral stability of the structure, including the overturning effects of drift, under the factored loads given in Section A4.

The vertical bracing system for a multistory frame may be considered to function together with in-plane shear-resisting exterior and interior walls, floor slabs and roof decks, which are properly secured to the structural frames. The columns, girders, beams and diagonal members, when used as the vertical bracing system, may be considered to comprise a vertical cantilever, simply connected truss in the analyses for frame buckling and lateral instability. Axial deformation of all members in the vertical bracing system shall be included in the lateral stability analysis.

Girders and beams included in the vertical bracing system of a braced multistory frame shall be proportioned for axial force and moment caused by concurrent factored horizontal and gravity loads.

2. Unbraced Frames. In frames where lateral stability depends upon the bending stiffness of rigidly connected beams and columns, the effective length factor K of compression members shall be determined by structural analysis and shall not be less than unity.

Analysis of the required strength of unbraced multistory frames shall include the effects of frame instability and column axial deformation under the factored loads given in Section A4.

In plastic design, the axial force in the columns caused by factored gravity plus factored horizontal loads shall not exceed $0.75\ A_g\ F_y$.

CHAPTER D

TENSION MEMBERS

Sec. 27.1403D. This chapter applies to prismatic members subject to axial tension caused by static forces acting through the centroidal axis. For members subject to combined axial tension and flexure, see Section H1. For members subject to fatigue, see Section K4. For tapered members, see Appendix F4. For threaded rods, see Section J3.

D1. DESIGN TENSILE STRENGTH

The design strength of tension members $\phi_t P_n$ shall be the lower value obtained according to the limit states of yielding in the gross section and fracture in the net section.

a. For yielding in the gross section:

$$\phi_t = 0.90$$

$$P_n = F_y A_g \qquad \text{(D1-1)}$$

b. For fracture in the net section:

$$\phi_t = 0.75$$

$$P_n = F_u A_e \qquad \text{(D1-2)}$$

WHERE:

A_e = effective net area, in.^{2}

A_g = gross area of member, in.^{2}

F_y = specified minimum yield stress, ksi

F_u = specified minimum tensile strength, ksi

P_n = nominal axial strength, kips

When members without holes are fully connected by welds, the effective net section used in Formula (D1-2) shall be computed using the smaller of the gross area of the member or the effective area of the welds as defined in Section J2. When holes are present in a welded member between end connections, or at the welded connection in the case of plug or slot welds, the net section through the holes shall be used in Formula (D1-2).

D2. BUILT-UP MEMBERS

The longitudinal spacing of connectors between elements in continuous contact consisting of a plate and a shape or two plates shall not exceed:

24 times the thickness of the thinner plate or 12 inches for painted members or unpainted members not subject to corrosion.

14 times the thickness of the thinner plate or 7 inches for unpainted members of weathering steel subject to atmospheric corrosion.

The longitudinal spacing of connectors between components should preferably limit the slenderness ratio in any component between the connectors to 300 or less.

Either perforated cover plates or tie plates without lacing may be used on the open sides of built-up tension members. Tie plates shall have a length not less than two thirds the distance between the lines of welds or fasteners connecting them to the components of the member. The thickness of such tie plates shall not be less than $^1/_{50}$ of the distance between these lines. The longitudinal spacing of intermittent welds or fasteners at tie plates shall not exceed 6 inches. The spacing of tie plates shall be such that the slenderness ratio of any component in the length between tie plates should preferably not exceed 300.

D3. EYEBARS AND PIN-CONNECTED MEMBERS

The design strength of eyebars shall be determined in accordance with Section D1a with A_g taken as the cross-sectional area of the body.

Eyebars shall be of uniform thickness, without reinforcement at the pin holes, and have circular heads whose periphery is concentric with the pin hole.

The radius of transition between the circular head and the eyebar body shall not be less than the head diameter.

The width of the body of the eyebars shall not exceed eight times its thickness.

The thickness can be less than $^1/_2$ inch only if external nuts are provided to tighten pin plates and filler plates into snug contact. The width b from the hole edge to the plate edge perpendicular to the direction of applied load shall be greater than two thirds and, for the purpose of calculation, not more than $^3/_4$ times the eyebar body width.

The pin diameter shall not be less than $^7/_8$ times the eyebar body width.

The pin-hole diameter shall not be more than $^1/_{32}$-inch greater than the pin diameter.

For steels having a yield stress greater than 70 ksi, the hole diameter shall not exceed five times the plate thickness and the width of the eyebar body shall be reduced accordingly. In pin-connected members, the pin hole shall be located midway between the edges of the member in the direction normal to the applied force. For pin-connected members in which the pin is expected to provide for relative movement between connected parts while under full load, the diameter of pin hole shall not be more than $^1/_{32}$ inch greater than the diameter of the pin. The width of the plate beyond the pin hole shall be not less than the effective width on either side of the pin hole.

In pin-connected plates other than eyebars, the design strength shall be determined according to Formula (D1-2) and the bearing strength of the projected area of pin shall be determined according to Section J8. The minimum net area beyond the bearing end of the pin hole, parallel to the axis of the member, shall not be less than two thirds of the net area required for strength across the pin hole.

The design strength of a pin-connected member $\phi_t P_n$ shall be the lowest value of the following limit states:

a. Tension on the net effective area:

$$\phi_t = 0.75$$

$$P_n = 2tb_{eff}F_u \qquad \text{(D3-1)}$$

b. Shear on the effective area:

$$\phi_{sf} = 0.75$$

$$P_n = A_{sf}F_y \qquad \text{(D3-2)}$$

c. Bearing on the projected area of the pin:

$$\phi = 1.0$$

$$P_n = A_{pb}F_y \qquad \text{(D3-3)}$$

WHERE:

a = shortest distance from edge of the pin hole to the edge of the member measured parallel to the direction of the force, in.

A_{pb} = projected bearing area, in.^{2}

A_{sf} = $2t\,(a + d/2)$, in.^{2}

b_{eff} = $2t + 0.63$, but not more than the actual distance from the edge of the hole to the edge of the part measured in the direction normal to the applied force, in.

d = pin diameter, in.

t = thickness of plate, in.

The corners beyond the pin hole may be cut 45 degrees to the axis of the member, provided the net area beyond the pin hole, on a plane perpendicular to the cut, is not less than that required beyond the pin hole parallel to the axis of the member.

Thickness limitations on both eyebars and pin-connected plates may be waived whenever external nuts are provided so as to tighten pin plates and filler plates into snug contact. When the plates are thus contained, the bearing strength shall be determined according to Section J8.

CHAPTER E

COLUMNS AND OTHER COMPRESSION MEMBERS

Sec. 27.1403E. This section applies to prismatic members subject to axial compression through the centroidal axis. For members subject to combined axial compression and flexure, see Chapter H. For tapered members, see Appendix F4.

E1. EFFECTIVE LENGTH AND SLENDERNESS LIMITATIONS

1. Effective Length. The effective length factor K shall be determined in accordance with Section C2.

2. Plastic Analysis. Plastic analysis, as limited in Section A5.1, is permitted if the column slenderness parameter λ_c defined by Formula (E2-4) does not exceed $1.5K$.

E2. DESIGN COMPRESSIVE STRENGTH

The design strength of compression members whose elements have width-thickness ratios less than λr of Section B5.1 is $\phi_c P_n$.

$$\phi_c = 0.85$$

$$P_n = A_g F_{cr} \tag{E2-1}$$

for $\lambda_c \leq 1.5$

$$F_{cr} = (0.658^{\lambda_c^2}) F_y \tag{E2-2}$$

for $\lambda_c > 1.5$

$$F_{cr} = \left[\frac{0.877}{\lambda_c^2}\right] F_y \tag{E2-3}$$

where

$$\lambda_c = \frac{Kl}{r\pi}\sqrt{\frac{F_y}{E}} \tag{E2-4}$$

A_g = gross area of member, in.^{2}
F_y = specified yield stress, ksi
E = modulus of elasticity, ksi
K = effective length factor
l = unbraced length of member, in.
r = governing radius of gyration about plane of buckling, in.

For members whose elements do not meet the requirements of Section B5.1, see Appendix B5.3.

E3. FLEXURAL-TORSIONAL BUCKLING

Singly symmetric and unsymmetric columns, such as angle or tee-shaped columns, and doubly symmetric columns such as cruciform or built-up columns with very thin walls, may require consideration of the limit states of flexural-torsional and torsional buckling. See Appendix E3 for the determination of design strength for these limit states.

E4. BUILT-UP MEMBERS

At the ends of built-up compression members bearing on base plates or milled surfaces, all components in contact with one another shall be connected by a weld having a length not less than the maximum width of the member or by bolts spaced longitudinally not more than four diameters apart for a distance equal to one and one-half times the maximum width of the member.

Along the length of built-up compression members between the end connections required above, longitudinal spacing for intermittent welds, bolts or rivets shall be adequate to provide for the transfer of calculated stress. However, where a component of a built-up compression member consists of an outside plate, except as provided in the next sentence, the maximum spacing shall not exceed the thickness of the thinner outside plate times $127/\sqrt{F_y}$ or 12 inches, when intermittent welds are provided along the edges of the components or when fasteners are provided on all gage lines at each section. When fasteners are staggered, the maximum spacing on each gage line shall not exceed the thickness of the thinner outside plate times $190/\sqrt{F_y}$ or 18 inches.

For unpainted built-up members made of weathering steel which will be exposed to atmospheric corrosion, the fasteners connecting a plate and a shape or two-plate components in contact with one another shall not exceed 14 times the thickness of the thinnest part or 7 inches, and the maximum edge distance shall not exceed eight times the thickness of the thinnest part, or 5 inches.

Compression members composed of two or more shapes shall be connected to one another at intervals such that the slenderness ratio $L/_r$ of either shape, between the fasteners, does not exceed the governing slenderness ratio of the built-up member. The least radius of gyration r shall be used in computing the slenderness ratio of each component part.

The design strength of built-up members composed of two or more shapes shall be determined in accordance with Section E2 or Appendix E3 subject to the following modification. If the buckling mode involves relative deformation that produce shear forces in the connectors between individual shapes, Kl/r is replaced by $(Kl/r)_m$ determined as follows:

a. for snug-tight bolted connectors:

$$\left(\frac{Kl}{r}\right)_m = \sqrt{\left(\frac{Kl}{r}\right)_o^2 + \left(\frac{a}{r_i}\right)^2} \qquad \text{(E4-1)}$$

b. for welded connectors and for fully tightened bolted connectors as required for slip-critical joints:

with $\dfrac{a}{r_i} > 50$

$$\left(\frac{Kl}{r}\right)_m = \sqrt{\left(\frac{Kl}{r}\right)_o^2 + \left(\frac{a}{r_i} - 50\right)^2} \qquad \text{(E4-2)}$$

with $\frac{a}{r_i} \leq 50$

$$\left(\frac{Kl}{r}\right)_m = \left(\frac{Kl}{r}\right)_o \qquad \text{(E4-3)}$$

where

$\left(\frac{Kl}{r}\right)_o$ = column slenderness of built-up member acting as a unit

$\frac{a}{r_i}$ = largest column slenderness of individual components

$\left(\frac{Kl}{r}\right)_m$ = modified column slenderness of built-up member

a = distance between connectors

r_i = minimum radius of gyration of individual component

Open sides of compression members built up from plates or shapes shall be provided with continuous cover plates perforated with a succession of access holes. The unsupported width of such plates at access holes, as defined in Section B5.1, is assumed to contribute to the design strength, provided that:

a. The width-thickness ratio conforms to the limitations of Section B5.1.

b. The ratio of length (in direction of stress) to width of hole shall not exceed two.

c. The clear distance between holes in the direction of stress shall be not less than the transverse distance between nearest lines of connecting fasteners or welds.

4. The periphery of the holes at all points shall have a minimum radius of $1^1/_2$ inches.

The function of perforated cover plates may be performed by lacing with tie plates at each end and at intermediate points if the lacing is interrupted. Tie plates shall be as near the ends as practicable. In main members providing design strength, the end tie plates shall have a length of not less than the distance between the lines of fasteners or welds connecting them to the components of the member. Intermediate tie plates shall have a length not less than $^1/_2$ of this distance. The thickness of tie plates shall not be less than $^1/_{50}$ of the distance between lines of welds or fasteners connecting them to the segments of the members. In welded construction, the welding on each line connecting a tie plate shall aggregate not less than $^1/_3$ the length of the plate. In bolted and riveted construction, the spacing in the direction of stress in tie plates shall not be more than six diameters and the tie plates shall be connected to each segment by at least three fasteners.

Lacing, including flat bars, angles, channels or other shapes employed as lacing, shall be so spaced that the L/r ratio of the flange included between their connections shall not exceed the governing slenderness ratio for the member as a whole. Lacing shall be proportioned to provide a shearing strength normal to the axis of the member equal to 2 percent of the compressive design strength of the member. The L/r ratio for lacing bars arranged in single systems shall not exceed 140. For double lacing this ratio shall not exceed 200. Double lacing bars shall be joined at their intersections. For lacing bars in compression, L may be taken as the unsupported length of the lacing bar between welds or fasteners connecting it to the components of the built-up member for single lacing, and 70 percent of that distance for double lacing. The inclination of lacing bars to the axis of the member should preferably be not less than 60° for single lacing and 45° for double lacing. When the distance between the lines of welds or fasteners in the flanges is more than 15 inches, the lacing shall be double or be made of angles.

E5. PIN-CONNECTED COMPRESSION MEMBERS

Pin-connections of pin-connected compression members shall conform to the requirements of Section D3 except Formulas (D1-1) and (D3-2) do not apply.

CHAPTER F

BEAMS AND OTHER FLEXURAL MEMBERS

Sec. 27.1403F. This section applies to singly or doubly symmetric beams including hybrid beams and girders loaded in the plane of symmetry. It also applies to channels loaded in a plane passing through the shear center parallel to the web or restrained against twisting at load points and points of support. For design flexural strength for members not covered in Section F1, see Appendix F1.7. For members subject to combined flexural and axial force, see Section H1. For unsymmetric beams and beams subject to torsion combined with flexure, see Section H2.

F1. DESIGN FOR FLEXURE

1. Unbraced Length for Plastic Analysis. Plastic analysis, as limited in Section A5, shall be permitted when the laterally unbraced length L_b of the compression flange at plastic hinge locations associated with the failure mechanism, for a compact section bent about the major axis, does not exceed L_{pd}, determined as follows:

a. For doubly symmetric and singly symmetric I-shaped members with the compression flange larger than the tension flange (including hybrid members) loaded in the plane of the web.

$$L_{pd} = \frac{3,600 + 2,200(M_1/M_p)}{F_y} r_y \qquad \text{(F1-1)}$$

WHERE:

F_y = specified minimum yield stress of the compression flange, ksi

M_1 = smaller moment at end of unbraced length of beam, kip-in.

M_p = plastic moment ($= F_y Z$ for homogeneous sections; computed from fully plastic stress distribution for hybrids), kip-in.

r_y = radius of gyration about minor axis, in.

(M_l/M_p) is positive when moments cause reverse curvature

b. For solid rectangular bars and symmetric box beams

$$L_{pd} = \frac{5,000 + 3,000(M_1/M_p)}{F_y} r_y \geq 3,000 \; r_y/F_y \qquad \text{(F1-2)}$$

There is no limit on L_b for members with circular or square cross sections or for any beam bent about its minor axis.

In the region of the last hinge to form, and in regions not adjacent to a plastic hinge, the flexural design strength shall be determined in accordance with Section F1.2.

2. Flexural Design Strength. The flexural design strength, determined by the limit state of lateral-torsional buckling, is $\phi_b M_n$, where the nominal strength M_n shall be determined in accordance with the following sections, and $\phi_b = 0.90$.

3. Compact Section Members with $L_b \leq L_r$. For laterally unsupported compact section members bent about the major axis:

$$M_n = C_b \left[M_p - (M_p - M_r) \left(\frac{L_b - L_p}{L_r - L_p} \right) \right] \leq M_p \qquad \text{(F1-3)}$$

WHERE:

C_b = $1.75 + 1.05(M_1/M_2) + 0.3\,(M_1/M_2)^2$ 2.3 where M_1 is the smaller and M_2 the larger end moment in the unbraced segment of the beam; M_1/M_2 is positive when the moments cause reverse curvature and negative when bent in single curvature.

C_b = 1.0 for unbraced cantilevers and for members where the moment within a significant portion of the unbraced segment is greater than or equal to the larger of the segment end moments. For the use of larger C_b values, recognized design procedures shall be used.

L_b = distance between points braced against lateral displacement of the compression flange, or between points braced to prevent twist of the cross section.

For I-shaped members including hybrid sections and channels bent about their major axis:

$$L_p = \frac{300 r_y}{\sqrt{F_{yf}}} \qquad \text{(F1-4)}$$

For solid rectangular bars and box beams:

$$L_p = \frac{3,750 r_y}{M_p} \sqrt{JA} \qquad \text{(F1-5)}$$

WHERE:

A = cross-sectional area, in.^{2}

J = torsional constant, in.^{4}

The limiting laterally unbraced length L_r and the corresponding buckling moment M_r shall be determined as follows:

a. For I-shaped members, doubly symmetric and singly symmetric with the compression flange larger than or equal to the tension flange, and channels loaded in the plane of the web:

$$L_r = \frac{r_y X_1}{(F_{yw} - F_r)} \sqrt{1 + \sqrt{1 + X_2 (F_{yw} - F_r)^2}} \qquad \text{(F1-6)}$$

$$M_r = (F_{yw} - F_r) S_x \qquad \text{(F1-7)}$$

WHERE:

$$X_1 = \frac{\pi}{S_x} \sqrt{\frac{EGJA}{2}} \qquad \text{(F1-8)}$$

$$X_2 = 4 \frac{C_w}{I_y} \left(\frac{S_x}{GJ} \right)^2 \qquad \text{(F1-9)}$$

S_x = section modulus about major axis, in.^{3}

E = modulus of elasticity of steel (29,000 ksi)

G = shear modulus of elasticity of steel (11,200 ksi)

F_{yw} = yield stress of web, ksi

I_y = moment of inertia about y-axis, in.^{4}

C_w = warping constant, in.^{6}

F_r = compressive residual stress in flange; 10 ksi for rolled shaped, 16.5 ksi for welded shapes

b. For symmetric box section bent about the major axis and loaded in the plane of symmetry, M_r and L_r shall be determined from Formulas 26-7 and 26-10, respectively.

c. For solid rectangular bars bent about the major axis:

$$L_r = \frac{57{,}000 r_y \sqrt{JA}}{M_r} \quad \text{(F1-10)}$$

$$M_r = F_y S_x \quad \text{(F1-11)}$$

4. Compact Section Members with $L_b > L_r$. For laterally unsupported members with compact section members bent about the major axis:

$$M_n = M_{cr} \leq C_b M_r \quad \text{(F1-12)}$$

where M_{cr} is the critical elastic moment, determined as follows:

a. For I-shaped members, doubly symmetric and singly symmetric with compression flange larger than the tension flange (including hybrid members) and channels loaded in the plane of the web:

$$M_{cr} = C_b \frac{\pi}{L_b} \sqrt{EI_y\, GJ + \left(\frac{\pi E}{L_b}\right)^2 I_y\, C_w} \quad \text{(F1-13)}$$

$$= \frac{C_b\, S_x\, X_1 \sqrt{2}}{L_b/r_y} \sqrt{1 + \frac{X_1^2\, X_2}{2(L_b/r_y)^2}}$$

b. For solid rectangular bars and symmetric box sections:

$$M_{cr} = \frac{57{,}000\ C_b \sqrt{JA}}{L_b/r_y} \quad \text{(F1-14)}$$

5. Tees and Double-angle Beams. The nominal strength of tees and double-angle beams loaded in the plane of symmetry, with flange and web slenderness ratios less than the corresponding values of λ_r in Table B5.1.

$$M_n = M_{cr} = \frac{C_b\, \pi \sqrt{EI_y GJ}}{L_b} \left[B + \sqrt{1 + B^2}\right] \leq M_y \quad \text{(F1-15)}$$

$$B = \pm\ 2.3\ (d/L_b) \sqrt{I_y/J} \quad \text{(F1-16)}$$

The plus sign for B applies when the stem is in tension and the minus sign applies when the stem is in compression.

6. Noncompact Plate Girders. The nominal strength of a doubly symmetric, single-web plate girder, including hybrid sections, shall be calculated by the provisions of Appendix F1.7 if $h_c/t_w \leq 970/\sqrt{F_{yf}}$ or by the provisions of Appendix G if $h_c/t_w > 970/\sqrt{F_{yf}}$.

7. Nominal Flexural Strength of Other Sections. There is no lateral-torsional buckling limit state for circular or square shapes or for any shape bent about its minor axis.

For the nominal strength M_n of other cross section types, including noncompact sections or sections with slender elements, see Appendix F1.7. See Appendix G for design of plate girders with slender webs.

F2. DESIGN FOR SHEAR

This section applies to the web (or webs in the case of multiple web members) of singly or doubly symmetric beams, including hybrid beams, subject to shear in the plane of symmetry, and channels subject to shear in the web. Where failure might occur by shear along a plane through fasteners, refer to Section J4. For members subjected to high shear from concentrated loads, see Section K1.7.

1. Web Area Determination. The web area A_w shall be taken as the overall depth d times the web thickness t_w.

2. Design Shear Strength. The design shear strength of webs is $\phi_v V_n$ where ϕ_v = 0.90 and the nominal shear strength V_n determined as follows:

For $\dfrac{h}{t_w} \le 187\sqrt{k/F_{yw}}$

$$V_n = 0.6\, F_{yw} A_w \qquad \text{(F2-1)}$$

for $187\sqrt{k/F_{yw}} < \dfrac{h}{t_w} \le 234\sqrt{k/F_{yw}}$

$$V_n = 0.6\, F_{yw} A_w \frac{187\sqrt{k/F_{yw}}}{h/t_w} \qquad \text{(F2-2)}$$

for $\dfrac{h}{t_w} > 234\sqrt{k/F_{yw}}$

$$V_n = A_w \frac{26{,}400k}{(h/t_w)^2} \qquad \text{(F2-3)}$$

The web plate buckling coefficient k is given by

$$k = 5 + \frac{5}{(a/h)^2} \qquad \text{(F2-4)}$$

Except that k shall be taken as 5 if a/h exceeds 3.0 or $[260/(h/t_w)]^2$. When stiffeners are not required, $k = 5$. In unstiffened girders, h/t shall not exceed 260.

Maximum (h/t_w) limits are given in Appendix G1.

An alternative design method for plate girders utilizing tension field action is given in Appendix G.

F3. TRANSVERSE STIFFENERS

Transverse stiffeners are not required when $h/t_w \le 418\sqrt{F_{yw}}$, or when the required shear V_u, as determined by structural analysis for the factored loads, is less than or equal to $\phi_v V_n$ for $k = 5$ given in Section F2. Transverse stiffeners used to develop the web design shear strength as provided in Section F2 shall have a moment of inertia about an axis in the web center for stiffener pairs or about the face in contact with the web plate for single stiffeners, which shall not be less than

$$j = \frac{2.5}{(a/h)^2} - 2 \geq 0.5 \qquad \text{(F3-1)}$$

Intermediate stiffeners may be stopped short of the tension flange, provided bearing is not needed to transmit a concentrated load or reaction. The weld by which intermediate stiffeners are attached to the web shall be terminated not less than four times or more than six times the web thickness from the near toe of the web-to-flange weld. When single stiffeners are used, they shall be attached to the compression flange, if it consists of a rectangular plate, to resist any uplift tendency due to torsion in the plate. When lateral bracing is attached to a stiffener or a pair of stiffeners, these in turn shall be connected to the compression flange to transmit 1 percent of the total flange stress, unless the flange is composed only of angles.

Bolts connecting stiffeners to the girder web shall be spaced not more than 12 inches on center. If intermittent fillet welds are used, the clear distance between welds shall not be more than 16 times the web thickness or more than 10 inches.

F4. WEB-TAPERED MEMBERS

See Appendix F4.

CHAPTER G

G. PLATE GIRDERS

Sec. 27.1403. Plate girders shall be distinguished from beams on the basis of the web slenderness ratio h_c/t_w. When this value is greater than $970/\sqrt{F_{yf}}$, the provisions of Appendix G shall apply for design flexural strength, otherwise Appendix F1.7 is applicable.

For design shear strength and transverse stiffener design, see appropriate sections in Chapter F, or see Appendices G3 and G4 if tension field action is utilized.

CHAPTER H

H. MEMBERS UNDER TORSION AND COMBINED FORCES

Sec. 27.1403. This section applies to prismatic members subjected to axial force and flexure about one or both axes of symmetry, with or without torsion, and torsion only. For web-tapered members, see Appendix F4.

H1. SYMMETRIC MEMBERS SUBJECT TO BENDING AND AXIAL FORCE

1. Doubly and Singly Symmetric Members in Flexure and Tension. The interaction of flexure and tension in symmetric shapes shall be limited by Formulas H1-1a and H1-1b.

for $\frac{P_u}{\phi P_n} \geq 0.2$

$$\frac{P_u}{\phi P_n} + \frac{8}{9}\left(\frac{M_{ux}}{\phi_b M_{nx}} + \frac{M_{uy}}{\phi_b M_{ny}}\right) \leq 1.0 \qquad \text{(H1-1a)}$$

for $\frac{P_u}{\phi P_n} < 0.2$

$$\frac{P_u}{2\phi P_n} + \left(\frac{M_{ux}}{\phi_b M_{nx}} + \frac{M_{uy}}{\phi_b M_{ny}}\right) \leq 1.0 \qquad \text{(H1-1b)}$$

WHERE:

P_u = required tensile strength, kips
P_n = nominal tensile strength determined in accordance with Section D1, kips
M_u = required flexural strength, kip-in.
M_n = nominal flexural strength determined in accordance with Section F1, kip-in.
ϕ_t = resistance factor for tension, $\phi_t = 0.90$ (see Section D1)
ϕ_b = resistance factor for flexure = 0.90

Second order effects may be considered in the determination of M_u for use in Formulas H1-1a and H1-1b. A more detailed analysis of the interaction of flexure and tension may be made in lieu of using Formulas H1-1a and H1-1b.

2. Doubly and Singly Symmetric Members in Flexure and Compression. The interaction of flexure and compression in symmetric shapes shall be limited by Formulas H1-1a and H1-1b where

P_u = required compressive strength, kips
P_n = nominal compressive strength determined in accordance with Section E2, kips
M_u = required flexural strength determined in accordance with Subsection a, below, kip-in.
M_n = nominal flexural strength determined in accordance with Subsection b, below, kip-in.
ϕ_c = resistance factor for compression, $\phi_c = 0.85$ (see Section E2)
ϕ_b = resistance factor for flexure = 0.90

a. Determination of M_u. In structures designed on the basis of elastic analysis, M_u may be determined from a second order elastic analysis using factored loads. In structures designed on the basis of plastic analysis, M_u shall be determined from a plastic analysis that satisfies the requirements of Sections C1 and C2. In structures designed on the basis of elastic first order analysis the following procedure for the determination of M_u may be used in lieu of a second order analysis:

$$M_u = B_1 M_{nt} + B_2 M_{lt} \qquad \text{(H1-2)}$$

WHERE:

M_{nt} = required flexural strength in member assuming there is no lateral translation of the frame, kip-in.

M_{lt} = required flexural strength in member as a result of lateral translation of the frame only, kip-in.

$$B_1 = \frac{C_m}{(1 - P_u/P_e)} \geq 1$$

P_e = $A_g F_y / \lambda^2_c$ where λ_c is defined by Formula E2-4 with $K \leq 1.0$ in the plane of bending.

C_m = a coefficient whose value shall be taken as follows:

i. For restrained compression members in frames braced against joint translation and not subject to transverse loading between their supports in the plane of bending,

$$C_m = 0.6 - 0.4(M_1/M_2) \qquad \text{(H1-4)}$$

where M_1/M_2 is the ratio of the smaller to larger moments at the ends of that portion of the member unbraced in the plane of bending under consideration, M_1/M_2 is positive when the member is bent in reverse curvature, negative when bent in single curvature.

ii. For compression members in frames braced against joint translation in the plane of loading and subjected to transverse loading between their supports, the value of C_m can be determined by rational analysis. In lieu of such analysis, the following values may be used:

for members whose ends are restrained .... $C_m = 0.85$

for members whose ends are unrestrained .... $C_m = 1.0$

$$B_2 = \frac{1}{1 - \Sigma P_u \left(\frac{\Delta_{oh}}{\Sigma HL}\right)} \qquad \text{(H1-5)}$$

or

$$B_2 = \frac{1}{1 - \frac{\Sigma P_u}{\Sigma P_e}} \qquad \text{(H1-6)}$$

ΣP_u = required axial load strength of all columns in a story, kips

Δ_{oh} = translation defletion of the story under consideration, in.

ΣH = sum of all story horizontal forces producing Δ_{oh}, kips

L = story height, in.

P_e = $A_g F_y / \lambda^2_c$, kips, where λ_c is the slenderness parameter defined by Formula E2-4, in which the effective length factor K in the plane of bending shall be determined in accordance with Section C2.2, but shall not be less than unity.

b. Determination of M_n. In the use of Formulas H1-1a and H1-1b, M_{nx} shall be determined in accordance with Section F1. The actual value of C_b specified in

Section F1.3 may be used, provided that the maximum moment M_{ux} occurs at the end of the member or at the end of an unbraced segment of a member. When the maximum moment occurs between the ends, M_{nx} shall be determined with C_b = 1.0. When Formula H1-2 is used for determining M_u, the maximum moment for a braced member bent about the strong axis and laterally braced only at its ends will occur at an end whenever the calculated value of B_1 is equal to or less than 1.

H2. UNSYMMETRIC MEMBERS AND MEMBERS UNDER TORSION AND COMBINED TORSION, FLEXURE AND/OR AXIAL FORCE

Sec. 27.1438. The design strength ϕF_y of the member shall equal or exceed the required strength expressed in terms of the normal stress f_{un} or the shear stress f_{uv}, determined by elastic analysis for the factored loads:

a. For the limit state of yielding under normal stress:

$$F_{un} \leq \phi F_y \qquad \text{(H2-1)}$$

$$\phi = 0.90$$

b. For the limit state of yielding under shear stress:

$$F_{uv} \text{ or } \leq 0.6\ \phi F_y \qquad \text{(H2-2)}$$

$$\phi = 0.90$$

For the limit state of buckling:

$$f_{un} \text{ or } f_{uv} \leq \phi_c\ F_{cr,} \text{ as applicable.} \qquad \text{(H2-3)}$$

WHERE:

ϕ_c 0.85 and F_{cr} shall be determined from Formula A-E3-2 or E3-3, as applicable.

Some constrained local yielding shall be permitted in areas adjacent to areas which remain elastic.

H3. ALTERNATE INTERACTION EQUATIONS FOR MEMBERS UNDER COMBINED STRESS

See Appendix H3.

CHAPTER I

COMPOSITE MEMBERS

Sec. 27.1403. General. This chapter applies to composite columns composed of rolled or built-up structural steel shapes, pipe or tubing and structural concrete acting together and to steel beams supporting a reinforced concrete slab so interconnected that the beams and the slab act together to resist bending. Simple and continuous composite beams with shear connectors and concrete-encased beams, constructed with or without temporary shores, included.

I1. DESIGN ASSUMPTIONS

Force Determination. In determining forces in members and connections of a structure that includes composite beams, consideration must be given to the effective sections at the time each increment of load is applied.

Elastic Analysis. For an elastic analysis of continuous composite beams without haunched ends, it is acceptable to assume that the stiffness of a beam is uniform throughout the beam length and may be computed using the moment of inertia of the composite transformed section in the positive moment region.

Plastic Analysis. When plastic analysis is used, the strength of flexural composite members shall be determined from plastic stress distributions as specified in I3.

Plastic Stress Distribution for Positive Moment. If the slab in the positive moment region is connected to the steel beam with shear connectors, a concrete stress of $0.85 f'_c$ shall be assumed uniformly distributed throughout the effective compression zone. Concrete tensile strength shall be neglected. A uniformly distributed steel stress of F_y shall be assumed throughout the tension zone and throughout the compression zone in the structural steel section. The net tensile force in the steel section shall be equal to the compressive force in the concrete slab.

Plastic Stress Distribution for Negative Moment. If the slab in the negative moment region is connected to the steel beam with shear connectors, a tensile stress of F_{yr} shall be assumed in all adequately developed longitudinal reinforcing bars within the effective width of the concrete slab. Concrete tensile strength shall be neglected. A uniformly distributed steel stress of F_y shall be assumed throughout the tension zone and throughout the compression zone in the structural steel section. The net compressive force in the steel section shall be equal to the total tensile force in the reinforcing steel.

Elastic Stress Distribution. When a determination of elastic stress distribution is required, strains in steel and concrete shall be assumed directly proportional to the distance from the neutral axis. The stress shall equal strain times E or E_c. Concrete tensile strength shall be neglected. Maximum stress in the steel shall not exceed F_y. Maximum compressive stress in the concrete shall not exceed $0.85f'_c$. In composite hybrid beams, the maximum stress in the steel flange shall not exceed F_{yf} but the strain in the web may exceed the yield strain; the stress shall be taken as F_{yw} such locations.

Fully Composite Beam. Shear connectors are provided in sufficient numbers to develop the maximum flexural strength of the composite beam. For elastic stress distribution it shall be assumed that no slip occurs.

Partially Composite Beam. The shear strength of shear connectors governs the flexural strength of the partially composite beam. Elastic computations such as those for deflections, fatigue and vibrations shall include the effect of slip.

Concrete-encased Beam. A beam totally encased in concrete cast integrally with the slab shall be assumed to be interconnected to the concrete by natural bond, without additional anchorage, provided that: (1) concrete cover over beam sides and soffit is at least 2 inches; (2) the top of the beam is at least $1^1/_2$ inches below the top and 2 inches above the bottom of the slab; and (3) concrete encasement contains adequate mesh or other reinforcing steel to prevent spalling of concrete.

Composite Column. A steel column fabricated from rolled or built-up steel shapes and encased on structural concrete or fabricated from steel pipe or tubing and filled with structural concrete.

I2. COMPRESSION MEMBERS

1. Limitations. To qualify as a composite column, the following limitations shall be met.

a. The cross-sectional area of the steel shape, pipe or tubing must comprise at least 4 percent of the total composite cross section.

b. Concrete encasement of a steel core shall be reinforced with longitudinal load carrying bars, longitudinal bars to restrain concrete and lateral ties. Longitudinal load carrying bars shall be continuous at framed levels; longitudinal restraining bars may be interrupted at framed levels. The spacing of ties shall be not greater than $^2/_3$ of the least dimension of the composite cross section. The cross-sectional area of the transverse and longitudinal reinforcement shall be at least 0.007 square inch per inch of bar spacing. The encasement shall provide at least 1.5 inches of clear cover outside of both transverse and longitudinal reinforcement.

c. Concrete shall have a specified compressive f'_c strength of not less than 3 ksi nor more than 8 ksi for normal-weight concrete and not less than 4 ksi for light-weight concrete.

d. The specified minimum yield stress of structural steel and reinforcing bars used in calculating the strength of a composite column shall not exceed 55 ksi.

e. The minimum wall thickness of structural steel pipe or tubing filled with concrete shall be equal to $b\sqrt{F_y/3E}$ for each face of width b in rectangular sections and $D\sqrt{F_y/8E}$ for circular sections of outside diameter D.

2. Design Strength. The design strength of axially loaded composite columns is $\phi_c P_n$, where $\phi_c = 0.85$ and the nominal axial compressive strength P_n shall be determined from Formulas E2-1 through E2-4 with the following modifications:

a.

A_s = gross area of steel shape, pipe or tubing, in.^{2} (replaces A_g)

r_m = radius of gyration of the steel shape, pipe or tubing except that for steel shapes it shall not be less than 0.3 times the overall thickness of the composite cross section in the plane of buckling, in. (replaces r)

b. Replace F_y with modified yield stress F_{my} from Formula I2-1 and replace E with modified modulus of elasticity E_m from Formula I2-2.

$$F_{my} = F_y = c_1 F_{yr} (A_r/A_s) + c_2 f'_c (A_c/A_s) \qquad \text{(I2-1)}$$

$$E_m = E + c_3 E_c (A_c/A_s) \qquad \text{(I2-2)}$$

WHERE:

A_c = area of concrete, in.^{2}

A_r = area of longitudinal reinforcing bars, in.^{2}

A_s = area of steel, in.2
E = modulus of elasticity of steel, ksi
E_c = modulus of elasticity of concrete*, ksi as given in Section 2608 (f) of the code
F_y = specified minimum yield stress of steel shape, pipe or tubing, ksi
F_{yr} = specified minimum yield stress of longitudinal reinforcing bars, ksi
F'_c = specified compressive strength of concrete, ksi
c_1,c_2,c_3= numerical coefficients. For concrete-filled pipe and tubing: $c_1 = 1.0$, $c_2 = 0.85$ and $c_3 = 0.4$; for concrete encased shapes $c_1 = 0.7$, $c_2 = 0.6$ and $c_3 = 0.2$

3. Columns with Multiple Steel Shapes. If the composite cross section includes two or more steel shapes, the shapes must be interconnected with lacing, tie plates or batten plates to prevent buckling of individual shapes before hardening of concrete.

4. Load Transfer. The portion of the design strength of axially loaded composite columns resisted by concrete shall be developed by direct bearing at connections. When the supporting concrete area is wider than the loaded area on one or more sides and otherwise restrained against lateral expansion on the remaining sides, the maximum design strength of concrete shall be $1.7\phi_c f'_c A_B$, where $\phi_c = 0.60$ is the resistance factor in bearing on concrete and A_B is the loaded area.

I3. FLEXURAL MEMBERS

1. Effective Width. The portion of the effective width of the concrete slab on each side of the beam center line shall not exceed:

a. One eighth of the beam span, center to center of supports;
b. One half the diameter to the centerline of the adjacent beam; or
c. The distance from the beam centerline to the edge of the slab.

2. Strength of Beams with Shear Connectors. 1. The positive design flexural strength $\phi_b M_n$ shall be determined as follows:

a. For h_c/t_w $640/\sqrt{F_{yf}}$:

$\phi_b = 0.85$; M_n shall be determined from the plastic stress distribution on the composite section.

b. For $h_c/t_w > 640/\sqrt{F_{yf}}$:

$\phi_b = 0.90$; M_n shall be determined from the superposition of elastic stresses, considering the effects of shoring.

The negative design flexural strength $\phi_b M_n$ shall be determined for the steel section alone, in accordance with the requirements of Section F.

---

*E_c may be computed from $E_c = w^{1.5}\sqrt{f'_c}$ where w, the unit weight of concrete, is expressed in lbs./cu.ft. and f'c is expressed in ksi.

Alternatively, the negative design flexural strength $\phi_b M_n$ may be computed with $\phi_b = 0.85$ and M_n determined from the plastic stress distribution on the composite section, provided that:

a. Steel beam is an adequately braced compact section, as defined in Section B5.

b. Shear connectors connect the slab to the steel beam in the negative moment region.

c. Slab reinforcement parallel to the steel beam, within the effective width of the slab, is properly developed.

3. Strength of Concrete-encased Beams. The design flexural strength $\phi_b M_n$ shall be computed with $\phi_b = 0.90$ and M_n determined from the superposition of elastic stresses, considering the effects of shoring.

Alternatively, the design flexural strength $\phi_b M_n$ may be computed with $\phi_b = 0.90$ and M_n determined from the plastic stress distribution on the steel section alone.

4. Strength During Construction. When temporary shores are not used during construction, the steel section alone shall have adequate strength to support all loads applied prior to the concrete attaining 75 percent of its specified strength f'_c. The design flexural strength of the steel section shall be determined in accordance with the requirements of Section F1.

5. Formed Steel Deck

a. General. The design flexural strength $\phi_b M_n$ of composite construction consisting of concrete slabs on formed steel deck connected to steel beams shall be determined by the applicable portions of Section I3.2, with the following modifications:

This section is applicable to decks with nominal rib height not greater than 3 inches. The average width of concrete rib or haunch w_r shall be not less than 2 inches, but shall not be taken in calculations as more than the minimum clear width near the top of the steel deck. See Section I3.5c for additional restrictions.

The concrete slab shall be connected to the steel beam with welded stud shear connectors $^3/_4$ inch or less in diameter (U.B.C. Standard No. 27-6). Studs may be welded either through the deck or directly to the steel beam. Stud shear connectors, after installation, shall extend not less than $1^1/_2$ inches above the top of the steel deck.

The slab thickness above the steel deck shall be not less than 2 inches.

b. Deck Ribs Oriented Perpendicular to Steel Beam. Concrete below the top of the steel deck shall be neglected in determining section properties and in calculating A_c for deck ribs oriented perpendicular to the steel beams.

The spacing of stud shear connectors along the length of a supporting beam shall not exceed 32 inches.

The nominal strength of a stud shear connector shall be the value stipulated in Section I5 multiplied by the following reduction factor:

$$\frac{0.85}{\sqrt{N_r}} (w_r/h_r) \, [(H_s/h_r) - 1.0] \le 1.0 \qquad \text{(I3-1)}$$

WHERE:

h_r = nominal rib height, in.

H_s = length of stud connector after welding, in., not to exceed the value (h_r + 3) in computations, although actual length may be greater

N_r = number of stud connectors in one rib at a beam intersection, not to exceed three in computations, although more than three studs may be installed

W_r = average width of concrete rib or haunch (as defined in Section I3.5a) in.

To resist uplift, steel deck shall be anchored to all supporting members at a spacing not to exceed 16 inches. Such anchorage may be provided by stud connectors, a combination of stud connectors and arc spot (puddle) welds or other devices specified by the designer.

c. Deck Ribs Oriented Parallel to Steel Beam. Concrete below the top of the steel deck may be included in determining section properties and shall be included in calculating A_c in Section I5.

Steel deck ribs over supporting beams may be split longitudinally and separated to form a concrete haunch.

When the nominal depth of steel deck is $1^1/_2$ inches or greater, the average width w_r of the supported haunch or rib shall be not less than 2 inches for the first stud in the transverse row plus 4 stud diameters for each additional stud.

The nominal strength of a stud shear connector shall be the value specified in Section I5, except that when w_r/h_r is less than 1.5, the value from Section I.5 shall be multiplied by the following reduction factor:

$$0.6\,(w_r/h_r)\,[(H_s/h_r) - 1.0] \le 1.0 \qquad \text{(I3-2)}$$

where h_r and H_s are as defined in Section I3.5b and w_r is the average width of concrete rib or haunch as defined in Section I3.5a.

6. Design Shear Strength. The design shear strength of composite beams shall be determined by the shear strength of the steel web, in accordance with Section F2.

I4. COMBINED COMPRESSION AND FLEXURE

Sec. 27.1404. The interaction of axial compression and flexure in the plane of symmetry on composite members shall be limited by Formulas H1-1 through H1-6 with the following modifications:

M_n = nominal flexural strength determined from plastic stress distribution on the composite cross section except as provided below, kip-in.

P_e = A_sF_{my}/λ_c^2, elastic buckling load, kips

F_{my} = modified yield stress, ksi, see Section I2

ϕ_b = resistance factor for flexure from Section I3

ϕ_c = 0.85

λ_c = column slenderness parameter defined by Formula E2-4 as modified in Section I2.2

When the axial term in Formulas H1-1a and H1-1b is less than 0.3, the nominal flexural strength M_n shall be determined by straight line transition between the nominal flexural strength determined from the plastic distribution on the composite cross sections at $(P_u/\phi_b P_n) = 0.3$ and the flexural strength at $P_u = 0$ as determined in Section I3. If shear connectors are required at $P_u = 0$, they shall be provided whenever $P_u/\phi_b P_n$ is less than 0.3.

I5. SHEAR CONNECTORS

This section applies to the design of stud and channel shear connectors. The design of connectors of other types, shall be in accordance with Section I6.

1. Materials. Shear connectors shall be headed steel studs not less than four stud diameters in length after installation, or hot-rolled steel channels. The stud connectors shall conform to the requirements of Section A3.6. The channel connectors shall conform to the requirements of Section A3. Shear connectors shall be embedded in concrete slabs made with ASTM C 33 aggregate or with rotary kiln produced aggregates conforming to ASTM C 330, with concrete unit weight not less than 90 pcf.

2. Horizontal Shear Force. Except for concrete-encased beams as defined in Section I1, the entire horizontal shear at the interface between the steel beam and the concrete slab shall be assumed to be transferred by shear connectors. For composite action with concrete subject to flexural compression, the total horizontal shear force between the point of maximum positive moment and the point of zero moment shall be taken as the smallest of the following: (1) $0.85 f'_c A_c$; (2) $A_s F_y$*; and (3) ΣQ_n;

WHERE:

f'_c = specified compressive strength of concrete, ksi
A_c = area of concrete slab within effective width, in.^{2}
A_s = area of steel cross section, in.^{2}
F_y = minimum specified yield stress, ksi
ΣQ_n = sum of nominal strengths of shear connectors between the point of maximum positive moment and the point of zero moment, kips

In continuous composite beams where longitudinal reinforcing steel in the negative moment regions is considered to act compositely with the steel beam, the total horizontal shear force between the point of maximum negative moment and the point of zero moment shall be taken as the smaller of $A_r F_{yr}$ and ΣQ_n;

WHERE:

A_r = area of adequately developed longitudinal reinforcing steel within the effective width of the concrete slab, in.2
F_{yr} = minimum specified yield stress of the reinforcing steel, ksi
ΣQ_n = sum of nominal strengths of shear connectors between the point of maximum negative moment and the point of zero moment, kips

*For hybrid beams, the yield force must be computed separately for each component of the cross section; $A_s F_y$ of the entire cross section is the sum of the component yield forces.

3. Strength of Stud Shear Connectors. The nominal strength of one stud shear connector embedded in a solid concrete slab is

$$Q_n = 0.5 A_{sc} \sqrt{f'_c E_c} \leq A_{sc} F_u \qquad (I5\text{-}1)$$

WHERE:

A_{sc} = cross-sectional area of a stud shear connector, in.^{2}

f'_c = specified compressive strength of concrete, ksi

F_u = minimum specified tensile strength of a stud shear connector, ksi

E_c = modulus of elasticity of concrete*, ksi

For a stud shear connector embedded in a slab on a formed steel deck, refer to Section I3 for reduction factors given by Formulas I3-1 and I3-2 as applicable. The reduction factors should be applied only to $0.5A_{sc} \sqrt{f'_c E_c}$ term in Formula I5-1.

4. Strength of Channel Shear Connectors. The nominal strength of one channel shear connector embedded in a solid concrete slab is

$$Q_n = 0.3 (t_f + 0.5 t_w) L_c \sqrt{f'_c E_c} \qquad (I5\text{-}2)$$

WHERE:

t_f = flange thickness of channel shear connector, in.

t_w = web thickness of channel shear connector, in.

L_c = length of channel shear connector, in.

5. Required Number of Shear Connectors. The number of shear connectors required between the section of maximum bending moment, positive or negative, and the adjacent section of zero moment shall be equal to the horizontal shear force as determined in Section I5.2 divided by the nominal strength of one shear connector as determined from Section I5.3 or Section I5.4.

6. Shear Connector Placement and Spacing. Shear connectors required each side of the point of maximum bending moment, positive or negative, may be distributed uniformly between that point and the adjacent points of zero moment. However, the number of shear connectors placed between any concentrated load and the nearest point of zero moment shall be sufficient to develop the maximum moment required at the concentrated load point.

Except for connectors installed in the ribs of formed steel decks, shear connectors shall have at least 1 inch of lateral concrete cover. Unless located over the web, the diameter of studs shall not be greater than 2.5 times the thickness of the flange to which they are welded. The minimum center to center spacing of stud connectors shall be 6 diameters along the longitudinal axis of the supporting composite beam and 4 diameters transverse to the longitudinal axis of the supporting composite beam, except that within the ribs of formed steel decks the center to center spacing may be as small as 4 diameters in any direction. The maximum center to center spacing of shear connectors shall not exceed 8 times the total slab thickness.

---

*E_c, in ksi, may be computed from $E_c = w^{1.5} \sqrt{f'_c}$ where w, the unit weight of concrete, is expressed in lbs./cu.ft. and f'_c is expressed in ksi.

I6. SPECIAL CASES

When composite construction does not conform to the requirements of Section I1 through Section I5, the strength of shear connectors and details of construction shall be established by a suitable test program.

CHAPTER J

CONNECTIONS, JOINTS AND FASTENERS

Sec. 27.1403.

J1. GENERAL PROVISIONS

1. Design Basis. Connections consist of connecting elements (e.g., stiffeners, gussets, angles, brackets) and connectors (welds, bolts, rivets). These components shall be proportioned so that their design strength equals or exceeds the required strength determined by (a) structural analysis for factored loads acting on the structure or (b) a specified proportion of the strength of the connected members, whichever is appropriate.

2. Simple Connections. Except as otherwise indicated in the design documents, connections of beams, girders or trusses shall be designed as flexible, and may ordinarily be proportioned for the reaction shears only. Flexible beam connections shall accommodate end rotations of unrestrained (simple) beams. To accomplish this, inelastic deformation in the connection is permitted.

3. Moment Connections. End connections of restrained beams, girders and trusses shall be designed for the combined effect of forces resulting from moment and shear induced by the rigidity of the connections.

4. Compression Members with Bearing Joints. When columns bear on bearing plates or are finished to bear at splices, there shall be sufficient connectors to hold all parts securely in place.

When other compression members are finished to bear, the splice material and its connectors shall be arranged to hold all parts in line and shall be proportioned for 50 percent of the factored strength of the member.

All compression joints shall be proportioned to resist any tension developed by the factored loads specified by Formula A4-6.

5. Minimum Strength of Connections. Except for lacing, sag rods or girts, connections providing design strength shall be designed to support a factored load not less than 10 kips.

6. Placement of Welds and Bolts. Groups of welds or bolts at the ends of any member which transmit axial force into that member shall be sized so that the center of gravity of the group coincides with the center of gravity of the member, unless provision is made for the eccentricity. The foregoing provision is not applicable to end connections of statically-loaded single angle, double angle and similar members.

7. Bolts in Combination with Welds. In new work, A307 bolts or high-strength bolts proportioned as bearing-type connections shall not be considered as sharing the load in combination with welds. Welds, if used, shall be provided to carry the entire force in the connection. High-strength bolts proportioned for slip-critical connections may be considered as sharing the load with the welds.

In making welded alterations to structures, existing rivets and high-strength bolts tightened to the requirements for slip-critical connections may be utilized for carrying loads resulting from existing dead loads, and the welding need only provide the additional design strength required.

8. High-strength Bolts in Combination with Rivets. In both new work and alterations, in connections designed as slip-critical connections in accordance with the provisions of Section J3, high-strength bolts may be designed to share the load with rivets.

9. Limitations on Bolted and Welded Connections. Fully tensioned high-strength bolts (see Table J3.1) or welds shall be used for the following connections:

Column splices in all tier structures 200 feet or more in height.

Column splices in tier structures 100 to 200 feet in height, if the least horizontal dimension is less than 40 percent of the height.

Column splices in tier structures less than 100 feet in height, if the least horizontal dimension is less than 25 percent of the height.

Connections of all beams and girders to columns and of any other beams and girders on which the bracing of columns is dependent, in structures over 125 feet in height.

In all structures carrying cranes of over 5-ton capacity: roof-truss splices and connections of trusses to columns, column splices, column bracing, knee braces and crane supports.

Connections for supports of running machinery, or of other live loads which produce impact or reversal of stress.

Any other connections stipulated on the design plans.

In all other cases connections may be made with A307 bolts or snug-tight high-strength bolts.

For the purpose of this Section, the height of a tier structure shall be taken as the vertical distance from the curb level to the highest point of the roof beams in the case of flat roofs, or to the mean height of the gable in the case of roofs having a slope of more than $2^2/_3$ in 12. Where the curb level has not been established, or where the structure does not adjoin a street, the mean level of the adjoining land shall be used instead of curb level. Penthouses may be excluded in computing the height of structure.

10. Splices In Heavy Sections

This paragraph applies to ASTM A6 Group 4 and 5 rolled shapes, or shapes built-up by welding plates more than 2 inches thick together to form the cross section*, and where the cross section is to be spliced and subject to primary tensile stresses due to tension or flexure. When tensile forces in these sections are to be transmitted through splices by full-penetration groove welds, material notch-toughness requirements as given in Section A3.1a, weld across hole details as given in J1.11, welding preheat requirements as given in J2.7 and the thermal-cut surface preparation and inspection requirements as given in M2.2 apply.

At tension splices in Group 4 and 55 shapes and built-up members of material more than 2 inches thick, weld tabs and backing shall be removed and the surfaces ground smooth.

When splicing ASTM A6 Group 4 and 5 rolled shapes or shapes built-up by welding plates more than 2 inches thick to form a cross section, and where the section is to be used as a primary compression member, all weld access holes required to facilitate groove welding operations shall satisfy the provisions of J1.11.

Alternatively, splicing of such members subject to compression, including members which are subject to tension due to wind or seismic loads, may be accomplished using splice details which do not induce large weld shrinkage strains such as partial penetration flange groove welds with fillet-welded surface lap plate splices on the web or with bolted or combination bolted/fillet-welded lap plate splices.

11. Beam Copes and Weld Access Holes

All weld access holes required to facilitate welding operations shall have a length from the toe of the weld preparation not less than $1^1/_2$ times the thickness of the material in which the hole is made. The height of the access hole shall be adequate for deposition of sound weld metal in the adjacent plates and provide clearance for weld tabs for the weld in the material in which the hole is made but not less than the thickness of the material. In hot-rolled shapes and built-up shapes, all beam copes and weld access holes shall be shaped free of notches or sharp reentrant corners except when fillet web-to-flange welds are used in built-up shapes, access holes are permitted to terminate perpendicular to the flange.

For Group 4 and 5 shapes and built-up shapes of material more than 2 inches thick, the thermally cut surfaces of beam copes and weld access holes shall be ground to bright metal and inspected by either magnetic particle or dye penetrant methods. If the curved transition portion of weld access holes and beam copes are formed by predrilled or sawed holes, that portion of the access hole or cope need not be ground. Weld access holes and beam copes in other shapes need not be ground nor inspected by dye penetrant or magnetic particle.

---

*When the individual elements of the cross section are spliced prior to being joined to form the cross section in accordance with ASW D1.1, Article 3.4.6, the applicable provisions of AWS D1.1 apply in lieu of the requirement of this section.

J2. WELDS

All provisions of U.B.C. Standard No. 27-6, American Welding Society *Structural Welding Code—Steel*, AWS D1.1, except Sections 2.3, 2.4, 2.5, 8.13.1, 9, and 10 as applicable, apply to work performed under this Specification.

1. Groove Welds

a. Effective Area. The effective area of groove welds shall be considered as the effective length of the weld times the effective throat thickness.

The effective length of a groove weld shall be the width of the part joined.

The effective throat thickness of a complete-penetration groove weld shall be the thickness of the thinner part joined.

The effective throat thickness of a partial-penetration groove weld shall be as shown in Table J2.1.

The effective throat thickness of a flare groove weld when flush to the surface of a bar or 90° bend in a formed section shall be as shown in Table J2.2. Random sections of production welds for each welding procedure, or such test sections as may be required by design documents, shall be used to verify that the effective throat is consistently obtained.

Larger effective throat thicknesses than those in Table J2.2 are permitted, provided the fabricator can establish by qualification that he can consistently provide such larger effective throat thicknesses. Qualification shall consist of sectioning the weld normal to its axis, at mid-length and terminal ends. Such sectioning shall be made on a number of combinations of material sizes representative of the range to be used in the fabrication or as required by the designer.

b. Limitations. The minimum effective throat thickness of a partial-penetration groove weld shall be as shown in Table J2.4. Weld size is determined by the thicker of the two parts joined, except that the weld size need not exceed the thickness of the thinnest part joined when a larger size is required by calculated strength. For this exception, particular care shall be taken to provide sufficient preheat for soundness of the weld.

TABLE J2.1
Effective Throat Thickness of Partial Penetration Groove Welds

<table>
<tr><th>Welding Process</th><th>Welding Position</th><th>Included Angle at Root of Groove</th><th>Effective Throat Thickness</th></tr>
<tr><td rowspan="3">Shielded metal arc
Submerged arc

Gas metal arc
Flux-cored arc</td><td rowspan="3">All</td><td>J or U joint</td><td rowspan="2">Depth of chamfer</td></tr>
<tr><td>Bevel or V joint
$\geq 60^\circ$</td></tr>
<tr><td>Bevel or V joint
$< 60^\circ$ but $\geq 45^\circ$</td><td>Depth of chamfer minus 1/8-in.</td></tr>
</table>

TABLE J2.2
Effective Throat Thickness of Flare Groove Welds

Type of Weld	Radius (R) of Bar or Bend	Effective Throat Thickness
Flare bevel groove	All	$^5/_{16}R$
Flare V-groove	All	$^1/_2R$[a]

[a]Use $^3/_8R$ for Gas Metal Arc Welding (except short circuiting transfer process) when $R \geq 1$ in.

2. Fillet Welds

a. Effective Area. The effective area of fillet welds shall be taken as the effective length times the effective throat thickness.

The effective length of fillet welds, except fillet welds in holes and slots, shall be the overall length of full-size fillets, including returns.

The effective throat thickness of a fillet weld shall be the shortest distance from the root of the joint to the face of the diagrammatic weld, except that for fillet welds made by the submerged arc process, the effective throat thickness shall be taken equal to the leg size for $^3/_8$ inch and smaller fillet welds, and equal to the theoretical throat plus 0.11 inch for fillet welds over $^3/_8$ inch.

For fillet welds in holes and slots, the effective length shall be the length of the centerline of the weld along the center of the plane through the throat. In the case of overlapping fillets, the effective area shall not exceed the nominal cross-sectional area of the hole or slot, in the plane of the faying surface.

b. Limitations. The *minimum size of fillet welds* shall be as shown in Table J2.5.

TABLE J2.4
Minimum Effective Throat Thickness of Partial-penetration Groove Welds

Material Thickness of Thicker Part Joined (in.)	Minimum Effective Throat Thickness[a] (in.)
To ¼ inclusive	⅛
Over ¼ to ½	3/16
Over ½ to ¾	¼
Over ¾ to 1½	5/16
Over 1½ to 2¼	⅜
Over 2¼ to 6	½
Over 6	⅝

[a]See Sect. J2.

TABLE J2.5
Minimum Size of Fillet Welds

Material Thickness of Thicker Part Joined (in.)	Minimum Size of Fillet Weld[a] (in.)
To $\frac{1}{4}$ inclusive	$\frac{1}{8}$
Over $\frac{1}{4}$ to $\frac{1}{2}$	$\frac{3}{16}$
Over $\frac{1}{2}$ to $\frac{3}{4}$	$\frac{1}{4}$
Over $\frac{3}{4}$	$\frac{5}{16}$

[a]Leg dimension of fillet welds.

Minimum weld size is determined by the thicker of the two parts joined, except that the weld size need not exceed the thickness of the thinner part. For this exception, particular care shall be taken to provide sufficient preheat for soundness of the weld. Weld sizes larger than the thinner part joined are permitted if required by calculated strength. In the as-welded condition, the distance between the edge of the base metal and the toe of the weld may be less than $^1/_{16}$ inch provided the weld size is clearly verifiable.

The *maximum size of fillet welds* that may be used along edges of connected parts shall be:

Along edges of material less than $^1/_4$-inch thick, not greater than the thickness of the material.

Along edges of material $^1/_4$ inch or more in thickness, not greater than the thickness of the material minus $^1/_{16}$ inch, unless the weld is especially designated on the drawings to be built out to obtain full-throat thickness.

The *effective length of fillet welds* designed on the basis of strength shall be not less than 4 times the nominal size, or else the size of the weld shall be considered not to exceed one fourth of its effective length. If longitudinal fillet welds are used alone in end connections of flat bar tension members, the length of each fillet weld shall be not less than the perpendicular distance between them. The transverse spacing of longitudinal fillet welds used in end connections of tension members shall not exceed 8 inches, unless the member is designed on the basis of effective net area in accordance with Section B3.

Intermittent fillet welds may be used to transfer calculated stress across a joint or faying surfaces when the strength required is less than that developed by a continuous fillet weld of the smallest permitted size, and to join components of built-up members. The effective length of any segment of intermittent fillet welding shall be not less than four times the weld size, with a minimum of $1^1/_2$ inches.

In *lap joints,* the minimum amount of lap shall be five times the thickness of the thinner part joined, but not less than 1 inch. Lap joints joining plates or bars subjected to axial stress shall be fillet welded along the end of both lapped parts, except where the deflection of the lapped parts is sufficiently restrained to prevent opening of the joint under maximum loading.

Side or end fillet welds terminating at ends or sides, respectively, of parts or members shall, wherever practical, be returned continuously around the corners for a distance not less than two times the nominal size of the weld. This provision shall apply to side and top fillet welds connecting brackets, beam seats and similar connections, on the plane about which bending moments are computed. For framing angles and simple end plate connections which depend upon flexibility of the outstanding legs for connection flexibility, end returns shall not exceed four times the nominal size of the weld. Fillet welds which occur on opposite sides of a common plane shall be interrupted at the corner common to both welds. End returns shall be indicated on the design and detail drawings.

Fillet welds in holes or slots may be used to transmit shear in lap joints or to prevent the buckling or separation of lapped parts and to join components of built-up members. Such fillet welds may overlap, subject to the provisions of Section J2. Fillet welds in holes or slots are not to be considered plug or slot welds.

3. Plug and Slot Welds

a. Effective Area. The effective shearing area of plug and slot welds shall be considered as the nominal cross-sectional area of the hole or slot in the plane of the faying surface.

b. Limitations. Plug or slot welds may be used to transmit shear in lap joints or to prevent buckling of lapped parts and to join component parts of built-up members.

The diameter of the holes for a plug weld shall not be less than the thickness of the part containing it plus $^5/_{16}$ inch, rounded to the next larger odd $^1/_{16}$ inch, or greater than two and one-fourth times the thickness of the weld metal.

The minimum center-to-center spacing of plug welds shall be four times the diameter of the hole.

The length of slot for a slot weld shall not exceed 10 times the thickness of the weld. The width of the slot shall not be less than the thickness of the part containing it plus $^5/_{16}$ inch, rounded to the next larger odd $^1/_{16}$ inch, nor shall it be larger than two and one-fourth times the thickness of the weld. The ends of the slot shall be semicircular or shall have the corners rounded to a radius not less than the thickness of the part containing it, except those ends, which extend to the edge of the part.

The minimum spacing of lines of slot welds in a direction transverse to their length shall be four times the width of the slot. The minimum center-to-center spacing in a longitudinal direction on any line shall be two times the length of the slot.

The thickness of plug or slot welds in material $^5/_8$ inch or less in thickness shall be equal to the thickness of the material. In material over $^5/_8$ inch in thickness, the thickness of the weld shall be at least one half the thickness of the material but not less than $^5/_8$ inch.

4. Design Strength. The design strength of welds shall be the lower value of ϕF_{BM} and ϕF_w, when applicable, where F_{BM} and F_w are the nominal strengths of the base material and the weld electrode material, respectively. The values of ϕ, F_{BM} and F_w and limitations thereon are given in Table J2.3.

5. Combination of Welds. If two or more of the general types of welds (groove, fillet, plug, slot) are combined in a single joint, the design strength of each shall be separately computed with reference to the axis of the group in order to determine the design strength of the combination.

6. Matching Steel. The choice of electrode for use with complete-penetration groove welds subject to tension normal to the effective area is dictated by the requirements for matching steels given in U.B.C. Standard No. 27-6.

7. MIXED WELD METAL

When notch-toughness is specified, the process consumables for all weld metal, tack welds, root pass and subsequent passes, deposited in a joint shall be compatible to assure notch-tough composite weld metal.

8. PREHEAT FOR HEAVY SHAPES

For A6 Group 4 and 5 shapes and welded built-up members made of plates more than 2 inches thick, a preheat equal to or greater than 350°F. shall be used when making groove-weld splices.

J3. BOLTS, THREADED PARTS AND RIVETS

1. High-strength Bolts. Except as otherwise provided in this standard, use of high-strength bolts shall conform to the provisions of U.B.C. Standard No. 27-7.

If required to be tightened to more than 50 percent of their minimum specified tensile strength, A449 bolts in tension and bearing-type shear connections shall have a F436 hardened washer installed under the bolt head, and the nuts shall meet the requirements of A563. When assembled, all joint surfaces, including those adjacent to the washers, shall be free of scale, except tight mill scale. Except as noted below, all A325 and A490 bolts shall be tightened to a bolt tension not less than that given in Table J3.1. Tightening shall be done by the turn-of-nut method, a direct tension indicator or by calibrated wrench.

TABLE J2.3
Design Strength of Welds

Types of Weld and Stress[a]	Material	Resistance Factor ϕ	Nominal strength F_{BM} or F_w	Required Weld strength level[b,c]
Complete Penetration Groove Weld				
Tension normal to effective area	Base	0.90	F_y	"Matching" weld must be used.
Compression normal to effective area	Base	0.90	F_y	Weld metal with a strength level equal to or less than "matching" may be used.
Tension or compression parallel to axis of weld				
Shear on effective area	Base Weld electrode	0.90 0.80	$0.60F_y$ $0.60F_{EXX}$	
Partial Penetration Groove Welds				
Compression normal to effective area	Base	0.90	F_y	Weld metal with a strength level equal to or less than "matching" weld metal may be used.
Tension or compression parallel to axis of weld[d]				
Shear parallel to axis of weld	Base[e] Weld electrode	0.75	$0.60F_{EXX}$	
Tension normal to effective area	Base Weld Electrode	0.90 0.80	F_y $0.60F_{EXX}$	
Fillet Welds				
Stress on effective area	Base[e] Weld electrode	0.75	$0.60F_{EXX}$	Weld metal with a strength level equal to or less than "matching" weld metal may be used.
Tension or compression parallel to axis of weld[d]	Base	0.90	F_y	
Plug or Slot Welds				
Shear parallel to faying surfaces (on effective area)	Base[e] Weld Electrode	0.75	$0.60F_{EXX}$	Weld metal with a strength level equal to or less than "matching" weld metal may be used.

[a]For definition of effective area, see Sect. J2.
[b]For "matching" weld metal, see Table 4.1.1, AWS D1.1.
[c]Weld metal one strength level stronger than "matching" weld metal will be permitted.
[d]Fillet welds and partial-penetration groove welds joining component elements of built-up members, such as flange-to-web connections, may be designed without regard to the tensile or compressive stress in these elements parallel to the axis of the welds.
[e]The design of connected material is governed by Sect. J4.

TABLE J3.1
Minimum Bolt Tension, kips[a]

Bolt Size, in.	A325 Bolts	A490 Bolts
1/2	12	15
5/8	19	24
3/4	28	35
7/8	39	49
1	51	64
1 1/8	56	80
1 1/4	71	102
1 3/8	85	121
1 1/2	103	148

[a]Equal to 0.70 of minimum tensile strength of bolts, rounded off to nearest kip, as specified in ASTM specifications for A325 and A490 bolts with UNC threads.

Bolts in connections not subject to tension loads, where slip can be permitted and where loosening or fatigue due to vibration or load fluctuations are not design considerations, need only to be tightened to the snug-tight condition. The snug-tight condition is defined as the tightness attained by a few impacts of an impact wrench or the full effort of a worker with an ordinary spud wrench and must bring the connected plies into firm contact. The nominal strength value given in Table J3.2 for bearing-type connections shall be used for bolts tightened to the snug-tight condition. Bolts to be tightened only to the snug-tight condition shall be clearly identified on the design and erection drawings.

2. Effective Bearing Area. The effective bearing area of bolts, threaded parts and rivets shall be the diameter multiplied by the length in bearing, except that for countersunk bolts and rivets one half the depth of the countersink shall be deducted.

3. Design Tension or Shear Strength. The design strength of bolts and threaded parts shall be taken as the product of the resistance factor ϕ and the nominal strength given in Table J3.2 of the unthreaded nominal body area of bolts and threaded parts other than upset rods (see Footnote c of Table J3.2). High-strength bolts required to support the applied load by means of direct tension shall be proportioned so that their average required strength, computed on the basis of nominal bolt area and independent of any initial tightening force, will not exceed the design strength. The applied load shall be the sum of the factored external loads and any tension resulting from prying action produced by deformation of the connected parts.

TABLE J3.2
Design Strength of Fasteners

Description of Fasteners	Tensile Strength: Resistance Factor φ	Tensile Strength: Nominal Strength, ksi	Shear Strength in Bearing-type Connections: Resistance Factor φ	Shear Strength in Bearing-type Connections: Nominal Strength ksi
A307 bolts	0.75	45.0[a]	0.60	27.0[b,e]
A325 bolts, when threads are *not* excluded from shear planes		90.0[d]	0.65	54.0[e]
A325 bolts, when threads *are* excluded from shear planes		90.0[d]		72.0[e]
A490 bolts, when threads are *not* excluded from shear planes		112.5[d]		67.5[e]
A490 bolts, when threads *are* excluded from the shear planes		112.5[d]		90.0[e]
Threaded parts meeting the requirements of Sect. A3, when threads are *not* excluded from the shear planes		$0.75F_u$[a,c]		$0.45F_u$
Threaded parts meeting the requirements of Sect. A3, when threads *are* excluded from the shear planes		$0.75F_u$[a,c]		$0.60F_u$
A502, Gr. 1, hot-driven rivets		45.0[a]		36.0[e]
A502, Gr. 2 & 3, hot-driven rivets		60.0[a]		48.0[e]

[a]Static loading only.
[b]Threads permitted in shear planes.
[c]The nominal tensile strength of the threaded portion of an upset rod, based upon the cross-sectional area at its major thread diameter, A_b shall be larger than the nominal body area of the rod before upsetting times F_y.
[d]For A325 and A490 bolts subject to tensile fatigue loading, see Appendix K4.
[e]When bearing-type connections used to splice tension members have a fastener pattern whose length, measured parallel to the line of force, exceeds 50 in., tabulated values shall be reduced by 20%.

TABLE J3.3
Tension Stress Limit (F_t), ksi, for Fasteners in Bearing-type Connections

Description of Fasteners	Threads Included in the Shear Plane	Threads Excluded from the Shear Plane
A307 bolts	$39 - 1.8f_v \le 30$	
A325 bolts	$85 - 1.8f_v \le 68$	$85 - 1.4f_v \le 68$
A490 bolts	$106 - 1.8f_v \le 84$	$106 - 1.4f_v \le 84$
Threaded parts A449 bolts over 1½-in. diameter	$0.73F_u - 1.8f_v \le 0.56F_u$	$0.73F_u - 1.4f_v \le 0.56F_u$
A502 Gr. 1 rivets	$44 - 1.3f_v \le 34$	
A502 Gr. 2 rivets	$59 - 1.3f_v \le 45$	

4. Combined Tension and Shear in Bearing-type Connections. Bolts and rivets subject to combined tension and shear shall be so proportioned that the tension stress f_t produced by factored loads on the nominal body area A_b does not exceed the values computed from the formulas in Table J3.3. The value of f_v, the shear produced by the same factored loads, shall not exceed the values for shear given in Section J3.3.

5. High-strength Bolts in Slip-critical Joints. The design shear resistance of slip-critical joints shall be determined by using the tabulated values from Table J3.4 multiplied by $\phi = 1.0$, except $\phi = 0.85$ for the long-slotted holes when the load is in the direction of the slot. The shear on the bolt due to service loads shall be less than the tabulated values. When the loading combination includes wind or seismic loads in addition to dead and live loads, the total of the combined load effects, at service loads, may be multiplied by 0.75 in accordance with ANSI 58.1.

When specified by the designer, the nominal slip resistance for connections having special faying surface conditions may be increased to the applicable values in RCSC Load and the Resistance Factor Design Specification.

When a bolt in a slip-critical connection is subjected to a service tensile force T, the nominal resistance in Table J3.4 shall be multiplied by the reduction factor $(1 - T/T_b)$ where T_b is the minimum pretension load from Table J3.1.

6. Bearing Strength at Bolt Holes. When L is not less than $1^1/_2d$ and the distance center to center of bolts is not less than $3d$, the design bearing strength on two or more bolts in the line of force is ϕR_n, where $\phi = 0.75$.

TABLE J3.4
Nominal Slip-critical Shear Strength, ksi, of High-strength Bolts[a]

Type of Bolt	Nominal Shear Strength		
	Standard Size Holes	Oversized and Short-slotted Holes	Long-slotted Holes[b]
A325	17	15	12
A490	21	18	15

[a]Class A (slip coefficient 0.33). Clean mill scale and blast cleaned surfaces with class A coatings. For design strengths with other coatings see RCSC "Load and Resistance Factor Design Specification for Structural Joints Using ASTM A325 or A490 Bolts."
[b]Tabulated values are for the case of load application transverse to the slot. When the load is parallel to the slot multiply tabulated values by 0.85.

In standard or short-slotted holes,

$$R_n = 2.4\ dtF_u \quad \text{(J3-1a)}$$

In long-slotted holes perpendicular to the load,

$$R_n = 2.0\ dtF_u \quad \text{(J3-1b)}$$

For the bolt closest to the edge, in all connections not covered by Formulas J3-1a and J3-1b, the design bearing of a single bolt, or two or more bolts in line of force, each with an end distance less than $1^1/_2 d$, shall be determined by ϕR_n, where $\phi = 0.75$.

$$R_n = LtF_u \quad \text{(J3-1c)}$$

If deformation around the bolt hole is not a design consideration and adequate spacing and edge distance as required by Sections J3.9 and J3.10 is provided, the following formula may be used in lieu of Formulas J3-1a and J3-1b, where ϕ = 0.75.

$$R_n = 3.0\ dtF_u \quad \text{(J3-1d)}$$

WHERE:

d = nominal dia. of bolt, in.

t = thickness of connected part, in.

F_u = specified tensile strength of connected part, ksi

L = distance in line of force from the center of a standard or oversized hole or from the center of the end of a slotted hole to an edge of a connected part, in.

7. Size and Use of Holes.

a. The *maximum sizes* of holes for rivets and bolts are given in Table J3.5, except that larger holes, required for tolerance on location of anchor bolts in concrete foundations, may be used in column base details.

TABLE J3.5
Nominal Hole Dimensions

Bolt Dia.	Hole Dimensions			
	Standard (Dia.)	Oversize (Dia.)	Short-slot (Width × length)	Long-slot (Width × length)
1/2	9/16	5/8	9/16 × 11/16	9/16 × 1 1/4
5/8	11/16	13/16	11/16 × 7/8	11/16 × 1 9/16
3/4	13/16	15/16	13/16 × 1	13/16 × 1 7/8
7/8	15/16	1 1/16	15/16 × 1 1/8	15/16 × 2 3/16
1	1 1/16	1 1/4	1 1/16 × 1 5/16	1 1/16 × 2 1/2
≥1 1/8	d + 1/16	d + 5/16	(d + 1/16) × (d + 3/8)	(d + 1/16) × (2.5 × d)

b. *Standard holes* shall be provided in member-to-member connections, unless oversized, short-slotted or long-slotted holes in bolted connections are approved by the designer. Finger shims up to 1/4 inch may be introduced into slip-critical connections designed on the basis of standard holes without reducing the nominal shear strength of the fastener to that specified for slotted holes.

c. *Oversized holes* may be used in any or all plies of slip-critical connections, but they shall not be used in bearing-type connections. Hardened washers shall be installed over oversized holes in an outer ply.

d. *Short-slotted holes* may be used in any or all plies of slip-critical or bearing-type connections. The slots may be used without regard to direction of loading in slip-critical connections, but the length shall be normal to the direction of the load in bearing-type connections. Washers shall be installed over short-slotted holes in an outer ply; when high-strength bolts are used, such washers shall be hardened.

e. *Long-slotted holes* may be used in only one of the connected parts of either a slip-critical or bearing-type connection at an individual faying surface. Long-slotted holes may be used without regard to direction of loading in slip-critical connections, but shall be normal to the direction of load in bearing-type connections. Where long-slotted holes are used in an outer ply, plate washers or a continuous bar with standard holes, having a size sufficient to completely cover the slot after installation, shall be provided. In high-strength bolted connections, such plate washers or continuous bars shall not be less than 5/16-inch thick and shall be of structural grade material, but need not be hardened. If hardened washers are required for use of high-strength bolts, the hardened washers shall be placed over the outer surface of the plate washer or bar.

f. When A490 bolts over 1 inch in diameter are used in slotted or oversize holes in external plies, a single hardened washer conforming to F436, except with 5/16- inch minimum thickness, shall be used in lieu of the standard washer.

8. Long Grips. A307 bolts providing design strength, and for which the grip exceeds five diameters, shall have their number increased 1 percent for each additional 1/16 inch in the grip.

TABLE J3.6
Values of Spacing Increment C_1, in.

Nominal Dia. of Fastener	Oversize Holes	Slotted Holes		
		Perpendicular to Line of Force	Parallel to Line of Force	
			Short-slots	Long-slots[a]
≤ 7/8	1/8	0	3/16	$1\frac{1}{2}d - \frac{1}{16}$
1	3/16	0	1/4	1 7/16
≥1 1/8	1/4	0	5/16	$1\frac{1}{2}d - \frac{1}{16}$

[a] When length of slot is less than maximum allowed in Table J3.5, C_1 may be reduced by the difference between the maximum and actual slot lengths.

9. Minimum Spacing. The distance between centers of standard, oversized or slotted fastener holes shall not be less than three times the nominal diameter of the fastener, or less than that required by the following paragraph, if applicable.

Along a line of transmitted forces, the distance between centers of holes shall not be less than $3d$ when Rn is determined by J3-1a and J3-1b. Otherwise the distance between centers of holes shall not be less than the following:

a. For standard holes:

$$\frac{P}{\phi F_u t} + \frac{d_h}{2} \qquad \text{(J3-2)}$$

WHERE:

ϕ = 0.75

P = force transmitted by one fastener to the critical connected part, kips

F_u = specified minimum tensile strength of the critical connected part, ksi

t = thickness of the critical connected part, in.

d_h = diameter of standard size hole, in.

b. For oversized and slotted holes, the distance required for standard holes in Subparagraph a, above, plus the applicable increment C_1 from Table J3.6, but the clear distance between holes shall not be less than one bolt diameter.

10. Minimum Edge Distance. The distance from the center of a standard hole to an edge of a connected part shall not be less than the applicable value from Table J3.7 or the value from Formula J3-3, as applicable.

Along a line of transmitted force, in the direction of the force, the distance from the center of a standard hole to the edge of the connected part shall not be less than $1^1/_2 d$ when R_n is determined by Formulas J3-1a or J3-1b. Otherwise the edge distance shall not be less than

$$\frac{P}{\phi F_u t} \qquad \text{(J3-3)}$$

where ϕ, P, F_u, t are defined in Section J3.9.

TABLE J3.7
Minimum Edge Distance, in.
(Center of Standard Hole[a] to Edge of Connected Part)

Nominal Rivet or Bolt Diameter (in.)	At Sheared Edges	At Rolled Edges of Plates, Shapes or Bars or Gas Cut Edges[b]
1/2	7/8	3/4
5/8	1 1/8	7/8
3/4	1 1/4	1
7/8	1 1/2[c]	1 1/8
1	1 3/4[c]	1 1/4
1 1/8	2	1 1/2
1 1/4	2 1/4	1 5/8
Over 1 1/4	1 3/4 × Diameter	1 1/4 × Diameter

[a]For oversized or slotted holes, see Table J3.8.
[b]All edge distances in this column may be reduced 1/8-in. when the hole is at a point where stress does not exceed 25% of the maximum design strength in the element.
[c]These may be 1 1/4 in. at the ends of beam connection angles.

The distance from the center of an oversized or slotted hole to an edge of a connected part shall not be less than that required for a standard hole plus the applicable increment C_2 from Table J3.8.

11. Maximum Edge Distance and Spacing. The maximum distance from the center of any rivet or bolt to the nearest edge of parts in contact shall be 12 times the thickness of the connected part under consideration, but shall not exceed 6 inches. Bolted joints in unpainted steel exposed to atmospheric corrosion require special limitations on pitch and edge distance, see Section E4.

J4. DESIGN SHEAR RUPTURE STRENGTH

The design strength for the limit state of rupture along a shear failure path in main members shall be taken as $\phi F_n A_{ns}$.

WHERE:

ϕ = 0.75

$F_n = 0.6 F_u$ (J4-1)

A_{ns} = net area subject to shear.

J5. CONNECTING ELEMENTS

This section applies to the design of connecting elements, such as stiffeners, gussets, angles and brackets and the panel zones of beam-to-column connections.

1. Eccentric Connections. Intersecting axially stressed members shall have their gravity axes intersect at one point, if practical; if not, provision shall be made for bending and shearing stresses due to the eccentricity.

TABLE J3.8
Values of Edge Distance Increment C_2, in.

Nominal Diameter of Fastener (in.)	Oversized Holes	Slotted Holes: Perpendicular to Edge: Short Slots	Slotted Holes: Perpendicular to Edge: Long Slots[a]	Slotted Holes: Parallel to Edge
≤ 7/8	1/16	1/8	3/4*d*	0
1	1/8	1/8		
≤ 1 1/8	1/8	3/16		

[a]When length of slot is less than maximum allowable (see Table J3.5), C_2 may be reduced by one-half the difference between the maximum and actual slot lengths.

2. Design Strength of Connecting Elements. The design strength ϕR_n of welded, bolted and riveted connecting elements statically loaded in tension (e.g., splice and gusset plates) shall be the lower value obtained according to the limit states of yielding, fracture of the connecting element and block shear rupture.

a. For yielding of the connecting element:

$\phi = 0.90$

$$R_n = A_g F_y \quad \text{(J5-1)}$$

b. For fracture of the connecting element where $A_n \leq 0.85 A_g$:

$$\phi = 0.75 \quad \text{(J5-2)}$$

$R_n = A_n F_u$

c. For block shear rupture: Block shear is a failure mode in which the resistance is determined by the sum of the shear strength on a failure path(s) and the tensile strength on a perpendicular segment. When ultimate strength on the net section is used to determine the resistance on one segment, yielding on the gross section shall be used on the perpendicular segment: $\phi = 0.75$. Design strength shall be the larger of the two failure modes.

At beam end connections where the top flange is coped, and in similar situations, failure can occur by shear along a plane through the fasteners, acting in combination with tension along a perpendicular plane. In such cases, the ultimate strength on the net section (shear or tension) shall be used to determine the resistance of one segment and yielding on the gross section (shear or tension) shall be used for the perpendicular segment, with $\phi = 0.75$ for both. By alternating the choice of which segment resistance is based on ultimate strength, two possible values of design strength are obtained. The larger value shall be taken as the design strength.

For all other connecting elements, the design strength ϕR_n shall be determined for the applicable limit state to insure that the design strength is equal to or greater than the required strength, where R_n is the nominal strength appropriate to the geometry and type of loading on the connecting element. The shear limit state is governed by:

$\phi = 0.80$

$R_n = 0.7 A_g F_y$ (J5-3)

6. FILLERS

In welded construction, any filler $^1/_4$ inch or more in thickness shall extend beyond the edges of the splice plate and shall be welded to the part on which it is fitted with sufficient weld to transmit the splice plate load, applied at the surface of the filler. The welds joining the splice plate to the filler shall be sufficient to transmit the splice plate load and shall be long enough to avoid overloading the filler along the toe of the weld. Any filler less than $^1/_4$-inch thick shall have its edges made flush with the edges of the splice plate and the weld size shall be the sum of the size necessary to carry the splice plus the thickness of the filler plate.

When bolts or rivets carrying loads pass through fillers thicker than $^1/_4$ inch except in connections designed as slip-critical connections, the fillers shall be extended beyond the splice material and the filler extension shall be secured by enough bolts or rivets to distribute the total stress in the member uniformly over the combined section of the member and the filler, or an equivalent number of fasteners shall be included in the connection.

J7. SPLICES

Groove-welded splices in plate girders and beams shall develop the full strength of the smaller spliced section. Other types of splices in cross sections of plate girders and beams shall develop the strength required by the forces at the point of splice.

J8. BEARING STRENGTH

The strength of surfaces in bearing is ϕR_n, where $\phi = 0.75$ and R_n is defined below for various types of bearing.

1. Milled or Finished Surfaces. For milled surfaces, pins in reamed, drilled or bored holes, and ends of fitted bearing stiffeners,

$$R_n = 2.0\, F_y A_{pb} \quad \text{(J8-1)}$$

WHERE:

F_y = specified minimum yield stress, ksi

A_{pb} = projected bearing area, in.^{2}

2. Expansion Rollers and Rockers. For expansion rollers and rockers,

$$R_n = 1.5\,(F_y - 13)\, ld/20 \quad \text{(J8-2)}$$

WHERE:

d = diameter, in.

l = length of bearing, in.

J9. COLUMN BASES AND BEARING ON CONCRETE

Proper provision shall be made to transfer the column loads and moments to the footings and foundations.

In the absence of code regulations, design bearing loads on concrete may be taken as $\phi_c P_p$:

On the full area of a concrete support .... $P_p = 0.85f'_c A_1$

On less than the full area of a concrete support ..... $P_p = 0.85f'_c A_1 \sqrt{A_2/A_1}$

WHERE:

ϕ_c = 0.60

A_1 = area of steel concentrically bearing on a concrete support, in.

A_2 = maximum area of the portion of the supporting surface that is geometrically similar to and concentric with the loaded area, in.^{2}

$\sqrt{A_2/A_1} \leq 2$

J10. ANCHOR BOLTS AND EMBEDMENTS

1. Anchor Bolts. Anchor bolts shall be designed to provide resistance to all design conditions on completed structures of tension and shear at the bases of columns, including the net tensile components of any bending moment which may result from column base restraint.

2. Embedments. The concrete structure shall be designed to safely support the loads from the embedment with an appropriate factor of safety to ensure that the embedment strength is not reduced as a result of local or gross failure of the supporting concrete structure.

The strength and design of the structural steel elements of the embedment shall be in accordance with this specification. Bolts, studs and bars functioning as embedment anchors resisting tensile loads shall be designed to transfer the design load to the concrete by means of bond, shear, bearing or a combination thereof.

Shear loads shall be considered to be transmitted by the embedment to the concrete by either shear lugs or shear friction.

The friction force V, kips, to resist shear shall be computed as follows:

$$V = \mu P \tag{J10-1}$$

WHERE:

P = normal force, kips

μ = coefficient of friction

The coefficient of friction μ shall be 0.90 for concrete placed against as- rolled steel with contact plane a full plate thickness below the concrete surface; 0.70 for concrete or grout placed against as-rolled steel with contact plane coincidental with the concrete surface; 0.55 for grouted conditions with the contact plane between grout and as-rolled steel above the concrete surface.

3. Prestressed Embedments. Anchorage to concrete structures by means of post-tensioned high-strength steel members is permissible. The material and the design requirements of the high-strength steel members and associated anchorage, as well as the fabrication and installation procedures, shall conform to the appropriate provisions of applicable codes.

CHAPTER K

STRENGTH DESIGN CONSIDERATIONS

Sec.27.1403K. This chapter covers additional member strength design considerations related to introduction of concentrated forces, ponding, torsion and fatigue.

K1. WEBS AND FLANGES WITH CONCENTRATED FORCES

1. Design Basis. Members with concentrated loads applied normal to *one flange* and symmetric to the web shall have a flange and web design strength sufficient to satisfy the local flange bending, web yielding strength, web crippling and sidesway web buckling criteria of Sections K1.2, K1.3, K1.4 and K1.5. Members with concentrated loads applied to *both flanges* shall have a web design strength sufficient to satisfy the web yielding, web crippling and column web buckling criteria of Sections K1.3, K1.4 and K1.6.

Where pairs of stiffeners are provided on opposite sides of the web, at concentrated loads, and extend at least half the depth of the member, Sections K1.2 and K1.3 need not be checked.

For column webs subject to high shears, see Section K1.7; for bearing stiffeners, see Section K1.8.

2. Local Flange Bending. The flange design strength in bending due to a tensile load shall be ϕR_n, kips

WHERE:

ϕ = 0.90

$R_n = 6.25 t_f^2 F_{yf}$ (K1-1)

F_{yf} = specified minimum yield stress of flange, ksi

t_f = thickness of the loaded flange, in.

If the length of loading measured across the member flange is less than $0.15b$, where b is the member flange width, Formula (K1-1) need not be checked.

3. Local Web Yielding. The design strength of the web at the toe of the fillet under concentrated loads shall be ϕR_n, kips, where $\phi = 1.0$ and R_n is determined as follows:

a. When the force to be resisted is a concentrated load producing tension or compression, applied at a distance from the member end that is greater than the depth of the member,

$$R_n = (5k + N)\, F_{yw} t_w \qquad \text{(K1-2)}$$

b. When the force to be resisted is a concentrated load applied at or near the end of the member,

$$R_n = (2.5k + N)\, F_{yw} t_w \qquad \text{(K1-3)}$$

WHERE:

F_{yw} = specified minimum yield stress of the web, ksi

N = length of bearing, in.

k = distance from outer face of flange to web toe of fillet, in.

t_w = web thickness, in.

4. Web Crippling. For unstiffened portions of webs of members under concentrated loads, the design compressive strength shall be ϕR_n, kips, where $\phi = 0.75$ and the nominal strength R_n is determined as follows:

a. When the concentrated load is applied at a distance not less than $d/2$ from the end of the member:

$$R_n = 135 t_w^2 \left[1 + 3 \left(\frac{N}{d} \right) \left(\frac{t_w}{t_f} \right)^{1.5} \right] \sqrt{F_{yw}\, t_f / t_w} \qquad \text{(K1-4)}$$

b. When the concentrated load is applied less than a distance $d/2$ from the end of the member:

$$R_n = 68 t_w^2 \left[1 + 3 \left(\frac{N}{d} \right) \left(\frac{t_w}{t_f} \right)^{1.5} \right] \sqrt{F_{yw}\, t_f / t_w} \qquad \text{(K1-5)}$$

WHERE:

d = overall depth of the member, in.

t_f = flange thickness, in.

If stiffeners are provided and extend at least one-half the web depth, Formulas (K1-4) and (K1-5) need not be checked.

5. Sidesway Web Buckling. For webs of members with flanges not restrained against relative movement by stiffeners or lateral bracing and subject to concentrated compressive loads, the design compressive strength shall be ϕR_n, kips, where $\phi = 0.85$ and the nominal strength R_n shall be determined as follows:

a. If the loaded flange is restrained against rotation and $(d_c/t_w)/(\rho/b_f)$ is less than 2.3:

$$R_n = \frac{12{,}000 t_w^3}{h} \left[1 + 0.4 \left(\frac{d_c/t_w}{l/b_f} \right)^3 \right] \qquad \text{(K1-6)}$$

b. If the loaded flange is *not* restrained against rotation and $(d_c/t_w)/(\rho/b_f)$ is less than 1.7:

WHERE:

l = largest laterally unbraced length along either flange at the point of load, in.

$$R_n = \frac{12,000t_w^3}{h}\left[0.4\left(\frac{d_c/t_w}{l/b_f}\right)^3\right] \quad \text{(K1-7)}$$

b_f = flange width, in.
t_w = web thickness, in.
d_c = $d - 2k$ = web depth clear of fillets, in.

Formulas (K1-6) and (K1-7) need not be checked providing $(d_c/t_w)/(\rho/b_f)$ exceeds 2.3 or 1.7, respectively, or for webs subject to distributed load.

If a concentrated load is located at a point where the web flexural stress due to factored load is below yielding, 24,000 may be used in lieu of 12,000 in Formulas (K1-6) and (K1-7).

6. Compression Buckling of the Web. For unstiffened portions of webs of members under concentrated loads to both flanges, the design compressive strength shall be ϕR_n, kips, where

$$\phi = 0.90$$

$$R_n = \frac{4,100t_w^3\sqrt{F_{yw}}}{d_c} \quad \text{(K1-8)}$$

R_n may be exceeded provided that a transverse stiffener or pair of stiffeners is attached to the web to satisfy Section F3.

7. Compression Members with Web Panels Subject to High Shear. For compression members subject to high shear stress in the web, the design web shear strength shall be ϕR_v, kips, where $\phi = 0.90$ and R_v shall be determined as follows:

a. For $P_u \leq 0.75\ P_n$:

$$R_v = 0.7\ F_y d_c t_w \quad \text{(K1-9)}$$

b. For $P_u > 0.75\ P_n$:

$$R_v = 0.7\ F_y d_c t_w\ [1.9 - 1.2\ (P_u/P_n)] \quad \text{(K1-10)}$$

WHERE:

P_u = required axial strength, kips
P_n = nominal axial strength, kips

8. Stiffener Requirements for Concentrated Loads. When required, stiffeners shall be placed in pairs at unframed ends of beams and girders. They shall be placed in pairs at points of concentrated load on the interior of beams, girders or columns if the load exceeds the nominal strength ϕR_n as determined from Sections K1.2 through K1.6, as applicable.

If the concentrated load, tension of compression exceeds the criteria for ϕR_n of Section K1.2 or K1.3, respectively, stiffeners need not extend more than one half the depth of the web, except as follows:

If concentrated compressive loads are applied to the members and if the load exceeds the compressive strength of the web ϕR_n given in Section K1.4 or K1.6, the stiffeners shall be designed as axially compressed members (columns) in accordance with requirements of Section E2 with an effective length equal to $0.75h$, a cross section composed of two stiffeners and a strip of the web having a width of $25t_w$, at interior stiffeners and $12t_w$ at the ends of members.

When the load normal to the flange is tensile, the stiffeners shall be welded to the loaded flange. When the load normal to the flange is compressive, the stiffeners shall either bear on or be welded to the loaded flange.

K2. PONDING

The roof system shall be investigated by structural analysis to assure adequate strength and stability under ponding conditions, unless the roof surface is provided with sufficient slope toward points of free drainage or adequate individual drains to prevent the accumulation of rainwater.

The roof system shall be considered stable and no further investigation is needed if:

$$C_p + 0.9C_s \leq 0.25 \qquad \text{(K2-1)}$$

and $I_d \geq 25\ (S^4)\ 10^{-6}$ (H2-2)

WHERE:

$$C_p = \frac{32L_s\ L_p^4}{10^7 I_p}$$

$$C_s = \frac{32SL_s^4}{10^7 I_s}$$

L_p = column spacing in direction of girder (length of primary members), ft.

L_s = column spacing perpendicular to direction of girder (length of secondary members), ft.

S = spacing of secondary members, ft.

I_p = moment of inertia of primary members, $in.^4$

I_s = moment of inertia of secondary members, $in.^4$

I_d = moment of inertia of the steel deck supported on secondary members, $in.^4$ per ft.

For trusses and steel joists, the moment of inertia I_s shall be decreased 15 percent when used in the above equation. A steel deck shall be considered a secondary member when it is directly supported by the primary members.

See Appendix K2 for an alternate determination of flat roof framing stiffness.

K3. TORSION

For limiting values of normal and shear stress, due to torsion and other loading, see Section H2. Some constrained local yielding may be permitted.

K4. FATIGUE

Few members or connections in conventional buildings need to be designed for fatigue, since most load changes in such structures occur only a small number of times or produce only minor stress fluctuations. The occurrence of full design wind or earthquake loads is too infrequent to warrant consideration in fatigue design. However, crane runways and supporting structures for machinery and equipment are often subject to fatigue loading conditions.

Members and their connections subject to fatigue loading shall be proportioned in accordance with the provisions of Appendix K4 for service loads.

CHAPTER L

SERVICEABILITY DESIGN CONSIDERATIONS

Sec. 27.1403L. This chapter is intended to provide design guidance for serviceability considerations not covered elsewhere. Serviceability is a state in which the function of a building, its appearance, maintainability, durability and comfort of its occupants are preserved under normal usage.

The general design requirement for serviceability is given in Section A5.4. Limiting values of structural behavior to ensure serviceability (e.g., maximum deflections, accelerations, etc.) shall be chosen with due regard to the intended function of the structure.

Where necessary, serviceability shall be checked using realistic loads for the appropriate serviceability limit state.

L1. CAMBER

If any special camber requirements are necessary to bring a loaded member into proper relation with the work of other trades, as for the attachment of runs of sash, the requirements shall be set forth in the design documents.

Beams and trusses detailed without specified camber shall be fabricated so that after erection any camber due to rolling or shop assembly shall be upward. If camber involves the erection of any member under a preload, this shall be noted in the design documents.

L2. EXPANSION AND CONTRACTION

Adequate provision shall be made for expansion and contraction appropriate to the service conditions of the structure.

L3. DEFLECTIONS, VIBRATION AND DRIFT

1. Deflections. Deformations in structural members and structural systems due to service loads shall not impair the serviceability of the structure.

2. Vibration. Vibration shall be considered in designing beams and girders supporting large areas free of partitions or other sources of damping, where vibration due to pedestrian traffic or other sources within the building might not be acceptable.

3. Drift. Lateral deflection or drift of structures due to code-specified wind or seismic loads shall not cause collision with adjacent structures or exceed the limiting values of such drifts which may be specified or appropriate.

L4. CONNECTION SLIP

For the design of slip-resistant connections, see Section J3.5.

L5. CORROSION

When appropriate, structural components shall be designed to tolerate corrosion or shall be protected against corrosion that may impair the strength or serviceability of the structure.

CHAPTER M

FABRICATION, ERECTION AND QUALITY CONTROL

Sec.27.1403M.

M1. SHOP DRAWINGS

Shop drawings giving complete information necessary for the fabrication of the component parts of the structure, including the location, type and size of all welds, bolts and rivets, shall be prepared in advance of the actual fabrication. These drawings shall clearly distinguish between shop and field welds and bolts and shall clearly identify slip-critical high-strength bolted connections.

Shop drawings shall be made in conformity with the best practice and with due regard to speed and economy in fabrication and erection.

M2. FABRICATION

1. Cambering, Curving and Straightening. Local application of heat or mechanical means may be used to introduce or correct camber, curvature and straightness. The temperature of heated areas, as measured by approved methods, shall not exceed 1,100°F. for A514 steel nor 1,200°F. for other steels.

2. Thermal Cutting. Thermal cutting shall preferably be done by machine. Thermally cut edges which will be subjected to substantial stress, or which are to have weld metal deposited on them, shall be reasonably free from notches or gouges; notches or gouges not more than $^1/_{16}$ inch deep will be permitted. Notches or gouges greater than $^3/_{16}$ inch deep that remain from cutting shall be removed by grinding or repaired by welding. All reentrant comers shall be shaped to provide a smooth transition. If a specific contour is required, it must be shown in the design documents.

M2.2 THERMAL CUTTING

Thermally cut free edges which will be subject to substantial tensile stress shall be free of gouges greater than $^3/_{16}$ inch deep and sharp notches; gouges greater than $^3/_{16}$ inch deep and sharp notches shall be removed by grinding or repaired by welding. Thermally cut edges which are to have weld deposited upon them shall be reasonably free of notches or gouges.

All reentrant comers shall be shaped to a smooth transition. If specific contour is required it must be shown on the contract documents.

Beam copes and weld access holes shall meet the geometrical requirements of Section J2.7. For beam copes and weld access holes in ASTM A6 Groups 4 and 5 shapes and welding built- up shapes with material thickness greater than 2 inches, a preheat temperature of not less than 150°F. shall be applied prior to thermal cutting.

3. Planing of Edges. Planing or finishing of sheared or thermally cut edges of plates or shapes will not be required unless specifically called for in the design documents or included in a stipulated edge preparation for welding.

4. Welding Construction. The technique of welding, the workmanship, appearance and quality of welds and the methods used in correcting nonconforming work shall be in accordance with "Section 3—Workmanship" and "Section 4—Technique" of the AWS *Structural Welding Code—Steel,* D1.1, U.B.C. Standard No. 27-6.

5. Bolted Construction. All parts of bolted members shall be pinned or bolted and rigidly held together while assembling. Use of a drift pin in bolt holes during assembling shall not distort the metal or enlarge the holes. Poor matching of holes shall be cause for rejection.

If the thickness of the material is not greater than the nominal diameter of the bolt plus $^1/_8$ inch, the holes may be punched. If the thickness of the material is greater than the nominal diameter of the bolt plus $^1/_8$ inch, the holes shall be either drilled or subpunched and reamed. The die for all subpunched holes, and the drill for all subdrilled holes, shall be at least $^1/_{16}$ inch smaller than the nominal diameter of the bolt. Holes in A514 steel plates over $^1/_2$ inch thick shall be drilled.

Fully inserted finger shims, with a total thickness of not more than $^1/_4$ inch within a joint, may be used in joints without changing the design load (based upon hole type) for the design of connections. The orientation of such shims is independent of the direction of application of the load.

The use of high-strength bolts shall conform to the requirements of the RCSC Load and Resistance Factor Design Specification for Structural Joints Using ASTM A325 or A490 Bolts.

6. Compression Joints. Compression joints which depend on contact bearing as part of the splice capacity shall have the bearing surfaces of individual fabricated pieces prepared by milling, sawing or other suitable means.

7. Dimensional Tolerances. Dimensional tolerances shall be as permitted in the *Code of Standard Practice* of the American Institute of Steel Construction, Inc., 1986 edition.

8. Finishing of Column Bases. Column bases and base plates shall be finished in accordance with the following requirements:

a. Steel bearing plates 2 inches or less in thickness may be used without milling, provided a satisfactory contact bearing is obtained. Steel bearing plates over 2 inches but not over 4 inches in thickness may be straightened by pressing or, if presses are not available, by milling for all bearing surfaces (except as noted in subparagraphs b and c of this section), to obtain a satisfactory contact bearing. Steel bearing plates over 4 inches in thickness shall be milled for all bearing surfaces (except as noted in subparagraphs b and c of this section).

b. Bottom surfaces of bearing plates and column bases which are grouted to ensure full bearing contact on foundations need not be milled.

c. Top surfaces of bearing plates need not be milled when full-penetration welds are provided between the column and the bearing plate.

M3. SHOP PAINTING

1. General Requirements. Shop painting and surface preparation shall be in accordance with the provisions of the *Code of Standard Practice* of the American Institute of Steel Construction, Inc., 1986 edition.

Unless otherwise specified, steelwork which will be concealed by interior building finish or will be in contact with concrete need not be painted. Unless specifically excluded, all other steelwork shall be given one coat of shop paint.

2. Inaccessible Surfaces. Except for contact surfaces, surfaces inaccessible after shop assembly shall be cleaned and painted prior to assembly, if required by the design documents.

3. Contact Surfaces. Paint is permitted unconditionally in bearing-type connections. For slip-critical connections where the design is based on special faying surface conditions in accordance with Section J3.5, shop contact surfaces shall be cleaned prior to assembly in accordance with the provisions of the *Code of Standard Practice* of the American Institute of Steel Construction, Inc., 1986 edition, but shall not be painted. Field contact surfaces and surfaces meeting the requirements of Section J3.5 shall be shop cleaned in accordance with the design documents, except as provided by Section M3.5.

4. Finished Surfaces. Machine-finished surfaces shall be protected against corrosion by a rust-inhibiting coating that can be removed prior to erection, or which has characteristics that make removal prior to erection unnecessary.

5. Surfaces Adjacent to Field Welds. Unless otherwise specified in the design documents, surfaces within 2 inches of any field weld location shall be free of materials that would prevent proper welding or produce toxic fumes during welding.

M4. ERECTION

1. Alignment of Column Bases. Column bases shall be set level and to correct elevation with full bearing on concrete or masonry.

2. Bracing. The frame of steel skeleton buildings shall be carried up true and plumb within the limits defined in the *Code of Standard Practice* of the American Institute of Steel Construction, Inc., 1986 edition. Temporary bracing shall be provided, in accordance with the requirements of the *Code of Standard Practice,* wherever necessary to take care of all loads to which the structure may be subjected, including equipment and the operation of same. Such bracing shall be left in place as long as may be required for safety.

3. Alignment. No permanent bolting or welding shall be performed until as much of the structure as will be stiffened thereby has been properly aligned.

4. Fit of Column Compression Joints. Lack of contact bearing not exceeding a gap of $^1/_{16}$ inch, regardless of the type of splice used (partial-penetration groove welded or bolted), shall be acceptable. If the gap exceeds $^1/_{16}$ inch, and if an engineering investigation shows that sufficient contact area does not exist, the gap shall be packed out with nontapered steel shims. Shims need not be other than mild steel, regardless of the grade of the main material.

5. Field Welding. Any shop paint on surfaces adjacent to joints to be field welded shall be wire brushed to reduce the paint film to a minimum.

Field welding of attachments to installed embedments in contact with concrete shall be done in such a manner as to avoid excessive thermal expansion of the embedment which could result in spalling or cracking of the concrete or excessive stress in the embedment anchors.

6. Field Painting. Responsibility for touch-up painting, cleaning and field painting shall be allocated in accordance with accepted local practices, and this allocation shall be set forth explicitly in the design documents.

7. Field Connections. As erection progresses, the work shall be securely bolted or welded to take care of all dead load, wind and erection stresses.

M5. QUALITY CONTROL

The fabricator shall provide quality control procedures to the extent that he deems necessary to assure that all work is performed in accordance with this Specification. In addition to the fabricator's quality control procedures, material and workmanship at all times may be subject to inspection by qualified inspectors representing the purchaser. If such inspection by representatives of the purchaser will be required, it shall be so stated in the design documents.

1. Cooperation. As far as possible, all inspection by representatives of the purchaser shall be made at the fabricator's plant. The fabricator shall cooperate with the inspector, permitting access for inspection to all places where work is being done. The purchaser's inspector shall schedule his work for minimum interruption to the work of the fabricator.

2. Rejections. Material or workmanship not in reasonable conformance with the provisions of this Specification may be rejected at any time during the progress of the work. The fabricator shall receive copies of all reports furnished to the purchaser by the inspection agency.

3. Inspection of Welding. The inspection of welding shall be performed in accordance with the provisions of Section 6 of the AWS *Structural Welding Code—Steel,* D1.1, in. U.B.C. Standard No. 27-6.

When visual inspection is required to be performed by AWS certified welding inspectors, it shall be so specified in the design documents.

When nondestructive testing is required, the process, extent and standards of acceptance shall be clearly defined in the design documents.

4. Inspection of Slip-critical High-strength Bolted Connections. The inspection of slip-critical high-strength bolted connections shall be in accordance with the provisions of the RCSC Load and Resistance Factor Design Specification for Structural Joints Using ASTM A325 or A490 Bolts.

5. Identification of Steel. The fabricator shall be able to demonstrate by a written procedure and by actual practice a method of material application and identification, visible at least through the "fit-up" operation, of the main structural elements of a shipping piece.

The identification method shall be capable of verifying proper material application as it relates to:

1. Material specification designation.
2. Heat number, if required.
3. Material test reports for special requirements.

APPENDIX B

DESIGN REQUIREMENTS

Sec. 27.1404B.

B5. LOCAL BUCKLING

3. Slender Compression Elements. Axially loaded members containing elements subject to compression which have a width-thickness ratio in excess of the applicable λ_r, as stipulated in Section B5.1, shall be proportioned according to this Appendix. Flexural members with slender compression elements shall be designed in accordance with Appendix F1.7. Rolled flexural members with proportions not covered by Appendix F1.7 shall be designed in accordance with this Appendix.

a. Unstiffened Compression Elements. The design strength of unstiffened compression elements whose width-thickness ratio exceeds the applicable limit λ_r, as stipulated in Section B5.1, shall be subject to a reduction factor Q_s. The value of Q_s shall be determined by Formulas (A-B5-1) through (A-B5-6), as applicable. When such elements comprise the compression flange of a flexural member, the maximum required bending stress shall not exceed $\phi_b F_y Q_s$, where $\phi_b = 0.90$. The design strength of axially loaded compression members shall be modified by the appropriate reduction factor Q_s, as provided in paragraph c.

For single angles:

When $76.0/\sqrt{F_y} < b/t < 155/\sqrt{F_y}$:

$$Q_s = 1.340 - 0.00447\,(b/t)\sqrt{F_y} \qquad \text{(A-B5-1)}$$

When $b/t \geq 155/\sqrt{F_y}$:

$$Q_s = 15,500/[F_y(b/t)^2] \qquad \text{(A-B5-2)}$$

For angles or plates projecting from columns or other compression members, and for projecting elements of compression flanges of girders:

When $95.0/\sqrt{F_y} < b/t < 176/\sqrt{F_y}$:

$$Q_s = 1.415 - 0.00437\,(b/t)\sqrt{F_y} \qquad \text{(A-B5-3)}$$

When $b/t \geq 176/\sqrt{F_y}$:

$$Q_s = 20,000/[F_y(b/t)^2] \qquad \text{(A-B5-4)}$$

For stems of tees:

When $127/\sqrt{F_y} < b/t < 176/\sqrt{F_y}$:

$$Q_s = 1.908 - 0.00715\ (b/t)\sqrt{F_y} \qquad \text{(A-B5-5)}$$

When $b/t \geq 176/\sqrt{f_y}$:

$$Q_s = 20,000/[F_y(b/t)^2] \qquad \text{(A-B5-6)}$$

WHERE:

b = width of unstiffened compression element as defined in Section B5.1, in.

t = thickness of unstiffened element, in.

F_y = specified minimum yield stress, ksi

Unstiffened elements of tees whose proportions exceed the limits of Section B5.1 shall conform to the limits given in Table A-B5.1.

b. Stiffened Compression Elements. When the width-thickness ratio of uniformly compressed stiffened elements (except perforated cover plates) exceeds the limit λ_r stipulated in Section B5.1, a reduced effective width b_e shall be used in computing the design properties of the section containing the element.

TABLE A-B5.1
Limiting Proportions for Tees

Shape	Ratio of Full Flange Width to Profile Depth	Ratio of Flange Thickness to Web or Stem Thickness
Built-up tees	≥ 0.50	≥ 1.25
Rolled tees	≥ 0.50	≥ 1.10

i. For flanges of square and rectangular sections of uniform thickness:

$$b_e = \frac{326t}{\sqrt{f}}\left[1 - \frac{64.9}{(b/t)\sqrt{f}}\right] \leq b \qquad \text{(A-B5-7)}$$

ii. For other uniformly compressed elements:

$$b_e = \frac{326t}{\sqrt{f}}\left[1 - \frac{57.2}{(b/t)\sqrt{f}}\right] \leq b \qquad \text{(A-B5-8)}$$

WHERE :

b = actual width of a stiffened compression element, as defined in Section B5.1, in.

b_e = reduced width, in.

t = element thickness, in.

f = computed elastic compressive stress in the stiffened elements, based on the design properties as specified in Section C of this Appendix, ksi. If unstiffened elements are included in the total cross section, f for the stiffened element must be such that the maximum compressive stress in the unstiffened element does not exceed ϕF_{cr} as defined in Appendix B5.3c with $Q = Q_s$ and $\phi_c = 0.85$, or $\phi_b F_y Q_s$ with $\phi_b = 0.90$, as applicable.

iii. For axially loaded circular sections:

Members with diameter-to-thickness ratios D/t greater than $3{,}300/F_y$, but having a diameter-to-thickness ratio of less than $13{,}000/F_y$;

$$Q = \frac{1,100}{F_y(D/t)} + \frac{2}{3} \qquad \text{(A-B5-9)}$$

WHERE:

D = outside diameter, in.

t = wall thickness, in.

c. Design Properties. Properties of sections shall be determined using the full cross section, except as follows:

In computing the moment of inertia and elastic section modulus of flexural members, the effective width of uniformly compressed stiffened elements, as determined in Appendix B5.3b, shall be used in determining effective cross-sectional properties.

For unstiffened elements of the cross section, Q_s is determined from Appendix B5.3a. For stiffened elements of the cross section

$$Q_a = \frac{\text{effective area}}{\text{actual area}} \qquad \text{(A-B5-10)}$$

where the effective area is equal to the summation of the effective areas of the cross section.

For axially loaded compression members the gross cross-sectional area and the radius of gyration r shall be computed on the basis of the actual cross section. However, when $\lambda_c\sqrt{Q} \leq 1.5$, the critical stress F_{cr} shall be determined by

$$F_{cr} = Q(0.658^{Q\lambda_c^2})F_y \qquad \text{(A-B5-11)}$$

WHERE:

$$Q = Q_s\, Q_a \tag{A-B5-12}$$

i. Cross sections composed entirely of unstiffened elements, $Q = Q_s (Q_a = 1.0)$
ii. Cross sections composed entirely of stiffened elements, $Q = Q_a (Q_s = 1.0)$
iii. Cross sections composed of both stiffened and unstiffened elements, $Q = Q_s Q_a$

When $\lambda_c \sqrt{Q} > 1.5$, the critical stress F_{cr} shall be determined by

$$F_{cr} = \left[\frac{0.877}{\lambda_c^2}\right] F_y \tag{A-B5-13}$$

APPENDIX E

COLUMNS AND OTHER COMPRESSION MEMBERS

Sec. 27.1404E.

E3. FLEXURAL-TORSIONAL BUCKLING

This section applies to the strength of singly symmetric and unsymmetric columns for the limiting states of flexural-torsional and torsional buckling.

Torsional buckling of symmetric shapes and flexural-torsional buckling of unsymmetric shapes are modes of buckling usually not considered in the design of hot-rolled columns. (Generally, either these modes do not govern or the critical load differs very little from the weak-axis planar buckling load.) Such buckling modes may, however, control the capacity of columns made from relatively thin plate elements and of unsymmetric columns.

The strength of compression members determined by the limit states of torsional and flexural-torsional buckling is $\phi_c P_n$,

WHERE:

ϕ = 0.85

P_n = nominal resistance in compression, kips

$= A_g F_{cr}$ (A-E3-1)

A_g = gross area of cross section, in.^{2}

Q = 1.0 for elements meeting the width-thickness ratios λ_r of Section B5.1

$= Q_s Q_a$ for elements not meeting the width-thickness ratios λ_r of Section B5.1 and determined in accordance with the provisions of Appendix B5.3

The nominal critical stress F_{cr} is determined as follows:

a. For $\lambda_e \sqrt{Q} \leq 1.5$:

$$F_{cr} = Q(0.65Q\lambda_e^2)F_y \tag{A-E3-2}$$

b. For $\lambda_e \sqrt{Q} > 1.5$:

$$F_{cr} = \left[\frac{0.877}{\lambda_e^2}\right] F_y \qquad \text{(A-E3-3)}$$

WHERE:

$$\lambda_e = \sqrt{F_y/F_e} \qquad \text{(A-E3-4)}$$

F_y = specified minimum yield stress of steel, ksi

The critical torsional or flexural-torsional elastic buckling stress F_e is determined as follows:

a. For doubly symmetric shapes the critical torsional elastic buckling stress is

$$F_e = \left[\frac{\pi^2 E C_w}{(K_z L)^2} + GJ\right] \frac{1}{I_x + I_y} \qquad \text{(A-E3-5)}$$

b. For singly symmetric shapes, where y is the axis of symmetry, the critical flexural-torsional elastic buckling stress is

$$F_e = \frac{F_{ey} + F_{ez}}{2H} \left(1 - \sqrt{1 - \frac{4F_{ey} F_{ez} H}{(F_{ey} + F_{ez})^2}}\right) \qquad \text{(A-E3-6)}$$

c. For unsymmetric shapes, the critical flexural-torsional elastic buckling stress F_e is the lowest root of the cubic equation

$$(F_e - F_{ex})(F_e - F_{ey})(F_e - F_{ez}) -$$
$$F_e^2(F_e - F_{ey})(x_o \sqrt{r_o})^2 -$$
$$F_e^2 (F_e - F_{ex})(y_o \sqrt{r_o})^2 = 0 \qquad \text{(A-E3-7)}$$

WHERE:

K_z = effective length factor for torsional buckling
E = modulus of elasticity, ksi
G = shear modulus, ksi
C = warping constant, in.^{6}
J = torsional constant, in.^{4}
I_x, I_y = moment of inertia about the principal axes,in.^{4}
X_o, y_o = coordinates of shear center with respect to the centroid, in.

$$\bar{r}_o^2 = x_o^2 + y_o^2 + \frac{I_x + I_y}{A} \qquad \text{(A-E3-8)}$$

$$H = 1 - \left(\frac{x_o^2 + y_o^2}{\bar{r}_o^2}\right) \qquad \text{(A-E3-9)}$$

$$F_{ex} = \frac{\pi^2 E}{(K_x L/r_x)^2} \qquad \text{(A-E3-10)}$$

$$F_{ey} = \frac{\pi^2 E}{(K_y L/r_y)^2} \qquad \text{(A-E3-11)}$$

$$F_{ez} = \left(\frac{\pi^2 E C_w}{(K_z L)^2} + \text{GJ}\right)\frac{1}{A\bar{r}_o^2} \qquad \text{(A-E3-12)}$$

WHERE:

A = cross-sectional area of member, in.^{2}

L = unbraced length, in.

K_x, K_y = effective length factors in x and y directions

r_x, r_y = radii of gyration about the principal axes, in.

APPENDIX F

BEAMS AND OTHER FLEXURAL MEMBERS

Sec. 27.1404F.

F1. DESIGN FOR FLEXURE

7. Nominal Flexural Strength. Table A-F1. 1 provides a tabular summary of Formulas (Fl-3) through (Fl-16) for determining the nominal flexural strength of beams and girders. For slenderness parameters of cross sections not included in Table A-Fl. l, see Appendix B5.3.

The nominal flexural strength M_n is the lowest value obtained according to the limit states of: (a) lateral-torsional buckling (LTB); (b) flange local buckling (FLB); and (c) web local buckling (WLB).

The nominal flexural strength M_n shall be determined as follows for each limit state:

For $\lambda \leq \lambda_p$:

$$M_n = M_p \qquad \text{(A-F1-1)}$$

For $\lambda_p < \lambda \leq \lambda_r$:

For the limit state of lateral-torsional buckling:

$$M_n = C_b \left[M_p - (M_p - M_r) \left(\frac{\lambda - \lambda_p}{\lambda_r - \lambda_p} \right) \right] \le M_p \qquad \text{(A-F1-2)}$$

For the limit states of flange and web local buckling:

$$M_n = M_p - (M_p - M_r) \left(\frac{\lambda - \lambda_p}{\lambda_r - \lambda_p} \right) \qquad \text{(A-F1-3)}$$

For $\lambda > \lambda_r$:

For the limit state of lateral-torsional buckling and for flange local buckling:

$$M_n = M_{cr} = S\, F_{cr} \qquad \text{(A-F1-4)}$$

For λ of the flange $> \lambda_r$ in shapes not included in Table A-F1.1, see Appendix B5.3.

For λ of the web $> \lambda_r$, see Appendix G.

For all slenderness parameters, the flexural strength of hybrid sections is limited by the flexural strength of equivalent homogeneous sections made up of the hybrid web and flange steel grade.

The terms used in the above equations are:

M_n = nominal flexural strength, kip-in.

M_p = plastic moment, kip-in.

M_{cr} = buckling moment, kip-in.

M_r = limiting buckling moment (equal to M_{cr} when $\lambda = \lambda_r$), kip-in.

λ = controlling slenderness parameter

= minor axis slenderness ratio L_b/r_y for lateral-torsional buckling

= flange width-thickness ratio b/t for flange local buckling as defined in Section B5.1

= web depth-thickness ratio h/t_w for web local buckling as defined in Section B5.1

λ_p = largest value of λ for which $M_n = M_p$

λ_r = largest value of λ for which buckling is inelastic

F_{cr} = critical stress, ksi

C_b = $1.75 + 1.05(M_1/M_2) + 0.3(M_1/M_2)^2 \le 2.3$ where M_1 is the smaller and M_2 the larger end-moment in the unbraced segment of the beam; M_1/M_2 is positive when the moments cause reverse curvature.

S = section modulus, in.^{3}

L_b = laterally unbraced length, in.

r_y = radius of gyration about minor axis, in.

The applicable limit states and equations for M_p, M_r, F_{cr}, λ, λ_p and λ_r are given in Table A-F1.1 for the shapes covered in this Appendix. The terms used in the table are:

A = cross-sectional area, in.^{2}
F_r = compressive residual stress in flange
= 10 ksi for rolled shapes
= 16.5 ksi for welded shapes
F_y = specified minimum yield strength, ksi
F_{yf} = yield strength of the flange, ksi
F_{yw} = yield strength of the web, ksi
J = torsional constant, in.^{4}
R_e = see Appendix G2
$(S_x)_{eff}$ = effective section modulus about major axis, in.^{3}
S_{xc} = section modulus of the outside fiber of the compression flange, in.^{3}
S_{xt} = section modulus of the outside fiber of the tension flange, in.^{3}
Z = plastic section modulus, in.^{3}
b = flange width, in.
d = overall depth, in.
h_c = twice the distance from the neutral axis to the inside face of the compression flange less the fillet or corner radius, in.
t_f = flange thickness, in.
t_w = web thickness, in.

TABLE A-F1.1
Nominal Strength Parameters

Shape	Plastic Moment M_p	Limit State of Buckling	Limiting Buckling Moment M_r
Channels and doubly and singly symmetric I-shaped beams (including hybrid beams) bent about major axis	$F_y Z_x$ (e)	LTB Doubly symmetric members and channels	$(F_{yw} - F_r)S_x$
		LTB Singly symmetric members	$(F_{yw} - F_r)S_{xc} \le F_{yt} S_{xt}$
		FLB	$(F_{yw} - F_r)S_x$
		WLB	$R_e F_{yt} S_x$
Channels and doubly symmetric I-shaped members bent about minor axis	$F_y Z_y$	FLB	$F_y S_y$
Solid symmetric shapes, except rectangular bars, bent about major axis	$F_y Z_x$	Not Applicable	
Solid rectangular bars bent about major axis	$F_y Z_x$	LTB	$F_y S_x$

TABLE A-F1.1 (cont'd)
Nominal Strength Parameters

Critical Stress F_{cr}	Slenderness Parameters λ	λ_p	λ_r	Limitations
$\frac{C_b X_1 \sqrt{2}}{\lambda}\sqrt{1+\frac{X_1^2 X_2}{2\lambda^2}}$ (b)	$\frac{L_b}{r_y}$	$\frac{300}{\sqrt{F_{yf}}}$	(a,b)	1. Applicable for I-shaped members if $h_c/t_w \leq 970/\sqrt{F_{yf}}$ when $h_c/t_w > 970/\sqrt{F_{yf}}$ See Appendix G 2. When $\lambda > \lambda_r$ a) Applicable for built-up channels if $b/d \leq 0.25$ and $t_f/t_w \leq 3.0$ b) Applicable for rolled channels if $b/d \leq 0.25$ and $t_f/t_w \leq 2.0$
(c)	$\frac{L_b}{r_y}$	$\frac{300}{\sqrt{F_{yf}}}$	Value of λ for which $M_{cr} = S_{xc}(F_{yf} - F_r)$	
(g)	$\frac{b}{t}$	$\frac{65}{\sqrt{F_{yf}}}$	(h)	
N.A.	$\frac{h_c}{t_w}$	$\frac{640}{\sqrt{F_{yf}}}$	$\frac{970}{\sqrt{F_{yf}}}$	
Same as for major axis				
Not Applicable				
$\frac{57{,}000 C_b \sqrt{JA}}{S_x}$	$\frac{L_b}{r_y}$	$\frac{3{,}750\sqrt{JA}}{M_p}$	$\frac{57{,}000\sqrt{JA}}{M_r}$	

TABLE A-F1.1 (cont'd)
Nominal Strength Parameters

Shape	Plastic Moment M_p	Limit State of Buckling	Limiting Buckling Moment M_r
Symmetric box sections loaded in a plane of symmetry	$F_y Z_x$	LTB	$(F_{yf} - F_r)S_x$
		FLB	$F_y S_x$
		WLB	Same as for I-shape
Circular Tubes	$F_y Z$	LTB	Not Applicable
		FLB	$M_n = \left(\frac{600}{D/t} + F_y\right)S^{(f)}$
		WLB	Not Applicable

a $$\lambda_r = \frac{X_1}{(F_{yw} - F_r)}\sqrt{1 + \sqrt{1 + X_2(F_{yw} - F_r)^2}}$$

b $$X_1 = \frac{\pi}{S_x}\sqrt{\frac{EGJA}{2}} \qquad X_2 = 4\frac{C_w}{I_y}\left(\frac{S_x}{GJ}\right)^2$$

c $$M_{cr} = \frac{57{,}000C_b}{L_b}\sqrt{I_yJ}\,(B_1 + \sqrt{(1 + B_2 + B_1^2)}) \le S_{xt}F_y$$

where

$B_1 = 2.25\,[2(I_{yc}/I_y) - 1](h/L_b)\sqrt{(I_y/J)}$ $\qquad B_2 = 25(1 - I_{yc}/I_y)(I_{yc}/J)(h/L_b)^2$

If the compression flange is larger than the tension flange, M_{cr} may be evaluated conservatively by the formula for doubly symmetric members, using for X_1 and X_2 the values for a symmetric section both of whose flanges are the same as the compression flange of the singly symmetric section.

TABLE A-F1.1 (cont'd)
Nominal Strength Parameters

Critical Stress F_{cr}	Slenderness Parameters λ	λ_p	λ_r	Limitations
$\frac{57{,}000 C_b \sqrt{JA}}{\lambda S_x}$	$\frac{L_b}{r_y}$	$\frac{3{,}750 \sqrt{JA}}{M_p}$	$\frac{57{,}000 \sqrt{JA}}{M_r}$	Applicable if $h_c/t_w \le 970/\sqrt{F_{yf}}$
$\frac{(S_x)_{eff}}{S_x} F_y{}^{(d)}$	$\frac{b}{t}$	$\frac{190}{F_y}$	$\frac{238}{\sqrt{(F_y - F_r)}}$	LTB applies only if $d > b$
Same as for I-shape				
Not Applicable				
$\frac{9{,}750}{D/t}$	D/t	$\frac{2{,}070}{F_y}$	$\frac{8{,}970}{F_y}$	$D/t < \frac{13{,}000}{F_y}$
Not Applicable				

[d] $(S_x)_{eff}$ is the section modulus for a section with a compression-flange width b_e given by $b_e = \frac{326\,t}{\sqrt{f}}\left(1 - \frac{64.9}{(b/t)\sqrt{f}}\right)$ for flanges of square and rectangular sections of uniform thickness

[e] Computed from fully plastic stress distribution for hybrid sections.

[f] This equation is to be used in place of Formula A-F1-3.

[g] $F_{cr} = \frac{20{,}000}{\lambda^2}$ for rolled shapes

$F_{cr} = \frac{11{,}200}{\lambda^2}$ for welded shapes

[h] $\lambda_r = \frac{141}{\sqrt{F_{yw} - 10}}$ for rolled shapes

$\lambda_r = \frac{106}{\sqrt{F_{yw} - 16.5}}$ for welded shapes

(Text continues on page 739.)

F4. WEB-TAPERED MEMBERS

The design of tapered members meeting the requirements of this section shall be governed by the provisions of Chapter F, except as modified by this Appendix.

1. General Requirements. In order to qualify under this Specification, a tapered member must meet the following requirements:

a. It shall possess at least one axis of symmetry which shall be perpendicular to the plane of bending if moments are present.

b. The flanges shall be of equal and constant area.

c. The depth shall vary linearly as

$$d = d_o \left(1 + \gamma \frac{z}{L}\right) \tag{A-F4-1}$$

WHERE:

d_o = depth at smaller end of member, in.

d_L = depth at larger end of member, in.

γ = $(d_L - d_o)/d_o \leq$ the smaller of $0.268(L/d_o)$ or 6.0

z = distance from the smaller end of member, in.

L = unbraced length of member measured between the center of gravity of the bracing members, in.

2. Design Tensile Strength. The design strength of tapered tension members shall be determined in accordance with Section D1.

3. Design Compressive Strength. The design strength of tapered compression members shall be determined in accordance with Section E2, using an effective slenderness parameter λ_{eff} computed as follows:

$$\lambda_{eff} = \frac{S}{\pi} \sqrt{\frac{QF_y}{E}} \tag{A-F4-2}$$

WHERE:

S = KL/r_{oy} for weak axis bending and $K\gamma L/r_{ox}$ for strong axis bending

K = effective length factor for a prismatic member

$K\gamma$ = effective length factor for a tapered member as determined by a rational analysis

r_{ox} = strong axis radius of gyration at the smaller end of a tapered member, in.

r_{oy} = weak axis radius of gyration at the smaller end of a tapered member, in.

F_y = specified minimum yield stress, ksi

Q = reduction factor

= 1.0 if all elements meet the limiting width-thickness ratios λ_r of Section B5.1

= Q_sQ_a, determined in accordance with Appendix B, if any stiffened and/or unstiffened elements exceed the ratios λ_r of Section B5.1

E = modulus of elasticity for steel, ksi

The smallest area of the tapered member shall be used for A_g in Formula (E2- 1).

4. Design Flexural Strength. The design flexural strength of tapered flexural members for the limit state of lateral-torsional buckling is $\phi_b M_n$, where $\phi_b = 0.90$ and the nominal strength is

$$M_n = (5/3)S'_x\ F_{b\gamma} \tag{A-F4-3}$$

WHERE:

S'_x = the section modulus of the critical section of the unbraced beam length under consideration

$$F_{b\gamma} = \frac{2}{3}\left[1.0 - \frac{F_y}{6B\sqrt{F_{s\gamma}^2 + F_{w\gamma}^2}}\right]F_y \leq 0.60F_y \tag{A-F4-4}$$

unless $F_{b\gamma} \leq F_y/3$, in which case

$$F_{b\gamma} = B\sqrt{F_{s\gamma}^2 + F_{w\gamma}^2} \tag{A-F4-5}$$

In the above equations,

$$F_{s\gamma} = \frac{12 \times 10^3}{h_s\ Ld_o/A_f} \tag{A-F4-6}$$

$$F_{w\gamma} = \frac{170 \times 10^3}{(h_w\ L/r_{To})^2} \tag{A-F4-7}$$

WHERE:

h_s = factor equal to $1.0 + 0.0230\gamma\sqrt{Ld_o/A_f}$

h_w = factor equal to $1.0 + 0.00385\ \gamma\sqrt{L/r_{To}}$

r_{To} = radius of gyration of a section at the smaller end, considering only the compression flange plus one third of the compression web area, taken about an axis in the plane of the web, in.

A_f = area of the compression flange, in.^{2}

and where B is determined as follows:

a. When the maximum moment M_2 in three adjacent segments of approximately equal unbraced length is located within the central segment and M_1 is the larger moment at one end of the three-segment portion of a member:*

$$B = 1.0 + 0.37\left(1.0 + \frac{M_1}{M_2}\right) + 0.50\gamma\left(1.0 + \frac{M_1}{M_2}\right) \geq 1.0 \tag{A-F4-8}$$

---

*M_1/M_2 is considered as negative when producing single curvature. In the rare case where M_1/M_2 is positive, it is recommended that it be taken as zero.

b. When the largest computed bending stress f_{b2} occurs at the larger end of two adjacent segments of approximately equal unbraced lengths and f_{b1} is the computed bending stress at the smaller end of the two-segment portion of a member:*

$$B = 1.0 + 0.58\left(1.0 + \frac{f_{b1}}{f_{b2}}\right) - 0.70\gamma\left(1.0 + \frac{f_{b1}}{f_{b2}}\right) \geq 1.0 \qquad \text{(A-F4-9)}$$

c. When the largest computed bending stress f_{b2}, occurs at the smaller end of two adjacent segments of approximately equal unbraced length and f_{b1} is the computed bending stress at the larger end of the two-segment portion of a member:**

$$B = 1.0 + 0.55\left(1.0 + \frac{f_{b1}}{f_{b2}}\right) + 2.20\gamma\left(1.0 + \frac{f_{b1}}{f_{b2}}\right) \geq 1.0 \qquad \text{(A-F4-10)}$$

In the foregoing, $\gamma = (d_L - d_o)/d_o$ is calculated for the unbraced length that contains the maximum computed bending stress.

d. When the computed bending stress at the smaller end of a tapered member or segment thereof is equal to zero:

$$B = \frac{1.75}{1.0 + 0.25\sqrt{\gamma}} \qquad \text{(A-F4-11)}$$

where $\gamma = (d_L - d_o)/d_o$ calculated for the unbraced length adjacent to the point of zero bending stress.

5. Design Shear Strength. The design shear strength of tapered flexural members shall be determined in accordance with Section F2.

6. Combined Flexure and Axial Force. For tapered members with a single web taper subject to compression and bending about the major axis, Formulas (H1-1) through (H1-3) apply, with the following modifications: P_n and P_{ex} shall be determined for the properties of the smaller end, using appropriate effective length factors. M_{nx}, M_u and M_{px} shall be determined for the larger end; $M_{nx} = (5/3)S'_x F_{b\gamma}$, where S'_x is the elastic section modulus of the larger end, and $F_{b\gamma}$ is the design flexural stress of tapered members. C_{mx} is replaced by C'_m, determined as follows:

a. When the member is subjected to end moments which cause single curvature bending and approximately equal computed moments at the ends:

---

*f_{b1}/f_{b2} is considered as negative when producing single curvature. If a point of contraflexure occurs in one of two adjacent unbraced segments, f_{b1}/f_{b2} is considered as positive. The ratio $f_{b1}/f_{b2} \neq 0$.

**f_{b1}/f_{b2} is considered as negative when producing single curvature. If a point of contraflexure occurs in one of two adjacent unbraced segments, f_{b1}/f_{b2} is considered as positive. The ratio $f_{b1}/f_{b2} \neq 0$.

$$C'_m = 1.0 + 0.1\left(\frac{P_u}{\phi_b P_{ex}}\right) + 0.3\left(\frac{P_u}{\phi_b P_{ex}}\right)^2 \qquad \text{(A-F4-12)}$$

b. When the computed bending moment at the smaller end of the unbraced length is equal to zero:

$$C'_m = 1.0 + 0.9\left(\frac{P_u}{\phi_b P_{ex}}\right) + 0.6\left(\frac{P_u}{\phi_b P_{ex}}\right)^2 \qquad \text{(A-F4-13)}$$

When the effective slenderness parameter $\lambda_{eff} \geq 1.0$ and combined stress is checked incrementally along the length,the actual area and the actual section modulus at the section under investigation may be used.

APPENDIX G

PLATE GIRDERS

Sec. 27.1404G.

G1. LIMITATIONS

Doubly and singly symmetric single-web nonhybrid and hybrid plate girders loaded in the plane of the web may be proportioned according to the provisions of this Appendix or Section F2, provided that these limits are satisfied.

a. For $\frac{a}{h} \leq 1.5$:

$$\frac{h}{t_w}\max = \frac{2,000}{\sqrt{F_{yf}}} \qquad \text{(A-G1-1)}$$

b. For $\frac{a}{h} > 1.5$:

$$\frac{h}{t_w}\max = \frac{14,000}{\sqrt{F_{yf}(F_{yf} + 16.5)}} \qquad \text{(A-G1-2)}$$

WHERE:

a = clear distance between transverse stiffeners, in.

h = clear distance between flanges less the fillet or comer radius for rolled shapes; and for built-up sections, the distance between adjacent lines of fasteners or the clear distance between flanges when welds are used, in.

t_w = web thickness, in.

F_{yf} = specified minimum yield stress of the flange, ksi

In unstiffened girders, h/t_w must be less than 260.

G2. DESIGN FLEXURAL STRENGTH

The design flexural strength for plate girders with slender webs ($h_c/t_w >$ $970/\sqrt{F_{yf}}$) shall be $\phi_b M_n$, where $\phi_b = 0.90$ and M_n is the lower value obtained according to the limit states of tension-flange yield and compression-flange buckling. When ($h_c/t_w > 970/\sqrt{F_{yf}}$, see Appendix F1.7.

For tension-flange yield:

$$M_n = S_{xt}\, R_{PG}\, R_e\, F_{yt} \qquad \text{(A-G2-1)}$$

For compression-flange buckling:

$$M_n = S_{xc}\, R_{PG}\, R_e\, F_{cr} \qquad \text{(A-G2-2)}$$

WHERE:

$$R_{PG} = 1 - 0.0005\, a_r \left(\frac{h_c}{t_w} - \frac{970}{\sqrt{F_{cr}}} \right) \le 1.0 \qquad \text{(A-G2-3)}$$

R_e = hybrid girder factor
= $1.0 - 0.1(1.3 + a_r)(0.81 - m) \le 1.0$ (for nonhybrid girders, $R_e = 1.0$)

a_r = ratio of web area to compression flange area

m = ratio of web yield stress to flange yield stress or F_{cr}

F_{cr} = critical compression flange stress, ksi

F_{yt} = yield stress of tension flange, ksi

S_{xc} = section modulus referred to compression flange, in.^{3}

S_{xt} = section modulus referred to tension flange, in.^{3}

h_c = twice the distance from the neutral axis to the inside face of the compression flange less the fillet or corner radius, in.

The critical stress F_{cr} to be used is dependent upon the slenderness parameters λ, λ_p, λ_r, and C_{PG} as follows:

$$F_{cr} = F_{yf} \qquad \text{(A-G2-4)}$$

$$F_{cr} = C_b F_{yf} \left[1 - \frac{1}{2} \left(\frac{\lambda - \lambda_p}{\lambda_r - \lambda_p} \right) \right] \le F_{yf} \qquad \text{(A-G2-5)}$$

$$F_{cr} = \frac{C_{PG}}{\lambda^2} \qquad \text{(A-G2-6)}$$

In the foregoing, the slenderness parameter shall be determined for both the limit state of lateral-torsional buckling and the limit state of flange local buckling; the slenderness parameter which results in the lowest value of F_{cr} governs.

For the limit state of lateral-torsional buckling:

$$\lambda = \frac{L_b}{r_T} \quad \text{(A-G2-7)}$$

$$\lambda_p = \frac{300}{\sqrt{F_{yf}}} \quad \text{(A-G2-8)}$$

$$\lambda_r = \frac{756}{\sqrt{F_{yf}}} \quad \text{(A-G2-9)}$$

$$C_{PG} = 286{,}000\ C_b \quad \text{(A-G2-10)}$$

$$\lambda = \frac{b_f}{2t_f} \quad \text{(A-G2-11)}$$

$$\lambda_p = \frac{65}{\sqrt{F_{yf}}} \quad \text{(A-G2-12)}$$

$$\lambda_r = \frac{150}{\sqrt{F_{yf}}} \quad \text{(A-G2–13)}$$

$$C_{PG} = 11{,}200 \quad \text{(A-G2-14)}$$

$$C_b = 1$$

The limit state of flexural web local buckling is not applicable.

G3. DESIGN SHEAR STRENGTH WITH TENSION FIELD ACTION

The design shear strength shall be $\phi_v V_n$, kips, where $\phi_v = 0.90$ and V_n is determined as follows:

a. For $h/t_w \leq 187\sqrt{k/F_{yw}}$:

$$V_n = 0.6\ A_w F_{yw} \quad \text{(A-G3-1)}$$

b. For $h/t_w > 187\sqrt{k/F_{yw}}$:

$$V_n = 0.6\ A_w F_{yw}\left(C_v + \frac{1 - C_v}{1.15\sqrt{1 + (a/h)^2}}\right) \quad \text{(A-G3-2)}$$

where

C_v = ratio of "critical" web stress, according to linear buckling theory, to the shear yield stress of web material

except for end-panels in nonhybrid plate girders, for all panels in hybrid and web-tapered plate girders and when a/h exceeds 3.0 or $[260/(h/t_w)]^2$. In these cases, tension field action is not permitted and

$$V_n = 0.6\ A_w\ F_{yw}\ C_v \quad \text{(A-G3-3)}$$

The web plate buckling coefficient k is given as

$$k = 5 + \frac{5}{(a/h)^2} \qquad \text{(A-G3-4)}$$

except that k shall be taken as 5.0 if a/h exceeds 3.0 or $[260/(h/t_w)]^2$. The shear coefficient C_v is determined as follows:

For $187\sqrt{\frac{k}{F_{yw}}} \le \frac{h}{t_w} \le 234\sqrt{\frac{k}{F_{yw}}}$:

$$C_v = \frac{187\sqrt{k/F_{yw}}}{h/t_w} \qquad \text{(A-G3-5)}$$

For $\frac{h}{t_w} > 234\sqrt{\frac{k}{F_{yw}}}$:

$$C_v = \frac{44{,}000\ k}{(h/t_w)^2 F_{yw}} \qquad \text{(A-G3-6)}$$

G4. TRANSVERSE STIFFENERS

Transverse stiffeners are not required in plate girders when $h/t_w \le 418/\sqrt{F_{yw}}$, or when the required shear V_u, as determined by structural analysis for the factored loads, is less than or equal to $0.6\phi A_w F_{yw} C_v$, where C_v is determined for $k = 5$ and $\phi = 0.90$. Stiffeners may be required in certain portions of a plate girder to develop the required shear or to satisfy the limitations given in Appendix G1.

The moment of inertia I_{st} of a transverse stiffener about an axis in the web center for stiffener pairs or about the face in contact with the web plate for single stiffeners shall not be less than $at^3_w j$, where

$$j = \frac{2.5}{(a/h)^2} - 2 \ge 0.5 \qquad \text{(A-G4-1)}$$

and the stiffener area A_{st} when designing for tension field action shall not be less than

$$\frac{F_{yw}}{F_{yst}}\left[0.15\ Dht_w\ (1 - C_v)\ \frac{V_u}{\phi_v V_n} - 18\ t_w^2\right] \ge 0 \qquad \text{(A-G4-2)}$$

WHERE:

F_{yst} = specified yield stress of the stiffener material, ksi

D = 1 for stiffeners in pairs

= 1.8 for single angle stiffeners

= 2.4 for single plate stiffeners

C_v and V_v are defined in Appendix G3, and V_u is the required shear at the location of the stiffener.

G5. FLEXURE-SHEAR INTERACTION

Plate girders with webs that depend on tension field action must satisfy flexure-shear interaction criteria.

When stiffeners are required and

$$\frac{0.6\ V_n}{M_n} \leq \frac{V_u}{M_u} \leq \frac{V_n}{0.75\ M_n}$$

the following interaction equation must be satisfied:

$$\frac{M_u}{M_n} + .625\ \frac{V_u}{V_n} \leq 1.375\ \phi \qquad \text{(A-G5-1)}$$

where M_n is the nominal flexural strength of plate girders from Appendix G2, $\phi = 0.90$ and V_n is the nominal shear strength from Appendix G3, except that M_u may not exceed ϕM_n ($\phi = 0.90$) and V_u may not exceed $\phi V_n (\phi = 0.90)$.

APPENDIX H

MEMBERS UNDER TORSION AND COMBINED FORCES

Sec.27.1404H.

H3. ALTERNATE INTERACTION EQUATIONS FOR MEMBERS UNDER COMBINED STRESS

For biaxially loaded I-shaped members used in braced frames only, the following interaction equations may be used in lieu of Formulas (H1-1a) and H1-1b).

$$\left(\frac{M_{ux}}{\phi_b\ M'_{px}}\right)^{\zeta} + \left(\frac{M_{uy}}{\phi_b\ M'_{py}}\right)^{\zeta} \leq 1.0 \qquad \text{(A-H3-1)}$$

$$\left(\frac{C_{mx}\ M_{ux}}{\phi_b\ M'_{nx}}\right)^{\eta} + \left(\frac{C_{my}\ M_{uy}}{\phi_b M'_{ny}}\right)^{\eta} \leq 1.0 \qquad \text{(A-H3-2)}$$

For $0.5 \leq b_f / d \leq 1.0$:

$$\zeta = 1.6 - \frac{P_u / P_y}{2[\ln(P_u / P_y)]} \qquad \text{(A-H3-3)}$$

For $b_f / d \geq 0.3$:

$$\eta = 0.4 + \frac{P_u}{P_y} + \frac{b_f}{d} \geq 1.0 \qquad \text{(A-H3-4)}$$

$$= 1.0 \text{ for } b_f / d < 0.3$$

where

b_f = flange width, in.
d = member depth, in.

$$M'_{px} = 1.2\ M_{px}[1 - (P_u / P_y)] \leq M_{px} \qquad \text{(A-H3-5)}$$

$$M'_{py} = 1.2\ M_{py}[1 - (P_u/P_y)^2] \leq M_{py} \quad \text{(A-H3-6)}$$

$$M'_{nx} = M_{nx}\left(1 - \frac{P_u}{\phi_c P_n}\right)\left(1 - \frac{P_u}{P_{ex}}\right) \quad \text{(A-H3-7)}$$

$$M'_{ny} = M_{ny}\left(1 - \frac{P_u}{\phi_c P_n}\right)\left(1 - \frac{P_u}{P_{ey}}\right) \quad \text{(A-H3-8)}$$

WHERE:

P_n = nominal compressive strength determined in accordance with Section E2, kips

P_u = required axial strength, kips

P_y = compressive yield strength $A_g F_y$, kips

ϕ_b = resistance factor for flexure = 0.90

ϕ_c = resistance factor for compression = 0.85

P_e = Euler buckling strength $A_g F_y / \lambda^2{}_c$, where λ_c is the column slenderness parameter defined by Formula (E2-4), kips

M_u = required flexural strength, kip-in.

M_n = nominal flexural strength, determined in accordance with Section F1, kip-in.

M_p = plastic moment, kip-in.

C_m = coefficient defined in Section H1.

APPENDIX K

STRENGTH DESIGN CONSIDERATIONS

Sec.27.1404K.

K2. PONDING

The provisions of this Appendix may be used when a more exact determination of flat roof framing stiffness is needed than that given by the provision of Section K2 that $C_p + 0.9C_s \leq 0.25$.

For any combination of primary and secondary framing, the stress index is computed as

$$U_p = \left(\frac{\phi_b F_y - f_o}{f_o}\right)_p \text{ for the primary member} \quad \text{(A-K2-3)}$$

$$U_s = \left(\frac{\phi_b F_y - f_o}{f_o}\right)_s \text{ for the secondary member} \quad \text{(A-K2-4)}$$

WHERE:

f_o = the stress due to $1.2D + 1.2R$ (D = nominal dead load, R = nominal load due to rain water or ice exclusive of the ponding contribution)*

ϕ_b = resistance factor for flexure = 0.90 (Section F)

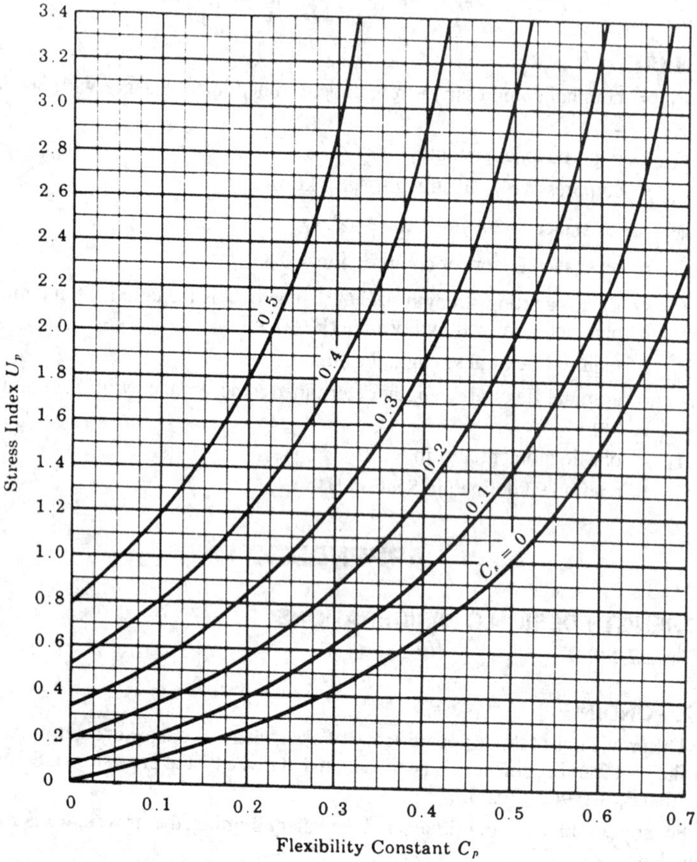
Stress Index U_p
3.4
3.2
3.0
2.8
2.6
2.4
2.2
2.0
1.8
1.6
1.4
1.2
1.0
0.8
0.6
0.4
0.2
0
0.5
0.4
0.3
0.2
0.1
$C_s = 0$
0
0.1
0.2
0.3
0.4
0.5
0.6
0.7
Flexibility Constant C_p

Fig. A-K2.1. Flexibility coefficients for combined primary and secondary systems

Enter Figure A-K2. 1 at the level of the computed stress index U_p determined for the primary beam; move horizontally to the computed C_s-value of the secondary beams and then downward to the abscissa scale. The combined stiffness of the primary and secondary framing is sufficient to prevent ponding if the flexibility con-

*Depending upon geographic location, this loading should include such amount of snow as might also be present.

stant read from this latter scale is more than the value of C_p computed for the given primary member; if not, a stiffer primary or secondary beam, or combination of both, is required. In the above,

$$C_p = \frac{32L_s\, L_p^4}{10^7 I_p}$$

$$C_s = \frac{32SL_s^4}{10^7 I_s}$$

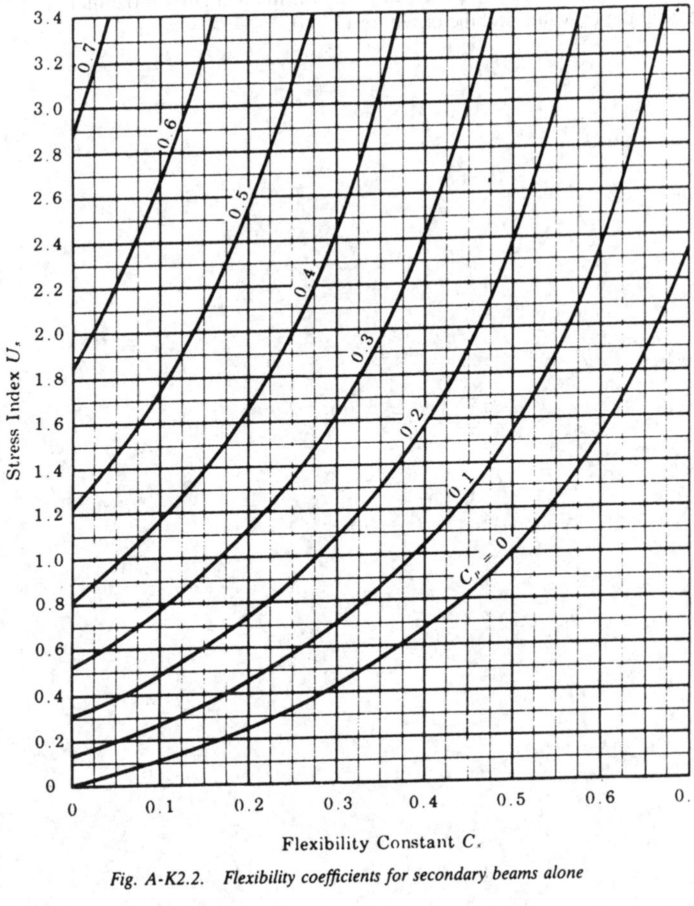
3.4
3.2
3.0
2.8
2.6
2.4
2.2
2.0
1.8
1.6
1.4
1.2
1.0
0.8
0.6
0.4
0.2
0
Stress Index U_s
0.7
0.6
0.5
0.4
0.3
0.2
0.1
$C_p = 0$
0
0.1
0.2
0.3
0.4
0.5
0.6
0.7
Flexibility Constant C_s

Fig. A-K2.2. Flexibility coefficients for secondary beams alone

WHERE:

L_p = column spacing in direction of girder (length of primary members), ft.

L_s = column spacing perpendicular to direction of girder (length of secondary members), ft.

S = spacing of secondary members, ft.

I_p = moment of inertia of primary members,in.^{4}

I_s = moment of inertia of secondary members, in.^{4}

Roof framing consisting of a series of equally spaced wall-bearing beams is considered as consisting of secondary members supported on an infinitely stiff primary member. For this case, enter Figure A-H2.2 with the computed stress index U_s. The limiting value of C_s is determined by the intercept of a horizontal line representing the U_s-value and the curve for $C_p = 0$.

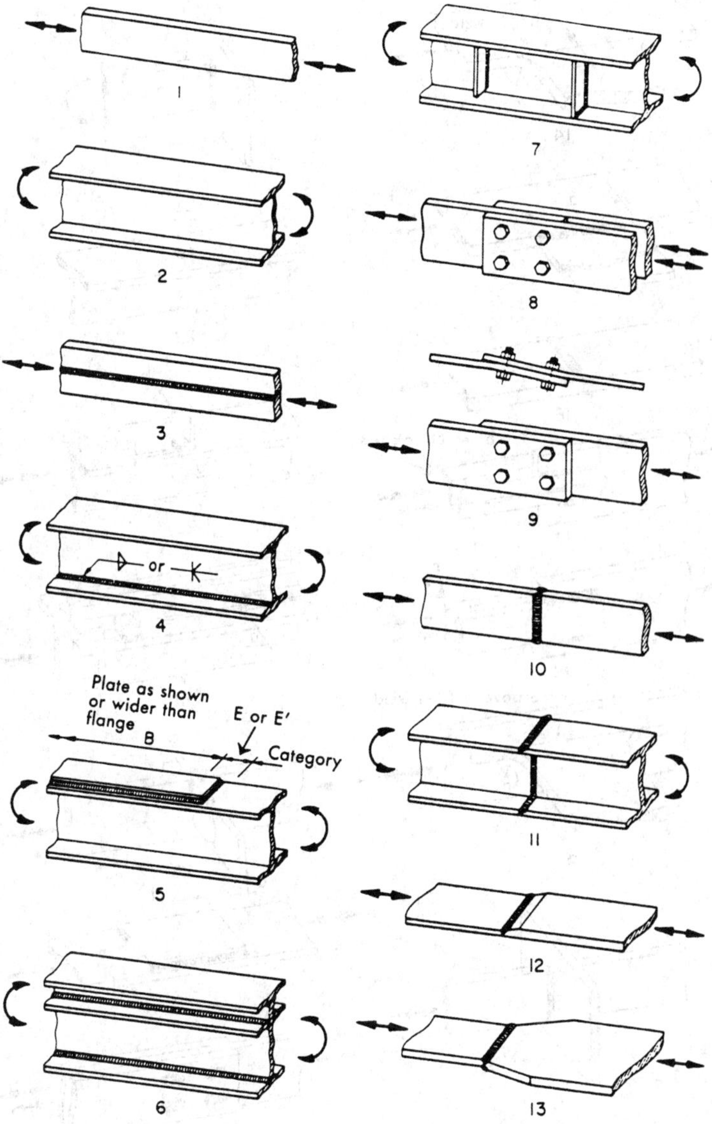
1
2
3
4
Plate as shown or wider than flange
B
E or E′
Category
5
6
7
8
9
10
11
12
13

Fig. A-K4.1. Illustrative examples

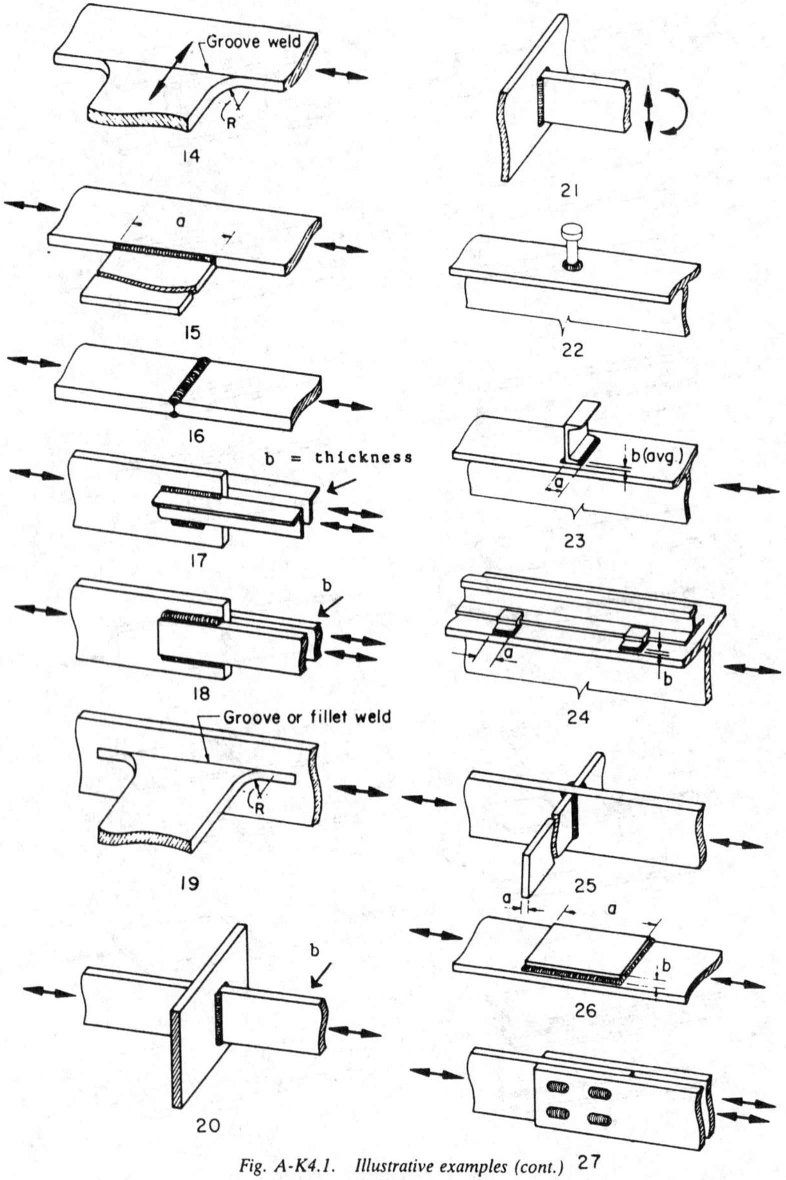
Groove weld
R
14
21
a
15
22
16
b = thickness
b(avg.)
a
23
17
b
a
b
18
24
Groove or fillet weld
R
19
25
a
a
b
b
26
20
27

Fig. A-K4.1. Illustrative examples (cont.)

The ponding deflection contributed by a metal deck is usually such a small part of the total ponding deflection of a roof panel that it is sufficient merely to limit its moment of inertia (per foot of width normal to its span) to 0.000025 times the fourth power of its span length. However, the stability against ponding of a roof consisting of a metal roof deck of relatively slender depth-span ratio, spanning between beams supported directly on columns, may need to be checked. This can be done using Figure A-K2.1 or A-K2.2 using as C_s the flexibility constant for one foot width of the roof deck ($S = 1.0$).

Since the shear rigidity of the web system steel joists and trusses is less than that of a solid plate, their moment of inertia should be taken as 85 percent of their chords.

K4. FATIGUE

Members and connections subject to fatigue loading shall be proportioned in accordance with the provisions of this Appendix.

Fatigue, as used in this Specification, is defined as the damage that may result in fracture after a sufficient number of fluctuations of stress. Stress range is defined as the magnitude of these fluctuations. In the case of a stress reversal, the stress range shall be computed as the numerical sum of maximum repeated tensile and compressive stresses or the sum of maximum shearing stresses of opposite direction at a given point, resulting from differing arrangement of live load.

1. Loading Conditions; Type and Location of Material. In the design of members and connections subject to repeated variation of live load, consideration shall be given to the number of stress cycles, the expected range of stress and the type and location of member or detail.

Loading conditions shall be classified according to Table A-K4.1.

The type and location of material shall be categorized according to Table A-K4.2.

2. Design Stress Range. The maximum range of stress at service loads shall not exceed the design stress range specified in Table A-K4.3.

3. Design Strength of Bolts in Tension. When subject to tensile fatigue loading, properly tightened A325 or A490 bolts shall be designed for the combined tensile design strength due to external and prying forces within limits given in Table A-K4.4.

TABLE A-K4.1
Number of Loading Cycles

Loading Condition	From	To
1	20,000[a]	100,000[b]
2	100,000	500,000[c]
3	500,000	2,000,000[d]
4	Over 2,000,000	

[a]Approximately equivalent to two applications every day for 25 years.
[b]Approximately equivalent to 10 applications every day for 25 years.
[c]Approximately equivalent to 50 applications every day for 25 years.
[d]Approximately equivalent to 200 applications every day for 25 years.

TABLE A-K4.2
Type and Location of Material

General Condition	Situation	Kind of Stress[a]	Stress Category (see Table A-K4.3)	Illustrative Example Nos. (see Fig. A-K4.1)[b]
Plain Material	Base metal with rolled or cleaned surface. Flame-cut edges with ANSI smoothness of 1,000 or less	T or Rev.	A	1,2
Built-up Members	Base metal and weld metal in members without attachments, built-up plates or shapes connected by continuous full-penetration groove welds or by continuous fillet welds parallel to the direction of applied stress	T or Rev.	B	3,4,5,6
	Base metal and weld metal in members without attachments, built-up plates, or shapes connected by full-penetration groove welds with backing bars not removed, or by partial-penetration groove welds parallel to the direction of applied stress	T or Rev.	B′	3,4,5,6
	Base metal at toe of welds on girder webs or flanges adjacent to welded transverse stiffeners	T or Rev.	C	7
	Base metal at ends of partial length welded coverplates narrower than the flange having square or tapered ends, with or without welds across the ends or wider than flange with welds across the ends			
	Flange thickness $\leq$ 0.8 in.	T or Rev.	E	5
	Flange thickness $>$ 0.8 in.	T or Rev.	E′	5
	Base metal at end of partial length welded coverplates wider than the flange without welds across the ends		E′	5

[a]"T" signifies range in tensile stress only; "Rev." signifies a range involving reversal of tensile or compressive stress; "S" signifies range in shear, including shear stress reversal.

[b]These examples are provided as guidelines and are not intended to exclude other reasonably similar situations.

[c]Allowable fatigue stress range for transverse partial-penetration and transverse fillet welds is a function of the effective throat, depth of penetration and plate thickness.

TABLE A-K4.2 (cont'd)
Type and Location of Material

General Condition	Situation	Kind of Stress[a]	Stress Category (see Table A-K4.3)	Illustrative Example Nos. (see Fig. A-K4.1)[b]
Groove Welds	Base metal and weld metal at full-penetration groove welded splices of parts of similar cross section ground flush, with grinding in the direction of applied stress and with weld soundness established by radiographic or ultrasonic inspection in accordance with the requirements of 9.25.2 or 9.25.3 of AWS D1.1, U.B.C. Standard No. 27-6.	T or Rev.	B	10,11
	Base metal and weld metal at full-penetration groove welded splices at transitions in width or thickness, with welds ground to provide slopes no steeper than 1 to 2½ with grinding in the direction of applied stress, and with weld soundness established by radiographic or ultrasonic inspection in accordance with the requirements of 9.25.2 or 9.25.3 of AWS D1.1, U.B.C. Standard No. 27-6.			
	A514 base metal	T or Rev.	B′	12,13
	Other base metals	T or Rev.	B	12,13
	Base metal and weld metal at full-penetration groove welded splices, with or without transitions having slopes no greater than 1 to 2½ when reinforcement is not removed but weld soundness is established by radiographic or ultrasonic inspection in accordance with requirements of 9.25.2 or 9.25.3 of AWS D1.1, U.B.C. Standard No. 27-6.	T or Rev.	C	10,11,12, 13
Partial-Penetration Groove Welds	Weld metal of partial-penetration transverse groove welds, based on effective throat area of the weld or welds	T or Rev.	F[c]	16

TABLE A-K4.2 (cont'd)
Type and Location of Material

General Condition	Situation	Kind of Stress[a]	Stress Category (see Table A-K4.3)	Illustrative Example Nos. (see Fig. A-K4.1)[b]
Fillet-welded Connections	Base metal at intermittent fillet welds	T or Rev.	E	
	Base metal at junction of axially loaded members with fillet-welded end connections. Welds shall be disposed about the axis of the member so as to balance weld stresses $b \leq 1$ in. $b > 1$ in.	 T or Rev. T or Rev.	 E E′	 17,18 17,18
	Base metal at members connected with transverse fillet welds $b \leq$ ½ in. $b >$ ½ in.	T or Rev.	C See Note c	20,21
Fillet Welds	Weld metal of continuous or intermittent longitudinal or transverse fillet welds	S	F[c]	15,17,18 20,21
Plug or Slot Welds	Base metal at plug or slot welds	T or Rev.	E	27
	Shear on plug or slot welds	S	F	27
Mechanically Fastened Connections	Base metal at gross section of high-strength bolted slip-critical connections, except axially loaded joints which induce out-of-plane bending in connected material	T or Rev.	B	8
	Base metal at net section of other mechanically fastened joints	T or Rev.	D	8,9
	Base metal at net section of fully tensioned high-strength, bolted-bearing connections	T or Rev.	B	8,9

TABLE A-K4.2 (cont'd)
Type and Location of Material

General Condition	Situation	Kind of Stress[a]	Stress Category (see Table A-K4.3)	Illustrative Example Nos. (see Fig. A-K4.1)[b]
Attachments	Base metal at details attached by full-penetration groove welds subject to longitudinal and/or transverse loading when the detail embodies a transition radius R with the weld termination ground smooth and for transverse loading, the weld soundness established by radiographic or ultrasonic inspection in accordance with 9.25.2 or 9.25.3 of AWS D1.1, U.B.C. Standard No. 27-6.			
	Longitudinal loading			
	$R > 24$ in.	T or Rev.	B	14
	24 in. $> R > 6$ in.	T or Rev.	C	14
	6 in. $> R > 2$ in.	T or Rev.	D	14
	2 in. $> R$	T or Rev.	E	14
	Detail base metal for transverse loading: equal thickness and reinforcement removed			
	$R > 24$ in.	T or Rev.	B	14
	24 in. $> R > 6$ in.	T or Rev.	C	14
	6 in. $> R > 2$ in.	T or Rev.	D	14
	2 in. $> R$	T or Rev.	E	14,15
	Detail base metal for transverse loading: equal thickness and reinforcement not removed			
	$R > 24$ in.	T or Rev.	C	14
	24 in. $> R > 6$ in.	T or Rev.	C	14
	6 in. $> R > 2$ in.	T or Rev.	D	14
	2 in. $> R$	T or Rev.	E	14,15

TABLE A-K4.2 (cont'd)
Type and Location of Material

General Condition	Situation	Kind of Stress[a]	Stress Category (see Table A-K4.3)	Illustrative Example Nos. (see Fig. A-K4.1)[b]
Attachments (cont'd)	Detail base metal for transverse loading: unequal thickness and reinforcement removed			
	$R > 2$ in.	T or Rev.	D	14
	2 in. $> R$	T or Rev.	E	14,15
	Detail base metal for transverse loading: unequal thickness and reinforcement not removed			
	all R	T or Rev.	E	14,15
	Detail base metal for transverse loading			
	$R > 6$ in.	T or Rev.	C	19
	6 in. $> R > 2$ in.	T or Rev.	D	19
	2 in. $> R$	T or Rev.	E	19
	Base metal at detail attached by full-penetration groove welds subject to longitudinal loading			
	$2 < a < 12b$ or 4 in.	T or Rev.	D	15
	$a > 12b$ or 4 in. when $b \leq 1$ in.	T or Rev.	E	15
	$a > 12b$ or 4 in. when $b > 1$ in.	T or Rev.	E′	15
	Base metal at detail attached by fillet welds or partial-penetration groove welds subject to longitudinal loading			
	$a < 2$ in.	T or Rev.	C	15,23,24, 25,26
	2 in. $< a < 12b$ or 4 in.	T or Rev.	D	15,23, 24,26
	$a > 12b$ or 4 in. when $b \leq 1$ in.	T or Rev.	E	15,23, 24,26
	$a > 12b$ or 4 in. when $b > 1$ in.	T or Rev.	E′	15,23, 24,26

TABLE A-K4.2 (cont'd)
Type and Location of Material

General Condition	Situation	Kind of Stress[a]	Stress Category (see Table A-K4.3)	Illustrative Example Nos. (see Fig. A-K4.1)[b]
Attachments (cont'd)	Base metal attached by fillet welds or partial-penetration groove welds subjected to longitudinal loading when the weld termination embodies a transition radius with the weld termination ground smooth:			
	$R > 2$ in.	T or Rev.	D	19
	$R \leq 2$ in.	T or Rev.	E	19
	Fillet-welded attachments where the weld termination embodies a transition radius, weld termination ground smooth, and main material subject to longitudinal loading: Detail base metal for transverse loading:			
	$R > 2$ in.	T or Rev.	D	19
	$R < 2$ in.	T or Rev.	E	19
	Base metal at stud-type shear connector attached by fillet weld or automatic end weld	T or Rev.	C	22
	Shear stress on nominal area of stud-type shear connectors	S	F	

TABLE A-K4.3
Allowable Stress Range, ksi

Category (From Table A-K4.2)	Loading Condition 1	Loading Condition 2	Loading Condition 3	Loading Condition 4
A	63	37	24	24
B	49	29	18	16
B′	39	23	15	12
C	35	21	13	10[a]
D	28	16	10	7
E	22	13	8	4.5
E′	16	9.2	5.8	2.6
F	15	12	9	8

[a]Flexural stress range of 12 ksi permitted at toe of stiffener welds or flanges.

TABLE A-K4.4
Design Strength of A325 or A490 Bolts Subject to Tension

Number of cycles	Design strength
Not more than 20,000	As specified in Section J3
From 20,000 to 500,000	$0.30\ A_b F_u$[a]
More than 500,000	$0.25\ A_b F_u$[a]

[a]At service loads.

NUMERICAL VALUES

TABLE 1
Design Strength as a Function of F_y

F_y (ksi)	Design Stress (ksi)				
	$0.54F_y$[a]	$0.56F_y$[b]	$0.63F_y$[c]	$0.85F_y$[d]	$0.90F_y$[e]
33	17.8	18.5	20.8	28.1	29.7
35	18.9	19.6	22.1	29.8	31.5
36	19.4	20.2	22.7	30.6	32.4
40	21.6	22.4	25.2	34.0	36.0
42	22.7	23.5	26.5	35.7	37.8
45	24.3	25.2	28.4	38.3	40.5
46	24.8	25.8	29.0	39.1	41.4
50	27.0	28.0	31.5	42.5	45.0
55	29.7	30.8	34.7	46.8	49.5
60	32.4	33.6	37.8	51.0	54.0
65	35.1	36.4	41.0	55.3	58.5
70	37.8	39.2	44.1	59.5	63.0
90	48.6	50.4	56.7	76.5	81.0
100	54.0	56.0	63.0	85.0	90.0

[a]See Sect. F2, Formulas F2-1 and F2-2
[b]See Sect. J5.2, Formula J5-3
[c]See Sect. K1.7, Formulas K1-9 and K1-10
[d]See Sect. E2, Formula E2-1
[e]See Sect. D1, Formula D1-1

TABLE 2
Design Strength as a Function of F_u

Item	ASTM Designation	F_y (ksi)	F_u (ksi)	Design Strength (ksi): Connected Part of Designated Steel: Tension $0.75 \times F_u$[a]	Bearing $0.75 \times 2.4F_u$[b]	Bolt or Threaded Part of Designated Steel: Tension $0.75 \times 0.75F_u$[c]	Shear $0.65 \times 0.45F_u$[d]	Shear $0.65 \times 0.6F_u$[e]
Shapes, Plates, Bars, Sheet and Tubing or Threaded Parts	A36	36	58–80	43.5	104	32.6	17.0	22.6
	A53	35	60	45.0	108	—	—	—
	[A242 A441 A588]	50	70	52.5	126	39.4	20.5	27.3
		46	67	50.3	121	37.7	19.6	26.1
		42	63	47.3	113	35.4	18.4	24.6
		40[f]	60	45.0	108	33.8	17.6	23.4
	A500	33/39[g]	45	33.8	81	—	—	—
		42/46[g]	58	43.5	104	—	—	—
		46/50[g]	62	46.5	112	—	—	—
	A501	36	58	43.5	104	—	—	—
	A529	42	60–85	45.0	108	33.8	17.6	23.4
	A570	40	55	41.3	99	—	—	—
		42	58	43.5	104	—	—	—
	A572	42	60	45.0	108	33.8	17.6	23.4
		50	65	48.8	117	36.6	19.0	25.4
		60	75	56.3	135	42.2	21.9	29.3
		65	80	60.0	144	45.0	23.4	31.2
	A514	100	110–130	82.5	198	61.9	32.2	42.9
		90	100–130	75.0	180	56.3	29.3	39.0
	A606	45	65	48.8	117	—	—	—
		50	70	52.5	126	—	—	—
	A607	45	60	45.0	108	—	—	—
		50	65	48.8	117	—	—	—
		55	70	52.5	126	—	—	—
		60	75	56.3	135	—	—	—
		65	80	60.0	144	—	—	—
		70	85	63.8	153	—	—	—
	A618	50	70	52.5	126	—	—	—
		50	65	48.8	117	—	—	—
Bolts	A449	92	120	—	—	67.5	35.1	46.8
		81	105	—	—	59.1	30.7	41.0
		58	90	—	—	50.6	26.3	35.1

[a]On effective net area, see Sects. D1, J5.2.
[b]Produced by fastener in shear, see Sect. J3.6. Note that smaller maximum design bearing stresses, as a function of hole spacing, may be required by Sects. J3.9 and J3.10.
[c]On nominal body area, see Table J3.2.
[d]Threads not excluded from shear plane, see Table J3.2.
[e]Threads excluded from shear plane, see Table J3.2.
[f]For A441 material only.
[g]Smaller value for circular shapes, larger for square or rectangular shapes.
Note: For dimensional and size limitations, see the appropriate Specification.

TABLE 3-36
Design Stress for Compression Members of 36 ksi Specified Yield Stress Steel, $\phi_c = 0.85$[a]

Kl/r	$\phi_c F_{cr}$ (ksi)	Kl/r	$\phi_c F_{cr}$ (ksi)	Kl/r	$\phi_c F_{cr}$ (ksi)	Kl/r	$\phi_c F_{cr}$ (ksi)	Kl/r	$\phi_c F_{cr}$ (ksi)
1	30.60	41	28.01	81	21.66	121	14.16	161	8.23
2	30.59	42	27.89	82	21.48	122	13.98	162	8.13
3	30.59	43	27.76	83	21.29	123	13.80	163	8.03
4	30.57	44	27.64	84	21.11	124	13.62	164	7.93
5	30.56	45	27.51	85	20.92	125	13.44	165	7.84
6	30.54	46	27.37	86	20.73	126	13.27	166	7.74
7	30.52	47	27.24	87	20.54	127	13.09	167	7.65
8	30.50	48	27.11	88	20.36	128	12.92	168	7.56
9	30.47	49	26.97	89	20.17	129	12.74	169	7.47
10	30.44	50	26.83	90	19.98	130	12.57	170	7.38
11	30.41	51	26.68	91	19.79	131	12.40	171	7.30
12	30.37	52	26.54	92	19.60	132	12.23	172	7.21
13	30.33	53	26.39	93	19.41	133	12.06	173	7.13
14	30.29	54	26.25	94	19.22	134	11.88	174	7.05
15	30.24	55	26.10	95	19.03	135	11.71	175	6.97
16	30.19	56	25.94	96	18.84	136	11.54	176	6.89
17	30.14	57	25.79	97	18.65	137	11.37	177	6.81
18	30.08	58	25.63	98	18.46	138	11.20	178	6.73
19	30.02	59	25.48	99	18.27	139	11.04	179	6.66
20	29.96	60	25.32	100	18.08	140	10.89	180	6.59
21	29.90	61	25.16	101	17.89	141	10.73	181	6.51
22	29.83	62	24.99	102	17.70	142	10.58	182	6.44
23	29.76	63	24.83	103	17.51	143	10.43	183	6.37
24	29.69	64	24.67	104	17.32	144	10.29	184	6.30
25	29.61	65	24.50	105	17.13	145	10.15	185	6.23
26	29.53	66	24.33	106	16.94	146	10.01	186	6.17
27	29.45	67	24.16	107	16.75	147	9.87	187	6.10
28	29.36	68	23.99	108	16.56	148	9.74	188	6.04
29	29.28	69	23.82	109	16.37	149	9.61	189	5.97
30	29.18	70	23.64	110	16.19	150	9.48	190	5.91
31	29.09	71	23.47	111	16.00	151	9.36	191	5.85
32	28.99	72	23.29	112	15.81	152	9.23	192	5.79
33	28.90	73	23.12	113	15.63	153	9.11	193	5.73
34	28.79	74	22.94	114	15.44	154	9.00	194	5.67
35	28.69	75	22.76	115	15.26	155	8.88	195	5.61
36	28.58	76	22.58	116	15.07	156	8.77	196	5.55
37	28.47	77	22.40	117	14.89	157	8.66	197	5.50
38	28.36	78	22.22	118	14.70	158	8.55	198	5.44
39	28.25	79	22.03	119	14.52	159	8.44	199	5.39
40	28.13	80	21.85	120	14.34	160	8.33	200	5.33

[a]When element width-to-thickness ratio exceeds λ_r, see Appendix B5.3.

TABLE 3-50
Design Stress for Compression Members of 50 ksi Specified Yield Stress Steel, $\phi_c = 0.85$[a]

$\frac{Kl}{r}$	$\phi_c F_{cr}$ (ksi)	$\frac{Kl}{r}$	$\phi_c F_{cr}$ (ksi)	$\frac{Kl}{r}$	$\phi_c F_{cr}$ (ksi)	$\frac{Kl}{r}$	$\phi_c F_{cr}$ (ksi)	$\frac{Kl}{r}$	$\phi_c F_{cr}$ (ksi)
1	42.50	41	37.59	81	26.31	121	14.57	161	8.23
2	42.49	42	37.36	82	26.00	122	14.33	162	8.13
3	42.47	43	37.13	83	25.68	123	14.10	163	8.03
4	42.45	44	36.89	84	25.37	124	13.88	164	7.93
5	42.42	45	36.65	85	25.06	125	13.66	165	7.84
6	42.39	46	36.41	86	24.75	126	13.44	166	7.74
7	42.35	47	36.16	87	24.44	127	13.23	167	7.65
8	42.30	48	35.91	88	24.13	128	13.02	168	7.56
9	42.25	49	35.66	89	23.82	129	12.82	169	7.47
10	42.19	50	35.40	90	23.51	130	12.62	170	7.38
11	42.13	51	35.14	91	23.20	131	12.43	171	7.30
12	42.05	52	34.88	92	22.89	132	12.25	172	7.21
13	41.98	53	34.61	93	22.58	133	12.06	173	7.13
14	41.90	54	34.34	94	22.28	134	11.88	174	7.05
15	41.81	55	34.07	95	21.97	135	11.71	175	6.97
16	41.71	56	33.79	96	21.67	136	11.54	176	6.89
17	41.61	57	33.51	97	21.36	137	11.37	177	6.81
18	41.51	58	33.23	98	21.06	138	11.20	178	6.73
19	41.39	59	32.95	99	20.76	139	11.04	179	6.66
20	41.28	60	32.67	100	20.46	140	10.89	180	6.59
21	41.15	61	32.38	101	20.16	141	10.73	181	6.51
22	41.02	62	32.09	102	19.86	142	10.58	182	6.44
23	40.89	63	31.80	103	19.57	143	10.43	183	6.37
24	40.75	64	31.50	104	19.28	144	10.29	184	6.30
25	40.60	65	31.21	105	18.98	145	10.15	185	6.23
26	40.45	66	30.91	106	18.69	146	10.01	186	6.17
27	40.29	67	30.61	107	18.40	147	9.87	187	6.10
28	40.13	68	30.31	108	18.12	148	9.74	188	6.04
29	39.97	69	30.01	109	17.83	149	9.61	189	5.97
30	39.79	70	29.70	110	17.55	150	9.48	190	5.91
31	39.62	71	29.40	111	17.27	151	9.36	191	5.85
32	39.43	72	29.09	112	16.99	152	9.23	192	5.79
33	39.25	73	28.79	113	16.71	153	9.11	193	5.73
34	39.06	74	28.48	114	16.42	154	9.00	194	5.67
35	38.86	75	28.17	115	16.13	155	8.88	195	5.61
36	38.66	76	27.86	116	15.86	156	8.77	196	5.55
37	38.45	77	27.55	117	15.59	157	8.66	197	5.50
38	38.24	78	27.24	118	15.32	158	8.55	198	5.44
39	38.03	79	26.93	119	15.07	159	8.44	199	5.39
40	37.81	80	26.62	120	14.82	160	8.33	200	5.33

[a]When element width-to-thickness ratio exceeds λ_r, see Appendix B5.3.

TABLE 4
Values of $\phi_c F_{cr}/F_y$, $\phi_c = 0.85$
For Determining Design Stress for Compression Members for Steel of Any Yield Stress[a]

All grades of steel

λ_c	$\phi_c F_{cr}/F_y$	λ_c	$\phi_c F_{cr}/F_y$	λ_c	$\phi_c F_{cr}/F_y$	λ_c	$\phi_c F_{cr}/F_y$
0.02	0.850	0.82	0.641	1.62	0.284	2.42	0.127
0.04	0.849	0.84	0.632	1.64	0.277	2.44	0.125
0.06	0.849	0.86	0.623	1.66	0.271	2.46	0.123
0.08	0.848	0.88	0.614	1.68	0.264	2.48	0.121
0.10	0.846	0.90	0.605	1.70	0.258	2.50	0.119
0.12	0.845	0.92	0.596	1.72	0.252	2.52	0.117
0.14	0.843	0.94	0.587	1.74	0.246	2.54	0.116
0.16	0.841	0.96	0.578	1.76	0.241	2.56	0.114
0.18	0.839	0.98	0.568	1.78	0.235	2.58	0.112
0.20	0.836	1.00	0.559	1.80	0.230	2.60	0.110
0.22	0.833	1.02	0.550	1.82	0.225	2.62	0.109
0.24	0.830	1.04	0.540	1.84	0.220	2.64	0.107
0.26	0.826	1.06	0.531	1.86	0.215	2.66	0.105
0.28	0.823	1.08	0.521	1.88	0.211	2.68	0.104
0.30	0.819	1.10	0.512	1.90	0.206	2.70	0.102
0.32	0.814	1.12	0.503	1.92	0.202	2.72	0.101
0.34	0.810	1.14	0.493	1.94	0.198	2.74	0.099
0.36	0.805	1.16	0.484	1.96	0.194	2.76	0.098
0.38	0.800	1.18	0.474	1.98	0.190	2.78	0.096
0.40	0.795	1.20	0.465	2.00	0.186	2.80	0.095
0.42	0.789	1.22	0.456	2.02	0.183	2.82	0.094
0.44	0.784	1.24	0.446	2.04	0.179	2.84	0.092
0.46	0.778	1.26	0.437	2.06	0.176	2.86	0.091
0.48	0.772	1.28	0.428	2.08	0.172	2.88	0.090
0.50	0.765	1.30	0.419	2.10	0.169	2.90	0.089
0.52	0.759	1.32	0.410	2.12	0.166	2.92	0.087
0.54	0.752	1.34	0.401	2.14	0.163	2.94	0.086
0.56	0.745	1.36	0.392	2.16	0.160	2.96	0.085
0.58	0.738	1.38	0.383	2.18	0.157	2.98	0.084
0.60	0.731	1.40	0.374	2.20	0.154	3.00	0.083
0.62	0.724	1.42	0.365	2.22	0.151	3.02	0.082
0.64	0.716	1.44	0.357	2.24	0.149	3.04	0.081
0.66	0.708	1.46	0.348	2.26	0.146	3.06	0.080
0.68	0.700	1.48	0.339	2.28	0.143	3.08	0.079
0.70	0.692	1.50	0.331	2.30	0.141	3.10	0.078
0.72	0.684	1.52	0.323	2.32	0.138	3.12	0.077
0.74	0.676	1.54	0.314	2.34	0.136	3.14	0.076
0.76	0.667	1.56	0.306	2.36	0.134	3.16	0.075
0.78	0.659	1.58	0.299	2.38	0.132	3.18	0.074
0.80	0.650	1.60	0.291	2.40	0.129	3.20	0.073

[a]When element width-to-thickness ratios exceed λ_r, see Appendix B5.3.
Values of $\lambda_c > 2.24$ exceed Kl/r of 200 for $F_y = 36$.
Values of $\lambda_c > 2.64$ exceed Kl/r of 200 for $F_y = 50$.

TABLE 5
Values of Kl/r for F_y = 36 and 50 ksi

λ_c	Kl/r		λ_c	Kl/r	
	$F_y = 36$	$F_y = 50$		$F_y = 36$	$F_y = 50$
0.02	1.8	1.5	0.82	73.1	62.0
0.04	3.6	3.0	0.84	74.9	63.6
0.06	5.3	4.5	0.86	76.7	65.1
0.08	7.1	6.1	0.88	78.5	66.6
0.10	8.9	7.6	0.90	80.2	68.1
0.12	10.7	9.1	0.92	82.0	69.6
0.14	12.5	10.6	0.94	83.8	71.1
0.16	14.3	12.1	0.96	85.6	72.6
0.18	16.0	13.6	0.98	87.4	74.1
0.20	17.8	15.1	1.00	89.2	75.7
0.22	19.6	16.6	1.02	90.9	77.2
0.24	21.4	18.2	1.04	92.7	78.7
0.26	23.2	19.7	1.06	94.5	80.2
0.28	25.0	21.2	1.08	96.3	81.7
0.30	26.7	22.7	1.10	98.1	83.2
0.32	28.5	24.2	1.12	99.9	84.7
0.34	30.3	25.7	1.14	101.6	86.3
0.36	32.1	27.2	1.16	103.4	87.8
0.38	33.9	28.8	1.18	105.2	89.3
0.40	35.7	30.3	1.20	107.0	90.8
0.42	37.4	31.8	1.22	108.8	92.3
0.44	39.2	33.3	1.24	110.6	93.8
0.46	41.0	34.8	1.26	112.3	95.3
0.48	42.8	36.3	1.28	114.1	96.8
0.50	44.6	37.8	1.30	115.9	98.4
0.52	46.4	39.3	1.32	117.7	99.9
0.54	48.1	40.9	1.34	119.5	101.4
0.56	49.9	42.4	1.36	121.3	102.9
0.58	51.7	43.9	1.38	123.0	104.4
0.60	53.5	45.4	1.40	124.8	105.9
0.62	55.3	46.9	1.42	126.6	107.4
0.64	57.1	48.4	1.44	128.4	108.9
0.66	58.8	49.9	1.46	130.2	110.5
0.68	60.6	51.4	1.48	132.0	112.0
0.70	62.4	53.0	1.50	133.7	113.5
0.72	64.2	54.5	1.52	135.5	115.0
0.74	66.0	56.0	1.54	137.3	116.5
0.76	67.8	57.5	1.56	139.1	118.0
0.78	69.5	59.0	1.58	140.9	119.5
0.80	71.3	60.5	1.60	142.7	121.1

TABLE 5 (cont'd)
Values of Kl/r for F_y = 36 and 50 ksi

λ_c	Kl/r		λ_c	Kl/r
	$F_y = 36$	$F_y = 50$		$F_y = 50$
1.62	144.4	122.6	2.42	183.1
1.64	146.2	124.1	2.44	184.6
1.66	148.0	125.6	2.46	186.1
1.68	149.8	127.1	2.48	187.6
1.70	151.6	128.6	2.50	189.1
1.72	153.4	130.1	2.52	190.7
1.74	155.1	131.6	2.54	192.2
1.76	156.9	133.2	2.56	193.7
1.78	158.7	134.7	2.58	195.2
1.80	160.5	136.2	2.60	196.7
1.82	162.3	137.7	2.62	198.2
1.84	164.1	139.2	2.64	199.7
1.86	165.8	140.7		
1.88	167.6	142.2		
1.90	169.4	143.8		
1.92	171.2	145.3		
1.94	173.0	146.8		
1.96	174.8	148.3		
1.98	176.5	149.8		
2.00	178.3	151.3		
2.02	180.1	152.8		
2.04	181.9	154.3		
2.06	183.7	155.9		
2.08	185.5	157.4		
2.10	187.2	158.9		
2.12	189.0	160.4		
2.14	190.8	161.9		
2.16	192.6	163.4		
2.18	194.4	164.9		
2.20	196.2	166.5		
2.22	197.9	168.0		
2.24	199.7	169.5		
2.26		171.0		
2.28		172.5		
2.30		174.0		
2.32		175.5		
2.34		177.0		
2.36		178.6		
2.38		180.1		
2.40		181.6		

Heavy line indicates Kl/r of 200.

TABLE 6
Slenderness Ratios of Elements as a Function of F_y From Table B5.1

Ratio	F_y (ksi)					
	36	42	46	50	60	65
$65/\sqrt{F_y}$	10.8	10.0	9.6	9.2	8.4	8.1
$76/\sqrt{F_y}$	12.7	11.7	11.2	10.7	9.8	9.4
$95/\sqrt{F_y}$	15.8	14.7	14.0	13.4	12.3	11.8
$106/\sqrt{F_y - 16.5}$	24.0	21.0	19.5	18.3	16.1	15.2
$127/\sqrt{F_y}$	21.2	19.6	18.7	18.0	16.4	15.8
$141/\sqrt{F_y - 10}$	27.7	24.9	23.5	22.3	19.9	19.0
$190/\sqrt{F_y}$	31.7	29.3	28.0	26.9	24.5	23.6
$238/\sqrt{F_y - 10}$	46.7	42.1	39.7	37.6	33.7	32.1
$238/\sqrt{F_y - 16.5}$	53.9	47.1	43.8	41.1	36.1	34.2
$253/\sqrt{F_y}$	42.2	39.0	37.3	35.8	32.7	31.4
$317/\sqrt{F_y - 10}$	62.2	56.0	52.8	50.1	44.8	42.7
$640/\sqrt{F_y}$	107	98.8	94.4	90.5	82.6	79.4
$970/\sqrt{F_y}$	162	150	143	137	125	120
$1{,}300/F_y$	36.1	31.0	28.3	26.0	21.7	20.0
$2{,}070/F_y$	57.5	49.3	45.0	41.4	34.5	31.8
$3{,}300/F_y$	91.7	78.6	71.7	66.0	55.0	50.8
$8{,}970/F_y$	249	214	195	179	150	138

TABLE 7
Values of C_b
For Use in Chapters F and G

$\frac{M_1}{M_2}$	C_b	$\frac{M_1}{M_2}$	C_b	$\frac{M_1}{M_2}$	C_b
−1.00	1.00	−0.45	1.34	0.10	1.86
−0.95	1.02	−0.40	1.38	0.15	1.91
−0.90	1.05	−0.35	1.42	0.20	1.97
−0.85	1.07	−0.30	1.46	0.25	2.03
−0.80	1.10	−0.25	1.51	0.30	2.09
−0.75	1.13	−0.20	1.55	0.35	2.15
−0.70	1.16	−0.15	1.60	0.40	2.22
−0.65	1.19	−0.10	1.65	0.45	2.28
−0.60	1.23	−0.05	1.70	≥0.47	2.30
−0.55	1.26	0	1.75		
−0.50	1.30	0.05	1.80		

Note 1: $C_b = 1.75 + 1.05(M_1/M_2) + 0.3\,(M_1/M_2)^2 \leq 2.3$
Note 2: M_1/M_2 positive for reverse curvature and negative for single curvature.

TABLE 8
Values of C_m
For Use in Section H1

$\frac{M_1}{M_2}$	C_m	$\frac{M_1}{M_2}$	C_m	$\frac{M_1}{M_2}$	C_m
−1.00	1.00	−0.45	0.78	0.10	0.56
−0.95	0.98	−0.40	0.76	0.15	0.54
−0.90	0.96	−0.35	0.74	0.20	0.52
−0.85	0.94	−0.30	0.72	0.25	0.50
−0.80	0.92	−0.25	0.70	0.30	0.48
−0.75	0.90	−0.20	0.68	0.35	0.46
−0.70	0.88	−0.15	0.66	0.40	0.44
−0.65	0.86	−0.10	0.64	0.45	0.42
−0.60	0.84	−0.05	0.62	0.50	0.40
				0.60	0.36
−0.55	0.82	0	0.60	0.80	0.28
−0.50	0.80	0.05	0.58	1.00	0.20

Note 1: $C_m = 0.6 - 0.4(M_1/M_2)$.
Note 2: M_1/M_2 is positive for reverse curvature and negative for single curvature.

TABLE 9
Values of P_e/A_g
For Use in Section H1 for Steel of Any Yield Stress

$\frac{Kl}{r}$	P_e/A_g (ksi)	$\frac{Kl}{r}$	P_e/A_g (ksi)	$\frac{Kl}{r}$	P_e/A_g (ksi)	$\frac{Kl}{r}$	P_e/A_g (ksi)	$\frac{Kl}{r}$	P_e/A_g (ksi)	$\frac{Kl}{r}$	P_e/A_g (ksi)
21	649.02	51	110.04	81	43.62	111	23.23	141	14.40	171	9.79
22	591.36	52	105.85	82	42.57	112	22.82	142	14.19	172	9.67
23	541.06	53	101.89	83	41.55	113	22.42	143	14.00	173	9.56
24	496.91	54	98.15	84	40.56	114	22.02	144	13.80	174	9.45
25	457.95	55	94.62	85	39.62	115	21.64	145	13.61	175	9.35
26	423.40	56	91.27	86	38.70	116	21.27	146	13.43	176	9.24
27	392.62	57	88.09	87	37.81	117	20.91	147	13.25	177	9.14
28	365.07	58	85.08	88	36.96	118	20.56	148	13.07	178	9.03
29	340.33	59	82.22	89	36.13	119	20.21	149	12.89	179	8.93
30	318.02	60	79.51	90	35.34	120	19.88	150	12.72	180	8.83
31	297.83	61	76.92	91	34.56	121	19.55	151	12.55	181	8.74
32	279.51	62	74.46	92	33.82	122	19.23	152	12.39	182	8.64
33	262.83	63	72.11	93	33.09	123	18.92	153	12.23	183	8.55
34	247.59	64	69.88	94	32.39	124	18.61	154	12.07	184	8.45
35	233.65	65	67.74	95	31.71	125	18.32	155	11.91	185	8.36
36	220.85	66	65.71	96	31.06	126	18.03	156	11.76	186	8.27
37	209.07	67	63.76	97	30.42	127	17.75	157	11.61	187	8.18
38	198.21	68	61.90	98	29.80	128	17.47	158	11.47	188	8.10
39	188.18	69	60.12	99	29.20	129	17.20	159	11.32	189	8.01
40	178.89	70	58.41	100	28.62	130	16.94	160	11.18	190	7.93
41	170.27	71	56.78	101	28.06	131	16.68	161	11.04	191	7.85
42	162.26	72	55.21	102	27.51	132	16.43	162	10.91	192	7.76
43	154.80	73	53.71	103	26.98	133	16.18	163	10.77	193	7.68
44	147.84	74	52.57	104	26.46	134	15.94	164	10.64	194	7.60
45	141.34	75	50.88	105	25.96	135	15.70	165	10.51	195	7.53
46	135.26	76	49.55	106	25.47	136	15.47	166	10.39	196	7.45
47	129.57	77	48.27	107	25.00	137	15.25	167	10.26	197	7.38
48	124.23	78	47.04	108	24.54	138	15.03	168	10.14	198	7.30
49	119.21	79	45.86	109	24.09	139	14.81	169	10.02	199	7.23
50	114.49	80	44.72	110	23.65	140	14.60	170	9.90	200	7.16

Note: $P_e/A_g = \dfrac{\pi^2 E}{(Kl/r)^2}$

TABLE 10-36

$\frac{\phi_v V_n}{A_w}$ (ksi) for Plate Girders by Section F2

For 36 ksi Yield Stress Steel, Tension Field Action Not Included

$\frac{h}{t_w}$	Aspect Ratio *a/h*: Stiffener Spacing to Web Depth													
	0.5	0.6	0.7	0.8	0.9	1.0	1.2	1.4	1.6	1.8	2.0	2.5	3.0	Over 3.0
60	19.4	19.4	19.4	19.4	19.4	19.4	19.4	19.4	19.4	19.4	19.4	19.4	19.4	19.4
70	19.4	19.4	19.4	19.4	19.4	19.4	19.4	19.4	19.4	19.4	19.4	19.4	19.4	19.4
80	19.4	19.4	19.4	19.4	19.4	19.4	19.4	19.4	19.4	19.4	18.9	18.2	17.9	16.9
90	19.4	19.4	19.4	19.4	19.4	19.4	19.4	18.5	17.8	17.2	16.8	16.2	15.9	14.7
100	19.4	19.4	19.4	19.4	19.4	19.2	17.6	16.6	16.0	15.5	14.9	13.8	13.2	11.9
110	19.4	19.4	19.4	19.4	18.4	17.4	16.0	14.8	13.7	12.8	12.3	11.4	10.9	9.8
120	19.4	19.4	19.4	18.1	16.9	16.0	14.0	12.5	11.5	10.8	10.3	9.6	9.2	8.3
130	19.4	19.4	18.2	16.7	15.6	14.1	11.9	10.6	9.8	9.2	8.8	8.2	7.8	7.0
140	19.4	18.8	16.9	15.5	13.5	12.1	10.3	9.2	8.4	7.9	7.6	7.0	6.7	6.1
150	19.4	17.6	15.7	13.5	11.8	10.6	8.9	8.0	7.3	6.9	6.6	6.1	5.9	5.3
160	18.9	16.5	14.1	11.9	10.4	9.3	7.9	7.0	6.5	6.1	5.8	5.4		4.6
170	17.8	15.5	12.5	10.5	9.2	8.2	7.0	6.2	5.7	5.4	5.1			4.1
180	16.8	13.9	11.1	9.4	8.2	7.3	6.2	5.5	5.1	4.8	4.6			3.7
200	14.9	11.2	9.0	7.6	6.6	5.9	5.0	4.5	4.1					3.0
220	12.3	9.3	7.5	6.3	5.5	4.9	4.2							2.5
240	10.3	7.8	6.3	5.3	4.6	4.1								2.1
260	8.8	6.6	5.3	4.5	3.9	3.5								1.8
280	7.6	5.7	4.6	3.9										
300	6.6	5.0	4.0											
320	5.8	4.4												

TABLE 10-50

$\frac{\phi_v V_n}{A_w}$ (ksi) for Plate Girders by Section F2

For 50 ksi Yield Stress Steel, Tension Field Action Not Included

$\frac{h}{t_w}$	Aspect Ratio *a/h*: Stiffener Spacing to Web Depth													
	0.5	0.6	0.7	0.8	0.9	1.0	1.2	1.4	1.6	1.8	2.0	2.5	3.0	Over 3.0
60	27.0	27.0	27.0	27.0	27.0	27.0	27.0	27.0	27.0	27.0	27.0	27.0	27.0	26.6
70	27.0	27.0	27.0	27.0	27.0	27.0	27.0	27.0	26.9	26.1	25.5	24.6	24.0	22.8
80	27.0	27.0	27.0	27.0	27.0	27.0	26.0	24.5	23.5	22.8	22.3	21.5	20.6	18.6
90	27.0	27.0	27.0	27.0	26.5	25.1	23.1	21.8	20.4	19.2	18.3	17.0	16.3	14.7
100	27.0	27.0	27.0	25.6	23.9	22.6	20.1	17.9	16.5	15.5	14.9	13.8	13.2	11.9
110	27.0	27.0	25.3	23.2	21.7	19.6	16.6	14.8	13.7	12.8	12.3	11.4	10.9	9.8
120	27.0	25.9	23.2	21.1	18.4	16.5	14.0	12.5	11.5	10.8	10.3	9.6	9.2	8.3
130	27.0	23.9	21.4	18.0	15.7	14.1	11.9	10.6	9.8	9.2	8.8	8.2	7.8	7.0
140	25.5	22.2	18.4	15.5	13.5	12.1	10.3	9.2	8.4	7.9	7.6	7.0	6.7	6.1
150	23.8	19.9	16.1	13.5	11.8	10.6	8.9	8.0	7.3	6.9	6.6	6.1	5.9	5.3
160	22.3	17.5	14.1	11.9	10.4	9.3	7.9	7.0	6.5	6.1	5.8	5.4		4.6
170	20.6	15.5	12.5	10.5	9.2	8.2	7.0	6.2	5.7	5.4	5.1			4.1
180	18.3	13.9	11.1	9.4	8.2	7.3	6.2	5.5	5.1	4.8	4.6			3.7
200	14.9	11.2	9.0	7.6	6.6	5.9	5.0	4.5	4.1					3.0
220	12.3	9.3	7.5	6.3	5.5	4.9	4.2							2.5
240	10.3	7.8	6.3	5.3	4.6	4.1								2.1
260	8.8	6.6	5.3	4.5	3.9	3.5								
280	7.6	5.7	4.6	3.9										

TABLE 11-36

$\frac{\phi_v V_n}{A_w}$ (ksi) for Plate Girders by Appendix G

For 36 ksi Yield Stress Steel, Tension Field Action Included[b]
(*Italic* values indicate gross area, as percent of ($h \times t_w$) required for pairs of intermediate stiffeners of 36 ksi yield stress steel with $V_u / \phi V_n = 1.0$.)[a]

$\frac{h}{t_w}$	Aspect Ratio a/h: Stiffener Spacing to Web Depth													
	0.5	0.6	0.7	0.8	0.9	1.0	1.2	1.4	1.6	1.8	2.0	2.5	3.0	Over 3.0[c]
60	19.4	19.4	19.4	19.4	19.4	19.4	19.4	19.4	19.4	19.4	19.4	19.4	19.4	19.4
70	19.4	19.4	19.4	19.4	19.4	19.4	19.4	19.4	19.4	19.4	19.4	19.4	19.4	19.4
80	19.4	19.4	19.4	19.4	19.4	19.4	19.4	19.4	19.4	19.4	19.1	18.6	18.3	16.9
90	19.4	19.4	19.4	19.4	19.4	19.4	19.4	19.0	18.5	18.2	17.8	17.3	16.8	14.7
100	19.4	19.4	19.4	19.4	19.4	19.3	18.6	18.1	17.6	17.2	16.6	15.6	14.9	11.9
110	19.4	19.4	19.4	19.4	19.1	18.7	17.9	17.2	16.3	15.6	15.1	14.0	13.3	9.8
120	19.4	19.4	19.4	19.0	18.5	18.1	17.0	16.0	15.1	14.4	13.9	12.8	12.0	8.3
130	19.4	19.4	19.1	18.6	18.1	17.4	16.1	15.1	14.2	13.5	12.9	11.8	11.0	7.0
140	19.4	19.3	18.7	18.2	17.4	16.6	15.4	14.4	13.5	12.8	12.2	11.0	10.2	6.1
150	19.4	19.0	18.4	17.5	16.7	16.0	14.8	13.8	12.9	12.2	11.6	10.4	9.6	5.3
160	19.3	18.7	17.9	17.0	16.2	15.5	14.3	13.3	12.4	11.7	11.1	9.9		4.6
170	19.1	18.4	17.4	16.6	15.8	15.1	13.9	12.9	12.0	11.3 *0.3*	10.7 *0.4*			4.1
180	18.9	18.0	17.1	16.2	15.5	14.8	13.6 *0.2*	12.6 *0.7*	11.7 *1.1*	11.0 *1.3*	10.4 *1.5*			3.7
200	18.4	17.3	16.4	15.6 *0.1*	14.9 *0.9*	14.2 *1.4*	13.1 *2.1*	12.0 *2.5*	11.2 *2.8*					3.0
220	17.8	16.9	16.0 *1.1*	15.2 *2.0*	14.5 *2.6*	13.8 *3.0*	12.7 *3.6*							2.5
240	17.4	16.5 *1.5*	15.7 *2.7*	14.9 *3.4*	14.2 *3.9*	13.5 *4.3*								2.1
260	17.1 *1.3*	16.2 *3.0*	15.4 *4.0*	14.6 *4.6*	14.0 *5.0*	13.3 *5.4*								1.8
280	16.8 *2.7*	16.0 *4.2*	15.2 *5.0*	14.4 *5.6*										
300	16.6 *3.9*	15.8 *5.2*	15.0 *5.9*											
320	16.4 *4.9*	15.6 *6.0*												

[a]For area of single-angle and single-plate stiffeners, or when $V_u/\phi V_n < 1.0$, see Formula A-G4-2.
[b]For end-panels and all panels in hybrid and web-tapered plate girders use Table 10-36.
[c]Same as for Table 10-36.
Note: Girders so proportioned that the computed shear is less than that given in right-hand column do not require intermediate stiffeners.

TABLE 11-50

$\frac{\phi_v V_n}{A_w}$ (ksi) for Plate Girders by Appendix G

For 50 ksi Yield Stress Steel, Tension Field Action Included[b]

(*Italic* values indicate gross area, as percent of $(h \times t_w)$ required for pairs of intermediate stiffeners of 50 ksi yield stress steel with $V_u/\phi V_n = 1.0$.)[a]

$\frac{h}{t_w}$	Aspect Ratio a/h: Stiffener Spacing to Web Depth													
	0.5	0.6	0.7	0.8	0.9	1.0	1.2	1.4	1.6	1.8	2.0	2.5	3.0	Over 3.0[c]
60	27.0	27.0	27.0	27.0	27.0	27.0	27.0	27.0	27.0	27.0	27.0	27.0	27.0	26.6
70	27.0	27.0	27.0	27.0	27.0	27.0	27.0	27.0	26.9	26.5	26.1	25.4	24.9	22.8
80	27.0	27.0	27.0	27.0	27.0	27.0	26.5	25.8	25.1	24.6	24.1	23.3	22.4	18.6
90	27.0	27.0	27.0	27.0	26.8	26.3	25.3	24.4	23.4	22.5	21.7	20.2	19.2	14.7
100	27.0	27.0	27.0	26.5	25.9	25.3	24.0	22.5	21.4	20.4	19.6	18.0	17.0	11.9
110	27.0	27.0	26.5	25.8	25.1	24.2	22.4	21.0	19.8	18.8	18.0	16.4	15.3	9.8
120	27.0	26.7	25.9	25.1	24.0	23.0	21.2	19.8	18.6	17.6	16.8	15.2	14.1	8.3
130	27.0	26.2	25.4	24.1	23.0	22.0	20.3	18.9	17.7	16.7	15.9	14.2	13.1	7.0
140	26.7	25.8	24.5	23.3	22.2	21.3	19.6	18.2	17.0	16.0	15.1	13.5	12.3	6.1
150	26.3	25.2	23.9	22.7	21.6	20.7	19.0	17.6	16.4	15.4	14.5	12.9	11.7	5.3
160	26.0	24.6	23.3	22.2	21.1	20.2	18.5	17.1	15.9 *0.2*	14.9 *0.4*	14.0 *0.5*	12.4 *0.8*		4.6
170	25.6	24.1	22.8	21.7	20.7	19.8	18.1 *0.5*	16.7 *1.0*	15.5 *1.2*	14.5 *1.4*	13.6 *1.6*			4.1
180	25.1	23.7	22.4	21.3	20.3 *0.4*	19.4 *0.9*	17.8 *1.5*	16.4 *1.9*	15.2 *2.2*	14.2 *2.3*	13.3 *2.5*			3.7
200	24.3	23.0	21.8 *1.0*	20.8 *1.8*	19.8 *2.3*	18.9 *2.7*	17.3 *3.2*	15.9 *3.5*	14.7 *3.7*					3.0
220	23.7	22.5 *1.7*	21.4 *2.7*	20.4 *3.3*	19.4 *3.8*	18.5 *4.1*	16.9 *4.5*							2.5
240	23.2 *1.8*	22.1 *3.2*	21.0 *4.0*	20.0 *4.6*	19.1 *4.9*	18.2 *5.2*								2.1
260	23.0 *3.2*	21.8 *4.4*	20.8 *5.1*	19.8 *5.6*	18.8 *5.9*	18.0 *6.1*								
280	22.7 *4.4*	21.6 *5.4*	20.6 *6.0*	19.6 *6.4*										

[a]For area of single-angle and single-plate stiffeners, or when $V_u/\phi V_n < 1.0$, see Formula A-G4-2.
[b]For end-panels and all panels in hybrid and web-tapered plate girders use Table 10-50.
[c]Same as for Table 10-50.
Note: Girders so proportioned that the computed shear is less than that given in right-hand column do not require intermediate stiffeners.

TABLE 12
Nominal Horizontal Shear Load for One Connector Q_n, kips[a]
From Formulas I5-1 and I5-2

Connector[b]	Specified Compressive Strength of Concrete, f_c', ksi[d]		
	3.0	3.5	4.0
½-in. dia. × 2-in. hooked or headed stud	9.4	10.5	11.6
⅝-in. dia. × 2½-in. hooked or headed stud	14.6	16.4	18.1
¾-in. dia. × 3-in. hooked or headed stud	21.0	23.6	26.1
⅞-in. dia. × 3½-in. hooked or headed stud	28.6	32.1	35.5
Channel C3 × 4.1	10.2 L_c[c]	11.5 L_c[c]	12.7 L_c[c]
Channel C4 × 5.4	11.1 L_c[c]	12.4 L_c[c]	13.8 L_c[c]
Channel C5 × 6.7	11.9 L_c[c]	13.3 L_c[c]	14.7 L_c[c]

[a]Applicable only to concrete made with C33 aggregates.
[b]The design horizontal loads tabulated may also be used for studs longer than shown.
[c]L_c = length of channel, inches.
[d]$F_u > 0.5(f_c' w)^{.75}$, w = 145 lbs./cu.ft.

TABLE 13
Coefficients for Use with Concrete Made with C330 Aggregates to Adjust Values from Table 12 for Lightweight Concrete

Specified Compressive Strength of Concrete (f_c')	Air Dry Unit Weight of Concrete, pcf						
	90	95	100	105	110	115	120
≤ 4.0 ksi	0.73	0.76	0.78	0.81	0.83	0.86	0.88
≥ 5.0 ksi	0.82	0.85	0.87	0.91	0.93	0.96	0.99

UNIFORM BUILDING CODE STANDARD NO. 27-15

ALLOWABLE STRESS DESIGN AND PLASTIC DESIGN FOR STRUCTURAL STEEL BUILDINGS

Based on Specification for Structural Steel Buildings Allowable Stress Design and Plastic Design of the American Institute of Steel Construction, Inc. (June 1, 1989)

See Sections 2701 (a); 2702; 2710 (b), (e) 3, (g) 3, (g) 4, (g) 7, (h) 2 and (i) 1; and 2711 (e) 3 and (f) 2, Uniform Building Code

Part I of this standard contains the exceptions to the referenced specification. Part II of this standard is "Allowable Stress Design and Plastic Design for Structural Buildings" reproduced with permission of the publisher.

Part I

Scope

Sec. 27.1503. Except for the limitations, deletions, modifications or amendments set forth in this section, buildings or structures may be designed in accordance with Part II of this standard. When other codes, standards or specifications are referred to in this standard, they are to be considered as only an indication of an acceptable method or material that can be used with the approval of the building official. Part II of this standard is amended as follows:

1. **Sec. A1. Modify as follows:**

   This standard is intended as an alternative to U.B.C. Standard No. 27-14.

2. **Sec. A2.1. Modify the last sentence as follows:**

   For the design of cold-formed steel structural members, whose profiles contain rounded comers and slender flat elements, the provisions of U.B.C. Standard No. 27-9 shall apply.

3. **Sec. A4. Modify as follows:**

   The nominal loads shall be the minimum design loads required by the code.

4. **Secs. A4.1, A4.4 and A4.5. Delete.**

Part II

TABLE OF CONTENTS

CHAPTER A
GENERAL PROVISIONS

Sec. 27.1501A

A1. SCOPE

Modified—See Part I.

A2. LIMITS OF APPLICABILITY

1. Structural Steel Defined. As used in this Specification, the term *structural steel* refers to the steel elements of the structural steel frame essential to the support of the design loads. Such elements are generally enumerated in Section 2.1 of the AISC *Code of Standard Practice for Steel Buildings and Bridges*. For the design of cold-formed steel structural members, whose profiles contain rounded corners and slender flat elements, the provisions of U.B.C. Standard No. 27-9 shall apply. (Modified per Part I).

2. Types of Construction. Three basic types of construction and associated design assumptions are permissible under the respective conditions stated herein, and each will govern in a specific manner the size of members and the types and strength of their connections:

Type 1, commonly designated as "rigid-frame" (continuous frame), assumes that beam-to-column connections have sufficient rigidity to hold virtually unchanged the original angles between intersecting members.

Type 2, commonly designated as "simple framing" (unrestrained, free-ended), assumes that, insofar as gravity loading is concerned, ends of beams and girders are connected for shear only and are free to rotate under gravity load.

Type 3, commonly designated as "semi-rigid framing" (partially restrained), assumes that the connections of beams and girders possess a dependable and known moment capacity intermediate in degree between the rigidity of Type 1 and the flexibility of Type 2.

The design of all connections shall be consistent with the assumptions as to type of construction called for on the design drawings.

Type 1 construction is unconditionally permitted under this Specification. Two different methods of design are recognized. Within the limitations laid down in Section N1, members of continuous frames or continuous portions of frames may be proportioned, on the basis of their maximum predictable strength, to resist the specified design loads multiplied by the prescribed load factors. Otherwise, Type 1 construction shall be designed, within the limitations of Chapters A through M, to resist the stresses produced by the specified design loads, assuming moment distribution in accordance with the elastic theory.

Type 2 construction is permitted under this Specification, subject to the stipulations of the following paragraph, wherever applicable.

In buildings designed as Type 2 construction (i.e., with beam-to-column connections other than wind connections assumed flexible under gravity loading) the wind moments may be distributed among selected joints of the frame, provided:

1. Connections and connected members have adequate capacity to resist wind moments.

2. Girders are adequate to carry full gravity load as "simple beams."

3. Connections have adequate inelastic rotation capacity to avoid overstress of the fasteners or welds under combined gravity and wind loading.

Type 3 (semirigid) construction is permitted upon evidence the connections to be used are capable of furnishing, as a minimum, a predictable proportion of full end restraint. The proportioning of main members joined by such connections shall be predicated upon no greater degree of end restraint than this minimum.

Types 2 and 3 construction may necessitate some nonelastic, but self-limiting, deformation of a structural steel part.

A3. MATERIAL

1. Structural Steel. a. ASTM designations. Material conforming to one of the following standard specifications is approved for use under this Specification:

A 36, A 53 (Grade B), A 242, A 441, A 500, A 501, A 514, A 529, A 570 (Grade 40, 45 and 50), A 572, A588, A 606, A 607, A 618, A 709 and A 852.

Certified mill test reports or certified reports of tests made by the fabricator or a testing laboratory in accordance with ASTM A 6 or A 568, as applicable, and the governing specification shall constitute sufficient evidence of conformity with one of the above ASTM standards. Additionally, the fabricator shall, if requested, provide an affidavit stating the structural steel furnished meets the requirements of the grade specified.

b. Unidentified steel. Unidentified steel, if free from surface imperfections, is permitted for parts of minor importance, or for unimportant details, where the precise physical properties of the steel and its weldability would not affect the strength of the structure.

c. Heavy shapes. For A 6 Groups 4 and 5 rolled shapes to be used as members subject to primary tensile stresses due to tension or flexure, toughness need not be specified if splices are made by bolting. If such members are spliced using full penetration welds, the steel shall be specified in the contract documents to be supplied with Charpy V-Notch testing in accordance with ASTM A 6, Supplementary Requirement S5. The impact test shall meet a minimum average value of 20 ft-lbs. absorbed energy at 70°F. and shall be conducted in accordance with ASTM A673 with the following exceptions:

a. The center longitudinal axis of the specimens shall be located as near as practical to midway between the inner flange surface and the center of the flange thickness at the intersection with the web mid-thickness.

b. Tests shall be conducted by the producer on material selected from a location representing the top of each ingot or part of an ingot used to produce the product represented by these tests.

For plates exceeding 2 inches thick used for built-up members with bolted splices and subject to primary tensile stresses due to tension or flexure, material toughness need not be specified. If such members are spliced using full penetration welds, the steel shall be specified in the contract documents to be supplied with Charpy V-Notch testing in accordance with ASTM A 6, Supplementary Requirement S5. The impact test shall be conducted by the producer in accordance with ASTM A 673, Frequency P, and shall meet a minimum average value of 20 ft-lbs. absorbed energy at + 70°F.

The above supplementary toughness requirements shall also be considered for welded full-penetration joints other than splices in heavy rolled and built-up members subject to primary tensile stresses.

Additional requirements for joints in heavy rolled and built-up members are given in Sections J1.7, J1.8, J2.6, J2.7 and M2.2.

2. Steel Castings and Forgings. Cast steel shall conform to one of the following standard specifications:

A27, Grade 65-36 and A148 Grade 80-50.

Steel forgings shall conform to the following standard specification:

A668

Certified test reports shall constitute sufficient evidence of conformity with the standards.

Allowable stresses shall be the same as those provided for other steels, where applicable.

3. Rivets. Steel rivets shall conform to the following standard specification:

A502

Manufacturer's certification shall constitute sufficient evidence of conformity with the standard.

4. Bolts, Washers and Nuts. Steel bolts shall conform to one of the following standard specifications:

A307, A327, A449, A490, A563 and F436.

A449 bolts are permitted only in connections requiring bolt diameters greater than $1^1/_2$ inches and shall not be used in slip-critical connections.

Manufacturer's certification shall constitute sufficient evidence of conformity with the standards.

5. Anchor Bolts and Threaded Rods. Anchor bolt and threaded rod steel shall conform to one of the following standard specifications:

Structural Steel, ASTM A 36

A36, A194, Grade 7, A354, A449, A588 and A687.

Threads on bolts and rods shall conform to Unified Standard Series of ANSI B18.1-72 and shall have Class 2A tolerances.

Steel bolts conforming to other provisions of Section A3 are permitted as anchor bolts. A449 material is acceptable for high-strength anchor bolts and threaded rods of any diameter.

Manufacturer's certification shall constitute sufficient evidence of conformity with the standards.

6. Filler Metal and Flux for Welding. Welding electrodes and fluxes shall conform to one of the following specifications of the American Welding Society*:

A5.1, A5.5, A5.17, A5.18, A5.20, A5.23, A5.28 and A5.29.

Manufacturer's certification shall constitute sufficient evidence of conformity with the standards.

7. Stud Shear Connectors. Steel stud shear connectors shall conform to the requirement of U.B.C. Standard No. 27-6.

Manufacturer's certification shall constitute sufficient evidence of conformity with the code.

A4. LOADS AND FORCES

Modified. See Part I

The nominal loads shall be the minimum design loads required by the code.

1. Dead Load and Live Load. Deleted per Part I

2. Impact. For structures carrying live loads** which induce impact, the assumed live load shall be increased sufficiently to provide for same.

If not otherwise specified, the increase shall not be less than:

For supports of elevators	100%
For cab-operated traveling crane support girders and their connections	25%
For pendant-operated traveling crane support girders and their connections	10%
For supports of light machinery, shaft or motor driven	20%
For supports of reciprocating machinery or power driven units	50%
For hangers supporting floors and balconies	33%

3. Crane Runway Horizontal Forces. The lateral force on crane runways to provide for the effect of moving crane trolleys shall not be less than 20 percent of the sum of weights of the lifted load and of the crane trolley, but exclusive of other parts of the crane. The force shall be assumed to be applied at the top of the rails, acting in either direction normal to the runway rails, and shall be distributed with due regard for lateral stiffness of the structure supporting the rails.

The longitudinal tractive force shall not be less than 10 percent of the maximum wheel loads of the crane applied at the top of the rail, unless otherwise specified.

The crane runway shall also be designed for crane stop forces.

4. Wind. Deleted per Part I.

5. Other Forces. Deleted per Part I.

---

*Approval of these welding electrode specifications is given without regard to weld metal notch toughness requirements, which are generally not critical for building construction.

**Live loads on crane support girders shall be taken as the maximum crane wheel loads.

A5. DESIGN BASIS

1. Allowable Stresses. Except as provided in Chapter N, all structural members, connections and connectors shall be proportioned so the stresses due to the working loads do not exceed the allowable stresses specified in Chapters D through K. The allowable stresses specified in these chapters do not apply to peak stresses in regions of connections (see also Section B9), provided requirements of Chapter K are satisfied.

For provisions pertaining to plastic design, refer to Chapter N.

2. Wind and Seismic Stresses. Allowable stresses may be increased one third above the values otherwise provided when produced by wind or seismic loading, acting alone or in combination with the design dead and live loads, provided the required section computed on this basis is not less than that required for the design dead and live load and impact (if any) computed without the one third stress increase, and further provided that stresses are not otherwise required to be calculated on the basis of reduction factors applied to design loads in combinations.

3. Structural Analysis. The stresses in members, connections and connectors shall be determined by structural analysis for the loads defined in Section A4. Selection of the method of analysis is the prerogative of the responsible engineer.

4. Design for Serviceability and Other Considerations. The overall structure and the individual members, connections and connectors shall be checked for serviceability in accordance with Chapter L.

A6. REFERENCED CODES AND STANDARDS

Where codes and standards are referenced in this Specification, the editions of the following listed adoption dates are intended:

American Institute for Steel Construction

Code of Standard Practice for Steel Buildings and Bridges, 1986.

American National Standards Institute

B18.1-72

A58.1-82

American Society for Testing and Materials

A 6-87d	A 27-87	A 36-87
A 53-88	A 148-84	A 242-87
A 307-86a	A 325-86	A 354-86
A 441-85	A 449-87	A 490-85
A 500-84	A 501-84	A 514-87a
A 529-85	A 563-84	A 570-85
A 572-85	A 588-87	A 606-85
A 607-85	A 618-84	A 668-85a
A 687-84	C 33-86	C 330-87
F 436-86	A 502-83A	A 709-87b
A 852-85		

American Welding Society

D1.1-88	A5.1-81	A5.5-81
A5.17-80	A5.18-79	A5.20-79
A5.23-80	A5.28-79	A5.29-80

Research Council on Structural Connections

Specification for Structural Joints Using ASTM A 325 or A490 Bolts, 1985.

A7. DESIGN DOCUMENTS

1. Plans. The design plans shall show a complete design with sizes, sections and relative locations of the various members. Floor levels, column centers and offsets shall be dimensioned. Drawings shall be drawn to a scale large enough to show the information clearly.

Design documents shall indicate the type or types of construction as defined in Section A2.2 and shall include the loads and design requirements necessary for preparation of shop drawings including shears, moments and axial forces to be resisted by all members and their connections.

Where joints are to be assembled with high-strength bolts, design documents shall indicate the connection type (slip-critical, tension or bearing).

Camber of trusses, beams and girders, if required, shall be called for in the design documents. The requirements for stiffeners and bracing shall be shown on the design documents.

2. Standard Symbols and Nomenclature. Welding and inspection symbols used on plans and shop drawings shall preferably be the American Welding Society symbols. Other adequate welding symbols are permitted, provided a complete explanation thereof is shown in the design documents.

3. Notation for Welding. Notes shall be made in the design documents and on the shop drawings of those joints or groups of joints in which the welding sequence and technique of welding shall be carefully controlled to minimize distortion.

Weld lengths called for in the design documents and on the shop drawings shall be the net effective lengths.

CHAPTER B
DESIGN REQUIREMENTS

Sec. 27.1502B. This chapter contains provisions which are common to the Specification as a whole.

B1. GROSS AREA

The gross area of a member at any point shall be determined by summing the products of the thickness and the gross width of each element as measured normal to the axis of the member.

For angles, the gross width shall be the sum of the widths of the legs less the thickness.

B2. NET AREA

The net area, A_n, of a member is the sum of the products of the thickness and the net width of each element computed as follows:

The width of a bolt or rivet hole shall be taken as $^1/_{16}$ inch greater than the nominal dimension of the hole.

For a chain of holes extending across a part in any diagonal or zigzag line, the net width of the part shall be obtained by deducting from the gross width the sum of the diameters or slot dimensions as provided in Section J3.2, of all holes in the chain, and adding, for each gage space in the chain, the quantity

$$s^2/4g$$

WHERE:

s = longitudinal center-to-center spacing (pitch) of any two consecutive holes, in.

g = transverse center-to-center spacing (gage) between fastener gage lines, in.

For angles, the gage for holes in opposite adjacent legs shall be the sum of the gages from the back of the angles less the thickness.

The critical net area, A_n, of the part is obtained from that chain which gives the least net width.

In determining the net area across plug or slot welds, the weld metal shall not be considered as adding to the net area.

B3. EFFECTIVE NET AREA

When the load is transmitted directly to each of the cross-sectional elements by connectors, the effective net area, A_e, is equal to the net area A_n.

When the load is transmitted by bolts or rivets through some but not all of the cross-sectional elements of the member, the effective net area, A_e, shall be computed as:

$$A_e = UA_g \qquad \text{(B3-1)}$$

WHERE:

A_g = net area of the member, in.^{2}

U = reduction coefficient

When the load is transmitted by welds through some but not all of the cross-sectional elements of the member, the effective net area, A, shall be computed as:

$$A_c = UA_g \qquad \text{(B3-2)}$$

WHERE:

A_g = gross area of member, in.^{2}

Unless a larger coefficient is justified by tests or other criteria, the following values of U shall be used:

a. W, M or S shapes with flange widths not less than two thirds the depth, and structural tees cut from these shapes, provided the connection is to the flanges. Bolted or riveted connections shall have no fewer than three fasteners per line in the direction of stress . . . . $U = 0.90$

b. W, M or S shapes not meeting the conditions of Subparagraph a, structural tees cut from these shapes and all other shapes, including built-up cross sections. Bolted or riveted connections shall have no fewer than three fasteners per line in the direction of stress .... $U = 0.85$

c. All members with bolted or riveted connections having only two fasteners per line in the direction of stress .... $U = 0.75$

When load is transmitted by transverse welds to some but not all of the cross-sectional elements of W, M or S shapes and structural tees cut from these shapes, A_e, shall be taken as the area of the directly connected elements.

When the load is transmitted to a plate by longitudinal welds along both edges at the end of the plate, the length of the welds shall not be less than the width of the plate. The effective net area, A_e, shall be computed by Equation (B3-2).

Unless a larger coefficient can be justified by tests or other criteria, the following values of U shall be used:

a. When $l > 2w$ .... $U = 1.0$

b. When $2w > l > 1.5w$ .... $U = 0.87$

c. When $1.5w > l > w$ .... $U = 0.75$

WHERE:

l = weld length, in.

w = plate width (distance between welds), in.

Bolted and riveted splice and gusset plates and other connection fittings subject to tensile force shall be designed in accordance with the provisions of Section D1, where the effective net area shall be taken as the actual net area, except that, for the purpose of design calculations, it shall not be taken as greater than 85 percent of the gross area.

B4. STABILITY

General stability shall be provided for the structure as a whole and for each compression element.

Consideration shall be given to significant load effects resulting from the deflected shape of the structure or of individual elements of the lateral load resisting system, including effects on beams, columns, bracing, connections and shear walls.

B5. LOCAL BUCKLING

1. Classification of Steel Sections. Steel sections are classified as compact, noncompact and slender element sections. For a section to qualify as compact, its flanges must be continuously connected to the web or webs and the width-thickness ratios of its compression elements must not exceed the applicable limiting width-thickness ratios from Table B5.1. Steel sections that do not qualify as compact are classified as noncompact if the width-thickness ratios of the compression elements do not exceed the values shown for noncompact in Table B5.1. If the width-thickness ratios of any compression element exceed the latter applicable value, the section is classified as a slender element section.

For unstiffened elements which are supported along only one edge, parallel to the direction of the compression force, the width shall be taken as follows:

a. For flanges of I-shaped members and tees, the width *b* is half the full nominal width.

b. For legs of angles and flanges of channels and zees, the width *b* is the full nominal dimension.

c. For plates, the width *b* is the distance from the free edge to the first row of fasteners or line of welds.

d. For stems of tees, *d* is taken as the full nominal depth.

For stiffened elements, i.e., supported along two edges parallel to the direction of the compression force, the width shall be taken as follows:

a. For webs of rolled, built-up or formed sections, *h* is the clear distance between flanges.

b. For webs of rolled, built-up or formed sections, *d* is the full nominal depth.

c. For flange or diaphragm plates in built-up sections, the width *b* is the distance between adjacent lines of fasteners or lines of welds.

d. For flanges of rectangular hollow structural sections, the width *b* is the clear distance between webs less the inside corner radius on each side. If the corner radius is not known, the flat width may be taken as the total section width minus three times the thickness.

For tapered flanges of rolled sections, the thickness is the nominal value halfway between the free edge and the corresponding face of the web.

2. Slender Compression Elements. For the design of flexural and compressive sections with slender compressive elements, see Appendix B5.

B6. ROTATIONAL RESTRAINT AT POINTS OF SUPPORT

At points of support, beams, girders and trusses shall be restrained against rotation about their longitudinal axis.

B7. LIMITING SLENDERNESS RATIOS

For members whose design is based on compressive force, the slenderness ratio Kl/r preferably should not exceed 200. If this limit is exceeded, the allowable stress shall not exceed the value obtained from Equation (E2-2).

For members whose design is based on tensile force, the slenderness ratio L/r preferably should not exceed 300. The above limitation does not apply to rods in tension. Members which have been designed to perform as tension members in a structural system, but experience some compression loading, need not satisfy the compression slenderness limit.

B8. SIMPLE SPANS

Beams, girders and trusses designed on the basis of simple spans shall have an effective length equal to the distance between centers of gravity of the members to which they deliver their end reactions.

B9. END RESTRAINT

When designed on the assumption of full or partial end restraint due to continuous, semi-continuous or cantilever action, the beams, girders and trusses, as well

TABLE B5.1
Limiting Width-Thickness Ratios for Compression Elements

Description of Element	Width-Thickness Ratio	Limiting Width-Thickness Ratios: Compact	Limiting Width-Thickness Ratios: Noncompact[c]
Flanges of I-shaped rolled beams and channels in flexure[a]	b/t	$65/\sqrt{F_y}$	$95/\sqrt{F_y}$
Flanges of I-shaped welded beams in flexure	b/t	$65/\sqrt{F_y}$	$95/\sqrt{F_{yf}/k_c}$[e]
Outstanding legs of pairs of angles in continuous contact; angles or plates projecting from rolled beams or columns; stiffeners on plate girders	b/t	NA	$95/\sqrt{F_y}$
Angles or plates projecting from girders, built-up columns or other compression members; compression flanges of plate girders	b/t	NA	$95/\sqrt{F_y/k_c}$
Stems of tees	d/t	NA	$127/\sqrt{F_y}$
Unstiffened elements simply supported along one edge, such as legs of single-angle struts, legs of double-angle struts with separators and cross or star-shaped cross sections	b/t	NA	$76/\sqrt{F_y}$
Flanges of square and rectangular box and hollow structural sections of uniform thickness subject to bending or compression[d]; flange cover plates and diaphragm plates between lines of fasteners or welds	b/t	$190/\sqrt{F_y}$	$238/\sqrt{F_y}$
Unsupported width of cover plates perforated with a succession of access holes[b]	b/t	NA	$317/\sqrt{F_y}$
All other uniformly compressed stiffened elements, i.e., supported along two edges	b/t h/t_w	NA	$253/\sqrt{F_y}$
Webs in flexural compression[a]	d/t	$640/\sqrt{F_y}$	—
	h/t_w	—	$760/\sqrt{F_b}$
Webs in combined flexural and axial compression	d/t_w	for $f_a/F_y \leq 0.16$ $\frac{640}{\sqrt{F_y}}\left(1 - 3.74\frac{f_a}{F_y}\right)$	—
		for $f_a/F_y > 0.16$ $257/\sqrt{F_y}$	
	h/t_w	—	$760/\sqrt{F_b}$
Circular hollow sections In axial compression In flexure	D/t	 $3{,}300/F_y$ $3{,}300/F_y$	 — —

[a]For hybrid beams, use the yield strength of the flange F_{yf} instead of F_y.
[b]Assumes net area of plate at widest hole.
[c]For design of slender sections that exceed the noncompact limits see Appendix B5.
[d]See also Sect. F3.1.
[e]$k_c = \frac{4.05}{(h/t)^{0.46}}$ if $h/t > 70$, otherwise $k_c = 1.0$.

as the sections of the members to which they connect, shall be designed to carry the shears and moments so introduced, as well as all other forces, without exceeding at any point the unit stresses prescribed in Chapters D through F, except that some nonelastic but self-limiting deformation of a part of the connection is permitted when this is essential to avoid overstressing of fasteners.

B10. PROPORTIONS OF BEAMS AND GIRDERS

Rolled or welded shapes, plate girders and cover-plated beams shall, in general, be proportioned by the moment of inertia of the gross section. No deduction shall be made for shop or field bolt or rivet holes in either flange provided that

$$0.5F_u A_{fn} \geq 0.6F_y A_{fg} \tag{B10-1}$$

where A_{fg} is the gross flange area and A_{fn} is the net flange area, calculated in accordance with the provisions of Sections B1 and B2.

If

$$0.5F_u A_{fn} < 0.6F_y A_{fg} \tag{B10-2}$$

the member flexural properties shall be based on an effective tension flange area, A_{fe}:

$$A_{fe} = \frac{5}{6} \frac{F_u}{F_y} A_{fn} \tag{B10-3}$$

Hybrid girders may be proportioned by the moment of inertia of their gross section*, subject to the applicable provisions in Section G1, provided they are not required to resist an axial force greater than $0.15F_y$ times the area of the gross section, where F_y is the yield stress of the flange material. To qualify as hybrid girders, the flanges at any given section shall have the same cross-sectional area and be made of the same grade of steel.

Flanges of welded beams or girders may be varied in thickness or width by splicing a series of plates or by the use of cover plates.

The total cross-sectional area of cover plates of bolted or riveted girders shall not exceed 70 percent of the total flange area.

High-strength bolts, rivets or welds connecting flange to web, or cover plate to flange, shall be proportioned to resist the total horizontal shear resulting from the bending forces on the girder. The longitudinal distribution of these bolts, rivets or intermittent welds shall be in proportion to the intensity of the shear. However, the longitudinal spacing shall not exceed the maximum permitted for compression or tension members in Section D2 or E4, respectively. Bolts, rivets or welds connecting flange to web shall also be proportioned to transmit to the web any loads applied directly to the flange, unless provision is made to transmit such loads by direct bearing.

---

*No limit is placed on the web stresses produced by the applied bending moment for which a hybrid girder is designed, except as provided in Section K4 and Appendix K4.

Partial length cover plates shall be extended beyond the theoretical cutoff point and the extended portion shall be attached to the beam or girder by high-strength bolts in a slip-critical connection, rivets or fillet welds adequate, at the applicable stresses allowed in Sections J2.4, J3.4, or K4, to develop the cover plate's portion of the flexural stresses in the beam or girder at the theoretical cutoff point.

In addition, for welded cover plates, the welds connecting the cover plate termination to the beam or girder in the length a', defined below, shall be adequate, at the allowed stresses, to develop the cover plate's portion of the flexural stresses in the beam or girder at the distance a' from the end of the cover plate. The length a', measured from the end of the cover plate, shall be:

1. A distance equal to the width of the cover plate when there is a continuous weld equal to or larger than three fourths of the plate thickness across the end of the plate and continuous welds along both edges of the cover plate in the length a'.

2. A distance equal to $1^1/_2$ times the width of the cover plate when there is a continuous weld smaller than three fourths of the plate thickness across the end of the plate and continuous welds along both edges of the cover plate in the length a'.

3. A distance equal to 2 times the width of the cover plate when there is no weld across the end of the plate, but continuous welds along both edges of the cover plate in the length a'.

B11. PROPORTIONING OF CRANE GIRDERS

The flanges of plate girders supporting cranes or other moving loads shall be proportioned to resist the horizontal forces produced by such loads.

CHAPTER C

FRAMES AND OTHER STRUCTURES

This chapter specifies general requirements to assure stability of the structure as a whole.

C1. GENERAL

In addition to meeting the requirements of member strength and stiffness, frames and other continuous structures shall be designed to provide the needed deformation capacity and to assure overall frame stability.

C2. FRAME STABILITY

1. Braced Frames. In trusses and in those frames where lateral stability is provided by adequate attachment to diagonal bracing, to shear walls, to an adjacent structure having adequate lateral stability or to floor slabs or roof decks secured horizontally by walls or bracing systems parallel to the plane of the frame, the effective length factor K for the compression members shall be taken as unity, unless analysis shows that a small value is permitted.

2. Unbraced Frames. In frames where lateral stability is dependent upon the bending stiffness of rigidly connected beams and columns, the effective length Kl of compression members shall be determined by analysis and shall not be less than the actual unbraced length.

CHAPTER D
TENSION MEMBERS

This section applies to prismatic members subject to axial tension caused by forces acting through the centroidal axis. For members subject to combined axial tension and flexure, see Section H2. For members subject to fatigue, see Section K4. For tapered members, see Appendix F7. For threaded rods, see Section J3.

D1. ALLOWABLE STRESS

The allowable stress F_t shall not exceed $0.60F_y$ on the gross area nor $0.50F_u$ on the effective net area. In addition, pin-connected members shall meet the requirements of Section D3.1 at the pin hole.

Block shear strength shall be checked at end connections of tension members in accordance with Section J4.

Eyebars shall meet the requirements of Section D3.1.

D2. BUILT-UP MEMBERS

The longitudinal spacing of connectors between elements in continuous contact consisting of a plate and a shape or two plates shall not exceed:

24 times the thickness of the thinner plate, or 12 inches for painted members or unpainted members not subject to corrosion.

14 times the thickness of the thinner plate, or 7 inches for unpainted members of weathering steel subject to atmospheric corrosion.

In a tension member the longitudinal spacing of fasteners and intermittent welds connecting two or more shapes in contact shall not exceed 24 inches. Tension members composed of two or more shapes or plates separated by intermittent fillers shall be connected to one another at these fillers at intervals such that the slenderness ratio of either component between the fasteners does not exceed 300.

Either perforated cover plates or tie plates without lacing are permitted on the open sides of built-up tension members. Tie plates shall have a length of not less than two thirds the distance between the lines of welds or fasteners connecting them to the components of the member. The thickness of such tie plates shall not be less than one fiftieth of the distance between these lines. The longitudinal spacing of intermittent welds or fasteners at tie plates shall not exceed 6 inches.

The spacing of tie plates shall be such that the slenderness ratio of any component in the length between tie plates should preferably not exceed 300.

D3. PIN-CONNECTED MEMBERS

1. Allowable Stress. The allowable stress on the net area of the pinhole for pin-connected members is $0.45\ F_y$. The bearing stress on the projected area of the pin shall not exceed the stress allowed in Section J8.

The allowable stress on eyebars meeting the requirements of Section D3.3 is $0.60F_y$ on the body area.

2. Pin-connected Plates. The minimum net area beyond the pinhole, parallel to the axis of the member, shall not be less than two thirds of the net area across the pinhole.

The distance used in calculations, transverse to the axis of pin-connected plates or any individual element of a built-up member, from the edge of the pinhole to the edge of the member or element shall not exceed 4 times the thickness at the pinhole. For calculation purposes, the distance from the edge of the pinhole to the edge of the plate or to the edge of a separated element of a built-up member at the pinhole, shall not be assumed to be more than 1.25 times the diameter of the pinhole.

For pin-connected members in which the pin is expected to provide for relative movement between connected parts while under full load, the diameter of the pinhole shall not be more than $^1/_{32}$ inch greater than the diameter of the pin.

The corners beyond the pinhole may be cut at 45° to the axis of the member, provided the net area beyond the pinhole, on a plane perpendicular to the cut, is not less than that perpendicular to the direction of the applied load.

3. Eyebars. Eyebars shall be of uniform thickness, without reinforcement at the pinholes, and have circular heads whose periphery is concentric with the pinhole. The radius of the transition between the circular head and the eyebar body shall not be less than the diameter of the head.

For calculation purposes, the width of the body of an eyebar shall not exceed 8 times its thickness.

The thickness may be less than $^1/_2$ inch only if external nuts are provided to tighten pin plates and filler plates into snug contact. For calculation purposes, the distance from the hole edge to plate edge perpendicular to the direction of the applied load shall not be less than two thirds or greater than three fourths times the width of the eyebar body.

The pin diameter shall not be less than seven eights times the eyebar width.

The pinhole diameter shall be no more than $^1/_{32}$-inch greater than the pin diameter.

For steel having a yield stress greater than 70 ksi, the hole diameter shall not exceed 5 times the plate thickness and the width of the eyebar shall be reduced accordingly.

CHAPTER E

COLUMNS AND OTHER COMPRESSION MEMBERS

Sec. 27.1501E. This section applies to prismatic members with compact and noncompact sections subject to axial compression through the centroidal axis. For members with slender elements, see Appendix B5.2. For members subject to combined axial compression and flexure, see Chapter H. For tapered members, see Appendix F7.

E1. EFFECTIVE LENGTH AND SLENDERNESS RATIO

The effective-length factor K shall be determined in accordance with Section C2.

In determining the slenderness ratio of an axially loaded compression member, the length shall be taken as its effective length Kl and r as the corresponding radius of gyration. For limiting slenderness ratios, see Section B7.

E2. ALLOWABLE STRESS

On the gross section of axially loaded compression members whose cross sections meet the provisions of Table B5.1, when Kl/r, the largest effective slenderness ratio of any unbraced segment is less than C_c, the allowable stress is:

$$F_a = \frac{\left[1 - \frac{(Kl/r)^2}{2C_c^2}\right] F_y}{\frac{5}{3} + \frac{3(Kl/r)}{8C_c} - \frac{(Kl/r)^3}{8C_c^3}} \qquad \text{(E2-1)}$$

WHERE

$$C_c = \sqrt{\frac{2\pi^2 E}{23(Kl/r)^2}}$$

On the gross section of axially loaded compression members, when Kl/r exceeds C_c, the allowable stress is:

$$F_a = \frac{12\pi^2 E}{23(Kl/r)^2} \qquad \text{(E2-2)}$$

E3. FLEXURAL-TORSIONAL BUCKLING

Singly symmetric and unsymmetric columns, such as angles or tee-shaped columns, and doubly symmetric columns such as cruciform or built-up columns with very thin walls, may require consideration of flexural-torsional and torsional buckling.

E4. BUILT-UP MEMBERS

All parts of built-up compression members and the transverse spacing of their lines of fasteners shall meet the requirements of Section B7.

For spacing and edge distance requirements for weathering steel members, see Section J3.10.

At the ends of built-up compression members bearing on base plates or milled surfaces, all components in contact with one another shall be connected by rivets or bolts spaced longitudinally not more than four diameters apart for a distance equal to one and one-half times the maximum width of the member, or by continuous welds having a length not less than the maximum width of the member.

The longitudinal spacing for intermediate bolts, rivets or intermittent welds in built-up members shall be adequate to provide for the transfer of calculated stress. The maximum longitudinal spacing of bolts, rivets or intermittent welds connecting two rolled shapes in contact shall not exceed 24 inches. In addition, for painted members and unpainted members not subject to corrosion where the outside component consists of a plate, the maximum longitudinal spacing shall not exceed:

$127/\sqrt{F_y}$ times the thickness of the outside plate or 12 inches when fasteners are not staggered along adjacent gage lines.

$190/\sqrt{F_y}$ times the thickness of the outside plate or 18 inches when fasteners are staggered along adjacent gage lines.

Compression members composed of two or more rolled shapes separated by intermittent fillers shall be connected at these fillers at intervals such that the slenderness ratio Kl/r of either shape, between the fasteners, does not exceed three fourths times the governing slenderness ratio of the built-up member. The least radius of gyration r shall be used in computing the slenderness ratio of each component part. At least two intermediate connectors shall be used along the length of the built-up member.

All connections, including those at the ends, shall be welded or shall utilize high-strength bolts tightened to the requirements of Table J3.7.

Open sides of compression members built up from plates or shapes shall be provided with lacing having tie plates at each end and at intermediate points if the lacing is interrupted. Tie plates shall be as near the ends as practicable. In main members carrying calculated stress, the end tie plates shall have a length of not less than the distance between the lines of fasteners or welds connecting them to the components of the member. Intermediate tie plates shall have a length not less than one half of this distance. The thickness of tie plates shall not be less than one fiftieth of the distance between the lines of fasteners or welds connecting them to the components of the member. In bolted and riveted construction, the spacing in the direction of stress in tie plates shall not be more than 6 diameters and the tie plates shall be connected to each component by at least 3 fasteners. In welded construction, the welding on each line connecting a tie plate shall aggregate not less than one third the length of the plate.

Lacing, including flat bars, angles, channels or other shapes employed as lacing, shall be so spaced that the ratio l/r of the flange included between their connections shall not exceed three fourths times the governing ratio for the member as a whole. Lacing shall be proportioned to resist a shearing stress normal to the axis of the member equal to 2 percent of the total compressive stress in the member. The ratio l/r for lacing bars arranged in single systems shall not exceed 140. For double lacing this ratio shall not exceed 200. Double lacing bars shall be joined at their intersections. For lacing bars in compression the unsupported length of the lacing bar shall be taken as the distance between fasteners or welds connecting it to the components of the built-up member for single lacing, and 70 percent of that distance for double lacing. The inclination of lacing bars to the axis of the member shall preferably not be less than 60° for single lacing and 45° for double lacing. When the distance between the lines of fasteners or welds in the flanges is more than 15 inches, the lacing preferably shall be double or be made of angles.

The function of tie plates and lacing may be performed by continuous cover plates perforated with access holes. The unsupported width of such plates at access holes, as defined in Section B5, is assumed available to resist axial stress, provided that: the width-to-thickness ratio conforms to the limitations of Section B5; the ratio of length (in direction of stress) to width of holes shall not exceed 2; the clear distance between holes in the direction of stress shall not be less than the transverse distance between nearest lines of connecting fasteners or welds; and the periphery of the holes at all points shall have a minimum radius of $1^1/_2$ inches.

E5. PIN-CONNECTED COMPRESSION MEMBERS

Pin-connections of pin-connected compression members shall conform to the requirements of Section D3.

E6. COLUMN WEB SHEAR

Column connections must be investigated for concentrated force introduction in accordance with Section K1.

CHAPTER F

BEAMS AND OTHER FLEXURAL MEMBERS

Sec. 27.1501F. Beams shall be distinguished from plate girders on the basis of the web slenderness ratio h/t_w. When this value is greater than $760/\sqrt{F_b}$ the allowable bending stress is given in Chapter G. The allowable shear stresses and stiffener requirements are given in Chapter F unless tension field action is used, then the allowable shear stresses are given in Chapter G.

This chapter applies to singly or doubly symmetric beams including hybrid beams and girders loaded in the plane of symmetry. It also applies to channels loaded in a plane passing through the shear center parallel to the web or restrained against twisting at load points and points of support. For members subject to combined flexural and axial force, see Section H1.

F1. ALLOWABLE STRESS: STRONG AXIS BENDING OF I-SHAPED MEMBERS AND CHANNELS

1. Members with Compact Sections. For members with compact sections as defined in Section B5.1 (excluding hybrid beams and members with yield points greater than 65 ksi) symmetrical about, and loaded in, the plane of their minor axis the allowable stress is

$$F_b = 0.66F_y \tag{F1-1}$$

provided the flanges are connected continuously to the web or webs and the laterally unsupported length of the compression flange L_b does not exceed the value of L_c, as given by the smaller of:

$$\frac{76b_f}{\sqrt{F_y}} \text{ or } \frac{20,000}{(d/A_f)F_y} \tag{F1-2}$$

Members (including composite members and excluding hybrid members and members with yield points greater than 65 ksi) which meet the requirements for compact sections and are continuous over supports or rigidly framed to columns, may be proportioned for nine tenths of the negative moments produced by gravity loading when such moments are maximum at points of support, provided that, for such members, the maximum positive moment is increased by one-tenth of the average negative moments. This reduction shall not apply to moments produced by loading on cantilevers. If the negative moment is resisted by a column rigidly framed to the beam or girder, the one-tenth reduction is permitted in proportioning the column for the combined axial and bending loading, provided that the stress f_a due to any concurrent axial load on the member, does not exceed $0.15F_a$.

2. Members with Noncompact Sections. For members meeting the requirements of Section F1.1 except that their flanges are noncompact (excluding built-up members and members with yield points greater then 65 ksi), the allowable stress is

$$F_b = F_y \left[0.79 - 0.002 \frac{b_f}{2t_f} \sqrt{F_y} \right] \qquad \text{(F1-3)}$$

For built-up members meeting the requirements of Section F1.1 except that their flanges are noncompact and their webs are compact or noncompact (excluding hybrid girders and members with yield points greater than 65 ksi), the allowable stress is

$$F_b = F_y \left[0.79 - 0.002 \frac{b_f}{2t_f} \sqrt{\frac{F_y}{k_c}} \right] \qquad \text{(F1-4)}$$

WHERE:

$$k_c = \frac{4.05}{(h/t_w)^{0.46}} \quad \text{if } h/t_w > 70\text{, otherwise } k_c = 1.0.$$

For members with a noncompact section (Section B5), but not included above, and loaded through the shear center and braced laterally in the region of compression stress at intervals not exceeding $76b_f/\sqrt{f_y}$, the allowable stress is

$$F_b = 0.60f_y \qquad \text{(F1-5)}$$

3. Members with Compact or Noncompact Sections with Unbraced Length Greater than L_c. For flexural members with compact or noncompact sections as defined in Section B5.1, and with unbraced lengths greater than L_c as defined in Section F1.1, the allowable bending stress in tension is determined from Equation (F1-5).

For such members with an axis of symmetry in, and loaded in the plane of their web, the allowable bending stress in compression is determined as the larger value from Equations (F1-6) or (F1-7) and (F1-8), except that Equation (F1-8) is applicable only to sections with a compression flange that is solid and approximately rectangular in cross section and that has an area not less than the tension flange. Higher values of the allowable compressive stress are permitted if justified by a more precise analysis. Stresses shall not exceed those permitted by Chapter G, if applicable.

For channels bent about their major axis, the allowable compressive stress is determined from Equation (F1-8).

When

$$\sqrt{\frac{102 \times 10^3 C_b}{F_y}} \leq \frac{l}{r_T} \leq \sqrt{\frac{510 \times 10^3 C_b}{F_Y}}: \tag{F1-6}$$

$$F_b = \left[\frac{2}{3} - \frac{F_y (l/r_T)^2}{1530 \times 10^3 C_b}\right] F_y \leq 0.60 F_y \tag{F1-7}$$

When

$$\frac{l}{r_T} \geq \sqrt{\frac{510 \times 10^3 C_b}{F_y}} \tag{F1-8}$$

$$F_b = \frac{170 \times 10^3 C_b}{(l/r_T)^2} \leq 0.60 F_y$$

For any value of l/r_T:

$$F_b = \frac{12 \times 10^3 C_b}{ld/A_f} \leq 0.60 F_y$$

WHERE:

l = distance between cross sections braced against twist or lateral displacement of the compression flange, in. For cantilevers braced against twist only at the support, l may conservatively be taken as the actual length.

r_T = radius of gyration of a section comprising the compression flange plus one third of the compression web area, taken about an axis in the plane of the web, in.

A_f = area of the compression flange, in.^{2}

C_b = $1.75 + 1.05\,(M_1/M_2) + 0.3\,(M_1/M_2)^2$, but not more than 2.3*, where M_1, is the smaller and M_2 the larger bending moment at the ends of the unbraced length, taken about the strong axis of the member, and where M_1/M_2, the ratio of end moments, is positive when M_1 and M_2 have the same sign (reverse curvature bending) and negative when they are of opposite signs (single curvature bending). When the bending moment at any point within an unbraced length is larger than that at both ends of this length, the value of C_b shall be taken as unity. When computing F_{bx} to be used in Equation (H1-1), C_b may be computed by the equation given above for frames subject to joint translation, and it shall be taken as unity for frames braced against joint translation. C_b may conservatively be taken as unity for cantilever beams.

For hybrid plate girders, F_y for Equations (F1-6) and (F1-7) is the yield stress of the compression flange. Equation (F1-8) shall not apply to hybrid girders.

---

*It is conservative to take C_b as unity. For values smaller than 2.3, see Table 6 in the Numerical Values Section.

Section F1.3 does not apply to tee sections if the stem is in compression anywhere along the unbraced length.

F2. ALLOWABLE STRESS: WEAK AXIS BENDING OF I-SHAPED MEMBERS, SOLID BARS AND RECTANGULAR PLATES

Lateral bracing is not required for members loaded through the shear center about their weak axis or for members of equal strength about both axes.

1. Members with Compact Sections. For doubly symmetrical I- and H-shape members with compact flanges (Section B5) continuously connected to the web and bent about their weak axes (except members with yield points greater than 65 ksi); solid round and square bars; and solid rectangular sections bent about their weaker axes, the allowable stress is

$$F_b = 0.75\,F_y \tag{F2-1}$$

2. Members with Noncompact Sections. For members not meeting the requirements for compact sections of Section B5 and not covered in Section F3, bent about their minor axis, the allowable stress is

$$F_b = 0.60F_y \tag{F2-2}$$

Doubly symmetrical I- and H-shape members bent about their weak axes (except members with yield points greater than 65 ksi) with noncompact flanges (Section B5) continuously connected to the web may be designed on the basis of an allowable stress of

$$F_b = F_y\left[1.075 - 0.005\left(\frac{b_f}{2t_f}\right)\sqrt{F_y}\right] \tag{F2-3}$$

F3. ALLOWABLE STRESS: BENDING OF BOX MEMBERS, RECTANGULAR TUBES AND CIRCULAR TUBES

1. Members with Compact Sections. For members bent about their strong or weak axes, members with compact sections as defined in Section B5 and flanges continuously connected to the webs, the allowable stress is

$$F_b = 0.66F_y \tag{F3-1}$$

To be classified as a compact section, a box-shaped member shall have, in addition to the requirements in Section B5, a depth not greater than six times the width, a flange thickness not greater than two times the web thickness and a laterally unsupported length L_b less than or equal to

$$L_c = \left(1,950 + 1,200\,\frac{M_1}{M_2}\right)\frac{b}{F_y} \tag{F3-2}$$

except that it need not be less than 1,200 (b/F_y), where M_1 is the smaller and M_2 the larger bending moment at the ends of the unbraced length, taken about the strong axis of the member, and where M_1/M_2, the ratio of end moments, is positive when M_1 and M_2 have the same sign (reverse curvature bending) and negative when they are of opposite signs (single curvature bending).

2. Members with Noncompact Sections. For box-type and tubular flexural members that meet the noncompact section requirements of Section B5, the allowable stress is

$$F_b = 0.60F_y \qquad \text{(F3-3)}$$

Lateral bracing is not required for a box section whose depth is less than 6 times its width. Lateral-support requirements for box sections of larger depth-to-width ratios must be determined by special analysis.

F4. ALLOWABLE SHEAR STRESS

For $h/t_w \leq 380/\sqrt{F_y}$, on the overall depth times the web thickness, the allowable shear stress is

$$F_v = 0.40F_y \qquad \text{(F4-1)}$$

For $h/t_w \geq 380/\sqrt{F_y}$, the allowable shear stress is on the clear distance between flanges times the web thickness is

$$F_v = \frac{F_y}{2.89}(C_v) \leq 0.40\,F_y$$

WHERE:

$$C_v = \frac{45{,}000k_v}{F_y(h/t_w)^2} \quad \text{when } C_v \text{ is less than 0.8}$$

$$= \frac{190}{(h/t_w)}\sqrt{\frac{k_v}{F_y}} \quad \text{when } C_v \text{ is more than 0.8}$$

$$k_v = 4.00 + \frac{5.34}{(a/h)^2} \quad \text{when } a/h \text{ is less than 1.0}$$

$$= 5.34 + \frac{4.00}{(a/h)^2} \quad \text{when } a/h \text{ is more than 1.0}$$

t_w = thickness of web, in.

a = clear distance between transverse stiffeners, in.

h = clear distance between flanges at the section under investigation, in.

For shear rupture on coped beam end connections, see Section J4.

Maximum h/t_w limits are given in Chapter G.

An alternative design method for plate girders utilizing tension field action is given in Chapter G.

F5. TRANSVERSE STIFFENERS

Intermediate stiffeners are required when the ratio h/t_w is greater than 260 and the maximum web shear stress f_v is greater than that permitted by Equation (F4-2).

The spacing of intermediate stiffeners, when required, shall be such that the web shear stress will not exceed the value for F_v given by Equation (F4-2) or (G3-1), as applicable, and

$$\frac{a}{h} \le \left[\frac{260}{(h/t_w)}\right]^2 \text{ and } 3.0 \qquad \text{(F5-1)}$$

F6. BUILT-UP MEMBERS

Where two or more rolled beams or channels are used side-by-side to form a flexural member, they shall be connected together at intervals of not more than 5 feet. Through-bolts and separators are permitted, provided that, in beams having a depth of 12 inches or more, no fewer than two bolts shall be used at each separator location. When concentrated loads are carried from one beam to the other, or distributed between the beams, diaphragms having sufficient stiffness to distribute the load shall be riveted, bolted or welded between the beams.

F1. WEB-TAPERED MEMBERS

See Appendix F7.

CHAPTER G

PLATE GIRDERS

Sec. 27.1502G. Plate girders shall be distinguished from beams on the basis of the web slenderness ratio h/t_w. When this value is greater than $760/\sqrt{f_b}$, the provisions of this chapter shall apply for allowable bending stress, otherwise Chapter F is applicable.

For allowable shear stress and transverse stiffener design see appropriate sections in Chapter F or this chapter if tension field action is utilized.

G1. WEB SLENDERNESS LIMITATIONS

When no transverse stiffeners are provided or when transverse stiffeners are spaced more than one and one-half times the distance between flanges

$$\frac{h}{t_w} \le \frac{14{,}000}{\sqrt{F_{yf}\,(F_{yf} + 16.5)}} \qquad \text{(G1-1)}$$

When transverse stiffeners are provided, spaced not more than one and one-half times the distance between flanges

$$\frac{h}{t_w} \le \frac{2{,}000}{\sqrt{F_{yf}}} \qquad \text{(G1-2)}$$

G2. ALLOWABLE BENDING STRESS

When the web depth-to-thickness ratio exceeds $760/\sqrt{F_b}$, the maximum bending stress in the compression flange shall not exceed

$$F'_b \le F_b\, R_{PG}\, R_e \qquad \text{(G2-1)}$$

WHERE:

F_b = applicable bending stress given in Chapter F, ksi

$$R_{PG} = 1 - 0.0005\frac{A_w}{A_f}\left(\frac{h}{t} - \frac{760}{\sqrt{F_b}}\right) \leq 1.0$$

$$R_e = \frac{12 + \left(\frac{A_w}{A_f}\right)(3\alpha - \alpha^3)}{12 + 2\left(\frac{A_w}{A_f}\right)} \leq 1.0$$

(nonhybrid girders, $R_e = 1.0$)

WHERE:

A_w = area of web at the section under investigation, in.^{2}

A_f = area of compression flange, in.^{2}

α = $0.6\,F_{yw}\,/\,F_b \leq 1.0$

G3. ALLOWABLE SHEAR STRESS WITH TENSION FIELD ACTION

Except as herein provided, the largest average web shear, f_v in kips per square inch, computed for any condition of complete or partial loading, shall not exceed the value given by Equation (F4-2).

Alternatively, for girders other than hybrid girders, if intermediate stiffeners are provided and spaced to satisfy the provisions of Section G4 and if $C_v \leq 1$, the allowable shear including tension field action given by Equation (G3-1) is permitted in lieu of the value given by Equation (F4-2).

$$F_v = \frac{F_y}{2.89}\left[C_v + \frac{1 - C_v}{1.15\sqrt{1 + (a/h)^2}}\right] \leq 0.40F_y \qquad \text{(G3-1)*}$$

G4. TRANSVERSE STIFFENERS

Transverse stiffeners shall meet the requirements of Section F5.

In girders designed on the basis of tension field action, the spacing between stiffeners at end panels, at panels containing large holes, and at panels adjacent to panels containing large holes shall be such that f_v does not exceed the value given by Equation (F4-2).

Bolts and rivets connecting stiffeners to the girder web shall be spaced not more than 12 inches on center. If intermittent fillet welds are used, the clear distance between welds shall not be more than 16 times the web thickness or more than 10 inches.

---

*Equation (G3-1) recognizes the contribution of tension field action.

The moment of inertia, I_{st}, of a pair of intermediate stiffeners, or a single intermediate stiffener, with reference to an axis in the plane of the web, shall be limited as follows:

$$I_{st} \geq \left(\frac{h}{50}\right)^4 \qquad \text{(G4-1)}$$

The gross area (total area, when stiffeners are furnished in pairs), in square inches, of intermediate stiffeners spaced as required for Equation (G3-1) shall not be less than

$$A_{st} = \frac{1 - C_v}{2}\left[\frac{a}{h} - \frac{(a/h)^2}{\sqrt{1 + (a/h)^2}}\right] YDht \qquad \text{(G4-2)}$$

When the greatest shear stress f_v in a panel is less than that permitted by Equation (G3-1), the reduction of this gross area requirement is permitted in like proportion.

Intermediate stiffeners required by Equation (G3-1) shall be connected for a total shear transfer, in kips per linear inch of single stiffener or pair of stiffeners, not less than

$$f_{vs} = h\sqrt{\left(\frac{F_y}{340}\right)^3} \qquad \text{(G4-3)}$$

where F_y = yield stress of web steel.

This shear transfer may be reduced in the same proportion that the largest computed shear stress, f_v, in the adjacent panels is less than that permitted by Equation (G3-1). However, rivets and welds in intermediate stiffeners which are required to transmit to the web an applied concentrated load or reaction shall be proportioned for not less than the applied load or reaction.

Intermediate stiffeners may be stopped short of the tension flange, provided bearing is not needed to transmit a concentrated load or reaction. The weld by which intermediate stiffeners are attached to the web shall not be terminated closer than four times or more than six times the web thickness from the near toe of the web-to-flange weld. When single stiffeners are used, they shall be attached to the compression flange, if it consists of a rectangular plate, to resist any uplift tendency due to torsion in the plate. When lateral bracing is attached to a stiffener, or a pair of stiffeners, in turn, these shall be connected to the compression flange to transmit 1 percent of the total flange stress, unless the flange is composed only of angles.

G5. COMBINED SHEAR AND TENSION STRESS

Plate girder webs which depend upon tension field action, as provided in Equation (G3-1), shall be so proportioned that bending tensile stress, due to moment in the plane of the girder web, shall not exceed $0.60F_y$ or

$$\left(0.825 - 0.375\frac{f_v}{F_v}\right) F_y \tag{G5-1}$$

WHERE:

f_v = computed average web shear stress (total shear divided by web area), ksi.

F_y = allowable web shear stress according to Equation (G3-1), ksi.

The allowable shear stress in the webs of girders having flanges and webs with yield point greater than 65 ksi shall not exceed the values given by Equation (F4-2) if the flexural stress in the flange f_b exceeds $0.75F_b$.

CHAPTER H
COMBINED STRESSES

Sec. 27.1502H. The strength of members subjected to combined stresses shall be determined according to the provisions of this chapter.

This chapter pertains to doubly and singly symmetrical members only. See Chapter E for determination of F_a and Chapter F for determination of F_{bx} and F_{by}.

H1. AXIAL COMPRESSION AND BENDING

Members subjected to both axial compression and bending stresses shall be proportioned to satisfy the following requirements:

$$\frac{f_a}{F_a} + \frac{C_{mx} f_{bx}}{\left(1 - \frac{f_a}{F'_{ex}}\right) F_{bx}} + \frac{C_{my} f_{by}}{\left(1 - \frac{f_a}{F'_{ey}}\right) F_{by}} \leq 1.0 \tag{H1-1}$$

$$\frac{f_a}{0.060F_y} + \frac{f_{bx}}{F_{bx}} + \frac{f_{by}}{F_{by}} \leq 1.0 \tag{H1-2}$$

When $f_a/F_a \leq 0.15$, Equation (H1-3) is permitted in lieu of Equations (H1-1) and (H1-2):

$$\frac{f_a}{F_a} + \frac{f_{bx}}{F_{bx}} + \frac{f_{by}}{F_{by}} \leq 1.0 \tag{H1-3}$$

In Equations (H1-1), (H1-2) and (H1-3), the subscripts x and y, combined with subscripts b, m and e, indicate the axis of bending about which a particular stress or design property applies, and

F_a = axial compressive stress that would be permitted if axial force alone existed, ksi.

F_b = compressive bending stress that would be permitted if bending moment alone existed, ksi.

$$F'_e = \frac{12\,\pi^2 E}{23(Kl_b/r_b)^2}$$

= Euler stress divided by a factor of safety, ksi (in the expression for F'_e, l_b is the actual unbraced length *in the plane of bending* and r_b is the corresponding radius of gyration. K is the effective length factor *in the plane of bending.)* As in the case of F_a, F_b and F'_e may be increased one third in accordance with Section A5.2.

f_a = computed axial stress, ksi.

f_b = computed compressive bending stress at the point under consideration, ksi.

C_m = Coefficient whose value shall be taken as follows:

a. For compression members in frames subject to joint translation (sidesway), $C_m = 0.85$.

b. For rotationally restrained compression members in frames braced against joint translation and not subject to transverse loading between their supports in the plane of bending,

$C_m = 0.6 - 0.4\ (M_1/M_2)$

where M_1/M_2 is the ratio of the smaller to larger moments at the ends of that portion of the member unbraced in the plane of bending under consideration. M_1/M_2 is positive when the member is bent in reverse curvature, negative when bent in single curvature.

c. For compression members in frames braced against joint translation in the plane of loading and subjected to transverse loading between their supports, the value of C_m may be determined by an analysis. However, in lieu of such analysis, the following values are permitted:

i. For members whose ends are restrained against rotation in the plane of bending . . . . $C_m = 0.85$

ii. For members whose ends are unrestrained against rotation in the plane of bending . . . . $C_m = 1.0$

H2. AXIAL TENSION AND BENDING

Members subject to both axial tension and bending stresses shall be proportioned at all points along their length to satisfy the following equation:

$$\frac{f_a}{F_t} + \frac{f_{bx}}{F_{bx}} + \frac{f_{by}}{F_{by}} \leq 1.0 \qquad \text{(H2-1)}$$

where f_b is the computed bending tensile stress, f_a is the computed axial tensile stress, F_b is the allowable bending stress and F_t, is the governing allowable tensile stress defined in Section D1.

However, the computed bending compressive stress arising from an independent load source relative to the axial tension, taken above, shall not exceed the applicable value required in Chapter F.

CHAPTER I
COMPOSITE CONSTRUCTION

Sec. 27.1502I. This chapter applies to steel beams supporting a reinforced concrete slab so interconnected that the beams and the slab act together to resist bending. Simple and continuous composite beams with shear connectors and concrete encased beams, constructed with or without temporary shores, are included.

I1. DEFINITION

Two cases of composite members are recognized: totally encased members which depend upon natural bond for interaction with the concrete, and those with shear connectors (mechanical anchorage to the slab) with the steel member not necessarily encased.

A beam totally encased in concrete cast integrally with the slab may be assumed to be connected to the concrete by natural bond, without additional anchorage, provided that:

1. Concrete cover over beam sides and soffit is at least 2 inches.
2. The top of the beam is at least $1^1/_2$ inches below the top and 2 inches above bottom of the slab.
3. Concrete encasement contains adequate mesh or other reinforcing steel throughout the whole depth and across the soffit of the beam to prevent spalling of the concrete. Shear connectors must be provided for composite action if the steel member is not totally eneased in concrete. The portion of the effective width of the concrete slab on each side of the beam centerline shall not exceed:

   a. One-eighth of the beam span, center-to-center of supports;
   b. One-half the distance to the centerline of the adjacent beam; or
   c. The distance from the beam centerline to the edge of the slab.

I2. DESIGN ASSUMPTIONS

1. Encased beams shall be proportioned to support, unassisted, all dead loads applied prior to the hardening of the concrete (unless these loads are supported temporarily on shoring) and, acting in conjunction with the slab, to support all dead and live loads applied after hardening of the concrete, without exceeding a computed bending stress of $0.66F_y$ where F_y is the yield stress of the steel beam. The bending stress produced by loads after the concrete has hardened shall be computed on the basis of the section properties of the composite section. Concrete tension stresses shall be neglected. Alternatively, the steel beam alone may be proportioned to resist, unassisted, the positive moment produced by all loads, live and dead, using a bending stress equal to $0.76F_y$, in which case temporary shoring is not required.

2. When shear connectors are used in accordance with Section I4, the composite section shall be proportioned to support all of the loads without exceeding the allowable stress prescribed in Section F1.1, even when the steel section is not shored during construction. In positive moment areas, the steel section is exempt from compact flange criteria (Section B5) and there is no limit on the unsupported length of the compression flange.

Reinforcement parallel to the beam within the effective width of the slab, when anchored in accordance with the provisions of the applicable building code, may be included in computing the properties of composite sections, provided shear connectors are furnished in accordance with the requirements of Section I4. The section properties of the composite section shall be computed in accordance with the elastic theory. Concrete tension stresses shall be neglected. For stress computations, the compression area of lightweight or normal weight concrete shall be treated as an equivalent area of steel by dividing it by the modular ratio n for normal weight concrete of the strength specified when determining the section properties. For deflection calculations, the transformed section properties shall be based on the appropriate modular ratio n for the strength and weight concrete specified, where $n = E/E_c$.

In cases where it is not feasible or necessary to provide adequate connectors to satisfy the horizontal shear requirements for full composite action, the effective section modulus shall be determined as

$$S_{eff} = S_s + \sqrt{\frac{V'_h}{V_h}}\,(S_{tr} - S_s) \qquad \text{(I2-1)}$$

WHERE:

V_h and V'_h are defined in Section I4.

S_s = section modulus of the steel beam referred to its bottom flange, in.^{3}

S_{tr} = section modulus of the transformed composite section referred to its bottom flange, based upon maximum permitted effective width of concrete flange (Section I1), in.^{3}

For composite beams constructed without temporary shoring, stresses in the steel section shall not exceed $0.90F_y$. Stresses shall be computed assuming the steel section alone resists all loads applied before the concrete has reached 75 percent of its required strength and the effective composite section resists all loads applied after that time.

The actual section modulus of the transformed composite section shall be used in calculating the concrete flexural compression stress and, for construction without temporary shores, this stress shall be based upon loading applied after the concrete has reached 75 percent of its required strength. The stress in the concrete shall not exceed $0.45 f'_c$.

I3. END SHEAR

The web and the end connections of the steel beam shall be designed to carry the total reaction.

I4. SHEAR CONNECTORS

Except in the case of encased beams, as defined in Section I2.1, the entire horizontal shear at the junction of the steel beam and the concrete slab shall be assumed to be transferred by shear connectors welded to the top flange of the beam and embedded in the concrete. For full composite action with concrete subject to flexural compression, the total horizontal shear to be resisted between the point of maximum positive moment and points of zero moment shall be taken as the smaller value using Equations (I4-1) and (I4-2):

$$V'_h = 0.85 f'_c A_c/2 \qquad \text{(I4-1)*}$$

and

$$V_h = f_y A_s/2 \qquad \text{(I4-2)}$$

WHERE:

f'_c = specified compression strength of concrete, ksi.

A_c = actual area of effective concrete flange defined in Section I1, in.^{2}

A_s = area of steel beam, in.^{2}

In continuous composite beams where longitudinal reinforcing steel is considered to act compositely with the steel beam in the negative moment regions, the total horizontal shear to be resisted by shear connectors between an interior support and each adjacent point of contraflexure shall be taken as

$$V_h = f_{yr} A_{sr}/2 \qquad \text{(I4-3)}$$

WHERE:

A_{sr} = total area of longitudinal reinforcing steel at the interior support located within the effective flange width specified in Section I1, in.^{2}

F_{yr} = specified minimum yield stress of the longitudinal reinforcing steel, ksi.

For full composite action, the number of connectors resisting the horizontal shear, V_h, each side of the point of maximum moment, shall not be less than that determined by the relationship V_h/q, where q, the allowable shear load for one connector, is given in Table I4.1 for flat soffit concrete slabs made with C33 aggregates. For flat soffit concrete slabs made with rotary kiln-produced aggregates, conforming to C330 with concrete unit weight not less than 90 pcf, the allowable shear load for one connector is obtained by multiplying the values from Table I4.1 by the coefficient from Table I4.2.

For partial composite action with concrete subject to flexural compression, the horizontal shear V'_h to be used in computing S_{eff} shall be taken as the product of q times the number of connectors furnished between the point of maximum moment and the nearest point of zero moment.

The value of V'_h shall not be less than one fourth the smaller value of Equation (I4-1), using the maximum permitted effective width of the concrete flange, or Equation (I4-2). The effective moment of inertia for deflection computations shall be determined by:

$$I_{eff} = I_s + \sqrt{\frac{V'_h}{V_h}}(I_{tr} - I_s) \qquad \text{(I4-4)}$$

WHERE:

I_s = moment of inertia of the steel beam, in.^{4}

I_{tr} = moment of inertia of the transformed composite section, in.^{4}

---

*The term $1/2\, F_{yr} A'_s$, shall be added to the right-hand side of Equation (I4-1) if longitudinal reinforcing steel with area A'_s located within the effective width of the concrete flange is included in the properties of the composite section.

Table I4.1
Allowable Horizontal Shear Load for One Connector (q), kips[a]

Connector[b]	Specified Compressive Strength of Concrete (f'_c), ksi		
	3.0	3.5	≥4.0
½″ dia. × 2″ hooked or headed stud	5.1	5.5	5.9
⅝″ dia. × 2½″ hooked or headed stud	8.0	8.6	9.2
¾″ dia. × 3″ hooked or headed stud	11.5	12.5	13.3
⅞″ dia. × 3½″ hooked or headed stud	15.6	16.8	18.0
Channel C3 × 4.1	4.3w[c]	4.7w[c]	5.0w[c]
Channel C4 × 5.4	4.6w[c]	5.0w[c]	5.3w[c]
Channel C5 × 6.7	4.9w[c]	5.3w[c]	5.6w[c]

[a]Applicable only to concrete made with ASTM C33 aggregates.
[b]The allowable horizontal loads tabulated are also permitted for studs longer than shown.
[c]w = length of channel, in.

Table I4.2
Coefficients for Use with Concrete Made with C330 Aggregates

Specified Compressive Strength of Concrete (f'_c)	Air Dry Unit Weight of Concrete, pcf						
	90	95	100	105	110	115	120
≤4.0 ksi	0.73	0.76	0.78	0.81	0.83	0.86	0.88
≥5.0 ksi	0.82	0.85	0.87	0.91	0.93	0.96	0.99

The connectors required on each side of the point of maximum moment in an area of positive bending may be uniformly distributed between that point and adjacent points of zero moment, except that N_2, the number of shear connectors required between any concentrated load in that area and the nearest point of zero moment, shall not be less than that determined by Equation (I4-5).

$$N_2 = \frac{N_1\left[\dfrac{M\beta}{M_{\max}} - 1\right]}{\beta - 1} \qquad \text{(I4-5)}$$

WHERE:

M = moment (less than the maximum moment) at a concentrated load point

N_1 = number of connectors required between point of maximum moment and point of zero moment, determined by the relationship V_h/q or V'_h/q, as applicable

$$\beta = \frac{S_{tr}}{S_s} \text{ or } \frac{S_{eff}}{S_s}, \text{ as applicable}$$

For a continuous beam, connectors required in the region of negative bending may be uniformly distributed between the point of maximum moment and each point of zero moment.

Shear connectors shall have at least 1 inch of lateral concrete cover, except for connectors installed in the ribs of formed steel decks. Unless located directly over the web, the diameter of studs shall not be greater than $2^1/_2$ times the thickness of the flange to which they are welded. The minimum center-to-center spacing of stud connectors shall be 6 diameters along the longitudinal axis of the supporting composite beam and 4 diameters transverse to the longitudinal axis of the supporting composite beam. The maximum center-to-center spacing of stud connectors shall not exceed 8 times the total slab thickness.

I5. COMPOSITE BEAMS OR GIRDERS WITH FORMED STEEL DECK

Composite construction of concrete slabs on formed steel deck connected to steel beams or girders shall be designed by the applicable portions of Sections I1 through I4, with the following modifications.

1. General. 1. Section I5 is applicable to decks with nominal rib height not greater than 3 inches.

2. The average width of concrete rib or haunch w_r shall not be less than 2 inches, but shall not be taken in calculations as more than the minimum clear width near the top of the steel deck. See Section I5.3, Subparagraphs 2 and 3, for additional provisions.

3. The concrete slab shall be connected to the steel beam or girder with welded stud shear connectors $^3/_4$ in. or less in diameter (U.B.C. Standard No. 27-6, AWS D1.1, Section 4, Part F). Studs may be welded through the deck or directly to the steel member.

4. Stud shear connectors shall extend not less than $1^1/_2$ inches above the top of the steel deck after installation.

5. The slab thickness above the steel deck shall not be less than 2 inches.

2. Deck Ribs Oriented Perpendicular to Steel Beam or Girder. 1. Concrete below the top of the steel deck shall be neglected when determining section properties and in calculating A_c for Equation (I4-1).

2. The spacing of stud shear connectors along the length of a supporting beam or girder shall not exceed 36 inches.

3. The allowable horizontal shear load per stud connector q shall be the value stipulated in Section I4 (Tables I4.1 and I4.2) multiplied by the following reduction factor:

$$\left(\frac{0.85}{\sqrt{N_r}}\right)\left(\frac{w_r}{h_r}\right)\left(\frac{H_s}{h_r} - 1.0\right) \leq 1.0 \qquad \text{(I5-1)}$$

WHERE:

h_r = nominal rib height, in

H_s = length of stud connector after welding, in., not to exceed the value $(hr + 3)$ in computations, although the actual length may be greater.

N_r = number of stud connectors on a beam in one rib, not to exceed 3 in computations, although more than 3 studs may be installed.

w_r = average width of concrete rib, in. (see Section I5.1, Subparagraph 2).

4. To resist uplift, the steel deck shall be anchored to all compositely designed steel beams or girders at a spacing not to exceed 16 inches. Such anchorage may be provided by stud connectors, a combination of stud connectors and arc spot (puddle) welds, or other devices specified by the designer.

3. Deck Ribs Oriented Parallel to Steel Beam or Girder. 1. Concrete below the top of the steel deck may be included when determining section properties and shall be included in calculating A_c for Equation (I4-1).

2. Steel deck ribs over supporting beams or girders may be split longitudinally and separated to form a concrete haunch.

3. When the nominal depth of steel deck is $1^1/_2$ inch or greater, the average width w_r of the supported haunch or rib shall not be less than 2 inches for the first stud in the transverse row plus four stud diameters for each additional stud.

4. The allowable horizontal shear load per stud connector q shall be the value stipulated in Section I4 (Tables I4.1 and I4.2), except when the ratio w_r/h_r is less than 1.5, the allowable load shall be multiplied by the following reduction factor:

$$0.6\left(\frac{w_r}{h_r}\right)\left(\frac{H_s}{h_r} - 1.0\right) \leq 1.0 \qquad \text{(I5-2)}$$

where h_r and H_s are as defined in Section 15.2 and w_r is the average width of concrete rib or haunch (see Section I5.1, Subparagraph 2, and Section I5.3, Subparagraph 3).

I6. SPECIAL CASES

When composite construction does not conform to the requirements of Sections I1 through I5, the allowable load per shear connector must be established by a suitable test program.

CHAPTER J

CONNECTIONS, JOINTS AND FASTENERS

Sec. 27.1502J. This chapter applies to connections consisting of connecting elements (plates, stiffeners, gussets, angles, brackets) and connectors (welds, bolts, rivets).

J1. GENERAL PROVISIONS

1. Design Basis. Connections shall be proportioned so that the calculated stress is less than the allowable stress determined (1) by structural analysis for loads acting on the structure or (2) as a specified proportion of the strength of the connected members, whichever is appropriate.

2. Simple Connections. Except as otherwise indicated in the design documents, connections of beams, girders or trusses shall be designed as flexible and ordinarily may be proportioned for the reaction shears only. Flexible beam connections shall accommodate end rotations of unrestrained (simple) beams. To accomplish this, in elastic deformation in the connection is permitted.

3. Moment Connections. End connections of restrained beams, girders and trusses shall be designed for the combined effect of forces resulting from moment and shear induced by the rigidity of the connections.

4. Compression Members with Bearing Joints. When columns bear on bearing plates or are finished to bear at splices, there shall be sufficient connectors to hold all parts securely in place.

When other compression members are finished to bear, the splice material and its connectors shall be arranged to hold all parts in line and shall be proportioned for 50 percent of the strength of the member.

All compression joints shall be proportioned to resist any tension developed by the specified lateral loads acting in conjunction with 75 percent of the calculated dead-load stress and no live load.

5. Connections of Tension and Compression Members in Trusses. The connections at ends of tension or compression members in trusses shall develop the force due to the design load, but not less than 50 percent of the effective strength of the member, unless a smaller percentage is justified by engineering analysis that considers other factors including handling, shipping and erection.

6. Minimum Connections. Connections carrying calculated stresses, except for lacing, sag bars and girts, shall be designed to support not less than 6 kips.

7. Splices in Heavy Sections. This section applies to A6 Group 4 and 5 rolled shapes, or shapes built-up by welding plates more than 2 inches thick together to form the cross section*, and where the cross section is to be spliced and subject to primary tensile stresses due to tension or flexure.

---

*When the individual elements of the cross section are spliced prior to being joined to form the cross section in accordance with U.B.C. Standard No. 27-6, AWS D1.1, Article 3.4.6, the applicable provisions of U.B.C. Standard No. 27-6, AWS D1.1 apply in lieu of the requirements of this Section.

When tensile forces in these sections are to be transmitted through splices by full-penetration groove welds, material notch-toughness requirements as given in Section A3.1c, weld access holes details as given in Section J1.8, compatible welding procedures as given in Section J2.6, welding preheat requirements as given in Section J2.7 and thermal cut surface preparation and inspection requirements as given in Section M2.2 apply.

At tension splices in these sections, weld tabs and backing shall be removed and the surfaces ground smooth.

When splicing these sections, and where the section is to be used as a primary compression member, all weld access holes required to facilitate groove welding operations shall satisfy the provisions of Section J1.8.

Alternatively, splicing of such members subject to compression, including members which are subject to tension due to wind or seismic loads, may be accomplished using splice details which do not induce large weld shrinkage strains such as partial-penetration flange groove welds with fillet-welded surface lap plate splices on the web, or with bolted or combination bolted/fillet-welded lap plate splices.

8. Beam Copes and Weld Access Holes. All weld access holes required to facilitate welding operations shall have a length from the toe of the weld preparation not less than one and one-half times the thickness of the material in which the hole is made. The height of the access hole shall be adequate for deposition of sound weld metal in the adjacent plates and provide clearance for weld tabs. In hot-rolled shapes and built-up shapes, all beam copes and weld access holes shall be shaped free of notches or sharp reentrant corners except that, when fillet web-to-flange welds are used in built-up shapes, access holes are permitted to terminate perpendicular to the flange.

For Group 4 and 5 shapes and built-up shapes of material more than 2 inches thick, the thermally cut surfaces of beam copes and weld access holes shall be ground to bright metal and inspected by either magnetic particle or dye penetrant methods. If the curved transition portion of weld access holes and beam copes are formed by predrilled or sawed holes, that portion of the access hole or cope need not be ground. Weld access holes and beam copes in other shapes need not be ground or inspected by dye penetrant or magnetic particle.

9. Placement of Welds, Bolts and Rivets. Groups of welds, bolts or rivets at the ends of any member which transmit axial stress into that member shall be sized so the center of gravity of the group coincides with the center of gravity of the member, unless provision is made for the eccentricity. The foregoing provision is not applicable to end connections of statically loaded single-angle, double-angle and similar members. Eccentricity between the gravity axes of such members and the gage lines for their riveted or bolted end connections may be neglected in statically loaded members, but shall be considered in members subject to fatigue loading.

See Section E4 for placement of fasteners in built-up members made of weathering steel.

10. Bolts in Combination with Welds. In new work, A307 bolts or high-strength bolts used in bearing-type connections shall not be considered as sharing the stress in combination with welds. Welds, if used, shall be provided to carry the entire stress in the connection. High-strength bolts proportioned for slip-critical connections may be considered as sharing the stress with the welds.

In making welded alterations to structures, existing rivets and high-strength bolts tightened to the requirements for slip-critical connections are permitted for carrying stresses resulting from loads present at the time of alteration, and the welding need be adequate to carry only the additional stress.

11. High-strength Bolts in Slip-critical Connections in Combination with Rivets. In both new work and alterations, high-strength bolts in slip-critical connections may be considered as sharing the load with rivets.

12. Limitations on Bolted and Welded Connections. Fully-tensioned high-strength bolts (see Table J3.7) or welds shall be used for the following connections:

Column splices in all tier structures 200 feet or more in height

Column splices in tier structures 100 to 200 feet in height, if the least horizontal dimension is less than 40 percent of the height

Column splices in tier structures less than 100 feet in height, if the least horizontal dimension is less than 25 percent of the height

Connections of all beams and girders to columns and of any other beams and girders on which the bracing of columns is dependent, in structures over 125 feet in height

In all structures carrying cranes of over 5-ton capacity: roof truss splices and connections of trusses to columns, column splices, column bracing, knee braces and crane supports

Connections for supports of running machinery or of other live loads which produce impactor reversal of stress

Any other connections stipulated on the design plans

In all other cases, connections may be made with high-strength bolts tightened to the snug-tight condition or with A307 bolts

For the purpose of this section, the height of a tier structure shall be taken as the vertical distance from the curb level to the highest point of the roof beams in the case of flat roofs, or to the mean height of the gable in the case of roofs having a rise of more than $2^2/_3$ in 12. Where the curb level has not been established, or where the structure does not adjoin a street, the mean level of the adjoining land shall be used instead of curb level. Penthouses may be excluded in computing the height of the structure.

J2. WELDS

All provisions of U.B.C. Standard No. 27-6. American Welding Society Structural Welding Code Steel, AWS D1.1, except Sections 2.3, 2.4, 2.5, 8.13.1, 9 and 10, apply to work performed under this Specification.

1. Groove Welds

a. Effective area. The effective area of groove welds shall be considered as the effective length of the weld times the effective throat thickness.

The effective length of a groove weld shall be the width of the part joined.

The effective throat thickness of a complete-penetration groove weld shall be the thickness of the thinner part joined.

The effective throat thickness of a partial-penetration groove weld shall be as shown in Table J2.1.

The effective throat thickness of a flare groove weld when flush to the surface of a bar or 90° bend in a formed section shall be as shown in Table J2.2. Random sections of production welds for each welding procedure, or such test sections as may be required by design documents, shall be used to verify that the effective throat is consistently obtained.

Larger effective throat thicknesses than those in Table J2.2 are permitted, provided the fabricator can establish by qualification that the fabricator can consistently provide such larger effective throat thicknesses. Qualification shall consist of sectioning the weld normal to its axis, at mid-length and terminal ends. Such sectioning shall be made on a number of combinations of material sizes representative of the range to be used in the fabrication or as required by the designer.

b. Limitations. The minimum effective throat thickness of a partial-penetration groove weld shall be as shown in Table J2.3. Minimum effective throat thickness is determined by the thicker of the two parts joined, except that the weld size need not exceed the thickness of the thinnest part joined. For this exception, particular care shall be taken to provide sufficient preheat for soundness of the weld.

2. Fillet Welds

a. Effective area. The effective area of fillet welds shall be taken as the effective length times the effective throat thickness.

TABLE J2.1
Effective Throat Thickness of Partial-penetration Groove Welds

Welding Process	Welding Position	Included Angle at Root of Groove	Effective Throat Thickness
Shielded metal arc Submerged arc Gas metal arc Flux-cored arc	All	J or U joint	Depth of chamfer
		Bevel or V joint ≥ 60°	
		Bevel or V joint < 60° but ≥ 45°	Depth of chamfer minus ⅛-in.

TABLE J2.2
Effective Throat Thickness of Flare Groove Welds

Type of Weld	Radius (R) of Bar or Bend	Effective Throat Thickness
Flare bevel groove	All	$^5/_{16}R$
Flare V-groove	All	$^1/_2R$[a]

[a]Use $^3/_8R$ for Gas Metal Arc Welding (except short circuiting transfer process) when $R \geq$ ½-in.

TABLE J2.3
Minimum Effective Throat Thickness of Partial-penetration Groove Welds

Material Thickness of Thicker Part Joined (in.)	Minimum Effective Throat Thickness[a] (in.)
To ¼ inclusive	⅛
Over ¼ to ½	$^3/_{16}$
Over ½ to ¾	¼
Over ¾ to 1½	$^5/_{16}$
Over 1½ to 2¼	⅜
Over 2¼ to 6	½
Over 6	⅝

[a]See Sect. J2.

The effective length of fillet welds, except fillet welds in holes and slots, shall be the overall length of full-size fillets, including returns.

The effective throat thickness of a fillet weld shall be the shortest distance from the root of the joint to the face of the diagrammatic weld, except that for fillet welds made by the submerged arc process, the effective throat thickness shall be taken equal to the leg size for $^3/_8$-inch and smaller fillet welds, and equal to the theoretical throat plus 0.11 inch for fillet welds larger than $^3/_8$ inch.

For fillet welds in holes and slots, the effective length shall be the length of the centerline of the weld along the center of the plane through the throat. In the case of overlapping fillets, the effective area shall not exceed the nominal cross-sectional area of the hole or slot in the plane of the faying surface.

b. Limitations. The *minimum size of fillet welds* shall be as shown in Table J2.4. Minimum weld size is dependent upon the thicker of the two parts joined, except that the weld size need not exceed the thickness of the thinner part. For this exception, particular care shall be taken to provide sufficient preheat for soundness of the weld. Weld sizes larger than the thinner part joined are permitted if required by calculated strength. In the as-welded condition, the distance between the edge of the base metal and the toe of the weld may be less than $^1/_{16}$ inch provided the weld size is clearly verifiable.

The *maximum size of fillet welds* that is permitted along edges of connected parts shall be:

- Material less than $^1/_4$ inch thick, not greater than the thickness of the material.
- Material $^1/_4$ inch or more in thickness, not greater than the thickness of the material minus $^1/_{16}$ inch, unless the weld is especially designated on the drawings to be built out to obtain full-throat thickness.

TABLE J2.4
Minimum Size of Fillet Welds

Material Thickness of Thicker Part Joined (in.)	Minimum Size of Fillet Weld[a] (in.)
To 1/4 inclusive	1/8
Over 1/4 to 1/2	3/16
Over 1/2 to 3/4	1/4
Over 3/4	5/16

[a]Leg dimension of fillet welds. Single-pass welds must be used.

The *minimum effective length of fillet welds* designed on the basis of strength shall be not less than 4 times the nominal size, or else the size of the weld shall be considered not to exceed one fourth of its effective length. If longitudinal fillet welds are used alone in end connections of flat bar tension members, the length of each fillet weld shall not be less than the perpendicular distance between them. The transverse spacing of longitudinal fillet welds used in end connections of tension members shall not exceed 8 inches, unless the member is designed on the basis of effective net area in accordance with Section B3.

Intermittent fillet welds are permitted to transfer calculated stress across a joint or faying surfaces when the strength required is less than that developed by a continuous fillet weld of the smallest permitted size, and to join components of built-up members. The effective length of any segment of intermittent fillet welding shall not be less than four times the weld size, with a minimum of $1^1/_2$ inches.

In *lap joints*, the minimum lap shall be five times the thickness of the thinner part joined, but not less than 1 inch. Lap joints joining plates or bars subjected to axial stress shall be fillet welded along the end of both lapped parts, except where the deflection of the lapped parts is sufficiently restrained to prevent opening of the joint under maximum loading.

Fillet welds in holes or slots are permitted to transmit shear in lap joints or to prevent the buckling or separation of lapped parts and to join components of built-up members. Such fillet welds may overlap, subject to the provisions of Section J2. Fillet welds in holes or slots are not to be considered plug or slot welds.

Side or end fillet welds terminating at ends or sides, respectively, of parts or members shall, wherever practicable, be returned continuously around the corners for a distance not less than 2 times the nominal size of the weld. This provision shall apply to side and top fillet welds connecting brackets, beam seats and similar connections, on the plane about which bending moments are computed. For framing angles and simple end plate connections which depend upon flexibility of the outstanding legs for connection flexibility, end returns shall not exceed four times the nominal size of the weld. Fillet welds which occur on opposite sides of a common plane shall be interrupted at the corner common to both welds. End returns shall be indicated on the design and detail drawings.

3. Plug and Slot Welds.

a. Effective area. The effective shearing area of plug and slot welds shall be considered as the nominal cross-sectional area of the hole or slot in the plane of the faying surface.

b. Limitations. Plug or slot welds are permitted to transmit shear in lap joints or to prevent buckling of lapped parts and to join component parts of built-up members.

The diameter of the hole for a plug weld shall not be less than the thickness of the part containing it plus $^5/_{16}$ inch, rounded to the next larger odd $^1/_{16}$ inch, nor greater than the minimum diameter plus $^1/_8$ inch or $2^1/_4$ times the thickness of the weld.

The minimum center-to-center spacing of plug welds shall be four times the diameter of the hole.

The minimum spacing of lines of slot welds in a direction transverse to their length shall be four times the width of the slot. The minimum center-to-center spacing in a longitudinal direction on any line shall be two times the length of the slot.

The length of slot for a slot weld shall not exceed 10 times the thickness of the weld. The width of the slot shall not be less than the thickness of the part containing it plus $^5/_{16}$ inch, rounded to the next larger odd $^1/_{16}$ inch, nor shall it be larger than $2^1/_4$ times the thickness of the weld. The ends of the slot shall be semicircular or shall have the corners rounded to a radius not less than the thickness of the part containing it, except those ends which extend to the edge of the part.

The thickness of plug or slot welds in material $^5/_8$ inch or less in thickness shall be equal to the thickness of the material. In material over $^5/_8$ inch thick, the thickness of the weld shall be at least one half the thickness of the material but not less than $^5/_8$ inch.

4. Allowable Stresses. Except as modified by the provisions of Section K4, welds shall be proportioned to meet the stress requirements given in Table J2.5.

5. Combination of Welds. If two or more of the general types of weld (groove, fillet, plug, slot) are combined in a single joint, the effective capacity of each shall be separately computed with reference to the axis of the group in order to determine the allowable capacity of the combination.

TABLE J2.5
Allowable Stress on Welds[f]

Type of Weld and Stress[a]	Allowable Stress	Required Weld Strength Level[b,c]
Complete-penetration Groove Welds		
Tension normal to effective area	Same as base metal	"Matching" weld metal shall be used.
Compression normal to effective area	Same as base metal	Weld metal with a strength level equal to or less than "matching" weld metal is permitted.
Tension or compression parallel to axis of weld	Same as base metal	
Shear on effective area	0.30 × nominal tensile strength of weld metal (ksi)	
Partial-penetration Groove Welds[d]		
Compression normal to effective area	Same as base metal	Weld metal with a strength level equal to or less than "matching" weld metal is permitted.
Tension or compression parallel to axis of weld[e]	Same as base metal	
Shear parallel to axis of weld	0.30 × nominal tensile strength of weld metal (ksi)	
Tension normal to effective area	0.30 × nominal tensile strength of weld metal (ksi), except tensile stress on base metal shall not exceed 0.60 × yield stress of base metal	
Fillet Welds		
Shear on effective area	0.30 × nominal tensile strength of weld metal (ksi)	Weld metal with a strength level equal to or less than "matching" weld metal is permitted.
Tension or compression Parallel to axis of weld[e]	Same as base metal	
Plug and Slot Welds		
Shear parallel to faying surfaces (on effective area)	0.30 × nominal tensile strength of weld metal (ksi)	Weld metal with a strength level equal to or less than "matching" weld metal is permitted.

[a]For definition of effective area, see Sect. J2.
[b]For "matching" weld metal, see Table 4.1.1, AWS D1.1.
[c]Weld metal one strength level stronger than "matching" weld metal will be permitted.
[d]See Sect. J2.1b for a limitation on use of partial-penetration groove welded joints.
[e]Fillet welds and partial-penetration groove welds joining the component elements of built-up members, such as flange-to-web connections, may be designed without regard to the tensile or compressive stress in these elements parallel to the axis of the welds.
[f]The design of connected material is governed by Chapters D through G. Also see Commentary Sect. J2.4.

6. Mixed Weld Metal. When notch-toughness is specified, the process consumables for all weld metal, tack welds, root pass and subsequent passes, deposited in a joint shall be compatible to assure notch-tough composite weld metal.

7. Preheat for Heavy Shapes. For ASTM A6 Group 4 and 5 shapes and welded built-up members made of plates more than 2 inches thick, a preheat equal to or greater than 350°F. shall be used when making groove weld splices.

J3. BOLTS, THREADED PARTS AND RIVETS

1. High-strength Bolts. Except as otherwise provided in this Specification, use of high-strength bolts shall conform to the provisions of the *Specification for Structural Joints Using ASTM A325 or A490 Bolts* approved by the Research Council on Structural Connections of the Engineering Foundation (RCSC).

If required to be tightened to more than 50 percent of their minimum specified tensile strength, A449 bolts in tension and bearing-type shear connections shall have an F436 hardened washer installed under the bolt head, and the nuts shall meet the requirements of A563.

2. Size and Use of Holes. a. The *maximum sizes* of holes for bolts are given in Table J3.1, except that larger holes, required for tolerance on location of anchor bolts in concrete foundations, are permitted in column base details.

b. *Standard holes* shall be provided in member-to-member connections, unless oversized, short-slotted or long-slotted holes in bolted connections are approved by the designer. Finger shims up to $^{1}/_{4}$ inch may be introduced into slip-critical connections designed on the basis of standard holes without reducing the allowable shear stress of the fastener.

TABLE J3.1
Nominal Hole Dimensions

Bolt Dia.	Hole Dimensions			
	Standard (Dia.)	Oversize (Dia.)	Short-slot (Width × length)	Long-slot (Width × length)
1/2	9/16	5/8	9/16 × 11/16	9/16 × 1 1/4
5/8	11/16	13/16	11/16 × 7/8	11/16 × 1 9/16
3/4	13/16	15/16	13/16 × 1	13/16 × 1 7/8
7/8	15/16	1 1/16	15/16 × 1 1/8	15/16 × 2 3/16
1	1 1/16	1 1/4	1 1/16 × 1 5/16	1 1/16 × 2 1/2
≥1 1/8	d + 1/16	d + 5/16	(d + 1/16) × (d + 3/8)	(d + 1/16) × (2.5 × d)

c. *Oversized holes* are permitted in any or all plies of slip-critical connections, but they shall not be used in bearing-type connections. Hardened washers shall be installed over oversized holes in an outer ply.

d. *Short-slotted holes* are permitted in any or all plies of slip-critical or bearing-type connections. The slots are permitted without regard to direction of loading in slip-critical connections, but the length shall be normal to the direction of the load in bearing-type connections. Washers shall be installed over short-slotted holes in an outer ply; when high-strength bolts are used, such washers shall be hardened.

e. *Long-slotted holes* are permitted in only one of the connected parts of either a slip-critical or bearing-type connection at an individual faying surface. Long-slotted holes are permitted without regard to direction of loading in slip-critical connections, but shall be normal to the direction of load in bearing-type connections. Where long-slotted holes are used in an outer ply, plate washers or a continuous bar with standard holes, having a size sufficient to completely cover the slot after installation, shall be provided. In high-strength bolted connections, such plate washers or continuous bars shall not be less than $^5/_{16}$ inch thick and shall be of structural grade material, but need not be hardened. If hardened washers are required for use of high-strength bolts, the hardened washers shall be placed over the outer surface of the plate washer or bar.

f. When A490 bolts over 1-inch diameter are used in slotted or oversize holes in external plies, a single hardened washer conforming to ASTM F 436, except with $^5/_{16}$ inch minimum thickness, shall be used in lieu of the standard washer.

3. Effective Bearing Area. The effective bearing area of bolts, threaded parts and rivets shall be the diameter multiplied by the length in bearing, except that for countersunk bolts and rivets one half the depth of the countersink shall be deducted.

4. Allowable Tension and Shear. Allowable tension and shear stresses on bolts, threaded parts and rivets shall be as given in Table J3.2, in ksi of the nominal body area of rivets (before driving) or the unthreaded nominal body area of bolts and threaded parts other than upset rods (see Footnote c, Table J3.2). High-strength bolts supporting applied load by direct tension shall be so proportioned that their average tensile stress, computed on the basis of nominal bolt area and independent of any initial tightening force, will not exceed the appropriate stress given in Table J3.2. The applied load shall be the sum of the external load and any tension resulting from prying action produced by deformation of the connected parts.

When specified by the designer, the nominal slip resistance for connections having special faying surface conditions may be increased to the applicable values in the *RCSC Specification for Structural Joints Using ASTM A325 or A490 Bolts*.

Finger shims up to $^1/_4$ inch may be introduced into slip-critical connections designed on the basis of standard holes without reducing the allowable shear stress of the fastener to that specified for slotted holes.

Design for bolts, threaded parts and rivets subject to fatigue loading shall be in accordance with Appendix K4.3.

TABLE J3.2
Allowable Stress on Fasteners, ksi

Description of Fasteners	Allowable Tension[g] (F_t)	Allowable Shear[g] (F_v)				
		Slip-critical Connections[e,i]				Bearing-type Connections[i]
		Standard size Holes	Oversized and Short-slotted Holes	Long-slotted holes: Transverse[j] Load	Long-slotted holes: Parallel[j] Load	
A502, Gr. 1, hot-driven rivets	23.0[a]					17.5[f]
A502, Gr. 2 and 3, hot-driven rivets	29.0[a]					22.0[f]
A307 bolts	20.0[a]					10.0[b,f]
Threaded parts meeting the requirements of Sects. A3.1 and A3.4 and A449 bolts meeting the requirements of Sect. A3.4, when threads are not excluded from shear planes	$0.33F_u$[a,c,h]					$0.17F_u$[h]
Threaded parts meeting the requirements of Sects. A3.1 and A3.4, and A449 bolts meeting the requirements of Sect. A3.4, when threads are excluded from shear planes	$0.33F_u$[a,h]					$0.22F_u$[h]
A325 bolts, when threads are not excluded from shear planes	44.0[d]	17.0	15.0	12.0	10.0	21.0[f]
A325 bolts, when threads are excluded from shear planes	44.0[d]	17.0	15.0	12.0	10.0	30.0[f]
A490 bolts, when threads are not excluded from shear planes	54.0[d]	21.0	18.0	15.0	13.0	28.0[f]
A490 bolts, when threads are excluded from shear planes	54.0[d]	21.0	18.0	15.0	13.0	40.0[f]

[a] Static loading only.
[b] Threads permitted in shear planes.
[c] The tensile capacity of the threaded portion of an upset rod, based upon the cross-sectional area at its major thread diameter A_b shall be larger than the nominal body area of the rod before upsetting times $0.60F_y$.
[d] For A325 and A490 bolts subject to tensile fatigue loading, see Appendix K4.3.
[e] Class A (slip coefficient 0.33). Clean mill scale and blast-cleaned surfaces with Class A coatings. When specified by the designer, the allowable shear stress, F_v, for slip-critical connections having special faying surface conditions may be increased to the applicable value given in the RCSC Specification.
[f] When bearing-type connections used to splice tension members have a fastener pattern whose length, measured parallel to the line of force, exceeds 50 in., tabulated values shall be reduced by 20%.
[g] See Sect. A5.2
[h] See Table 2, Numerical Values Section for values for specific ASTM steel specifications.
[i] For limitations on use of oversized and slotted holes, see Sect. J3.2.
[j] Direction of load application relative to long axis of slot.

5. Combined Tension and Shear in Bearing-type Connections. Bolts and rivets subject to combined shear and tension shall be so proportioned that the tension stress F_t in ksi on the nominal body area A_b produced by forces applied to the connected parts, shall not exceed the values computed from the equations in Table J3.3, where f_v, the shear stress produced by the same forces, shall not exceed the value for shear given in Table J3.2. When allowable stresses are increased for wind or seismic loads in accordance with Section A5.2, the constants in the equations listed in Table J3.3 shall be increased by one third, but the coefficient applied to f_v shall not be increased.

6. Combined Tension and Shear in Slip-critical Joints. For A32S and A490 bolts used in slip-critical connections, the maximum shear stress allowed by Table J3.2 shall be multiplied by the reduction factor $(1 - f_t A_b / T_b)$, where f_t is the average tensile stress due to a direct load applied to all of the bolts in a connection and T_b is the pretension load of the bolt specified in Table J3.7. When allowable stresses are increased for wind or seismic loads in accordance with the provisions of Section A5.2, the reduced allowable shear stress shall be increased by one third.

7. Allowable Bearing at Bolt Holes. On the projected area of bolts and rivets in shear connections with the end distance in the line of force not less than $1^1/_2\,d$ and the distance center-to-center of bolts not less than $3d$:

1. In standard- or short-slotted holes with two or more bolts in the line of force,

$$F_p = 1.2\,F_u \qquad \text{(J3-1)}$$

TABLE J3.3
Allowable Tension Stress F_t for Fasteners in Bearing-type Connections

Description of Fasteners	Threads Included in Shear Plane	Threads Excluded from Shear Plane
A307 bolts	$26 - 1.8f_v \le 20$	
A325 bolts	$\sqrt{(44)^2 - 4.39f_v^2}$	$\sqrt{(44)^2 - 2.15f_v^2}$
A490 bolts	$\sqrt{(54)^2 - 3.75f_v^2}$	$\sqrt{(54)^2 - 1.82f_v^2}$
Threaded parts, A449 bolts over 1½-in. dia.	$0.43F_u - 1.8f_v \le 0.33F_u$	$0.43F_u - 1.4f_v \le 0.33F_u$
A502 Gr. 1 rivets	$30 - 1.3f_v \le 23$	
A502 Gr. 2 rivets	$38 - 1.3f_v \le 29$	

WHERE:

F_p = allowable bearing stress, ksi

2. In long-slotted holes with the axis of the slot perpendicular to the direction of load and with two or more bolts in the line of force,

$$F_p = 1.0\,F_u \qquad \text{(J3-2)}$$

On the projected area of the bolt or rivet closest to the edge in standard- or short-slotted holes with the edge distance less than $1^1/_2\,d$ and in all connections with a single bolt in the line of force:

$$F_p = L_c F_u / 2d \leq 1.2F_u \qquad \text{(J3-3)}$$

WHERE:

L_e = distance from the free edge to center of the bolt, in.

d = bolt dia., in.

If deformation around the hole is not a design consideration and adequate spacing and edge distance is as required by Sections J3.8 and J3.9, the following equation is permitted in lieu of Equation (J3-1):

$$F_p = 1.5F_u \qquad \text{(J3-4)}$$

and the limit in Equation (J3-3) shall be increased to $1.5F_u$.

8. Minimum Spacing. The distance between centers of standard, oversized or slotted fastener holes shall not be less than two and two-thirds times the nominal diameter of the fastener or less than that required by the following paragraph, if applicable.

Along a line of transmitted forces, the distance between centers of holes s shall not be less than $3d$ when F_p is determined by Equations (J3-1) and (J3-2). Otherwise, the distance between centers of holes shall not be less than the following:

a. For standard holes:

$$s \leq 2P/F_u t + d/2 \qquad \text{(J3-5)}$$

WHERE:

P = force transmitted by one fastener to the critical connected part, kips

F_u = specified minimum tensile strength of the critical connected part, ksi

t = thickness of the critical connected part, in.

b. For oversized and slotted holes, the distance required for standard holes in Subparagraph a (above), plus the applicable increment C_1 from Table J3.4, but the clear distance between holes shall not be less than one bolt diameter.

9. Minimum Edge Distance. The distance from the center of a standard hole to an edge of a connected part shall not be less than the applicable value from Table J3.5 or the value from Equation (J3-6), as applicable.

Along a line of transmitted force, in the direction of the force, the distance from the center of a standard hole to the edge of the connected part L_e shall not be less than $1^1/_2 d$ when F_p is determined by Equations (J3-1) or (J3-2). Otherwise the edge distance shall not be less than

$$L_e \leq 2P/F_u t \qquad \text{(J3-6)}$$

where P, F_u, t are defined in Section J3.8.

TABLE J3.4
Values of Spacing Increment C_1, in.

Nominal Dia. of Fastener	Oversize Holes	Slotted Holes		
		Perpendicular to Line of Force	Parallel to Line of Force	
			Short-slots	Long-slots[a]
≤ 7/8	1/8	0	3/16	$1\frac{1}{2}d - \frac{1}{16}$
1	3/16	0	1/4	1 7/16
≥1 1/8	1/4	0	5/16	$1\frac{1}{2}d - \frac{1}{16}$

[a]When length of slot is less than maximum allowed in Table J3.1, C_1 may be reduced by the difference between the maximum and actual slot lengths.

TABLE J3.5
Minimum Edge Distance, in.
(Center of Standard Hole[a] to Edge of Connected Part)

Nominal Bolt or Rivet Dia. (in.)	At Sheared Edges	At Rolled Edges of Plates, Shapes or Bars, Gas Cut or Saw-cut Edges[b]
1/2	7/8	3/4
5/8	1 1/8	7/8
3/4	1 1/4	1
7/8	1 1/2[c]	1 1/8
1	1 3/4[c]	1 1/4
1 1/8	2	1 1/2
1 1/4	2 1/4	1 5/8
Over 1 1/4	1 3/4 × Dia.	1 1/4 × Dia.

[a]For oversized or slotted holes, see Table J3.6.
[b]All edge distances in this column may be reduced 1/8-in. when the hole is at a point where stress does not exceed 25% of the maximum design strength in the element.
[c]These may be 1 1/4 in. at the ends of beam connection angles.

The distance from the center of an oversized or slotted hole to an edge of a connected part shall not be less than required for a standard hole plus the applicable increment C_2 from Table J3.6.

10. Maximum Edge Distance and Spacing. The maximum distance from the center of any rivet or bolt to the nearest edge of parts in contact shall be 12 times the thickness of the connected part under consideration, but shall not exceed 6 inches. Bolted joints in unpainted steel exposed to atmospheric corrosion require special limitations on pitch and edge distance.

TABLE J3.6

Values of Edge Distance Increment C_2, in.

Nominal Dia. of Fastener (in.)	Oversized Holes	Slotted Holes		
		Perpendicular to Edge		Parallel to Edge
		Short Slots	Long Slots[a]	
≤ 7/8	1/16	1/8	3/4d	0
1	1/8	1/8		
≤1 1/8	1/8	3/16		

[a]When length of slot is less than maximum allowable (see Table J3.1), C_2 may be reduced by one-half the difference between the maximum and actual slot lengths.

For unpainted, built-up members made of weathering steel which will be exposed to atmospheric corrosion, the spacing of fasteners connecting a plate and a shape or two-plate components in contact shall not exceed 14 times the thickness of the thinnest part or 7 inches, and the maximum edge distance shall not exceed eight times the thickness of the thinnest part, or 5 inches.

11. Long Grips. A307 bolts which carry calculated stress, with a grip exceeding five diameters, shall have their number increased 1 percent for each additional 1/16 inch in the grip.

TABLE J3.7

Minimum Pretension for Fully-tightened Bolts, kips[a]

Bolt Size, in.	A325 Bolts	A490 Bolts
1/2	12	15
5/8	19	24
3/4	28	35
7/8	39	49
1	51	64
1 1/8	56	80
1 1/4	71	102
1 3/8	85	121
1 1/2	103	148

[a]Equal to 0.70 of minimum tensile strength of bolts, rounded off to nearest kip, as specified in ASTM specifications for A325 and A490 bolts with UNC threads.

J4. ALLOWABLE SHEAR RUPTURE

At beam end connections where the top flange is coped, and in similar situations where failure might occur by shear along a plane through the fasteners, or by a combination of shear along a plane through the fasteners plus tension along a perpendicular plane:

$$F_v = 0.30F_u \qquad \text{(J4-1)}$$

acting on the net shear area A_v and,

$$F_t = 0.50F_u \qquad \text{(J4-2)}$$

acting on the net tension area A_t.

The minimum net failure path on the periphery of welded connections shall be checked.*

J5. CONNECTING ELEMENTS

This section applies to the design of connecting elements, such as stiffeners, gussets, angles and brackets and the panel zones of beam-to-column connections.

1. Eccentric Connections. Intersecting axially stressed members shall have their gravity axes intersect at one point, if practicable; if not, provision shall be made for bending and shearing stresses due to the eccentricity.

2. Allowable Shear Rupture. For situations where failure might occur by shear along a plane through the fasteners, or by a combination of shear along a plane through the fasteners plus tension along a perpendicular plane, see Section J4.

J6. FILLERS

In welded construction, any filler $^1/_4$ inch or more in thickness shall extend beyond the edges of the splice plate and shall be welded to the part on which it is fitted with sufficient weld to transmit the splice plate stress, applied at the surface of the filler as an eccentric load. The welds joining the splice plate to the filler shall be sufficient to transmit the splice plate stress and shall be long enough to avoid overstressing the filler along the toe of the weld. Any filler less than $^1/_4$-inch thick shall have its edges flush with the edges of the splice plate and the weld size shall be the sum of the size necessary to carry the splice plate stress plus the thickness of the filler plate.

When bolts or rivets carrying computed stress pass through fillers thicker than $^1/_4$ inch,except in slip-critical connections assembled with high-strength bolts, the fillers shall be extended beyond the splice material and the filler extension shall be secured by enough bolts or rivets to distribute the total stress in the member uniformly over the combined section of the member and the filler, or an equivalent number of fasteners shall be included in the connection. Fillers between $^1/_4$-inch and $^3/_4$-inch thick, inclusive, need not be extended and developed, provided the allowable shear stress in the bolts is reduced by the factor, $0.4\,(t-0.25)$, where t is the total thickness of the fillers, up to $^3/_4$ inch.

---

*See Section B2.

J7. SPLICES

Groove welded splices in plate girders and beams shall develop the full strength of the smaller spliced section. Other types of splices in cross sections of plate girders and beams shall develop the strength required by the stresses at the point of splice.

J8. ALLOWABLE BEARING STRESS

On contact area of milled surfaces and ends of fitted bearing stiffeners; on projected area of pins in reamed, drilled or bored holes:

$$F_p = 0.90F_y^* \quad \text{(J8-1)}$$

Expansion rollers and rockers, kips per linear inch:

$$F_p = \left(\frac{F_y - 13}{20}\right) 0.66d \quad \text{(J8-2)}$$

where d is the diameter of roller or rocker, inch.

J9. COLUMN BASES AND BEARING ON MASONRY AND CONCRETE

Proper provision shall be made to transfer the column loads and moments to the footings and foundations.

In the absence of code regulations, the following stresses apply:

On sandstone and limestone . . . . $F_p = 0.40$ ksi
On brick in cement mortar . . . . $F_p = 0.25$ ksi
On the full area of a concrete support . . . . $F_p = 0.35f'_c$
On less than the full area of a concrete support . . . . $F_p = 0.35f'_c$

WHERE:

f'_c = specified compressive strength of concrete, ksi
A_1 = area of steel concentrically bearing on a concrete support, in.^{2}
A_2 = maximum area of the portion of the supporting surface that is geometrically similar to and concentric with the loaded area, in.^{2}

J10. ANCHOR BOLTS

Anchor bolts shall be designed to provide resistance to all conditions on completed structures of tension and shear at the bases of columns, including the net tensile components of any bending moment which may result from fixation or partial fixation of columns.

---

*When parts in contact have different yield stresses, F_y shall be the smaller value.

CHAPTER K
SPECIAL DESIGN CONSIDERATIONS

Sec. 27.1502K. This chapter covers member strength design considerations related to concentrated forces, ponding, torsion and fatigue.

K1. WEBS AND FLANGES UNDER CONCENTRATED FORCES

1. Design Basis. Members with concentrated loads applied normal to *one flange* and symmetric to the web shall have a flange and web proportioned to satisfy the local flange bending, web yielding strength, web crippling and sidesway web buckling criteria of Sections K1.2, K1.3, K1.4 and K1.5. Members with concentrated loads applied to *both flanges* shall have a web proportioned to satisfy the web yielding, web crippling and column web buckling criteria of Sections K1.3, K1.4 and K1.6.

Where pairs of stiffeners are provided on opposite sides of the web, at concentrated loads, and extend at least half the depth of the member, Sections K1.2 and K1.3 need not be checked.

For column webs subject to high shears, see Section K1.7; for bearing stiffeners, see Section K1.8.

2. Local Flange Bending. A pair of stiffeners shall be provided opposite the tension flange or flange plate of the beam or girder framing into the member when the thickness of the member flange t_f is less than

$$0.4 \sqrt{\frac{P_{bf}}{F_{yc}}} \qquad \text{(K1-1)}$$

WHERE:

F_{yc} = column yield stress, ksi

P_{bf} = the computed force delivered by the flange or moment connection plate multiplied by $^5/_3$, when the computed force is due to live and dead load only, or by $^4/_3$, when the computed force is due to live and dead load in conjunction with wind or earthquake forces, kips.

If the length of loading measured across the member flange is less than $0.15b$, where b is the member flange width, Equation (K1-1) need not be checked.

3. Local Web Yielding. Bearing stiffeners shall be provided in beams and welded plate girders if the compressive stress at the web toe of the fillets resulting from concentrated loads exceeds $0.66F_y$.

a. When the force to be resisted is a concentrated load producing tension or compression, applied at a distance from the member end that is greater than the depth of the member,

$$\frac{R}{t_w(N + 5k)} \leq 0.66F_y \qquad \text{(K1-2)}$$

b. When the force to be resisted is a concentrated load applied at or near the end of the member,

$$\frac{R}{t_w(N + 2.5k)} \le 0.66F_y \qquad \text{(K1-3)}$$

WHERE:

R = concentrated load or reaction, kips

t_w = thickness of web, in.

N = length of bearing (not less than k for end reactions), in.

k = distance from outer face of flange to web toe of fillet, in.

4. Web Crippling. Bearing stiffeners shall be provided in the webs of members under concentrated loads, when the compressive force exceeds the following limits:

a. When the concentrated load is applied at a distance not less than $d/2$ from the end of the member:

$$R = 67.5t_w^2\left[1 + 3\left(\frac{N}{d}\right)\left(\frac{t_w}{t_f}\right)^{1.5}\right]\sqrt{F_{yw}t_f/t_w} \qquad \text{(K1-4)}$$

b. When the concentrated load is applied less than a distance $d/2$ from the end of the member:

$$R = 34t_w^2\left[1 + 3\left(\frac{N}{d}\right)\left(\frac{t_w}{t_f}\right)^{1.5}\right]\sqrt{F_{yw}t_f/t_w} \qquad \text{(K1-5)}$$

WHERE:

F_{yw} = specified minimum yield stress of beam web, ksi

d = overall depth of the member, in.

t_f = flange thickness, in.

If stiffeners are provided and extend at least one-half the web depth, Equations (K1-4) and (K1-5) need not be checked.

5. Sidesway Web Buckling. Bearing stiffeners shall be provided in the webs of members with flanges not restrained against relative movement by stiffeners or lateral bracing and subject to concentrated compressive loads, when the compressive force exceeds the following limits:

a. If the loaded flange is restrained against rotation and $(d_c/t_w)/(l/b_f)$ is less than 2.3:

$$R = \frac{6,800t_w^3}{h}\left[1 + 0.4\left(\frac{d_c/t_w}{l/b_f}\right)^3\right] \qquad \text{(K1-6)}$$

b. If the loaded flange is not restrained against rotation and $(d_c/t_w)/(l/b_f)$ is less than 1.7:

$$R = \frac{6,800t_w^3}{h}\left[0.4\left(\frac{d_c/t_w}{l/b_f}\right)^3\right] \tag{K1-7}$$

WHERE:

l = largest laterally unbraced length along either flange at the point of load, in.

b_f = flange width, in.

d_c = $d - 2k$ = web depth clear of fillets, in.

Equations (K1-6) and (K1-7) need not be checked providing $(d_c/t_w)/(l/b_f)$ exceeds 2.3 or 1.7, respectively, or for webs subject to uniformly distributed load.

6. Compression Buckling of the Web. A stiffener or a pair of stiffeners shall be provided opposite the compression flange when the web depth clear of fillets d_c is greater than

$$\frac{4,100t_{wc}{}^3\sqrt{F_{yc}}}{P_{bf}} \tag{K1-8}$$

WHERE:

t_{wc} = thickness of column web, in.

7. Compression Members with Web Panels Subject to High Shear. Members subject to high shear stress in the web should be checked for conformance with Section F4.

8. Stiffener Requirements for Concentrated Loads. Stiffeners shall be placed in pairs at unframed ends or at points of concentrated loads on the interior of beams, girders or columns if required by Section K1.2 through K1.6, as applicable.

If required by Sections K1.2, K1.3 or Equation (K1-9), stiffeners need not extend more than one half the depth of the web, except as follows:

If stiffeners are required by Sections K1.4 or K1.6, the stiffeners shall be designed as axially compressed members (columns) in accordance with requirements of Section E2 with an effective length equal to $0.75h$, a cross section composed of two stiffeners and a strip of the web having a width of $25t_w$ at interior stiffeners and $12t_w$ at the ends of members.

When the load normal to the flange is tensile, the stiffeners shall be welded to the loaded flange. When the load normal to the flange is compressive, the stiffeners shall either bear on or be welded to the loaded flange.

When flanges or moment connection plates for end connections of beams and girders are welded to the flange of an I- or H-shape column, a pair of column-web stiffeners having a combined cross-sectional area A_{st} not less than that computed from Equation (K1-9) shall be provided whenever the calculated value of A_{st} is positive.

$$A_{st} = \frac{P_{bf} - F_{yc}t_{wc}(t_b + 5k)}{F_{yst}} \tag{K1-9}$$

WHERE

F_{yst} = stiffener yield stress, ksi

k = distance between outer face of column flange and web toe of its fillet, if column is a rolled shape, or equivalent distance if column is welded shape, in.

t_b = thickness of flange or moment connection plate delivering concentrated force, in.

Stiffeners required by the provisions of Equation (K1-9) and Sections K1.2 and K1.6 shall comply with the following criteria:

1. The width of each stiffener plus one-half the thickness of the column web shall not be less than one third the width of the flange or moment connection plate delivering the concentrated force.

2. The thickness of stiffeners shall be not less than one half the thickness of the flange or plate delivering the concentrated load.

3. The weld joining stiffeners to the column web shall be sized to carry the force in the stiffener caused by unbalanced moments on opposite sides of the column.

K2. PONDING

The roof system shall be investigated by structural analysis to assure adequate strength and stability under ponding conditions, unless the roof surface is provided with sufficient slope toward points of free drainage or adequate individual drains to prevent the accumulation of rainwater.

The roof system shall be considered stable and not requiring further investigation if:

$$C_p + 09\ C_s \leq 0.25 \qquad \text{(K2-1)}$$

$$\text{and } I_d \geq 25\ (S^4)\ 10^{-6} \qquad \text{(K2-2)}$$

WHERE

$$C_p = \frac{32L_s\ L_p^4}{10^7 I_p}$$

$$C_s = \frac{32SL_s^4}{10^7 I_s}$$

L_p = column spacing in direction of girder (length of primary members), ft.

L_s = column spacing perpendicular to direction of girder (length of secondary members), ft.

S = spacing of secondary members, ft.

I_p = moment of inertia of primary members, in.^{4}

I_s = moment of inertia of secondary members, in.^{4}

I_d = moment of inertia of the steel deck supported on secondary members, in.^{4} per ft.

For trusses and steel joists, the moment of inertia I_s shall be decreased 15 percent when used in the above equation. A steel deck shall be considered a secondary member when it is directly supported by the primary members.

Total bending stress due to dead loads, gravity live loads (if any) and ponding shall not exceed $0.80F_y$ for primary and secondary members. Stresses due to wind or seismic forces need not be included in a ponding analysis.

K3. TORSION

The effects of torsion shall be considered in the design of members and the normal and shearing stresses due to torsion shall be added to those from all other loads, with the resultants not exceeding the allowable values.

K4. FATIGUE

Members and their connections subject to fatigue loading shall be proportioned in accordance with the provisions of Appendix K4.

Few members or connections in conventional buildings need to be designed for fatigue, since most load changes in such structures occur only a small number of times or produce only minor stress fluctuations. The occurrence of full design wind or earthquake loads is too infrequent to warrant consideration in fatigue design. However, crane runways and supporting structures for machinery and equipment are often subject to fatigue loading conditions.

CHAPTER L
SERVICEABILITY DESIGN CONSIDERATIONS

Sec. 27.1502L. This chapter provides design guidance for serviceability considerations not covered elsewhere. Serviceability is a state in which the function of a building, its appearance, maintainability, durability and comfort of its occupants are preserved under normal usage.

Limiting values of structural behavior to ensure serviceability (e.g., maximum deflections, accelerations, etc.) shall be chosen with due regard to the intended function of the structure.

L1. CAMBER

If any special camber requirements are necessary to bring a loaded member into proper relation with the work of other trades, the requirements shall be set forth in the design documents.

Trusses of 80 feet or greater span generally shall be cambered for approximately the dead-load deflection. Crane girders of 75 feet or greater span generally shall be cambered for approximately the dead-load deflection plus one half the live-load deflection.

Beams and trusses detailed without specified camber shall be fabricated so that after erection any camber due to rolling or shop assembly shall be upward. If camber involves the erection of any member under a preload, this shall be noted in the design documents.

L2. EXPANSION AND CONTRACTION

Provision shall be made for expansion and contraction appropriate to the service conditions of the structure.

L3. DEFLECTION, VIBRATION AND DRIFT

1. **Deflection.** Beams and girders supporting floors and roofs shall be proportioned with due regard to the deflection produced by the design loads. Beams and girders supporting plastered ceilings shall be so proportioned that the maximum live-load deflection does not exceed $^1/_{360}$ of the span.

2. **Vibration.** Beams and girders supporting large open floor areas free of partitions or other sources of damping shall be designed with due regard for vibration.

L4. CONNECTION SLIP

For the design of slip-resistant connections see Section J3.

L5. CORROSION

When appropriate, structural components shall be designed to tolerate corrosion or shall be protected against corrosion that impairs the strength or serviceability of the structure.

Where beams are exposed they shall be sealed against corrosion of interior surfaces or spaced sufficiently far apart to permit cleaning and painting.

CHAPTER M
FABRICATION, ERECTION AND QUALITY CONTROL

Sec. 27.1502M.

M1. SHOP DRAWINGS

Shop drawings giving complete information necessary for the fabrication of the component parts of the structure, including the location, type and size of all welds, bolts and rivets, shall be prepared in advance of the actual fabrication. These drawings shall clearly distinguish between shop and field welds and bolts and shall clearly identify type of high strength bolted connection (snug-tight or fully tightened bearing, or slip-critical).

Shop drawings shall be made in conformity with the best practice and with due regard to speed and economy in fabrication and erection.

M2. FABRICATION

1. **Cambering, Curving and Straightening.** Local application of heat or mechanical means are permitted to introduce or correct camber, curvature and straightness. The temperature of heated areas, as measured by approved methods, shall not exceed 1,050°F. for A852 steel, 1,100°F. for A514 steel nor 1,200°F. for other steels. The same limits apply for equivalent grades of A709 steels.

2. **Thermal Cutting.** Thermally cut free edges which will be subject to substantial tensile stress shall be free of gouges greater than $^3/_{16}$ inch. Gouges greater than $^3/_{16}$-inch deep and sharp notches shall be removed by grinding or repaired by welding. Thermally cut edges which are to have weld deposited upon them shall be reasonably free of notches or gouges.

All reentrant corners shall be shaped to a smooth transition. If specific contour is required, it must be shown on the contract documents.

Beam copes and weld access holes shall meet the geometrical requirements of Section J1.8. Beam copes and weld access holes in A6 Group 4 and 5 shapes and welded built-up shapes with material thickness greater than 2 inches shall be preheated to a temperature of not less than 150°F. prior to thermal cutting.

3. Planing of Edges. Planing or finishing of sheared or thermally cut edges of plates or shapes will not be required unless specifically called for in the design documents or included in a stipulated edge preparation for welding.

4. Welded Construction. The technique of welding, the workmanship, appearance and quality of welds, and the methods used in correcting nonconforming work shall be in accordance with "Section 3—Workmanship" and "Section 4—Technique" of the AWS *Structural Welding Code—Steel,* D1.1, U.B.C. Standard No. 27-6.

5. High-strength Bolted Construction—Assembly. All parts of bolted members shall be pinned or bolted and held together rigidly while assembling. Use of a drift pin in bolt holes during assembling shall not distort the metal or enlarge the holes. Poor matching of holes shall be cause for rejection.

If the thickness of the material is not greater than the nominal diameter of the bolt plus $^1/_8$ inch, the holes may be punched. If the thickness of the material is greater than the nominal diameter of the bolt plus $^1/_8$ inch, the holes shall be either drilled or sub-punched and reamed. The die for all sub-punched holes and the drill for all sub-drilled holes shall beat least $^1/_{16}$ inch smaller than the nominal diameter of the bolt. Holes in A514 steel plates over $^1/_2$-inch thick shall be drilled.

Surfaces of high-strength-bolted parts in contact with the bolt head and nut shall not have a slope of more than 1:20 with respect to a plane normal to the bolt axis. Where the surface of a high-strength-bolted part has a slope of more than 1:20, a beveled washer shall be used to compensate for the lack of parallelism. High-strength-bolted parts shall fit solidly together when assembled and shall not be separated by gaskets or any other interposed compressible materials.

The orientation of fully inserted finger shims, with a total thickness of not more than $^1/_4$ inch within a joint, is independent of the direction of application of the load.

When assembled, all joint surfaces, including surfaces adjacent to the bolt head and nut, shall be free of scale, except tight mill scale, and shall be free of dirt or other foreign material. Burrs that would prevent solid seating of the connected parts in the snug-tight condition shall be removed. Contact surfaces within slip-critical connections shall be free of oil, paint, lacquer or other coatings, except as listed in Table 3 of the RCSC *Specification for Structural Joints Using ASTM A325 or A490 Bolts*.

The use of high-strength bolts shall conform to the requirements of the RCSC *Specification for Structural Joints Using ASTM A325 or A490 Bolts*.

G. Compression Joints. Compression joints which depend on contact bearing as part of the splice capacity shall have the bearing surfaces of individual fabricated pieces prepared by milling, sawing or other suitable means.

7. Dimensional Tolerances. Dimensional tolerances shall be as permitted in the *Code of Standard Practice* of the American Institute of Steel Construction, Inc.

8. Finishing of Column Bases. Column bases and base plates shall be finished in accordance with the following requirements:

a. Rolled steel bearing plates 2 inches or less in thickness are permitted without milling, provided a satisfactory contact bearing is obtained; rolled steel bearing plates over 2 inches but not over 4 inches in thickness may be straightened by pressing, or if presses are not available, by milling for all bearing surfaces (except as noted in Subparagraphs c. and d. of this section), to obtain a satisfactory contact bearing; rolled steel bearing plates over 4 inches thick shall be milled for all bearing surfaces (except as noted in Subparagraphs c. and d. of this section).

b. Column bases other than rolled steel bearing plates shall be milled for all bearing surfaces (except as noted in Subparagraphs c. and d. of this section).

c. The bottom surfaces of bearing plates and column bases which are grouted to ensure full bearing contact on foundations need not be milled.

d. The top surfaces of base plates with columns full-penetration welded need not be pressed or milled.

M3. SHOP PAINTING

1. General Requirements. Shop painting and surface preparation shall be in accordance with the provisions of the *Code of Standard Practice* of the American Institute of Steel Construction, Inc.

Unless otherwise specified, steelwork which will be concealed by interior building finish or will be in contact with concrete need not be painted. Unless specifically excluded, all other steelwork shall be given one coat of shop paint.

2. Inaccessible Surfaces. Except for contact surfaces, surfaces inaccessible after shop assembly shall be cleaned and painted prior to assembly, if required by the design documents.

3. Contact Surfaces. Paint is permitted unconditionally in bearing-type connections. For slip-critical connections, the faying surface requirements shall be in accordance with the RCSC *Specification for Structural Joints Using ASTM A325 or A490 Bolts,* paragraph 3. (b).

4. Finished Surfaces. Machine-finished surfaces shall be protected against corrosion by a rust-inhibiting coating that can be removed prior to erection, or which has characteristics that make removal prior to erection unnecessary.

5. Surfaces Adjacent to Field Welds. Unless otherwise specified in the design documents, surfaces within 2 inches of any field weld location shall be free of materials that would prevent proper welding or produce toxic fumes during welding.

M4. ERECTION

1. Alignment of Column Bases. Column bases shall be set level and to correct elevation with full bearing on concrete or masonry.

2. Bracing. The frame of steel skeleton buildings shall be carried up true and plumb within the limits defined in the *Code of Standard Practice* of the American

Institute of Steel Construction. Temporary bracing shall be provided, in accordance with the requirements of the *Code of Standard Practice,* wherever necessary to take care of all loads to which the structure may be subjected, including equipment and the operation of same. Such bracing shall be left in place as long as may be required for safety.

Wherever piles of material erection equipment or other loads are supported during erection, proper provision shall be made to take care of stresses resulting from such loads.

3. Alignment. No permanent bolting or welding shall be performed until as much of the structure as will be stiffened thereby has been properly aligned.

4. Fit of Column Compression Joints. Lack of contact bearing not exceeding a gap of $^1/_{16}$ inch, regardless of the type of splice used (partial-penetration, groove-welded or bolted), shall be acceptable. If the gap exceeds $^1/_{16}$ inch, but is less than $^1/_4$ inch, and if an engineering investigation shows sufficient contact area does not exist, the gap shall be packed with nontapered steel shims. Shims may be of mild steel, regardless of the grade of the main material.

5. Field Welding. Shop paint on surfaces adjacent to welds shall be wire-brushed to reduce paint film to a minimum.

6. Field Painting. Responsibility for touch-up painting, cleaning and field-painting shall be allocated in accordance with accepted local practices, and this allocation shall be set forth explicitly in the design documents.

7. Field Connections. As erection progresses, the work shall be securely bolted or welded to take care of all dead load, wind and erection stresses.

M5. QUALITY CONTROL

The fabricator shall provide quality control procedures to the extent that he deems necessary to assure that all work is performed in accordance with this Specification. In addition to the fabricator's quality control procedures, material and workmanship at all times may be subject to inspection by qualified inspectors representing the purchaser. If such inspection by representatives of the purchaser will be required, it shall be so stated in design documents.

1. Cooperation. As far as possible, all inspection by representatives of the purchaser shall be made at the fabricator's plant. The fabricator shall cooperate with the inspector, permitting access for inspection to all places where work is being done. The purchaser's inspector shall schedule his work for minimum interruption to the work of the fabricator.

2. Rejections. Material or workmanship not in reasonable conformance with the provisions of this Specification may be rejected at any time during the progress of the work. The fabricator shall receive copies of all reports furnished to the purchaser by the inspection agency.

3. Inspection of Welding. The inspection of welding shall be performed in accordance with the provisions of Section 6 of the AWS *Structural Welding Code—Steel,* D1.1, U.B.C. Standard No. 27-6.

When nondestructive testing is required, the process, extent and standards of acceptance shall be defined clearly in the design documents.

4. Inspection of Slip-critical, High-strength Bolted Connections. The inspection of slip-critical, high-strength bolted connections shall be in accordance with the provisions of the RCSC *Allowable Stress Design Specification for Structural Joints Using ASTM A325 or A490 Bolts.*

5. Identification of Steel. The fabricator shall be able to demonstrate by a written procedure and by actual practice a method of material application and identification, visible at least through the "fit-up" operation, of the main structural elements of a shipping piece.

The identification method shall be capable of verifying proper material application as it relates to:

1. Material specification designation;
2. Heat number, if required;
3. Material test reports for special requirements.

CHAPTER N
PLASTIC DESIGN

Sec. 27.1502N.

N1. SCOPE

Subject to the limitations contained herein, simple and continuous beams, braced and unbraced planar rigid frames, and similar parts of structures rigidly constructed so as to be continuous over at least one interior support,* are permitted to be proportioned on the basis of plastic design, i.e., on the basis of their maximum strength. This strength, as determined by rational analysis, shall not be less than that required to support a factored load equal to 1.7 times the given live load and dead load, or 1.3 times these loads acting in conjunction with 1.3 times any specified wind or earthquake forces.

Rigid frames shall satisfy the requirements for Type I construction in the plane of the frame, as provided in Section A2.2. This does not preclude the use of some simple connections, provided provisions of Section N3 are satisfied. Type 2 construction is permitted for members between rigid frames. Connections joining a portion of a structure designed on the basis of plastic behavior with a portion not so designed need be no more rigid than ordinary seat-and-top-angle or ordinary web connections.

Where plastic design is used as the basis for proportioning continuous beams and structural frames, the provisions relating to allowable stress are waived. Except as modified by these rules, however, all other pertinent provisions of Chapters A through M shall govern.

Crane runways shall not be designed continuous over interior vertical supports on the basis of maximum strength. However, rigid frame bents supporting crane runways may be considered as coming within the scope of the rules.

---

*As used here, "interior support" includes a rigid-frame knee formed by the junction of a column and a sloping or horizontal beam or girder.

N2. STRUCTURAL STEEL

Structural steel shall conform to one of the following specifications: A36, A242, A441, A529, A572 and A588.

N3. BASIS FOR MAXIMUM STRENGTH DETERMINATION

For one- or two-story frames, the maximum strength is permitted to be determined by a routine plastic analysis procedure and ignore the frame instability effect ($P\Delta$). For braced multistory frames, provisions shall be made to include the frame instability effect in the design of bracing system and frame members. For unbraced multistory frames, the frame instability effect shall be included directly in the calculations for maximum strength.

1. Stability of Braced Frames. The vertical bracing system for a plastically designed braced multistory frame shall be adequate, as determined by an analysis, to:

1. Prevent buckling of the structure under factored gravity loads.

2. Maintain the lateral stability of the structure, including the overturning effects of drift, under factored gravity plus factored horizontal loads.

It is permitted to consider that the vertical bracing system functions together with inplane shear-resisting exterior and interior walls, floor slabs and roof decks, if these walls, slabs and decks are secured to the structural frames. The columns, girders, beams and diagonal members, when used as the vertical bracing system, could be considered to comprise a vertical-cantilever, simply connected truss in the analyses for frame buckling and lateral stability. Axial deformation of all members in the vertical bracing system shall be included in the lateral stability analysis. The axial force in these members caused by factored gravity plus factored horizontal loads shall not exceed $0.85P_y$, where P_y is the product of yield stress times the profile area of the member.

Girders and beams included in the vertical bracing system of a braced multistory frame shall be proportioned for axial force and moment caused by the concurrent factored horizontal and gravity loads, in accordance with Equation (N4-2), with P_{cr}, taken as the maximum axial strength of the beam, based on the actual slenderness ratio between braced points in the plane of bending.

2. Stability of Unbraced Frames. The strength of an unbraced multistory frame shall be determined by an analysis which includes the effect of frame instability and column axial deformation. Such a frame shall be designed to be stable under (1) factored gravity loads and (2) factored gravity loads plus factored horizontal loads. The axial force in the columns at factored load levels shall not exceed $0.75P_y$.

N4. COLUMNS

In the plane of bending of columns which would develop a plastic hinge at ultimate loading, the slenderness ratio l/r shall not exceed C_c, defined in Section E2.

The maximum strength of an axially loaded compression member shall be taken as

$$P_{cr} = 1.7F_aA \qquad \text{(N4-1)}$$

where A is the gross area of the member and F_a, as defined by Equation (E2-1), is based upon the applicable slenderness ratio.

Members subject to combined axial load and bending moment shall be proportioned to satisfy the following interaction formulas:

$$\frac{P}{P_{cr}} + \frac{C_m M}{\left(1 - \frac{P}{P_e}\right) M_M} \leq 1.0 \qquad \text{(N4-2)}$$

$$\frac{P}{P_y} + \frac{M}{1.18 M_p} \leq 1.0; M \leq M_p \qquad \text{(N4-3)}$$

WHERE:

M = maximum factored moment, kip-ft

P = factored axial load, kips

P_e = Euler buckling load, kips

= $(23/12)F'_c A$, where F'_c is as defined in Section H1.

C_m = coefficient defined in Section H1.

M_m = maximum moment that can be resisted by the member in the absence of axial load, kip-ft

M_p = plastic moment, kip-ft

= $F_y Z$

Z = plastic section modulus, in.

For columns braced in the weak direction:

$$M_m = M_{px} \qquad \text{(N4-4)}$$

For columns unbraced in the weak direction:

$$M_m = \left[1.07 - \frac{(l/r_y)\sqrt{F_y}}{3160}\right] M_{px} \leq M_{px} \qquad \text{(N4-5)}$$

N5. SHEAR

Unless reinforced by diagonal stiffeners or a doubler plate, the webs of columns, beams and girders, including areas within the boundaries of the connections, shall be so proportioned that

$$V \leq 0.55 F_y t_w d \qquad \text{(N5-1)}$$

WHERE:

V = shear that would be produced by the required factored loading, kips

d = depth of the member, in.

t_w = web thickness, in.

N6. WEB CRIPPLING

Web stiffeners are required on a member at a point of load application where a plastic hinge would form.

At points on a member where the concentrated load delivered by the flanges of a member framing into it would produce web crippling opposite the compression flange or high-tensile stress in the connection of the tension flange, web stiffeners are required in accordance with the provisions of Section K1.

N7. MINIMUM THICKNESS (WIDTH-THICKNESS RATIOS)

The width-thickness ratio for flanges of rolled W, M or S shapes and similar builtup, single-web shapes subjected to compression involving hinge rotation under ultimate loading shall not exceed the following values:

F_y	$b_f/2t_f$
36	8.5
42	8.0
45	7.4
50	7.0
55	6.6
60	6.3
65	6.0

It is permitted to take the thickness of sloping flanges as their average thickness.

The width-thickness ratio of similarly compressed flange plates in box sections and cover plates shall not exceed $190/\sqrt{F_y}$.. For this purpose, the width of a cover plate shall be taken as the distance between longitudinal lines of connecting rivets, high-strength bolts or welds.

The depth-thickness ratio of webs of members subject to plastic bending shall not exceed the value given by Equation (N7-1) or (N7-2), as applicable.

$$\frac{d}{t} = \frac{412}{\sqrt{F_y}}\left(1 - 1.4\frac{P}{P_y}\right) \text{ when } \frac{P}{P_y} \leq 0.27 \qquad \text{(N7-1)}$$

$$\frac{d}{t} = \frac{257}{\sqrt{F_y}} \text{ when } \frac{P}{P_y} > 0.27 \qquad \text{(N7-2)}$$

N8. CONNECTIONS

All connections, the rigidity of which is essential to the continuity assumed as the basis of the analysis, shall be capable of resisting the moments, shears and axial loads to which they would be subjected by the full factored loading, or any probable partial distribution thereof.

Corner connections (haunches) that are tapered or curved for architectural reasons shall be so proportioned that the full plastic bending strength of the section adjacent to the connection can be developed, if required.

Stiffeners shall be used, as required, to preserve the flange continuity of interrupted members at their junction with other members in a continuous frame. Such stiffeners shall be placed in pairs on opposite sides of the web of the member which extends continuously through the joint.

High-strength bolts, A307 bolts, rivets and welds shall be proportioned to resist the forces produced at factored load, using stresses equal to 1.7 times those given in Chapters A through M. In general, groove welds are preferable to fillet welds, but their use is not mandatory.

High-strength bolts are permitted in joints having painted contact surfaces when these joints are of such size that the slip required to produce bearing would not interfere with the formation, at factored loading, of the plastic hinges assumed in the design.

N9. LATERAL BRACING

Members shall be braced adequately to resist lateral and torsional displacements at the plastic hinge locations associated with the failure mechanism. The laterally unsupported distance l_{cr} from such braced hinge locations to similarly braced adjacent points on the member or frame shall not exceed the value determined from Equation (N9-1) or (N9-2), as applicable.

$$\frac{l_{cr}}{r_y} = \frac{1,375}{F_y} + 25 \text{ when } +1.0 > \frac{M}{M_p} > -0.5 \qquad \text{(N9-1)}$$

$$\frac{l_{cr}}{r_y} = \frac{1,375}{F_y} \text{ when } -0.5 \geq \frac{M}{M_p} > -1.0 \qquad \text{(N9-2)}$$

WHERE:

r_y = radius of gyration of the member about its weak axis, in.

M = lesser of the moments at the ends of the unbraced segment, kip-ft.

M/M_p = end moment ratio, positive when the segment is bent in reverse curvature and negative when bent in single curvature

The foregoing provisions need not apply in the region of the last hinge to form in the failure mechanism assumed as the basis for proportioning a given member, nor in members oriented with their weak axis normal to the plane of bending. However, in the region of the last hinge to form, and in regions not adjacent to a plastic hinge, the maximum distance between points of lateral support shall be such as to satisfy the requirements of Equations (F1-5), (F1-6), or (F1-7), as well as Equations (H1-1) and (H1-2). For this case, the values of f_a and f_a shall be computed from the moment and axial force at factored loading, divided by the applicable load factor.

Members built into a masonry wall and having their web perpendicular to this wall can be assumed to be laterally supported with respect to their weak axis of bending.

N10. FABRICATION

The provisions of Chapters A through M with respect to workmanship shall govern the fabrication of structures, or portions of structures, designed on the basis of maximum strength, subject to the following limitations:

1. The use of sheared edges shall be avoided in locations subject to plastic hinge rotation at factored loading. If used, they shall be finished smooth by grinding, chipping or planing.

2. In locations subject to plastic hinge rotation at factored loading, holes for rivets or bolts in the tension area shall be sub-punched and reamed or drilled full size.

APPENDIX B

DESIGN REQUIREMENTS

Sec. 27.1503.

B5. LOCAL BUCKLING

2. Slender Compression Elements. Axially loaded members and flexural members containing elements subject to compression which have a width-thickness ratio in excess of the applicable noncompact value, as stipulated in Section B5.1 shall be proportioned according to this Appendix.

a. Unstiffened Compression Elements. The allowable stress of unstiffened compression elements whose width-thickness ratio exceeds the applicable noncompact value as stipulated in Section B5.1 shall be subject to a reduction factor Q_s. The value of Q_s shall be determined by Equations (A-B5-1) through (A-B5-6), as applicable, where b is the width of the unstiffened element as defined in Section B5.1. When such elements comprise the compression flange of a flexural member, the maximum allowable bending stress shall not exceed $0.60\,F_yQ_s$ nor the applicable value as provided in Section F1.3. The allowable stress of axially loaded compression members shall be modified by the appropriate reduction factor Q, as provided in paragraph c.

For single angles:

When $76.0/\sqrt{F_y} < b/t < 155/\sqrt{F_y}$: (A-B5-1)

$$Q_s = 1.340 - 0.00447(b/t)\sqrt{F_y}$$

When $b/t \geq 155/\sqrt{F_y}$: (A-B5-2)

$$Q_s = 15,500/[F_y(b/t)^2]$$

For angles or plates projecting from columns or other compression members, and for projecting elements of compression flanges of beams and girders:

When $95.0/\sqrt{F_y/k_c} < b/t < 195/\sqrt{F_y/k_c}$ (A-B5-3)

$$Q_s = 1.293 - 0.00309(b/t)\sqrt{F_y/k_c}$$

When $b/t > 195/\sqrt{F_y/k_c}$ (A-B5-4)

$$Q_s = 26,200k_c/[F_y(b/t)^2]$$

For stems of tees:

When $127/\sqrt{F_y} < b/t < 176/\sqrt{F_y}$: (A-B5-5)

$$Q_s = 1.908 - 0.00715(b/t)\sqrt{F_y}$$

When $b/t > 176/\sqrt{F_y}$ (A-B5-6)

$$Q_s = 20,000/[F_y(b/t)^2]$$

WHERE:

b = width of unstiffened compression element as defined in Section B5.1

t = thickness of unstiffened element, in.

F_y = specified minimum yield stress, ksi

$k_c = \dfrac{4.05}{(h/t)^{.46}}$ if $h/t > 70$, otherwise $k_c = 1.0$

Unstiffened elements of tees whose proportions exceed the limits of Section B5.1 shall conform to the limits given in Table A-B5.1.

b. Stiffened Compression Elements. When the width-thickness ratio of uniformly compressed stiffened elements (except perforated cover plates) exceeds the noncompact limit stipulated in Section B5.1, a reduced effective width b_e shall be used in computing the design properties of the section containing the element, except that the ratio b_e/t need not be taken as less than the applicable value permitted in Section B5.1.

For the flanges of square and rectangular sections of uniform thickness:

$$b_e = \frac{253t}{\sqrt{f}}\left[1 - \frac{50.3}{(b/t)\sqrt{f}}\right] \leq b \quad \text{(A-B5-7)}$$

For other uniformly compressed elements:

$$b_e = \frac{253t}{\sqrt{f}}\left[1 - \frac{44.3}{(b/t)\sqrt{f}}\right] \leq b \quad \text{(A-B5-8)}$$

WHERE:

b = actual width of a stiffened compression element, as defined in Section B5.1, in.

b_e = reduced width, in.

t = element thickness, in.

f = computed compressive stress (axial plus bending stresses) in the stiffened elements, based on the design properties as specified in Appendix B5.2, ksi. If unstiffened elements are included in the total cross section, f for the stiffened element must be such that the maximum compressive stress in the unstiffened element does not exceed $F_a Q_s$ or $F_b Q_s$, as applicable.

Table A-B5.1
Limiting Proportions for Channels and Tees

Shape	Ratio of full flange width to profile depth	Ratio of flange thickness to web or stem thickness
Built-up or rolled channels	≤0.25	≤3.0
	≤0.50	≤2.0
Built-up tees	≥0.50	≥1.25
Rolled tees	≥0.50	≥1.10

When the allowable stresses are increased due to wind or seismic loading in accordance with the provisions of Section A5.2, the effective width b_e shall be determined on the basis of 0.75 times the stress caused by wind or seismic loading acting alone or in combination with the design dead and live loading.

For axially loaded circular sections:

Members with diameter-to-thickness ratios D/t greater than $3{,}300/F_y$, but having a diameter-to-thickness ratio of less than $13{,}000/F_y$, shall not exceed the smaller value determined by Section E2 nor

$$F_a = \frac{662}{D/t} + 0.40F_y \qquad \text{(A-B5-9)}$$

WHERE:

D = outside diameter, in.

t = wall thickness, in.

c. Design Properties. Properties of sections shall be determined using the full cross section, except as follows:

In computing the moment of inertia and section modulus of flexural members, the effective width of uniformly compressed stiffened elements, as determined in Appendix B5.2b, shall be used in determining effective cross-sectional properties.

For stiffened elements of the cross section

$$Q_a = \frac{\text{effective area}}{\text{actual area}} \qquad \text{(A-B5-10)}$$

For unstiffened elements of the cross section, Q_s is determined from Appendix B5.2a.

For axially loaded compression members the gross cross-sectional area and the radius of gyration r shall be computed on the basis of the actual cross section.

The allowable stress for axially loaded compression members containing unstiffened or stiffened elements shall not exceed

$$F_a = \frac{Q\left[1 - \frac{(Kl/r)^2}{2C'_c{}^2}\right]F_y}{\frac{5}{3} + \frac{3(Kl/r)}{8C'_c} - \frac{(Kl/r)^3}{8C'_c{}^3}} \qquad \text{(A-B5-11)}$$

when Kl/r *is* less than $C'c$, where

$$C'_c = \sqrt{\frac{2\pi^2 E}{QF_y}}$$

and

$Q = Q_s Q_a$

a. Cross sections composed entirely of unstiffened elements,
$Q = Q_s$ i.e. ($Q_a = 1.0$)

b. Cross sections composed entirely of stiffened elements,
$Q = Q_a$ i.e. ($Q_s = 1.0$)

c. Cross sections composed of both stiffened and unstiffened elements,
$Q = Q_s Q_a$

When Kl/r exceeds C'_c:

$$F_a = \frac{12\pi^2 E}{23(Kl/r)^2} \qquad \text{(A-B5-12)}$$

d. Combined Axial and Flexural Stress. In applying the provisions of Chapter H to members subject to combined axial and flexural stress and containing stiffened elements whose width-thickness ratio exceeds the applicable noncompact limit given in Section B5.1, the stresses F_a, f_{bx} and f_{by} shall be calculated on the basis of the section properties as provided in Appendix B5.2c, as applicable. The allowable bending stress F_b for members containing unstiffened elements whose width-thickness ratio exceeds the noncompact limit given in Section B5.1 shall be the smaller value, $0.60F_yQ_s$, or that provided in Section F1.3. The term $f_a/0.60F_y$ in Equations (H1-2) and (A-F7-13) shall be replaced by $f_a/0.60F_yQ$.

APPENDIX F
BEAMS AND OTHER FLEXURAL MEMBERS

Sec. 27.1504.

F7. WEB-TAPERED MEMBERS

The design of tapered members meeting the requirements of this section shall be governed by the provisions of Chapter F, except as modified by this Appendix.

1. General Requirements. In order to qualify under this Specification, a tapered member must meet the following requirements:

a. It shall possess at least one axis of symmetry which shall be perpendicular to the plane of bending if moments are present.

b. The flanges shall be of equal and constant area.

c. The depth shall vary linearly as

$$d = d_o \left(1 + \gamma \frac{z}{L}\right) \qquad \text{(A-F7-1)}$$

WHERE:

d_o = depth at smaller end of member, in.

d_L = depth at larger end of member, in.

γ = $(d_L - d_o)/d_o \leq$ the smaller of 0.268 (L/d_o)or 6.0

z = distance from the smaller end of member, in.

L = unbraced length of member measured between the center of gravity of the bracing members, in.

2. Allowable Tensile Stress. The allowable tensile stress of tapered tension members shall be determined in accordance with Section D1.

3. Allowable Compressive Stress. On the gross section of axially loaded tapered compression members, the allowable compressive stress, in kips per square inch, shall not exceed the following:

$$F_{a\gamma} = \frac{\left(1.0 - \dfrac{S^2}{2C_c^2}\right) F_y}{\dfrac{5}{3} + \dfrac{3S}{8C_c} - \dfrac{S^3}{8C_c^3}} \qquad \text{(A-F7-2)}$$

When the effective slenderness ratio S exceeds C_c:

$$F_{a\gamma} = \frac{12\pi^2 E}{23S^2} \qquad \text{(A-F7-3)}$$

WHERE

S = Kl/r_{oy} for weak axis bending and $K_\gamma l/r_{ox}$ for strong axis bending

K = effective length factor for a prismatic member

K_γ = effective length factor for a tapered member as determined by an analysis

l = actual unbraced length of member, in.

r_{ox} = strong axis radius of gyration at the smaller end of a tapered member, in.

r_{oy} = weak axis radius of gyration at the smaller end of a tapered member, in.

4. Allowable Flexural Stress. Tension and compression stresses on extreme fibers of tapered flexural members, in kips per square inch, shall not exceed the following values:

$$F_{b\gamma} = \frac{2}{3}\left[1.0 - \frac{F_y}{6B\sqrt{F_{s\gamma}^2 + F_{w\gamma}^2}}\right]F_2 \leq 0.60F_y \qquad \text{(A-F7-4)}$$

unless $F_{b\gamma} < F_y/3$, in which case

$$F_{b\gamma} = B\sqrt{F_{s\gamma}^2 + F_{w\gamma}^2} \qquad \text{(A-F7-5)}$$

In the above equations,

$$F_{s\gamma} = \frac{12 \times 10^3}{H_s\, Ld_o/A_f} \qquad \text{(A-F7-6)}$$

$$F_{w\gamma} = \frac{170 \times 10^3}{(h_w\, L/r_{To})^2} \qquad \text{(A-F7-7)}$$

WHERE:

h_s = factor equal to $1.0 + 0.0230y\sqrt{Ld_o/A_f}$

h_w = factor equal to $1.0 + 0.00385\sqrt{L/r_{To}}$

r_{To} = radius of gyration to a section at the smaller end, considering only the compression flange plus one third of the compression web area, taken about an axis in the plane of the web, in.

A_f = area of the compression flange, in.^{2}

and where B is determined as follows:

a. When the maximum moment M_2 in three adjacent segments of approximately equal unbraced length is located within the central segment and M_1 is the larger moment at one end of the three-segment portion of a member:*

$$B = 1.0 + 0.37\left(1.0 + \frac{M_1}{M_2}\right) + 0.50\gamma\left(1.0 + \frac{M_1}{M_2}\right) \geq 1.0 \qquad \text{(A-F7-8)}$$

b. When the largest computed bending stress f_{b2} occurs at the larger end of two adjacent segments of approximately equal unbraced lengths and f_{b1}, is the computed bending stress at the smaller end of the two-segment portion of a member:*

$$B = 1.0 + 0.58\left(1.0 + \frac{f_{b1}}{f_{b2}}\right) - 0.70\gamma\left(1.0 + \frac{f_{b1}}{f_{b2}}\right) \geq 1.0 \qquad \text{(A-F7-9)}$$

---

*M_1/M_2 is considered as negative when producing single curvature. In the rare case where M_1/M_2 is positive, it is recommended it be taken as zero.

c. When the largest computed bending stress f_{b2} occurs at the smaller end of two adjacent segments of approximately equal unbraced length and f_{bl} is the computed bending stress at the larger end of the two-segment portion of a member:**

$$B = 1.0 + 0.55\left(1.0 + \frac{f_{b1}}{f_{b2}}\right) + 2.20\gamma\left(1.0 + \frac{f_{b1}}{f_{b2}}\right) \geq 1.0 \qquad \text{(A-F7-10)}$$

In the foregoing, $\gamma = (d_L - d_o)/d_o$ is calculated for the unbraced length containing the maximum computed bending stress.

d. When the computed bending stress at the smaller end of a tapered member or segment thereof is equal to zero:

$$B = \frac{1.75}{1.0 + 0.25\sqrt{\gamma}} \qquad \text{(A-F7-11)}$$

where $\gamma = (d_L - d_o)/d_o$ calculated for the unbraced length adjacent to the point of zero bending stress.

5. Allowable Shear. The allowable shear stress of tapered flexural members shall be in accordance with Section F4.

6. Combined Flexure and Axial Force. Tapered members and unbraced segments thereof subjected to both axial compression and bending stresses shall be proportioned to satisfy the following requirement:

$$\left(\frac{F_{ao}}{F_{a\gamma}}\right) + \frac{C'_m}{\left(1 - \frac{F_{ao}}{F'_{e\gamma}}\right)}\left(\frac{f_{bl}}{F'_{b\gamma}}\right) \leq 1.0 \qquad \text{(A-F7-12)}$$

$$\frac{f_a}{0.60F_y} + \frac{f_b}{F_{b\gamma}} \leq 1.0 \qquad \text{(A-F7-13)}$$

When $f_{ao}/F_a\gamma < 0.15$, Equation (A-F7-14) is permitted in lieu of Equations (A-F7-12) and (A-F7-13).

$$\left(\frac{f_a}{F_{a\gamma}}\right) + \left(\frac{f_b}{F_{b\gamma}}\right) \leq 1.0 \qquad \text{(A-F7-14)}$$

WHERE:

$F^a\gamma$ = axial compressive stress permitted in the absence of bending moment, ksi

$F^b\gamma$ = bending stress permitted in the absence of axial force, ksi

---

**f_{bl}/f_{b2} is considered as negative when producing single curvature. If a point of contraflexure occurs in one of two adjacent unbraced segments, f_{bl}/f_{b2} is considered as positive. The ratio f_{bl}/f_{b2} = 0.

F'^{e}_{γ} = Euler stress divided by factor of safety, ksi, equal to

$$\frac{12\pi^2 E}{23(K_\gamma l_b / r_{bo})^2}$$

where l_b is the actual unbraced length in the plane of bending and r_{bo} is the corresponding radius of gyration at its smaller end

f_{ao} = computed axial stress at the smaller end of the member or unbraced segment thereof, as applicable, ksi

f_{bl} = computed bending stress at the larger end of the member or unbraced segment thereof, as applicable, ksi

C'_m = coefficient applied to bending term in interaction equation

$$= 1.0 + 0.1\left(\frac{f_{ao}}{F'_{e\gamma}}\right) + 0.6\left(\frac{f_{ao}}{F'_{e\gamma}}\right)^2$$

when the member is subjected to end moments which cause single curvature bending and approximately equal computed bending stresses at the ends

$$= 1.0 + 0.9\left(\frac{f_{ao}}{F'_{e\gamma}}\right) + 0.6\left(\frac{f_{ao}}{F'_{e\gamma}}\right)^2$$

when the computed bending stress at the smaller end of the unbraced length is equal to zero.

When $Kl/r \geq C_c$ and combined stresses are checked incrementally along the length, f_{ao} may be replaced by f_a and f_{bl} may be replaced by f_b, in Equations (A-F7-12) and (A-F7-14).

APPENDIX K
STRENGTH DESIGN CONSIDERATIONS

Sec. 27.1505.

K4. FATIGUE

Members and connections subject to fatigue loading shall be proportioned in accordance with the provisions of this Appendix.

Fatigue, as used in this Specification, is defined as the damage that may result in fracture after a sufficient number of fluctuations of stress. Stress range is defined as the magnitude of these fluctuations. In the case of a stress reversal, the stress range shall be computed as the numerical sum of maximum repeated tensile and compressive stresses or the sum of maximum shearing stresses of opposite direction at a given point, resulting from differing arrangement of live load.

1. Loading Conditions; Type and Location of Material. In the design of members and connections subject to repeated variation of live load, consideration shall be given to the number of stress cycles, the expected range of stress and the type and location of member or detail.

Loading conditions shall be classified according to Table A-K4.1.

The type and location of material shall be categorized according to Table A-K4.2.

2. Allowable Stress Range. The maximum stress shall not exceed the basic allowable stress provided in Chapters A through M of this Specification and the maximum range of stress shall not exceed that given in Table A-K4.1.

TABLE A-K4.1
Number of Loading Cycles

Loading Condition	From	To
1	20,000[a]	100,000[b]
2	100,000	500,000[c]
3	500,000	2,000,000[d]
4	Over 2,000,000	

[a]Approximately equivalent to two applications every day for 25 years.
[b]Approximately equivalent to 10 applications every day for 25 years.
[c]Approximately equivalent to 50 applications every day for 25 years.
[d]Approximately equivalent to 200 applications every day for 25 years

3. Tensile Fatigue. When subject to tensile fatigue loading, the tensile stress in A325 or A490 bolts due to the combined applied load and prying forces shall not exceed the following values, and the prying force shall not exceed 60 percent of the externally applied load.

Number of Cycles	A325	A490
Not more than 20,000	44	54
From 20,000 to 500,000	40	49
More than 500,000	31	38

Bolts must be tensioned to the requirements of Table J3.7.

The use of other bolts and threaded parts subjected to tensile fatigue loading is not permitted.

TABLE A-K4.2
Stress Category Classifications

General Condition	Situation	Kind of Stress[a]	Stress Category (see Table A-K4.3)	Illustrative Example Nos. (see Fig. A-K4.1)[b]
Plain Material	Base metal with rolled or cleaned surface. Flame-cut edges with ANSI smoothness of 1,000 or less	T or Rev.	A	1,2
Built-up Members	Base metal in members without attachments, built-up plates or shapes connected by continuous full-penetration groove welds or by continuous fillet welds parallel to the direction of applied stress	T or Rev.	B	3,4,5,6
	Base metal in members without attachments, built-up plates, or shapes connected by full-penetration groove welds with backing bars not removed, or by partial-penetration groove welds parallel to the direction of applied stress	T or Rev.	B′	3,4,5,6
	Base metal at toe welds on girder webs or flanges adjacent to welded transverse stiffeners	T or Rev.	C	7
	Base metal at ends of partial length welded cover plates narrower than the flange having square or tapered ends, with or without welds across the ends or wider than flange with welds across the ends			
	Flange thickness ≤ 0.8 in.	T or Rev.	E	5
	Flange thickness > 0.8 in.	T or Rev.	E′	5
	Base metal at end of partial length welded cover plates wider than the flange without welds across the ends		E′	5

[a] "T" signifies range in tensile stress only; "Rev." signifies a range involving reversal of tensile or compressive stress; "S" signifies range in shear, including shear stress reversal.
[b] These examples are provided as guidelines and are not intended to exclude other reasonably similar situations.
[c] Allowable fatigue stress range for transverse partial-penetration and transverse fillet welds is a function of the effective throat, depth of penetration and plate thickness. See Frank and Fisher (1979).

TABLE A-K4.2 (cont'd)
Type and Location of Material

General Condition	Situation	Kind of Stress[a]	Stress Category (see Table A-K4.3)	Illustrative Example Nos. (see Fig. A-K4.1)[b]
Groove Welds	Base metal and weld metal at full-penetration groove welded splices of parts of similar cross section ground flush, with grinding in the direction of applied stress and with weld soundness established by radiographic or ultrasonic inspection in accordance with the requirements of 9.25.2 or 9.25.3 of AWS D1.1	T or Rev.	B	10,11
	Base metal and weld metal at full-penetration groove welded splices at transitions in width or thickness, with welds ground to provide slopes no steeper than 1 to 2½ with grinding in the direction of applied stress, and with weld soundness established by radiographic or ultrasonic inspection in accordance with the requirements of 9.25.2 or 9.25.3 of AWS D1.1			
	A514 base metal	T or Rev.	B′	12,13
	Other base metals	T or Rev.	B	12,13
	Base metal and weld metal at full-penetration groove welded splices, with or without transitions having slopes no greater than 1 to 2½ when reinforcement is not removed but weld soundness is established by radiographic or ultrasonic inspection in accordance with requirements of 9.25.2 or 9.25.3 of AWS D1.1	T or Rev.	C	10,11,12, 13
Partial-Penetration Groove Welds	Weld metal of partial-penetration transverse groove welds, based on effective throat area of the weld or welds	T or Rev.	F[c]	16

TABLE A-K4.2 (cont'd)
Type and Location of Material

General Condition	Situation	Kind of Stress[a]	Stress Category (see Table A-K4.3)	Illustrative Example Nos. (see Fig. A-K4.1)[b]
Fillet-welded Connections	Base metal at intermittent fillet welds	T or Rev.	E	
	Base metal at junction of axially loaded members with fillet-welded end connections. Welds shall be disposed about the axis of the member so as to balance weld stresses $b \leq 1$ in. $b > 1$ in.	 T or Rev. T or Rev.	 E E′	 17,18 17,18
	Base metal at members connected with transverse fillet welds $b \leq ½$ in. $b > ½$ in.	 T or Rev.	 C See Note c	 20,21
Fillet Welds	Weld metal of continuous or intermittent longitudinal or transverse fillet welds	S	F[c]	15,17,18 20,21
Plug or Slot Welds	Base metal at plug or slot welds	T or Rev.	E	27
	Shear on plug or slot welds	S	F	27
Mechanically Fastened Connections	Base metal at gross section of high-strength bolted slip-critical connections, except axially loaded joints which induce out-of-plane bending in connected material	T or Rev.	B	8
	Base metal at net section of other mechanically fastened joints	T or Rev.	D	8,9
	Base metal at net section of fully tensioned high-strength, bolted-bearing connections	T or Rev.	B	8,9

TABLE A-K4.2 (cont'd)
Type and Location of Material

General Condition	Situation	Kind of Stress[a]	Stress Category (see Table A-K4.3)	Illustrative Example Nos. (see Fig. A-K4.1)[b]
Attachments	Base metal at details attached by full-penetration groove welds subject to longitudinal and/or transverse loading when the detail embodies a transition radius *R* with the weld termination ground smooth and for transverse loading, the weld soundness established by radiographic or ultrasonic inspection in accordance with 9.25.2 or 9.25.3 of AWS D1.1			
	Longitudinal loading			
	$R > 24$ in.	T or Rev.	B	14
	24 in. $> R > 6$ in.	T or Rev.	C	14
	6 in. $> R > 2$ in.	T or Rev.	D	14
	2 in. $> R$	T or Rev.	E	14
	Detail base metal for transverse loading: equal thickness and reinforcement removed			
	$R > 24$ in.	T or Rev.	B	14
	24 in. $> R > 6$ in.	T or Rev.	C	14
	6 in. $> R > 2$ in.	T or Rev.	D	14
	2 in. $> R$	T or Rev.	E	14,15
	Detail base metal for transverse loading: equal thickness and reinforcement not removed			
	$R > 24$ in.	T or Rev.	C	14
	24 in. $> R > 6$ in.	T or Rev.	C	14
	6 in. $> R > 2$ in.	T or Rev.	D	14
	2 in. $> R$	T or Rev.	E	14,15

TABLE A-K4.2 (cont'd)
Type and Location of Material

General Condition	Situation	Kind of Stress[a]	Stress Category (see Table A-K4.3)	Illustrative Example Nos. (see Fig. A-K4.1)[b]
Attachments (cont'd)	Detail base metal for transverse loading: unequal thickness and reinforcement removed			
	$R > 2$ in.	T or Rev.	D	14
	2 in. $> R$	T or Rev.	E	14,15
	Detail base metal for transverse loading: unequal thickness and reinforcement not removed			
	all R	T or Rev.	E	14,15
	Detail base metal for transverse loading			
	$R > 6$ in.	T or Rev.	C	19
	6 in. $> R >$ 2 in.	T or Rev.	D	19
	2 in. $> R$	T or Rev.	E	19
	Base metal at detail attached by full-penetration groove welds subject to longitudinal loading			
	$2 < a < 12b$ or 4 in.	T or Rev.	D	15
	$a > 12b$ or 4 in. when $b \le 1$ in.	T or Rev.	E	15
	$a > 12b$ or 4 in. when $b > 1$ in.	T or Rev.	E′	15
	Base metal at detail attached by fillet welds or partial-penetration groove welds subject to longitudinal loading			
	$a < 2$ in.	T or Rev.	C	15,23,24, 25,26
	2 in. $< a < 12b$ or 4 in.	T or Rev.	D	15,23, 24,26
	$a > 12b$ or 4 in. when $b \le 1$ in.	T or Rev.	E	15,23, 24,26
	$a > 12b$ or 4 in. when $b > 1$ in.	T or Rev.	E′	15,23, 24,26

TABLE A-K4.2 (cont'd)
Type and Location of Material

General Condition	Situation	Kind of Stress[a]	Stress Category (see Table A-K4.3)	Illustrative Example Nos. (see Fig. A-K4.1)[b]
Attachments (cont'd)	Base metal attached by fillet welds or partial-penetration groove welds subjected to longitudinal loading when the weld termination embodies a transition radius with the weld termination ground smooth:			
	$R > 2$ in.	T or Rev.	D	19
	$R \leq 2$ in.	T or Rev.	E	19
	Fillet-welded attachments where the weld termination embodies a transition radius, weld termination ground smooth, and main material subject to longitudinal loading: Detail base metal for transverse loading:			
	$R > 2$ in.	T or Rev.	D	19
	$R < 2$ in.	T or Rev.	E	19
	Base metal at stud-type shear connector attached by fillet weld or automatic end weld	T or Rev.	C	22
	Shear stress on nominal area of stud-type shear connectors	S	F	

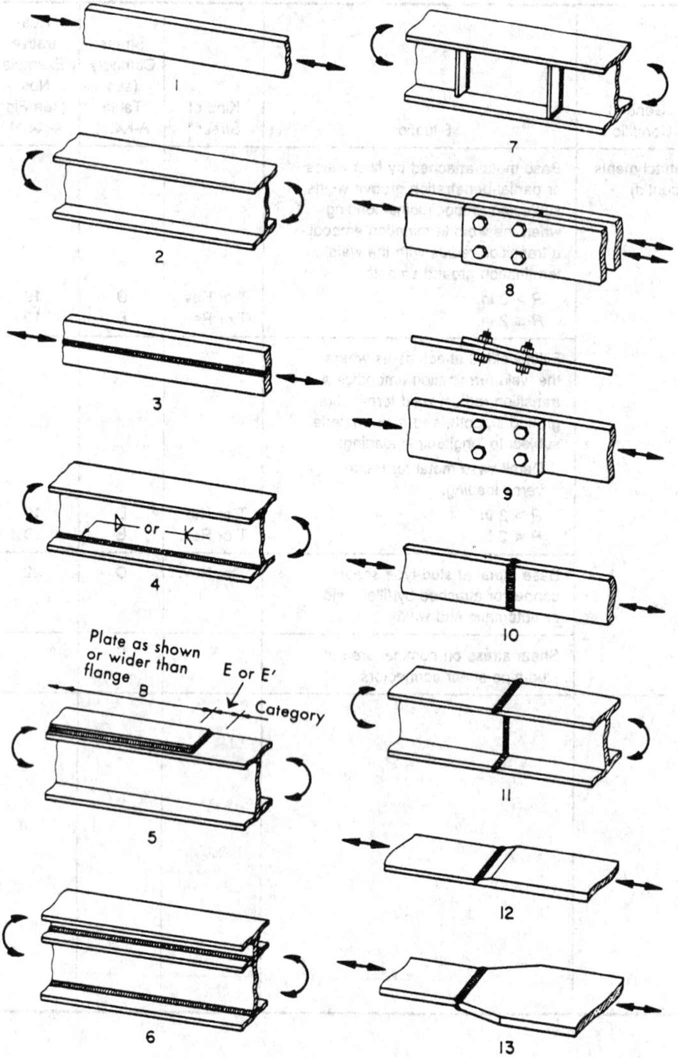
1
2
3
or
4
Plate as shown
or wider than
flange
B
E or E′
Category
5
6
7
8
9
10
11
12
13

Illustrative examples

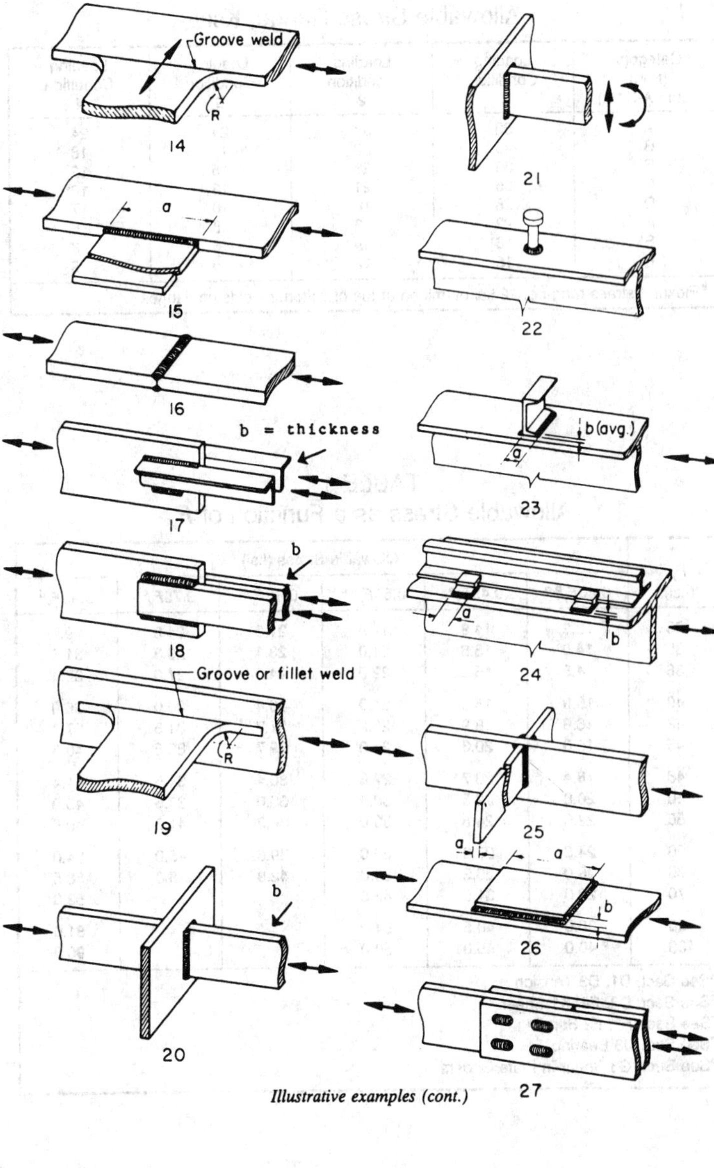
Groove weld
R
14
a
15
16
b = thickness
17
b
18
Groove or fillet weld
R
19
b
20
21
22
b(avg.)
a
23
a
b
24
25
a
a
b
26
27

Illustrative examples (cont.)

TABLE A-K4.3
Allowable Stress Range, Ksi

Category (from Table A-K4.2)	Loading Condition 1	Loading Condition 2	Loading Condition 3	Loading Condition 4
A	63	37	24	24
B	49	29	18	16
B′	39	23	15	12
C	35	21	13	10[a]
D	28	16	10	7
E	22	13	8	5
E′	16	9	6	3
F	15	12	9	8

[a] Flexural stress range of 12 ksi permitted at toe of stiffener welds on flanges

TABLE 1
Allowable Stress as a Function of F_y

F_y (ksi)	Allowable Stress (ksi)					
	$0.40F_y$[b,e]	$0.45F_y$[a]	$0.60F_y$[a,c]	$0.66F_y$[c]	$0.75F_y$[c]	$0.90F_y$[d]
33	13.2	14.9	19.8	21.8	24.8	29.7
35	14.0	15.8	21.0	23.1	26.3	31.5
36	14.5	16.2	22.0	24.0	27.0	32.4
40	16.0	18.0	24.0	26.4	30.0	36.0
42	16.8	18.9	25.2	27.7	31.5	37.8
45	18.0	20.3	27.0	29.7	33.8	40.5
46	18.4	20.7	27.6	30.4	34.5	41.4
50	20.0	22.5	30.0	33.0	37.5	45.0
55	22.0	24.8	33.0	36.3	41.3	49.5
60	24.0	27.0	36.0	39.6	45.0	54.0
65	26.0	29.3	39.0	42.9	48.8	58.5
70	28.0	31.5	42.0			63.0
90	36.0	40.5	54.0			81.0
100	40.0	45.0	60.0			90.0

[a] See Sect. D1, D3 Tension
[b] See Sect. D3, F4, K1 Shear
[c] See Sect. F1, F2 Bending
[d] See Sect. J8 Bearing
[e] See Sect. G3 Shear in Plate Girders

TABLE 2
Allowable Stresses as a Function of F_u

Item	ASTM Designation	F_y (ksi)	F_u (ksi)	Allowable Stress (ksi): Connected Part of Designated Steel		Allowable Stress (ksi): Bolt or Threaded Part of Designated Steel		
				Tension $0.5F_u$[a]	Bearing $1.2F_u$[b]	Tension $0.33F_u$[c]	Shear $0.17F_u$[d]	Shear $0.22F_u$[e]
Shapes, Plates, Bars, Sheet and Tubing, or Threaded Parts	A36	36	58—80	29.0	69.6	19.1	9.9	12.8
	A53	35	60	30.0	72.0	—	—	—
	[A242]	50	70	35.0	84.0	23.1	11.9	15.4
	[A441]	46	67	33.5	80.4	22.1	11.4	14.7
	[A588]	42	63	31.5	75.6	20.8	10.7	13.9
		40[f]	60	30.0	72.0	19.8	10.2	13.2
	A500	33/39[g]	45	22.5	54.0	—	—	—
		42/46[g]	58	29.0	69.6	—	—	—
		46/50[g]	62	31.0	74.4	—	—	—
	A501	36	58	29.0	69.6	—	—	—
	A529	42	60—85	30.0	72.0	19.8	10.2	13.2
	A570	40	55	27.5	66.0	—	—	—
		42	58	29.0	69.6	—	-	-
	A572	42	60	30.0	72.0	19.8	10.2	13.2
		50	65	32.5	78.0	21.5	11.1	14.3
		60	75	37.5	90.0	24.8	12.8	16.5
		65	80	40.0	96.0	26.4	13.6	17.6
	A514	100	110—130	55.0	132	36.3	18.7	24.2
		90	100—130	50.0	120	33.0	17.0	22.0
	A606	45	65	32.5	78.0	—	—	—
		50	70	35.0	84.0	—	—	—
	A607	45	60	30.0	72.0	—	—	—
		50	65	32.5	78.0	—	—	—
		55	70	35.0	84.0	—	—	—
		60	75	37.5	90.0	—	—	—
		65	80	40.0	96.0	—	—	—
		70	85	42.5	102	—	—	—
	A618	50	70	35.0	84.0	—	—	—
		50	65	32.5	78.0	—	—	—
	A852	70	90—110	45.0	108	—	—	—
Bolts	A449	92	120	—	—	39.6	20.4	26.4
		81	105	—	—	34.7	17.9	23.1
		58	90	—	—	29.7	15.3	19.8

[a] On effective net area, see Sects. D1, J4.
[b] Produced by fastener in shear, see Sect. J3.7. Note that smaller maximum design bearing stresses, as a function of hole spacing, may be required by Sects. J3.8 and J3.9.
[c] On nominal body area, see Table J3.2.
[d] Threads not excluded from shear plane, see Table J3.2.
[e] Threads excluded from shear plane, see Table J3.2.
[f] For A441 material only.
[g] Smaller value for circular shapes, larger for square or rectangular shapes.
Note: For dimensional and size limitations, see the appropriate ASTM Specification.

TABLE 3
VALUES OF C_a

For Determining Allowable Stress When $Kl/r \le C_c$ for Steel of Any Yield Stress (by Eq. $F_a = C_aF_y$)[a]

$\frac{Kl/r}{C_c}$	C_a	$\frac{Kl/r}{C_c}$	C_a	$\frac{Kl/r}{C_c}$	C_a	$\frac{Kl/r}{C_c}$	C_a
.01	.599	.26	.548	.51	.472	.76	.375
.02	.597	.27	.546	.52	.469	.77	.371
.03	.596	.28	.543	.53	.465	.78	.366
.04	.594	.29	.540	.54	.462	.79	.362
.05	.593	.30	.538	.55	.458	.80	.357
.06	.591	.31	.535	.56	.455	.81	.353
.07	.589	.32	.532	.57	.451	.82	.348
.08	.588	.33	.529	.58	.447	.83	.344
.09	.586	.34	.527	.59	.444	.84	.339
.10	.584	.35	.524	.60	.440	.85	.335
.11	.582	.36	.521	.61	.436	.86	.330
.12	.580	.37	.518	.62	.432	.87	.325
.13	.578	.38	.515	.63	.428	.88	.321
.14	.576	.39	.512	.64	.424	.89	.316
.15	.574	.40	.509	.65	.420	.90	.311
.16	.572	.41	.506	.66	.416	.91	.306
.17	.570	.42	.502	.67	.412	.92	.301
.18	.568	.43	.499	.68	.408	.93	.296
.19	.565	.44	.496	.69	.404	.94	.291
.20	.563	.45	.493	.70	.400	.95	.286
.21	.561	.46	.489	.71	.396	.96	.281
.22	.558	.47	.486	.72	.392	.97	.276
.23	.556	.48	.483	.73	.388	.98	.271
.24	.553	.49	.479	.74	.384	.99	.266
.25	.551	.50	.476	.75	.379	1.00	.261

[a]When ratios exceed the noncompact section limits of Sect. B5.1, use $\frac{Kl/r}{C_c'}$ in lieu of $\frac{Kl/r}{C_c}$ values and equation $F_a = C_aQ_aQ_sF_y$ (Appendix Sect. B5).

All grades of steel

TABLE 4
VALUES OF C_c

For Use with Equations (E2-1) and (E2-2) and in Table 3

F_y (ksi)	C_c	F_y (ksi)	C_c
33	131.7	46	111.6
35	127.9	50	107.0
36	126.1	55	102.0
39	121.2	60	97.7
40	119.6	65	93.8
42	116.7	90	79.8
45	112.8	100	75.7

TABLE 5
Slenderness Ratios of Elements as a Function of F_y

Specification Section and Ratios	F_y (ksi) 36	42	46	50	60	65
Table B5.1						
$65/\sqrt{F_y}$	10.8	10.0	9.6	9.2	8.4	8.1
$190/\sqrt{F_y}$	31.7	29.3	28.0	26.9	24.5	23.6
$640/\sqrt{F_y}$	106.7	98.8	94.4	90.5	82.6	79.4
$257/\sqrt{F_y}$	42.8	39.7	37.9	36.3	33.2	31.9
Sect. F1.2						
$\sqrt{\dfrac{102 \times 10^3 C_b}{F_y}}$	$53\sqrt{C_b}$	$49\sqrt{C_b}$	$47\sqrt{C_b}$	$45\sqrt{C_b}$	$41\sqrt{C_b}$	$40\sqrt{C_b}$
$\sqrt{\dfrac{510 \times 10^3 C_b}{F_y}}$	$119\sqrt{C_b}$	$110\sqrt{C_b}$	$105\sqrt{C_b}$	$101\sqrt{C_b}$	$92\sqrt{C_b}$	$89\sqrt{C_b}$
Table B5.1						
$76/\sqrt{F_y}$	12.7	11.7	11.2	10.7	9.8	9.4
$95/\sqrt{F_y}$	15.8	14.7	14.0	13.4	12.3	11.8
$127/\sqrt{F_y}$	21.2	19.6	18.7	18.0	16.4	15.8
Table B5.1						
$238/\sqrt{F_y}$	39.7	36.7	35.1	33.7	30.7	29.5
$317/\sqrt{F_y}$	52.8	48.9	46.7	44.8	40.9	39.3
$253/\sqrt{F_y}$	42.2	39.0	37.3	35.8	32.7	31.4
Table B5.1—Appendix B5.2b						
$3300/F_y$	91.7	78.6	71.7	66.0	55.0	50.8
$13000/F_y$	361	310	283	260	217	200
Sect. G1						
$\dfrac{14000}{\sqrt{F_y(F_y + 16.5)}}$	322	282	261	243	207	192
$2000/\sqrt{F_y}$	333	309	295	283	258	248

TABLE 6
Values of C_b

For Use in Equations (F1-6), (F1-7) and (F1-8)

$\frac{M_1}{M_2}$	C_b	$\frac{M_1}{M_2}$	C_b	$\frac{M_1}{M_2}$	C_b
−1.00	1.00	−0.45	1.34	0.10	1.86
−0.95	1.02	−0.40	1.38	0.15	1.91
−0.90	1.05	−0.35	1.42	0.20	1.97
−0.85	1.07	−0.30	1.46	0.25	2.03
−0.80	1.10	−0.25	1.51	0.30	2.09
−0.75	1.13	−0.20	1.55	0.35	2.15
−0.70	1.16	−0.15	1.60	0.40	2.22
−0.65	1.19	−0.10	1.65	0.45	2.28
−0.60	1.23	−0.05	1.70	≥0.47	2.30
−0.55	1.26	0	1.75		
−0.50	1.30	0.05	1.80		

Note 1: $C_b = 1.75 + 1.05(M_1/M_2) + 0.3\,(M_1/M_2)^2 \leq 2.3$
Note 2: M_1/M_2 positive for reverse curvature and negative for single curvature.

TABLE 7
Values of C_m

For Use in Equation (H1-1)

$\frac{M_1}{M_2}$	C_m	$\frac{M_1}{M_2}$	C_m	$\frac{M_1}{M_2}$	C_m
−1.00	1.00	−0.45	0.78	0.10	0.56
−0.95	0.98	−0.40	0.76	0.15	0.54
−0.90	0.96	−0.35	0.74	0.20	0.52
−0.85	0.94	−0.30	0.72	0.25	0.50
−0.80	0.92	−0.25	0.70	0.30	0.48
−0.75	0.90	−0.20	0.68	0.35	0.46
−0.70	0.88	−0.15	0.66	0.40	0.44
−0.65	0.86	−0.10	0.64	0.45	0.42
−0.60	0.84	−0.05	0.62	0.50	0.40
				0.60	0.36
−0.55	0.82	0	0.60	0.80	0.28
−0.50	0.80	0.05	0.58	1.00	0.20

Note 1: $C_m = 0.6 - 0.4(M_1/M_2)$
Note 2: M_1/M_2 is positive for reverse curvature and negative for single curvature.

TABLE 8
Values of F'_e

For Use in Equation (H1-1), for Steel of Any Yield Stress

All grades of steel

$\frac{Kl_b}{r_b}$	F'_e (ksi)	$\frac{Kl_b}{r_b}$	F'_e (ksi)	$\frac{Kl_b}{r_b}$	F'_e (ksi)	$\frac{Kl_b}{r_b}$	F'_e (ksi)	$\frac{Kl_b}{r_b}$	F'_e (ksi)	$\frac{Kl_b}{r_b}$	F'_e (ksi)
21	338.62	51	57.41	81	22.76	111	12.12	141	7.51	171	5.11
22	308.54	52	55.23	82	22.21	112	11.90	142	7.41	172	5.05
23	282.29	53	53.16	83	21.68	113	11.69	143	7.30	173	4.99
24	259.26	54	51.21	84	21.16	114	11.49	144	7.20	174	4.93
25	238.93	55	49.37	85	20.67	115	11.29	145	7.10	175	4.88
26	220.90	56	47.62	86	20.19	116	11.10	146	7.01	176	4.82
27	204.84	57	45.96	87	19.73	117	10.91	147	6.91	177	4.77
28	190.47	58	44.39	88	19.28	118	10.72	148	6.82	178	4.71
29	177.56	59	42.90	89	18.85	119	10.55	149	6.73	179	4.66
30	165.92	60	41.48	90	18.44	120	10.37	150	6.64	180	4.61
31	155.39	61	40.13	91	18.03	121	10.20	151	6.55	181	4.56
32	145.83	62	38.85	92	17.64	122	10.03	152	6.46	182	4.51
33	137.13	63	37.62	93	17.27	123	9.87	153	6.38	183	4.46
34	129.18	64	36.46	94	16.90	124	9.71	154	6.30	184	4.41
35	121.90	65	35.34	95	16.55	125	9.56	155	6.22	185	4.36
36	115.22	66	34.28	96	16.20	126	9.41	156	6.14	186	4.32
37	109.08	67	33.27	97	15.87	127	9.26	157	6.06	187	4.27
38	103.42	68	32.29	98	15.55	128	9.11	158	5.98	188	4.23
39	98.18	69	31.37	99	15.24	129	8.97	159	5.91	189	4.18
40	93.33	70	30.48	100	14.93	130	8.84	160	5.83	190	4.14
41	88.83	71	29.62	101	14.64	131	8.70	161	5.76	191	4.09
42	84.65	72	28.81	102	14.35	132	8.57	162	5.69	192	4.05
43	80.76	73	28.02	103	14.08	133	8.44	163	5.62	193	4.01
44	77.13	74	27.27	104	13.81	134	8.32	164	5.55	194	3.97
45	73.74	75	26.55	105	13.54	135	8.19	165	5.49	195	3.93
46	70.57	76	25.85	106	13.29	136	8.07	166	5.42	196	3.89
47	67.60	77	25.19	107	13.04	137	7.96	167	5.35	197	3.85
48	64.81	78	24.54	108	12.80	138	7.84	168	5.29	198	3.81
49	62.20	79	23.93	109	12.57	139	7.73	169	5.23	199	3.77
50	59.73	80	23.33	110	12.34	140	7.62	170	5.17	200	3.73

Note: $F'_e = \frac{12\pi^2 E}{23(Kl_b/r_b)^2}$

SYMBOLS

Sec. 27.2507. The section numbers in parentheses after the definition of a symbol refers to the section where the symbol is first used.

A Gross area of an axially loaded compression member, in.^{2} (N4)

A_b Nominal body area of a fastener, in.^{2} (J3.5); area of an upset rod based upon the major diameter of its threads, i.e., the diameter of a coaxial cylinder which would bound the crests of the threads, in.^{2} (J3.4)

A_c Actual area of effective concrete flange in composite design, in.^{2} (I4)

A_e Effective net area of an axially loaded tension member, in.^{2} (B3)

A_f Area of compression flange, in.^{2} (Fl.1)

A_{fe} Effective tension flange area, in.^{2} (B10)

A_{fg} Gross beam flange area, in.^{2} (B10)

A_{fn} Net beam flange area, in.^{2} (B10)

A_g Gross area of member, in.^{2} (B3)

A_n Net area of an axially loaded tension member, in.^{2} (B2)

A_s Area of steel beam in composite design, in.^{2} (I4)

$A's$ Area of compressive reinforcing steel, in.^{2} (I4)

A_{sr} Area of reinforcing steel providing composite action at point of negative moment, in.^{2} (I4)

A_{st} Cross-sectional area of stiffener or pair of stiffeners, in.^{2} (G4)

A_t Net tension area, in.^{2} (J4)

A_v Net shear area, in.^{2} (J4)

A_w Area of girder web, in.^{2} (G2)

A_1 Area of steel concentrically bearing on a concrete support, in.^{2} (J9)

A_2 Maximum area of the portion of the supporting surface that is geometrically similar to and concentric with the loaded area, in.^{2} (J9)

B Bending coefficient dependent upon computed moment or stress at the ends of unbraced segments of a tapered member (Appendix F7.4)

C_a Coefficient used in Table 4 of Numerical Values

C_b Bending coefficient dependent upon moment gradient (F1. 3)

C_c Column slenderness ratio separating elastic and inelastic buckling (E2)

C'_c Slenderness ratio of compression elements (Appendix B5.2)

C_h Coefficient used in Table 12 of Numerical Values

C_m Coefficient applied to bending term in interaction equation for prismatic members and dependent upon column curvature caused by applied moments (H1)

$C'm$ Coefficient applied to bending term in interaction equation for tapered members and dependent upon axial stress at the small end of the member (Appendix F7.6)

C_p Stiffness factor for primary member in a flat roof (K2)

C_s Stiffness factor for secondary member in a flat roof (K2)

C_v Ratio of "critical" web stress, according to the linear buckling theory, to the shear yield stress of web material (F4)

C_1 Increment used in computing minimum spacing of oversized and slotted holes (J3.8)

C_2 Increment used in computing minimum edge distance for oversized and slotted holes (J3.9)

D Factor depending upon type of transverse stiffeners (G4); outside diameter of tubular member, in. (Appendix B5.2)

E Modulus of elasticity of steel (29,000 ksi) (E2)

E_c Modulus of elasticity of concrete, ksi (I2)

F_a Axial compressive stress permitted in a prismatic member in the absence of bending moment, ksi (E2)

$F_{a}\gamma$ Axial compressive stress permitted in a tapered member in the absence of bending moment, ksi (Appendix F7.3)

F_b Bending stress permitted in a prismatic member in the absence of axial force, ksi (F1.1)

F'_b Allowable bending stress in compression flange of plate girders as reduced for hybrid girders or because of large web depth-to-thickness ratio, ksi (G2)

$F_{a}\gamma$ Bending stress permitted in a tapered member in the absence of axial force, ksi (Appendix F7.6)

F'_e Euler stress for a prismatic member divided by factor of safety, ksi (H1)

$F'_{e}\gamma$ Euler stress for a tapered member divided by factor of safety, ksi (Appendix F7.6)

F_p Allowable bearing stress, ksi (J3.7)

$F_{s\gamma}$ St. Venant torsion resistance bending stress in a tapered member, ksi (Appendix F7.4)

F_t Allowable axial tensile stress, ksi (D1)

F_u Specified minimum tensile strength of the type of steel or fastener being used, ksi (B10)

F_v Allowable shear stress, ksi (F4)

$F_{w\gamma}$ Flange warping torsion resistance bending stress in a tapered member, ksi(Appendix F7.4)

F_y Specified minimum yield stress of the type of steel being used, ksi (B5.1). As used in this Specification, "yield stress" denotes either the specified minimum yield point (for those steels with a yield point) or specified minimum yield strength (for those steels without a yield point)

F_{yc} Specified minimum column yield stress, ksi (K1.2)

F_{yf} Specified minimum yield stress of flange, ksi (Table B5.1)

F_{yr} Specified minimum yield stress of the longitudinal reinforcing steel, ksi (I4)

F_{yst} Specified minimum stiffener yield stress, ksi (K1.8)

F_{yw} Specified minimum yield stress of beam web, ksi (B5.1)

H_s Length of a stud shear connector after welding, in. (I5.2)

I_d Moment of inertia of steel deck supported on secondary members, in.^{4} (K2)

I_{eff} Effective moment of inertia of composite sections for direction computations, in.^{4} (I4)

I_p Moment of inertia of primary member in flat roof framing, in.^{4} (K2)

I_s Moment of inertia of secondary member in flat roof framing, in.^{4} (K2); moment of inertia of steel beam in composite construction, in.^{4} (I4)

I_{tr} Moment of inertia of transformed composite section, in.^{4} (I4)

K Effective length factor for a prismatic member (B7)

K_γ Effective length factor for a tapered member (Appendix F7.3)

L Unbraced length of tensile members, in. (B7); actual unbraced length of a column, in. (C2); unbraced length of member measured between the centers of gravity of the bracing members, in. (Appendix F7.1)

L_c Maximum unbraced length of the compression flange at which the allowable bending stress may be taken at 0.66 F_y or as determined by Specification Equation (F1-3) or Equation (F2-3), when applicable, ft. (F1)

L_e Distance from free edge to center of the bolt, in. (J3.6)

L_p Length of primary member in flat roof framing, ft (K2)

L_s Length of secondary member in flat roof framing, ft (K2)

M Moment, kip-ft. (I4); maximum factored bending moment, kip-ft (N4)

M_1 Smaller moment at end of unbraced length of beam-column (F3.1); larger moment at one end of three-segment portion of a tapered member (Appendix F7.4)

M_2 Larger moment at end of unbraced length of beam-column (F3.1); maximum moment in three adjacent segments of a tapered member (Appendix F7.4)

M_m Critical moment that can be resisted by a plastically designed member in the absence of axial load, kip-ft (N4)

M_p Plastic moment, kip-ft (N4)

N Length of bearing of applied load, in. (K1.3)

N_r Number of stud shear connectors on a beam in one transverse rib of a metal deck, not to exceed 3 in calculations (I5.2)

N_1 Number of shear connectors required between point of maximum moment and point of zero moment (I4)

N_2 Number of shear connectors required between concentrated load and point of zero moment (I4)

P Force transmitted by a fastener, kips (J3.8); factored axial load, kips (N3); normal force, kips (J10.2); axial load, kips (C1)

P_{bf} Factored beam flange or connection plate force in a restrained connection, kips (K1.2)

P_{cr} Maximum strength of an axially loaded compression member or beam, kips (N3.1)

P_e Euler buckling load, kips (N4)

P_y Plastic axial load, equal to profile area times specified minimum yield stress, kips (N3.1)

Q Full reduction factor for slender compression elements (Appendix B5.2)

Q_a Ratio of effective profile area of an axially loaded member to its total profile area (Appendix B5.2)

Q_s Axial stress reduction factor where width-thickness ratio of unstiffened elements exceeds noncompact section limits given in Section B5 (Appendix B5.2)

R Reaction or concentrated load applied to beam or girder, kips (K1.3); radius, in. (J2.1)

R_{PG} Plate girder bending strength reduction factor (G2)

R_e Hybrid girder factor (G2)

S Spacing of secondary members in a flat roof, ft (H2); governing slenderness ratio of a tapered member (Appendix F7.3)

S_{eff} Effective section modulus corresponding to partial composite action, in.^{3} (I2)

S_s Section modulus of steel beam used in composite design, referred to the bottom flange, in.^{3} (I2)

S_{tr} Section modulus of transformed composite cross section, referred to the bottom flange; based upon maximum permitted effective width of concrete flange, in.^{3} (I2)

T_b Specified pretension of a high-strength bolt, kips (J3.6)

U Reduction coefficient used in calculating effective net area (B3)

V Shear produced by factored loading, kips (N5); friction force, kips (J10.2)

V_h Total horizontal shear to be resisted by connectors under full composite action, kips (I2)

V'_h Total horizontal shear provided by the connectors providing partial composite action, kips (I2)

Y Ratio of yield stress of web steel to yield stress of stiffener steel (G4)

Z Plastic section modulus, in.^{3} (N4)

a Clear distance between transverse stiffeners, in. (F4); dimension parallel to the direction of stress, in. (Appendix K4)

a' Distance beyond theoretical cut-off point required at ends of welded partial length cover plate to develop stress, in. (B10)

b Actual width of stiffened and unstiffened compression elements as defined in Section B5.1, in.; dimension normal to the direction of stress, in. (Appendix K4)

b_e Effective width of stiffened compression element, in. (Appendix B5.2)

b_f Flange width of rolled beam or plate girder, in. (F1.1)

d Depth of beam or girder, in. (B5.1); diameter of a roller or rocker bearing, in. (J8); nominal diameter of a fastener, in. (J3.7)

d_L Depth at the larger end of a tapered member, in. (Appendix F7.1)

d_c Web depth clear of fillets, in. (K1.5)

d_o Depth at the smaller end of a tapered member or unbraced segment thereof, in. (Appendix F7.1)

f Axial compression stress on member based on effective area, ksi (Appendix B5.2)

f_a Computed axial stress, ksi (B5.1)

f_{ao} Computed axial stress at the smaller end of a tapered member or unbraced segment thereof, ksi (Appendix F7.6)

f_b Computed bending stress, ksi (H1)

f_{b1} Smallest computed bending stress at one end of a tapered segment, ksi (Appendix F7.4)

f_{b2} Largest computed bending stress at one end of a tapered segment, ksi (Appendix F7.4)

f_{bl} Computed bending stress at the larger end of a tapered member or unbraced segment thereof, ksi (Appendix F7.6)

f'_c Specified compression strength of concrete, ksi (I2)

f_t Computed tensile stress, ksi (J3.6)

f_v Computed shear stress, ksi (F5)

f_{vs} Shear between girder web and transverse stiffeners, kips per linear in. of single stiffener or pair of stiffeners (G4)

g Transverse spacing between fastener gage lines, in. (B2)

h Clear distance between flanges of a beam or girder at the section under investigation, in. (B5)

h_r Nominal rib height for steel deck, in. (I5.2)

h_s Factor applied to the unbraced length of a tapered member (Appendix F7.4)

h_w Factor applied to the unbraced length of a tapered member (Appendix F7.4)

k Distance from outer face of flange to web toe of fillet of rolled shape or equivalent distance on welded section, in. (K1.3)

k_c Compression element restraint coefficient (B5)

k_v Shear buckling coefficient for girder webs (F4)

l For beams, distance between cross sections braced against twist or lateral displacement of the compression flange, in. (F1.3); for columns, actual unbraced length of member, in. (B7); unsupported length of a lacing bar, in. (E4); weld length, in. (B3); largest laterally unbraced length along either flange at the point of load, in. (K1.5)

l_b Actual unbraced length in plane of bending, in. (H1)

l_{cr} Critical unbraced length adjacent to plastic hinge, in. (N9)

n Modular ratio (E/E_c) (I2)

q Allowable horizontal shear to be resisted by a shear connector, kips (I4)

r Governing radius of gyration, in. (B7)

r_T Radius of gyration of a section comprising the compression flange plus one third of the compression web area, taken about an axis in the plane of the web, in. (F1.3)

r_{To} Radius of gyration at the smaller end of a tapered member or unbraced segment thereof, considering only the compression flange plus one third of the compression web area, taken about an axis in the plane of the web, in. (Appendix F7.4)

r_b Radius of gyration about axis of concurrent bending, in. (H1)

r_{bo} Radius of gyration about axis of concurrent bending at the smaller end of a tapered member or unbraced segment thereof, in. (Appendix F7.6)

r_o Radius of gyration at the smaller end of a tapered member, in. (Appendix F7.3)

s Longitudinal center-to-center spacing (pitch) of any two consecutive holes, in. (B2)

t Thickness of a connected part, in. (13.9); wall thickness of a tubular member, in. (Appendix B5); compression element thickness, in. (B5.1); filler thickness, in. (J6)

t_b Thickness of beam flange or moment connection plate at rigid beam-to-column connection, in. (K1.8)

tf Flange thickness, in. (F1.1)

t_w Web thickness, in. (B5.1)

t_{wc} Column web thickness, in. (K1.6)

w Length of channel shear connectors, in. (I4); plate width (distance between welds), in. (B3)

w_r Average width of rib or haunch of concrete slab on formed steel deck, in. (I5.1)

x Subscript relating symbol to strong axis bending

y Subscript relating symbol to weak axis bending

z Distance from the smaller end of a tapered member, in. (Appendix F7.3)

α $= 0.6\ F_{yw}/F_b < 1.0$ (G2)

β Ratio S_{tr}/S_s or S_{eff}/S_s (I4)

γ Tapering ratio of a tapered member or unbraced segment of a tapered member (Appendix F7.1); subscript relating symbol to tapered members

Δ Displacement of the neutral axis of a loaded member from its position when the member is not loaded, in. (C1)

μ Coefficient of friction (J10.2)

UNIFORM BUILDING CODE STANDARD NO. 28-1

STANDARD FOR ALUMINUM STRUCTURES

Based on Specifications for Aluminum Structures of The Aluminum Association (December, 1986)

See Sections 2801 (a), 2802 (a) and (b), 2803 (a), (b) and (d), 2804 (c), (e) and (f) and Table No. 28-F, Uniform Building Code

Scope

Sec. 28.101. This standard covers design of aluminum alloy load-carrying members.

Materials

Sec. 28.102. The principal materials to which this standard applies are aluminum alloys registered with The Aluminum Association. Those frequently used for structural members are listed in Table No. 28-1-A. Applicable ASTM Specifications are Designations B 209, B 210, B 211, B 221, B 241, B 247, B 308 and B 429.

Design

Sec. 28.103. Design shall be in accordance with Chapter 28 and other applicable provisions of the Uniform Building Code.

Properties of section, such as cross-sectional area, moment of inertia, section modulus, radius of gyration, etc., shall be determined by accepted methods of engineering design. Computations of forces, moments, stresses and deflection shall be in accordance with accepted principles of elastic structural analyses.

Allowable Stresses

Sec. 28.104. Allowable stresses shall be determined in accordance with the provisions of Chapter 28 of the Uniform Building Code.

Special Design Rules

Sec. 28.105. (a) Combined Compression and Bending. A member subjected to axial compression and carrying a bending moment due to lateral or eccentric loads shall be proportioned in accordance with the following formulas:

1. Bending moment at center equal to or greater than 0.9 of maximum bending moment in span:

$$\frac{f_a}{F_a} + \frac{f_b}{F_b\,(1 - f_a/F_{ec})} \leqq 1$$

2. Bending moment at center equal to or less than 0.5 of maximum bending moment in span:

$$\frac{f_a}{F_a} + \frac{f_b}{F_b} \leqq 1$$

3. Bending moment at center between 0.5 and 0.9 maximum bending moment in span:

$$\frac{f_a}{F_a} + \frac{f_b}{F_b\left[1 - \left(\frac{2\,M_c}{M_m} - 1\right)\frac{f_a}{F_{ec}}\right]} \leqq 1$$

WHERE:

M_c = bending moment at center of span.

M_m = maximum bending moment in span.

(b) **Torsion and Shear in Tubes.** Allowable shear stresses in round or oval tubes due to torsion or transverse shear loads shall be determined from Specification 20 in Table No. 28-C of the Uniform Building Code with the ratio *h/t* replaced by an equivalent *h/t* given by the following:

$$\text{Equivalent}\ \frac{h}{t} = 2.9\left(\frac{R}{t}\right)^{5/8}\left(\frac{L_t}{R}\right)^{1/4}$$

WHERE:

L_t = length of tube between circumferential stiffeners, inches. Equivalent (h/t) = value to be substituted for h/t in Specification 20 in Table No. 28-C of the Uniform Building Code.

(c) **Combined Shear, Compression and Bending.** Allowable combinations of shear, compression and bending, as in the web of a beam column or the wall of a tube, shall be determined from the following formula:

$$\frac{f_a}{F_a} + \frac{f_b}{F_b} + \left(\frac{f_s}{F_s}\right)^2 \leqq 1.0$$

(d) **Stiffeners for Outstanding Flanges.** Outstanding flanges stiffened by lips or bulbs at the free edge shall be considered as supported on both edges if the radius of gyration of the lip or bulb meets the following requirement:

$$r_L = \frac{b}{5}$$

For simple rectangular lips having the same thickness as the flange, as in the case of formed sheet construction, the preceding requirement can be expressed as:

$$b_L = b/3$$

WHERE:

b_L = clear width of lip, inches.

Allowable stresses for flanges with lips or bulbs meeting the foregoing requirements shall be determined from Specifications 15 and 16 in Table No. 28-C of the Uniform Building Code. The area of stiffening lips or bulbs may be included with the area of the rest of the section in calculating the stresses caused by the loads.

(e) **Horizontal Stiffeners for Shear Webs.** If a horizontal stiffener is used on a beam web, it shall be located so that the distance from the toe of the compression flange to the centroid of the stiffener is 0.4 of the distance from the toe of the compression flange to the toe of the tension flange. The horizontal stiffener shall have a moment of inertia about the web of the beam not less than that given by the expression:

$$I_h = 2\alpha f\, th^3 \left[\left(1 + \frac{6A_h}{ht}\right)\left(\frac{s}{h}\right)^2 + 0.4\right]10^{-6}$$

WHERE:

α = 1, for stiffener consisting of equal members on both sides of the web.
α = 3.5, for stiffener consisting of member on only one side of web.
A_h = gross area of cross section of horizontal stiffener, inches².

For stiffener consisting of equal members on both sides of the web, the moment of inertia I_h shall be the sum of the moments of inertia about the center line of the web. For a stiffener consisting of a member on one side only, the moment of inertia shall be taken about the face of the web in contact with the stiffener.

(f) **Vertical Stiffeners for Shear Webs.** Stiffeners applied to beam webs to resist shear buckling shall have a moment of inertia not less than the value given by the following expressions:

$$\frac{s}{h} \leqq 0.4, \qquad I_s = \frac{n_a V h^2}{22{,}400}\left(\frac{s}{h}\right)$$

$$\frac{s}{h} \geqq 0.4, \qquad I_s = \frac{n_a V h^2}{140{,}000}\left(\frac{h}{s}\right)$$

When a stiffener is composed of a pair of members, one on each side of the web, the stiffener spacing s shall be the clear distance between the pairs of stiffeners. When a stiffener is composed of a member on one side only of the web the stiffener spacing s shall be the distance between rivet lines or other connecting lines.

For a stiffener composed of members of equal size on each side of the web, the moment of inertia of the stiffener shall be computed about the center line of the web. For a stiffener composed of a member on one side only of the web, the moment of inertia of the stiffener shall be computed about the face of the web in contact with the stiffener.

In the determination of the required moment of inertia of stiffeners, the distance h shall always be taken as the full clear height of the web regardless of whether or not a horizontal stiffener is present.

Stiffeners shall extend from flange to flange but need not be connected to either flange.

Unless the outer edge of a stiffener is continuously stiffened, its thickness shall be not less than one twelfth the clear width of the outstanding leg.

Vertical stiffeners shall, where possible, be placed in pairs at end bearings and at points of support of concentrated loads. They shall be connected to the web by enough rivets, or other means, to transmit the load. Such stiffeners shall be fitted to form a tight and uniform bearing against the loaded flanges unless welds, designed to transmit the full reaction or load, are provided between flange and stiffener.

Only that part of a stiffener cross section which lies outside the fillet of the flange angle shall be considered as effective in bearing. Bearing stiffeners shall not be joggled.

The moment of inertia of the bearing stiffener shall be not less than that given by the following expression:

$$I_b = I_s + \frac{P h^2 n_u}{\pi^2 E}$$

WHERE:

I_b = required moment of inertia of bearing stiffener, inches⁴.

(g) **Special Provisions for Thin Sections.** 1. **Appearance of buckling.** For very thin sections the allowable compressive stresses given in Specifications 9, 15, 16, 18 and 19 of Table No. 28-C of the Uniform Building Code may result in visible local buckling, even though an adequate margin of safety is provided against ultimate failure. In applications where any appearance of buckling must be avoided, the allowable stresses for thin sections shall not exceed the value of F_{ab} given by the following formulas:

SPECIFICATION	ALLOWABLE STRESS, F_{ab} ksi
9, 16	$F_{ab} = \dfrac{\pi^2 E}{n_a\,(1.6b/t)^2}$
15	$F_{ab} = \dfrac{\pi^2 E}{n_a\,(5.1b/t)^2}$
18	$F_{ab} = \dfrac{\pi^2 E}{n_a\,(0.67h/t)^2}$
19	$F_{ab} = \dfrac{\pi^2 E}{n_a\,(0.29h/t)^2}$

2. **Weighted average allowable compressive stress.** The cross section of a compression member may be composed of several thin elements, for which allowable stresses are determined by Specification 8, 9 or 10 of Table No. 28-C of the Uniform Building Code. The allowable compressive stress for the section as a whole may be considered to be the weighted average allowable stress for the individual elements, where the allowable stress for each element is weighted in accordance with the ratio of the area of the element to the total area of the section. The allowable compressive stress for the section as a whole used as a column must not exceed that given by Specification 7 of Table No. 28-C of the Uniform Building Code.

Weighted average allowable compressive stresses for beam flanges may be calculated in the same way, where the allowable stresses for individual elements are determined from Specifications 15 through 19 of Table No. 28-C of the Uniform Building Code. The beam flange may be considered to consist of the flange proper plus one-sixth of the area of the web or webs.

3. **Trapezoidal formed sheet beams.** The weighted average allowable compressive stress for a trapezoidal formed sheet beam, calculated according to paragraph 2 is:

$$F_{ba} = \frac{F_{bf} + F_{bh}\left(\dfrac{h}{3b}\right)}{1 + \dfrac{h}{3b}}$$

WHERE:

F_{ba} = weighted average allowable compressive stress for beam flange, ksi.

F_{bf} = allowable stress for flange proper based on Specification 16 of Table No. 28-C of the Uniform Building Code.

F_{bh} = allowable stress for webs based on Specification 18 or 19 of Table No. 28-C of the Uniform Building Code.

The foregoing formula may also be applied to the allowable tensile stress in trapezoidal formed sheet beams, if the designer wishes to take full advantage of the strength of the section. In this case, F_{ba} is the weighted average allowable tensile stress, F_{bf} is determined from Specification 2 in Table No. 28-C of the Uniform Building Code, and F_{bh} is given by Specification 4 in Table No. 28-C of the Uniform Building Code.

In regions of negative bending moment (for example, at interior supports of multiple span beams) the allowable tensile stress on the tension flange of a formed sheet beam shall not exceed the compressive stress that would be allowed on the same flange if it were in compression.

4. **Effect of local buckling on column strength.** An additional limitation must be placed on the allowable stress for very thin walled columns whose cross section is a rectangular tube or a formed sheet shape such that the flanges consist of flat elements supported on both edges. If the b/t for the flange of such a column is less than the value of S_2 in Specification 9 of Table No. 28-C of the Uniform Building Code, or less than 0.6 of the maximum slenderness ratio (L/r) for the column, no additional reduction in allowable stress is necessary. However, if the maximum b/t for the flange is greater than the value of S_2 from Specification 9 of Table No. 28-C of the Uniform Building Code, and also greater than 0.6 of the maximum slenderness ratio for the column, the allowable column stress shall not exceed the value given by

$$F_{rc} = \frac{\pi^2 E}{n_u \, (L/r)^{2/3} \, (1.6b/t)^{4/3}}$$

WHERE:

F_{rc} = reduced allowable stress on column, ksi.

The allowable stress also shall not exceed the value given by Specification 9 of Table No. 28-C of the Uniform Building Code.

5. **Effect of local buckling on beam strength.** The allowable compressive bending stress for single web beams whose flanges consist of thin, flat elements supported on one edge also shall be reduced in the case where the value of b/t for the flange is greater than the value of S_2 from Specification 15 of Table No. 28-C of the Uniform Building Code, and also greater than 0.16 (L_b/r_y). In this case, the allowable beam stress shall not exceed

$$F_{rb} = \frac{\pi^2 E}{n_y \, (L_b/1.2r_y)^{2/3} \, (5.1b/t)^{4/3}}$$

WHERE:

F_{rb} = reduced allowable compressive bending stress in beam flange, ksi.

L_b/r_y = slenderness ratio for beam.

6. **Effective width for calculation of deflection of thin gage sections.** As noted in paragraph 1, the allowable compressive stresses given in Specifications 9, 15, 16, 18 and 19 of Table No 28-C of the Uniform Building Code, may result in some local buckling at design loads for very thin sections even though an adequate margin of safety is provided against ultimate failure. This local buckling may result in increased deflections for sections containing thin elements with b/t value exceeding 1.65 S_2, where the value of S_2 is obtained for the element in question from Specifications 9, 15, 16, 18 and 19 of Table No. 28-C of the Uniform Building Code.

Where deflection at design loads is critical, the effective width concept may be used to determine an effective section to be used in deflection calculations. The effective width b_e of a thin element subjected to direct compression stresses is:

$$\text{If } f_a \leqq n_a F_{ab}, \quad b_e = b$$
$$\text{If } f_a > n_a F_{ab}, \quad b_e = b\sqrt{n_a F_{ab}/f_a}$$

WHERE:

b_e = effective width of flat plate element to be used in deflection calculations, inches.

F_{ab} = allowable stress for element from Subsection (g), ksi.

The same expression may be used to calculate the effective width on the compression side of a web in bending, with the compressive bending stress due to the applied loads, f_b, replacing f_a.

7. **Web crippling.** For structural formed sheet roofing and siding, allowable interior reactions and concentrated loads for flat webs shall not exceed

$$P_c = 600\frac{F_{cy}dt^2}{w}\left(6 + 0.04\frac{N}{t}\right)\left[1.1 - 0.1\left(\frac{\theta}{90}\right)\sqrt{\frac{r}{t}}\right] \text{ for } \frac{w}{t} \leq C_p$$

$$\text{and } P_c = 1{,}500\ Ed\ (N + w)\left(\frac{t}{w}\right)^3 \text{ for } \frac{w}{t} > C_p$$

$$\text{in which } C_p = \frac{2.5E\left(\dfrac{N}{w} + 1\right)}{F_{cy}\left(6 + 0.04\dfrac{N}{t}\right)\left[1.1 - 0.1\left(\dfrac{\theta}{90}\right)\sqrt{\dfrac{r}{t}}\right]}$$

Allowable end reactions shall not exceed

$$P_c = 600\frac{F_{cy}dt^2}{w}\left(3 + 0.04\frac{N}{t}\right)\left[1.1 - 0.1\left(\frac{\theta}{90}\right)\sqrt{\frac{r}{t}}\right] \text{ for } \frac{w}{t} \leq C_p$$

$$\text{and } P_c = 1{,}500\ Ed\left(N + \frac{w}{2}\right)\left(\frac{t}{w}\right)^3 \text{ for } \frac{w}{t} > C_p$$

$$\text{in which } C_p = \frac{1.25E\left(\dfrac{2N}{w} + 1\right)}{F_{cy}\left(3 + 0.04\dfrac{N}{t}\right)\left[1.1 - 0.1\left(\dfrac{\theta}{90}\right)\sqrt{\dfrac{r}{t}}\right]}$$

WHERE:

F_{cy} = minimum compressive yield strength of sheet, in kips per square inch.
N = length of bearing at reaction or concentrated load, inches.
P_c = allowable reaction or concentrated load per web, pounds.
r = bend radius at juncture of flange and web of trapezoidal section, measured to inside surface of bend, inches.
t = sheet thickness, inches.
w = slope width of web (shear element spanning between flats) of trapezoidal section, inches.
θ = angle between plane of web of trapezoidal section and plane of bearing surface ($\theta \leq 90$), degrees.
d = depth (vertical projection), inches.

(h) **Fatigue,** For up to 100,000 repetitions of maximum live load, if nonwelded, and 20,000 repetitions of maximum live load if welded, allowable stresses shall be determined in accordance with Table No. 28-C of the Uniform Building Code, and Section 28.106 provided that the structural members are free of re-entrant corners and other unusual stress raisers. For repetitions of loads in excess of these values allowable stresses shall be determined by a special analysis.

(i) **Compression in Single-web Beams.** The formulas of Specification 11 of Table No. 28-C of the Uniform Building Code, for single-web beams and girders, are based on an approximation in which the term L_b/r_y replaces a more complicated expression involving several different properties of the beam cross section. Because of this approximation, the formulas give very conservative results for certain conditions, namely for values of L_b/r_y exceeding about 50; for load distributions such that the bending moment near the center of the beam is appreciably less than the maximum bending moment in the beam; and for beams with transverse loads applied to the bottom flange. If the designer wishes to compute more precise values of allowable compressive stress for these cases, the value of r_y in Specification 11 of Table No. 28-C of the Uniform Building Code may be replaced by an "effective r_y" given by one of the following formulas:

Beam spans subjected to end moment only or to transverse loads applied at the neutral axis of the beam:

$$\text{Effective } r_y = \frac{k_b}{1.7}\sqrt{\frac{I_y d}{S_c}\sqrt{1+0.152\frac{J}{I_y}\left(\frac{L_b}{d}\right)^2}}$$

Beams subjected to transverse loads applied on the top or bottom flange (where the load is free to move laterally with the beam if the beam should buckle):

Effective r_y =

$$\frac{k_b}{1.7}\sqrt{\frac{I_y d}{S_c}\left[\pm 0.5+\sqrt{1.25+0.152\frac{J}{I_y}\left(\frac{L_b}{d}\right)^2}\right]}$$

The plus sign in front of the term "0.5" applies if the load is on the bottom flange, the minus sign if the load is on the top flange.

Effective r_y = value to be substituted for r_y in Specification 11 of Table No. 28-C of the Uniform Building Code.

The terms appearing in the above formulas are defined in the Uniform Building Code.

Values of the coefficient k_b follow:

BEAMS RESTRAINED AGAINST LATERAL DISPLACEMENT AT BOTH ENDS OF SPAN	VALUE OF COEFFICIENT K_b
Uniform bending moment, uniform transverse load, or two equal concentrated loads equidistant from the center of the span	1.00
Bending moment varying uniformly from a value of M_1 at one end to M_2 at the other end	
$M_1/M_2 = 0.5$	1.14
$M_1/M_2 = 0$	1.33
$M_1/M_2 = -0.5$	1.53
$M_1/M_2 = -1.0$	1.60
Concentrated load at center of span	1.16
CANTILEVER BEAMS	
Concentrated load at end of span	1.13
Uniform transverse load	1.43

(j) **Compression in Elastically Supported Flanges.** Allowable compressive stresses in elastically supported flanges, such as the compression flange of a standing seam roof or of a hat-shaped beam loaded with the two flanges in compression, shall be determined from Specification No. 11 with the following effective value of L_b/r_y substituted in the formulas for allowable stress.

$$\text{Effective } \frac{L_b}{r_y} = 2.7 \sqrt[4]{\frac{E A_c^2}{\beta I_{yc}}}$$

WHERE:

β = spring constant (transverse force in kips applied to a 1-inch length of the member at the compression flange to cause a 1-inch deflection of the flange), ksi.

Mechanical Connections

Sec. 28.106. (a) Riveted and Bolted Connections. Aluminum alloys used for rivets and bolts shall be those listed in Table No. 28-A of the Uniform Building Code. Nuts for ¼-inch bolts and smaller shall be 2024-T4. Nuts for larger diameter bolts shall be alloy 6061-T6 or 6262-T9. Flat washers shall be Alclad 2024-T4. Spring lock washers shall be alloy 7075-T6. For improved corrosion resistance, a .0002-inch minimum thickness anodic coating may be applied to alloy 2024 bolts.

1. **Allowable loads.** The allowable loads on rivets and bolts shall be calculated using the allowable bearing stresses in Table No. 28-C of the Uniform Building Code, and the allowable shear stresses in Table No. 28-A of the Uniform Building Code. The allowable bearing stress depends on the ratio of edge distance to rivet or bolt diameter where the edge distance is the distance from the center of the rivet or bolt to the edge of the load-carrying member toward which the pressure of the rivet or bolt is directed.

Allowable bearing stresses on bolts apply to either threaded or unthreaded surfaces.

2. **Effective diameter.** The effective diameter of rivets shall be taken as the hole diameter but shall not exceed the nominal diameter of the rivet by 4 percent for cold driven rivets and 7 percent for hot driven rivets. The effective diameter of bolts shall be taken as the nominal diameter of the bolt.

3. **Shear area.** The effective area of a rivet or bolt in any shear plane shall be based on the effective diameter except that for bolts with threads included in the shear plane the effective shear area shall be based on the root diameter.

4. **Bearing area.** The effective bearing area of rivets or bolts shall be the effective diameter multiplied by the length in bearing except that for countersunk rivets, half of the depth of the countersink shall be deducted from the length.

5. **Arrangements and strength of connections.** Insofar as possible, connections shall be arranged so that the center of resistance of the connection shall coincide with the resultant line of action of the load. Where eccentricity exists members and connections shall be proportioned to take into account any eccentricity of loading at the connections.

6. **Net section.** The net section of a riveted or bolted tension member shall be determined as the sum of the net sections of its component parts. The net section of a part is the product of the thickness of the part multiplied by its least net width. The net width for a chain of holes extending across the part in any straight or broken line shall be obtained by deducting from the gross width the sum of the diameters of all the holes in the chain and adding $s^2/4g$ for each gage space in the chain. In the correction quantity $s^2/4g$, s denotes spacing parallel to the direction of the load (pitch) of any two successive holes in the chain, in inches, and g refers to gage, the spacing perpendicular to the direction of the load of the same holes, in inches.

The net section of the part shall be obtained from that chain which gives the least net width. The hole diameter to be deducted shall be the actual hole diameter for drilled or reamed holes and the hole diameter plus 1/32 inch for punched holes.

For angles, the gross width shall be the sum of the widths of the legs less the thickness. The gage for holes in opposite legs shall be the sum of the gages from the back of the angles less the thickness.

For splice members, the thickness shall be only that part of the thickness of the member that has been developed by rivets or bolts, beyond the section considered.

7. **Effective sections of angles.** If a discontinuous angle (single or paired) in tension is connected to one side of a gusset plate, the effective net section shall be the net section of the connected leg plus one third of the section of the outstanding leg unless the outstanding leg is connected by a lug angle. In the latter case, the effective net section shall be the entire net section of the angle. The lug angle shall be designed to develop at least one half the total load in the member and shall be connected to the main member by at least two fasteners.

For double angles placed back to back and connected to both sides of a gusset plate, the effective net section shall be the net section of the connected legs plus two-thirds of the section of the outstanding legs.

For intermediate joints of continuous angles, the effective net area shall be the gross sectional area less deductions for holes.

8. **Grip of rivets and bolts.** If the grip (total thickness of metal being fastened) of rivets or bolts carrying calculated stress exceeds four and one-half times the diameter, the allowable load per rivet or bolt shall be reduced. The reduced allowable load shall be the normal allowable load divided by $[\frac{1}{2} + G/(9D)]$ in which G is the grip and D is the nominal diameter of the rivet or bolt. If the grip of

the rivet exceeds six times the diameter, special care shall be taken to insure that holes will be filled completely.

9. **Spacing of rivets and bolts.** Minimum distance of rivet centers shall be three times the nominal rivet diameter; minimum distance of bolt centers shall be two and one-half times the nominal bolt diameter. In built-up compression members the pitch in the direction of stress shall be such that the allowable stress on the individual outside sheets and shapes treated as columns having a length equal to the rivet or bolt pitch exceeds the calculated stress. The gage at right angles to the direction of stress shall be such that the allowable stress in the outside sheets, calculated from Specification 9 of Table No. 28-C of the Uniform Building Code, exceeds the calculated stress. In this case the width b may be taken as $0.8s$ where s is the gage in inches.

10. **Stitch rivets and bolts.** Where two or more web plates are in contact, there shall be stitch rivets or bolts to make them act in unison. In compression members, the pitch and gage of such rivets or bolts shall be determined as outlined in paragraph 9. In tension members, the maximum pitch or gage of such rivets or bolts shall not exceed a distance, in inches, equal to $(3 + 20t)$ in which t is the thickness of the outside plates, in inches.

11. **Edge distance of rivets or bolts.** The distance from the center of rivet or bolt under computed stress to the edge of the sheet or shape toward which the pressure is directed shall be twice the nominal diameter of the rivet or bolt. When a shorter edge distance is used the allowable bearing stress as determined by Table No. 28-C of the Uniform Building Code shall be reduced by the ratio: actual edge distance/twice rivet or bolt diameter. The edge distance shall be not less than 1.5 times the rivet or bolt diameter to sheared, sawed, rolled or planed edges.

12. **Blind rivets.** Blind rivets may be used only when the grip lengths and rivet-hole tolerances are as recommended by the respective manufacturers.

13. **Hollow-end rivets.** If hollow-end rivets with solid cross sections for a portion of the length are used the strength of these rivets may be taken equal to the strength of solid rivets of the same material, provided that the bottom of the cavity is at least 25 percent of the rivet diameter from the plane of shear as measured toward the hollow end; and, further, provided that they are used in locations where they will not be subjected to appreciable tensile stresses.

14. **Lock bolts.** Lock bolts may be used when installed in conformance with the lock bolt manufacturer's recommended practices and provided the body diameter and bearing areas under the head and nut, or their equivalent, are not less than those of a conventional nut and bolt.

(b) Thread Forming (Tapping) Screws and Metal Stitching Staples. If joints carrying calculated loads are to be made with thread forming screws or metal stitches, allowable strength values for these connections shall be established on the basis of specific acceptable tests.

(c) Fasteners for Structural Formed Sheet Roofing and Siding. 1. **General.** Fasteners shall have tensile and tensile anchorage strengths in resisting back loads, or uplift, in excess of the strength of the connection between fastener and sheet.

2. **Allowable loads for fasteners.** The allowable tensile load per fastener shall be

P_t = (1/2.2) × (minimum strength of connection between fastener and sheet).

3. **Allowable loads for specific fasteners.** The allowable loads for the specific fasteners listed, expressed in pounds, shall be used unless other allowable loads can be justified. Allowable loads for fasteners not listed shall be based on the results of tests and shall comply with the provisions of Section 28.106 (c) 1 and 2 above.

A. No. 14 stainless steel alloy self-tapping screws, hex head, cadmium plated, with composite aluminum-neoprene washer, the aluminum portion of which has minimum dimensions of 0.050-inch thickness and 5/8-inch OD, or with a stainless steel-neoprene washer, the stainless steel portion of which has minimum dimensions of 0.038-inch (No. 20 gage) thickness and 5/8-inch OD. In crowns,

$$P_t = 140\,t\,F_{ty}$$

and in valleys,

$$P_t = 170t\,F_{ty}$$

For steel supporting members, screw holes should be made with a No. 8 drill for No. 14-gage through No. 11-gage material, a No. 4 drill for No. 10-gage up to 3/16 inch and a No. 1 drill for 3/16 inch and thicker.

B. Stainless steel alloy welded studs, 5/16-inch-diameter base, 3/16-inch-diameter serrated top, with field-installed swaged aluminum cap of ½-inch diameter,

$$P_t = 230$$

Fabrication

Sec. 28.107. (a) **Laying Out.** Hole centers may be center punched and cutoff lines may be punched or scribed. Center punching and scribing shall not be used where such marks would remain on fabricated material.

A temperature correction shall be applied where necessary in the layout of critical dimensions. The coefficient of expansion shall be taken as 0.000013 per degree Fahrenheit.

(b) **Cutting.** Material may be sheared, sawed, cut with a router or arc cut. All edges which have been cut by the arc process shall be planed to remove edge cracks.

Cut edges shall be true, smooth and free from excessive burrs or ragged breaks.

Re-entrant cuts shall be avoided wherever possible. If used, they shall be filleted by drilling prior to cutting.

Oxygen cutting of aluminum alloys shall not be permitted.

(c) **Heating.** Structural material shall not be heated.

> **EXCEPTION:** Material may be heated to a temperature not exceeding 400°F. for a period not exceeding 30 minutes in order to facilitate bending. Such heating shall be done only when proper temperature controls and supervision are provided to insure that the limitations on temperature and time are carefully observed.

(d) **Punching, Drilling and Reaming.** The following rules for punching, drilling and reaming shall be observed:

1. Rivet or bolt holes may be either punched or drilled. Punching shall not be used if the metal thickness is greater than the diameter of the hole. The amount by which the diameter of a sub-punched hole is less than that of the finished hole shall be at least one fourth the thickness of the piece and in no case less than 1/32 inch.

2. The finished diameter of holes for cold-driven rivets shall be not more than 4 percent greater than the nominal diameter of the rivet.

3. The finished diameter of holes for hot-driven rivets shall be not more than 7 percent greater than the nominal diameter of the rivet.

4. The finished diameter of holes for bolts shall be not more than 1/16 inch larger than the nominal bolt diameter.

5. If any holes must be enlarged to admit the rivets or bolts, they shall be reamed. Poor matching of holes shall be cause for rejection. Holes shall not be drifted in such a manner as to distort the metal. All chips lodged between contacting surfaces shall be removed before assembly.

(e) **Riveting.** 1. **Driven head.** The driven head of aluminum alloy rivets shall be of the flat or the cone-point type with dimensions as follows:

A. Flat heads shall have a diameter not less than 1.4 times the nominal rivet diameter and a height not less than 0.4 times the nominal rivet diameter.

B. Cone-point heads shall have a diameter not less than 1.4 times the nominal rivet diameter and a height to the apex of the cone not less than 0.65 times the nominal rivet diameter. The included angle at the apex of the cone shall be approximately 127 degrees.

2. **Hole filling.** Rivets shall fill holes completely. Rivet heads shall be concentric with the rivet holes and shall be in proper contact with the surface of the metal.

3. **Defective rivets.** Defective rivets shall be removed by drilling.

(f) **Painting.** 1. **General.** Structures of the alloys covered by these standards are not ordinarily painted (with the exception of 2014-T6 when exposed to corrosive environments). Surfaces shall be painted where:

A. The aluminum alloy parts are in contact with, or are fastened to, steel members or other dissimilar materials.

B. The structures are to be exposed to extremely corrosive conditions, or for reason of appearance. Painting procedure is covered in the following paragraphs, and methods of cleaning and preparation are found in Subsection (g). (Treatment and painting of the structure in accordance with United States Military Specification MIL-T-704 is also acceptable.)

2. **Contact with dissimilar materials.** Where the aluminum alloy parts are in contact with, or are fastened to, steel members or other dissimilar materials, the aluminum shall be kept from direct contact with the steel or other dissimilar material by painting as follows:

A. Aluminum surfaces to be placed in contact with steel shall be given one coat of zinc chromate primer in accordance with Federal Specification TT-P-645 or the equivalent, or one coat of a suitable nonhardening joint compound capable of excluding moisture from the joint during prolonged service. Where severe corrosion conditions are expected additional protection can be obtained by applying the joint compound in addition to the zinc chromate primer. Zinc chromate paint shall be allowed to dry hard (air dry 24 hours) before assembly of the parts. The steel surfaces to be placed in contact with aluminum shall be painted with good quality priming paint, such as zinc chromate primer in accordance with Federal Specification TT-P-645, followed by one coat of paint consisting of 2 pounds of aluminum paste pigment (ASTM Specification D96266, Type 2, Class B) per gallon of varnish meeting Federal Specification TT-V-81d, Type II, or the equivalent. Stainless steel, or aluminized, hot-dip galvanized or electrogalvanized steel placed in contact with aluminum need not be painted.

B. When aluminum is in direct contact with wood, fiberboard or other porous material that may absorb water, an insulating barrier shall be installed between the aluminum and the porous material. Such aluminum surfaces shall be given a heavy coat of alkali-resistant bituminous paint or other coating providing equivalent protection before installation. Aluminum in contact with concrete or masonry shall be similarly protected in cases where moisture is present and corrodents can be entrapped between the surfaces.

C. Aluminum surfaces to be embedded in concrete ordinarily need not be painted, unless corrosive components are added to the concrete or unless the concrete is subjected for extended periods to extremely corrosive conditions. In such cases, aluminum surfaces shall be given one coat of suitable quality paint, such as zinc chromate primer conforming to Federal Specification TT-P-645 or equivalent, or shall be wrapped with a suitable plastic tape applied in such a manner as to provide adequate protection at the overlap.

D. Water that comes in contact with aluminum after first running over a heavy metal such as copper may contain trace quantities of the dissimilar metal or its corrosion product, which will cause corrosion of the aluminum. Protection shall be obtained by painting or plastic coating the dissimilar metal or by designing the structure so that the drainage from the dissimilar metal is diverted away from the aluminum.

3. **Overall painting.** Structures of the alloys covered by this standard are either not ordinarily painted for surface protection (with the exception of 2014-T6 when exposed to corrosive environments) or are made of prepainted aluminum components. There may be applications where the structures are to be exposed to extremely corrosive conditions. In these cases overall painting shall be specified.

(g) **Cleaning and Treatment of Metal Surfaces.** Prior to field painting of structures, all surfaces to be painted shall be cleaned immediately before painting by a method that will remove all dirt, oil, grease, chips and other foreign substances.

Exposed metal surfaces shall be cleaned with a suitable chemical cleaner such as a solution of phosphoric acid and organic solvents meeting United States Military Specification MIL-M-10578. If the metal is more than 1/8 inch thick, sandblasting may be used.

Welded Construction

Sec. 28.108. (a) **Filler Wire.** Verification shall be provided to show that the choice of filler metal for general purpose welding is appropriate.

(b) **Columns and Single-web Beams with Welds at Locations Other Than Ends and Cantilever Columns and Single-web Beams.** The allowable stresses determined in accordance with the provisions of Chapter 28 of the Uniform Building Code apply to members supported at both ends with welds at the ends only (not farther from the supports than 0.05 L from the ends).

For columns with transverse welds at locations other than the supports, cantilever columns with transverse welds at or near the supported end and columns with longitudinal welds having A_w equal to or greater than 15 percent of A, the effect of welding on column strength shall be taken into account by using an increased slenderness ratio L_w/r, in the column formula, as follows:

(Formula appears on the following page.)

$$\text{If } \frac{L}{r} > \sqrt{\frac{250{,}000}{F_{cyw}}}; \frac{L_w}{r} = \frac{L}{r}$$

$$\text{If } \frac{L}{r} \leq \sqrt{\frac{250{,}000}{F_{cyw}}};$$

$$\frac{L_w}{r} = \frac{L}{r} \sqrt{\frac{1 + 100 \dfrac{L_h}{L}}{1 + \left(\dfrac{L_h}{L}\right)\left(\dfrac{L}{r}\right)^2\left(\dfrac{F_{cyw}}{2500}\right)}}$$

The above formulas assume that the entire cross section within the length L_h is affected by the heat of welding. If only part of the cross section is so affected, the allowable stress based on L_w/r shall be substituted for F_w in the formula in Section 2802 (b) of the Uniform Building Code.

(c) **Welding Fabrication.** Welding of aluminum shall be in accordance with approved nationally recognized standards.

Testing

Sec. 28.109. (a) **General.** Testing shall be considered an acceptable method for substantiating the design of aluminum alloy load-carrying members. Tests shall be conducted by an independent testing laboratory or by a manufacturer's testing laboratory.

(b) **Test Loading and Behavior.** In order to test a structure or load-carrying member adequately, the loading shall be applied in a fashion that reasonably approximates the application of the loading during service. Further, the structure or member shall be supported in a manner that is no more sustaining to the structure than will be the supports available when the structure is in service.

Determination of allowable load-carrying capacity shall be made on the basis that the member, assembly or connection shall be capable of sustaining during the test without failure a total load, including the weight of the test specimen, equal to twice the live load plus one and one-half the dead load. Furthermore, harmful local distortions shall not develop during the test at a total load, including the weight of the test specimen, equal to the dead load plus one and one-half times the live load.

The factors by which the design live and dead loads are multiplied to determine the test loads are reduced to three fourths of the values given in the preceding paragraph when wind or seismic forces represent all or a portion of the live load, provided the structure or member meets the test requirements with the full load factors applied to the dead load and to that portion of the live load not attributable to wind or seismic forces.

Differences that may exist between nominal section properties and those of tested sections shall be considered.

TABLE NO. 28-1-A—MINIMUM MECHANICAL PROPERTIES FOR ALUMINUM ALLOYS
Values Are Given in Units of ksi (1000 lb/in^2)

ALLOY AND TEMPER	PRODUCT[1]	THICKNESS RANGE[1] in.	TENSION F_{tu}[2] ksi	TENSION F_{ty}[2] ksi	COMPRESSION F_{cy} ksi	SHEAR F_{su} ksi	SHEAR F_{sy} ksi	BEARING F_{bu} ksi	BEARING F_{by} ksi	COMPRESSIVE MODULUS OF ELASTICITY[3] E ksi
1100-H12	Sheet, Plate; Rolled Rod & Bar; Drawn Tube	All	14	11	10	9	6.5	28	18	10,100
-H14	Sheet, Plate; Rolled Rod & Bar; Drawn Tube	All	16	14	13	10	8	32	21	10,100
2014-T6	Sheet	0.040-0.249	66	58	59	40	33	125	93	10,900
-T651	Plate	0.250-2.000	67	59	58	40	34	127	94	10,900
-T6, -T6510[1]	Extrusions	All	60	53	55	35	31	114	85	10,900
-T6, -T651	Rolled Rod & Bar; Drawn Tube	All	65	55	53	38	32	124	88	10,900
Alclad 2014-T6	Sheet	0.020-0.039	63	55	56	38	32	120	88	10,800
-T6	Sheet	0.040-0.249	64	57	58	39	33	122	91	10,800
-T651	Plate	0.250-0.499	64	57	56	39	33	122	91	10,800
3003-H12	Sheet & Plate	0.017-2.000	17	12	10	11	7	34	19	10,100
-H14	Sheet & Plate	0.009-1.000	20	17	14	12	10	40	25	10,100
-H16	Sheet	0.006-0.162	24	21	18	14	12	46	31	10,100
-H18	Sheet	0.006-0.128	27	24	20	15	14	49	34	10,100
3003-H12	Drawn Tube	All	17	12	11	11	7	34	19	10,100
-H14	Drawn Tube	All	20	17	16	12	10	40	25	10,100
-H16	Drawn Tube	All	24	21	19	14	12	46	31	10,100
-H18	Drawn Tube	All	27	24	21	15	14	49	34	10,100
Alclad 3003-H12	Sheet & Plate	0.017-2.000	16	11	9	10	6.5	32	18	10,100
-H14	Sheet & Plate	0.009-1.000	19	16	13	12	9	38	24	10,100
-H16	Sheet	0.006-0.162	23	20	17	14	12	44	30	10,100
-H18	Sheet	0.006-0.128	26	23	19	15	13	47	32	10,100

(Continued)

TABLE NO. 28-1-A—MINIMUM MECHANICAL PROPERTIES FOR ALUMINUM ALLOYS—(Continued)
Values Are Given in Units of ksi (1000 lb/in²)

Alclad 3003-H14	Drawn Tube	0.010-0.500	19	16	15	12	9	38	24	10,100
-H18	Drawn Tube	0.010-0.500	26	23	20	15	13	47	32	10,100
3004-H32	Sheet & Plate	0.017-2.000	28	21	18	17	12	56	36	10,100
-H34	Sheet & Plate	0.009-1.000	32	25	22	19	14	64	40	10,100
-H36	Sheet	0.006-0.162	35	28	25	20	16	70	45	10,100
3004-H34	Drawn Tube	0.018-0.450	32	25	24	19	14	64	40	10,100
-H36	Drawn Tube	0.018-0.450	35	28	27	20	16	70	45	10,100
Alclad 3004-H32	Sheet	0.017-0.249	27	20	17	16	12	54	34	10,100
-H34	Sheet	0.009-0.249	31	24	21	18	14	62	38	10,100
-H36	Sheet	0.006-0.162	34	27	24	19	16	68	43	10,100
-H14	Sheet	0.009-0.249	32	26	22	19	15	64	39	10,100
-H16	Sheet	0.006-0.050	35	30	28	20	17	66	45	10,100
-H16	Sheet	0.051-0.162	35	30	26	20	17	66	45	10,100
-H131, -H241, -H341	Sheet	0.024-0.050	31	26	22	18	15	62	39	10,100
-H151, -H261, -H361	Sheet	0.024-0.050	34	30	28	19	17	66	45	10,100
3005-H25	Sheet	0.013-0.050	26	22	20	15	13	49	35	10,100
3006-H391	Sheet	0.010-0.050	31	27	27	20	16	60	44	10,100
3105-H25	Sheet	0.013-0.080	23	19	17	14	11	44	28	10,100
5005-H12	Sheet & Plate	0.018-2.000	18	14	13	11	8	34	22	10,100
-H14	Sheet & Plate	0.009-1.000	21	17	15	12	10	40	25	10,100
-H16	Sheet	0.006-0.162	24	20	18	14	12	48	30	10,100
-H32	Sheet & Plate	0.017-2.000	17	12	11	11	7	34	20	10,100
-H34	Sheet & Plate	0.009-1.000	20	15	14	12	8.5	40	24	10,100
-H36	Sheet	0.006-0.162	23	18	16	13	11	48	29	10,100

ALLOY AND TEMPER	PRODUCT[1]	THICKNESS RANGE[1] in.	TENSION		COMPRESSION	SHEAR		BEARING		COMPRESSIVE MODULUS OF ELASTICITY[3]
			F_{tu}[2] ksi	F_{ty}[2] ksi	F_{cy} ksi	F_{su} ksi	F_{sy} ksi	F_{bu} ksi	F_{by} ksi	E ksi
5050-H32	Sheet	0.017-0.249	22	16	14	14	9	44	27	10,100
-H34	Sheet	0.009-0.249	25	20	18	15	12	50	32	10,100
-H32	Rolled Rod & Bar; Drawn Tube	All	22	16	15	13	9	44	27	10,100
-H34	Rolled Rod & Bar; Drawn Tube	All	25	20	19	15	12	50	32	10,100
5052-H32	Sheet & Plate; Rolled Rod & Bar; Drawn Tube	All	31	23	21	19	13	60	39	10,200
-H34	Sheet & Plate; Rolled Rod & Bar; Drawn Tube	All	34	26	24	20	15	65	44	10,200
-H36	Sheet	0.006-0.162	37	29	26	22	17	70	46	10,200
5083-H111	Extrusions	up thru 0.500	40	24	21	24	14	78	41	10,400
-H111	Extrusions	0.501 & over	40	24	21	23	14	78	38	10,400
-H321	Sheet & Plate	0.188-1.500	44	31	26	26	18	84	53	10,400
-H323	Sheet	0.051-0.249	45	34	32	26	20	88	58	10,400
-H343	Sheet	0.051-0.249	50	39	37	29	23	95	66	10,400
-H321	Plate	1.501-3.000	41	29	24	24	17	78	49	10,400
5086-H111	Extrusions	up thru 0.500	36	21	18	21	12	70	36	10,400
-H111	Extrusions	0.501 & over	36	21	18	21	12	70	34	10,400
-H112	Plate	0.250-0.499	36	18	17	22	10	72	31	10,400
-H112	Plate	0.500-1.000	35	16	16	21	9	70	28	10,400
-H112	Plate	1.001-2.000	35	14	15	21	8	70	28	10,400
-H112	Plate	2.001-3.000	34	14	15	21	8	68	28	10,400
-H32	Sheet & Plate; Drawn Tube	All	40	28	26	24	16	78	48	10,400
-H34	Sheet & Plate; Drawn Tube	All	44	34	32	26	20	84	58	10,400
5154-H38	Sheet	0.006-0.128	45	35	33	24	20	81	56	10,300

(Continued)

TABLE NO. 28-1-A—MINIMUM MECHANICAL PROPERTIES FOR ALUMINUM ALLOYS—(Continued)
Values Are Given in Units of ksi (1000 lb/in²)

5454-H111	Extrusions	up thru 0.500	33	19	16	20	11	64	32	10,400
-H111	Extrusions	0.501 & over	33	19	16	19	11	64	30	10,400
-H112	Extrusions	up thru 5.000	31	12	13	19	7	62	24	10,400
-H32	Sheet & Plate	0.020-2.000	36	26	24	21	15	70	44	10,400
-H34	Sheet & Plate	0.020-1.000	39	29	27	23	17	74	49	10,400
5456-H111	Extrusions	up thru 0.500	42	26	22	25	15	82	44	10,400
-H111	Extrusions	0.501 & over	42	26	22	24	15	82	42	10,400
-H112	Extrusions	up thru 5.000	41	19	20	24	11	82	38	10,400
-H321	Sheet & Plate	0.188-1.250	46	33	27	27	19	87	56	10,400
-H321	Plate	1.251-1.500	44	31	25	25	18	84	53	10,400
-H321	Plate	1.501-3.000	41	29	25	25	17	82	49	10,400
-H323	Sheet	0.051-0.249	48	36	34	28	21	94	61	10,400
-H343	Sheet	0.051-0.249	53	41	39	31	24	101	70	10,400
6005-T5	Extrusions	up thru 0.500	38	35	35	24	20	80	56	10,100
6061-T6, -T651	Sheet & Plate	0.010-4.000	42	35	35	27	20	88	58	10,100
-T6, -T6510[1]	Extrusions	up thru 3.000	38	35	35	24	20	80	56	10,100
-T6, -T651	Rolled Rod & Bar	up thru 8.000	42	35	35	27	20	88	56	10,100
-T6	Drawn Tube	0.025-0.500	42	35	35	27	20	88	56	10,100
-T6	Pipe	up thru 0.999	42	35	35	27	20	88	56	10,100
-T6	Pipe	over 0.999	38	35	35	24	20	80	56	10,100
6063-T5	Extrusions	up thru 0.500	22	16	16	13	9	46	26	10,100
-T5	Extrusions	over 0.500	21	15	15	12	8.5	44	24	10,100
-T6	Extrusions	All	30	25	25	19	14	63	40	10,100
	Pipe									
6351-T5	Extrusions	up thru 1.00	38	35	35	24	20	80	56	10,100

[1]Values also apply to -T6511 temper.

[2]F_{tu} and F_{ty} are minimum specified values (except for Alclad 3004-H14, -H16 and F_{ty} for Alclad 3003-H18) other strength properties are corresponding minimum expected values.

[3]For deflection calculations an average modulus of elasticity is used; numerically this is 100 ksi lower than the values in this column.

TABLE NO. 28-1-B—MINIMUM MECHANICAL PROPERTIES FOR WELDED ALUMINUM ALLOYS[1]
(Gas Tungsten Arc or Gas Metal Arc Welding with No Postweld Heat Treatment)

ALLOY AND TEMPER	PRODUCT AND THICKNESS RANGE (Inch)	TENSION		COMPRESSION	SHEAR		BEARING	
		F_{tuw}[1] ksi	F_{tyw}[2] ksi	F_{cyw}[2] ksi	F_{suw} ksi	F_{syw} ksi	F_{buw} ksi	F_{byw} ksi
1100-H12, -H14	All	11	4.5	4.5	8	2.5	23	8
3003-H12, -H14, -H16, -H18	All	14	7	7	10	4	30	12
Alclad 3003-H12, -H14, -H16, -H18	All	13	6	6	10	3.5	30	11
3004-H32, -H34, -H36	All	22	11	11	14	6.5	46	20
Alclad 3004-H32, -H34, -H14, -H16	All	21	11	11	13	6.5	44	19
3005-H25	Sheet 0.013-0.050	17	9	9	12	5	36	15
5005-H12, -H14, -H32, -H34	All	14	7	7	9	4	28	10
5050-H32, -H34	All	18	8	8	12	4.5	36	12
5052-H32, -H34	All	25	13	13	16	7.5	50	19
5083-H111	Extrusions	39	21	20	23	12	78	32
-H321	Sheet & Plate 0.188-1.500	40	24	24	24	14	80	36
-H321	Plate 1.501-3.000	39	23	23	24	13	78	34
-H323, -H343	Sheet	40	24	24	24	14	80	36
5086-H111	Extrusions	35	18	17	21	10	70	28
-H112	Plate 0.250-0.499	35	17	17	21	9.5	70	28
-H112	Plate 0.500-1.000	35	16	16	21	9	70	28
-H112	Plate 1.001-2.000	35	14	14	21	8	70	28
-H32, -H34	Sheet & Plate	35	19	19	21	11	70	28

(Continued)

TABLE NO. 28-1-B—MINIMUM MECHANICAL PROPERTIES FOR WELDED ALUMINUM ALLOYS[1]—(Continued)
(Gas Tungsten Arc or Gas Metal Arc Welding With No Postweld Heat Treatment)

5086-H111	Extrusions	35	18	17	21	10	70	28
-H112	Plate 0.250-0.499	35	17	17	21	9.5	70	28
-H112	Plate 0.500-1.000	35	16	16	21	9	70	28
-H112	Plate 1.001-2.000	35	14	14	21	8	70	28
-H32, -H34	Sheet & Plate	35	19	19	21	11	70	28
5154-H38	Sheet	30	15	15	19	8.5	60	23
5454-H111	Extrusions	31	16	15	19	9.5	62	24
-H112	Extrusions	31	12	12	19	7	62	24
-H32, -H34	Sheet & Plate	31	16	16	19	9.5	62	24
5456-H111	Extrusions	41	24	22	24	14	82	38
-H112	Extrusions	41	19	19	24	11	82	38
-H321	Sheet & Plate 0.188-1.500	42	26	24	25	15	84	38
-H321	Plate 1.501-3.000	41	24	23	25	14	82	36
-H323, -H343	Sheet	42	26	26	25	15	84	38
6005-T5	Extrusions Up to 0.250	24	17	17	15	10	50	30
6061-T6, -T651[3]	All	24	20	20	15	12	50	30
-T6, -T651[4]	Over 0.375	24	15	15	15	9	50	30
6063-T5, -T6	All	17	11	11	11	6.5	34	22
6351-T5[1]	Extrusions	24	20	20	15	12	50	30
-T5[4]	Over 0.375	24	15	15	15	9	50	30

[1]Filler wires used are those recommended in Table No. 28-1-C. Values of F_{tuw} are ASME weld qualification test values.

[2]0.2 percent offset in 10-inch gauge length across a butt weld.

[3]Values when welded with 5183, 5356 or 5556 alloy filler wire regardless of thickness. Values also apply to thicknesses less than 0.375 inch when welded with 4043, 5154, 5254 or 5554 alloy filler wire.

[4]Values when welded with 4043, 5154, 5254 or 5554 alloy filler wire.

UNIFORM BUILDING CODE STANDARD NO. 29-1

SOILS CLASSIFICATION

Based on Standard Method D 2487-69 of the American Society for Testing and Materials. Extracted, with permission, from the Annual Book of ASTM Standards, copyright American Society for Testing and Materials, 1916 Race Street, Philadelphia, PA 19103.

See Sections 2901 (b) and 2904 (a), Uniform Building Code

Scope

Sec. 29.101. This standard describes a system for classifying mineral and organo-mineral soils for engineering purposes based on laboratory determination of particle-size characteristics, liquid limit and plasticity index.

Apparatus

Sec. 29.102. Apparatus of an approved type shall be used to perform the following tests and procedures: Preparation of soil samples, liquid limit test, plastic limit test and particle size analysis.

Sampling

Sec. 29.103. Sampling shall be conducted in accordance with approved methods for soil investigation and sampling by auger borings, for Penetration Test and Split-barrel Sampling of Soils, and for Thin-walled Tube Sampling of Soils.

The sample shall be carefully identified as to origin by a boring number and sample number in conjunction with a job number, a geologic stratum, a pedologic horizon or a location description with respect to a permanent monument, a grid system or a station number and offset with respect to a stated center line.

The sample should also be described in accordance with an approved visual-manual procedure. (A soil which is composed primarily of undecayed or partially decayed organic matter and has a fibrous texture, dark brown to black color, and organic odor should be designated as a highly organic soil, PT, and not subjected to the classification procedures described hereafter.)

Test Sample

Sec. 29.104. Test samples shall represent that portion of the field sample finer than the 3-inch sieve and shall be obtained as follows:

Air dry the field sample; weigh the field sample; and separate the field sample into two fractions on a 3-inch sieve. Weigh the fraction retained on the 3-inch sieve. Compute the percentage of plus 3-inch material in the field sample and note this percentage as auxiliary information. Thoroughly mix the fraction passing the 3-inch sieve and select test samples.

Preliminary Classification Procedure

Sec. 29.105. Procedure for the determination of percentage finer than the No. 200 sieve is as follows:

1. From the material passing the 3-inch sieve, select a test sample and determine the percentage of the test sample finer than the No. 200 sieve. (This step may be omitted if the soil can obviously be classified as fine-grained by visual inspection.)

2. Classify the soil as coarse-grained if more than 50 percent of the test sample is retained on the No. 200 sieve.

3. Classify the soil as fine-grained if 50 percent or more of the test sample passes the No. 200 sieve.

Procedure for Classification of Coarse-grained Soils (More than 50 Percent Retained on No. 200 Sieve)

Sec. 29.106. Select test samples from the material passing the 3-inch sieve for the determination of particle size characteristics, liquid limit and plasticity index. Determine the cumulative particle size distribution of the fraction coarser than the No. 200 sieve.

Classify the sample as *gravel,* G, if 50 percent or more of the coarse fraction (plus No. 200 sieve) is retained on the No. 4 sieve. Classify the sample as *sand,* S, if more than 50 percent of the coarse fraction (plus No. 200 sieve) passes the No. 4 sieve.

If less than 5 percent of the test sample passed the No. 200 sieve, compute the coefficient of uniformity, C_u, and coefficient of curvature, C_z, as given in Formulas 29-1-1 and 29-1-2:

$$C_u = \frac{D_{60}}{D_{10}} \quad \text{(29-1-1)}$$

$$C_z = \frac{(D_{30})^2}{D_{10} \times D_{60}} \quad \text{(29-1-2)}$$

in which D_{10}, D_{30} and D_{60} are the particle size diameters corresponding respectively to 10, 30 and 60 percent passing on the cumulative particle size distribution curve.

Classify the sample as well-graded gravel, GW, or well-graded sand, SW, if C_u is greater than 4 for gravel and 6 for sand, and C_z is between 1 and 3. Classify the sample as poorly graded gravel, GP, or poorly graded sand, SP, if either the C_u or the C_z criteria for well-graded soils are not satisfied.

If more than 12 percent of the test sample passed the No. 200 sieve, determine the liquid limit and the plasticity index of a portion of the test sample passing the No. 40 sieve in accordance with approved methods.

Classify the sample as silty gravel, GM, or silty sand, SM, if the results of the limits tests show that the fines are silty, that is, the plot of the liquid limit versus plasticity index falls below the "A" line (see Plasticity Table No. 29-1-A) or the plasticity index is less than 4.

Classify the sample as clayey gravel, GC, or clayey sand, SC, if the fines are clayey, that is, the plot of liquid limit versus plasticity index falls above the "A" line and the plasticity index is greater than 7.

If the fines are intermediate between silt and clay, that is, the plot of liquid limit versus plasticity index falls on or practically on the "A" line or falls above the "A" line but the plasticity index is in the range of 4 to 7, the soil should be given a borderline classification, such as GM-GC or SM-SC.

If 5 to 12 percent of the test sample passed the No. 200 sieve, the soil should be given a borderline classification based on both its gradation and limit test characteristics, such as GW-GC or SP-SM. (In doubtful cases the rule is to favor the less plastic classification. Example: a gravel with 10 percent fines, a C_u of 20, a C_z of 2.0, and a plasticity index of 6 would be classified as GW-GM rather than GW-GC.)

Procedure for Classification of Fine-grained Soils (50 Percent or More Passing No. 200 Sieve)

Sec. 29.107. From the material passing the 3-inch sieve, select a test sample for the determination of the liquid limit and plasticity index. The method for wet preparation shall be used for soils containing organic matter or irreversible mineral colloids.

Determine the liquid limit and the plasticity index of a portion of the test sample passing the No. 40 sieve.

Classify the soil as inorganic clay, C, if the plot of liquid limit versus plasticity index falls above the "A" line and the plasticity index is greater than 7.

Classify the soil as inorganic clay of low to medium plasticity, CL, if the liquid limit is less than 50 and the plot of liquid limit versus plasticity index falls above the "A" line and the plasticity index is greater than 7. See area identified as CL on the Plasticity Chart of Table No. 29-1-A.

Classify the soil as inorganic clay of high plasticity, CH, if the liquid limit is greater than 50 and the plot of liquid limit versus plasticity index falls above the "A" line. In cases where the liquid limit exceeds 100 or the plasticity index exceeds 60, the plasticity chart may be expanded by maintaining the same scales on both axes and extending the "A" line at the indicated slope. See area identified as CH on the Plasticity Chart, Table No. 29-1-A.

Classify the soil as inorganic silt, M, if the plot of liquid limit versus plasticity index falls below the "A" line or if the plasticity index is less than 4, unless it is suspected that organic matter is present in sufficient amounts to influence the soil properties, then tentatively classify the soil as organic silt or clay, O.

If the soil has a dark color and an organic odor when moist and warm, a second liquid limit test should be performed on a test sample which has been oven dried at 110 ± 5°C. for 24 hours.

Classify the soil as organic silt or clay, O, if the liquid limit after oven drying is less than three fourths of the liquid limit of the original sample determined before drying.

Classify the soil as inorganic silt of low plasticity, ML, or as organic silt of low plasticity, ML, or as organic silt or silt-clay of low plasticity, OL, if the liquid limit is less than 50 and the plot of liquid limit versus plasticity index falls below the "A" line or the plasticity index is less than 4. See area identified as ML and OL on the Plasticity Chart, Table No. 29-1-A.

Classify the soil as inorganic silt of medium to high plasticity, MH, or as organic clay or silt-clay of medium to high plasticity, OH, if the liquid limit is more than 50 and the plot of liquid limit versus plasticity index falls below the "A" line. See area identified as MH and OH on the Plasticity Chart of Table No. 29-1-A.

In order to indicate their borderline characteristics, some fine-grained soils should be classified by dual symbols.

If the plot of liquid limit versus plasticity index falls on or practically on the "A" line or above the "A" line where the plasticity index is in the range of 4 to 7, the soil should be given an appropriate borderline classification such as CL-ML or CH-OH.

If the plot of liquid limit versus plasticity index falls on or practically on the line liquid limit = 50, the soil should be given an appropriate borderline classification such as CL-CH or ML-MH. (In doubtful cases the rule for classification is to favor the more plastic classification. Example: a fine-grained soil with a liquid limit of 50 and a plasticity index of 22 would be classified as CH-MH rather than CL-ML.)

TABLE NO. 29-1-A—SOIL CLASSIFICATION CHART

MAJOR DIVISIONS			GROUP SYMBOLS	TYPICAL NAMES
COARSE-GRAINED SOILS More than 50% retained on No. 200 sieve*	GRAVELS 50% or more of coarse fraction retained on No. 4 sieve	CLEAN GRAVELS	GW	Well-graded gravels and gravel-sand mixtures, little or no fines
			GP	Poorly graded gravels and gravel-sand mixtures, little or no fines
		GRAVELS WITH FINES	GM	Silty gravels, gravel-sand-silt mixtures
			GC	Clayey gravels, gravel-sand-clay mixtures
	SANDS More than 50% of coarse fraction passes No. 4 sieve	CLEAN SANDS	SW	Well-graded sands and gravelly sands, little or no fines
			SP	Poorly graded sands and gravelly sands, little or no fines
		SANDS WITH FINES	SM	Silty sands, sand-silt mixtures
			SC	Clayey sands, sand-clay mixtures
FINE-GRAINED SOILS 50% or more passes No. 200 sieve*	SILTS AND CLAYS Liquid limit 50% or less		ML	Inorganic silts, very fine sands, rock flour, silty or clayey fine sands
			CL	Inorganic clays of low to medium plasticity, gravelly clays, sandy clays, silty clays, lean clays
			OL	Organic silts and organic silty clays of low plasticity
	SILTS AND CLAYS Liquid limit greater than 50%		MH	Inorganic silts, micaceous or diatomaceous fine sands or silts, elastic silts
			CH	Inorganic clays of high plasticity, fat clays
			OH	Organic clays of medium to high plasticity
	Highly Organic Soils		PT	Peat, muck and other highly organic soils

*Based on the material passing the 3-inch sieve.

(Continued)

TABLE NO. 29-1-A—SOIL CLASSIFICATION CHART—(Continued)

CLASSIFICATION CRITERIA		
CLASSIFICATION ON BASIS OF PERCENTAGE OF FINES Less than 5% Pass No. 200 sieve GW, GP, SW, SP More than 12% Pass No. 200 sieve GM, GC, SM, SC 5% to 12% Pass No. 200 sieve Borderline Classification requiring use of dual symbols	$C_u = D_{60}/D_{10}$ Greater than 4 $C_z = \frac{(D_{30})^2}{D_{10} \times D_{60}}$ Between 1 and 3	
	Not meeting both criteria for GW	
	Atterberg limits plot below "A"-line or plasticity index less than	Atterberg limits plotting in hatched area are borderline classifications requiring use of dual symbols
	Atterberg limits plot below "A"-line and plasticity index greater than 7	
	$C_u = D_{60}/D_{10}$ Greater than 6 $C_z = \frac{(D_{30})^2}{D_{10} \times D_{60}}$ Between 1 and 3	
	Not meeting both criteria for SW	
	Atterberg limits plot below "A" line or plasticity index less than 4	Atterberg limits plotting in hatched area are borderline classifications requiring use of dual symbols
	Atterberg limits plot above "A"-line and plasticity index greater than 7	

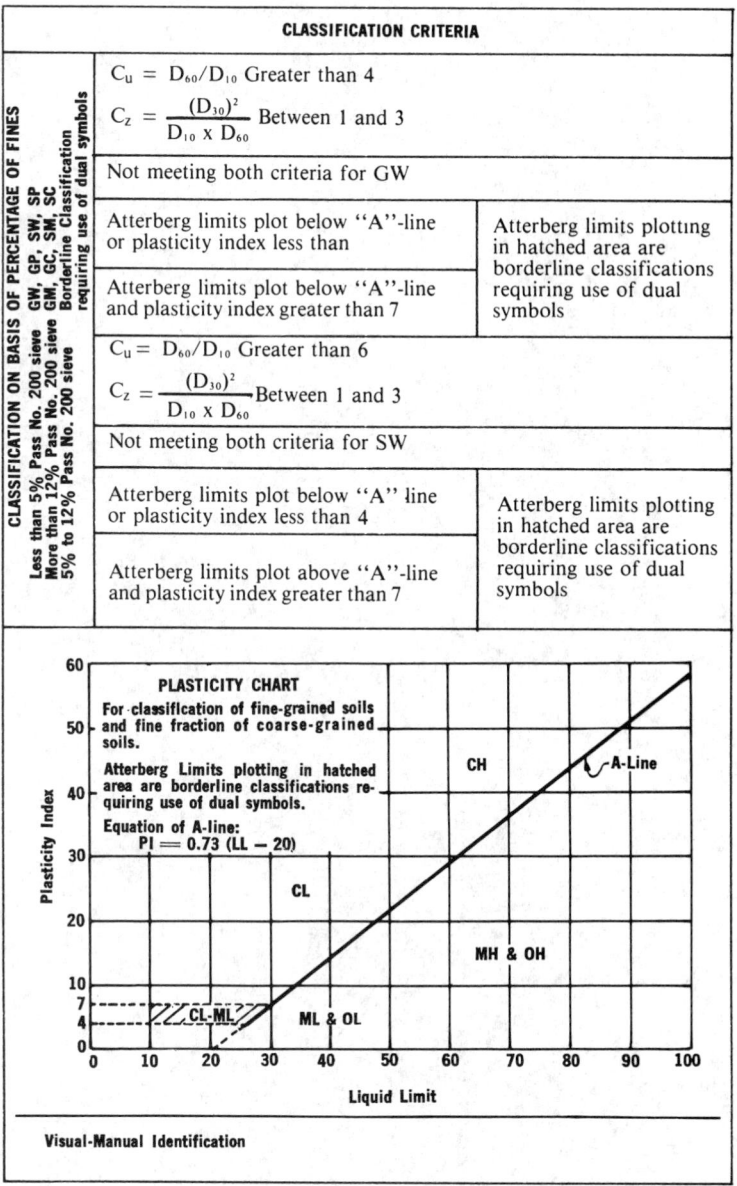

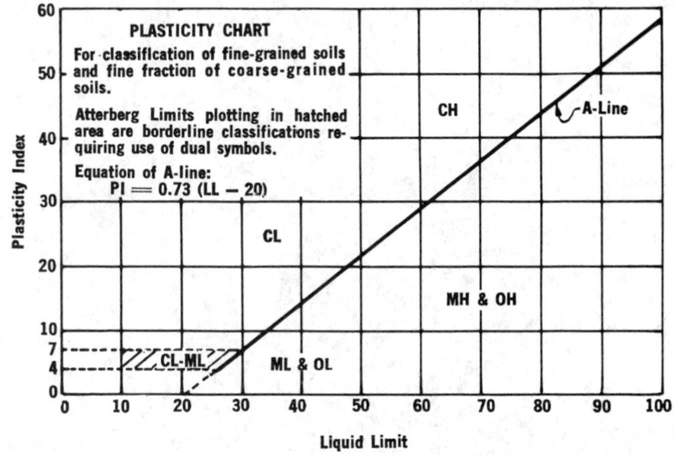
PLASTICITY CHART
For classification of fine-grained soils and fine fraction of coarse-grained soils.
Atterberg Limits plotting in hatched area are borderline classifications requiring use of dual symbols.
Equation of A-line:
PI = 0.73 (LL − 20)
CH
A-Line
CL
MH & OH
CL-ML
ML & OL
Plasticity Index
Liquid Limit
0
4
7
10
20
30
40
50
60
70
80
90
100

Visual-Manual Identification

UNIFORM BUILDING CODE STANDARD NO. 29-2

EXPANSION INDEX TEST

Based on Recommendations of the Los Angeles Section ASCE Soil Committee

See Sections 2901 (b) and 2904 (b), Uniform Building Code

Scope

Sec. 29.201. The expansion index test is designed to measure a basic index property of the soil and in this respect is comparable to other index tests such as the Atterberg limits. In formulating the test procedures no attempt has been made to duplicate any particular moisture or loading conditions which may occur in the field. Rather, an attempt has been made to control all variables which influence the expansive characteristics of a particular soil and still retain a practical test for general engineering usage.

Apparatus

Sec. 29.202. (a) **Mold.** The mold shall be cylindrical in shape, made of metal and have the capacity and dimensions indicated in Figure No. 29-2-1. It shall have a detachable collar inscribed with a mark 2.00 inches above the base. The lower section of the mold is designed to retain a removable stainless steel ring 1.00 inch in height, 4.01-inch internal diameter and 0.120-inch wall thickness.

(b) **Tamper.** A metal tamper having a 2-inch-diameter circular face and weighing 5.5 pounds shall be equipped with a suitable arrangement to control height of drop to a free fall of 12 inches above the top of the soil.

(c) **Balance.** A balance or scale of at least 1000-gram capacity sensitive to 0.1 gram.

(d) **Drying Oven.** A thermostatically controlled drying oven capable of maintaining a temperature of 230 plus or minus 9°F., for drying moisture samples.

(e) **Straight Edge.** Steel straight edge 12 inches in length and having one bevelled edge.

(f) **Sieves.** A No. 4 sieve conforming to the requirements of the specifications for sieves for testing purposes.

(g) **Mixing Tools.** Miscellaneous tools such as mixing pans, spoons, trowels, spatula, etc., or a suitable mechanical device for thoroughly mixing the sample of soil with increments of water.

Sample Preparation

Sec. 29.203. (a) **Preparation for Sieving.** If the soil sample is damp when received from the field, dry it until it becomes friable under a trowel. Drying may be in air or by use of drying apparatus such that the temperature of the sample does not exceed 140°F. Then thoroughly break up the aggregations in such a manner as to avoid reducing the natural size of the individual particles. If particles larger than ¼ inch are possibly expansive, such as claystone, shale or weathered volcanic rock, they should be broken down so as to pass the No. 4 sieve.

(b) **Sieving.** Sieve an adequate quantity of the representative pulverized soil over the No. 4 sieve. Record the percentage of coarse material retained on the No. 4 sieve and discard.

(c) **Sample.** Select a representative sample, weighing approximately 2 pounds or more, of the soil prepared as described in Subsections (a) and (b) above.

Specimen Preparation

Sec. 29.204. (a) **Moisture Determination.** Thoroughly mix the selected representative sample with sufficient distilled water to bring the soil to approximately optimum moisture content. After mixing, take a representative sample of the material for moisture determination, seal the remainder of the soil in a close-fitting airtight container for a period of at least six hours.

Weigh the moisture sample immediately and dry in an oven at 230 plus or minus 9°F., for at least 12 hours or to a constant weight to determine the moisture content. Moisture sample shall weigh not less than 300 grams.

(b) **Specimen Molding.** Form a specimen by compacting the cured soil in the 4-inch-diameter mold in two equal layers to give a total compacted depth of approximately 2 inches. Compact each layer by 15 uniformly distributed blows of the tamper dropping free from a height of 12 inches above the top of the soil, when a sleeve type rammer is used, or from 12 inches above the approximate elevation of each finally compacted layer when a stationary mounted type of tamper is used. During the compaction the mold shall rest on a uniform, rigid foundation, such as provided by a cube of concrete weighing at least 200 pounds.

(c) **Trim Specimen.** Following compaction, remove the upper and lower portions of the mold from the inner ring and carefully trim the top and bottom of the ring by means of the straight edge.

(d) **Saturation.** Weigh the compacted sample and determine the percent saturation. Adjust the moisture content to achieve 50 percent saturation by the addition of water or air drying the sample. Repeat steps (b) and (c) above.

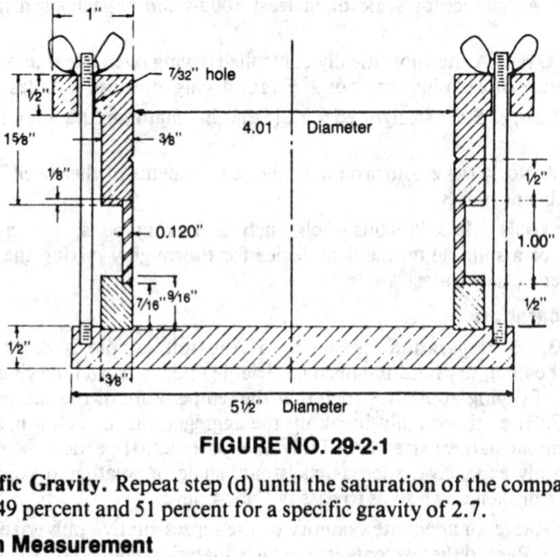
1"
7/32" hole
1/2"
15/8"
4.01 Diameter
3/8"
1/8"
1/2"
0.120"
1.00"
7/16"
9/16"
1/2"
1/2"
3/8"
51/2" Diameter

FIGURE NO. 29-2-1

(e) **Specific Gravity.** Repeat step (d) until the saturation of the compacted sample is between 49 percent and 51 percent for a specific gravity of 2.7.

Expansion Measurement

Sec. 29.205. (a) **Consolidometer.** Place the soil specimen in a consolidometer or equivalent loading device with porous stones at the top and bottom. Place on the specimen a total load of 12.63 pounds, including the weight of the upper porous stone and any unbalanced weight of the loading machine. Allow the specimen to consolidate under this load for a period of 10 minutes, after which time make the initial reading on the consolidometer dial indicator to an accuracy of 0.0005 inch.

(b) **Sample Submersion.** Submerge the sample in distilled water, making periodic readings on the dial indicator for a period of 24 hours or until the rate of expansion becomes less than 0.0002 inch per hour but not less than three hours submerged time.

(c) **Weighing.** Remove the sample from the loading machine after the final reading and weigh the specimen to the nearest 0.1 gram.

Calculations and Report

Sec. 29.206. (a) **Expansion Index.** Calculate the expansion index as follows:

$$E.I. = \frac{(\text{final thickness} - \text{initial thickness})}{\text{initial thickness}} \times 1000$$

Report the expansion index to the nearest whole number. If the initial sample thickness is greater than the final sample thickness, report the expansion index as 0. The molding moisture content and initial dry density of the specimen should accompany the expansion index in the complete presentation of results.

(b) **Weighted Expansion Index.** The weighted expansion index for a particular soil profile shall be determined as the summation of the products obtained by multiplying the expansion index by the factor appropriate to its elevation as indicated in Table No. 29-D of the Uniform Building Code.

UNIFORM BUILDING CODE STANDARD NO. 29-3

TREATED WOOD FOUNDATION SYSTEM

Based on National Forest Products Association, Technical Report No. 7

See Sections 2510 (a), 2901 (b) and 2907 (a), Uniform Building Code

Scope

Sec. 29.301. The basic design and construction requirements for Treated Wood Foundation Systems are set forth in this standard. Included are criteria for materials, preservative treatment, soil characteristics, environmental control, design loads and structural design.

Materials

Sec. 29.302. (a) **Lumber.** Lumber shall be of a species and grade for which allowable unit stresses are set forth in Table No. 25-A-1 of the Uniform Building Code and shall bear the grade mark of, or have a certificate of inspection issued by, an approved lumber grading or inspection bureau or agency.

(b) **Plywood.** All plywood shall be bonded with exterior glue and be grade marked indicating conformance with U.B.C. Standard No. 25-9 and shall bear the grade mark of an approved plywood inspection agency.

(c) **Fasteners in Preservative-treated Wood.** Fasteners in preservative-treated wood shall be approved silicon bronze or copper, stainless steel or hot-dipped zinc-coated steel conforming to Section 25.1717 (a) of U.B.C. Standard No. 25-17. Silicon bronze, copper and stainless steel fasteners are acceptable for all ground contact and moisture situations. Hot-dipped zinc-coated nails may be used for basement and crawl space wall construction where polyethylene sheeting is applied to the below-grade portion of the exterior wall and for wood basement floor construction, provided the polyethylene sheeting is placed in accordance with Section 29.303 (d). In addition, crawl space construction shall be located in soils having good drainage, such as GW, GP, SW, SP, GM, and SM types. Other types of steel or metal fasteners shall be permitted only if adequate comparative tests for corrosion resistance, including the effects associated with the wood treating chemicals, indicate an equal or better performance. Zinc-coated fasteners shall be coated after manufacture to their final form, including pointing, heating, threading or twisting, as applicable. Electrogalvanized nails or staples and hot-dipped zinc-coated staples shall not be used.

Framing anchors shall be of hot-dipped zinc-coated A-446 Grade A sheet steel conforming to U.B.C. Standard No. 27-1.

(d) **Gravel, Sand or Crushed Stone for Footings Fill.** Gravel shall be washed and well graded. The maximum size stone shall not exceed ¾ inch. Gravel shall be free from organic, clayey or silty soils.

Sand shall be coarse, not smaller than $^1/_{16}$-inch grains and shall be free from organic, clayey or silty soils.

Crushed stone shall have a maximum size of ½ inch.

(e) **Polyethylene Sheeting.** Polyethylene sheeting shall conform to requirements approved by the building official.

(f) **Sealants.** The materials used to attach the polyethylene sheets to each other or to the plywood shall be capable of adhering to those materials to form a continuous seal.

The material used for caulking joints in plywood sheathing shall be capable of adhering to the wood to provide a moisture seal under the conditions of temperature and moisture content at which it will be applied and used.

(g) **Preservative Treatment.** All lumber and plywood required to be preservative treated shall be pressure treated and bear the FDN grade mark. After treatment, each piece of lumber and plywood shall be dried to a moisture content not exceeding 19 percent. Each piece of treated lumber and plywood shall bear an approved quality mark or that of an approved inspection agency which maintains continuing supervision, testing and inspection over the quality of the product and shall be identified.

Where FDN lumber is cut or drilled after treatment, the cut surface shall be field treated with the following preservatives by repeated brushing, dipping or soaking until the wood absorbs no more preservative: ammoniacal copper arsenate (ACA), chromated copper arsenate (CCA), fluor chrome arsenate phenol (FCAP), acid copper chromate (ACC), or copper napthanate.

Copper napthenate shall be prepared with a solvent conforming to AWPA Standard P5. The preservative concentration shall contain a minimum of 2 percent copper metal. Preparations made by manufacturers of preservatives can also be used.

Waterborne preservatives ACA and CCA, Types A, B and C, shall have a minimum concentration of 3 percent in solution. Waterborne preservatives FCAP and ACC may be used for field treatment of material originally treated with CCA and ACA waterborne preservatives and the concentration of FCAP or ACC shall be a minimum of 5 percent in solution.

All lumber and plywood used in exterior foundation walls (except the upper top plate), all interior bearing wall framing and sheathing posts or other wood supports used in crawl spaces; all sleepers, joists, blocking and plywood subflooring used in basement floors; and all other plates, framing and sheathing in the ground or in direct contact with concrete shall be preservative treated. Where a significant portion of a bottom story wall is above adjacent ground level, such as when a building is situated on sloping terrain, the portion of wall to be considered as foundation wall shall be based on good engineering practice. Some members in such a wall may not require preservative treatment, such as window or door headers or the top plate. As a minimum, all exterior wall framing lumber and plywood sheathing less than 6 inches above finished grade shall be preservative treated.

(h) Soil Characteristics. Soils are defined herein in accordance with the Unified Soil Classification System (see U.B.C. Standard No. 29-1). Design properties are provided in Table No. 29-B, Uniform Building Code, or by a qualified soils engineer who by approval of the building official may assign other values based on soil tests or local experience.

Backfill of CH type (inorganic clays of high plasticity) or other types of expansive soils shall not be compacted dry. Backfill with MH soil types (inorganic silts, micaceous or diatomaceous fine sandy or silty soils, elastic silts) shall be well compacted to prevent surface water infiltration.

Organic soils, OL, OH and P_t are unsatisfactory for foundations unless specifically approved by the building official after a qualified soils engineer advises on the design of the entire soil-structural system.

Drainage and Moisture Control

Sec. 29.303. (a) General. The following sections present requirements to achieve dry and energy-efficient below-grade habitable space that is located above the permanent water table. Floors located below the permanent water table are not permitted unless special moisture control measures are designed by persons qualified in accordance with the authority having jurisdiction. [See Section 2905 (f), Uniform Building Code.]

(b) **Area Drainage.** Adjacent ground surface shall be sloped away from the structure with a gradient of at least ½ inch per foot for a distance of 6 feet or more. Provisions shall be made for drainage to prevent accumulation of surface water.

(c) **Subgrade Drainage.** A porous layer of gravel, crushed stone or sand shall be placed to a minimum thickness of 4 inches under basement floor slabs and all wall footings. For basement construction in MH and CH type soils, the porous layer under footings and slab shall be at least 6 inches thick.

Where there is basement space below grade, a sump shall be provided to drain the porous layer unless the foundation is installed in GW, GP, SW, SP, GM and SM type soils. The sump shall be at least 24-inch diameter or 20-inch square, shall extend at least 24 inches below the bottom of the basement floor slab and shall be capable of positive gravity or mechanical drainage to remove any accumulated water.

(d) **Sheeting and Caulking.** Polyethylene sheeting of 6-mil thickness shall be applied over the porous layer. A concrete slab shall be poured over the sheeting or a wood basement floor system shall be constructed on the sheeting. Where wood floors are used, the polyethylene sheeting shall be placed over wood sleepers supporting the floor joists. Sheeting should not extend beneath the wood footing plate.

In basement construction, joints between plywood panels in the foundation walls shall be sealed full length with caulking compound. Any unbacked panel joints shall be caulked at the time the panels are fastened to the framing.

Six-mil-thick polyethylene sheeting shall be applied over the below-grade portion of exterior basement walls prior to backfilling, except in GW, GP, SW, SP, GM and SM type soils. Joints in the polyethylene sheeting shall be lapped 6 inches and bonded with a sealant. The top edge of the polyethylene sheeting shall be bonded with a sealant to the plywood sheeting. A treated lumber or plywood strip shall be attached to the wall to cover the top edge of the polyethylene sheeting. The wood strip shall extend at least 2 inches above and 5 inches below finish grade level to protect the polyethylene from exposure to light and from mechanical damage at or near grade. The joint between the strip and the wall shall be caulked full length prior to fastening the strip to the wall. Alternatively, asbestos-cement board, brick, stucco or other covering appropriate to the architectural treatment may be used in place of the wood strip. The polyethylene sheeting shall extend down to the bottom of the wood footing plate but shall not overlap or extend into the gravel footing.

(e) **Perimeter Drainage Control.** The space between the side of a basement excavation and the exterior of a basement wall shall be backfilled for half the height of the excavation with the same material used for footings, except that for basements located in GW, GP, SW, SP, GM and SM type soils, or other sites that are well drained and acceptable to the authority having jurisdiction, the granular fill need not exceed a height of 1 foot above the footing. The top of this granular fill outside basement foundation walls and footings shall be covered with strips of 6-mil-thick polyethylene sheeting or type 30 felt, with adjacent strips lapped to provide for water seepage while preventing excessive infiltration of fine soils. Perforated sheeting or other filter membrane may also be used to control infiltration of fines.

(f) **Alternate Drainage System.** If a continuous concrete footing rather than a composite wood and gravel footing is used with the wood foundation in basement construction, the concrete shall be placed over a 4-inch-thick layer of gravel, crushed stone or sand that is arranged to allow drainage of water from the granular backfill outside the footing to the porous layer under the slab. Alternately, drainage across the concrete footing shall be provided by transverse pipes or drain tiles embedded in the concrete every 6 linear feet around the foundation.

(g) **Insulation.** Where insulation is applied between studs in exterior basement walls but the insulation is not flush with the exterior wall sheathing and does not extend down to the bottom plate, blocking shall be installed between the studs at the lower end of the insulation to prevent convection currents.

Design Loads

Sec. 29.304. (a) **General.** All parts of the wood foundation system shall be designed and constructed to provide safe support for all anticipated loads within the stress limits specified by the Uniform Building Code. Design loads shall be not less than those specified in Chapter 23 of the Uniform Building Code.

Design loads shall include downward forces acting on the wall from dead loads and roof and floor live loads, plus the lateral pressure from soil. Where applicable, the foundation also shall be designed to resist wind, earthquake and other static or dynamic forces. The foundation system shall be designed for the most severe distribution, concentration or combination of design loads deemed proper to act on the structure simultaneously.

(b) **Soil Loads.** Lateral pressure of the soil on the wall shall be considered in accordance with Section 2308 (b), Uniform Building Code.

Structural Design

Sec. 29.305. (a) **General.** Structural design of wood foundations shall be in accordance with established structural engineering and wood design practices as set forth in Chapter 25, Uniform Building Code.

(b) **Allowable Stresses.** Allowable unit stresses for lumber and plywood shall be as provided in Section 2504, Uniform Building Code. Design stresses for framing lumber shall be based on use under dry conditions (19 percent maximum moisture content), except that stresses for footing plates and crawl space framing shall be based on use under wet conditions. Design stresses for plywood sheathing shall be based on use under damp (moisture content 16 percent or more) conditions.

(c) **Allowable Loads on Fastenings.** Allowable loads for steel nails and framing anchors shall be in accordance with Section 2510, Uniform Building Code. Allowable loads for stainless steel Type 304 or 316, silicon bronze or copper nails shall be developed on a comparable basis to loads allowed for common steel nails. Allowable loads for stainless steel Type 304 or 316, silicon bronze or copper staples or other fasteners shall be in accordance with good engineering practice.

(d) **Footing Design.** The Treated Wood Foundation Systems incorporate a composite footing consisting of a wood footing plate and a layer of gravel, coarse sand or crushed stone. The wood footing plate distributes the axial design load from the framed wall to the gravel layer which in turn distributes it to the supporting soil.

Soil bearing pressure under the gravel, sand or crushed stone footings shall not exceed the allowable soil bearing values from Table No. 29-B of the Uniform Building Code except as permitted by Section 2906 of the Uniform Building Code.

Footing plate width shall be determined by allowable bearing pressure between the footing plate and the granular part of the footing. Gravel, sand or crushed stone under the footing plate shall be compacted to provide an allowable bearing capacity of 3000 psf when required by the design, otherwise an allowable bearing capacity of 2000 psf shall be assumed.

When the footing plate is wider than the bottom wall plate, the tension stress perpendicular to grain induced in the bottom face of the footing plate shall not exceed one-third the allowable unit shear stress for the footing plate. Use of plywood strips to reinforce the lumber footing plate is acceptable.

Thickness and width of the granular footing shall be determined by allowable bearing pressure between the gravel, sand or crushed stone and the supporting soil, assuming the downward load from the wood footing plate is distributed outward through the gravel, sand or crushed stone footing at an angle of 30 degrees from vertical at each edge of the footing plate. Additionally, the gravel, sand or crushed stone footing shall have a width not less than twice the width and a thickness not less than three-quarters the width of the wood footing plate and shall be confined laterally by backfill, granular fill, undisturbed soil, the foundation wall or other equivalent means.

The bottom of the wood footing plate shall not be above the maximum depth of frost penetration unless the gravel, sand or crushed stone footing extends to the maximum depth of frost penetration and is either connected to positive mechanical or gravity drainage, at or below the frost line, or is installed in GW, GP, SW, SP, GM and SM type soils where the permanent water table is below the frost line. A granular footing connected to a positively drained sump [see Section 29.303 (c)] by a trench filled with gravel, sand or crushed stone, or by an acceptable pipe connection, shall be considered to be drained to the level of the bottom of the sump or the bottom of the connecting trench or pipe, whichever is higher.

Where the bottom of the wood footing plate of a crawl space wall is not below the frost line, the top of the gravel, sand or crushed stone outside the wall shall be covered as required in Section 29.303 (e) for basement construction to prevent excessive infiltration of fine soils.

Where a wood footing plate is close to finished grade, such as when a deep granular footing is used to reach the frost line, the granular footing shall be protected against surface erosion or mechanical disturbance.

Posts and piers and their footings in basements or crawl spaces shall be in accordance with Sections 2516 and 2907, Uniform Building Code.

Footings under posts or piers may be of treated wood, treated wood and gravel, precast concrete or other approved material.

(e) **Foundation Wall Design.** Foundation wall studs shall be designed for stresses due to combined bending moment and axial loading resulting from lateral soil pressure and downward live and dead loads on the foundation wall, and for shear stresses due to lateral soil pressure. Top and bottom wall plates shall be designed for bearing of the studs on the plates. Joints in footing plate and upper top plate shall be staggered at least one stud space from joints in the adjacent plate to provide continuity between wall panels. Framing at openings in wall and floor systems and at other points of concentrated loads shall be designed with adequate capacity for the concentrated loads.

Plywood wall sheathing shall be designed for the shear and bending moment between studs due to soil pressures.

Joints, fastenings and connections in the wood foundation system shall be adequate to transfer all vertical and horizontal forces to the footing or to the applicable floor system. Connections at the top of the foundation wall shall be designed to transfer lateral soil load into the floor assembly. Lateral load at the bottom of a basement wall shall be transferred to the basement floor through bearing of the studs against the floor. Lateral load at the bottom of a crawl space wall shall be resisted by the soil inside the footing.

Foundation walls subject to racking loads due to earthquake, wind or differential soil pressure forces shall be designed with adequate shear strength to resist the most severe racking load or combination of loads, but earthquake and wind forces shall not be assumed to act simultaneously. Where a bottom wall plate of 1-inch nominal thickness has been used, the bottom of the wall shall be considered an unsupported panel edge when determining shear resistance of the wall.

(f) **Interior Load-bearing Walls.** Interior load-bearing walls in basements or crawl spaces shall be designed to carry the applicable dead and live loads in accordance with standard engineering practice and the requirements of the Uniform Building Code.

(g) **Basement Floor Design.** Concrete slab basement floors shall be designed in accordance with requirements of the Building Code but shall be not less than $3^1/_2$ inches in thickness.

Wood basement floors shall be designed to withstand axial forces and bending moments resulting from lateral soil pressures at the base of the exterior foundation walls and floor and live and dead loads. Floor framing shall be designed to meet joist deflection requirements of the Building Code.

Unless special provision is made to resist sliding caused by unbalanced lateral soil loads, wood basement floors shall be limited to applications where the differential depth of fill on opposing exterior foundation walls is 2 feet or less.

Joists in wood basement floors shall bear tightly against the narrow face of studs in the foundation wall or directly against a band joist which bears on the studs. Plywood subfloor shall be continuous overlapped joists or over butt joints between in-line joists. Where joists are parallel to the wall, sufficient blocking shall be provided between joists to transfer lateral forces from the base of the wall into the floor system.

Where required, resistance to uplift or restraint against buckling shall be provided by interior bearing walls or appropriately designed stub walls anchored in the supporting soil below.

Sleepers, joists, blocking and plywood subflooring used in basement floors shall meet the treatment requirements of Section 29.302 (g).

(h) **Uplift or Overtuning.** Design of the structure for uplift or overturning shall be in accordance with the requirements of the Uniform Building Code.

UNIFORM BUILDING CODE STANDARD NO. 29-4

DESIGN OF SLAB-ON-GRADE FOUNDATIONS TO RESIST THE EFFECTS OF EXPANSIVE SOILS

See Sections 2901 (b) and 2907 (e), Uniform Building Code

Part I

Design of Slab-On-Ground Foundations

Based on Design of Slab-On-Ground Foundations, of the Wire Reinforcement Institute, Inc. (August, 1981)

Scope

Sec. 29.401. This part covers a procedure for the design of slab-on-ground foundations to resist the effects of expansive soils in accordance with Chapter 29 of the Uniform Building Code. Use of this part shall be limited to buildings three stories or less in height in which gravity loads are transmitted to the foundation primarily by means of bearing walls constructed of masonry, wood or steel studs, and with or without masonry veneer.

Symbols and Notations

Sec. 29.402.

A_s = Area of steel reinforcing (sq. in. per foot) in slab—See Figure No. 29-4-10.

C_o = Overconsolidation coefficient—See Figure No. 29-4-3.

C_s = Soil slope coefficient—See Figure No. 29-4-2.

C_w = Climatic rating—See Figure No. 29-4-4.

E_c = Creep modulus of elasticity of concrete

f_y = Yield strength of reinforcing

I_c = Cracked moment of inertia of cross-section

k_l = Length modification factor-long direction—See Figure No. 29-4-9.

k_s = Length modification factor-short direction—See Figure No. 29-4-9.

L = Total length of slab in prime direction

L' = Total length of slab (width) perpendicular to L

L_c = Design cantilever length $(l_c k)$

l_c = Cantilever length as soil function

M_l = Design moment in long direction

M_s = Design moment in short direction

PI = Plasticity index

S = Maximum spacing of beams—See Figure No. 29-4-6.

V = Design shear force (total)

w = Weight per square foot of building and slab

q_u = Unconfined compressive strength of soil

$1\text{-}c$ = Soil/climatic rating factor—See Figure No. 29-4-5.

Δ = Deflection of slab, in.

Foundation Investigation

Sec. 29.403. A foundation investigation of the site shall be conducted in accordance with the provisions of Uniform Building Code Section 2905.

Design Procedure

Sec. 29.404. (a) **Loads.** The foundation shall be designed for a uniformly distributed load which shall be determined by dividing the actual dead and live loads for which the superstructure is designed, plus the dead and live loads contributed by the foundation, by the area of the foundation.

> **EXCEPTIONS:** 1. For one-story metal and wood stud buildings, with or without masonry veneer, and where the design floor live load is 50 pounds per square foot or less, a uniformly distributed load of 200 pounds per square foot may be assumed in lieu of calculating the effects of specific dead and live loads.
>
> 2. Those conditions where concentrated loads are of such magnitude that they must be considered are not covered by this part.

(b) **Determining the Effective Plasticity Index.** The effective plasticity index to be used in the design shall be determined in accordance with the following procedures:

1. The plasticity index shall be determined for the upper 15 feet of the soil layers and where the plasticity index varies between layers shall be weighted in accordance with the procedures outlined in Figure No. 29-4-1.
2. Where the natural ground slopes the plasticity index shall be increased by the factor C_s determined in accordance with Figure No. 29-4-2.
3. Where the unconfined compressive strength of the foundation materials exceeds 6000 pounds per square foot, the plasticity index shall be modified by the factor C_o determined in accordance with Figure No. 29-4-3. Where the unconfined compressive strength of the foundation materials is less than 6000 pounds per square foot, the plasticity index may be modified by the factor C_o determined in accordance with Figure No. 29-4-3.

The value of the effective plasticity index is that determined from the following equation:

$$\text{Effective P.I.} = \text{weighted P.I.} \times C_s \times C_o$$

Other factors which are capable of modifying the plasticity index such as fineness of soil particles and the moisture condition at the time of construction shall be considered.

Beams Spacing and Location

Sec. 29.405. Reinforced concrete beams shall be provided around the perimeter of the slab, and interior beams shall be placed at spacings not to exceed that determined from Figure No. 29-4-6. Slabs of irregular shape shall be divided into rectangles (which may overlap) so that the resulting overall boundary of the rectangles is coincident with that of the slab perimeter. See Figure No. 29-4-7.

Beam Design

Sec. 29.406. The following formulas shall be used to calculate the moment, shear and deflection and are based on the assumption that the zone of seasonal moisture changes under the perimeter of the slab is such that the beams resist loads as a cantilever of length L_c:

$$M = \frac{w L' (L_c)^2}{2}$$

$$V = w L' L_c$$

$$\Delta = \frac{w L' (L_c)^4}{4 E_c I_c}$$

The calculations shall be performed for both the long and short directions. Deflection shall not exceed $L_c/480$.

Slab Reinforcing

Sec. 29.407. The minimum slab thickness shall be 4 inches, and the maximum spacing of reinforcing bars shall be 18 inches. The amount of reinforcing shall be determined in accordance with Figure No. 29-4-10. Slab reinforcing shall be placed in both directions at the specified amounts and spacing.

Part II
Design of Post-tensioned Slabs On Ground
Based on Design Specification of the Post-Tensioning Institute

Scope

Sec. 29.408. This part covers a procedure for the design of slab-on-ground foundations to resist the effects of expansive soils in accordance with Chapter 29 of the Uniform Building Code. Use of this part shall be limited to buildings three stories or less in height in which gravity loads are transmitted to the foundation primarily by means of bearing walls constructed of masonry, wood or steel studs, and with or without masonry veneer.

Symbols and Notations

Sec. 29.409.

A = Area of gross concrete cross section, in.^{2}

A_b = Bearing area beneath a tendon anchor, in.^{2}

A_b = Maximum area of the portion of the supporting surface that is geometrically similar to and concentric with the loaded area, in.^{2}

A_{bm} = Total area of concrete in the beams, in.

A_c = Activity ratio of clay

A_{sl} = Area of concrete in the slab, in.^{2}

$CE'A_c$ = Cation Exchange Activity

E_c = Long-term or creep modulus of elasticity of concrete, psi

E_s = Modulus of elasctiy of soil, psi

I = Gross moment of inertia, in.^{4}

L = Total slab length in the direction being considered, ft.

M_l = Design moment in the long direction, ft.-kips/ft.

M_s = Design moment in the short direction, ft.-kips/ft.

${}_nM_t$, ${}_nM_c$
${}_pM_t$, ${}_pM_c$
= Negative and positive bending moments including tension or compression in the extreme fibers, ft.-kips/ft.

N_T = Number of tendons

P = Perimeter loading on the slab, lbs./ft.

P_r = Prestressing force, kips

PI = Plasticity index
S = Beam spacing, ft.
S_B = Section modulus with respect to bottom fiber, in.^{3}
S_T = Section modulus with respect to top fiber, in.^{3}
V = Design shear force, kips/ft.
W = Slab width, ft.
W_{slab} = Slab weight, lbs.
b = Width of an individual stiffening beam, in.
$\bar{c}$ = Centroid of presressing force, in.
c_g = Centroid of gross concrete section, in.
d = Depth of stiffening beam (measured from top surface of slab to bottom of beam), in.
e = Eccentricity of post-tensioning force, in.
e_m = Edge moisture variation distance, ft.
f_B = Section modulus factor for bottom fiber
f_c = Allowable compressive stress in the concrete, psi
f'_c = 28-day compressive strength of concrete, psi
f'_{ci} = Concrete compressive strength at time of stressing tendons, psi
f_{bp} = Allowable bearing stress under anchorage, psi
f_{cr} = Tensile cracking stress in concrete, psi
f_p = Minimum residual prestress or compressive stress, psi
f_T = Section modulus factor for top fiber
f_t = Allowable tensile stress in concrete, psi
g = Moment of inertia factor
k = Depth-to-neutral axis ratio; also "kips"
n = Number of beams in a cross section
q_{allow} = Allowable soil bearing pressure, psf
q_u = Unconfined compressive strength of the soil, psf
r_1 = Area ratio
t = Slab thickness, in.
y_m = Maximum differential soil movement
v_c = Premissible Concrete Shear Stress, psi
v = Design Shear Stress, psi
α = Angle of tendon inclination
$\triangle$ = Expected differential deflection of slab under service load, in.
$\triangle_{allow}$ = Allowable differential deflection of slab, in.
$\triangle_c$ = Correction to expected differential deflection due to prestressing, percent
$\triangle_{cs}$ = Differential deflection occurring as a result of constructing over compressible soil, in.
$\triangle_{ns}$ = Differential deflection occurring in the "no swell" condition, in.
$\triangle_o$ = Expected differential deflection without prestressing, in.
δ = Expected settlement occurring in compressive soil, in.

Foundation Investigation

Sec. 29.410. A foundation investigation of the site shall be conducted in accordance with the provisions of Section 2905.

Structural Design Procedure

Sec. 29.411. (a) **General.** The design procedure for post-tensioned slabs constructed over expansive soils shall include the following steps:

1. Divide an irregular slab plan into overlapping rectangles and design each rectangular section separately (Figure No. 29-4-11).
2. Assume a trial section in both the long and short directions of the design rectangle.
3. Calculate the service moment the section will be expected to experience in each direction for either the center lift or edge lift conditions.
4. Determine the allowable moment capacity of the assumed section in each direction and compare to the expected service moment.
5. Determine if the trial sections will meet differential deflection criteria in each direction.
6. Calculate the expected shear force in the assumed sections.
7. Determine the maximum allowable shear capacity of the sections and compare to the expected shearing force.
8. Repeat steps 3 through 7 for the opposite swelling condition.
9. Check the design for the first swelling condition to ascertain if adjustments are necessary to compensate for any design changes resulting from the second design swelling condition (Step 8).
10. Check the effect of slab-subgrade friction to assure a residual compressive stress of 50 psi at the center of each design rectangle in both directions. Adjust post-tensioning force if necessary.
11. Calculate stresses due to any heavy concentrated loads on the slab and provide special load-transfer details when necessary.

(b) **Trial Section Assumptions.** 1. Assume beam depth and spacing. An initial estimate of the depth of the stiffening beam can be obtained from solving either Equation (20) or Equation (21) for the beam depth yielding the maximum allowable differential deflection. A preliminary estimate of the allowable differential deflection can be made as follows:

A. Determine the maximum distance over which the allowable differential deflection will occur, L or 6β, whichever is smaller. As a first approximation, use $\beta = 8$ feet.

B. Select the permissible deflection ratio, e.g.,

(a) Center lift

$$\frac{\Delta}{L \text{ or } 6\beta} = \frac{1}{360} \quad (1)$$

(b) Edge lift

$$\frac{\Delta}{L \text{ or } 6\beta} = \frac{1}{1700} \quad (2)$$

The 1/1700 deflection ratio is used only to initially estimate the required beam depth for the edge lift condition.

C. Assume a beam spacing and solve for beam depth, *d*:

(i) Center lift

$$\text{Set } X = \frac{(y_m L)^{0.205}(S)^{1.059}(P)^{0.523}(e_m)^{1.296}}{380\,\Delta} \quad \text{(3a)}$$

Then

$$\log_{10}(d) = \frac{1}{1.214}\log_{10}(X) \quad \text{(3b)}$$

or,

$$d = X^{0.824} \quad \text{(3c)}$$

(ii) Edge lift

$$\text{Set } X = \frac{(L)^{0.35}(S)^{0.88}(e_m)^{0.74}(y_m)^{0.76}}{12\,\Delta\,(P)^{0.01}} \quad \text{(4a)}$$

Then

$$\log_{10}(d) = \frac{1}{0.85}\log_{10}(X) \quad \text{(4b)}$$

or,

$$d = X^{1.176} \quad \text{(4c)}$$

In most cases, the depth of the beams should be the same for all beams in both directions.

2. Determine section properties. The moment of inertia, section modulus, cross-sectional area of the slab and eccentricity of the prestressing force shall be calculated for the trial beam depth determined above in accordance with normal structural engineering procedures.

(c) **Design Stresses.** Permissible design stresses shall be in accordance with Uniform Building Code Section 2618.

(d) **Prestress Losses.** Loss of prestress due to elastic shortening of the concrete, creep of concrete, shrinkage of concrete and steel relaxation shall be taken as 30,000 psi for wire and strand tendons and 20,000 psi for bar tendons, unless more exact determination of these individual losses can be made. Prestress losses due to intentional and unintentional curvature of the tendons shall be calculated in accordance with Uniform Building Code Section 2618.

(e) **Slab-Subgrade Friction.** The effective prestressing force in post-tensioned slabs-on-ground is reduced by the frictional resistance to movement of the slab on the subgrade during stressing as well as the frictional resistance to dimensional changes due to concrete shrinkage or temperature variations. The largest amount of prestress loss due to slab-subgrade friction occurs in the center regions of the slab. The greatest structural requirement for prestress force, however, is at the location of the maximum moment, which occurs at approximately one β length inward from the edge of the slab. For normal construction practices, the value of the coefficient of friction should be taken as 0.75 for slabs on polyethylene and 1.00 for slabs cast directly on a sand base.

To provide assurance against cracking resulting from subgrade frictional resistance to movements induced by prestressing, concrete shrinkage, or temperature variations, the prestressing force provided in each direction shall not be less than provided by Equation (5). For very short slabs where the β length is approximately equal to one half of the length of the design rectangle, a prestressing force equivalent to one-half the weight of the stiffened slab multiplied by the coefficient of friction shall be deducted from the total prestressing force in calculating the net prestressing force available to provide resistance to applied bending moments.

$$P_r \geq \frac{W_{slab}}{2000} + .05A \qquad (5)$$

The maximum spacing of tendons shall not exceed that which would produce a minimum average effective prestress of 50 psi after allowance for slab-subgrade friction. The maximum spacing of tendons placed in the slab portion of the cross section can be estimated from Figure No. 29-4-12 (coefficient of friction assumed to be 0.75). Tendon spacings obtained from Figure No. 29-4-12 may have to be reduced to provide sufficient post-tensioning force to satisfy moment requirements.

(f) **Maximum Design Moments.** The maximum moment will vary, depending upon the swelling mode and the slab direction being designed. Moments for the center lift condition will, in general, be greater than edge lift moments. Moments in the short direction will, in general, be slightly greater than moments in the long direction.

1. Center lift moment.

A. Long Direction. The following equations shall be used to calculate maximum design moments for center lift bending in the long direction:

$$M_\ell = A_o \left[B(e_m)^{1.238} + C \right] \qquad (6)$$

WHERE:

M_ℓ = Design moment in long direction, ft-kips/ft.

$$A_o = \frac{1}{727}\left[(L)^{0.013}(S)^{0.306}(d)^{0.688}(P)^{0.534}(y_m)^{0.193}\right] \qquad (7)$$

and for

$0 \leq e_m \leq 5 \quad B = 1, \quad C = 0$

$$5 < e_m \quad B = \left(\frac{y_m - 1}{3}\right) \leq 1.0, \qquad (8)$$

$$C = \left[8 - \left(\frac{P - 613}{255}\right)\right]\left[\frac{4 - y_m}{3}\right] \geq 0$$

B. Short direction. The maximum design moment in the short direction for center lift bending shall be calculated as follows:

$$M_s = \left[\frac{58 + e_m}{60}\right] M_\ell \qquad (9)$$

WHERE:

M_s = Design Moment in short direction, in ft-kips/ft.

2. Edge lift moment.

A. Long direction. The maximum design moment in the long direction for edge lift bending shall be calculated as follows:

$$M_\ell = \left[\frac{(S)^{0.10} (de_m)^{0.78} (y_m)^{0.66}}{7.2 (L)^{0.0065} (P)^{0.04}}\right] \qquad (10)$$

B. Short direction. The maximum design moment in the short direction for edge lift bending shall be calculated as follows:

$$M_s = (d)^{0.35} \left[\frac{19 + e_m}{57.75}\right] M_\ell \qquad (11)$$

(g) **Maximum Allowable Service and Cracking Moments.** 1. **Allowable service moments.** The maximum moments to which the assumed sections can be subjected, consistent with the design stresses, can be determined from the familiar bending stress formula, rearranged so as to be able to solve for the maximum allowable external moments. The sign convention adopted is to represent compressive forces and eccentricities above the neutral axis as positive. The form of Equations (12) through (17) has been adjusted for the sign difference between tensile and compressive stresses. The following equations for allowable service moments must be evaluated for both the long and short direction.

A. Negative bending moment, $_nM$

(i) Tension in top fiber

$$_nM_t = S_T \left(\frac{P_r}{A} + f_t\right) + P_r e \qquad (12)$$

WHERE:

S_T = Section modulus for top fiber, inches³

P_r = Prestressing force, kips

A = Cross-sectional area, inches²

f_t = Allowable tensile stress, kips/inches²

e = Eccentricity of prestressing force, inches

(ii) Compression in bottom fiber

$$_nM_c = S_B \left(f_c - \frac{P_r}{A} \right) + P_r e \tag{13}$$

WHERE:

S_B = Selection modulus for bottom fiber, inches^3

f_c = Allowable compressive stress, ksi

The maximum external negative moment that can be carried by the section is the smaller of the moments calculated by Equations (12) and (13).

B. Positive bending moment, $_pM$

(i) Tension in bottom fiber

$$_pM_t = S_B \left(\frac{P_r}{A} + f_t \right) - P_r e \tag{14}$$

(ii) Compression in top fiber

$$_pM_c = S_T \left(f_c - \frac{P_r}{A} \right) - P_r e \tag{15}$$

The maximum external positive service moment that can be carried by the section is the smaller of the moments calculated by Equations (14) and (15).

2. **Tensile cracking moments.** Stiffened slabs-on-ground are usually designed to be under-reinforced. As long as the actual moment acting in the slab is below the tensile cracking moment, the stiffening beams may be assumed to act in their elastic range, and the assumed use of the gross section in computing deflection criteria is justified.

A. Negative bending moment, $_nM_{cr}$

$$_nM_{cr} = S_T \left(\frac{P_r}{A} + f_{cr} \right) + P_r e \tag{16}$$

B. Positive bending moment, $_pM_{cr}$

$$_pM_{cr} = S_B \left(\frac{P_r}{A} + f_{cr} \right) - P_r e \tag{17}$$

3. Compare allowable and cracking moments to be expected service moment. The design moments expected to occur in both directions, as calculated from Equations (6) and (9) through (11) must be compared to the allowable moments determined in Equations (12) through (15). If either the short direction or long direction design moments exceed the allowable service moments, the moment capacity of the section must be increased. Means of increasing the moment capacity include:

A. Deepening the stiffening beams (for deficient negative and positive moment capacity);

B. Decreasing the beam spacing (for deficient negative and positive moment capacity);

C. Increasing the prestressing force (for deficient negative moment capacity);

D. Decreasing the prestress eccentricity by carrying tendons below the neutral axis (for deficient positive moment capacity).

If the moment capacity of the assumed section exceeds the design moment, economies may be realized by performing the opposite to the actions suggested above for increasing moment capacities.

(h) **Differential Deflection.** Allowable and expected differential deflections may be calculated from the equations presented in the following sections.

1. Relative stiffness length, β, may be calculated as follows:

$$\beta = \frac{1}{12} \sqrt[4]{\frac{E_c I}{E_s}} \qquad (18)$$

WHERE:

β = Relative stiffness length, in feet

E_c = Creep modulus of elasticity of concrete, psi

E_s = Modulus of elasticity of soil, psi

I = Gross moment of inertia of section, inches^4

If the creep modulus of elasticity of the concrete is not known, it can be closely approximated by using 0.5 of the normal or early life concrete modulus of elasticity. If the modulus of elasticity of the clay soil is not known, use 1000 psi.

2. **Differential deflection distance.** The differential deflection may not occur over the entire length of the slab, particularly if the slab is longer than approximately 50 feet. Thus, the effective distance for determining the allowable differential deflection is the smaller of the two distances, L or 6β both expressed in feet.

3. **Allowable differential deflection.**

A. Center lift.

$$\Delta_{allow} = \frac{12\ (L \text{ or } 6\beta)}{360} \qquad (1)$$

WHERE:

Δ_{allow} = Allowable differential deflection, in inches

L = Total slab length, in feet

β = Relative stiffness length, in feet

B. Edge lift.

$$\Delta_{allow} = \frac{12\ (L \text{ or } 6\beta)}{800} \qquad (19)$$

The more stringent allowable differential deflection for the edge lift is specified because edge lift deflections are normally much less than center lift deflections and stems of beams resisting positive moments may be unreinforced.

4. Expected differential deflection without prestressing.

A. Center lift.

$$\Delta_o = \left[\frac{(y_m L)^{0.205}(S)^{1.059}(P)^{0.523}(e_m)^{1.296}}{380\,(d)^{1.214}}\right] \tag{20}$$

WHERE:

Δ_o = Expected differential deflection, in inches

B. Edge lift.

$$\Delta_o = \left[\frac{(L)^{0.35}(S)^{0.88}(e_m)^{0.74}(y_m)^{0.76}}{15.90\,(d)^{0.85}(P)^{0.01}}\right] \tag{21}$$

5. Deflection reduction due to prestressing. Normally, most of the prestressing is placed in the slab, and the centroid of the prestressing force is above the center of gravity of the section. Because of this, any deflection due to negative bending must first overcome a slight amount of positive deflection or camber caused by the prestressing. This differential deflection advantage of prestressing can be calculated by:

A. Calculate the percent of differential deflection reduction.

$$\Delta_c = e\sqrt{\frac{6400}{9L}} \tag{22}$$

WHERE:

Δ_c = Differential deflection correction, in percent

e = Eccentricity of prestressing force, in inches

B. Calculate corrected differential deflection.

$$\Delta = \Delta_o\left[\frac{100-\Delta_c}{100}\right] \tag{23}$$

WHERE:

Δ = Expected deflection, in inches

The effect of prestressing usually adds to the deflection due to edge lift bending. However, deflections due to this bending mode are usually smaller than center lift deflections.

6. Compare expected to allowable differential deflection. If the expected differential deflection as calculated by either Equations (20) or (21) adjusted for the effect of prestressing exceeds that determined from Equations (1) or (19), respectively, the assumed section must be stiffened. This can be accomplished in at least three ways:

A. Deepening the stiffening beams,

B. Decreasing the beam spacing, or

C. Adding additional prestressing tendons above the neutral axis.

(i) **Shear.** 1. **Expected service shear.** Expected values of service shear forces in kips per foot of width or length of slab shall be calculated from the following formulas:

A. Center lift.

(a) Short direction shear.

$$V_s = \frac{1}{1350}\left[(L)^{0.19}(S)^{0.45}(d)^{0.20}(P)^{0.54}(y_m)^{0.04}(e_m)^{0.97}\right] \quad (24)$$

(b) Long direction shear.

$$V_\ell = \frac{1}{1940}\left[(L)^{0.09}(S)^{0.71}(d)^{0.43}(P)^{0.44}(y_m)^{0.16}(e_m)^{0.93}\right] \quad (25)$$

B. Edge lift.

For both directions:

$$V = \left[\frac{(L)^{0.07}(d)^{0.40}(P)^{0.03}(e_m)^{0.16}(y_m)^{0.67}}{3.0\,(S)^{0.015}}\right] \quad (26)$$

WHERE:

V, V_s, V_l

= Shear force, in kips/ft.

2. **Allowable shear stresses.**

A. Nominal total design shear stress, v. Only the beams may be considered in calculating the cross-sectional area resisting shear force.

$$v = \frac{VW}{ndb} \quad (27)$$

WHERE:

V = Total shear force acting on the section, kips

B. Nominal permissible shear stress, v_c. Unless the permissible shear stress can be determined by testing or by more rigorous analysis, the maximum shear stress permitted shall be given by

$$v_c = 1.5\sqrt{f'_c} \quad (28)$$

where v_c and f'_c are both expressed in psi

3. Compare v to v_c. If v exceeds v_c, shear reinforcement must be provided. Possible alternatives to reinforcement include:

A. Increasing the beam depth,

B. Increasing the beam width, or

C. Increasing the number of beams (decrease beam spacing).

4. **Shear reduction due to prestressing.** An advantage of curved or draped prestressing tendon in beam stems is that due to the upward force exerted by the tendon on the concrete, shear compensation in an amount equal to $P_r \sin\alpha$ is obtained. The design shear force carried by the beams is reduced accordingly. Figure No. 29-4-13 shows the effect of draped prestressing tendons on shear reduction.

(j) **Calculation of Stress in Slabs Due to Load Bearing Partitions.** The equation for the tensile stress in a slab beneath a bearing partition may be derived from beam-on-elastic foundation theory. The maximum moment directly under a point load, *P,* in such a beam is given by

$$M_{max} = -\frac{P\beta}{4} \qquad (29)$$

WHERE:

M_{max} = The maximum moment (in-lb) per linear foot of bearing partition in a direction at right angles with the bearing partition

$$\beta = \left[\frac{4E_cI}{kb}\right]^{1/4}, \text{ relative stiffness length in inches} \qquad (30)$$

WHERE:

E_c = Creep modulus at elasticity of concrete

I = Moment of inertia of loaded slab width

B = Assumed beam (slab) width

k = Soil modulus

P = Bearing partition load in lb/ft of length, + upward

$$\frac{I}{B} = \frac{t^3}{12}$$

with the concrete and soil properties generally assumed ($E_c = 1.5 \times 10^6$ psi, k = 4 pci),

$$\frac{4E_c}{k} = 1.5 \times 10^6 \text{ in.}$$

and β becomes:

$$\beta = 18.8_t^{3/4}$$

therefore

$$M_{max} = -\frac{18.8\,Pt^{3/4}}{4} = -4.7\,Pt^{3/4} \qquad (31)$$

The equation for tensile stress, f_t, is

$$f_t = \frac{M_{max}C}{I} - f_p \tag{32}$$

where f_p = minimum compressive stress in the concrete due to prestressing (usually 50 psi).
Since

$$\frac{I}{C} = \frac{b\ t^3}{12}\left(\frac{2}{t}\right) = \frac{b\ t^2}{6}$$

and

b = 12 in. (one linear foot of bearing partition)

then

$$\frac{I}{C} = 2t^2$$

Thus, the tensile stress is

$$f_t = \frac{4.7\ P\ t^{3/4}}{2\ t^2} - f_p$$

$$f_t = 2.35\ \frac{P}{t^{1.25}} - f_p \tag{33}$$

The constant 2.35 depends upon the assumed value of subgrade modulus, k. The following table illustrates the variation in this constant for values of the subgrade modulus:

Type of Subgrade	K, lb/in³	c
Lightly compacted, high plastic, compressible soil	4	2.35
Compacted, low plastic soil	40	1.34
Stiff, compacted, select granular or stabilized fill	400	0.74

If the allowable tensile stress is exceeded by the results of the above analysis, a thicker slab section shall be used under the loaded area, or a stiffening beam shall be placed directly beneath the concentrated line load.

APPENDIX A
A Procedure for Estimation of the Amount of Climate Controlled Differential Movement of Expansive Soils

In general, the amount of differential movement to be expected in a given expansive soil should be based on recommendations supplied by a registered geotechnical engineer. The geotechnical engineer may use various soil testing procedures to provide a basis for these recommendations. A procedure developed in part through the PTI sponsored research project at Texas A & M University that may be used by geotechnical engineers (in conjunction with accumulated experience with local soils conditions) as an aid for estimation of expected differential movements of expansive soils is presented in this appendix. This procedure is applicable only in those cases where site conditions have been corrected so that soil moisture conditions are controlled by the climate alone.

The information necessary to determine the differential movement using the procedure in this appendix is the type and amount of clay, the depth to constant or equilibrium suction, the edge moisture variation distance, the magnitude of the equilibrium suction, and the field moisture velocity. With this information either known or estimated, differential movements may be selected from Tables Nos. 29-4-A to 29-4-O for the center lift condition, or Tables Nos. 29-4-P to 29-4-DD for the edge lift condition.

Procedures for determining or estimating the necessary items of soil information are as follows:

1. Select a Thornthwaite Moisture Index from Figure No. 29-4-14 or Figure No. 29-4-15. Alternatively, extreme annual values of the Thornthwaite Index may be calculated for a given site using Thornthwaite's procedures.
2. Obtain an estimate of the edge moisture variation distance, e_m, for both edge lift and center lift loading conditions from Figure No. 29-4-16.
3. Determine the percent of clay in the soil and the predominant clay mineral. The predominant type of clay can be determined by performing the following tests and calculations and by using Figure No. 29-4-17.
   (a) Determine the plastic limit (P.L.) and the plasticity index (P.I.) of the soil.
   (b) Determine the percentage of clay sizes in the material passing the U.S. No. 200 sieve (Hydrometer Test).
   (c) Calculate the activity ratio of the soil:

$$A_c = \frac{\text{P.I.}}{(\text{Percent passing U.S. No. 200 sieve} \leq 0.002 \text{ mm})} \qquad (1)$$

   (d) Calculate the Cation Exchange Activity. A discussion of procedures for determining Cation Exchange Capacity for use in calculating Cation Exchange Activity is presented in Appendix C.

$$CEA_c = \frac{\text{P.L.}^{1.17}}{(\text{Percent passing U.S. No. 200 sieve} \leq 0.002 \text{ mm})} \qquad (1)$$

   (e) Enter Figure. No. 29-4-17 with the A_c and CEA_c. The soil type is determined by the intersection of the two entries. Note that the same mineral type is obtained from Figure. No. 29-4-17 for a significant range of values of A_c and CEA_c. This indicates that the determination of the mineral type is relatively insensitive to the precision by which the Atterberg Limits and other soil parameters have been determined. In the case of doubt as to the predominant mineral type, the clay may be conservatively classified as montmorillonite.

4. Depth to constant soil suction can be estimated as the depth below which the ratio of water content to plastic limit is constant. At times it will be the depth to an inert material, an unweathered shale, or to a high water table. Constant soil suction can be estimated with reasonable accuracy from Figure No. 29-4-18 if it is not actually determined in the laboratory; however, for most practical applications, the design soil suction value will seldom exceed a magnitude of *pF* 3.6.
5. Moisture velocity can be approximated by using a velocity equal to one half of the Thornthwaite Moisture Index (expressed in inches/year) for the construction site, converted to inches/month. To allow for extreme local variations in moisture velocity, this value shall not be assumed to be less than 0.5 in./month, and the maximum moisture velocity shall be 0.7 in./month.
6. Using values of edge moisture distance variation, e_m, percent clay, predominant clay mineral (kaolinite, illite, or montmorillonite), depth to constant suction, soil suction *pF,* and velocity of moisture flow determined in steps 1 through 5 above, enter the appropriate table, Tables Nos. 29-4-A to 29-4-O for center lift and Tables Nos. 29-4-P to 29-4-DD for edge lift, and find the corresponding soil differential movements, y_m. The values of swell presented in the tables were obtained from a computer program based on the permeability of clays and the total potential of the soil water.

APPENDIX B
Simplified Procedures for Determining Cation Exchange Capacity and Cation Exchange Activity

Simplified Procedure for Determining Cation Exchange Capacity Using a Spectrophotometer

The cation exchange capacity of soil samples may be determined by comparative means in the standard spectrophotometer device. This method of determining the cation exchange capacity is used by the U.S. Soil Conservation Service. Data obtained by this method should be comparable with data for similar soils that have been measured by the U.S. Conservation Service. This simplified procedure is:

1. Place 10 grams of clay soil in a beaker and 100 ml of neutral 1 N ammonium acetate (NH_4Ac) is added. This solution is allowed to stand overnight.
2. Filter the solution of Step 1 by washing through filter paper with 50 ml of NH_4Ac.
3. Wash the material retained on the filter paper of Step 2 with two 150 ml washings of isopropyl alcohol, using suction. The isopropyl alcohol wash fluid should be added in increments of approximately 25 ml and the sample allowed to drain well between additions.
4. Transfer the soil and filter paper to a 800-ml flack. Add 50 ml $MgCI_2$ solution and allow to set at least 30 minutes but preferably 24 hours.
5. Under suction, filter the fluid resulting from Step 4.
6. Normally the solution of $MgCI_2$ must be diluted before it is placed in the spectrophotometer in Step 10. The dilution will vary from one piece of equipment to the next. The calculations given at the end of this section assume that 200 ml of distilled water have been used to dilute 1 ml of the $MgCI_2$ solution. The 200-to-1 dilution is fairly typical.
7. Prepare a standard curve by using 10 μg of nitrogen (in the NH_4 form) per ml of a standard solution in a 50 ml volumetric flask. Adjust the volume to approximately 25 ml, add 1 ml of 10 percent tartrate solution, and shake. Add 2 ml of Nessler's aliquot with rapid mixing. Add sufficient distilled water to bring the total volume to 50 ml. Allow color to develop for 30 minutes.
8. Repeat Step 7 for 1.0, 2.0, 4.0, and 8.0 ml aliquots of standard solution.
9. Insert the standard solution resulting from Steps 7 and 8 into the spectrophotometer. Record readings and plot the results to construct a standard curve. (The spectrophotometer is calibrated beforehand with distilled water.)
10. Extract 2.0 ml of sample aliquot from Step 6 and add 25 ml of distilled water in a 50 ml volumetric flask. Add 1 ml of 10 percent tartrate and shake. Add 2 ml of Nessler's aliquot with rapid mixing. Add sufficient distilled water to bring the total volume to 50 ml. Let the solution stand for 30 minutes and then insert into the spectrophotometer and record the transparency reading.
11. Typical calculations:

Weight of dry soil	=	10.64 grams
Spectrophotometer	=	81 percent
	=	24.5 μg/g from Standard Curve

Conversion:

$$\frac{24.5\ \mu g}{2ml./aliquot} \times \frac{200\ ml}{1\ ml} \times \frac{50\ ml}{10.64\ \mu g} \times \frac{1}{1000\ \mu/mg} \times$$

$$\frac{1}{14\ mg/meq} \times 100\ g. = 82.2\ meq/100g$$

Equation for Cation Exchange Capacity

A 1979 study at Texas Tech University resulted in the following proposed modifications to the Pearring and Holt equations for Clay Activity, Cation Exchange Capacity, and Cation Exchange Activity:

Clay Activity $Ac = \dfrac{PI}{\%\ Clay}$

Cation Exchange Capacity:

$CEC = (P.L.)^{1.17}$

Cation Exchange Activity:

$$CEAc = \frac{(P.L.)^{1.17}}{\%\ Clay}$$

NOMENCLATURE:

P.I. = Plasticity Index
P.L. = Plastic Limit
% Clay = % Passing U.S. No. 200 Sieve $\leq$ 0.002 mm.

Comparison of Methods of Determining Cation Exchange Capacity and Predominant Clay Mineral

A comparison of values of Cation Exchange Capacity using atomic absorption and spectrophotometer techniques is presented in Table No. 29-4-EE.

Comparison of clay mineral determination between atomic absorption of the correlation equations presented above is presented in Table No. 29-4-FF and Figure No. 29-4-19.

DETERMINING THE WEIGHTED PLASTICITY INDEX (P.I.)

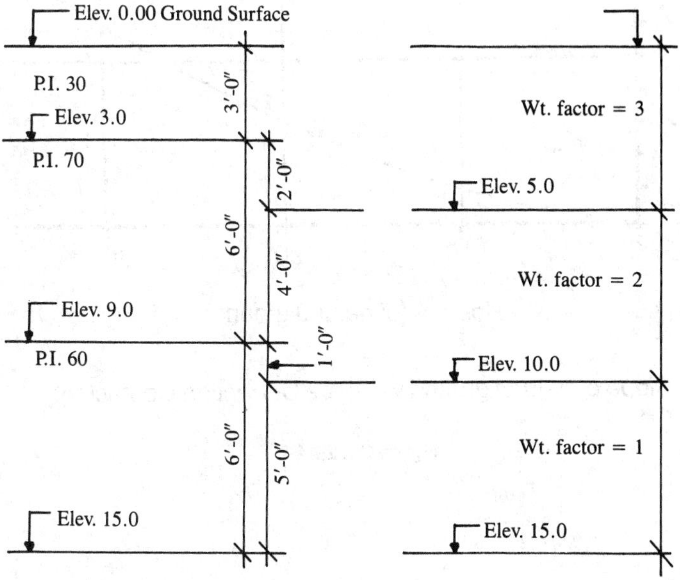

Elev. 0.00 Ground Surface
P.I. 30
3'-0"
Elev. 3.0
P.I. 70
2'-0"
6'-0"
4'-0"
Elev. 9.0
P.I. 60
1'-0"
6'-0"
5'-0"
Elev. 15.0
Wt. factor = 3
Elev. 5.0
Wt. factor = 2
Elev. 10.0
Wt. factor = 1
Elev. 15.0

Weight Factor F	Depth D	$F \times D$	$P.I.$	$F \times D \times$ P.I.	
3	3	9	30	=	270
3	2	6	70	=	420
2	4	8	70	=	560
2	1	2	60	=	120
1	5	5	60	=	300
		30			1670

Weighted P.I. = 1670/30 = 55.67
= 56

Figure No. 29-4-1

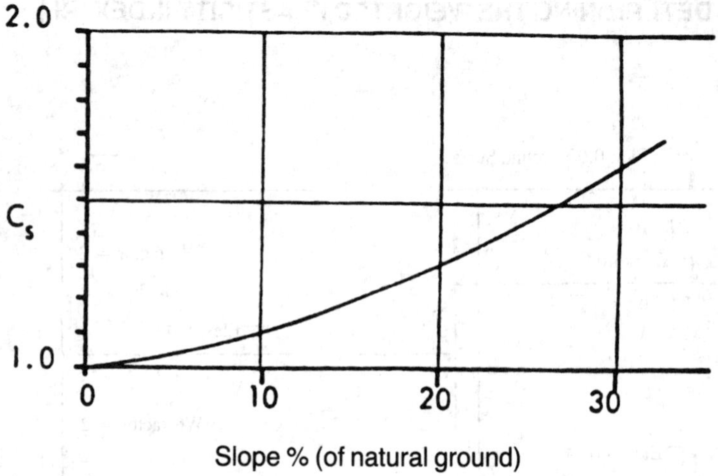
2.0
C_s
1.0
0
10
20
30
Slope % (of natural ground)

Slope of natural ground vs. slope Correction Coefficient

Figure No. 29-4-2

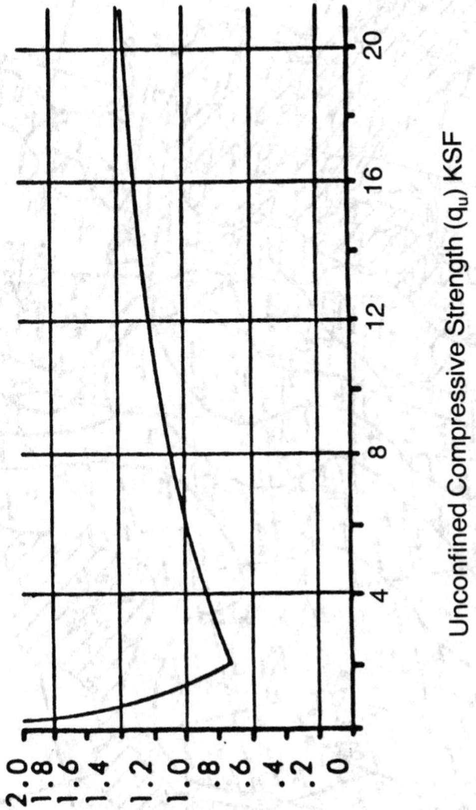

C_o
2.0
1.8
1.6
1.4
1.2
1.0
.8
.6
.4
.2
0
4
8
12
16
20
Unconfined Compressive Strength (q_u) KSF

Unconfined Compressive Strength vs. Overconsolidated Correction Coefficient

Figure No. 29-4-3

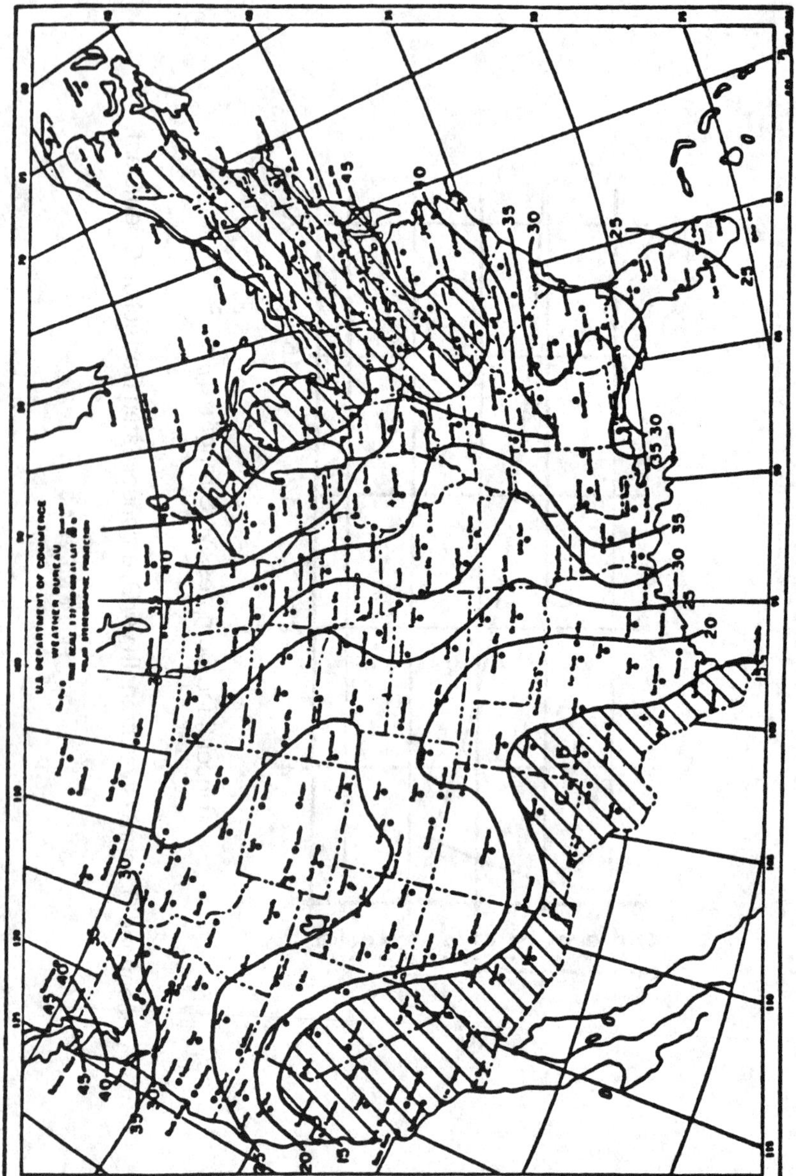
U.S. DEPARTMENT OF COMMERCE
WEATHER BUREAU

Climatic Rating (C_w) Chart

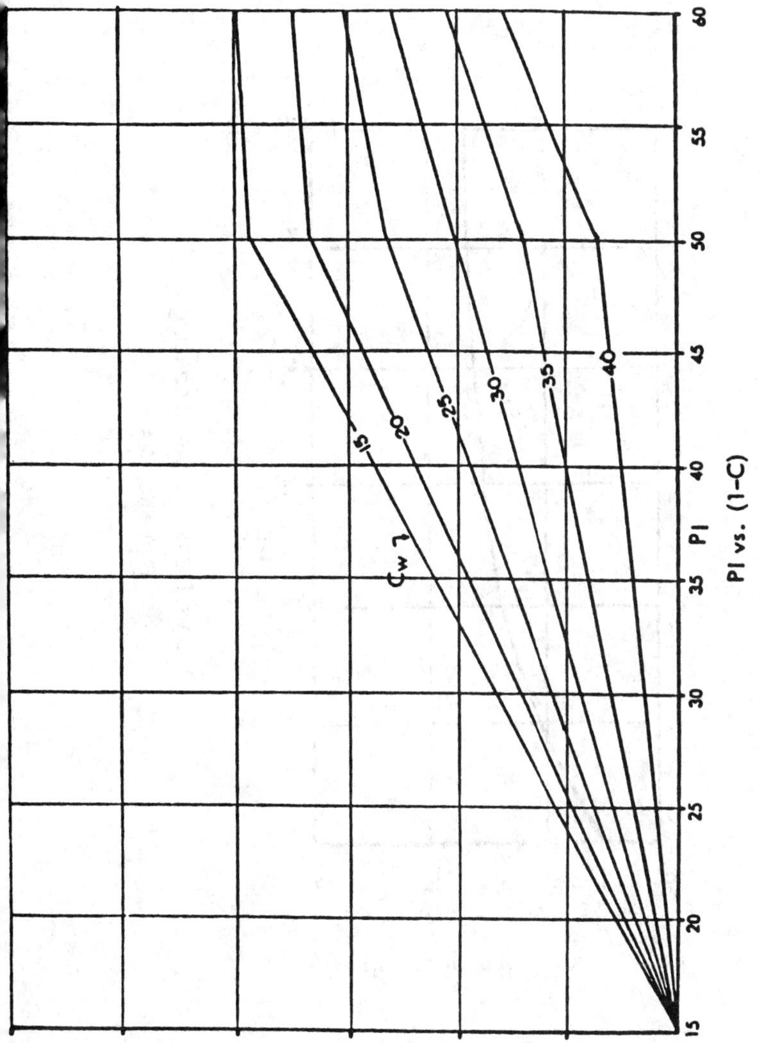

1-C
0
.1
.2
.3
.4
.5
.6
PI
15
20
25
30
35
40
45
50
55
60
Cw 7
15
20
25
30
35
40
PI vs. (1–C)

Figure No. 29-4-5

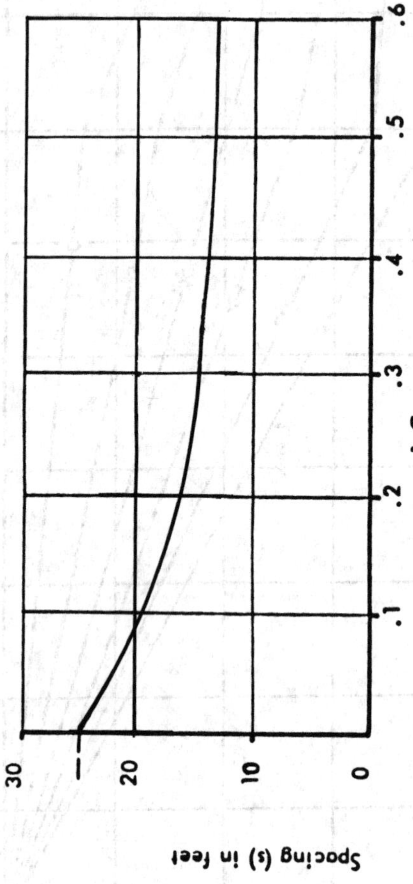

30
20
10
0
Spacing (s) in feet
.1
.2
.3
.4
.5
.6
1–C

1-C vs. Maximum beam spacing

Figure No. 29-4-6

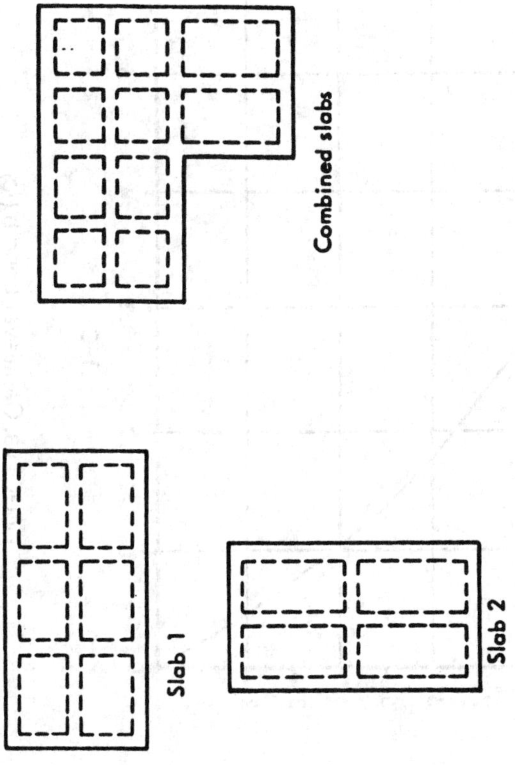
Combined slabs
Slab 1
Slab 2

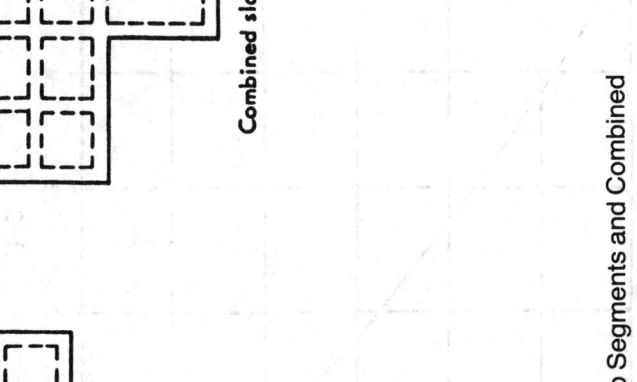

Slab Segments and Combined

Figure No. 29-4-7

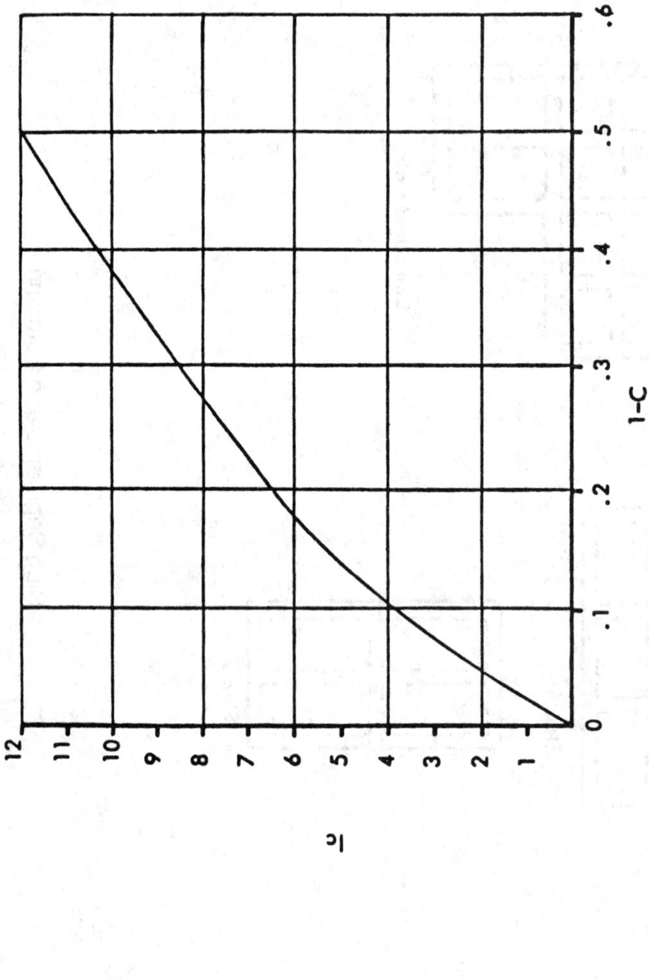
12
11
10
9
8
7
6
5
4
3
2
1
0
.1
.2
.3
.4
.5
.6
1–C
lc

(1-C) vs. Cantilever Length (*lc*)

Figure No. 29-4-8

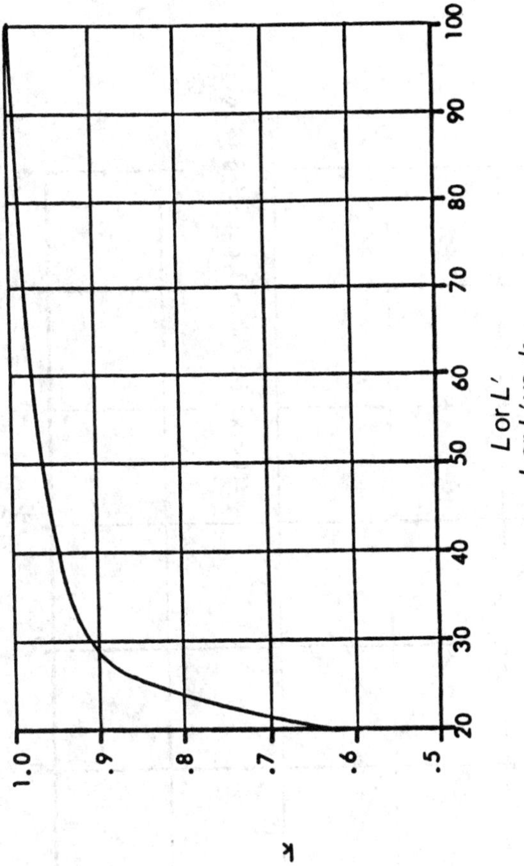
1.0
.9
.8
.7
.6
.5
k
20
30
40
50
60
70
80
90
100
L or L'

L or *L'* vs. *k*

Figure No. 29-4-9

SLAB REINFORCING

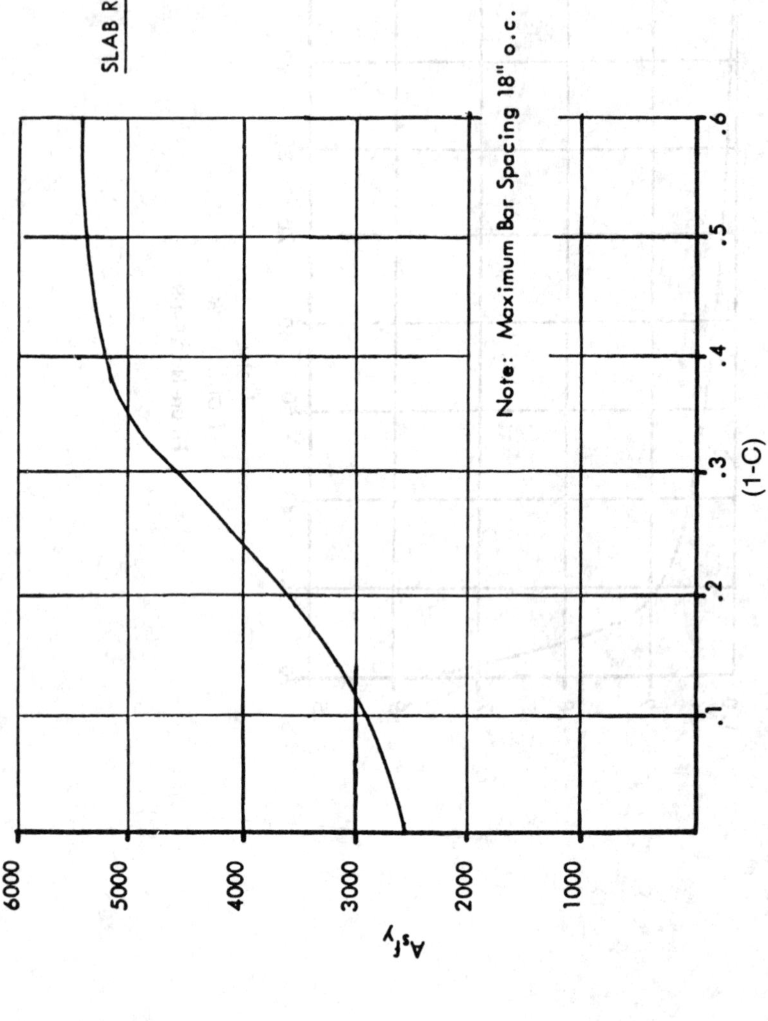
Note: Maximum Bar Spacing 18" o.c.
6000
5000
4000
3000
2000
1000
A_sf_y
.1
.2
.3
.4
.5
.6
(1-C)

(1-C) vs. A_sf_y

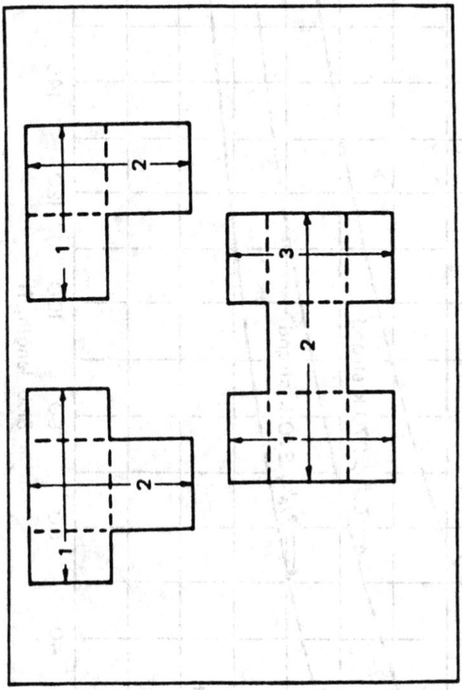
1
2
1
2
1
2
3

Figure No. 29-4-11. Design rectangles for slabs of irregular shape.

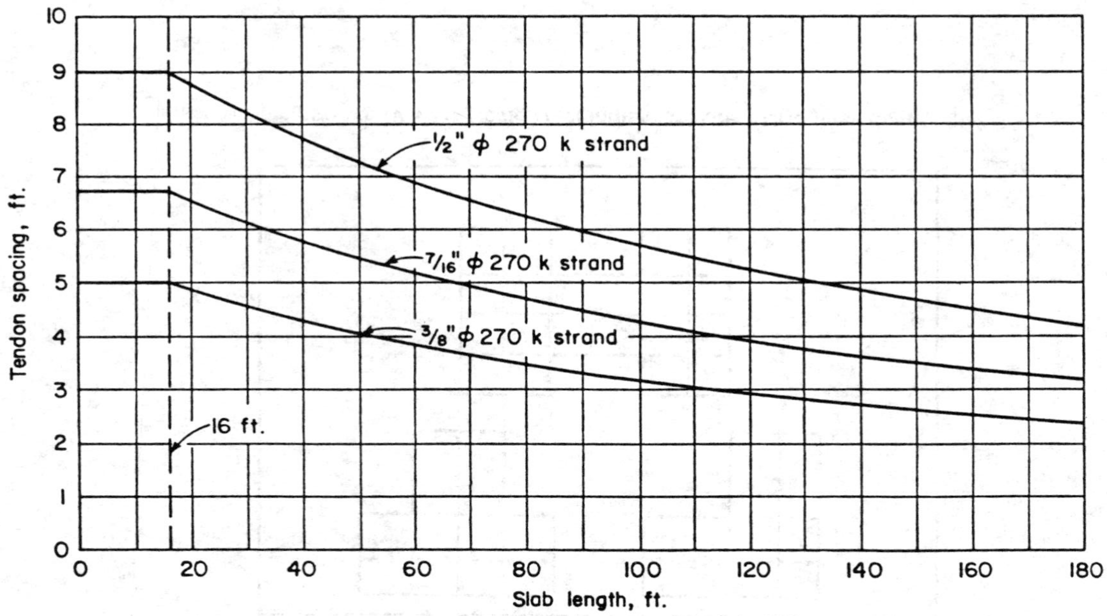

Tendon spacing, ft.
10
9
8
7
6
5
4
3
2
1
0
20
40
60
80
100
120
140
160
180
Slab length, ft.
½" φ 270 k strand
7/16" φ 270 k strand
3/8" φ 270 k strand
16 ft.

Figure No. 29-4-12. Maximum slab tendon spacing to overcome slab-subgrade friction (friction coefficient = 0.75) and retain 50 psi residual prestress compression at midpoint of stiffened slab on

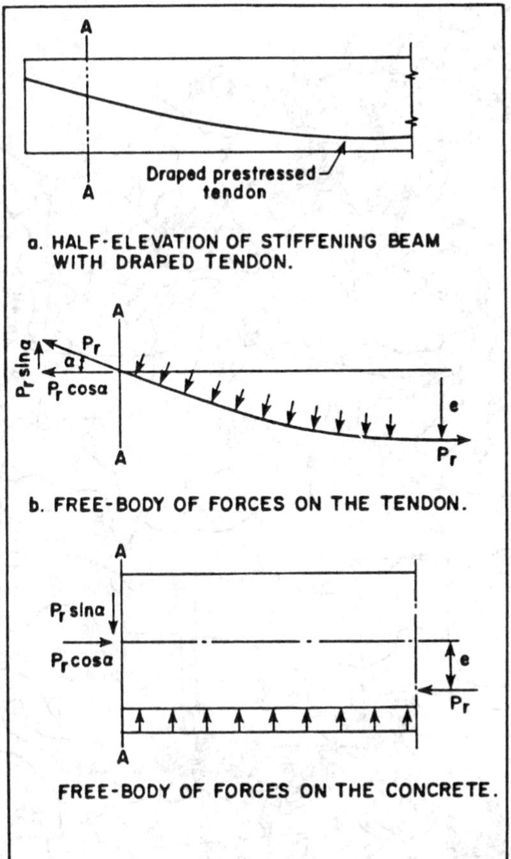
A
A
Draped prestressed tendon
a. HALF-ELEVATION OF STIFFENING BEAM WITH DRAPED TENDON.
A
Pr sina
Pr
a
Pr cosa
e
A
Pr
b. FREE-BODY OF FORCES ON THE TENDON.
A
Pr sina
Pr cosa
e
Pr
A
FREE-BODY OF FORCES ON THE CONCRETE.

Figure No. 29-4-13. Free-body diagrams for draped beam tendon and concrete section.

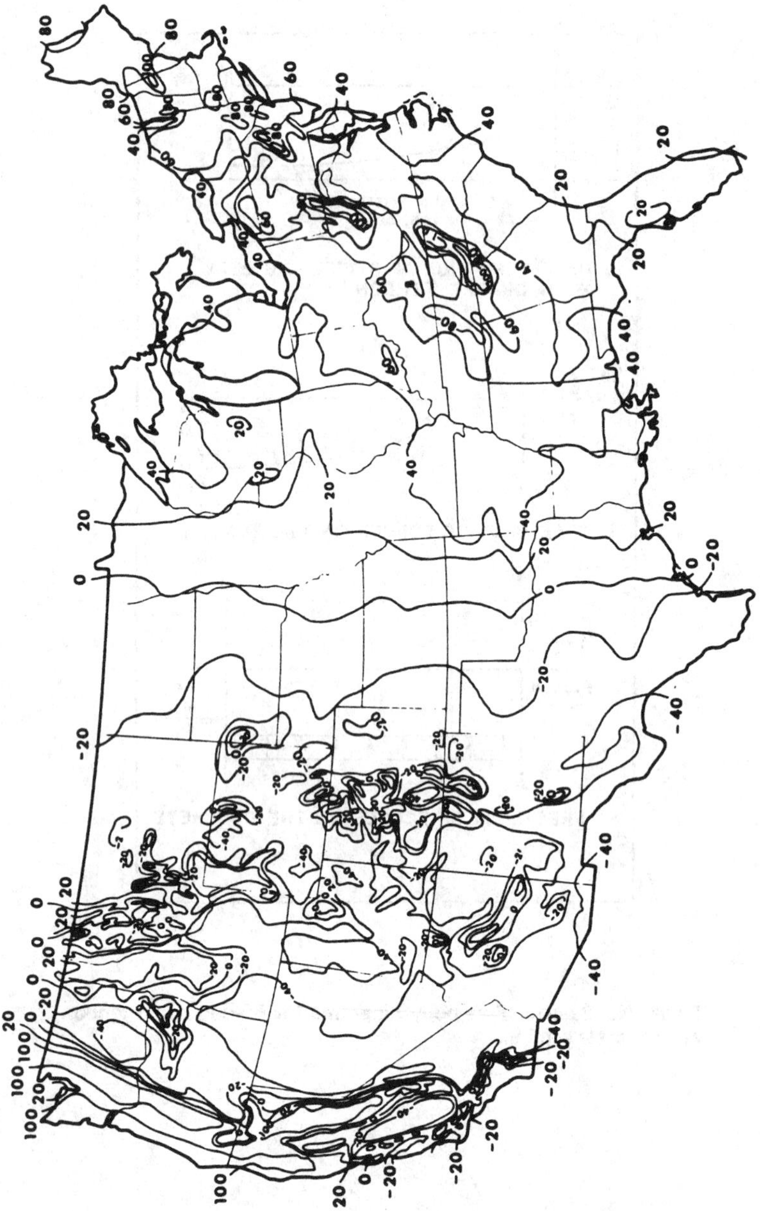

Figure No. 29-4-14. Thornthwaite Moisture Index distribution in the United States.

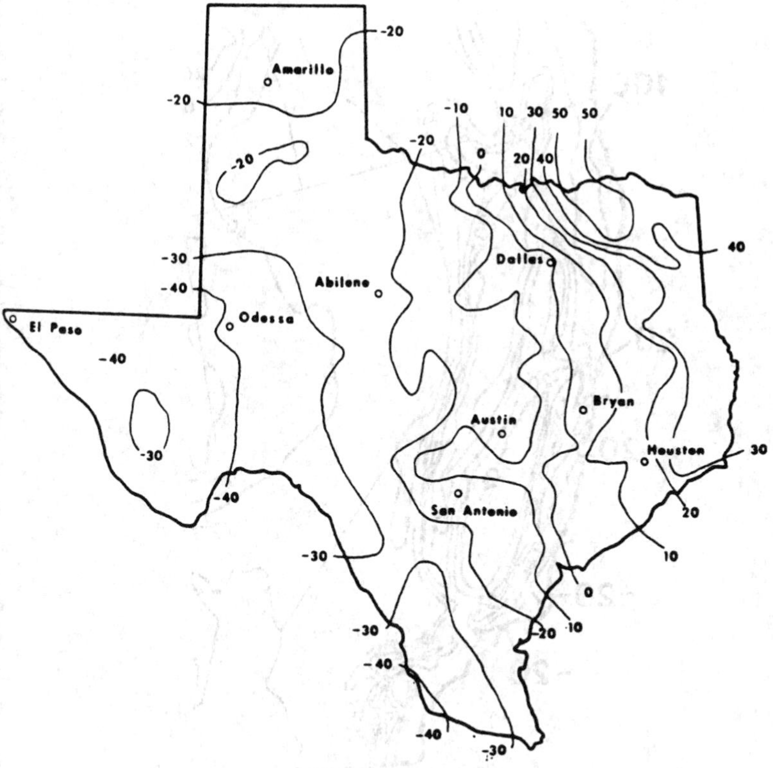
Amarillo
El Paso
Odessa
Abilene
Dallas
Austin
Bryan
Houston
San Antonio
-20
-10
0
10
20
30
40
50
-30
-40

Figure No. 29-4-15 (a). Thornthwaite Index for Texas (20 year average. 1955-1974).

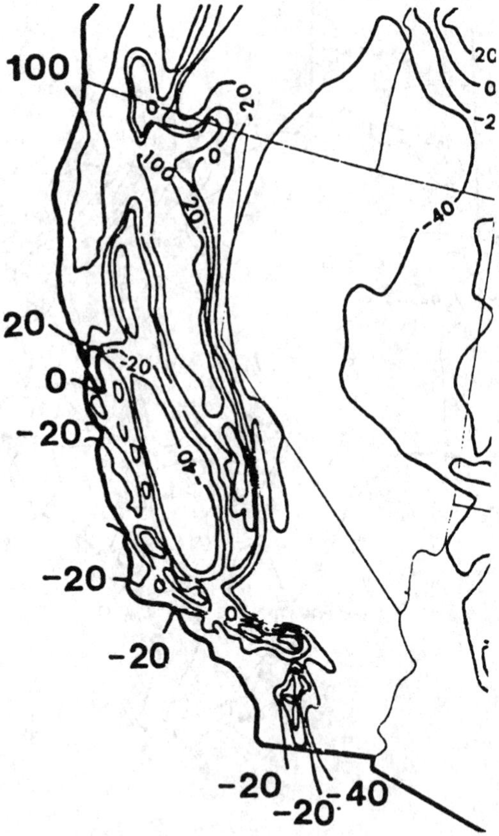
100
20
0
-20
-20
-20
-20
-20
-40
-20
0
-2
-40
100
0
20
-20
0
40

Figure No. 29-4-15 (b). Thornthwaite Moisture Index distribution in California.

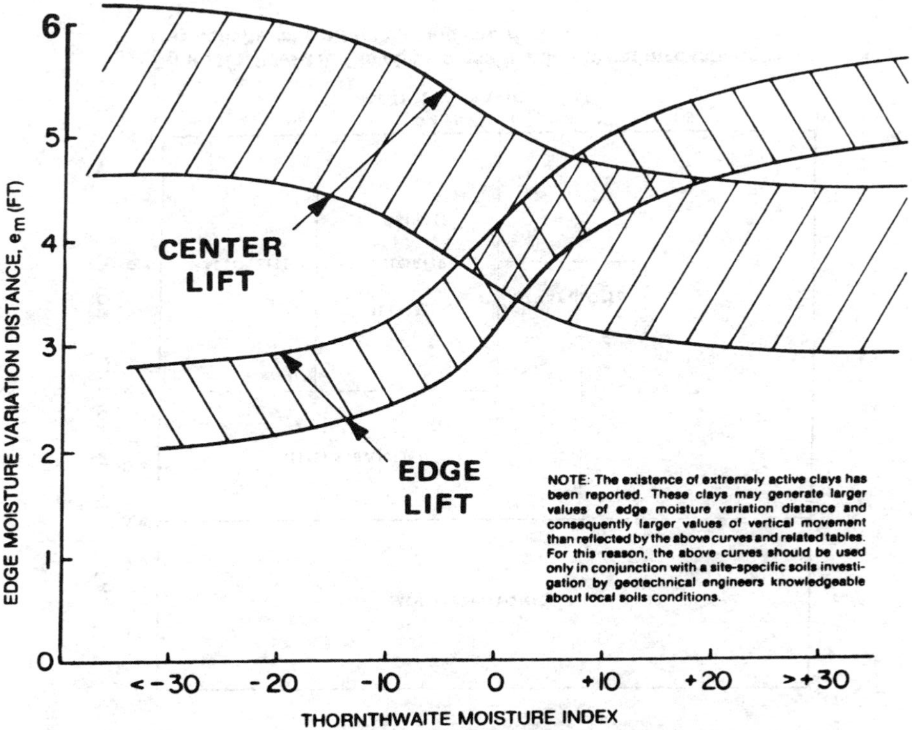
6
5
4
3
2
1
0
EDGE MOISTURE VARIATION DISTANCE, e_m (FT)
CENTER LIFT
EDGE LIFT
NOTE: The existence of extremely active clays has been reported. These clays may generate larger values of edge moisture variation distance and consequently larger values of vertical movement than reflected by the above curves and related tables. For this reason, the above curves should be used only in conjunction with a site-specific soils investigation by geotechnical engineers knowledgeable about local soils conditions.
< -30
-20
-10
0
+10
+20
> +30
THORNTHWAITE MOISTURE INDEX

Figure No. 29-4-16. Approximate relationship between Thornthwaite Index and moisture variation distance.

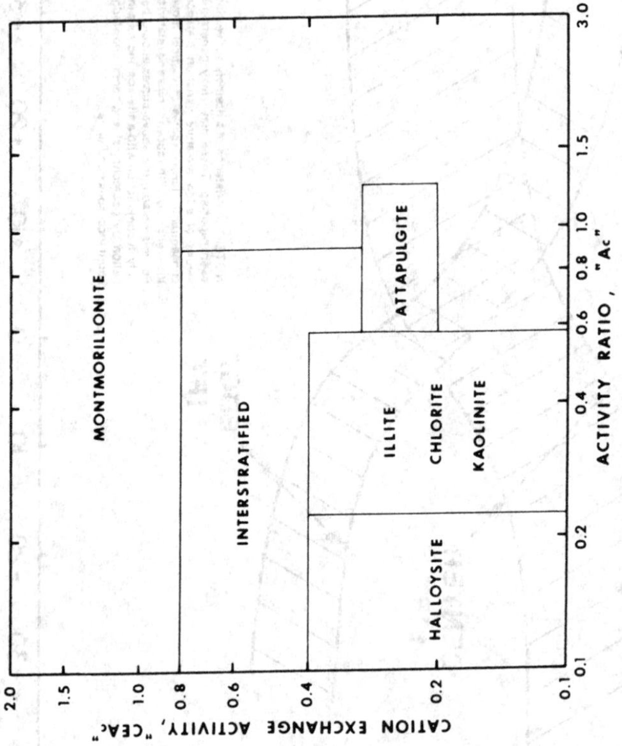
MONTMORILLONITE
INTERSTRATIFIED
ATTAPULGITE
ILLITE
CHLORITE
KAOLINITE
HALLOYSITE
CATION EXCHANGE ACTIVITY, "CEAc"
2.0
1.5
1.0
0.8
0.6
0.4
0.2
0.1
ACTIVITY RATIO, "Ac"
0.1
0.2
0.4
0.6
0.8
1.0
1.5
3.0

Figure No. 29-4-17. Clay type classification to cation exchange and clay activity ratio after Pearring and Holt.

NOTE: For practical applications, the maximum value of pF will seldom exceed a magnitude of 3.6.

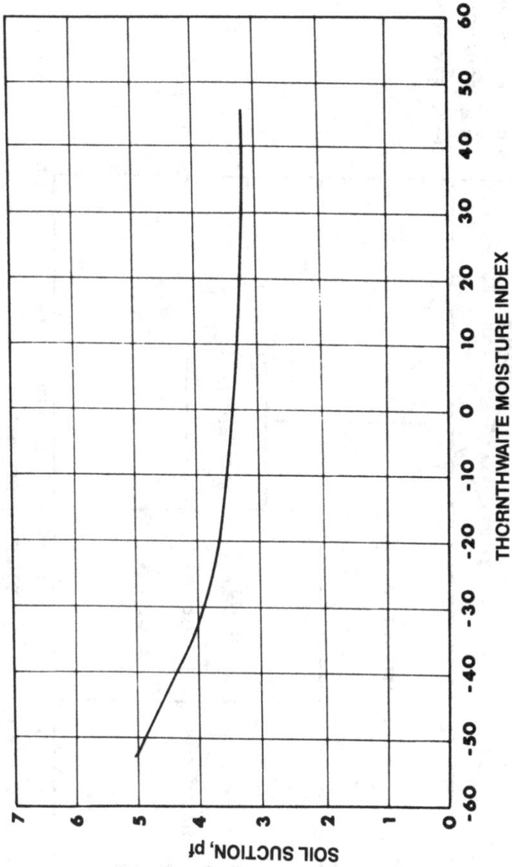
SOIL SUCTION, pf
0
1
2
3
4
5
6
7
THORNTHWAITE MOISTURE INDEX
-60
-50
-40
-30
-20
-10
0
10
20
30
40
50
60

Figure No. 29-4-18. Variation of constant soil suction with Thornthwaite Index.

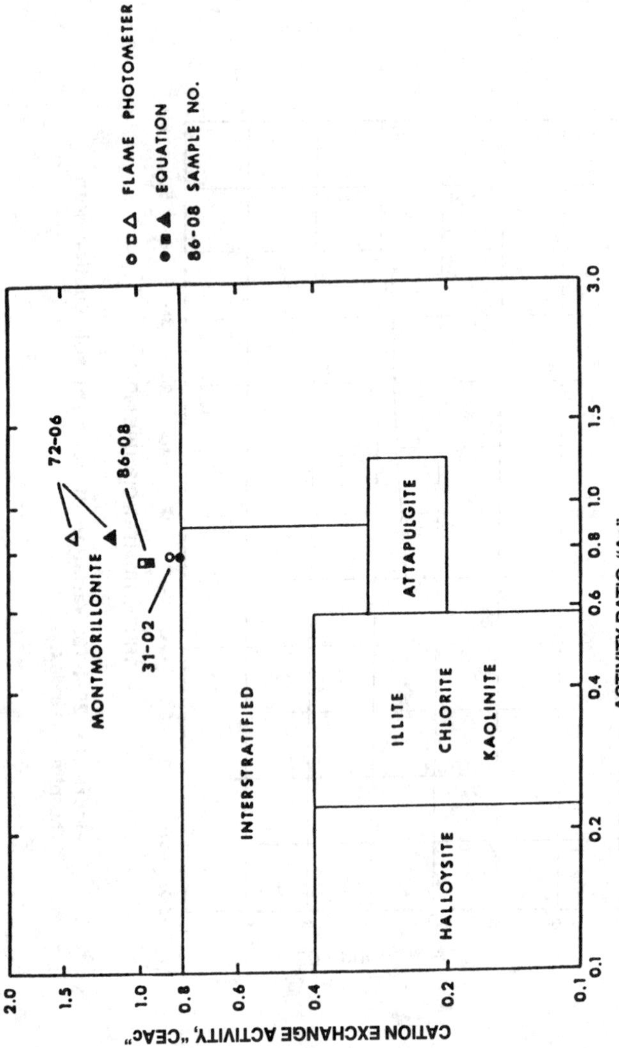
○ □ △ FLAME PHOTOMETER
● ■ ▲ EQUATION
86-08 SAMPLE NO.
MONTMORILLONITE
72-06
86-08
31-02
INTERSTRATIFIED
ATTAPULGITE
ILLITE
CHLORITE
KAOLINITE
HALLOYSITE
CATION EXCHANGE ACTIVITY, "CEAc"
2.0
1.5
1.0
0.8
0.6
0.4
0.2
0.1
ACTIVITY RATIO, "Ac"
0.1
0.2
0.4
0.6
0.8
1.0
1.5
3.0

Figure No 29-4-19. Comparison of Clay Mineral determination using Atomic Absorption and correlation equations.

Table No. 29-4-A. Differential Swell Occurring at the Perimeter of a Slab for a Center Lift Swelling Condition in Predominantly Kaolinite Clay Soil (30 Percent Clay).

Percent Clay (%)	Depth to Constant Suction (FT)	Constant Suction (pF)	Velocity of Moisture Flow (inches/month)	DIFFERENTIAL SWELL (IN) EDGE DISTANCE PENETRATION (FT)							
				1 FT	2 FT	3 FT	4 FT	5 FT	6 FT	7 FT	8 FT
30	3	3.2	0.1	0.001	0.001	0.002	0.002	0.003	0.004	0.004	0.005
			0.3	0.002	0.004	0.006	0.007	0.009	0.011	0.013	0.015
			0.5	0.003	0.005	0.008	0.011	0.015	0.018	0.021	0.025
			0.7	0.004	0.008	0.012	0.017	0.021	0.026	0.032	0.038
		3.4	0.1	0.001	0.002	0.003	0.004	0.006	0.007	0.008	0.009
			0.3	0.004	0.008	0.011	0.015	0.020	0.024	0.029	0.034
			0.5	0.006	0.012	0.019	0.026	0.034	0.044	0.054	0.067
			0.7	0.008	0.017	0.027	0.038	0.052	0.069	0.091	0.124
		3.6	0.1	0.003	0.006	0.009	0.012	0.015	0.019	0.022	0.026
			0.3	0.008	0.017	0.027	0.040	0.055	0.073	0.099	0.137
			0.5	0.014	0.030	0.050	0.077	0.117	0.192	0.370	0.881
			0.7	0.018	0.042	0.074	0.125	0.226	0.487	1.252	3.530
	5	3.2	0.1	0.001	0.003	0.004	0.005	0.007	0.008	0.010	0.012
			0.3	0.004	0.008	0.012	0.016	0.020	0.025	0.029	0.034
			0.5	0.007	0.013	0.020	0.028	0.035	0.043	0.051	0.060
			0.7	0.009	0.019	0.029	0.040	0.051	0.062	0.075	0.089
		3.4	0.1	0.003	0.005	0.008	0.011	0.014	0.017	0.020	0.023
			0.3	0.008	0.016	0.025	0.034	0.044	0.055	0.066	0.078
			0.5	0.014	0.028	0.043	0.060	0.079	0.100	0.125	0.153
			0.7	0.018	0.039	0.062	0.088	0.119	0.157	0.207	0.279
		3.6	0.1	0.006	0.013	0.020	0.027	0.034	0.042	0.050	0.059
			0.3	0.019	0.040	0.063	0.091	0.123	0.163	0.217	0.300
			0.5	0.030	0.067	0.112	0.171	0.258	0.413	0.776	1.797
			0.7	0.042	0.096	0.166	0.276	0.486	1.009	2.499	6.879
	7	3.2	0.1	0.002	0.004	0.007	0.009	0.012	0.015	0.017	0.020
			0.3	0.007	0.015	0.022	0.030	0.038	0.046	0.055	0.063
			0.5	0.012	0.025	0.038	0.051	0.065	0.080	0.095	0.111
			0.7	0.017	0.035	0.053	0.073	0.093	0.115	0.139	0.164
		3.4	0.1	0.005	0.010	0.016	0.021	0.026	0.031	0.037	0.042
			0.3	0.015	0.030	0.046	0.063	0.081	0.100	0.121	0.142
			0.5	0.024	0.050	0.079	0.110	0.144	0.184	0.228	0.281
			0.7	0.034	0.071	0.113	0.616	0.218	0.287	0.379	0.514
		3.58	0.1	0.011	0.022	0.033	0.045	0.057	0.069	0.082	0.096
			0.3	0.032	0.066	0.124	0.147	0.197	0.257	0.332	0.436
			0.5	0.051	0.110	0.182	0.272	0.396	0.596	1.006	2.098
			0.7	0.071	0.157	0.269	0.431	0.712	1.346	3.081	8.129

Table No. 29-4-B. Differential Swell Occurring at the Perimeter of a Slab for a Center Lift Swelling Condition in Predominantly Kaolinite Clay Soil (40 Percent Clay).

Percent Clay (%)	Depth to Constant Suction (FT)	Constant Suction (pF)	Velocity of Moisture Flow (inches /month)	DIFFERENTIAL SWELL (INCHES) EDGE DISTANCE PENETRATION (FT) 1 FT	2 FT	3 FT	4 FT	5 FT	6 FT	7 FT	8 FT
40	3	3.2	0.1	0.001	0.001	0.002	0.002	0.004	0.005	0.005	0.006
			0.3	0.002	0.004	0.006	0.009	0.011	0.014	0.016	0.019
			0.5	0.004	0.008	0.012	0.016	0.020	0.024	0.029	0.034
			0.7	0.005	0.010	0.016	0.022	0.029	0.035	0.043	0.050
		3.4	0.1	0.002	0.004	0.005	0.007	0.008	0.009	0.011	0.014
			0.3	0.004	0.009	0.014	0.020	0.025	0.032	0.038	0.044
			0.5	0.007	0.016	0.074	0.037	0.046	0.058	0.073	0.090
			0.7	0.011	0.023	0.036	0.051	0.070	0.092	0.122	0.166
		3.6	0.1	0.003	0.007	0.011	0.015	0.020	0.024	0.029	0.034
			0.3	0.010	0.023	0.037	0.053	0.072	0.097	0.131	0.183
			0.5	0.018	0.040	0.066	0.102	0.157	0.256	0.496	1.181
			0.7	0.025	0.056	0.100	0.168	0.303	0.653	1.677	4.728
	5	3.2	0.1	0.002	0.004	0.006	0.007	0.009	0.011	0.013	0.015
			0.3	0.005	0.011	0.016	0.022	0.028	0.033	0.039	0.046
			0.5	0.009	0.018	0.027	0.037	0.047	0.057	0.068	0.080
			0.7	0.012	0.025	0.038	0.053	0.067	0.083	0.100	0.118
		3.4	0.1	0.003	0.007	0.011	0.015	0.019	0.023	0.027	0.031
			0.3	0.011	0.022	0.034	0.046	0.059	0.073	0.088	0.104
			0.5	0.018	0.037	0.148	0.081	0.106	0.134	0.167	0.206
			0.7	0.025	0.052	0.083	0.118	0.159	0.210	0.277	0.374
		3.6	0.1	0.008	0.017	0.027	0.036	0.046	0.057	0.068	0.079
			0.3	0.026	0.054	0.085	0.122	0.165	0.219	0.292	0.401
			0.5	0.041	0.090	0.150	0.229	0.346	0.553	1.040	2.408
			0.7	0.057	0.128	0.224	0.371	0.652	1.353	3.349	9.215
	7	3.2	0.1	0.003	0.006	0.010	0.013	0.017	0.020	0.023	0.027
			0.3	0.010	0.020	0.030	0.040	0.051	0.062	0.073	0.084
			0.5	0.016	0.033	0.051	0.069	0.087	0.107	0.127	0.148
			0.7	0.023	0.046	0.071	0.098	0.125	0.155	0.186	0.220
		3.4	0.1	0.006	0.013	0.020	0.027	0.034	0.041	0.048	0.056
			0.3	0.020	0.041	0.062	0.085	0.109	0.135	0.162	0.191
			0.5	0.033	0.069	0.107	0.148	0.194	0.246	0.306	0.377
			0.7	0.045	0.095	0.152	0.216	0.292	0.385	0.507	0.689
		3.58	0.1	0.014	0.029	0.044	0.060	0.076	0.093	0.110	0.129
			0.3	0.042	0.087	0.138	0.196	0.263	0.343	0.444	0.583
			0.5	0.069	0.148	0.244	0.365	0.531	0.799	1.348	2.791
			0.7	0.095	0.210	0.360	0.577	0.953	1.803	4.126	-

Table No. 29-4-C. Differential Swell Occurring at the Perimeter of a Slab for a Center Lift Swelling Condition in Predominantly Kaolinite Clay Soil (50 Percent Clay).

Percent Clay (%)	Depth to Constant Suction (FT)	Constant Suction (pF)	Velocity of Moisture Flow (inches /month)	DIFFERENTIAL SWELL (INCHES) EDGE DISTANCE PENETRATION (FT) 1 FT	2 FT	3 FT	4 FT	5 FT	6 FT	7 FT	8 FT
50	3	3.2	0.1	0.001	0.002	0.002	0.003	0.004	0.005	0.006	0.007
			0.3	0.003	0.005	0.008	0.011	0.014	0.018	0.021	0.024
			0.5	0.004	0.009	0.014	0.019	0.025	0.030	0.036	0.042
			0.7	0.006	0.013	0.020	0.028	0.036	0.044	0.053	0.063
		3.4	0.1	0.002	0.004	0.006	0.008	0.010	0.012	0.015	0.017
			0.3	0.006	0.012	0.018	0.025	0.032	0.040	0.048	0.057
			0.5	0.009	0.020	0.031	0.043	0.057	0.073	0.091	0.113
			0.7	0.013	0.028	0.044	0.064	0.086	0.115	0.153	0.207
		3.6	0.1	0.005	0.009	0.014	0.020	0.025	0.031	0.037	0.044
			0.3	0.014	0.029	0.046	0 067	0.091	0.123	0.165	0.230
			0.5	0.022	0.049	0.083	0.127	0.196	0.321	0.620	1.480
			0.7	0.031	0.070	0.124	0.210	0.380	0.818	2.103	5.926
	5	3.2	0.1	0.002	0.005	0.007	0.009	0.011	0.014	0.016	0.018
			0.3	0.007	0.014	0.020	0.027	0.035	0.042	0.050	0.057
			0.5	0.011	0.022	0.034	0.046	0.059	0.072	0.086	0.100
			0.7	0.015	0.031	0.048	0.066	0.084	0.104	0.125	0.148
		3.4	0.1	0.005	0.009	0.014	0.019	0.024	0.029	0.034	0.039
			0.3	0.013	0.027	0.042	0.058	0.074	0.092	0.110	0.130
			0.5	0.023	0.047	0.073	0.101	0.133	0.168	0.209	0.258
			0.7	0.031	0.066	0.105	0.148	0.200	0.264	0.347	0.469
		3.6	0.1	0.011	0.022	0.033	0.045	0.058	0.071	0.085	0.099
			0.3	0.031	0.066	0.106	0.151	0.206	0.274	0.365	0.502
			0.5	0.051	0.113	0.188	0.288	0.434	0.694	1.303	3.018
			0.7	0.071	0.160	0.281	0.465	0.817	1.696	4.196	-
	7	3.2	0.1	0.004	0.008	0.013	0.017	0.021	0.025	0.030	0.034
			0.3	0.012	0.024	0.037	0.050	0.064	0.077	0.091	0.106
			0.5	0.021	0.042	0.064	0.086	0.110	0.134	0.159	0.186
			0.7	0.028	0.058	0.090	0.122	0.157	0.194	0.233	0.276
		3.4	0.1	0.008	0.017	0.025	0.034	0.043	0.052	0.061	0.070
			0.3	0.025	0.051	0.078	0.107	0.137	0.169	0.203	0.240
			0.5	0.041	0.085	0.133	0.185	0.243	0.308	0.383	0.472
			0.7	0.057	0.120	0.191	0.272	0.366	0.483	0.636	0.864
		3.58	0.1	0.018	0.036	0.055	0.074	0.095	0.116	0.138	0.161
			0.3	0.053	0.111	0.174	0.246	0.330	0.430	0.557	0.732
			0.5	0.086	0.186	0.306	0.457	0.666	1.001	1.690	3.499
			0.7	0.119	0.263	0.452	0.723	1.194	2.260	5.172	-

Table No. 29-4-D. Differential Swell Occurring at the Perimeter of a Slab for a Center Lift Swelling Condition in Predominantly Kaolinite Clay Soil (60 Percent Clay).

Percent Clay (%)	Depth to Constant Suction (FT)	Constant Suction (pF)	Velocity of Moisture Flow (inches /month)	DIFFERENTIAL SWELL (INCHES) EDGE DISTANCE PENETRATION (FT) 1 FT	2 FT	3 FT	4 FT	5 FT	6 FT	7 FT	8 FT
60	3	3.2	0.1	0.001	0.003	0.004	0.005	0.006	0.007	0.008	0.010
			0.3	0.003	0.007	0.010	0.014	0.018	0.021	0.025	0.029
			0.5	0.006	0.012	0.018	0.024	0.030	0.037	0.044	0.052
			0.7	0.008	0.017	0.025	0.034	0.044	0.054	0.065	0.077
		3.4	0.1	0.002	0.005	0.007	0.010	0.012	0.015	0.017	0.020
			0.3	0.007	0.014	0.022	0.030	0.038	0.047	0.057	0.068
			0.5	0.012	0.024	0.038	0.053	0.069	0.088	0.110	0.136
			0.7	0.016	0.033	0.053	0.077	0.104	0.138	0.184	0.249
		3.6	0.1	0.006	0.012	0.018	0.024	0.031	0.038	0.045	0.053
			0.3	0.017	0.035	0.056	0.081	0.110	0.148	0.199	0.278
			0.5	0.026	0.059	0.099	0.154	0.236	0.386	0.745	1.779
			0.7	0.036	0.083	0.149	0.252	0.455	0.983	2.527	7.124
	5	3.2	0.1	0.003	0.005	0.008	0.011	0.014	0.016	0.019	0.022
			0.3	0.008	0.016	0.025	0.033	0.042	0.051	0.060	0.069
			0.5	0.013	0.027	0.041	0.056	0.071	0.087	0.103	0.120
			0.7	0.019	0.038	0.058	0.080	0.102	0.126	0.151	0.178
		3.4	0.1	0.006	0.011	0.017	0.023	0.029	0.034	0.041	0.047
			0.3	0.016	0.033	0.051	0.069	0.089	0.110	0.132	0.156
			0.5	0.028	0.056	0.087	0.122	0.160	0.202	0.252	0.310
			0.7	0.037	0.078	0.125	0.177	0.240	0.316	0.417	0.564
		3.6	0.1	0.013	0.027	0.040	0.055	0.070	0.086	0.102	0.120
			0.3	0.038	0.080	0.077	0.182	0.248	0.329	0.439	0.604
			0.5	0.062	0.135	0.226	0.345	0.521	0.834	1.566	3.628
			0.7	0.086	0.193	0.337	0.559	0.982	2.039	5.049	-
	7	3.2	0.1	0.005	0.010	0.016	0.021	0.026	0.031	0.036	0.041
			0.3	0.015	0.030	0.046	0.061	0.078	0.094	0.111	0.128
			0.5	0.025	0.050	0.077	0.104	0.132	0.161	0.192	0.224
			0.7	0.034	0.070	0.108	0.147	0.189	0.233	0.281	0.332
		3.4	0.1	0.010	0.020	0.030	0.041	0.052	0.062	0.073	0.085
			0.3	0.030	0.061	0.093	0.128	0.164	0.202	0.243	0.287
			0.5	0.050	0.103	0.160	0.223	0.292	0.371	0.461	0.568
			0.7	0.069	0.144	0.229	0.326	0.440	0.580	0.765	1.038
		3.58	0.1	0.021	0.043	0.066	0.089	0.114	0.139	0.166	0.194
			0.3	0.063	0.131	0.208	0.295	0.396	0.516	0.669	0.879
			0.5	0.103	0.223	0.367	0.549	0.800	1.203	2.031	4.205
			0.7	0.142	0.316	0.543	0.870	1.436	2.717	6.217	-

Table No. 29-4-E. Differential Swell Occurring at the Perimeter of a Slab for a Center Lift Swelling Condition in Predominantly Kaolinite Clay Soil (70 Percent Clay).

Percent Clay (%)	Depth to Constant Suction (FT)	Constant Suction (pF)	Velocity of Moisture Flow (inches /month)	DIFFERENTIAL SWELL (INCHES) EDGE DISTANCE PENETRATION (FT) 1 FT	2 FT	3 FT	4 FT	5 FT	6 FT	7 FT	8 FT
70	3	3.2	0.1	0.001	0.003	0.004	0.005	0.007	0.008	0.010	0.011
			0.3	0.004	0.008	0.012	0.016	0.021	0.025	0.029	0.034
			0.5	0.006	0.013	0.020	0.027	0.035	0.042	0.051	0.060
			0.7	0.010	0.019	0.029	0.040	0.051	0.063	0.076	0.089
		3.4	0.1	0.003	0.005	0.008	0.011	0.014	0.017	0.020	0.023
			0.3	0.008	0.017	0.026	0.035	0.045	0.056	0.067	0.079
			0.5	0.014	0.028	0.044	0.062	0.081	0.103	0.129	0.159
			0.7	0.019	0.039	0.063	0.090	0.122	0.162	0.215	0.292
		3.6	0.1	0.006	0.013	0.020	0.027	0.035	0.043	0.052	0.061
			0.3	0.019	0.041	0.065	0.094	0.128	0.172	0.232	0.324
			0.5	0.032	0.069	0.117	0.180	0.276	0.451	0.871	2.079
			0.7	0.043	0.098	0.174	0.294	0.532	1.148	2.952	8.322
	5	3.2	0.1	0.003	0.006	0.009	0.013	0.016	0.019	0.022	0.026
			0.3	0.010	0.019	0.029	0.039	0.049	0.059	0.070	0.080
			0.5	0.016	0.032	0.048	0.065	0.083	0.101	0.120	0.140
			0.7	0.022	0.044	0.068	0.093	0.119	0.146	0.176	0.208
		3.4	0.1	0.006	0.012	0.019	0.026	0.033	0.039	0.046	0.054
			0.3	0.018	0.038	0.059	0.081	0.104	0.128	0.155	0.183
			0.5	0.031	0.065	0.101	0.141	0.185	0.235	0.293	0.361
			0.7	0.043	0.092	0.146	0.207	0.280	0.370	0.487	0.659
		3.6	0.1	0.015	0.030	0.046	0.063	0.081	0.099	0.119	0.139
			0.3	0.045	0.094	0.149	0.213	0.290	0.385	0.512	0.706
			0.5	0.072	0.158	0.264	0.404	0.609	0.974	1.830	4.239
			0.7	0.100	0.226	0.394	0.653	1.147	2.381	5.893	-
	7	3.2	0.1	0.006	0.011	0.017	0.023	0.029	0.035	0.041	0.047
			0.3	0.018	0.035	0.053	0.072	0.090	0.110	0.129	0.149
			0.5	0.030	0.059	0.090	0.121	0.154	0.188	0.224	0.262
			0.7	0.040	0.082	0.126	0.172	0.221	0.273	0.328	0.388
		3.4	0.1	0.012	0.024	0.036	0.048	0.060	0.073	0.086	0.099
			0.3	0.035	0.071	0.109	0.149	0.192	0.237	0.284	0.336
			0.5	0.057	0.119	0.186	0.260	0.341	0.432	0.538	0.663
			0.7	0.080	0.168	0.267	0.381	0.514	0.678	0.893	1.213
		3.58	0.1	0.025	0.050	0.077	0.104	0.133	0.163	0.194	0.227
			0.3	0.073	0.154	0.244	0.345	0.463	0.604	0.782	1.028
			0.5	0.120	0.260	0.429	0.642	0.935	1.406	2.373	4.913
			0.7	0.166	0.369	0.634	1.016	1.677	3.175	7.263	-

Table No. 29-4-F. Differential Swell Occurring at the Perimeter of a Slab for a Center Lift Swelling Condition in Predominantly Illite Clay Soil (30 Percent Clay).

Percent Clay (%)	Depth to Constant Suction (FT)	Constant Suction (pF)	Velocity of Moisture Flow (inches /month)	DIFFERENTIAL SWELL (INCHES) EDGE DISTANCE PENETRATION (FT)							
				1 FT	2 FT	3 FT	4 FT	5 FT	6 FT	7 FT	8 FT
30	3	3.2	0.1	0.002	0.003	0.004	0.005	0.006	0.007	0.008	0.010
			0.3	0.003	0.007	0.010	0.014	0.017	0.021	0.025	0.029
			0.5	0.006	0.012	0.018	0.024	0.030	0.037	0.044	0.051
			0.7	0.008	0.016	0.024	0.033	0.043	0.053	0.064	0.075
		3.4	0.1	0.003	0.005	0.007	0.010	0.012	0.015	0.017	0.020
			0.3	0.007	0.014	0.022	0.030	0.038	0.047	0.057	0.067
			0.5	0.011	0.024	0.037	0.052	0.068	0.087	0.109	0.135
			0.7	0.016	0.034	0.054	0.077	0.104	0.138	0.182	0.248
		3.6	0.1	0.005	0.011	0.017	0.023	0.030	0.037	0.044	0.051
			0.3	0.016	0.035	0.055	0.080	0.109	0.146	0.197	0.274
			0.5	0.027	0.058	0.098	0.152	0.234	0.382	0.737	1.760
			0.7	0.036	0.083	0.147	0.249	0.451	0.973	2.500	7.049
	5	3.2	0.1	0.003	0.006	0.008	0.011	0.014	0.016	0.019	0.022
			0.3	0.008	0.016	0.024	0.032	0.041	0.050	0.059	0.068
			0.5	0.013	0.027	0.041	0.055	0.070	0.086	0.102	0.119
			0.7	0.018	0.037	0.057	0.078	0.100	0.124	0.149	0.176
		3.4	0.1	0.005	0.011	0.016	0.022	0.028	0.034	0.040	0.046
			0.3	0.016	0.033	0.051	0.069	0.089	0.109	0.131	0.155
			0.5	0.027	0.055	0.086	0.120	0.157	0.200	0.248	0.306
			0.7	0.037	0.078	0.124	0.176	0.238	0.319	0.413	0.558
		3.6	0.1	0.012	0.025	0.039	0.053	0.068	0.084	0.100	0.118
			0.3	0.037	0.079	0.126	0.180	0.245	0.326	0.434	0.598
			0.5	0.062	0.134	0.224	0.342	0.516	0.825	1.551	3.591
			0.7	0.084	0.190	0.333	0.553	0.971	2.016	4.991	-
	7	3.2	0.1	0.005	0.010	0.015	0.020	0.025	0.030	0.035	0.041
			0.3	0.015	0.030	0.045	0.061	0.076	0.093	0.109	0.126
			0.5	0.025	0.050	0.076	0.103	0.131	0.160	0.190	0.221
			0.7	0.034	0.070	0.107	0.146	0.187	0.231	0.278	0.329
		3.4	0.1	0.010	0.020	0.030	0.041	0.051	0.062	0.073	0.084
			0.3	0.029	0.060	0.092	0.126	0.162	0.200	0.241	0.284
			0.5	0.048	0.102	0.158	0.221	0.288	0.367	0.456	0.562
			0.7	0.068	0.143	0.227	0.323	0.436	0.574	0.757	1.028
		3.58	0.1	0.021	0.042	0.065	0.088	0.113	0.138	0.164	0.191
			0.3	0.062	0.131	0.207	0.292	0.392	0.511	0.662	0.870
			0.5	0.103	0.221	0.363	0.543	0.792	1.191	2.010	4.162
			0.7	0.141	0.313	0.537	0.861	1.421	2.689	6.153	-

Table No. 29-4-G. Differential Swell Occurring at the Perimeter of a Slab for a Center Lift Swelling Condition in Predominantly Illite Clay Soil (40 Percent Clay).

Percent Clay (%)	Depth to Constant Suction (FT)	Constant Suction (pF)	Velocity of Moisture Flow (inches/month)	DIFFERENTIAL SWELL (INCHES)							
				EDGE DISTANCE PENETRATION (FT)							
				1 FT	2 FT	3 FT	4 FT	5 FT	6 FT	7 FT	8 FT
40	3	3.2	0.1	0.002	0.003	0.005	0.007	0.008	0.010	0.012	0.014
			0.3	0.005	0.010	0.015	0.020	0.026	0.031	0.037	0.042
			0.5	0.008	0.016	0.025	0.034	0.043	0.052	0.063	0.073
			0.7	0.011	0.023	0.035	0.048	0.062	0.076	0.092	0.109
		3.4	0.1	0.003	0.006	0.010	0.013	0.017	0.020	0.024	0.028
			0.3	0.010	0.021	0.032	0.043	0.055	0.068	0.082	0.098
			0.5	0.017	0.034	0.054	0.075	0.099	0.126	0.157	0.194
			0.7	0.023	0.048	0.077	0.110	0.149	0.198	0.263	0.357
		3.6	0.1	0.008	0.017	0.025	0.034	0.044	0.054	0.064	0.075
			0.3	0.023	0.050	0.080	0.115	0.157	0.211	0.284	0.396
			0.5	0.039	0.085	0.142	0.220	0.338	0.552	1.065	2.542
			0.7	0.053	0.120	0.213	0.360	0.651	1.405	3.611	-
	5	3.2	0.1	0.004	0.007	0.011	0.015	0.019	0.023	0.027	0.031
			0.3	0.012	0.024	0.035	0.047	0.060	0.072	0.085	0.098
			0.5	0.019	0.039	0.059	0.080	0.101	0.124	0.147	0.172
			0.7	0.026	0.054	0.083	0.113	0.145	0.179	0.215	0.254
		3.4	0.1	0.007	0.015	0.023	0.031	0.040	0.048	0.057	0.065
			0.3	0.023	0.047	0.073	0.099	0.128	0.157	0.189	0.224
			0.5	0.039	0.080	0.124	0.173	0.227	0.288	0.358	0.442
			0.7	0.053	0.112	0.178	0.254	0.343	0.452	0.596	0.805
		3.6	0.1	0.018	0.037	0.057	0.077	0.099	0.121	0.145	0.170
			0.3	0.054	0.114	0.182	0.261	0.354	0.471	0.627	0.863
			0.5	0.089	0.194	0.323	0.494	0.745	1.192	2.239	5.184
			0.7	0.122	0.275	0.482	0.799	1.403	2.912	7.207	-
	7	3.2	0.1	0.007	0.014	0.021	0.029	0.036	0.043	0.051	0.058
			0.3	0.022	0.043	0.065	0.088	0.111	0.134	0.158	0.183
			0.5	0.035	0.072	0.109	0.148	0.188	0.230	0.274	0.320
			0.7	0.049	0.100	0.154	0.210	0.270	0.330	0.401	0.474
		3.4	0.1	0.015	0.030	0.045	0.060	0.075	0.091	0.106	0.122
			0.3	0.042	0.087	0.134	0.183	0.234	0.289	0.348	0.410
			0.5	0.070	0.146	0.228	0.318	0.417	0.528	0.657	0.811
			0.7	0.098	0.207	0.328	0.466	0.629	0.829	1.093	1.484
		3.58	0.1	0.030	0.062	0.094	0.128	0.163	0.199	0.236	0.277
			0.3	0.090	0.188	0.298	0.422	0.566	0.738	0.956	1.256
			0.5	0.147	0.318	0.524	0.784	1.143	1.719	2.902	6.008
			0.7	0.203	0.451	0.775	1.242	2.051	3.883	8.882	-

Table No. 29-4-H. Differential Swell Occurring at the Perimeter of a Slab for a Center Lift Swelling Condition in Predominantly Illite Clay Soil (50 Percent Clay).

Percent Clay (%)	Depth to Constant Suction (FT)	Constant Suction (pF)	Velocity of Moisture Flow (inches/month)	DIFFERENTIAL SWELL (INCHES) EDGE DISTANCE PENETRATION (FT)							
				1 FT	2 FT	3 FT	4 FT	5 FT	6 FT	7 FT	8 FT
50	3	3.2	0.1	0.002	0.004	0.006	0.008	0.010	0.013	0.015	0.017
			0.3	0.006	0.013	0.019	0.026	0.033	0.040	0.047	0.055
			0.5	0.010	0.021	0.033	0.042	0.056	0.069	0.082	0.096
			0.7	0.014	0.030	0.046	0.063	0.081	0.099	0.120	0.142
		3.4	0.1	0.004	0.009	0.013	0.018	0.022	0.027	0.032	0.037
			0.3	0.013	0.026	0.041	0.056	0.072	0.089	0.107	0.127
			0.5	0.022	0.045	0.070	0.098	0.129	0.164	0.205	0.254
			0.7	0.030	0.063	0.101	0.144	0.196	0.260	0.344	0.467
		3.6	0.1	0.011	0.021	0.033	0.045	0.057	0.070	0.084	0.098
			0.3	0.031	0.065	0.105	0.150	0.206	0.276	0.372	0.518
			0.5	0.050	0.111	0.185	0.287	0.441	0.721	1.391	3.322
			0.7	0.069	0.156	0.278	0.470	0.851	1.836	4.720	-
	5	3.2	0.1	0.005	0.010	0.015	0.020	0.026	0.031	0.036	0.041
			0.3	0.015	0.030	0.046	0.062	0.078	0.094	0.111	0.128
			0.5	0.025	0.051	0.077	0.104	0.133	0.162	0.193	0.225
			0.7	0.035	0.071	0.110	0.148	0.190	0.235	0.282	0.333
		3.4	0.1	0.010	0.021	0.031	0.042	0.053	0.064	0.075	0.086
			0.3	0.031	0.062	0.096	0.131	0.167	0.207	0.248	0.293
			0.5	0.051	0.104	0.163	0.227	0.298	0.377	0.469	0.579
			0.7	0.070	0.147	0.233	0.332	0.449	0.592	0.779	1.054
		3.6	0.1	0.025	0.049	0.075	0.102	0.130	0.160	0.191	0.224
			0.3	0.071	0.150	0.239	0.341	0.463	0.615	0.820	1.129
			0.5	0.116	0.253	0.423	0.646	0.974	1.558	2.927	6.778
			0.7	0.159	0.359	0.629	1.043	1.834	3.807	9.422	-
	7	3.2	0.1	0.009	0.018	0.028	0.037	0.047	0.056	0.066	0.076
			0.3	0.028	0.056	0.085	0.114	0.144	0.175	0.206	0.238
			0.5	0.046	0.094	0.143	0.193	0.246	0.301	0.358	0.418
			0.7	0.064	0.131	0.201	0.275	0.353	0.436	0.524	0.620
		3.4	0.1	0.019	0.038	0.057	0.077	0.097	0.117	0.138	0.159
			0.3	0.055	0.114	0.175	0.239	0.307	0.378	0.455	0.537
			0.5	0.092	0.192	0.299	0.416	0.546	0.692	0.860	1.061
			0.7	0.129	0.271	0.429	0.610	0.823	1.085	1.429	1.940
		3.58	0.1	0.040	0.081	0.123	0.167	0.213	0.261	0.310	0.362
			0.3	0.117	0.246	0.389	0.551	0.739	0.965	1.250	1.642
			0.5	0.193	0.417	0.685	1.026	1.495	2.248	3.795	7.856
			0.7	0.265	0.590	1.013	1.624	2.682	5.075	-	-

Table No. 29-4-I. Differential Swell Occurring at the Perimeter of a Slab for a Center Lift Swelling Condition in Predominantly Illite Clay Soil (60 Percent Clay).

Percent Clay	Depth to Constant Suction	Constant Suction	Velocity of Moisture Flow	DIFFERENTIAL SWELL (INCHES)							
				EDGE DISTANCE PENETRATION (FT)							
(%)	(FT)	(pF)	(inches /month)	1 FT	2 FT	3 FT	4 FT	5 FT	6 FT	7 FT	8 FT
60	3	3.2	0.1	0.003	0.006	0.008	0.011	0.014	0.016	0.019	0.022
			0.3	0.008	0.016	0.024	0.033	0.041	0.050	0.059	0.068
			0.5	0.013	0.027	0.040	0.055	0.070	0.085	0.102	0.119
			0.7	0.018	0.037	0.067	0.078	0.100	0.123	0.148	0.176
		3.4	0.1	0.006	0.011	0.017	0.022	0.028	0.034	0.040	0.046
			0.3	0.016	0.033	0.051	0.069	0.089	0.110	0.133	0.157
			0.5	0.027	0.055	0.087	0.121	0.159	0.203	0.253	0.314
			0.7	0.037	0.078	0.124	0.178	0.241	0.320	0.424	0.576
		3.6	0.1	0.013	0.026	0.040	0.055	0.070	0.086	0.103	0.121
			0.3	0.038	0.080	0.129	0.185	0.254	0.340	0.459	0.639
			0.5	0.062	0.136	0.229	0.355	0.544	0.890	1.659	4.104
			0.7	0.085	0.194	0.344	0.582	1.052	2.268	5.831	-
	5	3.2	0.1	0.006	0.012	0.018	0.025	0.031	0.038	0.044	0.050
			0.3	0.018	0.037	0.056	0.075	0.095	0.116	0.137	0.158
			0.5	0.031	0.062	0.095	0.129	0.164	0.200	0.238	0.277
			0.7	0.043	0.088	0.134	0.183	0.235	0.290	0.348	0.411
		3.4	0.1	0.012	0.025	0.038	0.051	0.065	0.078	0.092	0.106
			0.3	0.038	0.077	0.118	0.161	0.206	0.255	0.306	0.361
			0.5	0.062	0.129	0.201	0.280	0.367	0.466	0.579	0.714
			0.7	0.086	0.181	0.288	0.410	0.554	0.730	0.962	1.301
		3.6	0.1	0.030	0.061	0.093	0.126	0.161	0.197	0.236	0.276
			0.3	0.088	0.185	0.295	0.421	0.572	0.761	1.013	1.394
			0.5	0.144	0.313	0.522	0.797	1.203	1.924	3.615	8.371
			0.7	0.197	0.444	0.778	1.289	2.265	4.702	-	-
	7	3.2	0.1	0.012	0.023	0.035	0.047	0.058	0.070	0.082	0.094
			0.3	0.035	0.069	0.105	0.141	0.178	0.216	0.255	0.294
			0.5	0.057	0.116	0.176	0.239	0.304	0.372	0.442	0.516
			0.7	0.079	0.162	0.249	0.340	0.436	0.538	0.647	0.766
		3.4	0.1	0.023	0.047	0.071	0.095	0.120	0.145	0.170	0.196
			0.3	0.069	0.141	0.216	0.294	0.379	0.467	0.562	0.663
			0.5	0.114	0.237	0.369	0.514	0.674	0.855	1.063	1.310
			0.7	0.156	0.333	0.528	0.752	1.015	1.340	1.764	2.395
		3.58	0.1	0.050	0.100	0.153	0.207	0.263	0.322	0.383	0.447
			0.3	0.145	0.304	0.481	0.681	0.912	1.192	1.543	2.028
			0.5	0.238	0.514	0.846	1.266	1.846	2.776	4.687	9.702
			0.7	0.328	0.730	1.252	2.006	3.312	6.268	-	-

Table No. 29-4-J. Differential Swell Occurring at the Perimeter of a Slab for a Center Lift Swelling Condition in Predominantly Illite Clay Soil (70 Percent Clay).

Percent Clay (%)	Depth to Constant Suction (FT)	Constant Suction (pF)	Velocity of Moisture Flow (inches /month)	DIFFERENTIAL SWELL (INCHES) EDGE DISTANCE PENETRATION (FT)							
				1 FT	2 FT	3 FT	4 FT	5 FT	6 FT	7 FT	8 FT
70	3	3.2	0.1	0.003	0.006	0.009	0.013	0.016	0.019	0.022	0.026
			0.3	0.009	0.019	0.028	0.038	0.048	0.059	0.069	0.080
			0.5	0.016	0.032	0.048	0.066	0.083	0.102	0.121	0.141
			0.7	0.021	0.044	0.068	0.092	0.119	0.147	0.177	0.209
		3.4	0.1	0.007	0.013	0.020	0.027	0.034	0.041	0.047	0.055
			0.3	0.019	0.039	0.061	0.083	0.106	0.131	0.158	0.187
			0.5	0.032	0.066	0.103	0.144	0.190	0.242	0.302	0.374
			0.7	0.044	0.093	0.148	0.212	0.287	0.381	0.510	0.686
		3.6	0.1	0.016	0.032	0.049	0.066	0.084	0.103	0.124	0.145
			0.3	0.045	0.095	0.153	0.220	0.302	0.405	0.545	0.761
			0.5	0.074	0.162	0.273	0.423	0.648	1.061	2.047	4.885
			0.7	0.101	0.231	0.409	0.692	1.251	2.700	6.940	-
	5	3.2	0.1	0.008	0.015	0.022	0.030	0.037	0.045	0.035	0.060
			0.3	0.022	0.044	0.067	0.090	0.114	0.138	0.163	0.189
			0.5	0.037	0.074	0.113	0.153	0.195	0.238	0.283	0.330
			0.7	0.051	0.104	0.159	0.218	0.279	0.345	0.414	0.489
		3.4	0.1	0.015	0.030	0.046	0.062	0.077	0.094	0.110	0.127
			0.3	0.044	0.091	0.140	0.191	0.245	0.303	0.364	0.430
			0.5	0.073	0.153	0.239	0.330	0.437	0.554	0.689	0.850
			0.7	0.102	0.215	0.342	0.487	0.659	0.869	1.145	1.548
		3.6	0.1	0.035	0.071	0.109	0.149	0.191	0.234	0.279	0.327
			0.3	0.104	0.219	0.350	0.501	0.680	0.904	1.204	1.659
			0.5	0.170	0.372	0.620	0.948	1.431	2.290	4.302	9.964
			0.7	0.234	0.528	0.925	1.534	2.696	5.597	-	-
	7	3.2	0.1	0.014	0.027	0.041	0.055	0.069	0.083	0.097	0.112
			0.3	0.040	0.082	0.124	0.167	0.212	0.257	0.303	0.350
			0.5	0.068	0.138	0.210	0.284	0.362	0.442	0.526	0.614
			0.7	0.094	0.193	0.296	0.404	0.519	0.640	0.771	0.911
		3.4	0.1	0.028	0.056	0.084	0.113	0.142	0.173	0.202	0.233
			0.3	0.082	0.167	0.257	0.352	0.451	0.556	0.669	0.789
			0.5	0.136	0.282	0.439	0.612	0.803	1.018	1.265	1.560
			0.7	0.188	0.396	0.629	0.895	1.209	1.594	2.100	2.851
		3.58	0.1	0.058	0.118	0.181	0.246	0.313	0.383	0.456	0.532
			0.3	0.173	0.362	0.573	0.812	1.088	1.419	1.838	2.415
			0.5	0.283	0.612	1.007	1.507	2.197	3.304	5.579	11.549
			0.7	0.391	0.869	1.490	2.388	3.943	7.462	-	-

Table No. 29-4-K. Differential Swell Occurring at the Perimeter of a Slab for a Center Lift Swelling Condition in Predominantly Montmorillonite Clay Soil (30 Percent Clay).

Percent Clay	Depth to Constant Suction	Constant Suction	Velocity of Moisture Flow (inches /month)	DIFFERENTIAL SHELL (INCHES)							
				EDGE DISTANCE PENETRATION (FT)							
(%)	(FT)	(pF)		1 FT	2 FT	3 FT	4 FT	5 FT	6 FT	7 FT	8 FT
30	3	3.2	0.1	0.001	0.003	0.004	0.005	0.007	0.008	0.009	0.011
			0.3	0.004	0.008	0.012	0.016	0.020	0.025	0.030	0.035
			0.5	0.006	0.013	0.020	0.027	0.035	0.043	0.051	0.060
			0.7	0.010	0.019	0.029	0.040	0.051	0.063	0.076	0.089
		3.4	0.1	0.003	0.005	0.008	0.011	0.014	0.017	0.020	0.023
			0.3	0.008	0.017	0.026	0.035	0.045	0.056	0.067	0.079
			0.5	0.014	0.028	0.044	0.062	0.081	0.102	0.128	0.159
			0.7	0.019	0.039	0.063	0.089	0.122	0.162	0.214	0.291
		3.6	0.1	0.006	0.013	0.020	0.027	0.035	0.043	0.052	0.061
			0.3	0.019	0.041	0.065	0.094	0.128	0.172	0.232	0.323
			0.5	0.031	0.069	0.116	0.179	0.275	0.450	0.868	2.073
			0.7	0.043	0.098	0.173	0.294	0.532	1.145	2.945	8.301
	5	3.2	0.1	0.003	0.006	0.010	0.013	0.016	0.019	0.022	0.026
			0.3	0.009	0.018	0.028	0.038	0.048	0.058	0.069	0.079
			0.5	0.016	0.032	0.048	0.065	0.083	0.101	0.120	0.140
			0.7	0.022	0.044	0.068	0.093	0.119	0.147	0.176	0.208
		3.4	0.1	0.006	0.013	0.019	0.026	0.033	0.039	0.046	0.054
			0.3	0.019	0.039	0.060	0.081	0.104	0.129	0.155	0.182
			0.5	0.032	0.065	0.102	0.141	0.186	0.235	0.293	0.361
			0.7	0.043	0.091	0.145	0.207	0.280	0.369	0.486	0.657
		3.6	0.1	0.015	0.030	0.047	0.063	0.081	0.099	0.119	0.139
			0.3	0.045	0.094	0.149	0.213	0.289	0.384	0.512	0.704
			0.5	0.072	0.158	0.264	0.403	0.607	0.972	1.826	2.514
			0.7	0.100	0.224	0.393	0.651	1.144	2.375	5.870	-
	7	3.2	0.1	0.006	0.012	0.017	0.023	0.029	0.035	0.041	0.047
			0.3	0.017	0.035	0.053	0.071	0.090	0.109	0.128	0.148
			0.5	0.029	0.059	0.089	0.121	0.154	0.188	0.223	0.261
			0.7	0.039	0.081	0.125	0.171	0.219	0.271	0.326	0.386
		3.4	0.1	0.012	0.024	0.036	0.048	0.061	0.074	0.086	0.099
			0.3	0.035	0.071	0.109	0.149	0.191	0.236	0.284	0.335
			0.5	0.058	0.120	0.187	0.261	0.342	0.433	0.537	0.662
			0.7	0.081	0.169	0.268	0.381	0.514	0.677	0.892	1.211
		3.58	0.1	0.024	0.050	0.076	0.104	0.132	0.162	0.193	0.225
			0.3	0.073	0.154	0.243	0.344	0.461	0.602	0.780	1.025
			0.5	0.120	0.259	0.427	0.639	0.932	1.402	2.367	4.900
			0.7	0.165	0.368	0.632	1.013	1.672	3.165	7.244	-

Table No. 29-4-L. Differential Swell Occurring at the Perimeter of a Slab for a Center Lift Swelling Condition in Predominantly Montmorillonite Clay Soil (40 Percent Clay).

Percent Clay (%)	Depth to Constant Suction (FT)	Constant Suction (pF)	Velocity of Moisture Flow (inches /month)	DIFFERENTIAL SWELL (INCHES) EDGE DISTANCE PENETRATION (FT)							
				1 FT	2 FT	3 FT	4 FT	5 FT	6 FT	7 FT	8 FT
40	3	3.2	0.1	0.002	0.004	0.006	0.008	0.010	0.012	0.014	0.016
			0.3	0.006	0.012	0.018	0.024	0.030	0.036	0.042	0.049
			0.5	0.009	0.019	0.029	0.040	0.050	0.062	0.074	0.086
			0.7	0.014	0.027	0.042	0.057	0.074	0.091	0.109	0.129
		3.4	0.1	0.004	0.008	0.012	0.016	0.021	0.025	0.029	0.034
			0.3	0.011	0.024	0.037	0.050	0.065	0.080	0.097	0.115
			0.5	0.019	0.040	0.063	0.088	0.116	0.148	0.185	0.229
			0.7	0.027	0.057	0.091	0.130	0.177	0.234	0.311	0.422
		3.6	0.1	0.010	0.019	0.030	0.040	0.051	0.063	0.076	0.089
			0.3	0.028	0.059	0.094	0.136	0.186	0.249	0.335	0.468
			0.5	0.046	0.100	0.168	0.260	0.399	0.652	1.258	3.004
			0.7	0.062	0.142	0.251	0.425	0.769	1.660	4.267	7.762
	5	3.2	0.1	0.004	0.009	0.013	0.018	0.022	0.027	0.032	0.037
			0.3	0.013	0.027	0.041	0.055	0.069	0.085	0.100	0.115
			0.5	0.023	0.046	0.069	0.094	0.120	0.147	0.174	0.203
			0.7	0.032	0.064	0.098	0.134	0.172	0.212	0.255	0.301
		3.4	0.1	0.010	0.019	0.028	0.038	0.048	0.058	0.068	0.079
			0.3	0.027	0.056	0.086	0.118	0.151	0.186	0.224	0.264
			0.5	0.045	0.094	0.147	0.205	0.269	0.341	0.424	0.522
			0.7	0.063	0.133	0.211	0.300	0.405	0.535	0.704	0.952
		3.6	0.1	0.021	0.044	0.067	0.092	0.117	0.144	0.172	0.201
			0.3	0.064	0.135	0.216	0.308	0.419	0.556	0.741	1.020
			0.5	0.105	0.229	0.382	0.584	0.880	1.408	2.645	6.127
			0.7	0.144	0.325	0.569	0.944	1.658	3.441	8.517	-
	7	3.2	0.1	0.009	0.018	0.026	0.035	0.043	0.052	0.061	0.070
			0.3	0.025	0.051	0.077	0.103	0.131	0.158	0.186	0.215
			0.5	0.042	0.085	0.129	0.175	0.223	0.272	0.324	0.378
			0.7	0.059	0.119	0.183	0.249	0.320	0.394	0.475	0.561
		3.4	0.1	0.017	0.035	0.052	0.070	0.088	0.106	0.125	0.144
			0.3	0.050	0.103	0.158	0.216	0.277	0.342	0.411	0.485
			0.5	0.084	0.173	0.270	0.377	0.494	0.626	0.778	0.960
			0.7	0.116	0.244	0.387	0.550	0.743	0.980	1.291	1.753
		3.56	0.1	0.033	0.066	0.101	0.136	0.173	0.211	0.251	0.292
			0.3	0.096	0.201	0.316	0.444	0.590	0.760	0.967	1.231
			0.5	0.158	0.339	0.553	0.815	1.160	1.668	2.583	4.748
			0.7	0.218	0.480	0.813	1.271	2.004	3.504	7.412	-

Table No. 29-4-M. Differential Swell Occurring at the Perimeter of a Slab for a Center Lift Swelling Condition in Predominantly Montmorillonite Clay Soil (50 Percent Clay).

Percent Clay (%)	Depth to Constant Suction (FT)	Constant Suction (pF)	Velocity of Moisture Flow (inches /month)	DIFFERENTIAL SWELL (INCHES) EDGE DISTANCE PENETRATION (FT) 1 FT	2 FT	3 FT	4 FT	5 FT	6 FT	7 FT	8 FT
50	3	3.2	0.1	0.003	0.005	0.008	0.010	0.013	0.016	0.018	0.021
			0.3	0.007	0.015	0.023	0.031	0.039	0.047	0.055	0.065
			0.5	0.012	0.026	0.038	0.052	0.066	0.081	0.097	0.113
			0.7	0.018	0.036	0.055	0.075	0.096	0.119	0.143	0.169
		3.4	0.1	0.006	0.011	0.016	0.022	0.027	0.033	0.038	0.044
			0.3	0.016	0.032	0.049	0.067	0.086	0.106	0.127	0.151
			0.5	0.026	0.053	0.083	0.116	0.153	0.195	0.243	0.301
			0.7	0.036	0.076	0.119	0.170	0.231	0.307	0.407	0.553
		3.6	0.1	0.012	0.025	0.038	0.052	0.067	0.082	0.099	0.116
			0.3	0.036	0.077	0.123	0.177	0.243	0.326	0.439	0.613
			0.5	0.059	0.131	0.220	0.340	0.522	0.854	1.648	3.935
			0.7	0.082	0.186	0.330	0.558	1.008	2.175	5.590	-
	5	3.2	0.1	0.006	0.012	0.018	0.024	0.030	0.036	0.042	0.048
			0.3	0.017	0.035	0.054	0.073	0.092	0.111	0.131	0.151
			0.5	0.030	0.060	0.091	0.124	0.157	0.192	0.228	0.266
			0.7	0.041	0.083	0.128	0.175	0.224	0.277	0.333	0.394
		3.4	0.1	0.012	0.024	0.037	0.049	0.062	0.075	0.089	0.102
			0.3	0.036	0.074	0.113	0.154	0.198	0.244	0.294	0.344
			0.5	0.059	0.123	0.193	0.268	0.352	0.446	0.555	0.684
			0.7	0.083	0.174	0.276	0.393	0.531	0.700	0.923	1.247
		3.6	0.1	0.029	0.058	0.089	0.121	0.154	0.189	0.226	0.264
			0.3	0.084	0.177	0.282	0.404	0.548	0.728	0.970	1.336
			0.5	0.137	0.299	0.500	0.764	1.152	1.844	3.464	8.025
			0.7	0.189	0.426	0.745	1.236	2.712	4.508	-	-
	7	3.2	0.1	0.011	0.022	0.034	0.044	0.056	0.067	0.078	0.090
			0.3	0.033	0.067	0.101	0.135	0.171	0.208	0.244	0.282
			0.5	0.055	0.111	0.169	0.229	0.291	0.356	0.423	0.495
			0.7	0.076	0.155	0.238	0.326	0.418	0.516	0.621	0.734
		3.4	0.1	0.023	0.045	0.068	0.091	0.115	0.139	0.163	0.188
			0.3	0.066	0.135	0.208	0.284	0.364	0.449	0.539	0.636
			0.5	0.106	0.226	0.354	0.493	0.646	0.819	1.019	1.256
			0.7	0.152	0.320	0.507	0.721	0.973	1.283	1.692	2.256
		3.56	0.1	0.042	0.087	0.131	0.178	0.226	0.276	0.328	0.382
			0.3	0.126	0.263	0.414	0.583	0.773	0.996	1.266	1.613
			0.5	0.207	0.444	0.724	1.068	1.519	2.185	3.382	6.219
			0.7	0.286	0.629	1.066	1.665	2.625	4.590	-	-

Table No. 29-4-N. Differential Swell Occurring at the Perimeter of a Slab for a Center Lift Swelling Condition in Predominantly Montmorillonite Clay Soil (60 Percent Clay).

Percent Clay (%)	Depth of Constant Suction (FT)	Constant Suction (pF)	Velocity of Moisture Flow (inches /month)	DIFFERENTIAL SWELL (INCHES) EDGE DISTANCE PENETRATION (FT) 1 FT	2 FT	3 FT	4 FT	5 FT	6 FT	7 FT	8 FT
60	3	3.2	0.1	0.003	0.006	0.009	0.013	0.016	0.019	0.022	0.026
			0.3	0.009	0.019	0.028	0.038	0.048	0.059	0.069	0.080
			0.5	0.015	0.031	0.048	0.065	0.082	0.101	0.120	0.140
			0.7	0.022	0.044	0.068	0.092	0.119	0.147	0.176	0.209
		3.4	0.1	0.006	0.013	0.019	0.026	0.033	0.040	0.047	0.054
			0.3	0.019	0.039	0.060	0.082	0.105	0.130	0.157	0.186
			0.5	0.031	0.065	0.102	0.143	0.189	0.240	0.300	0.372
			0.7	0.044	0.093	0.147	0.211	0.286	0.380	0.503	0.683
		3.6	0.1	0.015	0.031	0.048	0.065	0.083	0.102	0.122	0.144
			0.3	0.044	0.095	0.152	0.219	0.300	0.403	0.543	0.758
			0.5	0.073	0.161	0.272	0.420	0.645	1.056	2.037	4.865
			0.7	0.101	0.229	0.407	0.689	1.246	2.689	6.912	-
	5	3.2	0.1	0.008	0.015	0.023	0.030	0.038	0.045	0.053	0.060
			0.3	0.022	0.044	0.067	0.090	0.113	0.138	0.162	0.187
			0.5	0.037	0.074	0.113	0.153	0.194	0.237	0.282	0.329
			0.7	0.050	0.103	0.158	0.217	0.278	0.343	0.412	0.487
		3.4	0.1	0.015	0.030	0.043	0.061	0.077	0.093	0.109	0.126
			0.3	0.045	0.091	0.140	0.191	0.245	0.302	0.363	0.426
			0.5	0.073	0.152	0.237	0.331	0.435	0.551	0.686	0.846
			0.7	0.102	0.214	0.341	0.485	0.655	0.865	1.140	1.541
		3.6	0.1	0.035	0.071	0.109	0.149	0.190	0.233	0.279	0.326
			0.3	0.103	0.219	0.349	0.499	0.678	0.901	1.200	1.652
			0.5	0.169	0.370	0.618	0.945	1.425	2.280	4.284	9.923
			0.7	0.234	0.526	0.922	1.528	2.686	5.574	-	-
	7	3.2	0.1	0.013	0.027	0.041	0.055	0.069	0.083	0.097	0.111
			0.3	0.041	0.082	0.125	0.168	0.212	0.256	0.302	0.349
			0.5	0.068	0.137	0.209	0.283	0.360	0.441	0.524	0.612
			0.7	0.093	0.191	0.294	0.402	0.516	0.637	0.767	0.907
		3.4	0.1	0.027	0.055	0.083	0.112	0.142	0.171	0.201	0.232
			0.3	0.082	0.167	0.256	0.351	0.449	0.555	0.666	0.786
			0.5	0.135	0.280	0.438	0.609	0.799	1.013	1.260	1.553
			0.7	0.188	0.395	0.627	0.892	1.204	1.587	2.092	2.840
		3.56	0.1	0.053	0.107	0.163	0.221	0.281	0.342	0.407	0.474
			0.3	0.156	0.326	0.512	0.720	0.957	1.232	1.566	1.994
			0.5	0.256	0.549	0.895	1.320	1.879	2.702	4.182	8.216
			0.7	0.354	0.779	1.317	2.059	3.247	5.677	-	-

Table No. 29-4-O. Differential Swell Occurring at the Perimeter of a Slab for a Center Lift Swelling Condition in Predominantly Montmorillonite Clay Soil (70 Percent Clay).

Percent Clay (%)	Depth to Constant Suction (FT)	Constant Suction (pF)	Velocity of Moisture Flow (inches /month)	DIFFERENTIAL SWELL (INCHES) EDGE DISTANCE PENETRATION (FT)							
				1 FT	2 FT	3 FT	4 FT	5 FT	6 FT	7 FT	8 FT
70	3	3.2	0.1	0.004	0.007	0.011	0.015	0.019	0.023	0.026	0.030
			0.3	0.011	0.022	0.034	0.046	0.057	0.070	0.082	0.095
			0.5	0.018	0.037	0.057	0.077	0.098	0.120	0.143	0.167
			0.7	0.026	0.052	0.082	0.110	0.141	0.174	0.210	0.248
		3.4	0.1	0.007	0.015	0.023	0.031	0.039	0.048	0.056	0.065
			0.3	0.023	0.047	0.072	0.098	0.126	0.156	0.188	0.222
			0.5	0.038	0.078	0.122	0.171	0.225	0.287	0.358	0.443
			0.7	0.052	0.110	0.176	0.251	0.341	0.452	0.600	0.814
		3.6	0.1	0.018	0.037	0.056	0.077	0.098	0.121	0.145	0.171
			0.3	0.054	0.114	0.182	0.262	0.359	0.481	0.648	0.903
			0.5	0.088	0.192	0.324	0.502	0.769	1.258	2.428	5.796
			0.7	0.120	0.273	0.485	0.821	1.485	3.203	8.234	-
	5	3.2	0.1	0.009	0.017	0.026	0.035	0.044	0.053	0.062	0.071
			0.3	0.026	0.053	0.080	0.107	0.135	0.164	0.193	0.223
			0.5	0.044	0.088	0.134	0.182	0.231	0.283	0.336	0.392
			0.7	0.060	0.123	0.189	0.258	0.331	0.409	0.491	0.580
		3.4	0.1	0.018	0.036	0.055	0.073	0.092	0.111	0.131	0.151
			0.3	0.053	0.109	0.167	0.228	0.292	0.360	0.433	0.511
			0.5	0.088	0.182	0.284	0.395	0.519	0.658	0.818	1.008
			0.7	0.121	0.256	0.406	0.578	0.781	1.031	1.358	1.837
		3.6	0.1	0.042	0.086	0.131	0.178	0.227	0.278	0.332	0.389
			0.3	0.123	0.260	0.415	0.594	0.807	1.073	1.429	1.968
			0.5	0.202	0.441	0.737	1.126	1.698	2.717	5.104	11.822
			0.7	0.278	0.627	1.098	1.820	3.199	6.640	-	-
	7	3.2	0.1	0.016	0.032	0.049	0.065	0.082	0.098	0.115	0.132
			0.3	0.048	0.097	0.148	0.199	0.251	0.305	0.359	0.415
			0.5	0.081	0.163	0.249	0.338	0.429	0.525	0.624	0.729
			0.7	0.112	0.229	0.351	0.480	0.616	0.759	0.915	1.081
		3.4	0.1	0.032	0.066	0.099	0.134	0.168	0.204	0.240	0.276
			0.3	0.098	0.199	0.306	0.418	0.536	0.661	0.794	0.937
			0.5	0.162	0.334	0.522	0.727	0.952	1.207	1.501	1.851
			0.7	0.224	0.470	0.747	1.063	1.435	1.891	2.492	3.383
		3.56	0.1	0.063	0.128	0.194	0.263	0.334	0.407	0.484	0.563
			0.3	0.185	0.387	0.609	0.857	1.139	1.468	1.865	2.376
			0.5	0.305	0.655	1.067	1.573	2.239	3.219	4.983	9.162
			0.7	0.421	0.928	1.569	2.453	3.868	6.763	-	-

Table No. 29-4-P. Differential Swell Occurring at the Perimeter of a Slab for an Edge Lift Swelling Condition in Predominantly Kaolinite Clay Soil (30 Percent Clay).

Percent Clay (%)	Depth to Constant Suction (FT)	Constant Suction (pF)	Velocity of Moisture Flow (inches/month)	DIFFERENTIAL SWELL (INCHES) EDGE DISTANCE PENETRATION (FT)							
				1 FT	2 FT	3 FT	4 FT	5 FT	6 FT	7 FT	8 FT
30	3	3.2	0.1	0.001	0.001	0.002	0.002	0.003	0.003	0.004	0.004
			0.3	0.002	0.003	0.004	0.006	0.007	0.009	0.010	0.012
			0.5	0.003	0.005	0.007	0.010	0.012	0.014	0.017	0.019
			0.7	0.004	0.007	0.010	0.013	0.017	0.020	0.023	0.026
		3.4	0.1	0.001	0.002	0.003	0.004	0.005	0.006	0.007	0.008
			0.3	0.003	0.006	0.009	0.012	0.015	0.018	0.021	0.024
			0.5	0.005	0.010	0.015	0.020	0.025	0.029	0.033	0.037
			0.7	0.007	0.014	0.021	0.027	0.033	0.039	0.045	0.050
		3.6	0.1	0.003	0.005	0.008	0.010	0.013	0.015	0.017	0.020
			0.3	0.008	0.015	0.022	0.029	0.035	0.041	0.047	0.053
			0.5	0.013	0.025	0.035	0.046	0.055	0.064	0.072	0.080
			0.7	0.018	0.034	0.048	0.061	0.073	0.084	0.094	0.104
		3.8	0.1	0.006	0.013	0.018	0.024	0.030	0.035	0.040	0.045
			0.3	0.019	0.035	0.050	0.064	0.076	0.088	0.099	0.109
			0.5	0.031	0.056	0.078	0.097	0.114	0.129	0.143	0.156
			0.7	0.042	0.075	0.102	0.125	0.145	0.164	0.180	0.195
	5	3.2	0.1	0.001	0.002	0.003	0.004	0.005	0.007	0.008	0.009
			0.3	0.003	0.007	0.010	0.013	0.016	0.019	0.022	0.025
			0.5	0.006	0.011	0.016	0.021	0.027	0.032	0.037	0.041
			0.7	0.008	0.015	0.022	0.030	0.037	0.044	0.050	0.057
		3.4	0.1	0.002	0.005	0.007	0.009	0.012	0.014	0.016	0.018
			0.3	0.007	0.014	0.021	0.027	0.034	0.040	0.046	0.053
			0.5	0.012	0.023	0.034	0.045	0.055	0.065	0.075	0.084
			0.7	0.016	0.032	0.047	0.061	0.075	0.089	0.101	0.114
		3.6	0.1	0.006	0.012	0.017	0.023	0.028	0.034	0.039	0.044
			0.3	0.018	0.034	0.050	0.065	0.080	0.094	0.107	0.120
			0.5	0.029	0.056	0.081	0.104	0.126	0.147	0.167	0.186
			0.7	0.041	0.077	0.110	0.141	0.169	0.195	0.220	0.243
		3.8	0.1	0.014	0.028	0.042	0.055	0.067	0.079	0.091	0.102
			0.3	0.043	0.081	0.116	0.148	0.178	0.205	0.231	0.255
			0.5	0.072	0.131	0.183	0.228	0.270	0.307	0.342	0.374
			0.7	0.100	0.178	0.244	0.300	0.350	0.395	0.436	0.474
	7	3.2	0.1	0.002	0.004	0.006	0.008	0.009	0.011	0.013	0.015
			0.3	0.006	0.011	0.017	0.022	0.028	0.033	0.039	0.044
			0.5	0.010	0.019	0.028	0.037	0.046	0.055	0.064	0.072
			0.7	0.013	0.026	0.039	0.052	0.064	0.076	0.088	0.099
		3.4	0.1	0.004	0.008	0.012	0.016	0.020	0.024	0.028	0.032
			0.3	0.012	0.024	0.036	0.048	0.059	0.071	0.082	0.093
			0.5	0.021	0.041	0.060	0.079	0.097	0.115	0.132	0.149
			0.7	0.029	0.056	0.083	0.108	0.133	0.157	0.180	0.202
		3.6	0.1	0.010	0.020	0.030	0.040	0.050	0.059	0.069	0.078
			0.3	0.031	0.061	0.089	0.116	0.142	0.167	0.192	0.215
			0.5	0.052	0.100	0.145	0.187	0.227	0.264	0.300	0.335
			0.7	0.073	0.138	0.198	0.254	0.305	0.353	0.399	0.441
		3.8	0.1	-	-	-	-	-	-	-	-

Table No. 29-4-Q. Differential Swell Occurring at the Perimeter of a Slab for an Edge Lift Swelling Condition in Predominantly Kaolinite Clay Soil (40 Percent Clay).

Percent Clay (%)	Depth to Constant Suction (FT)	Constant Suction (pF)	Velocity of Moisture Flow (inches /month)	DIFFERENTIAL SWELL (INCHES) EDGE DISTANCE PENETRATION (FT)							
				1 FT	2 FT	3 FT	4 FT	5 FT	6 FT	7 FT	8 FT
40	3	3.2	0.1	0.001	0.001	0.002	0.003	0.003	0.004	0.005	0.005
			0.3	0.002	0.004	0.006	0.008	0.010	0.012	0.014	0.015
			0.5	0.003	0.007	0.010	0.013	0.016	0.019	0.022	0.025
			0.7	0.006	0.009	0.014	0.018	0.022	0.026	0.030	0.034
		3.4	0.1	0.001	0.003	0.004	0.006	0.007	0.008	0.010	0.011
			0.3	0.004	0.008	0.012	0.016	0.020	0.024	0.028	0.032
			0.5	0.007	0.014	0.020	0.027	0.033	0.039	0.045	0.050
			0.7	0.010	0.019	0.028	0.037	0.045	0.052	0.060	0.067
		3.6	0.1	0.004	0.007	0.010	0.014	0.017	0.020	0.023	0.026
			0.3	0.010	0.020	0.030	0.039	0.047	0.055	0.063	0.071
			0.5	0.017	0.033	0.047	0.061	0.074	0.086	0.097	0.108
			0.7	0.024	0.046	0.064	0.081	0.098	0.112	0.126	0.139
		3.8	0.1	0.009	0.017	0.025	0.032	0.040	0.046	0.053	0.060
			0.3	0.025	0.047	0.067	0.085	0.102	0.118	0.132	0.145
			0.5	0.041	0.075	0.104	0.129	0.152	0.173	0.192	0.209
			0.7	0.066	0.100	0.136	0.167	0.195	0.219	0.241	0.261
	5	3.2	0.1	0.002	0.003	0.004	0.006	0.007	0.009	0.010	0.012
			0.3	0.004	0.009	0.013	0.017	0.022	0.026	0.030	0.034
			0.5	0.007	0.015	0.022	0.029	0.035	0.042	0.049	0.056
			0.7	0.010	0.020	0.030	0.040	0.049	0.058	0.067	0.076
		3.4	0.1	0.003	0.006	0.009	0.012	0.016	0.019	0.022	0.025
			0.3	0.009	0.019	0.028	0.037	0.045	0.054	0.062	0.071
			0.5	0.016	0.031	0.046	0.060	0.074	0.087	0.100	0.113
			0.7	0.022	0.043	0.063	0.082	0.101	0.119	0.136	0.152
		3.6	0.1	0.008	0.016	0.023	0.031	0.038	0.045	0.052	0.059
			0.3	0.023	0.046	0.067	0.087	0.107	0.126	0.144	0.161
			0.5	0.039	0.075	0.108	0.140	0.169	0.197	0.223	0.249
			0.7	0.064	0.103	0.147	0.188	0.226	0.261	0.295	0.326
		3.8	0.1	0.019	0.038	0.056	0.073	0.090	0.106	0.121	0.136
			0.3	0.058	0.109	0.156	0.198	0.238	0.275	0.309	0.342
			0.5	0.096	0.176	0.245	0.306	0.361	0.411	0.458	0.501
			0.7	0.134	0.239	0.326	0.402	0.469	0.529	0.584	0.634
	7	3.2	0.1	0.003	0.005	0.008	0.010	0.013	0.015	0.018	0.020
			0.3	0.008	0.015	0.023	0.030	0.037	0.045	0.052	0.059
			0.5	0.013	0.025	0.038	0.050	0.062	0.074	0.085	0.097
			0.7	0.018	0.035	0.052	0.069	0.085	0.102	0.117	0.133
		3.4	0.1	0.006	0.011	0.016	0.022	0.027	0.032	0.038	0.043
			0.3	0.017	0.033	0.049	0.064	0.080	0.095	0.109	0.124
			0.5	0.028	0.054	0.080	0.105	0.130	0.154	0.177	0.200
			0.7	0.039	0.076	0.111	0.145	0.178	0.210	0.241	0.271
		3.6	0.1	0.014	0.027	0.041	0.054	0.067	0.080	0.092	0.105
			0.3	0.042	0.081	0.119	0.155	0.190	0.224	0.257	0.288
			0.5	0.069	0.134	0.194	0.250	0.304	0.354	0.402	0.448
			0.7	0.098	0.185	0.266	0.340	0.409	0.473	0.534	0.591
		3.8	0.1	-	-	-	-	-	-	-	-

Table No. 29-4-R. Differential Swell Occurring at the Perimeter of a Slab for an Edge Lift Swelling Condition in Predominantly Kaolinite Clay Soil (50 Percent Clay).

Percent Clay (%)	Depth to Constant Suction (FT)	Constant Suction (pF)	Velocity of Moisture Flow (inches /month)	DIFFERENTIAL SWELL (INCHES) EDGE DISTANCE PENETRATION (FT)							
				1 FT	2 FT	3 FT	4 FT	5 FT	6 FT	7 FT	8 FT
50	3	3.2	0.1	0.001	0.002	0.003	0.003	0.004	0.005	0.006	0.007
			0.3	0.003	0.005	0.007	0.010	0.012	0.015	0.017	0.019
			0.5	0.004	0.008	0.012	0.016	0.020	0.024	0.028	0.032
			0.7	0.006	0.012	0.017	0.023	0.028	0.033	0.038	0.043
		3.4	0.1	0.002	0.004	0.005	0.007	0.009	0.011	0.012	0.014
			0.3	0.005	0.011	0.016	0.021	0.025	0.030	0.035	0.040
			0.5	0.009	0.017	0.026	0.034	0.041	0.049	0.056	0.063
			0.7	0.012	0.024	0.035	0.046	0.056	0.066	0.075	0.084
		3.6	0.1	0.004	0.009	0.013	0.017	0.021	0.025	0.029	0.033
			0.3	0.013	0.025	0.037	0.048	0.059	0.069	0.079	0.089
			0.5	0.022	0.042	0.059	0.076	0.092	0.107	0.121	0.135
			0.7	0.030	0.056	0.080	0.102	0.122	0.141	0.158	0.175
		3.8	0.1	0.011	0.021	0.031	0.040	0.050	0.058	0.067	0.075
			0.3	0.032	0.059	0.084	0.107	0.128	0.147	0.165	0.182
			0.5	0.052	0.094	0.130	0.162	0.191	0.217	0.240	0.262
			0.7	0.071	0.126	0.171	0.210	0.244	0.275	0.302	0.328
	5	3.2	0.1	0.002	0.004	0.006	0.007	0.009	0.011	0.013	0.015
			0.3	0.006	0.011	0.016	0.022	0.027	0.032	0.037	0.043
			0.5	0.009	0.018	0.027	0.036	0.044	0.053	0.061	0.070
			0.7	0.013	0.025	0.038	0.050	0.062	0.073	0.084	0.096
		3.4	0.1	0.004	0.008	0.012	0.016	0.019	0.023	0.027	0.031
			0.3	0.012	0.023	0.035	0.046	0.057	0.068	0.078	0.088
			0.5	0.020	0.039	0.057	0.075	0.092	0.109	0.126	0.142
			0.7	0.028	0.054	0.079	0.103	0.126	0.149	0.170	0.191
		3.6	0.1	0.010	0.019	0.029	0.038	0.047	0.056	0.065	0.074
			0.3	0.029	0.057	0.084	0.109	0.134	0.158	0.180	0.202
			0.5	0.049	0.094	0.136	0.175	0.212	0.247	0.280	0.312
			0.7	0.068	0.129	0.185	0.236	0.283	0.328	0.369	0.408
		3.8	0.1	0.024	0.048	0.070	0.092	0.112	0.132	0.152	0.171
			0.3	0.072	0.137	0.195	0.249	0.298	0.344	0.387	0.428
			0.5	0.120	0.220	0.307	0.384	0.453	0.516	0.574	0.628
			0.7	0.168	0.299	0.409	0.504	0.588	0.663	0.732	0.795
	7	3.2	0.1	0.003	0.006	0.010	0.013	0.016	0.019	0.022	0.025
			0.3	0.010	0.019	0.028	0.038	0.047	0.056	0.065	0.074
			0.5	0.016	0.032	0.047	0.062	0.077	0.092	0.107	0.121
			0.7	0.022	0.044	0.066	0.087	0.107	0.127	0.147	0.167
		3.4	0.1	0.007	0.014	0.021	0.027	0.034	0.041	0.047	0.054
			0.3	0.021	0.041	0.061	0.080	0.100	0.119	0.137	0.156
			0.5	0.035	0.068	0.100	0.132	0.163	0.193	0.222	0.250
			0.7	0.048	0.095	0.139	0.182	0.223	0.263	0.302	0.339
		3.6	0.1	0.017	0.034	0.051	0.068	0.084	0.100	0.116	0.131
			0.3	0.052	0.102	0.149	0.195	0.239	0.281	0.322	0.361
			0.5	0.087	0.168	0.243	0.314	0.381	0.444	0.504	0.562
			0.7	0.122	0.232	0.333	0.426	0.512	0.593	0.669	0.741
		3.8	0.1	-	-	-	-	-	-	-	-

Table No. 29-4-S. Differential Swell Occurring at the Perimeter of a Slab for an Edge Lift Swelling Condition in Predominantly Kaolinite Clay Soil (60 Percent Clay).

Percent Clay	Depth to Constant Suction	Constant Suction	Velocity of Moisture Flow (inches /month)	DIFFERENTIAL SWELL (INCHES)							
				EDGE DISTANCE PENETRATION (FT)							
(%)	(FT)	(pF)		1 FT	2 FT	3 FT	4 FT	5 FT	6 FT	7 FT	8 FT
60	3	3.2	0.1	0.001	0.002	0.003	0.004	0.005	0.006	0.007	0.008
			0.3	0.003	0.006	0.009	0.012	0.015	0.018	0.021	0.023
			0.5	0.005	0.010	0.015	0.020	0.024	0.029	0.033	0.038
			0.7	0.007	0.014	0.021	0.027	0.033	0.040	0.046	0.052
		3.4	0.1	0.002	0.004	0.006	0.009	0.011	0.013	0.015	0.017
			0.3	0.006	0.013	0.019	0.025	0.031	0.036	0.042	0.048
			0.5	0.011	0.021	0.031	0.040	0.049	0.058	0.067	0.076
			0.7	0.015	0.029	0.042	0.055	0.067	0.079	0.090	0.101
		3.6	0.1	0.005	0.011	0.016	0.021	0.025	0.030	0.035	0.040
			0.3	0.016	0.031	0.045	0.058	0.071	0.083	0.095	0.106
			0.5	0.026	0.050	0.071	0.092	0.111	0.129	0.146	0.162
			0.7	0.036	0.068	0.097	0.123	0.147	0.169	0.190	0.210
		3.8	0.1	0.013	0.025	0.037	0.049	0.059	0.070	0.080	0.090
			0.3	0.038	0.071	0.101	0.129	0.154	0.177	0.199	0.219
			0.5	0.062	0.113	0.157	0.195	0.229	0.260	0.289	0.315
			0.7	0.085	0.151	0.205	0.252	0.293	0.330	0.363	0.394
	5	3.2	0.1	0.002	0.004	0.007	0.009	0.011	0.013	0.015	0.017
			0.3	0.007	0.013	0.020	0.026	0.032	0.039	0.045	0.051
			0.5	0.011	0.022	0.033	0.043	0.053	0.064	0.074	0.084
			0.7	0.015	0.031	0.045	0.060	0.074	0.088	0.101	0.115
		3.4	0.1	0.005	0.009	0.014	0.019	0.023	0.028	0.033	0.037
			0.3	0.014	0.028	0.042	0.055	0.068	0.081	0.094	0.106
			0.5	0.024	0.046	0.069	0.090	0.111	0.131	0.151	0.170
			0.7	0.033	0.065	0.095	0.124	0.152	0.179	0.205	0.230
		3.6	0.1	0.012	0.023	0.035	0.046	0.057	0.068	0.079	0.089
			0.3	0.035	0.069	0.101	0.132	0.161	0.189	0.217	0.243
			0.5	0.059	0.113	0.163	0.210	0.255	0.297	0.337	0.375
			0.7	0.082	0.155	0.222	0.284	0.341	0.394	0.444	0.491
		3.8	0.1	0.029	0.057	0.084	0.110	0.135	0.159	0.183	0.206
			0.3	0.087	0.164	0.235	0.299	0.358	0.414	0.466	0.515
			0.5	0.144	0.265	0.369	0.461	0.544	0.620	0.690	0.754
			0.7	0.201	0.360	0.492	0.606	0.707	0.798	0.880	0.956
	7	3.2	0.1	0.004	0.008	0.011	0.015	0.019	0.023	0.027	0.030
			0.3	0.011	0.023	0.034	0.045	0.056	0.067	0.078	0.089
			0.5	0.019	0.038	0.057	0.075	0.093	0.111	0.128	0.146
			0.7	0.027	0.053	0.079	0.104	0.129	0.153	0.177	0.201
		3.4	0.1	0.008	0.017	0.025	0.033	0.041	0.049	0.057	0.065
			0.3	0.025	0.049	0.073	0.097	0.120	0.143	0.165	0.187
			0.5	0.042	0.082	0.121	0.159	0.196	0.232	0.267	0.301
			0.7	0.058	0.114	0.167	0.219	0.268	0.316	0.363	0.408
		3.6	0.1	0.021	0.041	0.061	0.081	0.101	0.120	0.139	0.158
			0.3	0.063	0.122	0.179	0.234	0.287	0.338	0.387	0.434
			0.5	0.105	0.201	0.292	0.377	0.457	0.534	0.606	0.675
			0.7	0.147	0.279	0.400	0.512	0.616	0.713	0.804	0.891
		3.8	0.1	-	-	-	-	-	-	-	-

Table No. 29-4-T. Differential Swell Occurring at the Perimeter of a Slab for an Edge Lift Swelling Condition in Predominantly Kaolinite Clay Soil (70 Percent Clay).

Percent Clay	Depth to Constant Suction	Constant Suction	Velocity of Moisture Flow (inches /month)	DIFFERENTIAL SWELL (INCHES)							
				EDGE DISTANCE PENETRATION (FT)							
(%)	(FT)	(pF)		1 FT	2 FT	3 FT	4 FT	5 FT	6 FT	7 FT	8 FT
70	3	3.2	0.1	0.001	0.002	0.004	0.005	0.006	0.007	0.008	0.009
			0.3	0.004	0.007	0.011	0.014	0.017	0.021	0.024	0.027
			0.5	0.006	0.012	0.017	0.023	0.028	0.034	0.039	0.044
			0.7	0.008	0.016	0.024	0.032	0.039	0.046	0.054	0.061
		3.4	0.1	0.003	0.005	0.007	0.010	0.012	0.015	0.017	0.020
			0.3	0.008	0.015	0.022	0.029	0.036	0.042	0.049	0.056
			0.5	0.012	0.024	0.036	0.047	0.058	0.068	0.078	0.088
			0.7	0.017	0.034	0.049	0.064	0.079	0.092	0.106	0.118
		3.6	0.1	0.006	0.012	0.018	0.024	0.030	0.035	0.041	0.046
			0.3	0.018	0.036	0.052	0.068	0.083	0.097	0.111	0.124
			0.5	0.030	0.058	0.084	0.107	0.130	0.151	0.170	0.189
			0.7	0.042	0.079	0.113	0.143	0.172	0.198	0.222	0.245
		3.8	0.1	0.015	0.030	0.043	0.057	0.069	0.082	0.094	0.105
			0.3	0.044	0.083	0.119	0.150	0.180	0.207	0.232	0.256
			0.5	0.072	0.132	0.183	0.228	0.268	0.304	0.338	0.369
			0.7	0.099	0.176	0.240	0.295	0.343	0.386	0.425	0.460
	5	3.2	0.1	0.003	0.005	0.008	0.010	0.013	0.015	0.018	0.020
			0.3	0.008	0.015	0.023	0.031	0.038	0.045	0.053	0.060
			0.5	0.013	0.026	0.038	0.050	0.062	0.074	0.086	0.098
			0.7	0.018	0.036	0.053	0.070	0.086	0.103	0.119	0.134
		3.4	0.1	0.006	0.011	0.017	0.022	0.027	0.033	0.038	0.043
			0.3	0.017	0.033	0.049	0.064	0.080	0.095	0.110	0.124
			0.5	0.028	0.054	0.080	0.105	0.130	0.153	0.176	0.199
			0.7	0.039	0.075	0.111	0.145	0.177	0.209	0.239	0.268
		3.6	0.1	0.014	0.027	0.041	0.054	0.067	0.079	0.092	0.104
			0.3	0.041	0.080	0.118	0.154	0.188	0.221	0.253	0.284
			0.5	0.068	0.132	0.191	0.246	0.298	0.347	0.393	0.438
			0.7	0.096	0.181	0.259	0.331	0.398	0.460	0.518	0.574
		3.8	0.1	0.034	0.067	0.098	0.128	0.158	0.186	0.213	0.240
			0.3	0.102	0.192	0.274	0.349	0.419	0.483	0.544	0.601
			0.5	0.169	0.309	0.431	0.539	0.636	0.724	0.806	0.881
			0.7	0.235	0.420	0.575	0.708	0.826	0.932	1.028	1.117
	7	3.2	0.1	0.005	0.009	0.013	0.018	0.022	0.027	0.031	0.035
			0.3	0.013	0.027	0.040	0.053	0.066	0.079	0.091	0.104
			0.5	0.022	0.044	0.066	0.087	0.109	0.129	0.150	0.170
			0.7	0.031	0.062	0.092	0.121	0.150	0.179	0.207	0.234
		3.4	0.1	0.010	0.019	0.029	0.038	0.048	0.057	0.066	0.076
			0.3	0.029	0.058	0.086	0.113	0.140	0.167	0.193	0.218
			0.5	0.048	0.095	0.141	0.185	0.228	0.270	0.311	0.351
			0.7	0.068	0.133	0.195	0.256	0.314	0.370	0.424	0.476
		3.6	0.1	0.024	0.048	0.072	0.095	0.118	0.140	0.162	0.184
			0.3	0.073	0.143	0.209	0.274	0.335	0.395	0.452	0.508
			0.5	0.122	0.235	0.341	0.441	0.534	0.623	0.708	0.789
			0.7	0.172	0.326	0.468	0.598	0.719	0.833	0.940	1.041
		3.8	0.1	-	-	-	-	-	-	-	-

Table No. 29-4-U. Differential Swell Occurring at the Perimeter of a Slab for an Edge Lift Swelling Condition in Predominantly Illite Clay Soil (30 Percent Clay).

Percent Clay	Depth to Constant Suction	Constant Suction	Velocity of Moisture Flow	DIFFERENTIAL SWELL (INCHES)							
				EDGE DISTANCE PENETRATION (FT)							
(%)	(FT)	(pF)	(inches /month)	1 FT	2 FT	3 FT	4 FT	5 FT	6 FT	7 FT	8 FT
30	3	3.2	0.1	0.001	0.002	0.003	0.004	0.005	0.006	0.007	0.008
			0.3	0.003	0.006	0.009	0.012	0.015	0.017	0.020	0.023
			0.5	0.005	0.010	0.015	0.019	0.024	0.029	0.033	0.037
			0.7	0.007	0.014	0.020	0.027	0.033	0.039	0.045	0.051
		3.4	0.1	0.002	0.004	0.006	0.008	0.010	0.013	0.015	0.017
			0.3	0.006	0.013	0.019	0.025	0.030	0.036	0.042	0.047
			0.5	0.011	0.021	0.030	0.040	0.049	0.058	0.066	0.075
			0.7	0.015	0.029	0.042	0.054	0.067	0.078	0.089	0.100
		3.6	0.1	0.005	0.010	0.015	0.020	0.025	0.030	0.035	0.039
			0.3	0.016	0.030	0.044	0.057	0.070	0.082	0.094	0.105
			0.5	0.026	0.049	0.071	0.091	0.110	0.128	0.144	0.160
			0.7	0.036	0.067	0.096	0.121	0.145	0.168	0.188	0.208
		3.8	0.1	0.013	0.025	0.037	0.048	0.059	0.069	0.079	0.089
			0.3	0.038	0.071	0.100	0.127	0.152	0.175	0.197	0.217
			0.5	0.061	0.112	0.155	0.193	0.227	0.258	0.286	0.312
			0.7	0.084	0.149	0.203	0.250	0.290	0.327	0.360	0.390
	5	3.2	0.1	0.002	0.004	0.007	0.009	0.011	0.013	0.015	0.017
			0.3	0.007	0.013	0.019	0.026	0.032	0.038	0.045	0.051
			0.5	0.011	0.022	0.032	0.043	0.053	0.063	0.073	0.083
			0.7	0.015	0.030	0.045	0.059	0.073	0.087	0.100	0.114
		3.4	0.1	0.005	0.009	0.014	0.019	0.023	0.028	0.032	0.037
			0.3	0.014	0.028	0.041	0.055	0.068	0.080	0.093	0.105
			0.5	0.023	0.046	0.068	0.089	0.110	0.130	0.149	0.168
			0.7	0.033	0.064	0.094	0.123	0.150	0.177	0.202	0.227
		3.6	0.1	0.012	0.023	0.034	0.046	0.056	0.067	0.078	0.088
			0.3	0.035	0.068	0.100	0.130	0.159	0.187	0.214	0.241
			0.5	0.058	0.112	0.161	0.208	0.252	0.294	0.333	0.371
			0.7	0.081	0.154	0.220	0.281	0.337	0.390	0.439	0.486
		3.8	0.1	0.029	0.057	0.083	0.109	0.134	0.158	0.181	0.203
			0.3	0.086	0.163	0.232	0.296	0.355	0.409	0.461	0.509
			0.5	0.143	0.262	0.365	0.456	0.539	0.613	0.682	0.746
			0.7	0.199	0.356	0.487	0.600	0.699	0.789	0.871	0.946
	7	3.2	0.1	0.004	0.008	0.011	0.015	0.019	0.023	0.026	0.030
			0.3	0.011	0.023	0.034	0.045	0.056	0.067	0.077	0.088
			0.5	0.019	0.038	0.056	0.074	0.092	0.110	0.127	0.144
			0.7	0.027	0.052	0.078	0.103	0.127	0.152	0.175	0.198
		3.4	0.1	0.008	0.016	0.024	0.032	0.040	0.048	0.056	0.064
			0.3	0.025	0.049	0.072	0.096	0.119	0.141	0.163	0.185
			0.5	0.041	0.081	0.119	0.157	0.194	0.229	0.264	0.298
			0.7	0.068	0.113	0.166	0.217	0.266	0.313	0.359	0.404
		3.6	0.1	0.021	0.041	0.061	0.080	0.100	0.119	0.137	0.156
			0.3	0.062	0.121	0.177	0.232	0.284	0.334	0.383	0.430
			0.5	0.103	0.199	0.289	0.373	0.453	0.528	0.600	0.668
			0.7	0.145	0.276	0.396	0.507	0.609	0.706	0.796	0.882
		3.8	0.1	-	-	-	-	-	-	-	-

Table No. 29-4-V. Differential Swell Occurring at the Perimeter of a Slab for an Edge Lift Swelling Condition in Predominantly Illite Clay Soil (40 Percent Clay).

Percent Clay	Depth to Constant Suction	Constant Suction	Velocity of Moisture Flow (inches /month)	DIFFERENTIAL SWELL (INCHES) EDGE DISTANCE PENETRATION (FT)							
(%)	(FT)	(pF)		1 FT	2 FT	3 FT	4 FT	5 FT	6 FT	7 FT	8 FT
40	3	3.2	0.1	0.001	0.003	0.004	0.006	0.007	0.009	0.010	0.011
			0.3	0.004	0.009	0.013	0.017	0.021	0.025	0.029	0.033
			0.5	0.007	0.014	0.021	0.028	0.035	0.041	0.048	0.054
			0.7	0.010	0.020	0.029	0.039	0.048	0.057	0.065	0.074
		3.4	0.1	0.003	0.006	0.009	0.012	0.015	0.018	0.021	0.024
			0.3	0.009	0.018	0.027	0.035	0.044	0.052	0.060	0.068
			0.5	0.015	0.030	0.044	0.058	0.071	0.083	0.096	0.108
			0.7	0.021	0.041	0.060	0.079	0.096	0.113	0.129	0.145
		3.6	0.1	0.008	0.015	0.022	0.029	0.036	0.043	0.050	0.057
			0.3	0.022	0.044	0.064	0.083	0.101	0.119	0.136	0.152
			0.5	0.037	0.071	0.102	0.131	0.158	0.184	0.208	0.231
			0.7	0.051	0.097	0.138	0.175	0.210	0.242	0.272	0.300
		3.8	0.1	0.019	0.036	0.053	0.069	0.085	0.100	0.115	0.129
			0.3	0.054	0.102	0.145	0.184	0.220	0.253	0.284	0.313
			0.5	0.088	0.161	0.224	0.278	0.328	0.372	0.413	0.451
			0.7	0.122	0.216	0.294	0.360	0.419	0.472	0.519	0.563
	5	3.2	0.1	0.003	0.006	0.009	0.013	0.016	0.019	0.022	0.025
			0.3	0.009	0.019	0.028	0.037	0.046	0.055	0.064	0.073
			0.5	0.016	0.031	0.047	0.062	0.076	0.091	0.105	0.120
			0.7	0.022	0.044	0.065	0.085	0.106	0.125	0.145	0.164
		3.4	0.1	0.007	0.014	0.020	0.027	0.033	0.040	0.046	0.053
			0.3	0.020	0.040	0.060	0.079	0.097	0.116	0.134	0.152
			0.5	0.034	0.066	0.098	0.129	0.158	0.187	0.216	0.243
			0.7	0.047	0.092	0.135	0.177	0.217	0.255	0.292	0.328
		3.6	0.1	0.017	0.033	0.050	0.066	0.081	0.097	0.112	0.127
			0.3	0.050	0.098	0.144	0.188	0.230	0.271	0.310	0.347
			0.5	0.084	0.161	0.233	0.300	0.364	0.424	0.481	0.535
			0.7	0.117	0.222	0.317	0.405	0.487	0.563	0.634	0.701
		3.8	0.1	0.042	0.082	0.120	0.157	0.193	0.228	0.261	0.294
			0.3	0.124	0.235	0.335	0.427	0.512	0.591	0.665	0.735
			0.5	0.206	0.378	0.527	0.659	0.777	0.886	0.985	1.078
			0.7	0.288	0.514	0.703	0.866	1.010	1.139	1.257	1.366
	7	3.2	0.1	0.005	0.011	0.016	0.022	0.027	0.033	0.038	0.043
			0.3	0.016	0.033	0.049	0.065	0.080	0.096	0.112	0.127
			0.5	0.027	0.054	0.081	0.107	0.133	0.158	0.183	0.208
			0.7	0.038	0.076	0.112	0.149	0.184	0.219	0.253	0.286
		3.4	0.1	0.012	0.024	0.035	0.047	0.058	0.070	0.081	0.093
			0.3	0.036	0.070	0.105	0.138	0.171	0.204	0.236	0.267
			0.5	0.059	0.117	0.172	0.227	0.279	0.331	0.381	0.430
			0.7	0.083	0.163	0.239	0.313	0.384	0.452	0.518	0.583
		3.6	0.1	0.030	0.059	0.088	0.116	0.144	0.171	0.198	0.225
			0.3	0.089	0.175	0.256	0.335	0.410	0.483	0.553	0.621
			0.5	0.149	0.288	0.417	0.539	0.654	0.762	0.866	0.965
			0.7	0.210	0.399	0.572	0.731	0.880	1.019	1.149	1.273
		3.8	0.1	-	-	-	-	-	-	-	-

Table No. 29-4-W. Differential Swell Occurring at the Perimeter of a Slab for an Edge Lift Swelling Condition in Predominantly Illite Clay Soil (50 Percent Clay).

Percent Clay (%)	Depth to Constant Suction (FT)	Constant Suction (pF)	Velocity of Moisture Flow (inches/month)	DIFFERENTIAL SWELL (INCHES) EDGE DISTANCE PENETRATION (FT)							
				1 FT	2 FT	3 FT	4 FT	5 FT	6 FT	7 FT	8 FT
50	3	3.2	0.1	0.002	0.004	0.006	0.008	0.009	0.011	0.013	0.015
			0.3	0.006	0.011	0.017	0.022	0.028	0.033	0.038	0.044
			0.5	0.009	0.019	0.028	0.037	0.045	0.054	0.062	0.071
			0.7	0.013	0.026	0.038	0.051	0.062	0.074	0.086	0.097
		3.4	0.1	0.004	0.008	0.012	0.016	0.020	0.024	0.027	0.031
			0.3	0.012	0.024	0.035	0.046	0.057	0.068	0.078	0.089
			0.5	0.020	0.039	0.057	0.075	0.092	0.109	0.125	0.141
			0.7	0.028	0.054	0.079	0.103	0.126	0.148	0.169	0.189
		3.6	0.1	0.010	0.020	0.029	0.038	0.048	0.057	0.065	0.074
			0.3	0.029	0.057	0.083	0.108	0.132	0.155	0.178	0.199
			0.5	0.048	0.093	0.134	0.172	0.207	0.241	0.272	0.303
			0.7	0.067	0.127	0.180	0.229	0.274	0.316	0.356	0.392
		3.8	0.1	0.024	0.047	0.069	0.091	0.111	0.131	0.150	0.168
			0.3	0.071	0.133	0.189	0.240	0.287	0.331	0.371	0.409
			0.5	0.116	0.211	0.292	0.364	0.428	0.486	0.540	0.589
			0.7	0.159	0.282	0.384	0.471	0.548	0.616	0.679	0.736
	5	3.2	0.1	0.004	0.008	0.012	0.016	0.021	0.025	0.029	0.033
			0.3	0.012	0.025	0.037	0.049	0.061	0.072	0.084	0.096
			0.5	0.021	0.041	0.061	0.080	0.100	0.119	0.138	0.156
			0.7	0.029	0.057	0.085	0.112	0.138	0.164	0.190	0.215
		3.4	0.1	0.009	0.018	0.026	0.035	0.044	0.052	0.061	0.069
			0.3	0.027	0.052	0.078	0.103	0.127	0.152	0.175	0.198
			0.5	0.044	0.087	0.128	0.168	0.207	0.245	0.282	0.318
			0.7	0.062	0.121	0.177	0.231	0.283	0.334	0.382	0.429
		3.6	0.1	0.022	0.044	0.065	0.086	0.106	0.127	0.147	0.166
			0.3	0.066	0.129	0.188	0.246	0.301	0.354	0.405	0.454
			0.5	0.109	0.211	0.305	0.393	0.476	0.554	0.629	0.700
			0.7	0.153	0.290	0.415	0.530	0.636	0.736	0.829	0.917
		3.8	0.1	0.054	0.107	0.157	0.205	0.252	0.297	0.341	0.384
			0.3	0.162	0.307	0.438	0.558	0.669	0.773	0.870	0.961
			0.5	0.269	0.494	0.689	0.861	1.016	1.158	1.288	1.409
			0.7	0.376	0.672	0.919	1.132	1.320	1.490	1.644	1.785
	7	3.2	0.1	0.007	0.014	0.021	0.028	0.035	0.042	0.049	0.056
			0.3	0.021	0.043	0.064	0.085	0.105	0.126	0.146	0.166
			0.5	0.036	0.071	0.106	0.140	0.173	0.207	0.240	0.272
			0.7	0.050	0.099	0.147	0.194	0.240	0.286	0.331	0.375
		3.4	0.1	0.015	0.031	0.046	0.061	0.076	0.091	0.106	0.121
			0.3	0.046	0.092	0.137	0.181	0.224	0.266	0.308	0.349
			0.5	0.077	0.153	0.225	0.296	0.365	0.432	0.498	0.562
			0.7	0.109	0.213	0.313	0.409	0.501	0.591	0.678	0.762
		3.6	0.1	0.039	0.077	0.115	0.152	0.188	0.224	0.259	0.294
			0.3	0.117	0.228	0.335	0.437	0.536	0.631	0.723	0.811
			0.5	0.195	0.376	0.545	0.704	0.854	0.997	1.132	1.261
			0.7	0.274	0.522	0.748	0.956	1.150	1.332	1.503	1.664
		3.8	0.1	-	-	-	-	-	-	-	-

Table No. 29-4-X. Differential Swell Occurring at the Perimeter of a Slab for an Edge Lift Swelling Condition in Predominantly Illite Clay Soil (60 Percent Clay).

Percent Clay (%)	Depth to Constant Suction (FT)	Constant Suction (pF)	Velocity of Moisture Flow (inches/month)	DIFFERENTIAL SWELL (INCHES) EDGE DISTANCE PENETRATION (FT) 1 FT	2 FT	3 FT	4 FT	5 FT	6 FT	7 FT	8 FT
60	3	3.2	0.1	0.002	0.005	0.007	0.009	0.012	0.014	0.016	0.018
			0.3	0.007	0.014	0.021	0.027	0.034	0.041	0.047	0.054
			0.5	0.012	0.023	0.034	0.045	0.056	0.067	0.077	0.087
			0.7	0.016	0.032	0.047	0.062	0.077	0.092	0.106	0.119
		3.4	0.1	0.005	0.010	0.015	0.020	0.024	0.029	0.034	0.039
			0.3	0.015	0.029	0.043	0.057	0.071	0.084	0.097	0.110
			0.5	0.025	0.048	0.071	0.093	0.114	0.135	0.155	0.174
			0.7	0.034	0.067	0.097	0.127	0.155	0.182	0.208	0.234
		3.6	0.1	0.012	0.024	0.036	0.047	0.059	0.070	0.081	0.092
			0.3	0.036	0.070	0.103	0.134	0.164	0.192	0.219	0.245
			0.5	0.060	0.114	0.165	0.212	0.256	0.297	0.337	0.374
			0.7	0.083	0.156	0.223	0.283	0.339	0.391	0.439	0.485
		3.8	0.1	0.030	0.058	0.086	0.112	0.137	0.162	0.185	0.208
			0.3	0.088	0.165	0.234	0.297	0.355	0.409	0.459	0.506
			0.5	0.143	0.260	0.361	0.450	0.529	0.601	0.667	0.728
			0.7	0.196	0.348	0.474	0.582	0.677	0.761	0.838	0.909
	5	3.2	0.1	0.005	0.010	0.015	0.020	0.025	0.030	0.035	0.040
			0.3	0.015	0.030	0.045	0.060	0.075	0.089	0.104	0.118
			0.5	0.025	0.050	0.075	0.099	0.123	0.147	0.170	0.193
			0.7	0.036	0.070	0.104	0.138	0.171	0.203	0.234	0.265
		3.4	0.1	0.011	0.022	0.033	0.043	0.054	0.064	0.075	0.085
			0.3	0.033	0.065	0.096	0.127	0.157	0.187	0.216	0.245
			0.5	0.055	0.107	0.158	0.208	0.256	0.303	0.348	0.393
			0.7	0.076	0.149	0.219	0.286	0.350	0.412	0.472	0.530
		3.6	0.1	0.027	0.054	0.080	0.106	0.132	0.157	0.181	0.206
			0.3	0.081	0.159	0.233	0.303	0.371	0.437	0.500	0.561
			0.5	0.135	0.260	0.376	0.485	0.588	0.685	0.777	0.864
			0.7	0.189	0.358	0.512	0.654	0.786	0.908	1.024	1.133
		3.8	0.1	0.067	0.132	0.194	0.254	0.311	0.367	0.422	0.474
			0.3	0.201	0.379	0.541	0.690	0.827	0.955	1.074	1.187
			0.5	0.333	0.611	0.851	1.064	1.255	1.430	1.591	1.740
			0.7	0.465	0.830	1.135	1.398	1.631	1.840	2.030	2.205
	7	3.2	0.1	0.009	0.018	0.026	0.035	0.044	0.052	0.061	0.070
			0.3	0.026	0.053	0.079	0.104	0.130	0.155	0.180	0.205
			0.5	0.044	0.088	0.130	0.173	0.214	0.255	0.296	0.336
			0.7	0.062	0.122	0.182	0.240	0.297	0.353	0.408	0.463
		3.4	0.1	0.019	0.038	0.057	0.076	0.094	0.113	0.131	0.149
			0.3	0.057	0.114	0.169	0.223	0.276	0.329	0.380	0.431
			0.5	0.096	0.188	0.278	0.366	0.451	0.534	0.615	0.694
			0.7	0.134	0.263	0.386	0.505	0.619	0.730	0.837	0.941
		3.6	0.1	0.048	0.095	0.141	0.187	0.232	0.277	0.320	0.364
			0.3	0.144	0.282	0.414	0.540	0.662	0.779	0.893	1.002
			0.5	0.241	0.465	0.674	0.870	1.055	1.231	1.398	0.558
			0.7	0.339	0.644	0.924	1.181	1.421	1.645	1.856	2.055
		3.8	0.1								

Table No. 29-4-Y. Differential Swell Occurring at the Perimeter of a Slab for an Edge Lift Swelling Condition in Predominantly Illite Clay Soil (70 Percent Clay).

Percent Clay (%)	Depth to Constant Suction (FT)	Constant Suction (pF)	Velocity of Moisture Flow (inches /month)	DIFFERENTIAL SWELL (INCHES) EDGE DISTANCE PENETRATION (FT) 1 FT	2 FT	3 FT	4 FT	5 FT	6 FT	7 FT	8 FT
70	3	3.2	0.1	0.003	0.006	0.008	0.011	0.014	0.017	0.019	0.022
			0.3	0.008	0.017	0.025	0.033	0.041	0.048	0.056	0.064
			0.5	0.014	0.027	0.041	0.054	0.067	0.079	0.092	0.104
			0.7	0.019	0.038	0.056	0.074	0.092	0.109	0.126	0.142
		3.4	0.1	0.006	0.012	0.018	0.023	0.029	0.035	0.040	0.046
			0.3	0.018	0.035	0.052	0.068	0.084	0.100	0.115	0.130
			0.5	0.029	0.057	0.084	0.111	0.136	0.160	0.184	0.207
			0.7	0.041	0.079	0.116	0.151	0.186	0.217	0.248	0.278
		3.6	0.1	0.015	0.029	0.043	0.056	0.070	0.083	0.096	0.109
			0.3	0.043	0.084	0.123	0.159	0.195	0.229	0.261	0.292
			0.5	0.071	0.136	0.196	0.252	0.305	0.354	0.401	0.445
			0.7	0.099	0.186	0.265	0.337	0.403	0.465	0.523	0.577
		3.8	0.1	0.036	0.070	0.102	0.133	0.163	0.192	0.220	0.247
			0.3	0.104	0.196	0.279	0.354	0.422	0.486	0.546	0.602
			0.5	0.170	0.310	0.430	0.535	0.630	0.715	0.794	0.866
			0.7	0.234	0.415	0.564	0.692	0.805	0.906	0.998	1.082
	5	3.2	0.1	0.006	0.012	0.018	0.024	0.030	0.036	0.042	0.048
			0.3	0.018	0.036	0.054	0.072	0.089	0.106	0.124	0.141
			0.5	0.030	0.060	0.089	0.118	0.147	0.175	0.202	0.230
			0.7	0.042	0.084	0.124	0.164	0.203	0.241	0.279	0.315
		3.4	0.1	0.013	0.026	0.039	0.052	0.064	0.077	0.089	0.102
			0.3	0.039	0.077	0.115	0.151	0.187	0.223	0.258	0.292
			0.5	0.066	0.128	0.188	0.247	0.305	0.360	0.414	0.467
			0.7	0.091	0.177	0.260	0.340	0.417	0.490	0.562	0.631
		3.6	0.1	0.032	0.064	0.095	0.126	0.157	0.186	0.216	0.245
			0.3	0.097	0.189	0.277	0.361	0.442	0.520	0.595	0.667
			0.5	0.161	0.309	0.448	0.577	0.699	0.815	0.925	1.029
			0.7	0.225	0.426	0.610	0.779	0.936	1.081	1.219	1.348
		3.8	0.1	0.080	0.157	0.231	0.302	0.371	0.437	0.502	0.564
			0.3	0.239	0.452	0.644	0.821	0.984	1.136	1.279	1.413
			0.5	0.396	0.727	1.013	1.266	1.494	1.702	1.894	2.072
			0.7	0.563	0.988	1.361	1.664	1.941	2.190	2.417	2.625
	7	3.2	0.1	0.011	0.021	0.031	0.042	0.052	0.062	0.073	0.083
			0.3	0.031	0.063	0.094	0.124	0.155	0.185	0.215	0.244
			0.5	0.062	0.104	0.155	0.205	0.255	0.304	0.352	0.400
			0.7	0.074	0.146	0.216	0.285	0.354	0.420	0.486	0.551
		3.4	0.1	0.023	0.045	0.068	0.090	0.112	0.134	0.156	0.178
			0.3	0.068	0.136	0.201	0.266	0.329	0.391	0.453	0.513
			0.5	0.114	0.224	0.331	0.436	0.537	0.636	0.732	0.826
			0.7	0.160	0.313	0.459	0.601	0.737	0.869	0.996	1.120
		3.6	0.1	0.057	0.113	0.168	0.223	0.276	0.329	0.381	0.433
			0.3	0.172	0.335	0.492	0.643	0.788	0.928	1.063	1.193
			0.5	0.287	0.553	0.802	1.036	1.256	1.465	1.664	1.854
			0.7	0.403	0.767	1.099	1.406	1.691	1.958	2.209	2.447
		3.8	0.1	-	-	-	-	-	-	-	-

Table No. 29-4-Z. Differential Swell Occurring at the Perimeter of a Slab for an Edge Lift Swelling Condition in Predominantly Montmorillonite Clay Soil (30 Percent Clay).

Percent Clay (%)	Depth to Constant Suction (FT)	Constant Suction (pF)	Velocity of Moisture Flow (inches /month)	DIFFERENTIAL SWELL (INCHES) EDGE DISTANCE PENETRATION (FT) 1 FT	2 FT	3 FT	4 FT	5 FT	6 FT	7 FT	8 FT
30	3	3.2	0.1	0.001	0.002	0.004	0.005	0.006	0.007	0.008	0.009
			0.3	0.004	0.007	0.010	0.014	0.017	0.021	0.024	0.027
			0.5	0.006	0.012	0.017	0.023	0.028	0.034	0.039	0.044
			0.7	0.008	0.016	0.024	0.032	0.039	0.046	0.053	0.060
		3.4	0.1	0.003	0.005	0.007	0.010	0.012	0.015	0.017	0.019
			0.3	0.007	0.015	0.022	0.029	0.036	0.042	0.049	0.055
			0.5	0.012	0.024	0.036	0.047	0.058	0.068	0.078	0.088
			0.7	0.017	0.034	0.049	0.064	0.078	0.092	0.105	0.118
		3.6	0.1	0.006	0.012	0.018	0.024	0.030	0.035	0.041	0.046
			0.3	0.018	0.036	0.052	0.068	0.083	0.097	0.111	0.124
			0.5	0.030	0.058	0.083	0.107	0.129	0.150	0.170	0.189
			0.7	0.042	0.079	0.112	0.143	0.171	0.197	0.222	0.245
		3.8	0.1	0.015	0.030	0.043	0.057	0.069	0.082	0.093	0.105
			0.3	0.044	0.083	0.118	0.150	0.179	0.206	0.232	0.255
			0.5	0.072	0.132	0.182	0.227	0.267	0.303	0.337	0.368
			0.7	0.099	0.176	0.239	0.294	0.342	0.385	0.423	0.459
	5	3.2	0.1	0.003	0.005	0.008	0.010	0.013	0.015	0.018	0.020
			0.3	0.008	0.015	0.023	0.030	0.038	0.045	0.053	0.060
			0.5	0.013	0.026	0.038	0.050	0.062	0.074	0.086	0.098
			0.7	0.018	0.036	0.053	0.070	0.086	0.102	0.118	0.134
		3.4	0.1	0.006	0.011	0.016	0.022	0.027	0.033	0.038	0.043
			0.3	0.017	0.033	0.049	0.064	0.080	0.095	0.109	0.124
			0.5	0.028	0.054	0.080	0.105	0.129	0.153	0.176	0.198
			0.7	0.039	0.075	0.110	0.144	0.177	0.208	0.238	0.268
		3.6	0.1	0.014	0.027	0.041	0.054	0.066	0.079	0.092	0.104
			0.3	0.041	0.080	0.118	0.153	0.188	0.221	0.252	0.283
			0.5	0.068	0.131	0.190	0.245	0.297	0.346	0.392	0.437
			0.7	0.095	0.181	0.259	0.330	0.397	0.459	0.517	0.572
		3.8	0.1	0.034	0.067	0.098	0.128	0.157	0.186	0.213	0.239
			0.3	0.101	0.192	0.273	0.348	0.418	0.482	0.543	0.600
			0.5	0.168	0.308	0.430	0.537	0.634	0.722	0.804	0.879
			0.7	0.235	0.419	0.573	0.706	0.824	0.929	1.025	1.114
	7	3.2	0.1	0.004	0.009	0.013	0.018	0.022	0.027	0.031	0.035
			0.3	0.013	0.027	0.040	0.053	0.066	0.078	0.091	0.104
			0.5	0.022	0.044	0.066	0.087	0.108	0.129	0.150	0.170
			0.7	0.031	0.062	0.092	0.121	0.150	0.178	0.206	0.234
		3.4	0.1	0.010	0.019	0.029	0.038	0.048	0.057	0.066	0.075
			0.3	0.029	0.057	0.085	0.113	0.140	0.166	0.192	0.218
			0.5	0.048	0.095	0.141	0.185	0.228	0.270	0.311	0.361
			0.7	0.068	0.133	0.195	0.255	0.313	0.369	0.423	0.475
		3.6	0.1	0.024	0.048	0.071	0.095	0.117	0.140	0.162	0.184
			0.3	0.073	0.142	0.209	0.273	0.334	0.394	0.451	0.506
			0.5	0.122	0.235	0.340	0.439	0.533	0.622	0.706	0.787
			0.7	0.171	0.326	0.466	0.597	0.718	0.831	0.937	1.038
		3.8	0.1	-	-	-	-	-	-	-	-

Table No. 29-4-AA. Differential Swell Occurring at the Perimeter of a Slab for an Edge Lift Swelling Condition in Predominantly Montmorillonite Clay Soil (40 Percent Clay).

Percent Clay (%)	Depth to Constant Suction (FT)	Constant Suction (pF)	Velocity of Moisture Flow (inches /month)	DIFFERENTIAL SWELL (INCHES)							
				EDGE DISTANCE PENETRATION (FT)							
				1 FT	2 FT	3 FT	4 FT	5 FT	6 FT	7 FT	8 FT
40	3	3.2	0.1	0.002	0.003	0.005	0.007	0.008	0.010	0.012	0.013
			0.3	0.005	0.010	0.015	0.020	0.025	0.030	0.035	0.039
			0.5	0.009	0.017	0.025	0.033	0.041	0.049	0.056	0.064
			0.7	0.012	0.023	0.035	0.046	0.056	0.067	0.077	0.087
		3.4	0.1	0.004	0.007	0.011	0.014	0.018	0.021	0.025	0.028
			0.3	0.011	0.021	0.032	0.042	0.052	0.061	0.071	0.080
			0.5	0.018	0.035	0.052	0.068	0.084	0.099	0.113	0.128
			0.7	0.025	0.049	0.071	0.093	0.114	0.133	0.153	0.171
		3.6	0.1	0.009	0.018	0.026	0.035	0.043	0.051	0.059	0.067
			0.3	0.027	0.052	0.075	0.098	0.120	0.141	0.160	0.180
			0.5	0.044	0.084	0.121	0.155	0.187	0.218	0.246	0.274
			0.7	0.061	0.114	0.163	0.207	0.248	0.286	0.321	0.355
		3.8	0.1	0.022	0.043	0.063	0.082	0.100	0.118	0.135	0.152
			0.3	0.064	0.121	0.171	0.217	0.260	0.299	0.336	0.370
			0.5	0.105	0.191	0.264	0.329	0.387	0.440	0.488	0.533
			0.7	0.144	0.255	0.347	0.426	0.495	0.557	0.614	0.665
	5	3.2	0.1	0.004	0.007	0.011	0.015	0.019	0.022	0.026	0.030
			0.3	0.011	0.022	0.033	0.044	0.055	0.065	0.076	0.087
			0.5	0.019	0.037	0.055	0.073	0.090	0.107	0.125	0.141
			0.7	0.026	0.052	0.076	0.101	0.125	0.148	0.171	0.194
		3.4	0.1	0.008	0.016	0.024	0.032	0.039	0.047	0.055	0.062
			0.3	0.024	0.047	0.070	0.093	0.115	0.137	0.158	0.179
			0.5	0.040	0.078	0.116	0.152	0.187	0.221	0.255	0.287
			0.7	0.056	0.109	0.160	0.209	0.256	0.302	0.345	0.388
		3.6	0.1	0.020	0.039	0.059	0.078	0.096	0.115	0.133	0.150
			0.3	0.060	0.116	0.170	0.222	0.272	0.320	0.366	0.410
			0.5	0.099	0.190	0.275	0.355	0.430	0.501	0.568	0.633
			0.7	0.138	0.262	0.375	0.479	0.575	0.665	0.749	0.829
		3.8	0.1	0.049	0.096	0.142	0.186	0.228	0.269	0.309	0.347
			0.3	0.147	0.278	0.396	0.505	0.605	0.699	0.786	0.869
			0.5	0.244	0.447	0.623	0.779	0.919	1.047	1.164	1.274
			0.7	0.340	0.607	0.831	1.023	1.193	1.347	1.486	1.614
	7	3.2	0.1	0.006	0.013	0.019	0.026	0.032	0.038	0.045	0.051
			0.3	0.019	0.039	0.058	0.076	0.095	0.114	0.132	0.150
			0.5	0.032	0.064	0.095	0.126	0.157	0.187	0.217	0.246
			0.7	0.045	0.089	0.133	0.176	0.217	0.258	0.299	0.339
		3.4	0.1	0.014	0.028	0.042	0.055	0.069	0.083	0.096	0.109
			0.3	0.042	0.083	0.124	0.163	0.202	0.241	0.278	0.316
			0.5	0.070	0.138	0.204	0.268	0.330	0.391	0.450	0.508
			0.7	0.098	0.192	0.283	0.369	0.453	0.534	0.613	0.689
		3.6	0.1	0.035	0.070	0.104	0.137	0.170	0.202	0.235	0.266
			0.3	0.106	0.206	0.303	0.395	0.484	0.570	0.653	0.734
			0.5	0.176	0.340	0.493	0.637	0.772	0.901	1.023	1.140
			0.7	0.248	0.472	0.676	0.864	1.040	1.204	1.358	1.504
		3.8	0.1	-	-	-	-	-	-	-	-

Table No. 29-4-BB. Differential Swell Occurring at the Perimeter of a Slab for an Edge Lift Swelling Condition in Predominantly Montmorillonite Clay Soil (50 Percent Clay).

Percent Clay	Depth to Constant Suction	Constant Suction	Velocity of Moisture Flow	DIFFERENTIAL SWELL (INCHES)							
				EDGE DISTANCE PENETRATION (FT)							
(%)	(FT)	(pF)	(inches /month)	1 FT	2 FT	3 FT	4 FT	5 FT	6 FT	7 FT	8 FT
50	3	3.2	0.1	0.002	0.004	0.007	0.009	0.011	0.013	0.015	0.018
			0.3	0.007	0.013	0.020	0.026	0.033	0.039	0.045	0.052
			0.5	0.011	0.022	0.033	0.043	0.054	0.064	0.074	0.084
			0.7	0.016	0.031	0.045	0.060	0.074	0.088	0.101	0.115
		3.4	0.1	0.005	0.009	0.014	0.019	0.023	0.028	0.032	0.037
			0.3	0.014	0.028	0.042	0.055	0.068	0.080	0.093	0.105
			0.5	0.024	0.046	0.068	0.089	0.109	0.129	0.148	0.167
			0.7	0.033	0.064	0.093	0.122	0.149	0.175	0.200	0.224
		3.6	0.1	0.012	0.023	0.034	0.045	0.056	0.067	0.077	0.088
			0.3	0.035	0.068	0.099	0.128	0.157	0.184	0.210	0.235
			0.5	0.057	0.110	0.158	0.203	0.245	0.285	0.323	0.358
			0.7	0.079	0.150	0.213	0.271	0.325	0.375	0.421	0.465
		3.8	0.1	0.029	0.056	0.082	0.107	0.132	0.155	0.177	0.199
			0.3	0.084	0.158	0.224	0.285	0.340	0.392	0.440	0.485
			0.5	0.137	0.250	0.346	0.431	0.507	0.576	0.639	0.698
			0.7	0.188	0.334	0.454	0.558	0.649	0.730	0.804	0.871
	5	3.2	0.1	0.005	0.010	0.015	0.019	0.024	0.029	0.034	0.039
			0.3	0.015	0.029	0.044	0.058	0.072	0.086	0.100	0.133
			0.5	0.024	0.048	0.072	0.095	0.118	0.141	0.163	0.185
			0.7	0.034	0.067	0.100	0.132	0.163	0.194	0.224	0.254
		3.4	0.1	0.011	0.021	0.031	0.041	0.052	0.062	0.072	0.082
			0.3	0.031	0.062	0.092	0.122	0.151	0.179	0.207	0.235
			0.5	0.052	0.103	0.152	0.199	0.245	0.290	0.334	0.376
			0.7	0.073	0.143	0.210	0.274	0.335	0.395	0.452	0.508
		3.6	0.1	0.026	0.052	0.077	0.102	0.126	0.150	0.174	0.197
			0.3	0.078	0.152	0.223	0.291	0.356	0.419	0.479	0.538
			0.5	0.130	0.249	0.361	0.465	0.563	0.656	0.745	0.829
			0.7	0.181	0.343	0.491	0.627	0.753	0.871	0.981	1.086
		3.8	0.1	0.064	0.126	0.186	0.243	0.299	0.352	0.404	0.454
			0.3	0.192	0.364	0.519	0.661	0.793	0.915	1.030	1.138
			0.5	0.319	0.585	0.816	1.020	1.204	1.371	1.525	1.668
			0.7	0.445	0.796	1.088	1.340	1.563	1.764	1.946	2.114
	7	3.2	0.1	0.008	0.017	0.025	0.034	0.042	0.050	0.059	0.067
			0.3	0.025	0.050	0.075	0.100	0.125	0.149	0.173	0.197
			0.5	0.042	0.084	0.125	0.165	0.205	0.245	0.284	0.322
			0.7	0.059	0.117	0.174	0.230	0.285	0.339	0.391	0.443
		3.4	0.1	0.018	0.037	0.055	0.073	0.090	0.108	0.126	0.143
			0.3	0.055	0.109	0.162	0.214	0.265	0.315	0.365	0.413
			0.5	0.092	0.181	0.267	0.351	0.433	0.512	0.590	0.665
			0.7	0.129	0.252	0.370	0.484	0.594	0.700	0.802	0.902
		3.6	0.1	0.046	0.091	0.136	0.179	0.223	0.265	0.307	0.349
			0.3	0.138	0.270	0.397	0.518	0.635	0.747	0.856	0.961
			0.5	0.231	0.446	0.646	0.834	1.012	1.180	1.341	1.494
			0.7	0.325	0.618	0.885	1.132	1.362	1.577	1.779	1.970
		3.8	0.1	-	-	-	-	-	-	-	-

Table No. 29-4-CC. Differential Swell Occurring at the Perimeter of a Slab for an Edge Lift Swelling Condition in Predominantly Montmorillonite Clay Soil (60 Percent Clay).

Percent Clay (%)	Depth to Constant Suction (FT)	Constant Suction (pF)	Velocity of Moisture Flow (inches /month)	DIFFERENTIAL SWELL (INCHES) EDGE DISTANCE PENETRATION (FT) 1 FT	2 FT	3 FT	4 FT	5 FT	6 FT	7 FT	8 FT
60	3	3.2	0.1	0.003	0.006	0.008	0.011	0.014	0.016	0.019	0.022
			0.3	0.008	0.016	0.025	0.033	0.040	0.048	0.056	0.064
			0.5	0.014	0.027	0.041	0.054	0.066	0.079	0.091	0.104
			0.7	0.019	0.038	0.056	0.074	0.091	0.109	0.125	0.142
		3.4	0.1	0.006	0.012	0.017	0.023	0.029	0.035	0.040	0.046
			0.3	0.018	0.035	0.051	0.068	0.084	0.099	0.115	0.130
			0.5	0.029	0.067	0.084	0.110	0.135	0.160	0.183	0.206
			0.7	0.041	0.079	0.116	0.151	0.184	0.216	0.247	0.277
		3.6	0.1	0.014	0.029	0.043	0.056	0.070	0.083	0.096	0.109
			0.3	0.043	0.083	0.122	0.159	0.194	0.228	0.260	0.291
			0.5	0.071	0.136	0.195	0.251	0.303	0.352	0.399	0.433
			0.7	0.098	0.186	0.264	0.336	0.402	0.463	0.521	0.575
		3.8	0.1	0.035	0.069	0.102	0.133	0.163	0.191	0.219	0.246
			0.3	0.104	0.195	0.277	0.352	0.421	0.484	0.544	0.599
			0.5	0.169	0.309	0.428	0.533	0.627	0.712	0.790	0.863
			0.7	0.233	0.413	0.562	0.690	0.802	0.903	0.994	1.077
	5	3.2	0.1	0.006	0.012	0.018	0.024	0.030	0.036	0.042	0.048
			0.3	0.018	0.036	0.054	0.071	0.089	0.106	0.123	0.140
			0.5	0.030	0.060	0.090	0.118	0.146	0.174	0.202	0.229
			0.7	0.042	0.083	0.124	0.163	0.202	0.240	0.278	0.314
		3.4	0.1	0.013	0.026	0.039	0.051	0.064	0.076	0.089	0.101
			0.3	0.039	0.077	0.114	0.151	0.187	0.222	0.256	0.291
			0.5	0.065	0.127	0.188	0.246	0.303	0.359	0.413	0.465
			0.7	0.090	0.177	0.259	0.339	0.415	0.488	0.559	0.628
		3.6	0.1	0.032	0.064	0.095	0.126	0.156	0.186	0.215	0.244
			0.3	0.096	0.188	0.276	0.360	0.440	0.518	0.593	0.665
			0.5	0.160	0.308	0.446	0.575	0.697	0.812	0.921	1.025
			0.7	0.224	0.425	0.607	0.775	0.931	1.077	1.214	1.343
		3.8	0.1	0.080	0.156	0.230	0.301	0.369	0.436	0.500	0.562
			0.3	0.238	0.450	0.642	0.817	0.980	1.132	1.274	1.407
			0.5	0.395	0.724	1.009	1.261	1.488	1.695	1.886	2.063
			0.7	0.551	0.984	1.345	1.657	1.933	2.181	2.407	2.614
	7	3.2	0.1	0.010	0.021	0.031	0.042	0.052	0.062	0.072	0.083
			0.3	0.031	0.062	0.093	0.124	0.154	0.184	0.214	0.243
			0.5	0.052	0.104	0.155	0.205	0.254	0.303	0.351	0.398
			0.7	0.073	0.145	0.215	0.284	0.352	0.419	0.484	0.548
		3.4	0.1	0.023	0.045	0.067	0.090	0.112	0.134	0.155	0.177
			0.3	0.068	0.135	0.200	0.264	0.328	0.390	0.451	0.511
			0.5	0.113	0.223	0.330	0.434	0.535	0.633	0.729	0.823
			0.7	0.159	0.311	0.458	0.598	0.734	0.865	0.992	1.115
		3.6	0.1	0.057	0.113	0.168	0.222	0.275	0.328	0.380	0.431
			0.3	0.171	0.334	0.490	0.640	0.785	0.924	1.058	1.188
			0.5	0.286	0.551	0.799	1.031	1.251	1.459	1.658	1.847
			0.7	0.402	0.764	1.095	1.400	1.684	1.950	2.200	2.437
		3.8	0.1	-	-	-	-	-	-	-	-

Table No. 29-4-DD. Differential Swell Occurring at the Perimeter of a Slab for an Edge Lift Swelling Condition in Predominantly Montmorillonite Clay Soil (70 Percent Clay).

Percent Clay (%)	Depth to Constant Suction (FT)	Constant Suction (pF)	Velocity of Moisture Flow (inches /month)	DIFFERENTIAL SWELL (INCHES) EDGE DISTANCE PENETRATION (FT) 1 FT	2 FT	3 FT	4 FT	5 FT	6 FT	7 FT	8 FT
70	3	3.2	0.1	0.003	0.007	0.010	0.013	0.016	0.020	0.023	0.026
			0.3	0.010	0.020	0.029	0.039	0.048	0.058	0.067	0.076
			0.5	0.016	0.032	0.048	0.064	0.079	0.094	0.109	0.123
			0.7	0.023	0.045	0.067	0.088	0.109	0.129	0.149	0.169
		3.4	0.1	0.007	0.014	0.021	0.028	0.034	0.041	0.048	0.054
			0.3	0.021	0.041	0.061	0.081	0.100	0.118	0.137	0.155
			0.5	0.035	0.068	0.100	0.131	0.161	0.190	0.219	0.246
			0.7	0.048	0.094	0.138	0.179	0.219	0.258	0.294	0.330
		3.6	0.1	0.017	0.034	0.051	0.067	0.083	0.099	0.114	0.129
			0.3	0.051	0.099	0.145	0.189	0.231	0.271	0.310	0.347
			0.5	0.084	0.162	0.233	0.299	0.361	0.420	0.475	0.528
			0.7	0.117	0.221	0.314	0.400	0.479	0.552	0.620	0.684
		3.8	0.1	0.042	0.082	0.121	0.158	0.194	0.228	0.261	0.293
			0.3	0.124	0.233	0.330	0.419	0.501	0.577	0.648	0.714
			0.5	0.202	0.368	0.510	0.635	0.747	0.849	0.942	1.028
			0.7	0.277	0.492	0.669	0.822	0.955	1.075	1.184	1.284
	5	3.2	0.1	0.007	0.014	0.022	0.029	0.036	0.043	0.050	0.057
			0.3	0.022	0.043	0.064	0.085	0.106	0.126	0.147	0.167
			0.5	0.036	0.071	0.106	0.140	0.174	0.207	0.240	0.273
			0.7	0.050	0.099	0.147	0.195	0.241	0.286	0.331	0.374
		3.4	0.1	0.015	0.031	0.046	0.061	0.076	0.091	0.106	0.121
			0.3	0.046	0.092	0.136	0.179	0.222	0.264	0.306	0.346
			0.5	0.077	0.151	0.223	0.293	0.361	0.427	0.492	0.554
			0.7	0.108	0.210	0.309	0.403	0.494	0.582	0.666	0.748
		3.6	0.1	0.038	0.076	0.113	0.150	0.186	0.221	0.256	0.290
			0.3	0.115	0.224	0.329	0.429	0.525	0.617	0.706	0.792
			0.5	0.191	0.367	0.531	0.685	0.830	0.967	1.097	1.221
			0.7	0.267	0.506	0.724	0.924	1.110	1.283	1.446	1.600
		3.8	0.1	0.095	0.186	0.274	0.358	0.440	0.519	0.595	0.669
			0.3	0.283	0.536	0.764	0.974	1.168	1.348	1.517	1.677
			0.5	0.470	0.862	1.262	1.502	1.773	2.020	2.247	2.458
			0.7	0.656	1.172	1.603	1.974	2.303	2.598	2.867	3.114
	7	3.2	0.1	0.012	0.025	0.037	0.050	0.062	0.074	0.086	0.098
			0.3	0.037	0.074	0.111	0.147	0.183	0.219	0.255	0.290
			0.5	0.062	0.124	0.184	0.244	0.303	0.361	0.418	0.475
			0.7	0.087	0.173	0.256	0.339	0.419	0.499	0.577	0.653
		3.4	0.1	0.027	0.054	0.080	0.107	0.133	0.159	0.185	0.211
			0.3	0.081	0.160	0.238	0.315	0.390	0.464	0.537	0.609
			0.5	0.135	0.266	0.393	0.517	0.637	0.754	0.869	0.980
			0.7	0.189	0.371	0.545	0.713	0.875	1.031	1.182	1.329
		3.6	0.1	0.068	0.134	0.200	0.264	0.328	0.391	0.453	0.514
			0.3	0.204	0.398	0.584	0.763	0.935	1.101	1.261	1.415
			0.5	0.341	0.656	0.951	1.229	1.490	1.739	1.975	2.200
			0.7	0.479	0.910	1.304	1.668	2.006	2.323	2.621	2.903
		3.8	0.1	-	-	-	-	-	-	-	-
			0.3								
			0.5								

Table No. 29-4-EE.
Comparison of Methods of Determining Cation Exchange Capacity.

SOIL SAMPLE	CATION EXCHANGE CAPACITY (meq/100gm)	
	ATOMIC ABSORPTION	SPECTROPHOTOMETER[a]
01 - 01	21.1	20.2
31 - 02	28.2	26.2
53 - 05	14.7	7.0
72 - 06	71.4	72.8
73 - 06	21.6	18.9
86 - 08	45.0	50.0

[a] Bausch & Lomb "Spectronic-20"

Table No. 29-4-FF. Comparison of Clay Mineral Determination Methods.

SOIL SAMPLE	PERCENT CLAY	ATTERBERG LIMITS		C.E.C. (meq/100 gm)		Ac	CEAc		PREDOMINANT CLAY MINERAL		
		PL	PI	FLAME PHOTOMETER	CORRELATION EQUATION		FLAME PHOTOMETER	CORRELATION EQUATION	FLAME PHOTOMETER	CORRELATION EQUATION	X-RAY DEFRACTION ANALYSIS
31-02	33.5	16.5	26.6	28.2	26.6	0.79	0.84	0.80	Smectite	Smectite	Smectite
72-06	50.0	32.5	41.8	71.4	58.7	0.84	1.43	1.17	Smectite	Smectite	Smectite
86-08	47.0	25.1	36.4	45.0	43.4	0.77	0.96	0.92	Smectite	Smectite	Smectite

UNIFORM BUILDING CODE STANDARD NO. 31-1

BUILDING AND FACILITY ACCESS SPECIFICATIONS

See Sections 3101 (b), 3103 (b) 1 and 4, 3104 (a), 3105 (a), 3105 (b) 2 and 5, and 3105 (c) and (e), Uniform Building Code

Adoption of ANSI Standard

Sec. 31.101. Access to buildings and facilities in buildings shall be in accordance with American National Standard A117.1-1986, "Providing Accessibility and Usability for Physically Handicapped People," published by the American National Standards Institute, copyright 1986, 1430 Broadway, New York, New York 10018, as if set out at length herein.

When a provision of the standard adopted hereby is found to be in conflict with a provision of the Uniform Building Code, the provision of the Uniform Building Code takes precedence.

UNIFORM BUILDING CODE STANDARD NO. 32-5

ROOFING AGGREGATES

Material Standard of the International Conference of Building Officials

See Section 3201 (b) and Table No. 32-E, Uniform Building Code

Scope

Sec. 32.501. This standard covers the quality, grading and amounts to be applied of mineral roofing aggregate.

Characteristics

Sec. 32.502. The mineral aggregate at the time of application shall be hard, durable, opaque, chemically inert, free of clay, loam, sand or foreign substances, and surface dry to 0.5 percent by weight moisture content.

Grading

Sec. 32.503. The mineral aggregate shall conform to the sieve analysis requirements prescribed in Table No. 32-5-A.

TABLE NO. 32-5-A

SIEVE SIZE	PERCENTAGE PASSING	
	For Use With Embedment Coat of 60 Pounds per Roofing Square (Percent)	For Use With Embedment Coat of 50 Pounds per Roofing Square (Percent)
5/8"	100	100
1/2"	90-100	100
3/8"	25- 60	90-100
1/4"	0- 10	30- 70
No. 4	0- 2	0- 10
No. 8		0- 4
No. 10		0- 1
No. 20	0- 0.5	0- 0.5

Water Absorption

Sec. 32.504. Aggregate shall not absorb more than 5 percent of the dry weight of the aggregate when tested using any nationally recognized standard.

Translucency

Sec. 32.505. Aggregate shall have a translucency intensity of not more than "slight" when visually inspected.

Hardness

Sec. 32.506. Aggregate shall have a hardness factor of not more than 20 percent.

Application

Sec. 32.507. If the unit weight (loose) of the aggregate is 60 pounds per cubic foot, or more, the amount applied per roofing square shall be as specified in the Uniform Building Code.

If the unit weight (loose) is less than 60 pounds per cubic foot, the amount applied shall be as follows:

1. For an embedment coat of 60 pounds of asphalt per roofing square, not less than 5 cubic feet of aggregate per roofing square shall be applied.

2. For an embedment coat of 50 pounds of asphalt per roofing square, not less than 4 cubic feet of aggregate per roofing square shall be applied.

UNIFORM BUILDING CODE STANDARD NO. 32-7

TEST STANDARD FOR DETERMINING THE FIRE RETARDANCY OF ROOF-COVERING MATERIALS

Based on Standard Specification 790 October 5, 1983, of the Underwriters Laboratories Inc.

See Sections 1701 (b), 1713 (e) 3, 3201 (b), 3202, 5201 (f), 5207 (a) 2 and Table No 32-A, Uniform Building Code

General

Sec. 32.701. (a) **Scope.** These requirements cover the performance of roof-covering materials exposed to fire conditions, and are intended to indicate the characteristics of roof coverings when exposed to fire originating from sources outside a building on which the coverings may be installed. They are applicable to roof coverings intended for installation on either combustible or noncombustible decks when the roof coverings are applied as intended.

Class A roof coverings are effective against severe fire test exposures. Under such exposures, roof coverings of this class are not readily flammable, afford a fairly high degree of fire protection to the roof deck, do not slip from position, and are not expected to produce flying brands.

Class B roof coverings are effective against moderate fire test exposures. Under such exposures, roof coverings of this class are not readily flammable, afford a moderate degree of fire protection to the roof deck, do not slip from position, and are not expected to produce flying brands.

Class C roof coverings are effective against light fire test exposures. Under such exposures, roof coverings of this class are not readily flammable, afford a measurable degree of fire protection to the roof deck, do not slip from position and are not expected to produce flying brands.

Tests conducted in accordance with these requirements are intended to demonstrate the performance of roof coverings during the types and periods of exposure involved, but are not intended to determine the acceptability of roof coverings for use after exposure to fire.

Roof-covering materials are also required to comply with the requirements for construction, material specifications and performance as applicable to specific types, designs, sizes and arrangements. All such applicable additional requirements are not considered to be within the scope of these requirements for fire tests.

The terms "combustible" and "noncombustible" as used in the standard apply to decks as follows:

1. Combustible is a deck formed of wood (sheathing boards or plywood).
2. Noncombustible is a deck formed of metal, concrete or poured gypsum.

(b) **Test Apparatus.** As illustrated in Figure No. 32-7-1, the apparatus used for the tests described in Section 32.702 is to consist of the following:

1. A test deck to which the roof-covering materials to be tested are applied, mounted on a framework. The pitch of the framework is to be adjustable.

2. A construction of noncombustible boards, mounted on the front of the framework to simulate eaves and cornices.

3. A gas burner (for intermittent-flame, spread-of-flame and flying-brand tests) consisting of a 44-inch length of nominal 2-inch (2.38-inch outside diameter) pipe having a $^1/_2$-inch-wide, 36-inch-long slot in the side toward the test deck. The burner is to be supplied with gas at both ends through nominal 1-inch (1.32-inch outside diameter) pipe to provide uniform gas pressure at the burner assembly.

4. A blower and air duct for providing the required wind conditions. The air introduced by the blower is to be taken from outside the test room.

5. Adjustable fins mounted inside the air duct to straighten the airstream and reduce turbulence.

6. A baffle mounted on the back edge of the test deck to prevent backfiring under the deck.

7. Noncombustible boards extending from the sides and bottom of the air duct to the simulated-eaves-and-cornice construction mentioned in Item B (not used during burning-brand test).

The tests are to be conducted in a room vented to the outer air to relieve the air pressure created by the blower. During these tests, all doors and windows in the room are to be closed, and the room otherwise controlled as necessary to prevent outside wind and weather conditions from affecting the test results. Tests are not to be conducted if the room temperature is less than 50°F. or more than 90°F.

Figure No. 32-7-2 illustrates the essential elements of the rain test apparatus.

(c) **Preparation of Samples.** 1. **Deck construction.** Except for treated wood shingles or shakes for the intermittent-flame and the burning-brand tests, the test deck is to be $3^1/_3$ feet wide by $4^1/_3$ feet long and is to be made of kiln-dried No. 1 white pine or ponderosa pine lumber with not less than 8 percent or more than 12 percent moisture content. The lumber is to be free from large or loose knots, sapwood, rot or pitch pockets, and is to contain no edge knots. Individual deck boards are to be of nominal 1- by 8-inch lumber (dressed on four sides). If used for the Class C Burning-brand Test, the width of the deck board is to be such that the brands will be located directly over the spaces between the boards. The deck boards are to be laid across the shorter dimension of the test deck, spaced $^1/_4$ inch apart, and securely nailed to two nominal 2- by 4-inch wood battens located under and flush with the outer edges of the deck. Decks so constructed are to be even and uniform.

For the intermittent-flame, burning-brand and flying-brand tests on treated wood shingles and shakes, the test decks are to be constructed of nominal 1- by 4-inch lumber (dressed on four sides), spaced $^1/_2$ inch apart and securely nailed to two nominal 2- by 4-inch wood battens. The lumber is to be of the quality specified in the above paragraph.

At the manufacturer's option, the roof covering may be investigated when applied to plywood decks of the minimum thickness recommended by the manufacturer. The plywood (A-C grade, Group 1, exterior) is to have face and back veneers of Douglas fir. A plywood deck is to have $^1/_8$-inch vertical and horizontal joints, and all vertical joints are to be centered on nominal 2- by 4-inch wood battens. If the manufacturer specifies that the battens are also to be used for horizontal joints, the classification shall be so restricted.

A plywood deck to be used for the Intermittent-flame Test is to have a horizontal joint 8 inches from and parallel to the $3^1/_3$-foot-long leading edge. In addition, a vertical joint that is centered on the deck and extends from the leading edge of the deck to the horizontal joint is to be provided. As the lower $1^1/_2$ inches of this joint is not protected by the nominal 2- by 4-inch batten, due to the mounting arrangement of the carriage, the underside of this joint from the end of the 2 by 4 to the leading edge of the deck is to be covered by a piece of sheet steel 2 inches wide.

A plywood deck to be used for a Class A or Class B Burning-brand Test is to be provided with a horizontal joint that is $22^1/_2$ inches from and parallel to the leading edge of the deck. A deck to be used for a Class A test is to have a vertical joint centered on the deck and extending above the horizontal joint. A deck to be used for a Class B test is to be provided with two vertical joints, extending above the horizontal joint, and each located 10 inches from and parallel to the side edges of the deck. A plywood deck to be used for a Class C Burning-brand Test is to have five horizontal joints with at least $^1/_8$-inch spacing between joints in the plywood.

Unless the material to be tested is intended for use on noncombustible decks only, the test deck for the Spread-of-flame Test, on material other than wood shingles and shakes, is to be constructed in accordance with either the Intermittent-flame Test or the manufacturer's option above, except that (1) the vertical and horizontal joints need not be provided and (2) the length of the deck is to be 13 feet for Class C tests, 9 feet for Class B tests, and 8 feet for Class A tests. For tests on materials intended for use on noncombustible decks only, a noncombustible deck of the applicable length may be used. The test deck for wood shingles and shakes is to be constructed of nominal 1- by 4-inch lumber (dressed on four sides) spaced $1^1/_2$ inches apart, and securely nailed to two nominal 2- by 4-inch wood battens, except that the length of the deck is to be as specified above.

2. **Roof-covering application.** Representative samples of a roof-covering material are to be applied to test decks constructed in accordance with the applicable requirements described above. The assemblies are to be conditioned in accordance with subsection 3 below. The roof-covering material to be tested is to be applied in accordance with the manufacturer's instructions, to the applicable number of test decks as specified in Table No. 32-7-A. The material is to extend to, and be flush with, the edges of the deck, except for a 1-inch overhang at the leading edge.

3. **Conditioning.** The completed test assemblies are to be stored indoors at temperatures not lower than 60°F. or higher than 90°F. for the period of time necessary to cure the material, but not more than 60 days. Should storage conditions vary from those specified, the decks are to be stored until moisture determinations indicate that the deck lumber has no less than 8 percent or more than 12 percent moisture content. Test decks are to be stored so that each will be surrounded by freely circulating air.

Performance

Sec. 32.702. (a) **General.** The Intermittent-flame Test, the Spread-of-flame Test and the Burning-brand Test are applicable to all roof coverings. The Flying-brand Test, the Rain Test and the Weathering Test are conducted only on treated wood shingles and shakes.

> **EXCEPTION:** When the roof covering is limited to installation on noncombustible decks, the penetration tests, that is, the Intermittent-flame Test and the Burning-brand Test, need not be conducted.

For these tests, mortar (cementitious mixture, lime and water) is to be troweled into the joint formed by the leading edge of the roof-covering material and the framework of the carriage, to prevent air or the test flame from traveling under the material being tested.

During the tests, the test decks are to be subjected to an air current that flows uniformly over the top surface of the roof-covering material, as determined by a pretest calibration of the equipment using a bare $3^1/_3$- by $3^1/_4$-foot plywood deck. At points midway up the slope of the bare deck, with the deck positioned at an incline of 5 inches to the horizontal foot, the velocity of the air current is to be $12 \pm {}^1/_2$ miles per hour, as measured at the center and edges of the deck, with each measurement being $3^{11}/_{16}$ inches above the surface of the deck.

For these tests, the test decks are to be at an incline of 5 inches per horizontal foot; except that built-up roof coverings are to be tested at the maximum incline recommended by the manufacturer, but not more than 5 inches per horizontal foot.

(b) **Intermittent-flame Test.** A test deck is to be mounted on the framework at the required incline, and subjected to the specified air current. The test deck is then to be subjected to a luminous gas flame approximately triangular in shape, approximately 3 feet wide at the leading edge of the deck, and gradually narrowing to a width of approximately 6 inches at the top of the deck. Licks of flame may extend approximately an additional 1 to 2 feet. The gas supply is to be regulated so that the flame, if not augmented by combustion of the roof covering, develops a temperature of 1,400°F. ± 50°F. for a Class A or Class B test, and 1,300°F. ± 50°F. for a Class C test. The temperature is to be determined by a No. 14 B & S gage chromel-alumel wire thermocouple located 1 inch toward the source of flame from the lower edge of the first board of a bare deck formed of noncombustible material.

The flame is to be intermittently applied at intervals as specified in Table No. 32-7-B.

Following the last application of flame, air current is to be maintained until all evidence of flame, glow and smoke has disappeared from the exposed surface of the material being tested or until unacceptable results occur, but in no case is the air current to be maintained for more than one hour for a Class A or Class B test or ${}^1/_2$ hour for a Class C test.

During the Intermittent-flame Test, including the ON and OFF periods of flame application and the subsequent period of maintained airflow, the test deck is to be observed for the appearance of sustained flaming on the underside, production of flaming or glowing brands, displacement of portions of the test sample, and exposure or falling away of portions of the roof deck.

(c) **Spread-of-flame Test.** A test deck is to be mounted and luminous gas flame applied, as described in Section 32.702 (b), second paragraph, for the Intermittent-flame Tests.

For a Class A or Class B test, the gas flame is to be applied continuously for 10 minutes or until the spread of flame (flaming of the material being tested) permanently recedes from a point of maximum spread, whichever is the shorter duration. For a Class C test, the gas flame is to be applied for four minutes and then removed.

During and after the application of the test flame, the test sample is to be observed for the distance to which flaming of the material has spread, production of flaming or glowing brands, and displacement of portions of the test sample. The observation is to continue until the flame has permanently receded from a point of maximum spread.

(d) **Burning-brand Test.** 1. **General.** A test deck is to be mounted as described in Section 32.702 (b), second paragraph, for the Intermittent-flame Test, except that the framework is to be 60 inches from the air duct outlet (see Figure No. 32-7-1), and the gas piping and burner are to be removed so as not to obstruct the airflow.

2. **Size and construction of brands.** The brands to be used in these tests are to be as shown in Figure No. 32-7-3 and are to be constructed as follows. Prior to the test, the brands are to be conditioned in an oven at 105°F. to 120°F. for at least 24 hours.

The Class A brand is to consist of a grid, 12 inches square and approximately $2^1/_4$ inches thick, made of kiln-dried Douglas fir lumber that is free from knots and pitch pockets. The brand is to be made of 36 strips of lumber each $^3/_4$ by $^3/_4$ inch square by 12 inches long, placed in three layers of 12 strips each, with strips placed $^1/_4$ inch apart. These strips are to be placed at right angles to those in adjoining layers and are to be nailed, using $1^1/_2$-inch long No. 16 gage nails, or stapled using No. 16 gage steel wire staples having a $^7/_{32}$-inch crown and $1^1/_4$-inch legs, at each end of each strip on one face, and in a diagonal pattern as shown in Figure No. 32-7-3 on the other face. The dry weight of the finished brand is to be 2,000 grams $\pm$ 150 grams at the time of the test.

The Class B brand is to consist of a grid, 6 inches square and approximately $2^1/_4$ inches thick, made of kiln-dried Douglas fir lumber that is free from knots and pitch pockets. The brand is to be made of 18 strips of lumber $^3/_4$ by $^3/_4$ inch square and 6 inches long, placed in three layers of six strips each, with strips spaced $^1/_4$ inch apart. The strips are to be placed at right angles to those in adjoining layers and are to be nailed, using $1^1/_2$-inch-long No. 16 gage nails, or stapled using No. 16 gage steel wire staples having a $^7/_{32}$-inch crown and $1^1/_4$-inch legs, at each end of each strip on one face, and in a diagonal pattern as shown in Figure No. 32-7-3 on the other face. The dry weight of the finished brand is to be 500 grams $\pm$ 50 grams at the time of the test.

The Class C brand is to consist of a piece of kiln-dried nonresinous white pine lumber that is free from knots and pitch pockets. The brand is to measure $1^1/_2$ by $1^1/_2$ by $^{25}/_{32}$ inches and a saw kerf $^1/_8$ inch wide is to be cut across the center of both the top and bottom faces to a depth of one half the thickness of the brand and at right angles to each other. The dry weight of the finished brand is to be $9^1/_4$ grams $\pm$ $1^1/_4$ grams at the time of the test.

3. **Ignition of brands.** Before application to the test deck, the brands are to be ignited so as to burn freely in still air as described below. The flame of the gas burner used to ignite the brands is to essentially envelop the brands during the process of ignition. The temperature of the igniting flame is to be 1,630°F. $\pm$ 50°F. measured $2^5/_{16}$ inches above the top of the burner. The burner is to be shielded from drafts.

Class A brands are to be exposed to the flame for five minutes, during which time they are to be rotated to present each surface to the flame as follows:

Each 12- by 12-inch face for 30 seconds.

Each $2^1/_4$- by 12-inch face for 45 seconds.

Each 12- by 12-inch face again for 30 seconds.

Class B brands are to be exposed to the flame for four minutes, during which time they are to be rotated to present each surface to the flame as follows:

Each 6- by 6-inch face for 30 seconds.

Each $2^1/_4$- by 6-inch face for 30 seconds.

Each 6- by 6-inch face again for 30 seconds.

Class C brands are to be exposed to the flame for two minutes, during which time they are to be rotated to present each of the $1^1/_2$- by $1^1/_2$-inch faces to the flame for one minute.

4. **Test conditions.** A. **Class A.** A brand is to be placed on the surface of each test deck at the location considered most vulnerable (point of minimum coverage over deck joint) with respect to ignition of the deck, but in no case closer than 4 inches from either side or 12 inches from the top or bottom edge of the deck. The brand is to be placed so that the strips in both the upper and lower layers are parallel to the direction of airflow. The brand is to be secured to the deck by a No. 18 B & S gage soft iron wire.

If the roof covering is applied to a pine board deck, the brand ordinarily will be in the most vulnerable location when the upper edge of the brand is located 3 inches above a horizontal joint in the test deck. If the roof covering is applied to a plywood deck, the brand ordinarily will be in the most vulnerable location when the brand is placed so that it is centered laterally with respect to the vertical joint in the test deck, and the upper edge of the brand is located 3 inches above the horizontal joint.

B. **Class B.** A brand is to be placed on the surface of the test deck at each of the two locations considered most vulnerable (point of minimum coverage over deck joint) with respect to ignition of the deck. Each brand is to be positioned with its upper edge $1^1/_2$ inches above the selected joint in the deck boards, but in no case closer than 6 inches from each side or 12 inches from the top or bottom edge of the deck. The brands are to be placed so that the strips in both the upper and lower layers are parallel to the direction of airflow. They are to be secured to the deck by a No. 18 B & S gage soft iron wire. The second brand is not to be applied until all burning resulting from the first brand has ceased.

If the roof covering is applied to a pine board deck, the brands ordinarily will be in the most vulnerable location when the upper edge of each brand is located 3 inches above a horizontal joint in the test deck. If the roof covering is applied to a plywood deck, the brands ordinarily will be in the most vulnerable location when they are placed so that they are centered laterally with respect to a vertical joint in the test deck, and the upper edge of each brand is located $1^1/_2$ inches above the horizontal joint.

C. **Class C asphalt shingles.** Loose or unfastened portions of the shingles that can be bent up to 90 degrees without injury to the fastenings are to be cut away. Twenty ignited brands are then to be placed at one- or two-minute intervals in the areas of minimum coverage $^1/_2$ inch away from any cut edge of shingles in the course above that course on which the brand is placed. No brand is to be placed closer than 4 inches to the point where the previous brand was located.

Brands are to be located not closer than 2 inches to the joints between adjacent shingles on the same course. All brands are to be placed so that the center of each brand is directly over the space between the deck boards. Brands are to be held in position throughout the test by a No. 18 B & S gage soft iron wire stretched across the width of the deck. The saw kerf on the deck side of the brand is to be parallel to the direction of the airflow. The wire is to be placed in the other saw kerf.

If the roof covering is applied to plywood decks, the brands are to be placed centrally over the joints in the plywood deck.

D. **Sheet roofing or built-up covering assemblies.** Twenty ignited brands are to be placed at one- or two-minute intervals in the areas of minimum coverage. No brand is to be placed closer than 4 inches to the joint where a previous brand was located. All brands are to be placed so that the center of each brand is directly over the space between the deck boards. See "Asphalt shingles" for securing of brands in place and relative positioning of brand saw kerfs.

E. **Treated wood shingles and shakes.** Twenty ignited brands are to be placed on each treated wood shingle deck at one- or two-minute intervals. For treated wood shakes, 20 ignited brands are to be distributed at one- or two-minute intervals on each pair of decks. Each brand is to be centered over the $^1/_4$-inch joint between shakes or shingles so that the top edge of the brand is approximately $^1/_2$ inch below the butt of the shake or shingle in the course above. No brand is to be placed closer than 4 inches to the point where a previous brand was located. See "Asphalt shingles" for securing of brands in place and relative positioning of brand saw kerfs.

5. **Duration of tests.** Each individual test, whether Class A, Class B or Class C, is to be continued until the brand is consumed and until all evidence of flame, glow and smoke has disappeared from both the exposed surface of the material being tested and the underside of the test deck, or until unacceptable results occur, but not for more than $1^1/_2$ hours for a Class A or Class B test. The results of tests in which the brands do not show progressive and substantially complete consumption after application to the test deck are to be disregarded.

6. **Observations.** During the tests, observations are to be made for the appearance of sustained flaming on the underside of the test deck, production of flaming

or glowing brands of roof-covering material, displacement of the test sample and the exposure or falling away of portions of the roof deck.

(e) **Flying-brand Test.** This test applies to Class B and Class C treated wood shingles and shakes. If a Class A rating is desired, appropriate tests of increased severity are to be conducted.

A test deck is to be mounted and a luminous gas flame applied as described in Section 32.702 (b), second paragraph, for the Intermittent-flame Test.

The gas flame is to be applied continuously for (1) 10 minutes for a Class B test and (2) four minutes for a Class C test. The air current is to be maintained until all evidence of flame, glow and smoke has disappeared from the exposed surface of the material being tested to determine if flying brands will be developed. For treated wood shakes, the velocity of the air current is to be increased to 18 miles per hour after the gas flame is extinguished.

(f) **Rain Test.** The test decks are to be mounted in a framework at a slope of 4 inches per horizontal foot. Spray nozzles that deliver an average of 0.7 inch of water per hour at a temperature of 35°F. to 60°F. are to be mounted approximately 7 feet above the test decks. The test decks are to be exposed to 12 one-week conditioning cycles. Each cycle is to consist of 96 hours of water exposure followed by 72 hours of drying time at 140°F. The final drying cycle is to be controlled so that the moisture content of the deck lumber is between 8 and 12 percent. The conditioned decks are then to be tested in accordance with Table No. 32-7-A.

An alternative test cycle may be utilized at the manufacturer's option whereby two sets of six decks are to be alternately exposed to seven days (168 hours) of water exposures, followed by two days' (48 hours) draining and five days' (120 hours) curing at 140°F. This cycle is to be repeated seven times, except that the seventh water exposure is to be reduced to six days (144 hours).

(g) **Weathering Test.** The test decks are to be mounted outdoors at an incline of 5 inches to the horizontal foot, facing south. After each of one, two, three, five and 10 years of exposure, three test decks are to be brought indoors and conditioned until the deck lumber attains a moisture content between 8 and 12 percent. From each set of decks, one deck is to be subjected to the Intermittent-flame Test, one to the Burning-brand Test and one to the Flying-brand Test.

Conditions of Acceptance for Classification

Sec. 32.703. At no time during the Intermittent-flame, Spread-of-flame or Burning-brand Tests shall:

1. Any portion of the roof-covering material be blown or fall off the test deck in the form of flaming or glowing brands, or

2. The roof deck be exposed by breaking, sliding, cracking or warping of the roof covering, or

3. Portions of the roof deck fall away in the form of glowing particles.

For the purpose of the requirements, any piece of roof covering that continues to glow or flame upon landing on the test room floor is considered to be a glowing or flaming brand, respectively.

At no time during the Class A, Class B or Class C Intermittent-flame or Burning-brand tests shall there be sustained flaming of the underside of the deck.

EXCEPTION: If flaming does occur, another series of tests may be conducted and the results accepted provided no additional sustained flaming occurs.

For the Spread-of-flame Test, the flaming of the material shall not have spread beyond 6 feet for Class A, 8 feet for Class B and 13 feet (the top of the deck) for Class C. There shall have been no significant lateral spread of flame from the path directly exposed to the test flame.

For the Flying-brand Test on treated wood shingles and shakes, flying, flaming or glowing brands shall not be produced.

TABLE NO. 32-7-A—REQUIRED TESTS AND TEST ASSEMBLIES

MATERIAL TO BE TESTED	REQUIRED NUMBER OF TEST ASSEMBLIES[1]					
	Intermittent-flame Test	Spread-of-flame Test	Burning-brand Test	Flying-brand Test	Rain Test	Weathering Test
Other than wood shakes or shingles, for installation on:						
A. Combustible decks:						
1. Class A	2	2	4	NA	NA	NA
2. Class B or C	2	2	2	NA	NA	NA
B. Noncombustible decks only	NA	2	NA	NA	NA	NA
Wood shakes and shingles[2]:						
A. Class A	3 (2) [5]	3	6 (2) [5]	3 (2) [5]	6	15
B. Class B or C	3 (2) [5]	3	3 (2) [5]	3 (2) [5]	6	15

Notes:

NA—test is not required.

The number in parentheses is the number of samples from the Rain Test.

The number in brackets is the number of samples from the Weathering Test.

TABLE NO. 32-7-B—FLAME APPLICATION

CLASS	FLAME ON (minutes)	FLAME OFF (minutes)	NUMBER OF TEST CYCLES
A	2	2	15
B	2	2	8
C	1	2	3

FIGURE NO. 32-7-1—FIRE TEST APPARATUS

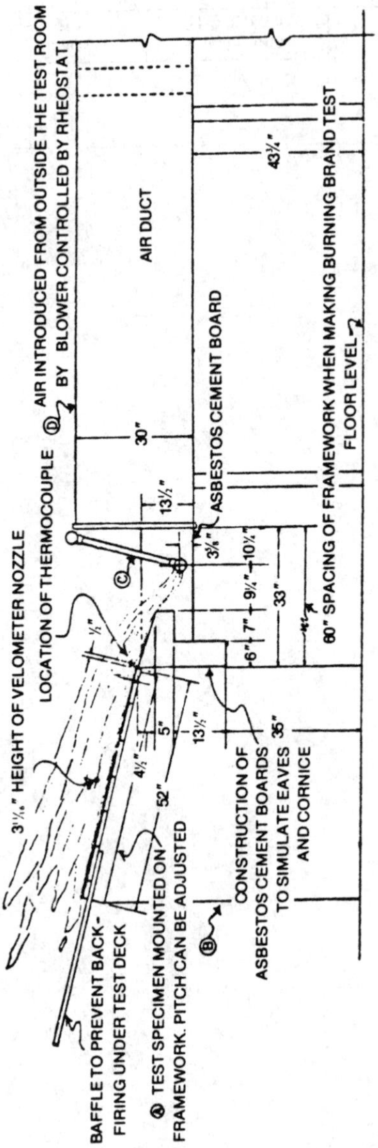

3¹¹⁄₁₆" HEIGHT OF VELOMETER NOZZLE
LOCATION OF THERMOCOUPLE
Ⓓ AIR INTRODUCED FROM OUTSIDE THE TEST ROOM BY BLOWER CONTROLLED BY RHEOSTAT
AIR DUCT
ASBESTOS CEMENT BOARD
Ⓒ
BAFFLE TO PREVENT BACK-FIRING UNDER TEST DECK
Ⓐ TEST SPECIMEN MOUNTED ON FRAMEWORK. PITCH CAN BE ADJUSTED
Ⓑ
CONSTRUCTION OF ASBESTOS CEMENT BOARDS TO SIMULATE EAVES AND CORNICE
60" SPACING OF FRAMEWORK WHEN MAKING BURNING BRAND TEST
FLOOR LEVEL
½"
52"
4½"
5"
13½"
35"
6"
7"
9¼"
10¼"
33"
3⅜"
13½"
30"
43¾"

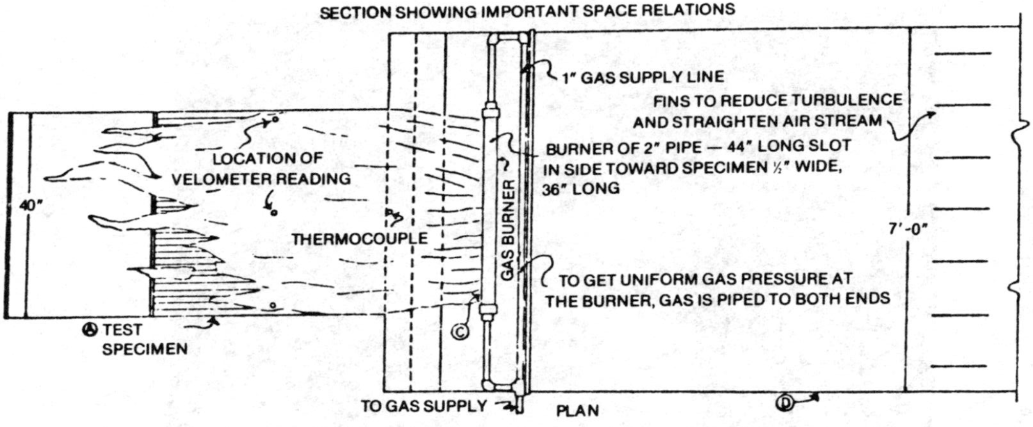
SECTION SHOWING IMPORTANT SPACE RELATIONS
1" GAS SUPPLY LINE
FINS TO REDUCE TURBULENCE AND STRAIGHTEN AIR STREAM
BURNER OF 2" PIPE — 44" LONG SLOT IN SIDE TOWARD SPECIMEN ½" WIDE, 36" LONG
LOCATION OF VELOMETER READING
40"
THERMOCOUPLE
GAS BURNER
7'-0"
TO GET UNIFORM GAS PRESSURE AT THE BURNER, GAS IS PIPED TO BOTH ENDS
A TEST SPECIMEN
C
TO GAS SUPPLY
D
PLAN

CONVERSION FACTORS:

½ inch = 12.7 mm

1 inch = 25.4 mm

Free outlet to be provided to relieve air pressure created by blower. Doors and windows in the room that houses the apparatus to be kept closed at all times during tests to prevent turbulence which would otherwise distort flame and prevent adequate control thereof.

FIGURE NO. 32-7-2
RAIN-TEST APPARATUS

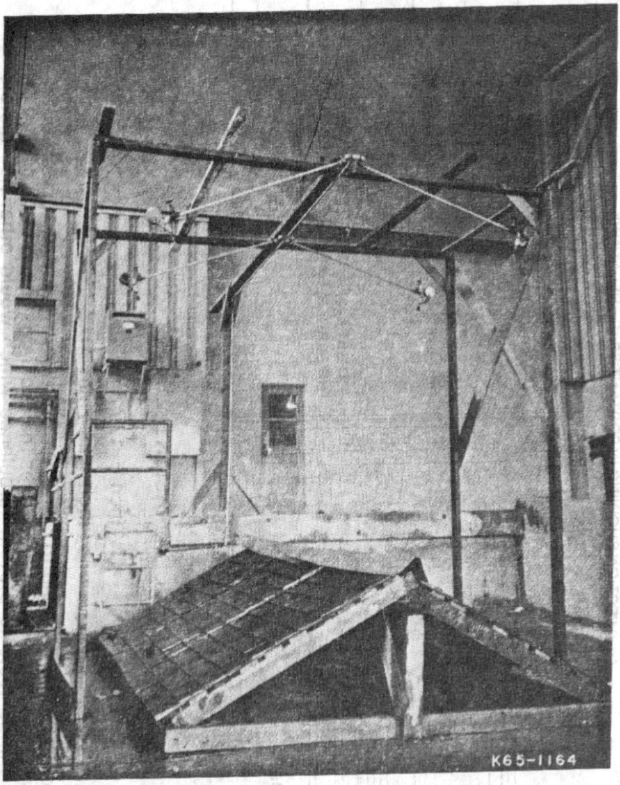
K65-1164

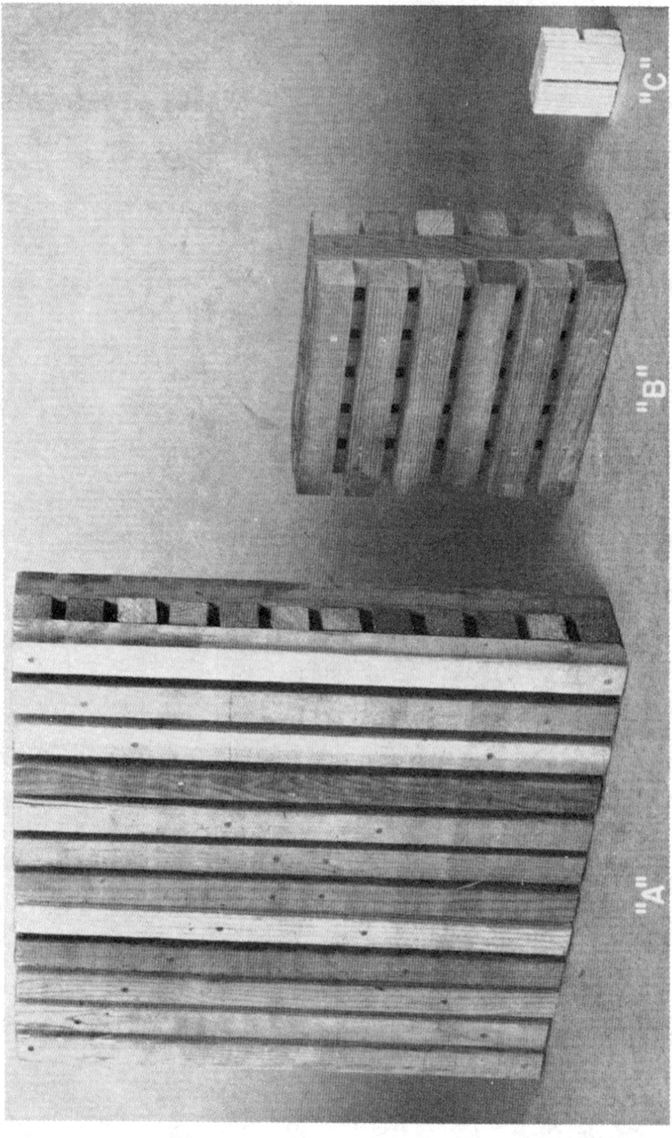
"A"
"B"
"C"

FIGURE NO. 32-7-3
"A," "B" AND "C" BRANDS

UNIFORM BUILDING CODE STANDARD NO. 32-8

WOOD SHAKES

Part I

Wood Shakes (Nonpreservative Treated)

Based on Grading and Packing Rules for Red Cedar Shakes of the Red Cedar Shingle & Handsplit Shake Bureau, 1975.

See Sections 3201 (b), 3202, and 3208 (a) 2 and (b) 10, Uniform Building Code

Scope

Sec. 32.801. Wood shakes regulated under this part shall be of an approved durable wood and shall be manufactured and graded No. 1 in accordance with this standard and their use shall be governed by the provisions of Chapter 32 of the Uniform Building Code.

Definitions

Sec. 32.802. (a) **General.** For the purposes of this part, certain words and phrases are defined as follows:

BUTT is the thicker end of the shake.

CHECK is any separation of the wood.

COURSE is a horizontal layer forming one of a series of layers on a roof or wall or in the packed bundle.

CRIMPS is a breaking down or collapse of wood cells during drying, characterized by a caved-in or corrugated appearance.

DECAY (ROT) is the decomposition of wood substance caused by action of wood-destroying fungi, resulting in softening, loss of strength and weight and change of texture and color.

EXPOSURE is the portion which, when applied, is exposed to the weather.

FEATHER TIP or shim is a condition of manufacture found on the thin ends of some shakes where the saw came out of the piece prematurely, producing a thin, flimsy, featherlike-tip that is uneven or has corners sawn off.

GRAIN is the direction, size, arrangement, appearance or quality of the fibers in wood. To have a specific meaning, the term must be qualified:

Cross Grain is a condition that should not be confused with the terms flat grain or edge grain, and that might better be termed "cross fiber," since it is a deviation of the wood fibers from the true parallel of the face of the shake. It is a defect when it runs from one face of the shake to the other within a longitudinal distance of 3 inches or less in that portion measured 6 inches from the butt. There is to be no excessive cross grain in the remainder of the shake.

Diagonal Grain is a condition where the grain of the wood does not run parallel to the edges of the shake. It is considered a defect when the grain diverges or slants 2 inches or more in width in 12 inches of length.

Edge Grain or Vertical Grain is wood cut in a plane approximately at right angles to the annual rings. A condition in which the rings form an angle of 45 degrees or more with the face of the piece.

Flat Grain is wood cut in a plane approximately tangential to the annual rings and means a condition in which the rings form an angle of less than 45 degrees with the face of the piece.

Torn Grain (Torn Fiber) is a fuzzy or whiskered appearance in the face of the shake. Usually caused by a dull saw or grain deviations.

HEARTWOOD (HEART) is the inner layer of a woody stem wholly composed of nonliving cells and usually differentiated from the outer enveloping layer (sapwood) by its darker color.

KNOT is that portion of a branch or limb which has been surrounded by subsequent growth of wood of the tree.

LINEAL INCH is the total width of any given number of shakes when laid edge to edge.

PLY is the minimum number of thicknesses, when applied, of shakes or at any point on the covered surface. This term is relative to exposure.

SAPWOOD is wood containing some living cells and forming the initial wood layer beneath the bark of the log. Sapwood may be lighter in color than heartwood.

SHIM. See **"Feather Tip."**

SQUARE PACK is a unit providing sufficient shakes for the coverage of a given area when the shakes are laid at the required exposure to the weather. (See Tables Nos. 32-8-A and 32-8-B.)

TIP is the thinner end of the shake.

WAVES are the washboard-like irregularities on the face of a shake.

WORMHOLE is a hole or passage burrowed by a worm or insect.

(b) **Shake Types.** Shake types shall be one of the following types:

1. **Handsplit-and-resawn** have split faces and sawn backs, and are produced by running split wood blanks or boards of proper thickness diagonally through a bandsaw to produce two tapered shakes from each blank.

2. **Shake hip** and **ridge** are two shakes that have one edge, each sawn on a bevel and fastened together to produce the cap for the hip or ridge of the roof.

3. **Straight-split** are manufactured by splitting from only one end of a block of wood, producing shakes which are the same thickness throughout.

4. **Tapersawn** are tapered pieces sawn both sides.

5. **Taper-split** are split both sides. A natural taper, from butt to tip, is achieved by reversing the block, end for end, with each split.

Quality Standards

Sec. 32.803. (a) **No. 1 Grade Shake.** Shakes shall be 100 percent clear, graded from the split face in the case of handsplit-and-resawn shakes and from the best face in the case of taper-split, taper-sawn and straight-split shakes.

Shakes shall be 100 percent heartwood, free of bark and sapwood, except that up to $^1/_8$ inch of sapwood is permitted on one edge.

Taper-split shakes and straight-split shakes shall be 100 percent edge-grain; tapersawn shakes may include up to 10 percent of flat-grain in the lineal inches of any bundle. Handsplit-and-resawn shakes may include up to 20 percent of flat-grain in the lineal inches of any bundle.

Curvature in the sawed face of handsplit-and-resawn shakes shall not exceed 1 inch from a level plane in the length of the shake. Excessive grain sweep on the face shall not be permitted. Knots, wormholes, decay, checks, crimps, waves and torn fiber are not permitted.

(b) **No. 2 Grade Tapersawn Shakes.** No. 2 grade tapersawn shakes shall be of sound and serviceable material, graded from the best face. Flat grain is allowed in the No. 2; sapwood is restricted to 1 inch in width in the first 10 inches above the butt. Defects such as knots, wormholes, decay, crimps, cross grain, waves or torn fiber are not allowed in the first $7^1/_2$, 9 and 12 inches from the butt in the 15-, 18- and 24-inch lengths, respectively, of the No. 2 grade tapersawn shakes. In the same product, grain characteristics, other than cross grain, are not considered defects; defects may be up to $1^1/_2$ inches in diameter, but aggregate defects must not exceed one half the width of the shakes.

Size

Sec. 32.804. (a) **Length.** 1. **No. 1 Grade Shake.** Nominal shake lengths shall be 15 inches, 18 inches or 24 inches, with a minus tolerance of $^1/_2$ inch and a plus tolerance of 2 inches. A variation, including shims or feather tips, of 1 inch from these nominal lengths shall be permitted in 5 percent of the lineal inches of shakes in any bundle. See Table No. 32-8-A. The 15-inch starter-finish course grade shall permit a tolerance of 1 inch over and under the nominal 15-inch length.

2. **No. 2 tapersawn grade shake.** For No. 2 grade tapersawn shakes, minimum lengths of 15-, 18- and 24-inch shakes shall be 14, 16 and 22 inches, respectively.

(b) **Thickness.** 1. **No. 1 Grade Shake.** Shake thickness shall be determined by measurement of the butt within $^1/_2$ inch from each edge. If corrugations or valleys exceed $^1/_2$ inch in depth, a minus tolerance of $^1/_8$ inch is permitted in the minimum specified thickness.

2. **No. 2 grade tapersawn shake.** No. 2 grade tapersawn shakes shall have one of two thicknesses at the butt, $^5/_8$ inch or $^3/_4$ inch with a minus tolerance of $^1/_{16}$ inch in 10 percent of a bundle.

(c) **Width.** 1. **No. 1 Grade Shake.** Shakes shall be of random widths, none narrower than 4 inches. Handsplit-and-resawn shakes shall have a maximum width of 14 inches.

2. **No. 2 grade tapersawn shake.** No. 2 grade tapersawn shakes shall have a minimum width of 3 inches; shakes less than 4 inches in width shall not constitute more than 10 percent of the running inches of each bundle. Edges shall be parallel within $^1/_2$ inch.

(d) **Edges.** Edges of shakes shall be parallel within 1 inch. Edges of taper-sawn shakes shall be parallel within $^5/_8$ inch.

Packing

Sec. 32.805. (a) **General.** Shakes shall be packed in straight courses in regular frames 18 to 20 inches wide. See Tables Nos. 32-8-A and 32-8-B.

(b) **Identification.** Each bundle of wood shakes graded under this standard shall bear the label of an approved inspection bureau or agency. The label shall be white base stock with predominantly blue ink and shall clearly indicate No. 1 grade.

Inspection.

Sec. 32.806. Shakes shall be adjudged off grade if the total lineal inches of defective shakes exceed 7 percent of the total lineal inches per bundle. See Table No. 32-8-A.

Reinspection

Sec. 32.807. In case of reinspection, 10 or more bundles selected at random shall constitute a fair sampling of the shipment. The 7 percent tolerance of defective shakes specified in Section 32.806 shall also apply for reinspection.

Part II

Wood Shakes Preservatively Treated

Scope

Sec. 32.821. Wood shakes regulated by this part shall be manufactured, preservative treated and graded in accordance with this standard, and their use shall be governed by the provisions of Chapter 32 of the Uniform Building Code.

Definitions

Sec. 32.822. For the purpose of this section certain words and phrases are defined as follows:

COVERED AREA refers specifically to that portion of the face which will be covered in place.

EXPOSED FACE refers specifically to that 10-inch or $7^1/_2$-inch section which will be exposed to the elements.

FACE refers to the entire best side of the shake, which would be expected to be installed facing up.

REVERSE refers to the entire reverse side which would be expected to be installed facing down.

TAPERSAWN SHAKES are sawn both sides with edges sawn and are 18 or 24 inches in length.

TIP ZONE refers to the final 4 inches or 3 inches (of a 24-inch or 18-inch shake respectively) adjacent to the tip.

Quality Standards

Sec. 32.823. (a) **Manufacture.** 1. **Length.** The length of shakes shall be 24 inches and 18 inches, allowing for a minus tolerance of $^1/_2$ inch and a plus tolerance of 2 inches.

A variation of a minus 1 inch, including shims and feathertips, would be permitted in 5 percent of lineal inches of shakes per bundle, provided that the shake thickness on both edges at the 22-inch and 16-inch lengths is at least $^1/_8$ inch.

Angled end trim at butt shall not exceed approximately $^1/_2$ inch per 4 inches of width.

2. **Thickness.** The green butt thickness of shakes shall be $^{13}/_{16}$ inch, with a minus tolerance of $^1/_8$ inch allowed in 10 percent of lineal inches of shakes per bundle. The maximum thickness shall not exceed $1^1/_{16}$ inches.

Tip thickness shall be $^1/_8$ to $^1/_4$ inch.

Thickness variation across the width limited by the above-stated maximums and minimums.

"Dish out" of thickness along length is allowed if it does not reduce the thickness more than $^1/_4$ inch on the exposed face and is not less than one half the standard thickness in the covered area.

3. **Width.** Minimum green width shall be 4 inches; maximum shall be 8 inches. When checking dry material, a maximum shrinkage allowance of $^1/_4$ inch under the 4-inch minimum will be considered.

Shakes shall be parallel within $^1/_2$ inch.

4. **Treatment.** Southern pine tapersawn shakes shall be preservative treated in accordance with U.B.C. Standard No. 25-12 (AWPB Standards LP-2 and LP-3).

(b) **Grade Defects Limited throughout Each Shake.** 1. **Compression wood.** Compression wood is prohibited if in readily identifiable and damaging form. Damaging form includes, but is not limited to, bands of compression wood exceeding $^1/_2$ inch in width, or bands running along an edge, or solid blocks of compression wood.

2. **Density.** Medium to dense grain is required measured across the entire butt. Not less than four complete annual rings per inch are permitted at any location.

3. **Heart or ring shakes.** Heart or ring shakes are prohibited.

4. **Slope of grain.** Diagonal or spiral grain shall not exceed 1 inch in 10 inches. Abnormal grain distortions on face are not permitted.

5. **Stain.** Medium blue stain is permitted.

6. **Unsound wood.** Unsound wood is prohibited on either face.

7. **Warp.** Facial curvature (bow), twist, or both, shall not exceed $^1/_4$ inch from a level plane.

(c) **Grade Defects Limited by Location.** 1. **General.** The shake shall be graded from the best face.

2. **Holes.** Well-scattered ambrosia beetle pin holes up to $^1/_{16}$ inch in diameter are allowed if not through the thickness and if limited to 6 per 10 inches of length on the face. All other types of knot, insect or mechanical holes are prohibited, except an occasional $^1/_2$-inch hole or encased pith knot is allowed along an edge of the covered area if not extending more than $^1/_2$ inch into the shake width.

3. **Knots.** Knots shall be measured by average facial dimensions.

Pith knots are prohibited on the face. They are allowed on reverse side only if the pith hole is not through the thickness.

Generally, no knots are permitted on the exposed face. However, 5 percent of the lineal inches of shakes per bundle may have up to a $1^1/_2$-inch cumulative area of sound or firm and tight knots.

Sound or firm and tight knots are limited to a 2-inch cumulative size located in the top one half of the shake at the tapered end.

Individual knots of any quality limited to a maximum size of $1^1/_2$ inches on the reverse face. A No. 2 shake may contain up to a $1^1/_2$-inch cumulative area of sound or firm and tight knots in the exposed $7^1/_2$- or $5^1/_2$-inch face.

4. **Grain.** Generally, vertical grain is required. On the exposed face, flat grain is allowed only along an edge of the face. Center of flat grain not permitted within $1^1/_2$ inches of center of shake. For No. 2 grade shakes, there are no restrictions on amount or location of flat grain in shake.

5. **Pitch pockets.** Pitch pockets are prohibited on the exposed face. They are allowed if not through in the covered area and on the reverse side, with the exception that through pitch pockets are allowed in the tip zone.

6. **Pith.** Pith is not allowed if contained within the thickness of a shake, or if along the surface of the exposed face. A superficial (split) pith is allowed in the covered area or on the reverse side.

7. **Wane.** Pencil wane is only allowed on the face. Wane on the reverse side is allowed, not to exceed one half the thickness by one sixth the width if located within one half the shake length from the butt; otherwise, wane in occasional pieces may be through the thickness if not reducing the face width by more than $^1/_2$ inch.

(d) **Reverse Face.** Other than the limitations described, the reverse face shall be free of defects which might prevent normal use.

Inspection

Sec. 32.824. Shakes shall be adjudged off grade if the total lineal inches of defective shakes exceeds 5 percent of the total lineal inches per bundle. See Table No. 32-8-A.

Reinspection

Sec. 32.825. In case of reinspection, 10 or more bundles selected at random shall constitute a fair sampling of the shipment. The 5 percent tolerance for defective materials per bundle specified in Section 32.824 shall also apply for reinspection.

Part III

Southern Yellow Pine, Black Gum/Sweetgum Tapersawn Shake Hip and Ridge Units

Scope

Sec. 32.831. Southern yellow pine, black gum/sweetgum tapersawn shake hip and ridge units regulated by this part shall be manufactured, treated and graded in accordance with this standard and their use shall be governed by the provisions of Chapter 32 of the Uniform Building Code.

Quality Standards

Sec. 32.832. Shake hip and ridge units shall be manufactured from only No. 1 grade tapersawn shakes.

Units shall be fabricated at point of attachment with alternating laps, and shall be correspondingly packed 12/12 per bundle.

Inner surface of units at the butt shall measure not less than 9 inches, with the width of the narrower pieces not less than $4^1/_2$ inches.

Units shall be joined with not less than two fasteners applied within 8 inches of the butt. Fasteners shall be a minimum of approximately 3 inches apart and shall be corrosion resistant. Either staples or nails are acceptable. Fasteners shall hold the assembly together until applied properly on the roof.

TABLE NO. 32-8-A—HANDSPLIT SHAKES SUMMARY OF SIZES, PACKING REGULATIONS AND COVERAGE

LENGTH AND THICKNESS	20" PACK		18" PACK		APPROXIMATE COVERAGE (In Square Feet) OF ONE SQUARE BASED ON FOLLOWING WEATHER EXPOSURES:[1]											
	No. of Courses per Bdl.	No. of Bdls. per Sq.	No. of Courses per Bdl.	No. of Bdls. per Sq.	51/2"	61/2"	7"	71/2"	8"	81/2"	10"	111/2"	13"	14"	15"	16"
18" × 1/2" Handsplit and resawn	10/10	4	9/9	5	55	65	70	75	80	85						
18" × 3/4" Handsplit and resawn	8/8	5	9/9	5	55	65	70	75	80	85						
24" × 3/8" Handsplit	10/10	4	9/9	5	—	65	70	75	80	85	100	115				
24" × 1/2" Handsplit and resawn	10/10	4	9/9	5	—	65	70	75	80	85	100	115				
24" × 3/4" Handsplit and resawn	8/8	5	9/9	5	—	65	70	75	80	85	100	115				
24" × 1/2" Taper split	10/10	4	9/9	5	—	65	70	75	80	85	100	115				
18" × 3/8" True edge Straight split	14 Straight	4	—	—	—	—	—	—	—	—	—	—	—	100	106	112
18" × 3/8" Straight split	19 Straight	5	—	—	65	75	80	90	95	100						
24" × 3/8" Straight split	16 Straight	5	—	—	—	65	70	75	80	85	100	115				
15" Starter finish course	8/8	5	9/9	5	Use supplementary with shakes applied not over 10" weather exposure											
	10/10	4														
18" × 5/8" Taper sawn	—	—	9/9	5	55	65	70	75	—	85	100					
24" × 5/8" Taper sawn	—	—	9/9	5	—	65	70	75	—	85	100	115				

[1]For maximum weather exposure on wall construction, see Table No. 25-L; on roof construction, see Table No. 32-8-B of the Uniform Building Code.

TABLE NO. 32-8-B—MAXIMUM WEATHER EXPOSURE

GRADE LENGTH	3 INCHES TO LESS THAN 4 INCHES IN 12 INCHES	4 INCHES IN 12 INCHES AND STEEPER
Wood Shakes[1]		
No. 1 18-inch	$7^1/_2$	$7^1/_2$
No. 1 24-inch	10	10
No. 2 18-inch Tapersawn Shakes	—	$5^1/_2$
No. 2 24-inch Tapersawn Shakes	—	$7^1/_2$

[1]Exposure of 24-inch by $^3/_8$-inch handsplit resawn shakes shall not exceed 5 inches regardless of the roof slope.

UNIFORM BUILDING CODE STANDARD NO. 32-11

WOOD SHINGLES

Based on the Standards of the Red Cedar Shingle and Handsplit Shake Bureau and Material Product Standards of the International Conference of Building Officials

See Sections 3201 (b), 3202, 3208 (a) 2 and 3208 (b) 11, Uniform Building Code

Scope

Sec. 32.1101. This standard provides a minimum specification for sawn wood shingles of No. 1 Grade, No. 2 Grade and No. 3 Grade. It covers length, width, thickness, grain, characteristics and color for these requirements, plus definitions and specifications.

Definitions

Sec. 32.1102. For the purpose of this standard, the following terms shall be construed as herein specified.

BUTT is the thicker end of the shingle.

CHECK is any separation of the wood.

COURSE is a horizontal layer forming one of a series of layers on a roof or wall or in the packed bundle.

CRIMPS are a breaking down or collapse of wood cells during drying, characterized by a caved-in or corrugated appearance.

DECAY (ROT) is the decomposition of wood substance caused by action of wood-destroying fungi, resulting in softening, loss of strength and weight and change of texture and color.

EXPOSURE is the portion which, when applied, is exposed to the weather.

GRAIN is the direction, size, arrangement, appearance or quality of the fibers in wood. To have a specific meaning, the term must be qualified:

CROSS GRAIN is a condition that should not be confused with the terms "flat" or "edge" grain, and that might better be termed "cross fiber," since it is a deviation of the wood fibers from the true parallel of the face of the shingle. It is a defect when it runs from one face of the shingle to the other within a longitudinal distance of 3 inches or less in that portion measured 6 inches from the butt. Excessive cross grain must not be present in the remainder of the shingle.

DIAGONAL GRAIN is a condition where the grain of the wood does not run parallel to the edges of the shingle. It is considered a defect when the grain diverges or slants 2 inches or more in width in 12 inches of length.

EDGE GRAIN OR VERTICAL GRAIN is wood cut in a plane approximately at right angles to the annual rings. A condition in which the rings form an angle of 45 degrees or more with the face of the piece.

FLAT GRAIN is a condition in shingles or lumber where the growth rings are flat or horizontal, as opposed to edge-grained or quartered material where the growth rings are on edge, or vertical to the surface. Wood cut in a plane approximately tangential to the annual rings and means a condition in which the rings form an angle of less than 45 degrees with the face of the piece.

FEATHER TIPS (or shim) is a condition of manufacture found on the thin ends of some shingles where the saw came out of the piece prematurely, producing a thin, flimsy, featherlike tip that is uneven or has corners sawn off.

HEARTWOOD (HEART) is the inner layer of a woody stem wholly composed of nonliving cells and usually differentiated from the outer enveloping layer (sapwood) by its darker color.

HIP AND RIDGE SHINGLE are two shingles that have one edge of each sawn on a bevel and fastened together to produce the cap for the hip or ridge of the roof. Hip and ridge units are manufactured from No. 1 Grade shingles.

KNOT is that portion of a branch or limb which has been surrounded by subsequent growth of wood of the tree.

LINEAL INCHES are the total width of any given number of shingles when laid edge to edge.

PLY is the minimum number of thicknesses, when applied, of shingles at any point on the covered surface. This term is related to exposure.

SAPWOOD is wood containing some living cells and forming the initial wood layer beneath the bark of the log. Sapwood may be lighter in color than heartwood.

SHIM. See Feather Tips.

SQUARE PACK is a unit providing sufficient shingles for the coverage of a given area when the shingles are laid at the specified exposure to the weather in Tables Nos. 25-L and 32-C of the code.

TIP is the thinner end of the shingle.

TORN FIBER (TORN GRAIN) is a fuzzy or whiskered appearance on the face of the shingle usually caused by a dull saw or grain deviations.

WAVES are washboard-like irregularities on the face of a shingle.

WORMHOLE is a hole or passage burrowed by a worm or insect.

Sec. 32.1103. (a) **General.** Each bundle of Nos. 1, 2 and 3 Grade wood shingles graded under this standard shall bear the label of an approved inspection bureau or agency. For No. 1 Grade, the label shall be of white base stock printed with predominantly blue ink and shall clearly indicate the No. 1 grade. For No. 2 Grade, the label shall be of white base stock printed with predominantly red ink and shall clearly indicate the No. 2 Grade. For No. 3 Grade, the label shall be of white base stock printed with predominantly black ink and shall clearly indicate the No. 3 Grade. All grades shall be well manufactured and neatly packed; they shall comply with or exceed the specifications herein established for quality.

(b) **Characteristics.** 1. **General.** Shingles characteristics shall be in accordance with the provisions of this section:

2. **No. 1 Grade.** No. 1 Grade shall be vertical grain or edge grain, be clear of defects and be 100 percent heartwood. Knots, wormholes, decay, checks, crimps, flat grain, cross grain and sapwood constitute natural characteristics that are not admissible. Defects in manufacturing, including shims, feather tips, diagonal grain, cross grain, waves and torn fiber, are likewise not admissible.

3. **No. 2 Grade.** In No. 2 Grade, sapwood is restricted to 1 inch in width in the first 10 inches above the butt. Grain characteristics, other than cross grain, are not considered defects. Defects such as knots, knotholes, wormholes, decay, checks, crimps, waves or torn fiber are not allowed in the first 10 inches, 11 inches and 16 inches from the butt in the 16-inch, 18-inch and 24-inch lengths, respectively. Defects may be up to 3 inches in diameter, but aggregate defects shall not exceed one half the width of the shingle.

4. **No. 3 Grade.** In No. 3 Grade, sapwood is permitted. Other grain deviations are not considered defects. Other defects, as listed above for No. 2 Grade, are not allowed in the first 6 inches from the butt for 16-inch and 18-inch lengths and 10 inches for 24-inch lengths. Defects may be up to 3 inches in diameter, but aggregate defects shall not exceed two-thirds the width of the shingle.

Length, Width, Thickness

Sec. 32.1104. (a) **Length.** 1. **No. 1 Grade.** For No. 1 Grade the minimum length shall be 16 inches. Shingles are usually manufactured in 16-inch, 18-inch and 24-inch lengths. A tolerance of 1 inch over the nominal length is allowed. A minus tolerance of 1/4 inch below the nominal length is allowed. A minus tolerance of 1 inch below the nominal length is permitted in not more than 10 percent of the running inches in the bundle.

2. **No. 2 Grade.** For No. 2 Grade the minimum lengths, including shims or feather tips for 16-inch, 18-inch and 24-inch shingles, shall be 15 inches, 16 inches and 20 inches, respectively.

3. **No. 3 Grade.** For No. 3 Grade the minimum lengths, including shims or feather tips for 16-inch, 18-inch and 24-inch shingles, shall be 14 inches, 16 inches and 18 inches, respectively.

(b) **Width.** Maximum width shall be 14 inches.

1. **No. 1 Grade.** Minimum width up to but not including 24-inch lengths, shall be 3 inches. Minimum width for shingles 24 inches and longer shall be 4 inches. In 16-inch and 18-inch shingles those less than 4 inches in width shall not constitute more than 10 percent of the running inches per bundle. Shingles shall be uniform in width; that is, with parallel sides. Edges shall be parallel within a tolerance of 1/4 inch.

2. **No. 2 Grade.** Minimum width shall be 3 inches. Not more than 20 percent of the running inches in each bundle shall be less than 4 inches wide. Edges shall be parallel within a tolerance of 1/4 inch in the 16-inch and 18-inch lengths and 3/8 inch in the 24-inch length.

3. **No. 3 Grade.** Minimum width shall be 3 inches except it may be 2 1/2 inches for the 16-inch length. Not more than 30 percent of the running inches in each bundle shall be less than 4 inches wide. Edges shall be parallel within a tolerance of 3/8 inch.

(c) **Thickness.** Shingles are measured for thickness at the butt ends and designated according to the number of pieces necessary to constitute a specific unit of thickness. At the time of manufacture, 16-inch shingles shall be 5/2 (the thickness of 5 butts will be 2 inches), 18 inches shall be 5/2 1/4 (5 butts measure 2 1/4 inches) and 24 inches shall be 4/2 (4 butts measure 2 inches). Shingles shall be uniform in thickness, but a minus tolerance of 3 percent is allowable to compensate for the difference in shrinkage due to seasoning or kiln drying. This tolerance is based on the total thickness of the bundle.

Inspection

Sec. 32.1105. Shingles shall be adjudged off grade if the total lineal inches of defective shingles exceed 4 percent of the total lineal inches per bundle.

Reinspection

Sec. 32.1106. In case of reinspection, 10 or more bundles selected at random shall constitute a fair sampling of the shipment. The 4 percent tolerance for defective shingles specified in Section 32.1105 shall also apply for reinspection.

UNIFORM BUILDING CODE STANDARD NO. 32-12

ROOF TILE

Recommended Standard of the International Conference of Building Officials

See Sections 3201 (b), 3202 and 3208 (b) 5, Uniform Building Code

Scope

Sec. 32.1201. This standard applies to all clay, concrete and other cement-based tiles. Supplementary tests justifying adequacy under loads prescribed in Chapter 23 shall be provided.

Basic Information

Sec. 32.1202. The following basic information shall be submitted.

1. Manufacturing data as applicable such as mix design, density, protective coatings, mixing, forming, extruding, firing, curing, coloring and glazing.

2. Dimensioned scale drawings and details noting thicknesses, lugs, lips, contours, water diverters, size and location of all fasteners.

3. Method of packaging and identification of components.

Report of Tests

Sec. 32.1203. A qualified representative of the independent testing agency shall witness the production, fabrication and installation of test specimens.

The test report must be in sufficient detail to identify specimen properties that could affect performance as a roof covering. The testing agency must verify and report dimensions, weight, density, moisture content and other relevant physical properties of the major components.

Required Tests

Sec. 32.1204. Tiles shall be tested for strength and water absorption as set forth in this standard.

Samples

Sec. 32.1205. A total of 10 representative samples shall be selected by the independent laboratory from the production line. The laboratory shall document production procedures as specified in Section 32.1203. Cement-based products shall be conditioned at a temperature of 73° ± 5°F. and 50 percent relative humidity for a period of 28 days. At the end of the conditioning period, the size and weight for each specimen shall be recorded.

Test Procedures

Sec. 32.1206. (a) **Strength Test.** 1. **Sample.** Five samples conditioned as specified in Section 32.1205 shall be subjected to the strength test.

2. **Procedure.** A. **Barrel-shaped ("Spanish") tile.** The supports for the sample shall be two knife edges of the rocker type with edges at least as long as the width of the sample. The loading knife edge may be either the fixed or the rocker type and shall be at least as long as the width of the sample.

Place the sample on the knife edges with the open side or turned-down edges down, so that the sample is supported by the knife edges at a span of 12 inches centered on the length of the sample. Apply the load at center of the span and sample width through the loading knife edge. Apply loads at rates not to exceed 10 pounds per second until failure and record the breaking load to the nearest 5 pounds.

B. **Other tile.** The test span shall be the maximum unsupported span specified for field installation. The sample shall be tested as shown in Figure No. 32-12-1 with the load applied at a uniform rate not exceeding 10 pounds per second until failure, which shall be recorded to the nearest pound. The test shall be repeated on the other specimens and the average breaking load determined.

3. **Conditions of acceptance.** A. **Barrel-shaped tile.** Barrel-shaped tiles are tiles having a minimum rise-to-width ratio of 1:4. The average breaking load shall not be less than 400 pounds with no single load less than 350 pounds.

B. **Other tiles.** The average breaking load shall not be less than 300 pounds for five consecutively tested samples or 250 pounds for any individual sample.

(b) **Water Absorption Test.** 1. **Sample.** A minimum of five samples from the tile fractured in the strength test shall be tested for water absorption. The sum of the dry weight for five samples at room temperature shall not be less than 12 pounds. A total of five or more samples of the ridge and other accessory tile not subjected to the strength test also shall be tested. The aggregate dry weight at room temperature of these samples shall be not less than 5 pounds.

2. **Procedure.** Loose particles shall be removed by scrubbing with a fiber brush and clean water. Samples shall be dried in a well-ventilated oven for 24 hours at a temperature of 221°F. varying not more than 3.6°F. After drying, the samples may be cooled at room temperature for 15 minutes after identifying and weighing to the nearest 0.01 gram. The samples shall then be immersed in filtered or distilled water for 48 hours at a temperature of 68°F., varying not more than 9°F. One sample shall be removed, surfaces wiped dry and weighed immediately. The process shall be repeated for each sample.

3. **Condition of acceptance.** No sample shall absorb more than 15 percent water of its dry weight.

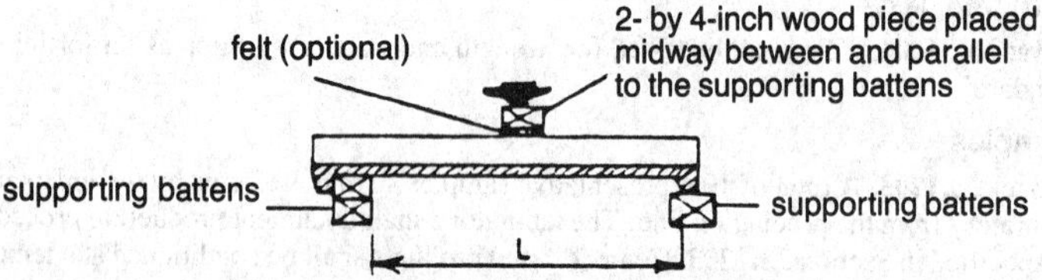
felt (optional)
2- by 4-inch wood piece placed midway between and parallel to the supporting battens
supporting battens
supporting battens
L

TRANSVERSE BREAKING STRENGTH

Notes:

L = Maximum unsupported span specified for field installation

The load shall be applied with a 2- by 4-inch (nominal size) wood piece laid flat and continuous from edge to edge of the tile. Where the effective width of tile exceeds 16 inches, the loads specified in Section 32.1206 (a) 2 shall be increased in proportion to the tile width.

FIGURE NO. 32-12-1

UNIFORM BUILDING CODE STANDARD NO. 32-13

MODIFIED BITUMEN, THERMOPLASTIC AND THERMOSET MEMBRANES USED FOR ROOF COVERINGS

Based on Standard Specifications D 412-87, D 471-79, D 570-81, D 624-86, D 638-84, D 751-79, D 816-82, D 1004-66 (1981), D 1204-84, D 2136-84 and D 2137-83 of the American Society for Testing and Materials

See Sections 3201 (b) and 3202, Uniform Building Code

Scope

Sec. 32.1301. (a) **General.** This standard covers the following membranes used for roof coverings.

(b) **Modified Bitumen Membranes.** Composite sheets consisting of bitumen modifiers and reinforcements. The material shall be of the following types of classes:

Type I—APP modified bitumen reinforced membrane composed primarily of asphalt blended with atactic polypropylene.

Type II—SBS modified bitumen reinforced membrane composed primarily of asphalt blended with styrene-butadiene-styrene.

Type III—Self-adhesive modified bitumen membrane composed primarily of asphalt blended with styrene-butadiene-styrene.

(c) **Thermoplastic Membranes.** Sheets composed of polymers and other proprietary ingredients whose chemical composition allows the sheet to be welded together by either heat or solvent throughout its service life.

(d) **Thermoset Membranes.** Sheets composed of polymers and other proprietary ingredients whose chemical composition vulcanizes or cross-links during its service life.

Physical Properties

Sec. 32.1302. The materials shall conform to the physical properties prescribed in Tables Nos. 32-13-A, 32-13-B, 32-13-C, 32-13-D and 32-13-E.

TABLE NO. 32-13-A—PROPERTIES OF THERMOSET REINFORCED MEMBRANES USED FOR ROOF COVERINGS

MATERIALS PROPERTIES	TEST[1] METHODS	UNITS	PHYSICAL PROPERTIES
Thickness	ASTM D 751-79	inches	⩾ 0.030
Breaking strength[2]	ASTM D 751-79	lb./inch	⩾ 90
Elongation at fabric break[3]	ASTM D 751-79	Percent	⩾ 15
Tear resistance	ASTM D 751-79	lb.	⩾ 25
Water absorption	ASTM D 471 166 hours at 73°F.	Weight change percent	⩽ 10
Dimensional stability	ASTM D 1204-84 24 hours at 130°F.	Percent	⩽ 2
Low temperature flexibility	ASTM D 2137-83	°F.	⩽ −30
Factory seam strength	ASTM D 751	lb./inch	⩾ 50[4]

[1]The test to be used shall be a method approved by the building official.

[2]Results of tensile strength after heat aging at 212°F. for 166 hours will remain at ⩾ 90. Accelerated weathering in xenon, carbon arc or QUV with water spray for 2,000 hours at 176°F. will not reduce the breaking strength to less than 90 pounds.

[3]Elongation at break shall not be reduced by heat aging or accelerated weathering by more than 20 percent.

[4]Or membrane rupture.

TABLE NO. 32-13-B—PROPERTIES OF THERMOSET NONREINFORCED MEMBRANES USED FOR ROOF COVERINGS

MATERIALS PROPERTIES	TEST[1] METHODS	UNITS	PHYSICAL PROPERTIES
Thickness	ASTM D 412-87	inches	⩾ 0.040
Tensile strength[2]	ASTM D 412-87	psi	⩾ 1000
Elongation[3]	ASTM D 412-87	Percent	⩾ 300
Tear resistance	ASTM D 624-86	lb./inch	⩾ 120
Water absorption	ASTM D 471-79 166 hours at 158°F.	Weight change percent	
Dimensional stability	ASTM D 1204-84 70 hours at 212°F.	Percent	⩽ 2.0
Low temperature flexibility	ASTM D 2137-83	°F.	⩽ −30
Factory seam strength	ASTM D 816-82	lb./inch	⩾ 30[4]

[1]The test to be used shall be a method approved by the building official.

[2]Results of tensile strength after heat aging at 212°F. for 166 hours will remain at ⩾ 1000. Accelerated weathering in xenon, carbon arc or QUV with water spray for 2,000 hours at 176°F. will not reduce the tensile strength to less than 1000 psi.

[3]Elongation shall not be reduced by heat aging or accelerated weathering to less than 200 percent.

[4]Or membrane rupture.

TABLE NO. 32-13-C—PROPERTIES OF THERMOPLASTIC REINFORCED MEMBRANES USED FOR ROOF COVERINGS

MATERIALS PROPERTIES	TEST[1] METHODS	UNITS	PHYSICAL PROPERTIES
Thickness	ASTM D 751-79	inches	⩾ 0.030
Breaking strength[2]	ASTM D 751-79	lb.	⩾ 90
Elongation at fabric break[3]	ASTM D 751-79	Percent	⩾ 15
Tear resistance	ASTM D 751-79	lb.	⩾ 20
Water absorption	ASTM D 570-81 166 hours at 158°F.	Weight change percent	⩽ 5.0
Dimensional stability	ASTM D 1204-84 6 hours at 176°F.	Percent	⩽ 1.0
Low temperature flexibility	ASTM D 2136-84	°F.	⩽ −30
Factory seam strength	ASTM D 751-79	lb./inch	⩾ 50[4]

[1]The test to be used shall be a method approved by the building official.

[2]Results of tensile strength after heat aging at 158°F. for 30 days will remain at ⩾ 90. Accelerated weathering in xenon, carbon arc or QUV with water spray for 2,000 hours at 145°F. will not reduce the breaking strength to less than 90 pounds.

[3]Elongation at break shall not be reduced by heat aging or accelerated weathering by more than 20 percent.

[4]Or membrane rupture.

TABLE NO. 32-13-D—PROPERTIES OF THERMOPLASTIC NONREINFORCED MEMBRANES USED FOR ROOF COVERINGS

MATERIALS PROPERTIES	TEST[1] METHODS	UNITS	PHYSICAL PROPERTIES
Thickness	ASTM D 638-84	inches	⩾ 0.045
Tensile strength[2]	ASTM D 638-84	psi	⩾ 1500
Elongation[3]	ASTM D 638-84	Percent	⩾ 250
Tear resistance	ASTM D 1004-66 (1981)	lb.	⩾ 10
Water absorption	ASTM D 570-81 166 hours at 158°F.	Weight change percent	⩽ 3.0
Dimensional stability	ASTM D 1204-84 6 hours at 176°F.	Percent	⩽ 2.0
Low temperature flexibility	ASTM D 2136-84	°F.	⩽ −30
Factory seam strength	ASTM D 638-84	psi	⩾ 1300[4]

[1]The test to be used shall be a method approved by the building official.

[2]Results of tensile strength after heat aging at 194°F. for 168 hours will remain at ⩾ 1000. Accelerated weathering in xenon, carbon arc or QUV with water spray for 2,000 hours at 145°F. will not reduce the tensile strength to less than 1000 psi.

[3]Elongation at break shall not be reduced by heat aging or accelerated weathering to less than 200 percent.

[4]Or membrane rupture.

TABLE NO. 32-13-E—PROPERTIES OF MODIFIED BITUMEN MEMBRANES USED FOR ROOF COVERINGS

MATERIAL PROPERTY	UNITS	PHYSICAL PROPERTIES[1]		
		TYPE I MEMBRANE	TYPE II MEMBRANE	TYPE III MEMBRANE
Thickness	mils	⩾ 120	⩾ 120	⩾ 40
Weight	lb./100 ft.[2]	⩾ 60	⩾ 60	⩾ 30
Tensile strength at 0°F.[2,3] machine or cross-machine direction	lb./in.	⩾ 100	⩾ 100	⩾ 50
Elongation at 0°F.[2,3] machine or cross-machine direction	Percent	⩾ 4	⩾ 4	⩾ 50
Strain energy at 0°F.[3]	lb. in./in.	⩾ 2	⩾ 2	N/A
Water absorption	Percent	⩽ 5	⩽ 5	⩽ 5
Low temperature flexibility[2]	°F.	⩽ 32	⩽ 5	⩽ 5
Dimensional stability	Percent	⩽ 1	⩽ 1	⩽ 1
Compound stability	°F.	⩾ 250	⩾ 220	N/A

[1]Tests shall be approved methods of evaluating the properties of roofing materials.

[2]Stated property is before and after heat condition at 158°F. for 2,000 hours. Accelerated weathering in xenon, carbon arc or QUV with water spray for 2,000 hours at 145°F. will not reduce the tensile strength by more than 5 percent or the elongation by more than 10 percent.

[3]Strain energy is the area under the load elongation curve obtained from the machine chart or computer system converted to units of pounds per inch per inch. This is required if one of the minimum values for tensile strength or elongation is not met. Ultimate elongation for this calculation shall be the elongation to the point the load is 5 percent of the tensile strength of the membrane after the maximum load has been reached.

UNIFORM BUILDING CODE STANDARD NO. 32-14

AUTOMATIC SMOKE AND HEAT VENTS

Standard of the International Conference of Building Officials
See Sections 3201 (b) and 3206 (a) and (d), Uniform Building Code

Scope

Sec. 32.1401. (a) **General.** This standard applies to thermally activated, automatic smoke and heat vents designed for installation on the roof of buildings as required by Section 3206 of the Building Code.

(b) **Instructions.** A copy of the installation and operating instructions shall be supplied with each unit. The instructions shall prescribe construction representative of that used in the examination and testing of the product.

Construction and Materials

Sec. 32.1402. The critical operating components of vents, such as heat sensors, hinges, latches, linkages and other mechanical parts, shall be constructed of corrosion-resistant materials.

Plastics shall be approved plastics as defined in the Building Code.

Vent design for minimum roof live load shall be of adequate strength and durability to withstand the design loads as prescribed in the Building Code.

Method of Activation

Sec. 32.1403. Releasing devices for vents shall be activated by heat. The heat-activated device shall be one of the following:

1. A fixed-temperature device having a melting temperature rating at least 30 degrees above the maximum expected ambient temperatures at the intended location.
2. A rate-of-rise device.
3. Approved, heat-sensitive glazing designed to shrink and drop out of the vent opening.

Test Procedures

Sec. 32.1404. (a) **General.** Recognized and accepted testing procedures and testing equipment shall be used.

(b) **Samples.** Samples submitted for acceptance tests shall be production units whose materials, design and specifications are representative of the models for which acceptance is sought. Written specifications shall be submitted for each model. Tests for multiple-sized models shall utilize the largest size unit for evaluations.

(c) **Heat Sensors.** Heat-sensing devices shall be capable of activation in accordance with the requirements of the simulated fire test.

(d) **Load Performance.** Vents shall be tested to open freely and fully against a live load of 10 pounds per square foot. Vents intended for installation in areas subject to snow loads shall be tested to open freely and fully against snow loads as determined by the building official.

(e) **Simulated Fire Test.** 1. **Requirements.** Vents shall be tested to open fully to operational position in five minutes when subjected to a precalibrated time-temperature gradient that heats the air within the vent cavity to 500°F. within the five-minute period. Where vents are operated by fixed-temperature fusible devices, the device shall be located in the expected flow pattern of hot gases and not shielded from fire temperatures. The actual load on the device shall not exceed its greatest load capacity.

2. **Calibration.** Correction of the test calibration may be accomplished by varying the height of the vent being tested or the height of the test-fuel pan.

3. **Test Method.** Test units shall be end-supported 35 inches above the fire test floor. Two Type K, chrome lus. alumel 18-gauge thermocouples shall be attached to the inside of the vent, 1 inch below the highest point of the cavity. The leads shall be connected to a recording potentiometer, 0 - 2000°F. range multipoint.

A one-square-foot steel test-fuel pan shall be centered under the test unit on the floor. Isopropyl alcohol shall be poured into the pan to a depth of 1/2 inch. The alcohol shall be ignited and a determination made as to the ability of the test unit to meet the test requirements.

During the test there shall not be any flame impingment on the test unit lid or dropout glazing.

4. **Repetitions.** Each unit tested shall successfully pass five simulated fire tests per mode of operation without mechanical or structural failure. Modes of operation tested shall include: (i) Activation of the manual release mechanism on units so equipped, and (ii) Activation of the heat-sensing device.

EXCEPTION: Drop-out glazing vents need be tested only once per unit. Release of the glazing is a normal test response.

Necessary resetting or replacement of the heat-sensing device shall not be considered a mechanical or structural failure.

Marking

Sec. 32.1405. Each unit shall bear a durable, visible label stating the name and location of the manufacturer, the model designation and the year of manufacture.

UNIFORM BUILDING CODE STANDARD NO. 33-1

POWER-OPERATED EXIT DOORS

Test Standard of the International Conference of Building Officials

See Sections 3301 (a) and 3304 (h), Uniform Building Code

Scope

Sec. 33.101. (a) **General.** These requirements and methods of test apply to power-operated swinging doors and combination sliding and swinging doors intended for installation in locations where conforming exits are required by Chapter 33.

(b) **Operators and Activators.** Power-operated doors may be provided with air, hydraulic or electric operators actuated from a floor, activating carpet, photoelectric device or other approved signaling device.

(c) **Fire Door Assemblies.** Power-operated doors intended for installation in openings where fire door assemblies are required shall, in addition to the requirements of this standard, be tested in accordance with Fire Tests of Door Assemblies, U.B.C. Standard No. 43-2.

General

Sec. 33.102. (a) **Panic Hardware.** Power-operated doors intended for installation in openings where panic hardware is required shall be tested with panic hardware on the doors.

(b) **Opening Degree.** When manually operated in the direction of egress, leaves of swinging doors or swing-out sections of sliding doors shall swing open to not less than 90 degrees from the closed position.

(c) **Locking Mechanisms.** Locking mechanisms on doors intended for locations which do not require panic hardware shall be of a type readily identified as locked, and the doors shall be posted with durable, permanent signs reading "THESE DOORS MUST REMAIN UNLOCKED DURING BUSINESS HOURS." Signs shall be 1-inch high block letters on a contrasting background. Signs shall be located on the header framing.

(d) **Swinging and Sliding Doors.** Each swing-out leaf of swinging or sliding doors with swinging sections shall be provided with durable signs in not less than 1-inch block letters on contrasting background reading, "IN EMERGENCY PUSH TO OPEN," or other approved wording. The sign shall be located at the closing edge of the door not less than 36 inches nor more than 60 inches above the floor. The sign shall read horizontally and may be in two lines.

(e) **Electrical Wiring and Devices.** Electrical wiring, electrical devices and controls shall be of a type tested and approved by the building official.

(f) **Testing.** Doors with power operators shall be examined and tested by an approved testing agency.

(g) **Test Report.** The test report shall contain engineering data and drawings, size and weight of door tested, wiring diagrams of electrical control systems, schematic drawings of mechanical controls and operating manuals. The report shall describe the mechanical operation of the power operator in sequence as the door opens and closes under normal and emergency conditions. The report shall set forth the tests performed in accordance with the provisions of this standard and the results thereof. The report shall additionally contain an analysis comparing each feature of the design against the performance test procedures contained herein.

(h) **Simulated Installation and Test Equipment.** Doors with power operators shall be installed in a simulated wall and door framing assembly in accordance with the manufacturer's instructions. The test specimen shall be not less than 3 feet wide by 7 feet high. A motor-driven or suitable mechanism shall be used to actuate the activating carpet. The rate of operation or number of cycles shall be three to five per minute. On sliding doors with a swing-out section additional operating endurance tests shall be conducted. A motor-driven mechanism or other approved means shall be used to push the swinging door section open and pull the swinging section closed at a rate of three to five cycles per minute, so that the latching mechanism and disconnect switches operate as in service. During the test the door specimen shall have only the lubrication which is provided by the manufacturer at the factory, or as may be recommended by the manufacturer in his installation instructions.

(i) **Endurance Tests.** The power operator shall function as intended to open and close the door for 100,000 cycles of operation without failure or excessive wear of parts. The release mechanism and disconnect switches of the swinging section in sliding doors shall function as intended for 250 cycles of operation without failure or excessive wear of parts. The opening and closing forces, and the speed of opening and closing, shall be recorded at the start of the endurance tests and shall again be recorded at the end of the endurance tests. Opening and closing forces at the beginning and at the end of the endurance test shall not exceed the maximum forces prescribed in these test procedures.

Swinging Doors

Sec. 33.103. (a) **Opening Size.** Each door opening, when the door is in the 90-degree open position, shall provide a clear opening width of not less than 32 inches, with no single leaf less than 24 inches in width.

(b) **Doors in Pairs.** Doors in pairs shall be equipped with a separate operator for each leaf unless tests with a tandem operator with one leaf jammed in a closed and in a partially open position indicates that the second leaf continues to operate or is free to swing into the open position without exceeding the maximum permitted manual opening pressures. On doors with mechanical controls, one mechanism shall be subjected to fault conditions; during the fault condition the second leaf shall be openable manually without exceeding the maximum permitted opening pressure.

(c) **Closing Mechanism.** Normal closing of doors shall be by spring action, pressure operated mechanism or electrically driven mechanism. The closing force measured at the closing stile shall not exceed 40 pounds at any point in the closing arc. The time of final 10 degrees of closing shall be not less than one and one-half seconds.

(d) **Operation.** Each possible fault condition that affects the power supply shall be introduced into the door and power operator assembly. Under each fault condition, single doors and each leaf of doors in pairs shall open to the 90-degree position with an applied pressure at the normal location of the push plate not exceeding 40 pounds.

(e) **In-swinging Doors.** Power-operated in-swinging doors are not recognized for determining exit width opening required to swing in the direction of egress.

(f) **Activating Carpets and Safety Mats.** Activating carpets and safety mats shall comply with the following provisions:

1. When carpets are used as the activating device, they shall have a width not less than 10 inches less than the clear width of the door opening with the center line of the carpet in the center line of the door opening. The width shall be measured between the exposed edges of the carpet tread surface excluding molded edge bevels or edge trim.

2. The length of activating carpets shall be not less than 42 inches. The length of activating carpets for doors exceeding 42 inches in width shall be not less than 56 inches. The length shall be measured from the center line of the door pivot to the exposed edge of the carpet tread surface excluding molded edge bevels or edge trim.

3. Doors serving one-way traffic only shall be provided with a safety mat having a length not less than the width of the widest leaf. A safety mat is one that will prevent the door from opening if there is pressure on the safety mat before pressure is applied to the activating mat, and one that will prevent the door from closing following normal door actuation until pressure on the safety mat is removed.

4. Doors serving both egress and ingress shall have a series of joined carpets on the swing side of the door arranged as follows:

A. One safety carpet or mat nearest to the door at least as long as the width of the door leaf;

B. One or more activating carpets to provide a total carpet length on the swing side of not less than two and one-half times the width of the widest door leaf.

Sliding Doors

Sec. 33.104. (a) **General.** Sliding doors shall comply with the following provisions:

1. Sliding leaves of sliding doors shall be provided with swinging sections arranged to swing in the direction of egress when pressure is applied at the location of normal push plates or on the crossbar of panic hardware on doors where panic hardware is required.

2. Operation of the swinging section shall disconnect the sliding door power operator.

3. Permanent stops shall be provided to prevent double swing.

4. Location of the breakaway tension adjustment, opening and closing speed adjustment, opening and closing snub speed adjustments, opening and closing power pressure adjustments, and similar controls shall be concealed and not readily accessible where they may be subject to tampering.

5. Doors shall be suspended from an overhead track. Operators and control levers or mechanisms shall be guarded.

(b) **Closing Mechanism.** The closing force of sliding doors at 24 inches of opening shall not exceed 30 pounds with a closing speed not in excess of 1.5 feet per second.

(c) **Opening Width.** The minimum clear width of the door opening with the swinging section or sections in the 90-degree open position shall not be less than 32 inches with no single leaf less than 24 inches in width.

(d) **Opening Forces.** The swinging section in sliding doors shall swing open into the full open position when an opening force not exceeding 40 pounds is applied at the normal push plate location or on the crossbar of panic hardware.

(e) **Fault Condition Introduced.** Under each possible fault condition that affects the power supply and with the sliding leaf or leaves retracted one-half the leaf width into its or their pocket, each swinging section shall open to the 90-degree position with an applied pressure at the normal location of the push plate not exceeding 40 pounds.

(f) **Sliding Doors Without Swing-out Section.** Power-operated sliding doors which are not provided with a swing-out section may be evaluated for conformance to the mechanical requirements and endurance tests provided in this standard. Power-operated sliding doors which are not provided with a swing-out section shall not be listed for use in locations where required exits are specified by the Uniform Building Code.

(g) **Activating Carpets, Safety Mats.** Activating carpets and safety mats shall conform to Section 33.103 (f).

Marking

Sec. 33.105. The name of the manufacturer, or trademark by which the manufacturer can be readily identified, shall be legibly marked on the operating equipment where it can be seen after installation. The type, model number or letter designation identifying the product as a listed device shall be provided on a label attached in a location as indicated in its listing.

UNIFORM BUILDING CODE STANDARD NO. 33-2

STAIRWAY IDENTIFICATION

Specification Standard of the International Conference of Building Officials

See Sections 3301 (a) and 3306 (p), Uniform Building Code

Scope

Sec. 33.201. Signs to provide information to the occupants and fire department personnel to ensure that they do not become confused during emergencies shall be installed in accordance with this standard.

General

Sec. 33.202. Standardized signs shall be installed in stairways when the building is four or more stories in height. The signs shall identify each stair landing and indicate the upper and lower termination of the stairway.

Sign Details

Sec. 33.203. (a) **Size.** Signs shall be a minimum 12 inches by 12 inches.

(b) **Stairway Location.** The stairway location, such as STAIR NO. 1 or WEST STAIR, shall be placed at the top of the sign in 1-inch-high block lettering with $^1/_4$-inch strokes.

(c) **Upper Terminus.** The stairway's upper terminus, such as ROOF ACCESS or NO ROOF ACCESS, shall be placed under the stairway identification in 1-inch-high block lettering with $^1/_4$-inch strokes.

(d) **Floor Level Number.** The floor level number shall be placed in the middle of the sign in 5-inch-high lettering with $^3/_4$-inch strokes. The mezzanine levels shall have the letter "M" preceding the floor number. Basement levels shall have the letter "B" preceding the floor number.

(e) **Lower Terminus.** The lower and upper terminus of the stairway shall be placed at the bottom of the sign in 1-inch-high block lettering with $^1/_4$-inch strokes.

Examples:

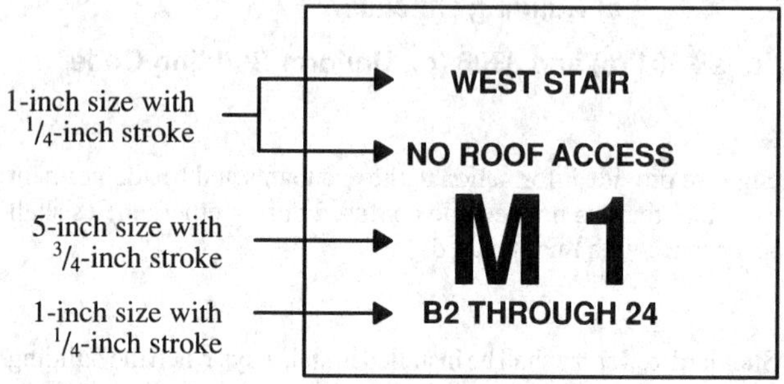
1-inch size with
1/4-inch stroke
5-inch size with
3/4-inch stroke
1-inch size with
1/4-inch stroke
WEST STAIR
NO ROOF ACCESS
M 1
B2 THROUGH 24

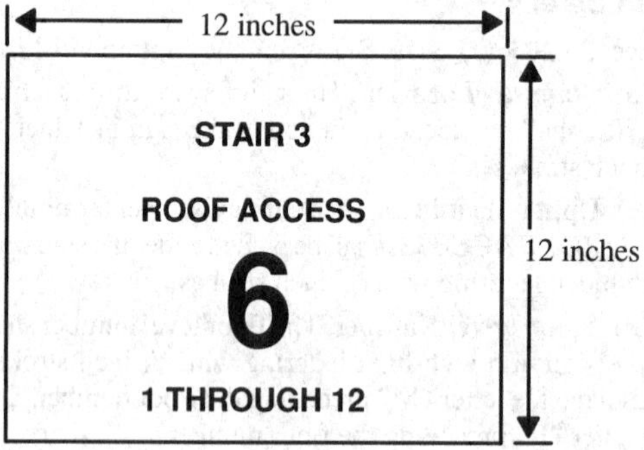
12 inches
12 inches
STAIR 3
ROOF ACCESS
6
1 THROUGH 12

UNIFORM BUILDING CODE STANDARD NO. 33-3

EXIT LADDER DEVICE

Test Standard of the International Conference of Building Officials

See Appendix Section 111 (a), Uniform Building Code

Scope

Sec. 33.301. This standard for exit ladder devices is applicable where such devices are permitted by the building official for installation on existing apartment houses and hotels in conformance with Appendix Section 111 (a) of the Uniform Building Code.

Instructions

Sec. 33.302. Installation shall be in accordance with the manufacturer's instructions. Instructions shall be illustrated and shall include directions and information adequate for attaining proper and safe installation of the product. Where exit ladder devices are intended for mounting on different support surfaces, specific installation instructions shall be provided for each surface.

General Design

Sec. 33.303. All load-bearing surfaces and supporting hardware shall be of noncombustible materials. Exit ladder devices shall have a minimum width of 12 inches when in the position intended for use. The design load shall be not less than 400 pounds for 16-foot length and 600 pounds for 25-foot length.

Performance

Sec. 33.304. (a) Exit ladder devices shall be capable of withstanding an applied load of four times the design load when installed in the manner intended for use. Test loads shall be applied for a period of one hour.

(b) Exit ladder devices of the retractable type shall, in addition to the static load requirements of Section 33.304 (a), be capable of withstanding the following tests:

1. Rung strength.
2. Rung-to-side-rail shear strength.
3. Release mechanism.
4. Low temperature.

Rung-strength Test

Sec. 33.305. Rungs of retractable exit ladder devices shall be capable of withstanding a load of 1000 pounds when applied to a 3½-inch-wide block resting at the center of the rung. The test load shall be applied for a period of one hour. The ladder shall remain operational following this test.

Rung-to-side-rail Shear Test

Sec. 33.306. Rungs of retractable exit ladder devices shall be capable of withstanding a load of 1000 pounds when applied to a 3½-inch-wide block resting on the center rung as near the side rail as possible. The test load shall be applied for a period of one hour. Upon removal of the test load the fasteners attaching the rung to the side rail shall show no evidence of failure. The ladder shall remain operational following this test.

Release Mechanism Test

Sec. 33.307. The release mechanism of retractable exit ladder devices shall operate with an average applied force of not more than 5 pounds for hand-operated releasing mechanisms and an average applied force of not more than 25 pounds for foot-pedal types of releasing mechanisms. For these tests, a force gauge shall be applied to the release mechanism, and the average of three consecutive readings shall be computed.

Low Temperature Operation Test

Sec. 33.308. Representative samples of the exit ladder device shall be subjected to a temperature of −40°C. in an environmental chamber for a period of 24 hours. The release mechanism shall be operated immediately upon removal from the chamber. The ladder device shall function as intended without any restriction of operation.

UNIFORM BUILDING CODE STANDARD NO. 33-4

PANIC HARDWARE

Based on Standard 305, July 30, 1979, of the Underwriters Laboratories Inc.

See Sections 3301 (a) and 3304 (d), Uniform Building Code

Scope

Sec. 33.401. (a) **General.** These requirements cover releasing devices actuated by a crossbar for outward-opening doors designed to facilitate the safe egress of persons from buildings in the event of panic or other emergency.

(b) **Installation.** A copy of the operating and installation instructions or equivalent information is to be furnished with the samples submitted for investigation for use as a guide in the examination and test of the mechanism. For this purpose a printed edition is not required.

Construction

Sec. 33.402. (a) **Assembly.** The mechanism shall be of a type which can be readily maintained in proper operating condition.

The mechanism shall be designed so as to release the door latch or latches when pressure is applied to the release bar in the direction of exit travel.

The ends of the release bar shall be curved, guarded or otherwise designed to prevent catching on the clothing of persons during exit.

The release mechanism shall not depend on springs to open the door latch or latches.

A locking or dogging device provided as part of the mechanism shall not prevent release of the door latch or latches when pressure is applied to the release bar in the direction of exit travel.

A dead-locking bolt shall not be employed unless it is released by the action of the release bar.

The projection of the release bar when in the depressed position shall not unduly restrict the exit opening.

(b) **Materials.** The materials employed shall have adequate mechanical strength to perform their intended function. A metal or alloy shall have a solidus point not less than 1000°F.

The materials employed shall minimize the likelihood of the release mechanism becoming inoperative due to corrosion.

Performance

Sec. 33.403. (a) **Endurance Test.** The release mechanism and latches shall function as intended for 100,000 cycles of operation without failure or excessive wear of the parts.

The assembly is to be installed on a simulated door and frame assembly in accordance with the manufacturer's instructions. A motor-driven mechanism is to actuate the release bar so as to release the latches and push the door open, as in service. The rate of operation is to be approximately 30 per minute. For this test, the assembly is to have the lubrication which is provided at the factory or recommended by the manufacturer.

(b) **Emergency Operation Test.** The release mechanism shall be so designed that a horizontal force of 15 pounds or less will actuate the release bar and latches. When the latched door is subjected to outward pressure as described below, a force of 50 pounds or less shall actuate the release bar.

The sample is to be subjected to the 15-pound test before and after the endurance test and subjected to the 50-pound test after the endurance test.

A horizontal force of 250 pounds is to be applied against the latching edge adjacent to the latch in the direction in which the door opens. A spring scale or similar means is to be used to measure the horizontal force which is applied against the center of the release bar.

For double doors, a horizontal force of 250 pounds is to be applied against the midpoint of the outer stile of each door.

The release bar is not to be deformed by the test; and a spacing of at least 1 inch is to be provided between the release bar and the door face when the horizontal force is applied against the center of the release bar.

Marking

Sec. 33.404. The manufacturer's or vendor's name and a distinctive type or model designation shall be plainly marked on the release-bar assembly.

If a manufacturer produces panic hardware assemblies at more than one factory, each such assembly shall have a distinctive marking or identifying symbol to identify it as the product of a particular factory.

UNIFORM BUILDING CODE STANDARD NO. 38-1

INSTALLATION OF SPRINKLER SYSTEMS

This standard, with certain exceptions, is based upon the National Fire Protection Association Standard for the Installation of Sprinkler Systems, NFPA 13-1987.

Part I of this standard contains the exceptions to NFPA 13-1989. Part II of this standard contains NFPA 13-1989 reproduced in its entirety with permission of the publisher.

See Sections 901 (c); 1807 (c); 3801 (b), (d) and (e); 3802 (f) 3, (g) and (h); 3901 (a); 3903 (d); 4204 (a); 5207 (a) 4 B and 6 B; 5208 (a) 4; 5603 (a); and Appendix 1108 (b), Uniform Building Code

Part I

Amendments

Sec. 38.101. The National Fire Protection Association standard adopted by this standard applies to the selection, installation, acceptance inspection and acceptance testing of sprinkler systems, except as follows:

1. Sec. 1-1 is amended by changing the note to read as follows:

Consult other recognized and accepted standards for additional requirements relating to water supplies.

2. Sec. 1-3 is amended by changing the definition of "authority having jurisdiction" to read as follows:

Authority Having Jurisdiction is the building official.

The definitions of "approved" and "listed" shall be as set forth in the Uniform Building Code.

Sec. 1-3 is further amended by deleting the definitions of the words "should" and "standard," by deleting the note following the definition of "sprinkler system," and by adding definitions for "acceptance" and "building official" to read as follows:

Acceptance is acceptance by the building official.

Building Official is the officer or other designated authority charged with the administration and enforcement of this standard, or the officer's or other designated authority's duly authorized representative.

3. Sec. 1-5 is revised to read as follows:

1-5.1. A sprinkler system installed under this standard shall be maintained in accordance with the Uniform Fire Code, Article 10.

1-5.2. The installer of the system shall provide the owner with written instructions and information relating to the care and maintenance of the sprinkler system, with special attention given to the sprinkler system devices.

4. Sec. 1-7 is amended to read as follows:

1-7.1. For the purpose of determining the level of protection to be provided by required sprinkler system installations, Table No. 1.7.1 shall be used.

For hazard classifications other than those indicated, see appropriate nationally recognized standards for design criteria.

When fire sprinkler systems are required in buildings of undetermined use, they shall be designed and installed to have a sprinkler density of not less than that required for an Ordinary Hazard Group 3 use with a minimum design area of 3,000 square feet.

Use is considered undetermined if not specified at time permit is issued.

Where a subsequent occupancy requires a system with greater capability, it shall be the responsibility of the occupant to upgrade the system to the required density for the new occupancy.

TABLE NO. 1.7.1
HAZARD CLASSIFICATION

OCCUPANCY OF BUILDING OR PORTION THEREOF	HAZARD CLASSIFICATION
Group A Occupancies used as meeting rooms, library reading rooms, restaurant seating areas, clubs, theaters, museums, health clubs, educational classrooms and churches. Group B Occupancies used as offices, data processing areas, colleges and universities. Group E Occupancies other than shops and laboratories. Group I Occupancy living and sleeping areas. Group R, Division 1 Occupancies.[1] Typically these uses are such that the quantity and combustibility of contents is such that relatively low-rate-of-heat-release fires would be expected.	Light
Group B Occupancies used for light manufacturing, commercial kitchens, laundries, automobile parking garages, bakeries, canneries, electronic plants, beverage manufacturing and glass products manufacturing plants not producing dust or fibers. Typically these uses are such that the quantity of combustibles is relatively low, the combustibility of contents is moderate, storage does not exceed 8 feet in height, and moderate-rate-of-heat-release fires would be expected.	Ordinary Group 1
Group B Occupancies used for chemical plant laboratories, mercantile, machine shops, printing plants, library stack areas, metal working, wood product assembly, textile manufacturing, confectionery products, cold storage warehouses,[2] cereal mills, service stations and repair garages. Typically these uses are such that the quantity of combustibles is moderate. The combustibility of contents is moderate, storage does not exceed 12 feet in height[2] and moderate-rate-of-heat-release fires would be expected.	Ordinary Group 2

TABLE NO. 1.7.1
HAZARD CLASSIFICATION—(Continued)

OCCUPANCY OF BUILDING OR PORTION THEREOF	HAZARD CLASSIFICATION
Group A Occupancies such as exhibition halls. Group B Occupancies used as tobacco products manufacturing, paper and pulp mills, piers and wharfs, and warehousing[2] of higher combustible contents (including packaging). Group H Occupancies used as feed mills, tire manufacturing, chemical plants, repair garages and woodworking. Group H, Division 6 Occupancies (except extra-hazard areas). Typically these uses are such that high-rate-of-heat-release fires would be expected and the spread of fire would be rapid.	Ordinary Group 3
Group H Occupancies used for printing (using inks with flashpoints below 100°F.), combustible hydraulic fluid-use areas such as die casting and metal extruding, upholstering with plastic foam, rubber reclaiming, compounding, drying, milling, vulcanizing, plywood and particle board manufacturing, saw mills, textile picking, opening, blending, garnetting, carding and combining of cotton, synthetics, wool shoddy or burlap. Typically these uses are such that a significant fire hazard exists.	Extra Hazard Group I
Group H Occupancies used as asphalt saturating, flammable liquids spraying, flow coating, open oil quenching, varnish and paint dipping, solvent cleaning and manufactured home or modular building manufacturing (where the finished building enclosure is present and has combustible interiors). These uses are such that a severe fire hazard exists.	Extra Hazard Group 2[3]

[1]See also Section 7-4.4.
[2]For high-piled storage, see U.F.C. Article 81.
[3]For additional or more stringent criteria, see U.F.C. Article 79 or 80.

5. Sec. 1-9.2 (m) is amended to read as follows:

1-9.2 (m). Manufacturing data sheets for sprinkler heads which contain at least the following information:

—Make
—Type
—K-factor
—Nominal orifice size
—Temperature rating
—Minimum operating pressures and discharge rates for proposed area of coverage

6. Sec. 1-11.2.2 is amended by substituting the phrase "nationally recognized standards" for "NFPA 24, Standard for the Installation of Private Fire Service Mains and their Appurtenances" in the second sentence.

7. Sec. 2-2.1.1 is amended by substituting the phrase "nationally recognized' for "NFPA" in the first and second sentences of Exception 4.

8. Table No. 2-2.1.1 (a) is amended by substituting the phrase "U.F.C. Standards Nos. 81-1 and 81-2" for "NFPA 231 and NFPA 231C" in the fifth row.

9. Sec. 2-2.3.4 (a) is amended by substituting the phrase "the Uniform Building Code" for "NFPA 14, Standard for the Installation of Standpipe and Hose Systems" in the first sentence of the text and in the first sentence of the exception.

10. Sec. 2-2.3.4 (b) is amended by substituting the phrase "the Uniform Building Code" for "NFPA 14, Standard for the Installation of Standpipe and Hose Systems."

11. Sec. 2-3.2 is amended by deleting the reference "See NFPA 24, Standard for the Installation of Private Fire Service Mains and their Appurtenances."

12. Sec. 2-4.1 is amended by deleting the reference "See NFPA 22, Standard for Water Tanks for Private Fire Protection."

13. Sec. 2-5.1 is amended by deleting the reference "See NFPA 22, Standard for Water Tanks for Private Protection."

14. Sec. 2-6.1.1 is amended by deleting the reference "See NFPA 22, Standard for Water Tanks for Private Fire Protection."

15. Sec. 2-7.6.1 is amended to read as follows:

2-7.6.1. All fire-extinguishing systems installed pursuant to this standard shall be installed in accordance with the requirements of Uniform Building Code Chapter 38. Fire hose threads used in connection with fire-extinguishing systems shall be National Standard hose thread or as approved by the chief.

16. Sec. 3-1.1.5 is amended to read as follows:

3-1.1.5. Other types of pipe or tube, such as plastic, may be used if it is investigated and found to be listed for this service.

17. Sec. 3-3.1 is amended to read as follows:

3-3.1. For sprinklers in storage racks, see Uniform Fire Code Standard No. 81-2.

18. Sec. 3-7.2.2 is amended by substituting the phrase "nationally recognized standards" for "NFPA 51B, Standard for Fire Prevention in Use of Cutting and Welding Processes" in the exception.

19. Sec. 3-10.1.12 is amended to read as follows:

3-10.1.12. When sprinkler piping is installed in storage racks as defined in U.F.C. Standard No. 81-2, piping shall be substantially supported from the storage rack structure or building in accordance with all applicable provisions of Section 3-15.

20. Sec. 3-11.2.4 is amended by substituting the phrase "other nationally recognized standards" for "NFPA 307, Standard for the Construction and Fire Protection of Marine Terminals, Piers and Wharfs" in the third sentence of Exception 1, and "NFPA 81, Standard for Fur Storage, Fumigation and Cleaning" in Exception 2.

21. Sec. 3-11.2.9.1 is amended by substituting the phrase "other nationally recognized standards" for "NFPA 13D, Standard for the Installation of Sprinkler Systems in One- and Two-family Dwellings and Mobile Homes."

22. Sec. 3-11.6.2 is amended by substituting the phrase "nationally recognized" for "NFPA" in Exception 4.

23. Sec. 3-12.1 is amended to read as follows:

3-12.1. Definition. A local alarm unit is an assembly of apparatus approved for the service and so constructed and installed that any flow of water from a sprinkler system equal to or greater than that from a single automatic sprinkler of the smallest orifice size installed on the system will result in an audible alarm on the premises within 2 minutes after such flow begins. For remote sprinkler water-flow alarm transmission, see Section 3-17.7.1.

24. Sec. 3-12.2 is amended to read as follows:

3-12.2. Local water-flow alarms shall be provided on each sprinkler system having more than five sprinklers and shall be located in an area approved by the chief.

25. Sec. 3-12.7.1 is amended by substituting the phrase "nationally recognized" for "NFPA" in the last line of the first paragraph and deleting Subsections (a), (b), (c) and (d).

26. Sec. 3-12.7.2 is amended to read as follows:

3-12-7.2. Electrically operated alarm attachments forming part of a local sprinkler water-flow alarm system may be of open circuit type and shall comply with U.F.C. Standard No. 14-1.

27. Sec. 4-1.1.1 is amended to read as follows:

4-1.1.1. The basic requirements for spacing, location and position of sprinklers are specified in this chapter and are based on the following principles and Table No. 4-1.1:

TABLE NO. 4-1.1
SPRINKLER SPACING, AREA OF COVERAGE, AND DEFLECTOR POSITION REQUIREMENTS

	HAZARD			
SPRINKLER SPACING[1]	**Light**	**Ordinary**	**Extra**	
4-2.1 Max. distance between sprinklers[2]	15	15	12	
4-2.1.5.1 Max. distance from wall[3]	7½	7½	6	
TYPE OF CEILING CONSTRUCTION	**AREA OF COVERAGE**[4]			**POSITION OF DEFLECTOR**[5]
Combustible smooth ceiling	200/225	130	90/100	1″-10″
Combustible smooth ceiling under beams	200/225	130	90/100	1″-14″
Noncombustible smooth ceiling	200/225	130	90/100	1″-12″
Noncombustible smooth ceiling under beams	200/225	130	90/100	1″-16″
Open wood joist—spaced 3′ or less o.c.	130	130	90/110	1″-6″

(Continued)

TABLE NO. 4-1.1 —(Continued)

TYPE OF CEILING CONSTRUCTION	AREA OF COVERAGE[4]			POSITION OF DEFLECTOR[5]
Open wood joist—spaced greater than 3′ o.c.	130	130	90/100	[6]
Open wood truss	130	130	90/100	[7]
Composite wood joist (16″ or less depth)	130	130	90/100	1″-6″
Composite wood joist (greater than 16″ depth)	[8]	[8]	[8]	
Open web steel beam	168	130	90/100	[9]
Open bar joist—combustible deck	200/225	130	90/100	1″-10″
Open bar joist—noncombustible deck	200/225	130	90/100	1″-12″
Beam and girder—in bays	200/225	130	90/100	1″-6″[10]
Beam and girder—under beam	200/225	130	90/100	1″-20″[11] 1″-4″[12]
Beam and girder—concrete tee with stems spaced more than 3′ to less than 7½′	200/225	130	90/100	[13]
Panel—in bay	168	130	90/100	1″-18″
Panel—under beam/girder	168	130	90/100	1″-22″[11,12] 1″-4″[12]

[1]See Section 4-4.19 for additional clarification regarding light-hazard sprinkler spacing from walls.

[2]The maximum distance between sprinklers in hydraulically calculated systems is determined by the "S" and "L" values as defined in Section 7-4.3.1.2.

[3]The maximum distance from a sprinkler to a wall in hydraulically calculated systems is determined by one half of the "S" and "L" values as defined in Section 7-4.3.1.2.

[4]The top number is the area of coverage for pipe schedule systems and the bottom number is the area of coverage for hydraulically calculated systems.

For high-piled storage, the area of coverage shall not exceed 100 square feet, except where the system has been designed in accordance with U.F.C. Standards Nos. 81-1 and 81-2 having a density less than 0.25 gallon per minute per square foot where the area of coverage may not exceed 130 square feet.

[5]Section 4-3.1, Exception 2, allows an alternate deflector location for sprinklers located per their listing.

[6]See smooth ceiling or beam and girder.

[7]See Section 4-2.4.1.

[8]National Fire Protection Association 13 is silent on area of coverage and location of sprinklers in composite wood joist construction having a depth greater than 16 inches. Therefore, it may be necessary to provide sprinklers in every joist space, or see Section 4-2.2.2.4.

[9]See Section 4-2.4.4.

[10]Deflectors of sprinklers under beams shall be located 1 to 4 inches below beams and not more than 14 inches below combustible ceilings or more than 16 inches below noncombustible ceilings.

(Continued)

[11]Below ceiling.
[12]Below beam.
[13]Sprinklers shall be located at or above a plan 1 inch below the level of the bottom of the stems of the tees and shall comply with Table No. 4-2.4.6.

28. Sec. 4-1.1.2 is amended by substituting the phrase "other nationally recognized standards" for "NFPA 13D, Standard for the Installation of Sprinkler Systems for One- and Two-family Dwellings and Mobile Homes."

29. Sec. 4-1.3.5 is amended to read as follows:

4-1.3.5. Standard Mill Construction refers to Type IV heavy-timber buildings in the Uniform Building Code.

30. Sec. 4-1.3.10 is amended to read as follows:

4-1.3.10. High-piled Storage. See Uniform Fire Code, Article 81.

31. Sec. 4-2.2.1 is amended by changing the last paragraph to read as follows:

4-2.2.1. High-piled combustible storage (as defined in the Uniform Fire Code)—40,000 square feet. Exception is retained.

32. Sec. 4-2.2.5 is amended in Exceptions 1 and 2 to read as follows:

EXCEPTIONS: 1. Sprinkler spacing may exceed 100 square feet but shall not exceed 130 square feet in systems hydraulically designed in accordance with U.F.C. Standards Nos. 81-1 and 81-2 for densities below 0.25 gallon per minute per square foot.

2. Where protection areas are specifically indicated in the design criteria of other NFPA standards and the Uniform Fire Code.

33. Sec. 4-2.2.6 is amended by substituting the phrase "nationally recognized" for "NFPA."

34. Sec. 4-2.5.1, the second sentence is amended to read as follows:

For in-rack sprinklers, the clear space shall be in accordance with U.F.C. Standards Nos. 81-1 and 81-2.

35. Sec. 4-4.7.2.4 is amended to read as follows:

4-4.7.2.4. Stairs enclosed in shafts of noncombustible construction shall have sprinklers provided at each floor landing.

36. Sec. 4-4.16.3 is amended by substituting the phrase "other nationally recognized standards" for "NFPA 81, Standard on Fur Storage, Fumigation and Cleaning" in the note.

37. Sec. 4-4.17.1 is amended by changing "(See NFPA 96, Standard for Vapor Removal from Cooking Equipment.)" to "(See Uniform Mechanical Code.)"

38. Sec., 4-4.18 is amended by changing "See NFPA 231C, Standard on Rack Storage of Materials" to "See Uniform Fire Code Standard No. 81-2."

39. Sec. 5-3.5 is amended by substituting the phrase "U.F.C. Standard No. 14-2" for "NFPA 72E, Standard on Automatic Fire Detectors."

40. Sec. 9-2.3.9.1 is amended by deleting the reference "See NFPA 24, Standard for the Installation of Fire Service Mains and their Appurtenances."

41. Sec. 9-2.4.1 is amended by substituting the phrase "other nationally recognized" for "appropriate NFPA."

42. Sec. 9-3.3.9.1 is amended by deleting the reference "See NFPA 24, Standard for the Installation of Fire Service Mains and their Appurtenances."

43. Chapter 10 is deleted.

44. Appendix Chapter D is deleted.

Part II

Contents

NFPA 13

Standard for the
Installation of Sprinkler Systems

1989 Edition

NOTICE: An asterisk (*) following the number or letter designating a paragraph indicates explanatory material on that paragraph in Appendix A.

Information on referenced publications can be found in Chapter 10 and Appendix C.

Chapter 1 General Information

1-1 Scope. This standard provides the minimum requirements for the design and installation of automatic sprinkler systems and of exposure protection sprinkler systems, including the character and adequacy of water supplies and the selection of sprinklers, piping, valves, and all materials and accessories; but not including the installation of private fire service mains and their appurtenances, the installation of fire pumps, the construction and installation of gravity and pressure tanks and towers.

NOTE: Consult other NFPA standards for additional requirements relating to water supplies.

1-2 Purpose. The purpose of this standard is to provide a reasonable degree of protection for life and property from fire through standardized installation requirements for sprinkler systems based upon sound engineering principles, test data, and field experience. The standard endeavors to continue the excellent record that has been established by standard sprinkler systems and meet the needs of changing technology. Nothing in this standard is intended to restrict new technologies or alternate arrangements, providing the level of safety prescribed by the standard is not lowered. Materials or devices not specifically designated by this standard shall be utilized in complete accord with all conditions, requirements, and limitations of their listings.

NOTE 1: A sprinkler system is a specialized fire protection system and requires knowledgeable and experienced design and installation.

NOTE 2: Since its inception, this document has been developed on the basis of standardized materials, devices, and design practices. However, certain paragraphs, such as 3-1.1.5, 4-1.1.3, and this one, allow the use of materials and devices not specifically designated by this standard, provided such use is within parameters established by testing and listing agencies. In using such materials or devices, it is important that all conditions, requirements, and limitations of the listing be fully understood and accepted, and that the installation is in complete accord with such listing requirements.

1-3* Definitions.

Approved. Acceptable to the "authority having jurisdiction."

NOTE: The National Fire Protection Association does not approve, inspect or certify any installations, procedures, equipment, or materials nor does it approve or evaluate testing laboratories. In determining the acceptability of installations or procedures, equipment or materials, the authority having jurisdiction may base acceptance on compliance with NFPA or other appropriate standards. In the absence of such standards, said authority may require evidence of proper installation, procedure or use. The authority having jurisdiction may also refer to the listings or labeling practices of an organization concerned with product evaluations which is in a position to determine compliance with appropriate standards for the current production of listed items.

Authority Having Jurisdiction. The "authority having jurisdiction" is the organization, office or individual responsible for "approving" equipment, an installation or a procedure.

NOTE: The phrase "authority having jurisdiction" is used in NFPA documents in a broad manner since jurisdictions and "approval" agencies vary as do their responsibilities. Where public safety is primary, the "authority having jurisdiction" may be a federal, state, local or other regional department or individual such as a fire chief, fire marshal, chief of a fire prevention bureau, labor department, health department, building official, electrical inspector, or others having statutory authority. For insurance purposes, an insurance inspection department, rating bureau, or other insurance company representative may be the "authority having jurisdiction." In many circumstances the property owner or his designated agent assumes the role of the "authority having jurisdiction"; at government installations, the commanding officer or departmental official may be the "authority having jurisdiction."

Dwelling Unit. One or more rooms arranged for the use of one or more individuals living together as in a single housekeeping unit normally having cooking, living, sanitary, and sleeping facilities.

For purposes of this standard, dwelling unit includes hotel rooms, dormitory rooms, apartments, condominiums, sleeping rooms in nursing homes, and similar living units.

Listed. Equipment or materials included in a list published by an organization acceptable to the "authority having jurisdiction" and concerned with product evaluation, that maintains periodic inspection of production of listed equipment or materials and whose listing states either that the equipment or material meets appropriate standards or has been tested and found suitable for use in a specified manner.

NOTE: The means for identifying listed equipment may vary for each organization concerned with product evaluation, some of which do not recognize equipment as listed unless it is also labeled. The "authority having jurisdiction" should utilize the system employed by the listing organization to identify a listed product.

Shall. Indicates a mandatory requirement.

Should. Indicates a recommendation or that which is advised but not required.

Sprinkler System. A sprinkler system, for fire protection purposes, is an integrated system of underground and overhead piping designed in accordance with fire protection engineering standards. The installation includes one or more automatic water supplies. The portion of the sprinkler system aboveground is a network of specially sized or hydraulically designed piping installed in a building, structure, or area, generally overhead, and to which sprinklers are attached in a systematic pattern. The valve controlling each system riser is located in the system riser or its supply piping. Each sprinkler system riser includes a device for actuating an alarm when the system is in operation. The system is usually activated by heat from a fire and discharges water over the fire area.

NOTE: The design and installation of water supply facilities such as gravity tanks, fire pumps, reservoirs or pressure tanks, and underground piping are covered by the following NFPA standards: NFPA 22, *Water Tanks for Private Fire Protection*; NFPA 20, *Installation of Centrifugal Fire Pumps*; and NFPA 24, *Installation of Private Fire Service Mains and Their Appurtenances.*

Standard. A document containing only mandatory provisions, using the word shall to indicate requirements. Explanatory material may be included only in the form of fine print notes, in footnotes, or in an appendix.

1-4 Other Publications. A selected list of other publications related to the installation of sprinkler systems is published at the end of this standard.

1-5 Maintenance.

1-5.1* A sprinkler system installed under this standard shall be properly maintained for efficient service. The owner is responsible for the condition of the sprinkler system and shall use due diligence in keeping the system in good operating condition.

1-5.2 The installing contractor shall provide the owner with:

(a) Instruction charts describing operation and proper maintenance of sprinkler devices.

(b) Publication titled NFPA 13A, *Recommended Practice for the Inspection, Testing and Maintenance of Sprinkler Systems.*

1-6 Classification of Sprinkler Systems.

1-6.1 This standard covers automatic sprinkler systems of the types listed below, and systems of outside sprinklers for protection against exposure fires covered specifically in Chapter 6. Manually operated deluge systems, used for certain special hazard conditions, are not specifically covered in this standard but certain provisions of this standard will be found applicable.

Wet-Pipe Systems (*See Section 5-1.*)

Dry-Pipe Systems (*See Section 5-2.*)

Preaction Systems (*See Section 5-3.*)

Deluge Systems (*See Section 5-3.*)

Combined Dry-Pipe and Preaction Systems (*See Section 5-4.*)

Sprinkler Systems — Special Types. Special purpose systems employing departures from the requirements of this standard, such as special water supplies and reduced pipe sizing, shall be installed in accordance with their listing.

1-7 Classification of Occupancies.

1-7.1* Occupancy classifications for this standard relate to sprinkler installations and their water supplies only. They are not intended to be a general classification of occupancy hazards.

1-7.2 Light Hazard Occupancies.

1-7.2.1* Light Hazard. Occupancies or portions of other occupancies where the quantity and/or combustibility of contents is low and fires with relatively low rates of heat release are expected.

1-7.3 Ordinary Hazard Occupancies.

1-7.3.1* Ordinary Hazard (Group 1). Occupancies or portions of other occupancies where combustibility is low, quantity of combustibles is moderate, stockpiles of combustibles do not exceed 8 ft (2.4 m), and fires with moderate rates of heat release are expected.

1-7.3.2* Ordinary Hazard (Group 2). Occupancies or portions of other occupancies where quantity and combustibility of contents is moderate, stockpiles do not exceed 12 ft (3.7 m), and fires with moderate rate of heat release are expected.

1-7.3.3* Ordinary Hazard (Group 3). Occupancies or portions of other occupancies where quantity and/or combustibility of contents is high, and fires of high rate of heat release are expected.

1-7.4* Extra Hazard Occupancies.

1-7.4.1* Extra Hazard Occupancies or portions of other occupancies where quantity and combustibility of contents is very high, and flammable and combustible liquids, dust, lint, or other materials are present introducing the probability of rapidly developing fires with high rates of heat release.

1-7.4.2 Extra Hazard Occupancies involve a wide range of variables that may produce severe fires. The following shall be used to evaluate the severity of Extra Hazard Occupancies:

Extra Hazard (Group 1) includes occupancies described in 1-7.4.1 with little or no flammable or combustible liquids.

Extra Hazard (Group 2) includes occupancies described in 1-7.4.1 with moderate to substantial amounts of flammable or combustible liquids or where shielding of combustibles is extensive.

1-8* Design and Installation.

1-8.1 Devices and Materials.

1-8.1.1 Only new sprinklers shall be employed in the installation of sprinkler systems.

1-8.1.2* When a sprinkler system is installed, only approved materials and devices shall be used.

1-8.1.3 Sprinkler systems shall be designed for a maximum working pressure of 175 psi (12.1 bars).

Exception: Higher design pressures may be used when all system components are rated for pressures higher than 175 psi (12.1 bars).

1-8.1.3.1 Interior system components subject to pressure shall be designed for a working pressure not less than 175 psi (12.1 bars).

1-9* Working Plans.

1-9.1 Working plans shall be submitted for approval to the authority having jurisdiction before any equipment is installed or remodeled. Deviation from approved plans will require permission of the authority having jurisdiction.

1-9.2* Working plans shall be drawn to an indicated scale, on sheets of uniform size, with a plan of each floor, made so that they can be easily duplicated, and shall show the following data:

(a) Name of owner and occupant

(b) Location, including street address

(c) Point of compass

(d) Ceiling construction

(e) Full height cross section

(f) Location of fire walls

(g) Location of partitions

(h) Occupancy of each area or room

(i) Location and size of concealed spaces, closets, attics, and bathrooms [*see 4-4.3 to 4-4.16 inclusive (except 4-4.5 and 4-4.6), and 4-4.19*]

(j) Any questionable small enclosures in which no sprinklers are to be installed

(k) Size of city main in street, pressure, and whether dead-end or circulating and, if dead-end, direction and distance to nearest circulating main, city main test results, and elevation relative to the test hydrant (*see B-2-1*)

(l) Other sources of water supply, with pressure or elevation

(m) Make, type, and nominal orifice size of sprinkler

(n) Temperature rating and location of high-temperature sprinklers

(o) Total area protected by each system on each floor

(p) Number of sprinklers on each riser per floor

(q) Make, type, model, and size of alarm or dry-pipe valve

(r) Make, type, model, and size of preaction or deluge valve

(s) Kind and location of alarm bells

(t) Total number of sprinklers on each dry-pipe system, preaction system, combined dry-pipe/preaction system, or deluge system

(u) Approximate capacity in gallons of each dry-pipe system

(v) Pipe type and schedule of wall thickness

(w) Nominal pipe size and cutting lengths of pipe (or center to center dimensions)

NOTE: Where typical branch lines prevail, it will be necessary to size only one line.

(x) Location and size of riser nipples

(y) Type of fittings and joints and location of all welds and bends

(z) Type and locations of hangers, sleeves, braces, and methods of securing sprinklers when applicable

(aa) All control valves, check valves, drain pipes, and test connections

(bb) Size and location of hand hose, hose outlets, and related equipment

(cc) Underground pipe size, length, location, weight, material, point of connection to city main; the type of valves, meters, and valve pits; and the depth that top of the pipe is laid below grade

(dd) Provision for flushing (*see 3-3.2*)

(ee) When the equipment is to be installed as an addition to an existing system enough of the existing system shall be indicated on the plans to make all conditions clear

(ff) For hydraulically designed systems, the material to be included on the hydraulic data nameplate

(gg) Name and address of contractor

(hh) Method of protection for nonmetallic piping

(ii) A graphical representation of the scale shall be provided on all plans.

1-10 Approval of Sprinkler Systems.

1-10.1 The installer shall perform all required acceptance tests (*see Section 1-11*), complete the Contractor's Material and Test Certificate(s) [*see Figures 1-10.1(a) and 1-10.1(b)*], and forward the certificate(s) to the authority having jurisdiction prior to asking for approval of the installation.

1-10.2 When the authority having jurisdiction desires to be present during the conduct of acceptance tests, the installer shall give advance notification of the time and date the testing will be performed.

1-11 Acceptance Tests.

1-11.1* Flushing of Piping. Underground mains and lead-in connections to system risers shall be flushed thoroughly before connection is made to sprinkler piping, in order to remove foreign materials which may have entered the underground during the course of the installation or which may have been present in existing piping. The minimum rate of flow shall be not less than the water demand rate of the system which is determined by the system design, or not less than that necessary to provide a velocity of 10 ft per second (3 m/s), whichever is greater. For all systems the flushing operations shall be continued for a sufficient time to ensure thorough cleaning. When planning the flushing operations, consideration shall be given to disposal of the water issuing from the test outlets.

Exception: When the flow rate, as listed in Table 1-11.1, cannot be verified or met, supply piping shall be flushed at the maximum flow rate available to the system under fire conditions.

Table 1-11.1 Flow Required to Produce a Velocity of 10 Ft per Second (3 m/s) in Pipes

Pipe Size (in.)	Flow Rate (gpm)	Flow Rate (L/min)
4	390	1476
6	880	3331
8	1560	5905
10	2440	9235
12	3520	13323

For SI Units: 1 in. = 25.4 mm; 1 gpm = 3.785 L/min.

CONTRACTOR'S MATERIAL & TEST CERTIFICATE FOR ABOVEGROUND PIPING

PROCEDURE

Upon completion of work, inspection and tests shall be made by the contractor's representative and witnessed by an owner's representative. All defects shall be corrected and system left in service before contractor's personnel finally leave the job.

A certificate shall be filled out and signed by both representatives. Copies shall be prepared for approving authorities, owners, and contractor. It is understood the owner's representative's signature in no way prejudices any claim against contractor for faulty material, poor workmanship, or failure to comply with approving authority's requirements or local ordinances.

PROPERTY NAME		DATE	
PROPERTY ADDRESS			
PLANS	ACCEPTED BY APPROVING AUTHORITIES (NAMES)		
	ADDRESS		
	INSTALLATION CONFORMS TO ACCEPTED PLANS	☐ YES	☐ NO
	EQUIPMENT USED IS APPROVED	☐ YES	☐ NO
	IF NO, EXPLAIN DEVIATIONS		
INSTRUCTIONS	HAS PERSON IN CHARGE OF FIRE EQUIPMENT BEEN INSTRUCTED AS TO LOCATION OF CONTROL VALVES AND CARE AND MAINTENANCE OF THIS NEW EQUIPMENT?	☐ YES	☐ NO
	IF NO, EXPLAIN		
	HAVE COPIES OF THE FOLLOWING BEEN LEFT ON THE PREMISES:	☐ YES	☐ NO
	1. SYSTEM COMPONENTS INSTRUCTIONS	☐ YES	☐ NO
	2. CARE AND MAINTENANCE INSTRUCTIONS	☐ YES	☐ NO
	3. NFPA 13A	☐ YES	☐ NO
LOCATION OF SYSTEM	SUPPLIES BUILDINGS		

SPRINKLERS

MAKE	MODEL	YEAR OF MANUFACTURE	ORIFICE SIZE	QUANTITY	TEMPERATURE RATING

PIPE AND FITTINGS

Type of Pipe ____________________

Type of Fittings ____________________

ALARM VALVE OR FLOW INDICATOR

ALARM DEVICE			MAXIMUM TIME TO OPERATE THROUGH TEST CONNECTION	
TYPE	MAKE	MODEL	MIN.	SEC.

DRY VALVE			Q.O.D.		
MAKE	MODEL	SERIAL NO.	MAKE	MODEL	SERIAL NO.

DRY PIPE OPERATING TEST

	TIME TO TRIP THRU TEST CONNECTION*		WATER PRESSURE	AIR PRESSURE	TRIP POINT AIR PRESSURE	TIME WATER REACHED TEST OUTLET*		ALARM OPERATED PROPERLY	
	MIN.	SEC.	PSI	PSI	PSI	MIN.	SEC.	YES	NO
Without Q.O.D.									
With Q.O.D.									

IF NO, EXPLAIN

* MEASURED FROM TIME INSPECTOR'S TEST CONNECTION IS OPENED.

85A (10-88) PRINTED IN U.S.A. (OVER)

Figure 1-10.1(a) Contractor's Material and Test Certificate for Aboveground Piping.

DELUGE & PREACTION VALVES	OPERATION ☐ PNEUMATIC ☐ ELECTRIC ☐ HYDRAULIC
	PIPING SUPERVISED ☐ YES ☐ NO	DETECTING MEDIA SUPERVISED ☐ YES ☐ NO
	DOES VALVE OPERATE FROM THE MANUAL TRIP AND/OR REMOTE CONTROL STATIONS ☐ YES ☐ NO
	IS THERE AN ACCESSIBLE FACILITY IN EACH CIRCUIT FOR TESTING ☐ YES ☐ NO	IF NO, EXPLAIN

MAKE	MODEL	DOES EACH CIRCUIT OPERATE SUPERVISION LOSS ALARM		DOES EACH CIRCUIT OPERATE VALVE RELEASE		MAXIMUM TIME TO OPERATE RELEASE	
		YES	NO	YES	NO	MIN.	SEC.

TEST DESCRIPTION

HYDROSTATIC: Hydrostatic tests shall be made at not less than 200 psi (13.6 bars) for two hours or 50 psi (3.4 bars) above static pressure in excess of 150 psi (10.2 bars) for two hours. Differential dry-pipe valve clappers shall be left open during test to prevent damage. All aboveground piping leakage shall be stopped.

PNEUMATIC: Establish 40 psi (2.7 bars) air pressure and measure drop which shall not exceed 1-1/2 psi (0.1 bars) in 24 hours. Test pressure tanks at normal water level and air pressure and measure air pressure drop which shall not exceed 1-1/2 psi (0.1 bars) in 24 hours.

TESTS	ALL PIPING HYDROSTATICALLY TESTED AT ______ PSI FOR ______ HRS. DRY PIPING PNEUMATICALLY TESTED ☐ YES ☐ NO EQUIPMENT OPERATES PROPERLY ☐ YES ☐ NO	IF NO, STATE REASON
	DO YOU CERTIFY AS THE SPRINKLER CONTRACTOR THAT ADDITIVES AND CORROSIVE CHEMICALS, SODIUM SILICATE OR DERIVATIVES OF SODIUM SILICATE, BRINE, OR OTHER CORROSIVE CHEMICALS WERE NOT USED FOR TESTING SYSTEMS OR STOPPING LEAKS? ☐ YES ☐ NO	
	DRAIN TEST READING OF GAGE LOCATED NEAR WATER SUPPLY TEST CONNECTION: ______ PSI	RESIDUAL PRESSURE WITH VALVE IN TEST CONNECTION OPEN WIDE ______ PSI
	UNDERGROUND MAINS AND LEAD IN CONNECTIONS TO SYSTEM RISERS FLUSHED BEFORE CONNECTION MADE TO SPRINKLER PIPING. VERIFIED BY COPY OF THE U FORM NO. 85B ☐ YES ☐ NO FLUSHED BY INSTALLER OF UNDER-GROUND SPRINKLER PIPING ☐ YES ☐ NO	OTHER EXPLAIN

BLANK TESTING GASKETS	NUMBER USED	LOCATIONS	NUMBER REMOVED

WELDING	WELDED PIPING ☐ YES ☐ NO		
	IF YES . . .		
	DO YOU CERTIFY AS THE SPRINKLER CONTRACTOR THAT WELDING PROCEDURES COMPLY WITH THE REQUIREMENTS OF AT LEAST AWS D10.9, LEVEL AR-3		☐ YES ☐ NO
	DO YOU CERTIFY THAT THE WELDING WAS PERFORMED BY WELDERS QUALIFIED IN COMPLIANCE WITH THE REQUIREMENTS OF AT LEAST AWS D10.9, LEVEL AR-3		☐ YES ☐ NO
	DO YOU CERTIFY THAT WELDING WAS CARRIED OUT IN COMPLIANCE WITH A DOCUMENTED QUALITY CONTROL PROCEDURE TO INSURE THAT ALL DISCS ARE RETRIEVED, THAT OPENINGS IN PIPING ARE SMOOTH, THAT SLAG AND OTHER WELDING RESIDUE ARE REMOVED, AND THAT THE INTERNAL DIAMETERS OF PIPING ARE NOT PENETRATED		☐ YES ☐ NO
CUTOUTS (DISCS)	DO YOU CERTIFY THAT YOU HAVE A CONTROL FEATURE TO ENSURE THAT ALL CUTOUTS (DISCS) ARE RETRIEVED?		☐ YES ☐ NO
HYDRAULIC DATA NAMEPLATE	NAME PLATE PROVIDED ☐ YES ☐ NO	IF NO, EXPLAIN	
REMARKS	DATE LEFT IN SERVICE WITH ALL CONTROL VALVES OPEN:		
SIGNATURES	NAME OF SPRINKLER CONTRACTOR		
	TESTS WITNESSED BY		
	FOR PROPERTY OWNER (SIGNED)	TITLE	DATE
	FOR SPRINKLER CONTRACTOR (SIGNED)	TITLE	DATE

ADDITIONAL EXPLANATION AND NOTES

85A BACK

Figure 1-10.1(a) (continued) Contractor's Material and Test Certificate for Aboveground Piping.

CONTRACTOR'S MATERIAL & TEST CERTIFICATE FOR UNDERGROUND PIPING

PROCEDURE

Upon completion of work, inspection and tests shall be made by the contractor's representative and witnessed by an owner's representative. All defects shall be corrected and system left in service before contractor's personnel finally leave the job.

A certificate shall be filled out and signed by both representatives. Copies shall be prepared for approving authorities, owners, and contractor. It is understood the owner's representative's signature in no way prejudices any claim against contractor for faulty material, poor workmanship, or failure to comply with approving authority's requirements or local ordinances.

PROPERTY NAME		DATE
PROPERTY ADDRESS		
PLANS	ACCEPTED BY APPROVING AUTHORITIES (NAMES)	
	ADDRESS	
	INSTALLATION CONFORMS TO ACCEPTED PLANS EQUIPMENT USED IS APPROVED IF NO, STATE DEVIATIONS	☐ YES ☐ NO ☐ YES ☐ NO
INSTRUCTIONS	HAS PERSON IN CHARGE OF FIRE EQUIPMENT BEEN INSTRUCTED AS TO LOCATION OF CONTROL VALVES AND CARE AND MAINTENANCE OF THIS NEW EQUIPMENT? IF NO, EXPLAIN	☐ YES ☐ NO
	HAVE COPIES OF APPROPRIATE INSTRUCTIONS AND CARE AND MAINTENANCE CHARTS BEEN LEFT ON PREMISES? IF NO, EXPLAIN	☐ YES ☐ NO
LOCATION	SUPPLIES BUILDINGS	
	PIPE TYPES AND CLASS	TYPE JOINT

UNDERGROUND PIPES AND JOINTS	PIPE CONFORMS TO ______ STANDARD ☐ YES ☐ NO FITTINGS CONFORM TO ______ STANDARD ☐ YES ☐ NO IF NO, EXPLAIN
	JOINTS NEEDING ANCHORAGE CLAMPED, STRAPPED, OR BLOCKED IN ACCORDANCE WITH ______ STANDARD ☐ YES ☐ NO IF NO, EXPLAIN
TEST DESCRIPTION	FLUSHING. Flow the required rate until water is clear as indicated by no collection of foreign material in burlap bags at outlets such as hydrants and blow-offs. Flush at flows not less than 390 GPM (1476 L/min) for 4-inch pipe, 880 GPM (3331 L/min) for 6-inch pipe, 1560 GPM (5905 L/min) for 8-inch pipe, 2440 GPM (9235 L/min) for 10-inch pipe, and 3520 GPM (13323 L/min) for 12-inch pipe. When supply cannot produce stipulated flow rates, obtain maximum available. HYDROSTATIC. Hydrostatic tests shall be made at not less than 200 psi (13.8 bars) for two hours or 50 psi (3.4 bars) above static pressure in excess of 150 psi (10.3 bars) for two hours. LEAKAGE. New pipe laid with rubber gasketed joints shall, if the workmanship is satisfactory, have little or no leakage at the joints. The amount of leakage at the joints shall not exceed 2 qts. per hr. (1.89 L/h) per 100 joints irrespective of pipe diameter. The leakage shall be distributed over all joints. If such leakage occurs at a few joints the installation shall be considered unsatisfactory and necessary repairs made. The amount of allowable leakage specified above may be increased by 1 fl oz per in. valve diameter per hr. (30 mL/25 mm/h) for each metal seated valve isolating the test section. If dry barrel hydrants are tested with the main valve open, so the hydrants are under pressure, an additional 5 oz per minute (150 mL/min) leakage is permitted for each hydrant.
FLUSHING TESTS	NEW UNDERGROUND PIPING FLUSHED ACCORDING TO ______ STANDARD ☐ YES ☐ NO BY (COMPANY) IF NO, EXPLAIN
	HOW FLUSHING FLOW WAS OBTAINED ☐ PUBLIC WATER ☐ TANK OR RESERVOIR ☐ FIRE PUMP THROUGH WHAT TYPE OPENING ☐ HYDRANT BUTT. ☐ OPEN PIPE
	LEAD-INS FLUSHED ACCORDING TO ______ STANDARD ☐ YES ☐ NO BY (COMPANY) IF NO, EXPLAIN
	HOW FLUSHING FLOW WAS OBTAINED ☐ PUBLIC WATER ☐ TANK OR RESERVOIR ☐ FIRE PUMP THROUGH WHAT TYPE OPENING ☐ Y CONN. TO FLANGE & SPIGOT ☐ OPEN PIPE

85B(10-88) PRINTED IN USA (OVER)

Figure 1-10.1(b) (continued) Contractor's Material and Test Certificate for Underground Piping.

HYDROSTATIC TEST	ALL NEW UNDERGROUND PIPING HYDROSTATICALLY TESTED AT ______ PSI FOR ______ HOURS		JOINTS COVERED ☐ YES ☐ NO
LEAKAGE TEST	TOTAL AMOUNT OF LEAKAGE MEASURED ______ GALS. ______ HOURS		
	ALLOWABLE LEAKAGE ______ GALS. ______ HOURS		
HYDRANTS	NUMBER INSTALLED	TYPE AND MAKE	ALL OPERATE SATISFACTORILY ☐ YES ☐ NO
CONTROL VALVES	WATER CONTROL VALVES LEFT WIDE OPEN IF NO, STATE REASON		☐ YES ☐ NO
	HOSE THREADS OF FIRE DEPARTMENT CONNECTIONS AND HYDRANTS INTERCHANGEABLE WITH THOSE OF FIRE DEPARTMENT ANSWERING ALARM		☐ YES ☐ NO
REMARKS	DATE LEFT IN SERVICE		
SIGNATURES	NAME OF INSTALLING CONTRACTOR		
	TESTS WITNESSED BY		
	FOR PROPERTY OWNER (SIGNED)	TITLE	DATE
	FOR INSTALLING CONTRACTOR (SIGNED)	TITLE	DATE

ADDITIONAL EXPLANATION AND NOTES

Figure 1-10.1(b) (continued) Contractor's Material and Test Certificate for Underground Piping.

1-11.1.1 Provision shall be made for the disposal of water issuing from test outlets to avoid property damage.

1-11.2 Hydrostatic Tests.

1-11.2.1* All new systems including yard piping shall be hydrostatically tested at not less than 200 psi (13.8 bars) pressure for 2 hours, or at 50 psi (3.4 bars) in excess of the maximum pressure, when the maximum pressure to be maintained in the system is in excess of 150 psi (10.3 bars).

The test pressure shall be read from a gage located at the low elevation point of the individual system or portion of the system being tested.

Exception: At seasons of the year that will not permit testing with water an interim test may be conducted with air pressure of at least 40 psi (2.8 bars) allowed to stand for 24 hours. The standard hydrostatic test shall be conducted when weather permits.

1-11.2.2* Permissible Leakage. The inside sprinkler piping shall be installed in such a manner that there will be no visible leakage when the system is subjected to the hydrostatic pressure test. Refer to NFPA 24, *Standard for the Installation of Private Fire Service Mains and Their Appurtenances*, for permissible leakage in underground piping. The amount of leakage shall be measured by pumping from a calibrated container.

1-11.2.3 Fire Department Connection. Piping between the check valve in the fire department inlet pipe and the outside connection shall be tested in the same manner as the balance of the system.

1-11.2.4 Corrosive Chemicals. Additives and corrosive chemicals, sodium silicate or derivatives of sodium silicate, brine or other corrosive chemicals shall not be used for testing systems or stopping leaks.

1-11.2.5 Test Blanks. Whenever a test blank is used it shall be of the self-indicating type. Test blanks shall have red painted lugs protruding beyond the flange in such a way as to clearly indicate their presence. The installer shall have all test blanks numbered so as to keep track of their use and assure their removal after the work is completed.

1-11.3 Test of Dry-Pipe Systems.

1-11.3.1 Differential Dry-Pipe Valves. The clapper of a differential type dry-pipe valve shall be held off its seat during any test in excess of 50 psi (3.4 bars) to prevent damaging the valve.

1-11.3.2 Air Test. In dry-pipe systems an air pressure of 40 psi (2.8 bars) shall be pumped up, allowed to stand 24 hours, and all leaks that allow a loss of pressure over 1½ psi (0.1 bar) for the 24 hours shall be stopped.

1-11.3.3 Operating Test of Dry-Pipe Valve. A working test of the dry-pipe valve alone and with a quick-opening device, if installed, shall be made before acceptance by opening the system test connection. Trip and water delivery times shall be measured from the time the inspector's test connection is opened and shall be recorded using the Contractor's Material and Test Certificate for Aboveground Piping.

1-11.4 Tests of Drainage Facilities. Tests of drainage facilities shall be made while the control valve is wide open. The main drain valve shall be opened and remain open until the system pressure stabilizes. (*See 2-9.1.*)

1-11.5 Each pressure reducing valve shall be tested upon completion of the initial installation to ensure proper pressure reduction at both maximum and normal inlet pressures.

1-12 Operation of Sprinkler System Control Valves by Contractors. When work on a sprinkler system requires that a contractor operate a valve controlling water supplies to a sprinkler system, the contractor shall inform the owner so that the owner may follow the normal valve supervision procedure.

1-13 Units. Metric units of measurement in this standard are in accordance with the modernized metric system known as the International System of Units (SI). Two units (liter and bar), outside of but recognized by SI, are commonly used in international fire protection. These units are listed in Table 1-13 with conversion factors.

Table 1-13 Metric Units of Measurement

Name of Unit	Unit Symbol	Conversion Factor
liter	L	1 gal = 3.785 L
liter per minute per square meter	(L/min)/m^2	1 gpm/ft^2 = 40.746 (L/min)/m^2
millimeter per minute	1 mm/min	1 gpm/ft^2 = 40.746 mm/min
cubic decimeter	dm^3	1 gal = 3.785 dm^3
pascal	Pa	1 psi = 6894.757 Pa
bar	bar	1 psi = 0.0689 bar
bar	bar	1 bar = 10^5 Pa

For additional conversions and information see ASTM E380, *Standard for Metric Practice.*

1-13.1 If a value for measurement as given in this standard is followed by an equivalent value in other units, the first stated is to be regarded as the requirement. A given equivalent value may be approximate.

1-13.2 The conversion procedure for the SI units has been to multiply the quantity by the conversion factor and then round the result to the appropriate number of significant digits.

Chapter 2 Water Supplies

2-1* General Provisions. Every automatic sprinkler system shall have at least one automatic water supply.

2-2* Water Supply Requirements for Sprinkler Systems.

2-2.1 General.

2-2.1.1 Water supply requirement tables shall be used in determining the minimum water supply requirements for Light, Ordinary, and Extra Hazard Occupancies. Occupancy classification shall be determined from Section 1-7.

Exception No. 1: Water supply requirements for dwelling units protected by residential sprinklers shall be in accordance with 7-4.4 in wet systems only.

Exception No. 2: The water supply requirements for ESFR and large-drop sprinkler systems shall be in accordance with Chapter 9.

Exception No. 3: The water supply requirements for exposure protection systems shall be in accordance with Chapter 6.

Exception No. 4: For hazard classifications other than those indicated, see appropriate NFPA standards for design criteria. When other NFPA standards have developed sprinkler system design criteria, they shall take precedence.

(a) Table 2-2.1.1(a) shall be used to determine the minimum volume of water and pressure normally required for a pipe schedule sprinkler system. The table is to be used only with experienced judgment.

(b) Table 2-2.1.1(b) shall be used to determine the minimum volume of water and pressure normally required for a hydraulically designed sprinkler system.

2-2.1.2 The following shall be used in applying Table 2-2.1.1(b).

2-2.1.3 The water supply for sprinklers only shall be calculated either from the area/density curves in Figure 2-2.1.1(b) in accordance with 2-2.2 or be based upon the room design method in accordance with 2-2.3.1 at the discretion of the designer.

2-2.2* Area/Density Method.

2-2.2.1 The water supply requirement for sprinklers only shall be calculated from the density curves in Figure 2-2.1.1(b). The calculations shall satisfy a single point on the appropriate design curve. It is not necessary to meet all points on the selected curve.

2-2.2.2 The densities and areas provided in Figure 2-2.1.1(b) are for use only with standard response sprinklers. For use of other types of sprinklers see 4-1.1.3.

2-2.2.3 For dry-pipe systems, increase the area of sprinkler operation by 30 percent without revising density.

2-2.2.4 When high-temperature sprinklers are used for Extra Hazard Occupancies, the area of sprinkler operation may be reduced by 25 percent without revising the density, but to not less than 2000 sq ft (186 m^2).

2-2.3* Room Design Method.

2-2.3.1 The water supply requirements for sprinklers only

(Continued)

Table 2-2.1.1(a) Guide to Water Supply Requirements for Pipe Schedule Sprinkler Systems

Occupancy Classification	Residual Pressure Required (see Note 1)	Acceptable Flow at Base of Riser (see Note 2)	Duration in Minutes
Light Hazard	15 psi	500-750 gpm (see Note 3)	30-60
Ordinary Hazard (Group 1)	15 psi or higher	700-1000 gpm	60-90
Ordinary Hazard (Group 2)	15 psi or higher	850-1500 gpm	60-90
Ordinary Hazard (Group 3)	Pressure and flow requirements for sprinklers and hose streams to be determined by authority having jurisdiction.		60-120
High-Piled Storage *(see 4-1.3.10)*	Pressure and flow requirements for sprinklers and hose streams to be determined by authority having jurisdiction. (*See Chapter 7 and NFPA 231 and NFPA 231C.*)		
High-Rise Buildings	Pressure and flow requirements for sprinklers and hose streams to be determined by authority having jurisdiction.		
Extra Hazard	Pressure and flow requirements for sprinklers and hose streams to be determined by authority having jurisdiction.		

For SI Units: 1 psi = 0.0689 bar; 1 gpm = 3.785 L/min.

Notes:

1. The pressure required at the base of the sprinkler riser(s) is defined as the residual pressure required at the elevation of the highest sprinkler plus the pressure required to reach this elevation.

2. The lower figure is the minimum flow including hose streams ordinarily acceptable for pipe schedule sprinkler systems. The higher flow should normally suffice for all cases under each group.

3. The requirement may be reduced to 250 gpm if building area is limited by size compartmentation or if building (including roof) is noncombustible construction.

Table 2-2.1.1(b) Table and Design Curves for Determining Density, Area of Sprinkler Operation, and Water Supply Requirements for Hydraulically Designed Sprinkler Systems

Minimum Water Supply Requirements

Hazard Classification	Sprinklers Only—gpm	Inside Hose—gpm	Total Combined Inside and Outside Hose—gpm	Duration in Minutes
Light	See 2-2.1.3	0, 50, or 100	100	30
Ord.—Gp. 1	See 2-2.1.3	0, 50, or 100	250	60-90
Ord.—Gp. 2	See 2-2.1.3	0, 50, or 100	250	60-90
Ord.—Gp. 3	See 2-2.1.3	0, 50, or 100	500	60-120
Ex. Haz.—Gp. 1	See 2-2.1.3	0, 50, or 100	500	90-120
Ex. Haz.—Gp. 2	See 2-2.1.3	0, 50, or 100	1000	120

For SI Units: 1 gpm = 3.785 L/min.

(Continued)

shall be based upon the room which creates the greatest demand. The density selected shall be that from Figure 2-2.1.1(b) corresponding to the room size. If the room is smaller than the smallest area shown in the applicable curve in Figure 2-2.1.1(b) see 2-2.4(a). If the room is larger than the largest area shown in the applicable curve, use the density for the largest area shown for all sprinklers in the room. All rooms shall be enclosed with construction having a fire-resistance rating equal to the water supply duration indicated in Table 2-2.1.1(b) with minimum protection of openings as follows:

(a) Light Hazard—automatic or self-closing doors.

Exception: When openings are not protected, calculations shall include the sprinklers in the room plus two sprinklers in the communicating space nearest each such unprotected opening unless the communicating space has only one sprinkler, in which case calculations shall be extended to the operation of that sprinkler. The selection of the room and communicating space sprinklers to be calculated shall be that which produces the greatest hydraulic demand.

(b) Ordinary and Extra Hazard—automatic or self-closing doors with appropriate fire-resistance ratings for the enclosure.

Density Curves

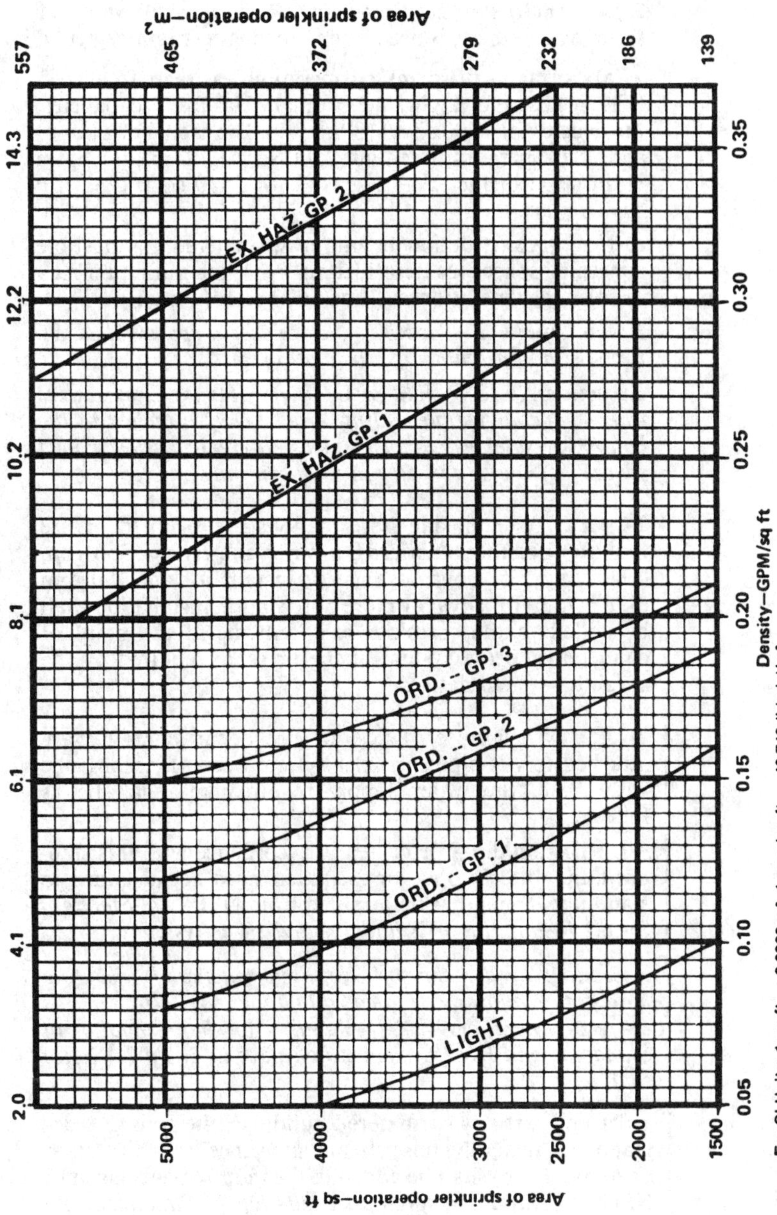
Density—(L/min) /m²
2.0
4.1
6.1
8.1
10.2
12.2
14.3
Area of sprinkler operation—m²
557
465
372
279
232
186
139
EX. HAZ. GP. 2
EX. HAZ. GP. 1
ORD. -- GP. 3
ORD. -- GP. 2
ORD. -- GP. 1
LIGHT
0.05
0.10
0.15
0.20
0.25
0.30
0.35
Density—GPM/sq ft
5000
4000
3000
2500
2000
1500
Area of sprinkler operation—sq ft

For SI Units: 1 sq ft = 0.0920 m²; 1 gpm/sq ft = 40.746 (L/min)/m².

Figure 2-2.1.1(b).

2-2.4* **Additional Requirements.** Regardless of which of the above methods is used, the following restrictions apply:

(a) For areas of sprinkler operation less than 1500 sq ft (139 m^2) used for Light and Ordinary Hazard Occupancies, the density for 1500 sq ft (139 m^2) shall be used. For areas of sprinkler operation less than 2500 sq ft (232 m^2) for Extra Hazard Occupancies, the density for 2500 sq ft (232 m^2) shall be used.

(b) For construction having unsprinklered combustible concealed spaces (as described in 4-4.4) the minimum area of sprinkler operation shall be 3000 sq ft (279 m^2).

Exception No. 1: Combustible concealed spaces filled entirely with noncombustible insulation.

Exception No. 2: Light or Ordinary Hazard Occupancies where noncombustible ceilings are directly attached to the bottom of solid wood joists so as to create enclosed joist spaces, each less than 160 cu ft (4.8 m^3) in volume.

2-2.4.1* When inside hose stations are planned or are required by other standards, a water allowance of 50 gpm (189 L/min) for a one hose station installation and 100 gpm (378 L/min) for a two or more hose station installation shall be added to the sprinkler requirements at the point of connection to the system at the pressure required by the sprinkler system design.

2-2.4.2 When hose valves for fire department use are attached to wet-pipe sprinkler system risers in accordance with 3-3.8, the water supply requirements shall be as follows:

(a) For buildings protected in accordance with this standard, the water supply for sprinklers need not be added to standpipe demand as determined from NFPA 14, *Standard for the Installation of Standpipe and Hose Systems.*

Exception: When the sprinkler system demand, including hose stream allowance indicated in Table 2-2.1.1(b), exceeds the requirements of NFPA 14, Standard for the Installation of Standpipe and Hose Systems, the values in Table 2-2.1.1(b) shall be used.

(b) For partially sprinklered buildings, the sprinkler demand, not including hose stream allowance, as indicated in Table 2-2.1.1(b) shall be added to the requirements given in NFPA 14, *Standard for the Installation of Standpipe and Hose Systems.*

2-2.4.3 Water demand of sprinklers installed in racks shall be added to the ceiling sprinkler water demand at the point of connection. Demands shall be balanced to the higher pressure.

2-2.4.4 Water allowance for outside hose shall be added to the sprinkler and inside hose requirement at the connection to the city water main, or at a yard hydrant, whichever is closer to the system riser.

2-2.4.5 The lower duration figures in Tables 2-2.1.1(a) and 2-2.1.1(b) are ordinarily acceptable where remote station waterflow alarm service or equivalent is provided.

2-2.4.6 When pumps, gravity tanks, or pressure tanks supply sprinklers only, requirements for inside and outside hose need not be considered in determining the size of such pumps or tanks.

2-3 Connections to Water Works Systems.

2-3.1 Acceptability.

2-3.1.1* General. A connection to a reliable water works system shall be an acceptable water supply source. The volume and pressure of a public water supply shall be determined from waterflow test data.

2-3.1.2 Meters. Meters are not recommended for use on sprinkler systems; however, where required by other authorities, they shall be of an approved type.

2-3.2* Capacity. The connection and arrangement of underground supply piping shall be capable of supplying the volume as required in Table 2-2.1.1(a) or 2-2.1.1(b). Pipe size shall be at least as large as the system riser. (*See NFPA 24, Standard for the Installation of Private Fire Service Mains and Their Appurtenances.*)

Exception: Unlined cast or ductile iron pipe shall not be less than 4 in. (102 mm) in size.

2-4 Gravity Tanks.

2-4.1 Acceptability. An elevated tank sized in accordance with Table 2-2.1.1(a) or 2-2.1.1(b) shall be an acceptable water supply source. (*See NFPA 22, Standard for Water Tanks for Private Fire Protection.*)

2-4.2 Capacity and Elevation. The capacity and elevation of the tank and the arrangement of the underground supply piping shall provide the volume and pressure required by Table 2-2.1.1(a) or 2-2.1.1(b) designs.

2-5 Pumps.

2-5.1* Acceptability. A single automatically controlled fire pump sized in accordance with Table 2-2.1.1(a) or 2-2.1.1(b) supplied under positive head shall be an acceptable water supply source. (*See NFPA 20, Standard for the Installation of Centrifugal Fire Pumps.*)

2-5.2* Supervision. When a single fire pump constitutes the sole sprinkler supply, it shall be provided with supervisory service from an approved central station, proprietary, remote station system or equivalent.

2-6 Pressure Tanks.

2-6.1 Acceptability.

2-6.1.1 A pressure tank sized in accordance with Table 2-2.1.1(a) or 2-2.1.1(b) is an acceptable water supply source. (*See NFPA 22, Standard for Water Tanks for Private Fire Protection.*)

2-6.1.2 Pressure tanks shall be provided with an approved means for automatically maintaining the required air pressure. When a pressure tank is the sole water supply there shall also be provided an approved trouble alarm to indicate low air pressure and low water level with the alarm supplied from an electrical branch circuit independent of the air compressor.

2-6.1.3 Pressure tanks shall not be used to supply other than sprinklers and hand hose attached to sprinkler piping.

2-6.2 Capacity. The required water capacity of a pressure tank shall be in accordance with 2-2.1.1 and shall include the extra capacity needed to fill dry-pipe or preaction systems when installed. The total volume shall be based on the water capacity, plus the air capacity required by 2-6.3.

2-6.3* Water Level and Air Pressure. Unless otherwise approved by the authority having jurisdiction, the pressure tank shall be kept two-thirds full of water, and an air pressure of at least 75 psi (5.2 bars) by the gage shall be maintained. When the bottom of the tank is located below the highest sprinklers served, the air pressure by the gage shall be at least 75 psi (5.2 bars) plus three times the pressure caused by the column of water in the sprinkler system above the tank bottom.

2-7 Fire Department Connections.

2-7.1* A fire department connection shall be provided as described in this section.

Exception No. 1: The fire department connection may be omitted for systems having 20 sprinklers or less.

Exception No. 2: When permission of the authority having jurisdiction has been obtained for its omission.

2-7.2* Size. Pipe size shall be 4 in. (102 mm) for fire engine connections and 6 in. (152 mm) for fire boat connections.

Exception No. 1: For hydraulically calculated systems, fire department connection pipe serving one system riser may be as small as the system riser.

Exception No. 2: A single fire department hose connection may be piped to a 3-in. (76-mm) or smaller connection.

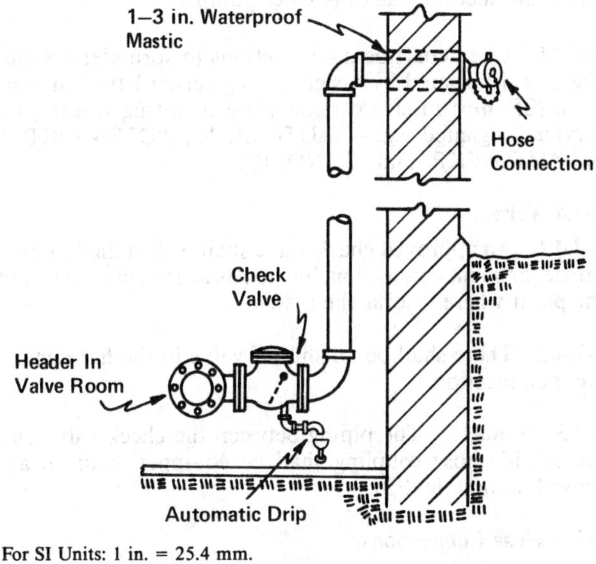
1–3 in. Waterproof Mastic
Hose Connection
Check Valve
Header In Valve Room
Automatic Drip

For SI Units: 1 in. = 25.4 mm.

Figure 2-7.1 Fire Department Connection.

2-7.3* Arrangement. (*See 3-9.2.5 and 3-9.2.6.*)

2-7.3.1 The fire department connection shall be made on the system side of a check valve in the water supply piping.

2-7.3.2 On wet-pipe systems with a single riser the connection shall be made on the system side of approved indicating, check, and alarm valves to the riser, unless the system is supplied by a fire department pumper connection in the yard. (*See 3-9.2.6.*)

2-7.3.3 On dry-pipe systems with a single riser the connection shall be made between the approved indicating valve and the dry-pipe valve, unless the system is supplied by a fire department pumper connection in the yard.

2-7.3.4 On systems with two or more risers, the connection shall be made on the system side of all shutoff valves controlling other water supplies, but on the supply side of the riser shutoff valves so that, with any one riser off, the connection will feed the remaining sprinklers, unless the sprinklers are supplied by a fire department pumper connection in the yard.

2-7.3.5 Fire department connections shall not be connected on the suction side of booster pumps.

2-7.3.6 Fire department connections to sprinkler systems shall be designated by a sign having raised letters at least 1 in. (25 mm) in size cast on plate or fitting reading for service designated: e.g.—"AUTOSPKR.," "OPEN SPKR.," or "AUTOSPKR. and STANDPIPE."

2-7.4 Valves.

2-7.4.1 An approved check valve shall be installed in each fire department connection, located as near as practicable to the point where it joins the system.

2-7.4.2 There shall be no shutoff valve in the fire department connection.

2-7.5 Drainage. The piping between the check valve and the outside hose coupling shall be equipped with an approved automatic drip.

2-7.6 Hose Connections.

2-7.6.1 The fire department connection(s) shall be internal threaded swivel fitting(s) having the NH standard thread, at least one of which shall be 2.5 — 7.5 NH standard thread, as specified in NFPA 1963, *Standard for Screw Threads and Gaskets for Fire Hose Connections.*

Exception: When local fire department connections do not conform to NFPA 1963, the authority having jurisdiction shall designate the connection to be used.

2-7.6.2 Hose connections shall be equipped with listed plugs or caps.

2-8 Arrangement of Water Supply Connections.

2-8.1 Connection Between Underground and Aboveground Piping. The connection between the system piping and underground piping shall be made with a suitable transition piece and shall be properly strapped or fastened by approved devices. The transition piece shall be protected against possible damage from corrosive agents, solvent attack, or mechanical damage.

2-8.2* Connection Passing Through or Under Foundation Walls. When system piping pierces a foundation wall below grade or is located under the foundation wall, clearance shall be provided to prevent breakage of the piping due to building settlement.

2-9 Water Supply Test Connections and Gages.

2-9.1* Test Connections. Test connections, which may also be used as drain pipes, shall be provided at locations that will permit flow tests to be made to determine whether water supplies and connections are in order. Such test connections shall be not less than the sizes specified in 3-6.2 and equipped with a shutoff valve. They shall be so installed that the valve may be opened wide for a sufficient time to assure a proper test without causing water damage. (*See 3-6.2 and 3-6.4.*)

2-9.2 Gages.

2-9.2.1 A pressure gage with a connection not smaller than ¼ in. (6.4 mm) shall be installed on the riser or feed main at or near each test connection. This gage connection shall be equipped with a shutoff valve and with provision for draining.

2-9.2.2 The required pressure gages shall be of an approved type and shall have a maximum limit not less than twice the normal working pressure at the point where installed. They shall be installed to permit removal, and shall be located where they will not be subject to freezing.

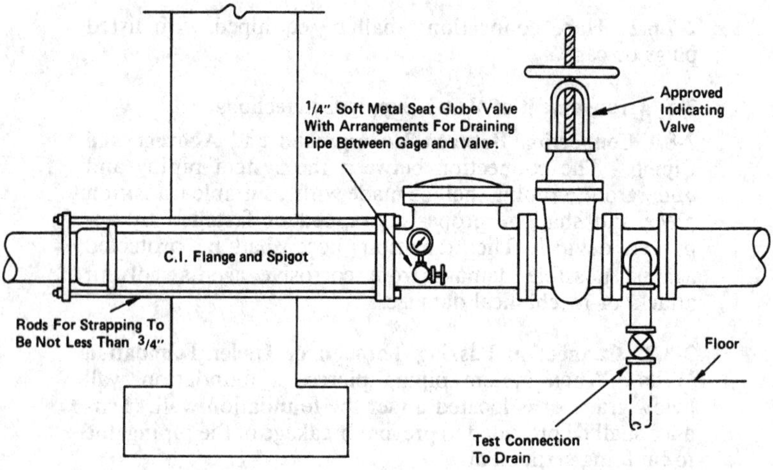

1/4" Soft Metal Seat Globe Valve With Arrangements For Draining Pipe Between Gage and Valve.
Approved Indicating Valve
C.I. Flange and Spigot
Rods For Strapping To Be Not Less Than 3/4"
Floor
Test Connection To Drain

For SI Units: 1 in. = 25.4 mm.

Figure 2-9.1 Water Supply Connection with Test Connection.

Chapter 3 System Components

3-1 Piping.

3-1.1 Piping Specifications.

3-1.1.1 Pipe or tube used in sprinkler systems shall meet or exceed the standards in Table 3-1.1.1 or be in accordance with 3-1.1.2 through 3-1.1.6. Pipe and tube used in sprinkler systems shall be designed to withstand a working pressure of not less than 175 psi (12.1 bars).

Table 3-1.1.1 Pipe or Tube Materials and Dimensions

Materials and Dimensions	Standard
Ferrous Piping (Welded and Seamless)	
†Spec. for Black and Hot-Dipped Zinc Coated (Galvanized) Welded and Seamless Steel Pipe for Fire Protection Use	ASTM A795
†Spec. for Welded and Seamless Steel Pipe	ANSI/ASTM A53
Wrought Steel Pipe	ANSI B36.10M
Spec. for Elec.-Resistance Welded Steel Pipe	ASTM A135
Copper Tube (Drawn, Seamless)	
†Spec. for Seamless Copper Tube	ASTM B75
†Spec. for Seamless Copper Water Tube	ASTM B88
Spec. for General Requirements for Wrought Seamless Copper and Copper-Alloy Tube	ASTM B251
Brazing Filler Metal (Classification BCuP-3 or BCuP-4)	AWS A5.8
Solder Metal, 95-5 (Tin-Antimony-Grade 95TA)	ASTM B32

†Denotes pipe or tubing suitable for bending (*see 3-1.1.7*) according to ASTM standards.

3-1.1.2* When welded and seamless steel pipe listed in Table 3-1.1.1 is used and joined by welding as referenced in 3-7.2 or by roll grooved pipe and couplings as referenced in 3-7.3, the minimum nominal wall thickness for pressures up to 300 psi (20.7 bars) shall be in accordance with Schedule 10 for sizes up to 5 in. (127 mm); 0.134 in. (3.40 mm) for 6 in. (152 mm); and 0.188 in. (4.78 mm) for 8- and 10-in. (203- and 254-mm) pipe; or as modified in 3-1.1.5, or as defined in 3-1.1.6.

3-1.1.3 When steel pipe listed in Table 3-1.1.1 is used and joined by threaded fittings referenced in 3-7.1 or by couplings used with pipe having cut grooves, the minimum wall thickness shall be in accordance with Schedule 30 [in sizes 8 in. (203 mm) and larger] or Schedule 40 [in sizes less than 8 in. (203 mm)] pipe for pressures up to 300 psi (20.7 bars).

3-1.1.4* Copper tube as specified in the standards listed in Table 3-1.1.1, used in sprinkler systems, shall have a wall thickness of Type K, L, or M.

3-1.1.5* Other types of pipe or tube may be used if investigated and listed for this service and installed in accordance with their listing limitations, including installation instructions. Pipe or tube shall not be listed for portions of an occupancy classification.

3-1.1.6 Whenever the word pipe is used in this standard it shall be understood to also mean tube.

3-1.1.7 Pipe Bending. Bending of steel pipe (Schedule 40) and copper tube (Types K and L) may be accomplished when bends are made in conformance with good installation practices and show no kinks, ripples, distortions, reduction in diameter, or any noticeable deviations from round. The minimum radius of a bend shall be 6 pipe diameters for pipe sizes 2 in. (51 mm) and smaller, and 5 pipe diameters for pipe sizes 2½ in. (64 mm) and larger.

3-2* Definitions. (*See Figure A-3-2.*)

Risers. The vertical pipes in a sprinkler system.

System Riser. The aboveground supply pipe directly connected to the water supply.

Feed Mains. Mains supplying risers or cross mains.

Cross Mains. Pipes directly supplying the lines in which the sprinklers are placed.

Branch Lines. Lines of pipe, from the point of attachment to the cross main (or similar connection) to the end sprinkler, in which the sprinklers are directly placed.

3-3 Special Provisions Applicable to Piping.

3-3.1 Rack Storage. For sprinklers in storage racks see NFPA 231C, *Standard for Rack Storage of Materials.*

3-3.2* Provision for Flushing Systems. All sprinkler systems shall be arranged for flushing. Readily removable fittings shall be provided at the end of all cross mains. All cross mains shall terminate in 1¼-in. (33-mm) or larger pipe. All branch lines on gridded systems shall be arranged to facilitate flushing.

3-3.3 Stair Towers. Stairs, towers, or other construction with incomplete floors, if piped on independent risers, shall be treated as one area with reference to pipe sizes.

3-3.4 Return Bends. Return bends shall be used when pendent sprinklers are supplied from a raw water source, mill pond, or from open-top reservoirs. Return bends shall be connected to the top of branch lines in order to avoid accumulation of sediment in the drop nipples.

Exception No. 1: Return bends are not required for deluge systems.

Exception No. 2: Return bends are not required when dry-pendent sprinklers are used.

3-3.5 Piping to Sprinklers Below Ceilings.

3-3.5.1 In new installations expected to supply sprinklers below a ceiling, minimum 1 in. (25 mm) outlets shall be provided.

Exception: Hexagonal bushings may be utilized to accommodate the temporary sprinklers and are to be removed with the sprinklers.

3-3.5.2 In revamping existing systems, a nipple not exceeding 4 in. (102 mm) in length and of the same pipe thread size as the sprinkler being removed may be used. All other piping shall be 1 in. (25 mm) which supplies a single sprinkler in an area.

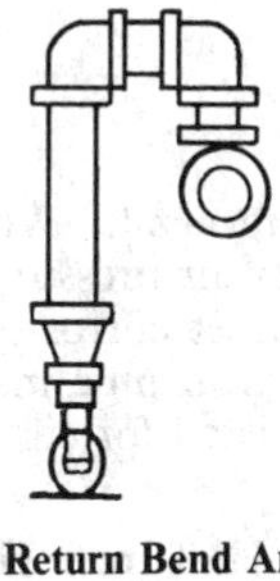

Figure 3-3.4 Return Bend Arrangement.

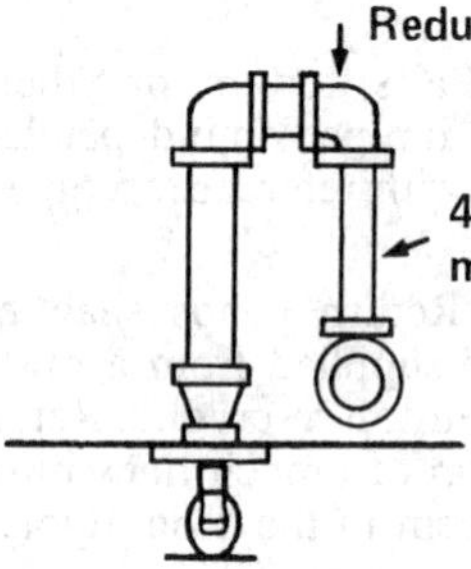
Reducing elbow
4″ length maximum

Figure 3-3.5.2(a) Nipple and Reducing Elbow Supplying Sprinkler Below Ceiling.

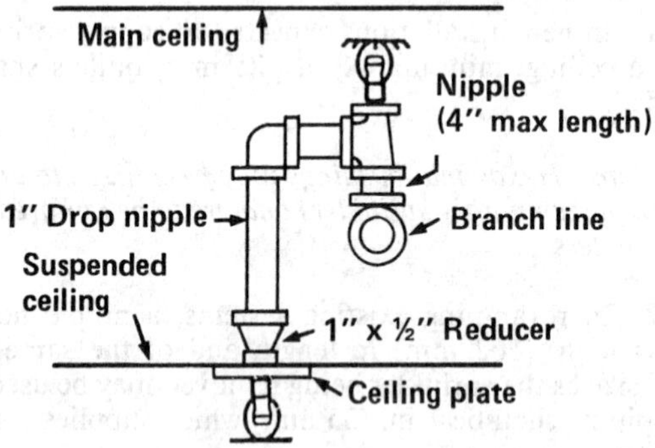
Main ceiling
Nipple (4″ max length)
1″ Drop nipple
Branch line
Suspended ceiling
1″ x ½″ Reducer
Ceiling plate

Figure 3-3.5.2(b) Sprinklers in Concealed Space and Below Ceiling.

3-3.6 Dry-Pipe Underground. When necessary to place pipe that will be under air pressure underground, the pipe shall be protected against corrosion (*see 3-5.2*), or unprotected cast or ductile iron pipe may be used when joined with a gasketed joint listed for air service underground.

3-3.7* One and One-Half-Inch Hose Connections. One

and one-half-inch [1½-in. (38-mm)] hose used for fire purposes only may be connected to wet sprinkler systems only, subject to the following restrictions:

(a) Hose station's supply pipes shall not be connected to any pipe smaller than 2½ in. (64 mm).

Exception: For hydraulically designed loops and grids the minimum size pipe between the hose station's supply pipe and the source may be 2 in. (51 mm).

(b) For piping serving a single hose station, pipe shall be minimum 1 in. (25 mm) for horizontal runs up to 20 ft (6.1 m), minimum 1¼ in. (33 mm) for the entire run for runs between 20 and 80 ft (6.1 and 24.4 m), and minimum 1½ in. (38 mm) for the entire run for runs greater than 80 ft (24.4 m). For piping serving multiple hose stations, runs shall be a minimum of 1½ in. (38 mm) throughout.

(c) Piping shall be at least 1 in. (25 mm) for vertical runs.

(d) When the pressure at any hose station outlet exceeds 100 psi (6.9 bars), an approved device shall be installed at the outlet to reduce the pressure at the outlet to 100 psi (6.9 bars).

3-3.8* Hose Connections for Fire Department Use. In buildings of Light or Ordinary Hazard Occupancy, 2½-in. (64-mm) hose valves for fire department use may be attached to wet-pipe sprinkler system risers. (*See 2-2.4.2.*) The following restrictions apply:

(a) Sprinklers shall be under separate floor control valves.

(b) The minimum size of the riser shall be 4 in. (102 mm) unless hydraulic calculations indicate a smaller size riser will satisfy sprinkler and hose stream demands.

(c) Each combined sprinkler and standpipe riser shall be equipped with a riser control valve to permit isolating a riser without interrupting the supply to other risers from the same source of supply.

(d) For fire department connections serving standpipe and sprinkler systems, refer to Section 2-7.

3-4 System Test Connections.

3-4.1 Wet Systems.

3-4.1.1* A test connection not less than 1 in. (25 mm) in diameter, terminating in a smooth bore corrosion-resistant orifice, giving a flow equivalent to one sprinkler of a type having the smallest orifice installed on the particular system, shall be provided to test each waterflow alarm device for each system. The test connection valve shall be readily accessible. The discharge shall be to the outside, to a drain connection capable of accepting full flow under system pressure or to another location where water damage will not result.

3-4.2* Dry-Pipe Systems. A test connection not less than 1 in. (25 mm) in diameter, terminating in a smooth bore corrosion-resistant orifice to provide a flow equivalent to one sprinkler of a type installed on the particular system, shall be installed on the end of the most distant sprinkler pipe in the upper story and be equipped with a readily accessible 1-in. (25-mm) shutoff valve and plug, at least one of which shall be brass. In lieu of a plug, a nipple and cap may be used.

3-4.3 Preaction Systems. A test connection shall be used on a preaction system using supervisory air.

3-4.4 Deluge Systems. A test connection is not required on a deluge system.

3-5* Protection of Piping.

3-5.1 Protection of Piping Against Freezing.

3-5.1.1 When portions of systems are subject to freezing and temperatures cannot be reliably maintained at or above 40°F (4°C) sprinklers shall be installed as a dry-pipe or preaction system.

Exception: Small unheated areas may be protected by antifreeze systems. (See Section 5-5.)

3-5.1.2* When water-filled supply pipes, risers, system risers, or feed mains pass through open areas, cold rooms, passageways, or other areas exposed to freezing, the pipe shall be protected against freezing by insulating coverings, frostproof casings, or other reliable means capable of maintaining a minimum temperature of 40°F (4°C).

3-5.2 Protection of Piping Against Corrosion.

3-5.2.1* When corrosive conditions are known to exist due to moisture or fumes from corrosive chemicals, or both, types of piping, fittings, and hangers that resist corrosion shall be used or a protective coating shall be applied to all unprotected exposed surfaces of the sprinkler system to resist corrosion. (*See 3-11.4.*)

3-5.2.2 When water supplies are known to have unusual corrosive properties and threaded or cut grooved steel pipe is to be used, wall thickness shall be in accordance with Schedule 30 [in sizes 8 in. (203 mm) or larger] or Schedule 40 [in sizes less than 8 in. (203 mm)].

3-5.2.3* Steel pipe, when exposed to weather, shall be externally galvanized or otherwise protected against corrosion.

3-5.2.4 When steel pipe is used underground as a connection from a system to sprinklers in a detached building, the pipe shall be protected against corrosion before being buried.

3-5.3 Protection of Piping Against Damage Where Subject to Earthquakes.

3-5.3.1* General. Sprinkler systems shall be protected to minimize or prevent pipe breakage where subject to earthquakes in accordance with the requirements of 3-5.3.

Exception: Alternative methods of providing earthquake protection of sprinkler systems based on a dynamic seismic analysis certified by a registered professional engineer such that system performance will be at least equal to that of the building structure under expected seismic forces.

3-5.3.2* Couplings. Listed flexible pipe couplings joining grooved end pipe shall be provided as flexure joints to allow individual sections of piping 3½ in. (89 mm) or larger to move differentially with the individual sections of the building to which it is attached. Couplings shall be arranged to coincide with structural separations within a building. They shall be installed:

(a) Within 24 in. (610 mm) of the top and bottom of all risers.

Exception No. 1: In risers less than 3 ft (0.9 m) in length flexible couplings may be omitted.

Exception No. 2: In risers 3 to 7 ft (0.9 to 2.1 m) in length, one flexible coupling is adequate.

(b) At the ceiling of each story in multistory buildings.

(c) On one side of concrete or masonry walls within 3 ft (0.9 m) of the wall surface.

(d)* At or near building expansion joints.

(e) At the top of drops to hose lines, rack sprinklers, and mezzanines, regardless of pipe size.

(f) At the top of drops exceeding 15 ft (4.6 m) in length to sprinklers or portions of systems, regardless of pipe size.

3-5.3.3* Swing Joints. Swing joints assembled with flexible fittings shall be installed where sprinkler piping, regardless of size, crosses building seismic joints.

3-5.3.4* Clearance. Clearance shall be provided around all piping extending through walls, floors, platforms, and foundations, including drains, fire department connections, and other auxiliary piping.

(a) Minimum clearance on all sides shall be not less than 1 in. (25 mm) for pipes 1 in. (25 mm) through 3½ in. (89 mm) and 2 in. (51 mm) for pipe sizes 4 in. (102 mm) and larger.

Exception No. 1: When clearance is provided by a pipe sleeve, a nominal diameter 2 in. (51 mm) larger than the nominal diameter of the pipe is acceptable for pipe sizes 1 in. (25 mm) through 3½ in. (89 mm) and the clearance provided by a pipe sleeve of nominal diameter 4 in. (102 mm) larger than the nominal diameter of the pipe is acceptable for pipe sizes 4 in. (102 mm) and larger.

Exception No. 2: No clearance is necessary for piping passing through gypsum board or equally frangible construction which is not required to have a fire-resistance rating.

Exception No. 3: No clearance is necessary if flexible couplings or swing joints are located within 1 ft (0.3 m) of each side of a wall.

(b) When required the clearance shall be filled with a flexible material such as mastic.

3-5.3.5 Sway Bracing.

3-5.3.5.1* Both lateral and longitudinal sway braces shall be sized and fastened such that the horizontal loads assigned to the braces in Table 3-5.3.5.1(1) do not exceed the allowable loads on the braces as shown in Table 3-5.3.5.1(2) and the allowable loads on fasteners as shown in Table 3-5.3.5.1(3). Sway bracing shall be tight and concentric. All parts and fittings of a brace shall lie in a straight line to avoid eccentric loadings on fittings and fasteners. For longitudinal braces only, the brace may be connected to a tab welded to the pipe in conformance with 3-7.2.

Exception: In lieu of using Table 3-5.3.5.1(1), horizontal loads for braces may be determined by analysis. Sway braces shall be designed to withstand a force in tension or compression equivalent to not less than half the weight of water-filled piping. For lateral braces, the load shall include all branch lines and mains within the zone of influence of the brace. For longitudinal braces, the load shall include all mains within the zone of influence of the brace. For individual braces the slenderness ratio l/r shall not exceed 200, where l is the length of the brace and r is the least radius of gyration, both in inches.

Table 3-5.3.5.1(1) Assigned Load Table
(Based on half the weight of the water-filled pipe)

Spacing of Lateral Braces (ft)	Spacing of Longitudinal Braces** (ft)	Assigned Load for Pipe Size to be Braced (lb) 2	2½	3	4	5	6	8
10	20	380	395	410	435	470	655	915
20	40	760	785	815	870	940	1305	1830
25	50	950	980	1020	1090	1175	1630	2290
30	60	1140	1180	1225	1305	1410	1960	2745
40	80	1515	1570	1630	1740	1880	2610	3660
50*		1895	1965	2035	2175	2350	3260	4575

*Permitted only under Exception No. 4 to 3-5.3.5.4.

**If branch lines are provided with lateral bracing or hung with U-hooks bent out at least 10 degrees from vertical, half the assigned load may be used for longitudinal braces.

Table 3-5.3.5.1(2)

Shape and Size	Least Radius of Gyration	Maximum Length for *l*/r—200	Maximum Horizontal Load (lb) 30° Angle From Vertical	45° Angle From Vertical	60° Angle From Vertical
Pipe (Schedule 40)	$= \frac{\sqrt{r_0^2 + r_1^2}}{2}$				
1 in.	.42	7′0″	1767	2500	3061
1¼ in.	.54	9′0″	2393	3385	4145
1½ in.	.623	10′4″	2858	4043	4955
2 in.	.787	13′1″	3828	5414	6630
Pipe (Schedule 10)	$= \frac{\sqrt{r_0^2 + r_1^2}}{2}$				
1 in.	.43	7′2″	1477	2090	2559
1¼ in.	.55	9′2″	1900	2687	3291
1½ in.	.634	10′7″	2194	3103	3800
2 in.	.802	13′4″	2771	3926	4803
Angles					
1½ × 1½ × ¼	.292	4′10″	2461	3481	4263
2 × 2 × ¼	.391	6′6″	3356	4746	5813
2½ × 2 × ¼	.424	7′0″	3792	5363	6569
2½ × 2½ × ¼	.491	8′2″	4257	6021	7374
3 × 2½ × ¼	.528	8′10″	4687	6628	8118
3 × 3 × ¼	.592	9′10″	5152	7286	8923

(Continued)

Table 3-5.3.5.1(2) — *(Continued)*

Shape and Size	Least Radius of Gyration	Maximum Length for l/r—200	Maximum Horizontal Load (lb) 30° Angle From Vertical	45° Angle From Vertical	60° Angle From Vertical
Rods	$= \frac{r}{2}$				
⅜	.094	1′6″	395	559	685
½	.125	2′6″	702	993	1217
⅝	.156	2′7″	1087	1537	1883
¾	.188	3′1″	1580	2235	2737
⅞	.219	3′7″	2151	3043	3726
Flats	= 0.29 h (where h is smaller of two side dimensions)				
1½ × ¼	.0725	1′2″	1118	1581	1936
2 × ¼	.0725	1′2″	1789	2530	3098
2 × ⅜	.109	1′9″	2683	3795	4648

Table 3-5.3.5.1(3)
Maximum Loads for Various Types of Fasteners to Structure

NOTE: Loads (given in pounds) are keyed to vertical angles of braces and orientation of connecting surface. These values are based on concentric loadings of the fastener. Use figures to determine proper reference within table. For angles between those shown, use most restrictive case. Braces should not be attached to light structure members.

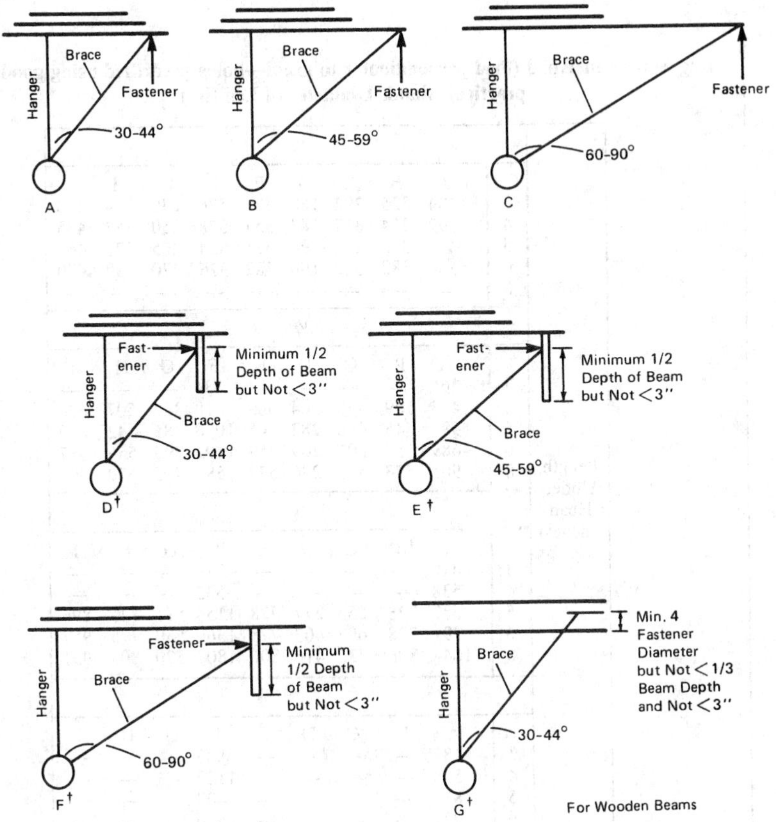
Hanger
Brace
Fastener
30-44°
A
Hanger
Brace
Fastener
45-59°
B
Hanger
Brace
Fastener
60-90°
C
Fast-ener
Minimum 1/2 Depth of Beam but Not <3"
Hanger
Brace
30-44°
D†
Fast-ener
Minimum 1/2 Depth of Beam but Not <3"
Hanger
Brace
45-59°
E†
Fastener
Minimum 1/2 Depth of Beam but Not <3"
Hanger
Brace
60-90°
F†
Min. 4 Fastener Diameter but Not <1/3 Beam Depth and Not <3"
Hanger
Brace
30-44°
G†
For Wooden Beams

(Continued)

†For wooden beams not less than 3 in. (76 mm).

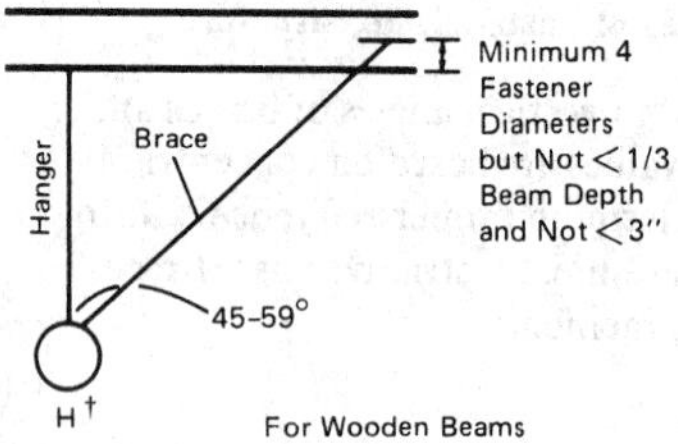
Minimum 4
Fastener
Diameters
but Not < 1/3
Beam Depth
and Not < 3"
Brace
Hanger
45-59°
H†
For Wooden Beams

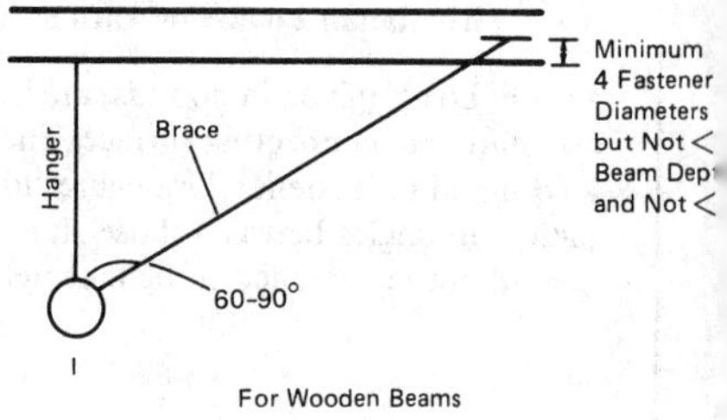
Minimum
4 Fastener
Diameters
but Not <
Beam Dep
and Not <
Brace
Hanger
60-90°
I
For Wooden Beams

†For wooden beams not less than 3 in. (76 mm).

Lag Screws in Wood (load perpendicular to grain—holes predrilled using good practice) Shank Diameter of Lag (in.)

Length Under Head (inches)	A	B	C	D	E	F	G	H	I
3/8									
3	304	325	292	168	325	526	230	324	400
4	392	354	317	183	354	678	250	352	435
5	476	375	336	194	375	824	265	373	461
6	564	382	342	196	382	976	270	380	470
8	—	—	—	—	—	—	—	—	—
1/2									
3	366	—	—	—	—	834	—	—	—
4	473	509	456	264	509	818	360	507	626
5	582	545	488	282	545	1008	385	542	670
6	689	559	501	209	559	1192	395	556	687
8	905	573	513	296	573	1586	405	570	704
5/8									
3	410	—	—	—	—	716	—	—	—
4	538	—	—	—	—	532	—	—	—
5	687	728	653	277	728	1154	515	725	896
6	791	778	697	403	778	1360	550	775	957
8	1044	806	723	416	806	1807	570	803	991
7/8									
3	487	—	—	—	—	843	—	—	—
4	548	—	—	—	—	1122	—	—	—
5	813	—	—	—	—	1407	—	—	—
6	971	—	—	—	—	1630	—	—	—
8	1297	1365	1223	685	1365	2244	965	1359	1678

Table 3-5.3.5.1 (3) (Continued)
Through Bolts in Wood (load perpendicular to grain)
Diameter of Bolt (in.)

Length of Bolt in Timber (in.)	⅜ ABCE	⅜ D	⅜ F	⅜ G	⅜ H	⅜ I	½ ABCE	½ D	½ F	½ G	½ H	½ I
1½	300	173	519	150	211	261	340	197	589	170	239	296
2	370	214	641	185	261	322	420	243	727	210	296	365
2½	460	266	796	230	324	400	550	318	952	275	387	478
3	480	277	831	240	338	417	630	364	1091	315	444	548
3⅝	460	268	797	230	324	400	720	416	1247	360	507	626
5½	—	—	—	—	—	—	680	393	1177	340	479	591

Length of Bolt in Timber (in.)	⅝ ABCE	⅝ D	⅝ F	⅝ G	⅝ H	⅝ I	⅞ ABCE	⅞ D	⅞ F	⅞ G	⅞ H	⅞ I
1½	390	225	675	195	275	339	470	272	614	235	331	409
2	470	272	814	235	331	409	580	335	1004	290	408	504
2½	620	358	1074	310	437	539	760	439	1316	380	535	661
3	710	410	1229	355	500	617	870	503	1506	435	613	757
3⅝	850	491	1472	425	599	739	1050	607	1818	525	739	913
5½	1020	590	1766	510	718	887	1580	913	2736	790	1113	1374

Expansion Shields in Concrete
Diameter of Bolt (in.)

Min. Depth of Hole (in.)	Diameter	A	B	C	D	E	F	G	H	I
2½	⅜	498	962	1173	678	962	962	925	1303	1609
3¼	⅜	—	—	—	—	—	—	925	1303	1609
3¾	⅜	—	—	—	—	—	—	925	1303	1609
4½	⅜	—	—	—	—	—	—	925	1303	1609
2½	½	—	—	—	—	—	—	1638	2306	2848
3¼	½	923	1782	2076	1200	1782	1597	1638	2306	2848
3¾	½	—	—	—	—	—	—	1638	2306	2848
4½	½	—	—	—	—	—	—	1638	2306	2848
2½	⅝	—	—	—	—	—	—	2080	2930	3617
3¼	⅝	—	—	—	—	—	—	2080	2930	3617
3¾	⅝	1480	2857	2637	1524	2857	2581	2080	2930	3617
4½	⅝	—	—	—	—	—	—	2080	2930	3617
2½	⅞	—	—	—	—	—	—	2470	4113	5078
3¼	⅞	—	—	—	—	—	—	2970	4113	5078
3¾	⅞	—	—	—	—	—	—	2970	4113	5078
4½	⅞	3070	4130	3702	2139	4130	5312	2970	4113	5078

Connections to Steel (values assume bolt perpendicular to mounting surface)
Diameter of Unfinished Steel Bolt (in.)

¼								
A	B	C	D	E	F	G	H	I
400	500	600	300	500	650	325	458	565

⅜								
A	B	C	D	E	F	G	H	I
900	1200	1400	800	1200	1550	735	1035	1278

½								
A	B	C	D	E	F	G	H	I
1600	2050	2550	1450	2050	2850	1300	1830	2260

⅝								
A	B	C	D	E	F	G	H	I
2500	3300	3950	2250	3300	4400	2045	2880	3557

For SI Units: 1 in. = 25.4 mm.

3-5.3.5.2 Longitudinal sway bracing spaced at a maximum of 80 ft (24 m) on center shall be provided for feed and cross mains.

3-5.3.5.3* Tops of risers shall be secured against drifting in any direction, utilizing a four-way sway brace.

3-5.3.5.4 Lateral sway bracing spaced at a maximum of 40 ft (12 m) on center shall be provided for feed and cross mains.

Exception No. 1: Lateral sway bracing may be omitted on pipes individually supported by rods less than 6 in. (152 mm) long.

Exception No. 2: U-type hangers used to support the mains may be used to satisfy the requirements for lateral sway bracing provided the legs are bent out at least 10 degrees from the vertical.

Exception No. 3: When flexible couplings are installed on mains other than as required in 3-5.3.2, a lateral brace shall be provided within 24 in. (610 mm) of every other coupling, but not more than 40 ft (12 m) on center.

Exception No. 4: When building primary structural members exceed 40 ft (12 m) on center, lateral braces may be spaced up to 50 ft (15.2 m) on center.

3-5.3.5.5 Bracing shall be attached directly to feed and cross mains.

3-5.3.5.6 A length of pipe shall not be braced to sections of the building that will move differentially.

3-5.3.5.7 The last length of pipe at the end of a feed or cross main shall be provided with a lateral brace. Lateral braces may also act as longitudinal braces if they are within 24 in. (610 mm) of the center line of the piping braced longitudinally.

3-5.3.5.8 Sway bracing is not required for branch lines.

Exception No. 1: The end sprinkler on a line shall be restrained against excessive movement by use of a wraparound U-hook (see Figure A-3-10.1) or by other approved means.

Exception No. 2: Branch lines 2½ in. (64 mm) or larger shall be provided with lateral bracing in accordance with 3-5.3.5.4.

3-5.3.5.9 C-type clamps used to attach hangers to the building structure in areas subject to earthquakes shall be equipped with a retaining strap or other approved means to prevent movement. (*See Figure A-3-10.1.*)

3-5.3.5.10 C-type clamps, with or without retaining straps, shall not be used to attach braces to the building structure.

3-6 Drainage.

3-6.1 Pitching of Piping for Drainage.

3-6.1.1* All sprinkler pipe and fittings shall be so installed that the system may be drained.

3-6.1.2 On wet-pipe systems, sprinkler pipes may be installed level. Trapped piping shall be drained in accordance with 3-6.3.

3-6.1.3 On those portions of preaction systems subject to freezing and on dry-pipe systems, sprinkler pipe on branch lines shall be pitched at least ½-in. in 10 ft (4 mm/m) and the pipe of cross and feed mains shall be given a pitch of not less than ¼-in. in 10 ft (2 mm/m). A pitch of ¾ to 1-in. (19 to 25-mm) shall be provided for short branch lines and ½-in. in 10 ft (4 mm/m) for cross and feed mains in refrigerated areas and in buildings of light construction that may settle under heavy loads.

3-6.2 System, Main Drain, or Sectional Drain Connections. [*See Figures 3-6.2 and A-3-4.1.1(b).*]

3-6.2.1 Provisions shall be made to properly drain all parts of the system.

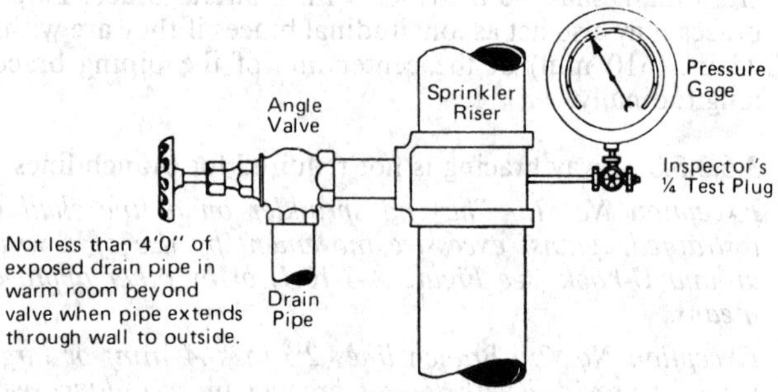
Pressure Gage
Sprinkler Riser
Angle Valve
Inspector's ¼ Test Plug
Not less than 4'0" of exposed drain pipe in warm room beyond valve when pipe extends through wall to outside.
Drain Pipe

For SI Units: 1 in. = 25.4 mm; 1 ft = 0.3048 m.

Figure 3-6.2 Drain Connection for System Riser.

3-6.2.2 Drain connections for systems supply risers and mains shall be sized as shown in Table 3-6.2.2.

Table 3-6.2.2

Riser or Main Size	Size of Drain Connection
Up to 2 in.	¾ in. or larger
2½ in., 3 in., 3½ in.	1¼ in. or larger
4 in. and larger	2 in. only

3-6.2.3 Each interior sectional control valve shall be provided with a drain connection sized as shown in Table 3-6.2.2 so as to drain that portion of the system controlled by the sectional valve. These drains shall discharge either outside or to a drain connection.

3-6.2.4 The test valves required by 2-9.1 may be used as main drain valves.

3-6.3 Auxiliary Drains.

3-6.3.1 Auxiliary drains shall be provided when a change in piping direction prevents drainage of sections of branch lines or mains through the main drain valve.

3-6.3.2 Auxiliary Drains for Wet-Pipe Systems.

3-6.3.2.1 When the capacity of trapped sections of pipes is 5 gal (18.9 L) or less, the auxiliary drain shall consist of a nipple and cap or brass plug not less than 3/4 in. (19 mm) in size.

Exception: Auxiliary drains are not required for piping that can be drained by removing a single pendent sprinkler.

3-6.3.2.2 When the capacity of isolated trapped sections of pipe is more than 5 gal (18.9 L) and less than 50 gal (189 L), the auxiliary drain shall consist of a valve not smaller than 3/4 in. (19 mm) in size and a plug, at least one of which shall be brass. In lieu of a plug, a nipple and cap may be used.

3-6.3.2.3* When the capacity of isolated trapped sections of pipe is 50 gal (189 L) or more, the auxiliary drain shall consist of a valve not smaller than 1 in. (25 mm), piped to an accessible location.

3-6.3.2.4 Tie-in drains are not required on wet-pipe systems.

3-6.3.3 Auxiliary Drains for Dry-Pipe Systems.

3-6.3.3.1 When capacity of trapped sections of pipe is 5 gal (18.9 L) or less, the auxiliary drain shall consist of a valve not smaller than 3/4 in. (19 mm) and a plug, at least one of which shall be brass. In lieu of a plug, a nipple and cap may be used.

Exception: Auxiliary drains are not required for a drop nipple when installed in accordance with 5-2.2.

3-6.3.3.2 When capacity of isolated trapped sections of pipe is more than 5 gal (18.9 L), the auxiliary drain shall consist of two 1-in. (25-mm) valves, and one 2-in. by 12-in.

(51-mm by 305-mm) condensate nipple or equivalent, accessibly located. (*See Figure 3-6.3.3.*)

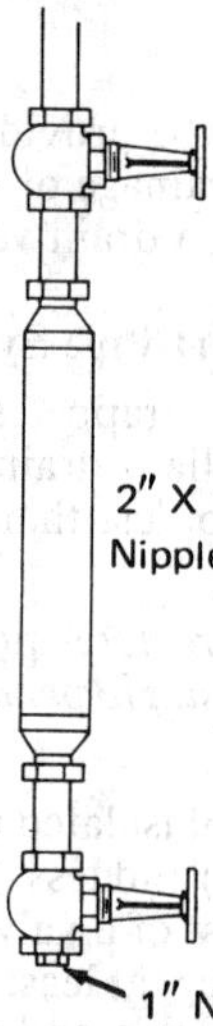
Dry System
Auxiliary Drain
1" Valve
2" X 12"
Nipple or Equivalent
1" Valve
1" Nipple and Cap or Plug

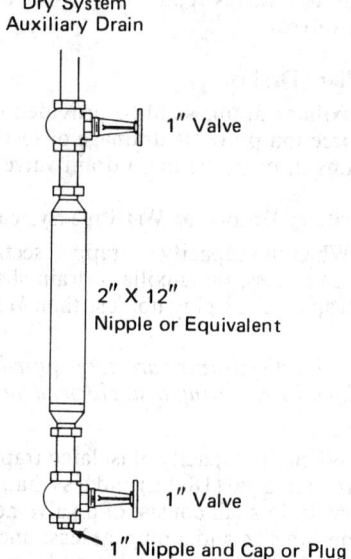

For SI Units: 1 in. = 25.4 mm; 1 ft = 0.3048 m.

Figure 3-6.3.3 Dry System Auxiliary Drain.

3-6.3.3.3* Tie-in drains shall be provided for multiple adjacent trapped branch lines and shall be a minimum of 1 in. (25 mm). Tie-in drain lines shall be pitched a minimum of ½ in. in 10 ft (4 mm/m).

3-6.3.4 Auxiliary Drains for Preaction Systems.

3-6.3.4.1 When trapped sections of pipe are in areas subject to freezing, auxiliary drains shall conform to 3-6.3.3.

3-6.3.4.2 When trapped sections of pipe are in areas not subject to freezing, auxiliary drains shall consist of a valve not smaller than ¾ in. (19 mm) and a plug, at least one of which shall be brass. In lieu of a plug, a nipple and cap may be used.

Exception: Auxiliary drains are not required for piping that can be drained by removing a single pendent sprinkler when capacity of the trapped sections of pipe is 5 gal (18.9 L) or less.

3-6.4 Discharge of Drain Valves.

3-6.4.1* Direct interconnections shall not be made between sewers and sprinkler drains of systems supplied by public water. The drain discharge shall be in conformity with any health or water department regulations.

3-6.4.2 When drain pipes are buried underground, approved corrosion-resistant pipe shall be used.

3-6.4.3 Drain pipes shall not terminate in blind spaces under the building.

3-6.4.4 When exposed, drain pipes shall be fitted with a turned down elbow.

3-6.4.5* Drain pipes shall be arranged so as not to expose any part of the sprinkler system to freezing conditions.

3-7 Joining of Pipe and Fittings.

3-7.1 Threaded Pipe and Fittings.

3-7.1.1 All threaded fittings and pipe shall have threads cut to ANSI/ASME standard B1.20.1. Care shall be taken that the pipe does not extend into the fitting sufficiently to reduce the waterway.

3-7.1.2* Steel pipe with wall thicknesses less than Schedule 30 [in sizes 8 in. (203 mm) and larger] or Schedule 40 [in sizes less than 8 in. (203 mm)] shall not be joined by threaded fittings, unless a threaded assembly has been investigated for suitability in automatic sprinkler installations and listed for this service.

3-7.1.3 Joint compound or tape shall be applied to the threads of the pipe and not in the fitting.

3-7.2* Welded Piping.

3-7.2.1 Welding methods that comply with all of the requirements of AWS D10.9, *Specification for Qualification of Welding Procedures and Welders for Piping and Tubing*, Level AR-3, are acceptable means of joining fire protection piping.

3-7.2.2* Welding sections of sprinkler piping in place inside the building shall not be permitted. Sections of branch lines, cross mains, or risers may be shop welded.

Exception: Welding sections of sprinkler piping in place inside new buildings under construction may be permitted only when the construction is noncombustible and no combustible contents are present and when the welding process is performed in accordance with NFPA 51B, Standard for Fire Prevention in Use of Cutting and Welding Processes.

3-7.2.3 Welding procedures, welders, and welding machine operators shall be qualified as required by 3-7.2.11.

3-7.2.4 Fittings used to join pipe shall be listed fabricated fittings, or manufactured in accordance with Table 3-8.1.1. Such fittings joined in conformance with a qualified welding procedure as set forth in this section are an acceptable product under this standard, provided that materials and wall thickness are compatible with other sections of this standard.

Exception: Fittings are not required when pipe ends are buttwelded.

3-7.2.5 No welding shall be performed if there is impingement of rain, snow, sleet, or high wind on the weld area of the pipe product.

3-7.2.6 When welding is performed:

(a)* Holes in piping for outlets shall be cut to the full inside diameter of fittings prior to welding in place of the fittings.

(b) Discs shall be retrieved.

(c) Openings cut into piping shall be smooth bore and all internal slag and welding residue shall be removed.

(d) Fittings shall not penetrate the internal diameter of the piping.

(e) Steel plates shall not be welded to the ends of piping or fittings.

(f) Fittings shall not be modified.

(g) Nuts, clips, eye rods, angle brackets, or other fasteners shall not be welded to pipe or fittings.

Exception: Tabs may be welded to pipe for longitudinal earthquake braces only. (See 3-5.3.5.1.)

3-7.2.7 When reducing a pipe size in the run of a main, cross main, or branch, a reducing fitting designed for that purpose shall be used.

3-7.2.8 Torch cutting and welding shall not be permitted as a means of modifying or repairing sprinkler systems.

3-7.2.9 When welding is planned, a contractor shall specify the section to be shop welded on drawings and the type of fittings or formations to be used.

3-7.2.10 Sections of shop welded piping shall be joined by means of flanged or flexible gasketed joints or other approved fittings.

Exception: See 3-7.2.2.

3-7.2.11 Qualifications.

3-7.2.11.1 A welding procedure shall be prepared and qualified before any welding is done. Qualification of the welding procedure to be used and the performance of welders and welding operators is required and shall comply with the requirements of American Welding Society standard AWS D10.9, Level AR-3.

3-7.2.11.2 Contractors or fabricators shall be responsible for all welding they install. Each contractor or fabricator shall have an established written quality assurance procedure related to control of the requirements of 3-7.2.6, available to the authority having jurisdiction.

3-7.2.11.3 Contractors or fabricators shall be responsible for qualifying any welding procedure that they intend to have used by personnel of their organization.

3-7.2.11.4 Contractors or fabricators shall be responsible for qualifying all of the welders and welding machine operators employed by them in compliance with the requirements of AWS D10.9, Level AR-3.

3-7.2.12 Records.

3-7.2.12.1 Welders or welding machine operators shall, upon completion of each weld, stamp an imprint of their identification into the side of the pipe adjacent to the weld.

3-7.2.12.2 Contractors or fabricators shall maintain certified records, which are available to the authority having jurisdiction, of the procedures used and the welders or welding machine operators employed by them along with their welding identification imprints. Records shall show the date and the results of procedure and performance qualifications.

3-7.3 Groove Joining Methods.

3-7.3.1 Pipe joined with mechanical grooved fittings shall be joined by a listed combination of fittings, gaskets, and grooves. When grooves are cut or rolled on the pipe they shall be dimensionally compatible with the fitting.

Exception: Steel pipe with wall thicknesses less than Schedule 30 [in sizes 8 in. (203 mm) and larger] or Schedule 40 [in sizes less than 8 in. (203 mm)] shall not be joined by fittings used with pipe having cut grooves.

3-7.3.2 Mechanical grooved couplings including gaskets used on dry-pipe systems shall be listed for dry-pipe service.

3-7.4* Brazed and Soldered Joints. Joints for the connection of copper tube shall be brazed.

Exception No. 1: Solder joints may be permitted for wet-pipe systems in Light Hazard Occupancies where the temperature classification of the installed sprinklers is Ordinary or Intermediate.

Exception No. 2: Solder joints may be permitted for wet-pipe systems in Ordinary Hazard (Group 1) Occupancies where the piping is concealed.

3-7.5 Other Types. Other types of joints shall be made or installed in accordance with the requirements of the listing for this service.

3-7.6 End Treatment. After cutting, pipe ends shall have burrs and fins removed.

3-7.6.1 When using listed fittings, the pipe and its end treatment shall be in accordance with the manufacturer's installation instructions and the listing.

3-8 Fittings.

3-8.1 Types of Fittings.

3-8.1.1 Fittings used in sprinkler systems shall be of the materials listed in Table 3-8.1.1 or in accordance with

3-8.1.2. The chemical properties, physical properties, and dimensions of the materials listed in Table 3-8.1.1 shall be at least equivalent to the standards cited in the table. Fittings used in sprinkler systems shall be designed to withstand the working pressures involved, but not less than 175 psi (12.1 bars) cold water [125 psi (8.6 bars) saturated steam] pressure.

Table 3-8.1.1 Fittings Materials and Dimensions

Material and Dimensions	Standard
Cast Iron	
Cast Iron Threaded Fittings, Class 125 and 250	ANSI B16.4
Cast Iron Pipe Flanges and Flanged Fittings	ANSI B16.1
Malleable Iron	
Malleable Iron Threaded Fittings, Class 150 and 300	ANSI B16.3
Steel	
Factory-made Wrought Steel Buttweld Fittings	ANSI B16.9
Buttwelding Ends for Pipe, Valves, Flanges and Fittings	ANSI B16.25
Spec. for Piping Fittings of Wrought Carbon Steel and Alloy Steel for Moderate and Elevated Temperatures	ASTM A234
Steel Pipe Flanges and Flanged Fittings	ANSI B16.5
Forged Steel Fittings, Socket Welded and Threaded	ANSI B16.11
Copper	
Wrought Copper and Bronze Solder-Joint Pressure Fittings	ANSI B16.22
Cast Bronze Solder-Joint Pressure Fittings	ANSI B16.18

3-8.1.2* Other types of fittings may be used, but only those investigated and listed for this service.

3-8.1.2.1* When unique characteristics of a fitting, such as a tendency to rotate, require support in addition to that required in Section 3-10, restraint shall be provided in accordance with its listing.

3-8.1.3 Fittings used in sprinkler systems shall be extra-heavy pattern where pressures exceed 175 psi (12.1 bars).

Exception No. 1: Standard weight pattern cast-iron fittings 2 in. (51 mm) in size and smaller may be used where pressures do not exceed 300 psi (20.7 bars).

Exception No. 2: Standard weight pattern malleable iron fittings 6 in. (152 mm) in size and smaller may be used where pressures do not exceed 300 psi (20.7 bars).

Exception No. 3: Fittings may be used for system pressures up to the limits specified in listings by a testing laboratory.

3-8.1.4 When water pressures are 175 psi to 300 psi (12.1 to 20.7 bars), extra heavy valves shall be used in accordance with their pressure ratings.

3-8.1.5* When individual floor/zone control valves are not provided, a flanged joint or mechanical coupling shall be used at the riser at each floor for connections to piping serving floor areas in excess of 5000 sq ft (465 m^2).

3-8.2* Couplings and Unions. Screwed unions shall not be used on pipe larger than 2 in. (51 mm). Couplings and unions of other than screwed-type shall be of types approved specifically for use in sprinkler systems. Unions, screwed or mechanical couplings, or flanges may be used to facilitate installation.

3-8.3 Reducers and Bushings. A one-piece reducing fitting shall be used wherever a change is made in the size of the pipe.

Exception No. 1: Hexagonal or face bushings may be used in reducing the size of openings of fittings when standard fittings of the required size are not available.

Exception No. 2: Hexagonal bushings as permitted in 3-3.5.1 are acceptable.

3-9 Valves.

3-9.1 Types of Valves to Be Used.

3-9.1.1 All valves on connections to water supplies and in supply pipes to sprinklers shall be listed indicating valves, unless a nonindicating valve, such as an underground gate valve with approved roadway box complete with T-wrench, is accepted by the authority having jurisdiction.

Such valves shall not close in less than 5 seconds when operated at maximum possible speed from the fully open position. This is to avoid damage to piping by water hammer.

The following may not incorporate indicating devices as part of the valve, but the valve assembly described shall qualify as an indicating valve:

(a) A listed underground gate valve equipped with a listed indicator post,

(b) A listed water control valve assembly with a reliable position indication connected to a remote supervisory station.

3-9.1.2 Drain valves and test valves shall be of approved type of 175 psi (12.1 bars) cold water [125 psi (8.6 bars) saturated steam] pressure rating.

3-9.1.3 Check valves shall be listed and installed in a vertical or horizontal position in accordance with their listing.

3-9.1.4 When wafer type valves are used, the disc may extend beyond the end of the valve body. Valve discs shall not interfere with the operation of other system components.

3-9.2* Valves Controlling Sprinkler Systems.

3-9.2.1* Each system shall be provided with a listed indicating valve so located as to control all sources of water supply except fire department connections.

3-9.2.2 At least one listed indicating valve shall be installed in each source of water supply except fire department connections.

3-9.2.3 Valves on connections to water supplies, sectional control valves, and other valves in supply pipes to sprinklers shall be supervised open by one of the following methods:

(a) Central station, proprietary, or remote station signaling service,

(b) Local signaling service that will cause the sounding of an audible signal at a constantly attended point,

(c) Locking valves open,

(d) Sealing of valves and approved weekly recorded inspection when valves are located within fenced enclosures under the control of the owner.

Exception No. 1: Underground gate valves with roadway boxes need not be supervised.

Exception No. 2: For floor control valves in high-rise buildings, see 3-12.6; for circulating closed-loop systems, see 5-6.1.6.

3-9.2.4 When there is more than one source of water supply, a check valve shall be installed in each connection.

Exception: When cushion tanks are used with automatic fire pumps, no check valve is required in the cushion tank connection.

3-9.2.5* A check valve shall be installed in each water supply connection if there is a fire department connection on the system.

3-9.2.6* When a single wet-pipe sprinkler system is equipped with a fire department connection the alarm valve is considered a check valve and an additional check valve shall not be required.

3-9.2.7 In a city connection serving as one source of supply, the city valve in the connection may serve as one of the required valves. A listed indicating valve or an indicator post valve shall be installed on the system side of the check valve. (*See Figure A-3-9.2.5.*)

Exception: When a wet-pipe sprinkler system is equipped with an (alarm) check valve, a gate valve is not required on the system side of the (alarm) check valve.

3-9.3 Pressure Reducing Valves.

3-9.3.1 In portions of systems where all components are not listed for pressure greater than 175 psi (12.1 bar) and the potential exists for normal (nonfire condition) water pressure in excess of 175, a listed pressure reducing valve shall be installed and set for an outlet pressure not exceeding 165 psi (11.4 bar) at the maximum inlet pressure.

3-9.3.2 Pressure gages shall be installed on the inlet and outlet sides of each pressure reducing valve.

3-9.3.3 A relief valve of not less than ½ in. (13 mm) in size shall be provided on the discharge side of the pressure reducing valve set to operate at a pressure not exceeding 175 psi (12.1 bar).

3-9.3.4 A listed indicating valve shall be provided on the inlet side of each pressure reducing valve.

Exception: Where the pressure reducing valve meets the listing requirements for use as an indicating valve.

3-9.4* Identification of Valves. When there is more than one control valve, permanently marked identification signs indicating the portion of the system controlled by each valve shall be provided.

Embossed plastic tape, pencil, ink, crayon, etc., shall not be considered permanent markings. The sign shall be secured with noncorrosive wire, chain, or other means.

3-10 Hangers.

3-10.1* General. Type of hangers and installation methods shall be in accordance with the requirements of Section 3-10.

Exception: Hangers and installation methods certified by a registered professional engineer for the following:

(a) Designed to support five times the weight of the water-filled pipe plus 250 lb (114 kg) at each point of piping support.

(b) These points of support are enough to support the sprinkler system.

(c) Ferrous materials are used for hanger components.

Detailed calculations shall be submitted, when required by the reviewing authority, showing stresses developed both in hangers and piping, and safety factors allowed.

3-10.1.1 Hangers and their components shall be ferrous.

Exception: Nonferrous components that have been proven by fire tests to be adequate for the hazard application, are listed for this purpose, and are in compliance with the other requirements of this section.

3-10.1.2 The components of hanger assemblies that directly attach to the pipe or to the building structure shall be listed.

Exception: Mild steel hangers formed from rods need not be listed.

3-10.1.3* Sprinkler piping or hangers shall not be used to support nonsystem components.

3-10.1.4 Sprinkler piping shall be substantially supported from the building structure, which must support the added load of the water-filled pipe plus a minimum of 250 lb (114 kg) applied at the point of hanging.

3-10.1.5 Sprinkler piping shall be supported independently of the ceiling sheathing.

Exception: Toggle hangers shall be used only for the support of pipe 1½ in. (38 mm) or smaller in size under ceilings of hollow tile or metal lath and plaster.

3-10.1.6 When sprinkler piping is installed below ductwork, piping shall be substantially supported from the building structure or from the steel angles supporting the ductwork provided the angles conform to Tables 3-10.1.7(a) and 3-10.1.7(b).

3-10.1.7* For trapeze hangers, the minimum size of steel angle or pipe span between purlins or joists shall be such that the available section modulus of the trapeze member from Table 3-10.1.7(b) equals or exceeds the section modulus required in Table 3-10.1.7(a).

Any other sizes or shapes giving equal or greater section modulus will be acceptable. All angles are to be used with the longer leg vertical. The trapeze member shall be secured to prevent slippage. When a pipe is suspended from a pipe trapeze, ring, strap, or clevis, hangers of the size corresponding to the suspended pipe shall be used on both ends.

3-10.1.8 The size of hanger rods and fasteners required to support the steel angle iron or pipe indicated in Table 3-10.1.7(a) shall comply with 3-10.4.

3-10.1.9 Eye rods and ring hangers shall be secured with necessary lock washers to prevent lateral motion at the point of support.

3-10.1.10 Holes through concrete beams may also be considered as a substitute for hangers for the support of pipes.

Table 3-10.1.7(a) Section Modulus Required for Trapeze Members (in.³)

Span of Trapeze	Pipe Size											
	1 in.	1¼ in.	1½ in.	2 in.	2½ in.	3 in.	3½ in.	4 in.	5 in.	6 in.	8 in.	10 in.
1 ft 6 in.	.08 .08	.09 .09	.09 .09	.09 .10	.10 .11	.11 .12	.12 .13	.13 .15	.15 .18	.18 .22	.24 .30	.32 .41
2 ft 0 in.	.11 .11	.12 .12	.12 .12	.13 .13	.13 .15	.15 .16	.16 .18	.17 .20	.20 .24	.24 .29	.32 .40	.43 .55
2 ft 6 in.	.14 .14	.14 .15	.15 .15	.16 .16	.17 .18	.18 .21	.20 .22	.21 .25	.25 .30	.30 .36	.40 .50	.54 .68
3 ft 0 in.	.17 .17	.17 .18	.18 .18	.19 .20	.20 .22	.22 .25	.24 .27	.26 .30	.31 .36	.36 .43	.48 .60	.65 .82
4 ft 0 in.	.22 .22	.23 .24	.24 .24	.25 .26	.27 .29	.29 .33	.32 .36	.34 .40	.41 .48	.48 .58	.64 .80	.87 1.09
5 ft 0 in.	.28 .28	.29 .29	.30 .30	.31 .33	.34 .37	.37 .41	.40 .45	.43 .49	.51 .60	.59 .72	.80 1.00	1.08 1.37
6 ft 0 in.	.33 .34	.35 .35	.36 .36	.38 .39	.41 .44	.44 .49	.48 .54	.51 .59	.61 .72	.71 .87	.97 1.20	1.30 1.64
7 ft 0 in.	.39 .39	.40 .41	.41 .43	.44 .46	.47 .51	.52 .58	.55 .63	.60 .69	.71 .84	.83 1.01	1.13 1.41	1.52 1.92
8 ft 0 in.	.44 .45	.46 .47	.47 .49	.50 .52	.54 .59	.59 .66	.63 .72	.68 .79	.81 .96	.95 1.16	1.29 1.61	1.73 2.19
9 ft 0 in.	.50 .50	.52 .53	.53 .55	.56 .59	.61 .66	.66 .74	.71 .81	.77 .89	.92 1.08	1.07 1.30	1.45 1.81	1.95 2.46
10 ft 0 in.	.56 .56	.58 .59	.59 .61	.63 .65	.68 .74	.74 .82	.79 .90	.85 .99	1.02 1.20	1.19 1.44	1.61 2.01	2.17 2.74

For SI units: 1 in. = 25.4 mm; 1 ft = 0.3048m.

Top values are for Schedule 10 pipe; bottom values are for Schedule 40 Pipe.

Note: The table is based on a maximum allowable bending stress of 15 KSI and a midspan concentrated load from 15 ft of water-filled pipe, plus 250 lb.

3-10.1.11 Maximum Distance Between Hangers.

3-10.1.11.1* For steel pipe sizes 1½ in. (38 mm) and larger, the maximum distance between hangers shall be 15 ft (4.5 m). For steel pipe sizes less than 1½ in. (38 mm), the maximum distance between hangers shall be 12 ft (3.6 m).

Exception No. 1: Threaded lightweight steel pipe shall have a maximum distance between hangers not exceeding 12 ft (3.6 m) for pipe sizes 3 in. (76 mm) or less.

Exception No. 2: The maximum distance between hangers may be modified in accordance with other paragraphs of Section 3-10.

3-10.1.11.2* For copper tubes as specified in Table 3-1.1.1 the maximum distance between hangers shall not exceed that in Table 3-10.1.11.2.

3-10.1.12 When sprinkler piping is installed in storage racks as defined in NFPA 231C, *Standard for Rack Storage of Materials*, piping shall be substantially supported from the storage rack structure or building in accordance with all applicable provisions of Section 3-10.

3-10.2 Hangers in Concrete.

3-10.2.1 Listed inserts set in concrete may be installed for the support of hangers. Wood plugs shall not be used.

3-10.2.2 Listed expansion shields for supporting pipes under concrete construction may be used in a horizontal position in the sides of beams. In concrete having gravel or crushed stone aggregate, expansion shields may be used in the vertical position to support pipes 4 in. (102 mm) or less in diameter.

3-10.2.3 For the support of pipes 5 in. (127 mm) and larger, expansion shields if used in the vertical position shall alternate with hangers connected directly to the structural members such as trusses and girders, or to the sides of concrete beams. In the absence of convenient structural members, pipes 5 in. (127 mm) and larger may be supported entirely by expansion shields in the vertical position, but spaced not over 10 ft (3 m) apart.

3-10.2.4 Expansion shields shall not be used in ceilings of gypsum or similar soft material. In cinder concrete, expan-

Table 3-10.1.7(b) Available Section Moduli of Common Trapeze Hangers

Pipe	Modulus
Schedule 10	
1 in.	.12
1¼ in.	.19
1½ in.	.26
2 in.	.42
2½ in.	.69
3 in.	1.04
3½ in.	1.38
4 in.	1.76
5 in.	3.03
6 in.	4.35
Schedule 40	
1 in.	.13
1¼ in.	.23
1½ in.	.33
2 in.	.56
2½ in.	1.06
3 in.	1.72
3½ in.	2.39
4 in.	3.21
5 in.	5.45
6 in.	8.50

Angles	Modulus
1½ X 1½ X 3/16	.10
2 X 2 X 1/8	.13
2 X 1½ X 3/16	.18
2 X 2 X 3/16	.19
2 X 2 X 1/4	.25
2½ X 1½ X 3/16	.28
2½ X 2 X 3/16	.29
2 X 2 X 5/16	.30
2½ X 2½ X 3/16	.30
2 X 2 X 3/8	.35
2½ X 2½ X 1/4	.39
3 X 2 X 3/16	.41
3 X 2½ X 3/16	.43
3 X 3 X 3/16	.44
2½ X 2½ X 5/16	.48
3 X 2 X 1/4	.54
2½ X 2 X 3/8	.55
2½ X 2½ X 3/8	.57
3 X 3 X 1/4	.58
3 X 3 X 5/16	.71
2½ X 2½ X 1/2	.72
3½ X 2½ X 1/4	.75
3 X 2½ X 3/8	.81
3 X 3 X 3/8	.83
3½ X 2½ X 5/16	.93
3 X 3 X 7/16	.95
4 X 4 X 1/4	1.05
3 X 3 X 1/2	1.07
4 X 3 X 5/16	1.23
4 X 4 X 5/16	1.29
4 X 3 X 3/8	1.46
4 X 4 X 3/8	1.52
5 X 3½ X 5/16	1.94
4 X 4 X 1/2	1.97
4 X 4 X 5/8	2.40
4 X 4 X 3/4	2.81
6 X 4 X 3/8	3.32
6 X 4 X 1/2	4.33
6 X 4 X 3/4	6.25
6 X 6 X 1	8.57

For SI Units: 1 in. = 25.4 mm; 1 ft. = 0.3048 m.

Table 3-10.1.11.2 Hanger Spacing for Copper Tube

Tube Size	Maximum Hanger Spacing
¾ in.—1 in.	8 ft
1¼ in.—1½ in.	10 ft
2 in.—3 in.	12 ft
3½ in.—8 in.	15 ft

For SI units: 1 in. = 25.4 mm; 1 ft = 0.3048 m.

sion shields shall not be used except on branch lines where they shall alternate with through bolts or hangers attached to beams.

3-10.2.5 When expansion shields are used in the vertical position, the holes shall be drilled to provide uniform contact with the shield over its entire circumference. Depth of the hole shall be not less than specified for the type of shield used.

3-10.2.6 Holes for expansion shields in the side of concrete beams shall be above the center line of the beam or above the bottom reinforcement steel rods.

3-10.3 Powder-Driven Studs and Welding Studs.

3-10.3.1* Powder-driven studs, welding studs, and the tools used for installing these devices shall be listed by a testing laboratory and installed within the limits of pipe size, installation position, and construction material into which they are installed as expressed in individual listings or approvals.

3-10.3.2 The ability of concrete to hold the studs varies widely according to type of aggregate and quality of concrete, and it shall be established in each case by testing concrete on the job to determine that the studs will hold a minimum load of 750 lb (341 kg) for 2-in. (51 mm) or smaller pipe, 1000 lb (454 kg) for 2½-, 3-, or 3½-in. (64-, 76-, or 89-mm) pipe, and 1200 lb (545 kg) for 4- or 5-in. (102- or 127-mm) pipe.

3-10.3.3 When increaser couplings are used, they shall be attached directly to the powder-driven stud or welding stud.

3-10.3.4 Welded studs or other hanger parts shall not be attached by welding to steel less than U.S. Standard, 12 gage.

3-10.4 Rods and "U" Hooks.

3-10.4.1 Hanger rod size shall be the same as that approved for use with the hanger assembly and the size of rods shall not be less than that given in Table 3-10.4.1.

Exception: Rods of smaller diameter may be used when the hanger assembly has been tested and listed by a testing laboratory and installed within the limits of pipe sizes expressed in individual listings or approvals. For rolled threads, the rod size shall not be less than the root diameter of the thread.

Table 3-10.4.1 Hanger Rod Sizes

Pipe Size	Dia. of Rod in.	Dia. of Rod mm	Pipe Size	Dia. of Rod in.	Dia. of Rod mm
Up to and including 4 in.	3/8	9.5	5, 6, and 8 in.	1/2	12.7
			10 and 12 in.	5/8	15.9

For SI Units: 1 in. = 25.4 mm.

3-10.4.2 U-Hooks. The size of the rod material of U-hooks shall not be less than that given in Table 3-10.4.2. Drive screws shall be used only in a horizontal position as in the side of a beam in conjunction with U-hangers only.

Table 3-10.4.2 U-Hook Rod Sizes

Pipe Size	Hook Material Diameter in.	Hook Material Diameter mm
Up to 2 in.	5/16	7.9
2½ in. to 6 in.	3/8	9.5
8 in.	1/2	12.7

For SI Units: 1 in. = 25.4 mm.

3-10.4.3 The size of the rod material for eye rods shall not be less than specified in Table 3-10.4.3.

Table 3-10.4.3 Eye Rod Sizes

Pipe Size	Diameter of Rod With Bent Eye in.	mm	With Welded Eye in.	mm
Up to 4 in.	3/8	9.5	3/8	9.5
5-6 in.	1/2	12.7	1/2	12.7
8 in.	3/4	19.1	1/2	12.7

For SI Units: 1 in. = 25.4 mm.

3-10.4.4 Threaded sections of rods shall not be formed or bent.

3-10.4.5 Screws. For ceiling flanges and U-hooks, screw dimensions shall not be less than those given in Table 3-10.4.5.

Exception: When the thickness of planking and thickness of flange do not permit the use of screws 2 in. (51 mm) long, screws 1¾ in. (44 mm) long may be permitted with hangers spaced not over 10 ft (3 m) apart. When the thickness of beams or joists does not permit the use of screws 2½ in. (64 mm) long, screws 2 in. (51 mm) long may be permitted with hangers spaced not over 10 ft (3 m) apart.

Table 3-10.4.5 Screw Dimension for Ceiling Flanges and U-Hooks

Pipe Size	2 Screw Flanges
Up to 2 in.	Wood Screw No. 18 × 1½ in.
Pipe Size	**3 Screw Flanges**
Up to 2 in.	Wood Screw No. 18 × 1½ in.
2½ in., 3 in., 3½ in.	Lag Screw 3/8 in. × 2 in.
4 in., 5 in., 6 in.	Lag Screw 1/2 in. × 2 in.
8 in.	Lag Screw 5/8 in. × 2 in.
Pipe Size	**4 Screw Flanges**
Up to 2 in.	Wood Screw No. 18 × 1½ in.
2½ in., 3 in., 3½ in.	Lag Screw 3/8 in. × 1½ in.
4 in., 5 in., 6 in.	Lag Screw 1/2 in. × 2 in.
8 in.	Lag Screw 5/8 in. × 2 in.
Pipe Size	**U-Hooks**
Up to 2 in.	Drive Screw No. 16 × 2 in.
2½ in., 3 in., 3½ in.	Lag Screw 3/8 in. × 2½ in.
4 in., 5 in., 6 in.	Lag Screw 1/2 in. × 3 in.
8 in.	Lag Screw 5/8 in. × 3 in.

For SI Units: 1 in. = 25.4 mm.

3-10.4.6 The size bolt or lag (coach) screw used with an eye rod or flange on the side of the beam shall not be less than specified in Table 3-10.4.6.

Table 3-10.4.6 Minimum Bolt or Lag Screw Sizes

Size of Pipe	Size of Bolt or Lag Screw in.	Size of Bolt or Lag Screw mm	Length of Lag Screw Used with Wood Beams in.	Length of Lag Screw Used with Wood Beams mm
Up to and including 2 in.	3/8	9.5	2½	64
2½ to 6 in. (inclusive)	½	12.7	3	76
8 in.	5/8	15.9	3	76

Exception: When the thickness of beams or joists does not permit the use of screws 2½ in. (64 mm), screws 2 in. (51 mm) may be permitted with hangers spaced not over 10 ft (3 m) apart.

3-10.4.7 Wood screws shall not be driven. Nails are not acceptable for fastening hangers.

3-10.4.8 Screws in the side of a timber or joist shall be not less than 2½ in. (64 mm) from the lower edge when supporting branch lines, and not less than 3 in. (76 mm) when supporting main lines. This shall not apply to 2-in. (51-mm) or thicker nailing strips resting on top of steel beams.

3-10.4.9 The minimum plank thickness and the minimum width of the lower face of beams or joists in which lag screw rods are used shall be as given in Table 3-10.4.9.

Table 3-10.4.9
Minimum Plank Thicknesses and Beam or Joist Widths

Pipe Size	Nominal Plank Thickness in.	Nominal Plank Thickness mm	Nominal Width of Beam or Joist Face in.	Nominal Width of Beam or Joist Face mm
Up to 2 in.	3	76	2	51
2½ in. to 3½ in.	4	102	2	51
4 in. and 5 in.	4	102	3	76
6 in.	4	102	4	102

3-10.4.10 Lag screw rods shall not be used for support of pipes larger than 6 in. (152 mm). All holes for lag screw rods shall be predrilled 1/8 in. (3.2 mm) less in diameter than the root diameter of the lag screw thread.

3-10.5 Location of Hangers on Branch Lines. This subsection applies to the support of steel pipe or copper tube as specified in 3-1.1.1, subject to the provisions of 3-10.1.11.

3-10.5.1 On branch lines, there shall be not less than one hanger for each length of pipe.

Exception: Hangers may be located as provided in 3-10.5.2 to 3-10.5.5 inclusive.

3-10.5.2* When sprinklers are spaced less than 6 ft (1.8 m) apart, hangers may be spaced up to a maximum of 12 ft (3.7 m). (*See Figure A-3-10.5.2.*)

3-10.5.3 Starter lengths less than 6 ft (1.8 m) do not require a hanger, except on the end line of a side-feed system or where an intermediate cross main hanger has been omitted.

3-10.5.4 The distance between a hanger and the center line of an upright sprinkler shall not be less than 3 in. (76 mm).

3-10.5.5* The unsupported length between the end sprinkler and the last hanger on the line shall not be greater than 36 in. (914 mm) for 1-in. (25-mm) pipe or 48 in. (1219 mm) for 1¼-in. (33-mm) or larger pipe. When either of these limits is exceeded, the pipe shall be extended beyond the end sprinkler and supported by an additional hanger. (*See 3-8.1.2.1.*)

Exception: When the maximum pressure at the sprinkler exceeds 100 psi (6.9 bars), and a branch line above a ceiling supplies sprinklers in a pendent position below the ceiling the hanger assembly supporting the pipe supplying an end sprinkler in a pendent position shall be of a type that prevents upward movement of the pipe. [See Figure A-3-10.5.5(a).]

The unsupported length between the end sprinkler in a pendent position or drop nipple and the last hanger on the branch line shall not be greater than 12 in. (305 mm) for steel pipe or 6 in. (152 mm) for copper pipe. When this limit is exceeded, the pipe shall be extended beyond the end sprinkler and supported by an additional hanger. The hanger closest to the sprinkler shall be of a type that clamps to and prevents upward movement of the piping. [See Figure A-3-10.5.5(a).]

3-10.5.6* The length of an unsupported armover to a sprinkler shall not exceed 24 in. (610 mm) for steel pipe or 12 in. (305 mm) for copper tube. (*See 3-8.1.2.1.*)

Exception: When the maximum pressure at the sprinkler exceeds 100 psi and a branch line above a ceiling supplies sprinklers in a pendent position below the ceiling, the length of an unsupported armover to a sprinkler or drop nipple shall not exceed 12 in. (305 mm) for steel pipe and 6 in. (152 mm) for copper tube.

When the limits of unsupported armover lengths of 3-10.5.6 or this Exception are exceeded, the hanger closest to the sprinkler shall be of a type that prevents upward movement of the piping. [See Figure A-3-10.5.5(a).]

3-10.5.7 Wall mounted sidewall sprinklers shall be restrained to prevent movement.

3-10.6 Location of Hangers on Cross Mains. This subsection applies to the support of steel pipe only as specified in 3-1.1.1, subject to the provisions of 3-10.1.11. Intermediate hangers shall not be omitted for copper tube.

3-10.6.1* On cross mains, there shall be at least one hanger between each two branch lines.

Exception No. 1: In bays having two branch lines, the intermediate hanger may be omitted provided that a hanger attached to a purlin is installed on each branch line located as near to the cross main as the location of the purlin permits. [See Figure A-3-10.6.1(a).] Remaining branch line hangers shall be installed in accordance with 3-10.5.

Exception No. 2: In bays having three or more branch lines, either side or centerfeed, one (only) intermediate hanger may be omitted provided that a hanger attached to a purlin is installed on each branch line located as near to the cross main as the location of the purlin permits. [See Figures A-3-10.6.1(b) and A-3-10.6.1(c).] Remaining branch line hangers shall be installed in accordance with 3-10.5.

3-10.6.2 At the end of the cross main, intermediate trapeze hangers shall be installed unless the cross main is extended to the next framing member with an ordinary hanger installed at this point, in which event an intermediate hanger may be omitted in accordance with 3-10.6.1, Exceptions No. 1 and No. 2.

3-10.7 Support of Risers.

3-10.7.1 Risers shall be supported by attachments directly to the riser or by hangers located on the horizontal connections close to the riser.

3-10.7.2 In multistory buildings, riser supports shall be provided at the lowest level, at each alternate level above, above and below offsets, and at the top of the riser. Supports above the lowest level shall also restrain the pipe to prevent movement by an upward thrust when flexible fittings are used. Where risers are supported from the ground, the ground support constitutes the first level or riser support. Where risers are offset or do not rise from the ground, the first ceiling level above the offset constitutes the first level of riser support.

3-10.7.3 Sprinkler and tank risers in vertical shafts, or in buildings with ceilings over 25 ft (7.6 m) high, shall have at least one support for each riser pipe section.

3-10.7.4 Clamps supporting pipe by means of set screws shall not be used.

3-11 Sprinklers.

3-11.1 Types of Sprinklers. Some of the commonly used sprinklers are as follows:

(a) *Upright Sprinklers.* Sprinklers designed to be installed in such a way that the water spray is directed upwards against the deflector.

(b) *Pendent Sprinklers.* Sprinklers designed to be installed in such a way that the water stream is directed downward against the deflector.

(c) *Sidewall Sprinklers.* Sprinklers having special deflectors that are designed to discharge most of the water away from the nearby wall in a pattern resembling one quarter of a sphere, with a small portion of the discharge directed at the wall behind the sprinkler.

(d) *Extended Coverage Sidewall Sprinklers.* Sprinklers with special extended, directional, discharge patterns.

(e) *Open Sprinklers.* Sprinklers from which the actuating elements have been removed.

(f) *Corrosion-Resistant Sprinklers.* Sprinklers with special coatings or platings to be used in an atmosphere that would corrode an uncoated sprinkler.

(g) *Nozzles.* Devices for use in applications requiring special discharge patterns, directional spray, fine spray, or other unusual discharge characteristics.

(h)* *Dry-Pendent Sprinklers.* Sprinklers for use in a pendent position in a dry-pipe system or a wet-pipe system with the seal in a heated area.

(i)* *Dry Upright Sprinklers.* Sprinklers that are designed to be installed in an upright position, on a wet-pipe system, to extend into an unheated area with a seal in a heated area.

(j) *Ornamental Sprinklers.* Sprinklers that have been painted or plated by the manufacturer.

(k) *Flush Sprinklers.* Sprinklers in which all or part of the body, including the shank thread, is mounted above the lower plane of the ceiling.

(l) *Recessed Sprinklers.* Sprinklers in which all or part of the body, other than the shank thread, is mounted within a recessed housing.

(m) *Concealed Sprinklers.* Recessed sprinklers with cover plates.

(n) *Old-Style Sprinklers.* Sprinklers that direct only from 40 to 60 percent of the total water initially in a downward direction and that are designed to be installed with the deflector either upright or pendent.

(o) *Residential Sprinklers.* Sprinklers that have been specifically listed for use in residential occupancies.

(p) *Intermediate Level Sprinklers.* Sprinklers equipped with integral shields to protect their operating elements from the discharge of sprinklers installed at higher elevations.

(q) *Special Sprinklers.* Sprinklers that have been tested and listed as prescribed in 4-1.1.3.

(r) *Quick-Response Sprinklers.* A type of special sprinkler incorporating a fast-actuating heat-responsive element.

(s) *Large-Drop Sprinklers:* Listed large-drop sprinklers are characterized by a K factor between 11.0 and 11.5, and proven ability to meet prescribed penetration, cooling, and distribution criteria prescribed in large-drop sprinkler examination requirements. The deflector/discharge characteristics of large-drop sprinklers generate drops of such size and velocity as to enable effective penetration of the high-velocity fire plume.

3-11.2 Use of Sprinklers.

3-11.2.1* Only listed sprinklers shall be used and shall be installed in accordance with their listing.

Exception: When construction features or other special situations require unusual water distribution, listed sprinklers may be installed in other positions than anticipated by their listing to achieve specific results.

3-11.2.2 Sprinklers shall not be altered in any respect or have any type of ornamentation or coating applied after shipment from the place of manufacture.

3-11.2.3 Sprinklers shall not be used for system working pressures exceeding 175 psi (12.1 bars).

Exception: Higher design pressures may be used when sprinklers are listed for those pressures.

3-11.2.4 Old-style sprinklers shall not be used in a new installation.

Exception No. 1: For installation under piers and wharves where construction features require an upward discharge to wet the underside of decks and structural members supporting the decks, a sprinkler that projects water upward to wet the overhead shall be used. This can be accomplished by using standard pendent sprinklers installed in an upright position or by the use of old-style sprinklers. See NFPA 307, Standard for the Construction and Fire Protection of Marine Terminals, Piers, and Wharves.

Exception No. 2: Old-style sprinklers shall be installed in fur storage vaults. See 4-4.16.3. Also see NFPA 81, Standard for Fur Storage, Fumigation and Cleaning.

Exception No. 3: Listed old-style sprinklers may be used when construction features or other special situations require unique water distribution.

3-11.2.5 Sidewall sprinklers shall be installed only in Light Hazard Occupancies.

Exception: Sidewall sprinklers specifically listed for use in Ordinary Hazard Occupancies.

3-11.2.6 Extended coverage sidewall sprinklers shall be installed only in accordance with their listing.

3-11.2.7 Open sprinklers may be used to protect special hazards, for protection against exposures, or in other special locations.

3-11.2.8 Escutcheon Plates.

3-11.2.8.1 When nonmetallic ceiling plates (escutcheons) are used they shall be listed.

3-11.2.8.2 Escutcheon plates used to create a recessed or flush type sprinkler shall be part of a listed sprinkler assembly.

3-11.2.9 Residential Sprinklers.

3-11.2.9.1* Residential sprinklers may be used in dwelling units located in any occupancy provided they are installed in conformance with their listing and the positioning requirements of NFPA 13D, *Standard for the Installation of Sprinkler Systems in One- and Two-Family Dwellings and Mobile Homes.* One-half inch or larger orifice residential sprinklers may be used in dry-pipe systems when the design area is in compliance with Chapter 2.

3-11.2.9.2 When residential sprinklers are installed within a compartment as defined in 7-4.4, all sprinklers shall be from the same manufacturer and have the same heat-response element including temperature rating.

3-11.3 Replacement of Sprinklers.

3-11.3.1 When sprinklers are replaced, the replacement sprinkler shall be of the same type, orifice, and temperature rating unless conditions require a different type sprinkler be installed. The replacement sprinkler shall then be of a type, orifice, and temperature rating to suit the new conditions.

3-11.3.2 Old-style sprinklers may be replaced with old-style sprinklers, or with the appropriate pendent or upright sprinkler.

3-11.3.3 Old-style sprinklers shall not be used to replace pendent or upright sprinklers.

3-11.3.4 Extreme care shall be exercised when replacing horizontal sidewall and extended coverage sidewall sprinklers to assure the correct replacement sprinkler is installed.

3-11.3.5 Sprinklers that have been painted or coated, except by the manufacturer, shall be replaced and shall not be cleaned by use of chemicals, abrasives, or other means. (*See 3-11.9.2.*)

3-11.4 Corrosion-Resistant, Wax-Coated, or Similar Sprinklers.

3-11.4.1* Listed corrosion-resistant or special coated sprinklers shall be installed in locations where chemicals, moisture, or other corrosive vapors sufficient to cause corrosion of such devices exist.

3-11.4.2 Care shall be taken in the handling and installation of wax-coated or similar sprinklers to avoid damaging the coating.

3-11.4.3 Corrosion-resistant coatings shall be applied only by the manufacturer of the sprinkler.

Exception: Any damage to the protective coating occurring at the time of installation shall be repaired at once using only the coating of the manufacturer of the sprinkler in the approved manner so that none of the sprinkler will be exposed after installation has been completed.

3-11.5* Sprinkler Discharge Characteristics and Identification.

3-11.5.1 Table 3-11.5 shows the K factor, relative discharge, and identification for sprinklers having different orifice sizes.

Exception: Special listed sprinklers may have pipe threads different from those shown in Table 3-11.5.

3-11.5.2 For Light Hazard Occupancies not requiring as much water as is discharged by a nominal ½-in. (12.7-mm) orifice sprinkler operating at 7 psi (0.5 bar), sprinklers having a smaller orifice may be used subject to the following restrictions:

(a) The system shall be hydraulically calculated. (*See Section 8-1.*)

(b) Small orifice sprinklers shall not be used on dry-pipe, preaction, or combined dry-pipe and preaction systems.

Exception: Outside sprinklers for protection from exposure fires installed in conformance with Chapter 6.

(c) An approved strainer shall be provided in the riser or feed main that supplies sprinklers having orifices smaller than ⅜ in. (9.5 mm).

Table 3-11.5 Sprinkler Discharge Characteristics Identification

Nominal Orifice Size (in.)[1]	Orifice Type	K Factor[2]	Percent of Nominal ½ in. Discharge	Thread Type	Pintle	Nominal Orifice Size Marked On Frame
¼	Small	1.3-1.5	25	½ in. NPT	Yes	Yes
5/16	Small	1.8-2.0	33.3	½ in. NPT	Yes	Yes
⅜	Small	2.6-2.9	50	½ in. NPT	Yes	Yes
7/16	Small	4.0-4.4	75	½ in. NPT	Yes	Yes
½	Standard	5.3-5.8	100	½ in. NPT	No	No
17/32	Large	7.4-8.2	140	¾ in. NPT	No	No
				or ½ in. NPT	Yes	Yes
⅝	Extra Large	11.0-11.5	200	¾ in. NPT	Yes	Special Deflector

[1]See A-3-11.5.2

[2]K factor is the constant in the formula $Q = K\sqrt{P}$

Where Q = Flow in gpm
P = Pressure in psi

For SI Units: $Qm = Km\sqrt{Pm}$

Where Qm = Flow in L/min
Pm = Pressure in bars
$Km = 14\ K$

Table 3-11.6.1 Temperature Ratings, Classifications, and Color Codings

Max. Ceiling Temp. °F	°C	Temperature Rating °F	°C	Temperature Classification	Color Code	Glass Bulb Colors
100	38	135 to 170	57 to 77	Ordinary	Uncolored or Black	Orange or Red
150	66	175 to 225	79 to 107	Intermediate	White	Yellow or Green
225	107	250 to 300	121 to 149	High	Blue	Blue
300	149	325 to 375	163 to 191	Extra High	Red	Purple
375	191	400 to 475	204 to 246	Very Extra High	Green	Black
475	246	500 to 575	260 to 302	Ultra High	Orange	Black
625	329	650	343	Ultra High	Orange	Black

3-11.5.3 For locations or conditions requiring more water than is discharged by a nominal ½-in. (12.7-mm) orifice sprinkler, a sprinkler having a larger orifice may be used.

3-11.5.4 Sprinklers having orifice sizes exceeding ½ in. (12.7 mm) and having ½ in. NPT shall not be installed in new sprinkler systems.

3-11.6* Temperature Ratings, Classifications, and Color Coding.

3-11.6.1 The standard temperature ratings of automatic sprinklers are shown in Table 3-11.6.1. Automatic sprinklers shall have their frame arms colored in accordance with the color code designated in Table 3-11.6.1, with the following Exceptions:

Exception No. 1: The color identification for corrosion-resistant sprinklers may be a dot on the top of the deflector, the color of the coating material, or colored frame arms.

Exception No. 2: Color identification is not required for ornamental sprinklers such as factory plated or factory painted sprinklers, or for recessed, flush, or concealed sprinklers.

3-11.6.2 Ordinary temperature rated sprinklers shall be used throughout buildings.

Exception No. 1: Where maximum ceiling temperatures exceed 100°F (38°C), sprinklers with temperature ratings in accordance with the maximum ceiling temperatures of Table 3-11.6.1 shall be used.

Exception No. 2: Intermediate and high-temperature sprinklers may be used throughout Ordinary and Extra Hazard Occupancies.

Exception No. 3: Sprinklers of intermediate and high temperature classifications shall be installed in specific locations as required by 3-11.6.3 and 5-6.1.4.1.

Exception No. 4: When permitted or required by other NFPA standards.

3-11.6.3 The following practices shall be observed to provide sprinklers of other than ordinary temperature classification unless maximum expected temperatures are otherwise determined, or unless high-temperature sprinklers are used throughout [*see Tables 3-11.6.3(a) and 3-11.6.3(b) and Figure 3-11.6.3(a)*]:

(a) Sprinklers near unit heaters. Sprinklers in the heater zone shall be high and sprinklers in the danger zone intermediate temperature classification.

(b) Sprinklers located within 12 in. (305 mm) to one side or 30 in. (762 mm) above an uncovered steam main, heating coil, or radiator shall be intermediate temperature classification.

(c) Sprinklers within 7 ft (2.1 m) of a low-pressure blowoff valve that discharges free in a large room shall be high temperature classification.

(d) Sprinklers under glass or plastic skylights exposed to the direct rays of the sun shall be intermediate temperature classification.

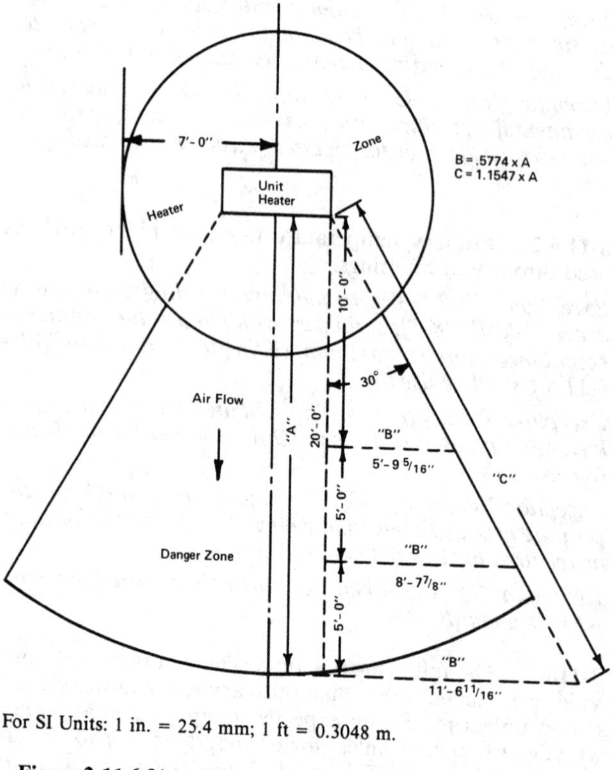
7'-0"
Zone
B = .5774 x A
C = 1.1547 x A
Unit
Heater
Heater
10'-0"
30°
Air Flow
"A"
20'-0"
"B"
5'-9 5/16"
"C"
5'-0"
Danger Zone
"B"
8'-7 7/8"
5'-0"
"B"
11'-6 11/16"

For SI Units: 1 in. = 25.4 mm; 1 ft = 0.3048 m.

Figure 3-11.6.3(a) Heater and Danger Zones at Unit Heaters.

Table 3-11.6.3(a) Temperature Ratings of Sprinklers Based on Distance from Heat Sources

Type of Heat Condition	Ordinary Degree Rating	Intermediate Degree Rating	High Degree Rating
1. Heating Ducts (a) Above	More than 2 ft 6 in.	2 ft 6 in. or less	—
(b) Side and Below	More than 1 ft 0 in.	1 ft 0 in. or less	—
(c) Diffuser Downward Discharge Horizontal Discharge	Any distance except as shown under Intermediate	*Downward:* Cylinder with 1 ft 0 in. radius from edge, extending 1 ft 0 in. below and 2 ft 6 in. above *Horizontal:* Semi-cylinder with 2 ft 6 in. radius in direction of flow, extending 1 ft 0 in. below and 2 ft 6 in. above	—
2. Unit Heater (a) Horizontal Discharge	—	*Discharge Side:* 7 ft 0 in. to 20 ft 0 in. radius pie-shaped cylinder [see Figure 3-11.6.3(a)] extending 7 ft 0 in. above and 2 ft 0 in. below heater; also 7 ft 0 in. radius cylinder more than 7 ft 0 in. above unit heater	7 ft 0 in. radius cylinder extending 7 ft 0 in. above and 2 ft 0 in. below unit heater
(b) Vertical Downward Discharge [Note: For sprinklers below unit heater, see Figure 3-11.6.3(a).]	—	7 ft 0 in. radius cylinder extending upward from an elevation 7 ft 0 in. above unit heater	7 ft 0 in. radius cylinder extending from the top of the unit heater to an elevation 7 ft 0 in. above unit heater
3. Steam Mains (Uncovered) (a) Above	More than 2 ft 6 in.	2 ft 6 in. or less	—
(b) Side and Below	More than 1 ft 0 in.	1 ft 0 in. or less	—
(c) Blowoff Valve	More than 7 ft 0 in.	—	7 ft 0 in. or less

For SI Units: 1 in. = 25.4 mm; 1 ft = 0.3048 m.

Table 3-11.6.3(b) Ratings of Sprinklers in Specified Locations

Location	Ordinary Degree Rating	Intermediate Degree Rating	High Degree Rating
Skylights	—	Glass or plastic	—
Attics	Ventilated	Unventilated	—
Peaked Roof: Metal or thin boards; concealed or not concealed; insulated or uninsulated	Ventilated	Unventilated	—
Flat Roof: Metal, not concealed; insulated or uninsulated	Ventilated or unventilated	Note: For uninsulated roof, climate and occupancy may require Intermediate sprinklers. Check on job.	—
Flat Roof: Metal; concealed; insulated or uninsulated	Ventilated	Unventilated	—
Show Windows	Ventilated	Unventilated	—

Note: A check of job condition by means of thermometers may be necessary.

(e) Sprinklers in an unventilated concealed space under an uninsulated roof, or in an unventilated attic, shall be of intermediate temperature classification.

(f) Sprinklers in unventilated show windows having high-powered electric lights near the ceiling shall be intermediate temperature classification.

(g) For sprinklers protecting commercial-type cooking equipment and ventilation systems, temperature classifications of intermediate, high, or extra high shall be provided as determined by use of a temperature measuring device. (*See 4-4.17.2.*)

3-11.6.4 In case of change of occupancy involving temperature change, the sprinklers shall be changed accordingly.

3-11.7* Stock of Spare Sprinklers.

3-11.7.1 There shall be maintained on the premises a supply of spare sprinklers (never less than 6) so that any sprinklers that have operated or been damaged in any way may be promptly replaced. These sprinklers shall correspond to the types and temperature ratings of the sprinklers in the property. The sprinklers shall be kept in a cabinet located where the temperature to which they are subjected will at no time exceed 100°F (38°C).

3-11.7.2 A special sprinkler wrench shall also be provided and kept in the cabinet, to be used in the removal and installation of sprinklers.

3-11.7.3 The stock of spare sprinklers shall be as follows:

(a) For equipments not over 300 sprinklers, not less than 6 sprinklers.

(b) For equipments 300 to 1,000 sprinklers, not less than 12 sprinklers.

(c) For equipments above 1,000 sprinklers, not less than 24 sprinklers.

(d) Stock of spare sprinklers shall include all types and ratings installed.

3-11.8* Guards and Shields. Sprinklers that are so located as to be subject to mechanical injury (in either the upright or the pendent position) shall be protected with listed guards.

3-11.9 Painting and Ornamental Finishes.

3-11.9.1* When the sprinkler piping is given any kind of coating, such as whitewash or paint, care shall be exercised to see that no automatic sprinklers are coated.

3-11.9.2* Sprinklers shall not be painted and any sprinklers that have been painted shall be replaced with new listed sprinklers of the same characteristics.

Exception: Factory-applied coatings to sprinkler frames for identifying sprinklers of different temperature ratings in accordance with 3-11.6.1.

3-11.9.3 Ornamental finishes shall not be applied to sprinklers by anyone other than the sprinkler manufacturer and only sprinklers listed with such finishes shall be used.

3-12 Sprinkler Alarms.

3-12.1 Definition. A local alarm unit is an assembly of apparatus approved for the service and so constructed and installed that any flow of water from a sprinkler system equal to or greater than that from a single automatic sprinkler of the smallest orifice size installed on the system will result in an audible alarm on the premises within 5 minutes after such flow begins. For remote sprinkler waterflow alarm transmission see 3-12.7.1.

3-12.2* Where Required. Local waterflow alarms shall be provided on all sprinkler systems having more than 20 sprinklers.

3-12.3 Waterflow Detecting Devices.

3-12.3.1 Wet-Pipe Systems. The alarm apparatus for a wet-pipe system shall consist of a listed alarm check valve or other listed waterflow detecting alarm device with the necessary attachments required to give an alarm.

3-12.3.2 Dry-Pipe Systems. The alarm apparatus for a dry-pipe system shall consist of listed alarm attachments to the dry-pipe valve. When a dry-pipe valve is located on the system side of an alarm valve, the actuating device of the alarms for the dry-pipe valve may be connected to the alarms on the wet-pipe system.

3-12.3.3* Preaction and Deluge Systems. In addition to the waterflow alarms required for systems having more than 20 sprinklers, all deluge and preaction systems shall be provided with listed alarm attachments actuated by the detection system.

3-12.3.4* Waterflow alarm indicators (paddle-type) shall not be installed in dry-pipe, preaction, or deluge systems.

3-12.4 Attachments — General.

3-12.4.1* An alarm unit shall include a listed mechanical alarm, horn, or siren, or a listed weatherproof electric gong, bell, horn, or siren.

3-12.4.2* Outdoor mechanical or electrically operated bells shall be of weatherproof and guarded type.

3-12.4.3 On each alarm check valve used under conditions of variable water pressure, a retarding device shall be installed. Valves shall be provided in the connections to retarding devices, to permit repair or removal without shutting off sprinklers; these valves shall be so arranged that they may be locked or sealed in the open position.

3-12.4.4 Alarm valves, dry-pipe, preaction, and deluge valves shall be fitted with an alarm bypass test connection for an electric alarm switch, water motor gong, or both. This pipe connection shall be made on the water supply side of the system and provided with a control valve and drain for the alarm piping. A check valve shall be installed in the pipe connection from the intermediate chamber of a dry-pipe valve.

3-12.4.5 A control valve shall be installed in connection with a pressure-type contactor or water-motor-operated alarm devices, and such valves shall be of the type that will clearly indicate whether they are open or closed and be so constructed that they may be locked or sealed in the open position. The control valve for the retarding chamber on alarm check valves of wet-pipe systems may be accepted as complying with this paragraph.

3-12.5* Attachments — Mechanically Operated. For all types of sprinkler systems employing water-motor-operated alarms, an approved ¾-in. (19-mm) strainer shall be installed at the alarm outlet of the waterflow detecting device except that when a retarding chamber is used in connection with an alarm valve, the strainer shall be located at the outlet of the retarding chamber unless the retarding chamber is provided with an approved integral strainer in its outlet. Water-motor-operated devices shall be protected from the weather, and shall be properly aligned and so installed as not to get out of adjustment. All piping to these devices shall be galvanized or brass or other approved corrosion-resistant material of a size not less than 3/4 in. (19 mm).

3-12.6 Alarm Attachments — High-rise Buildings. When a fire must be fought internally due to the height of a building, the following additional alarm supervision must be provided:

(a) When each sprinkler system on each floor is equipped with a separate waterflow device, it shall be connected to an alarm system in such a manner that operation of one sprinkler will actuate the alarm system, and the location of the operated flow device shall be indicated on an annunciator and/or register. The annunciator or register shall be located at grade level at the normal point of fire department access, at a constantly attended building security control center, or both locations.

Exception: When the location within the protected buildings where supervisory or alarm signals are received is not under constant supervision by qualified personnel in the employ of the owner, a connection shall be provided to transmit a signal to a remote or central station.

(b) A distinct trouble signal shall be provided to indicate a condition that will impair the satisfactory operation of the sprinkler system. This shall include but not be limited to monitoring control valves, building temperatures, fire pump power supplies and running conditions, and water tank levels and temperatures. Pressure supervision shall also be provided on pressure tanks.

3-12.7 Attachments — Electrically Operated.

3-12.7.1 Electrically operated alarm attachments forming part of an auxiliary, central station, proprietary, or remote station signaling system shall be installed in accordance with the following applicable NFPA standards:

(a) NFPA 71, *Standard for the Installation, Maintenance, and Use of Signaling Systems for Central Station Service,*

(b) NFPA 72B, *Standard for the Installation, Maintenance, and Use of Auxiliary Protective Signaling Systems for Fire Alarm Service,*

(c) NFPA 72C, *Standard for the Installation, Maintenance, and Use of Remote Station Protective Signaling Systems,*

(d) NFPA 72D, *Standard for the Installation, Maintenance, and Use of Proprietary Protective Signaling Systems.*

3-12.7.2* The circuits of electrical alarm attachments forming part of a local sprinkler waterflow alarm system need not be supervised.

Exception: If the local sprinkler waterflow alarm system is part of a required local fire alarm system, it shall be installed in accordance with NFPA 72A, Standard for the Installation, Maintenance, and Use of Local Protective Signaling Systems.

3-12.7.3 Waterflow detecting devices, including the associated alarm circuits, shall be tested by an actual waterflow through use of a test connection. (*See 3-12.8.*)

3-12.7.4 Outdoor electric alarm devices shall be of a type specifically listed for outdoor use, and the outdoor wiring shall be in approved conduit, properly protected from the entrance of water in addition to the requirements of 3-12.7.1 and 3-12.7.2.

3-12.8 Drains. Drains from alarm devices shall be so arranged that there will be no danger of freezing, and so that there will be no overflowing at the alarm apparatus at domestic connections or elsewhere with the sprinkler drains wide open and under system pressure. (*See 3-6.4.*)

Chapter 4 Spacing, Location, and Position of Sprinklers

4-1 General Information.

4-1.1* Basic Requirements.

4-1.1.1* The basic requirements for spacing, location, and position of sprinklers are specified in this chapter and are based on the following principles:

(a) Sprinklers installed throughout the premises,

(b) Sprinklers located so as not to exceed maximum protection area per sprinkler,

(c) Sprinklers positioned and located so as to optimize performance with respect to activation time and distribution,

(d) And as specified herein.

Exception No. 1: See 4-4.3, 4-4.4, and 4-4.19.2 for locations from which sprinklers may be omitted.

Exception No. 2: Special sprinklers may be installed in accordance with 4-1.1.3.

Exception No. 3: When sprinklers are specifically tested and test results prove that deviations from clearance requirements to structural members offer no obstruction to spray discharge, they may be positioned and located accordingly.

Exception No. 4: Clearance between sprinklers and ceilings may exceed the maximum specified in Sections 4-3 and 4-5.4 provided that, for the conditions of occupancy protected, tests or calculations show comparable sensitivity and performance of the sprinklers to those installed in conformance with Sections 4-3 and 4-5.4.

4-1.1.2 Residential sprinklers shall be installed in conformance with their listing and the positioning requirements of NFPA 13D, *Standard for the Installation of Sprinkler Systems for One- and Two-Family Dwellings and Mobile Homes.*

4-1.1.3 Special sprinklers may be installed with protection areas, locations, and distances between sprinklers differing from those specified in Sections 4-2 and 4-5 when found suitable for such use based on: fire tests related to the hazard category; tests to evaluate distribution, wetting of floors and walls, interference to distribution by structural elements; and tests to characterize response sensitivity, when installed in accordance with any special sprinkler listing limitation.

Exception No. 1: No sprinkler shall be installed to protect an area greater than 400 sq ft (36 m^2).

Exception No. 2: Maximum area of coverage for individual extended coverage pendent and upright sprinklers shall be limited to areas having coverage with equal-sided dimensions.

4-1.2* When partial sprinkler systems are installed, the requirements of this standard shall be used insofar as they are applicable. The authority having jurisdiction shall be consulted in each case.

4-1.3 Definitions.

4-1.3.1 Smooth Ceiling Construction. The term *smooth ceiling construction* as used in this standard includes:

(a) Flat slab, pan-type reinforced concrete, concrete joist less than 3 ft (0.9 m) on centers.

(b) Continuous smooth bays formed by wood, concrete, or steel beams spaced more than 7½ ft (2.3 m) on centers — beams supported by columns, girders, or trusses.

(c) Smooth roof or floor decks supported directly on girders or trusses spaced more than 7½ ft (2.3 m) on centers.

(d) Smooth monolithic ceilings of at least ¾ in. (19 mm) of plaster on metal lath or a combination of materials of equivalent fire-resistive rating attached to the underside of wood joists, wood trusses, and bar joists.

(e) Open web-type steel beams, regardless of spacing.

(f) Smooth shell-type roofs, such as folded plates, hyperbolic paraboloids, saddles, domes, and long barrel shells.

(g) In (b) through (f) above, the roof and floor decks may be noncombustible or combustible. Item (b) would include standard mill construction.

(h) Suspended ceilings of noncombustible construction.

(i) Suspended ceilings of combustible construction where there is a full complement of sprinklers in the space immediately above such a ceiling and the space is unfloored and unoccupied.

(j) Smooth monolithic ceilings with fire resistance less than that specified under item (d) attached to the underside of wood joists, wood trusses, and bar joists.

(k) Combustible suspended ceilings arranged other than as specified under item (i).

4-1.3.2 Beam and Girder Construction. The term *beam and girder construction* as used in this standard includes noncombustible and combustible roof or floor decks supported by wood beams of 4 in. (102 mm) or greater nominal thickness, or concrete or steel beams spaced 3 to 7½ ft (0.9 to 2.3 m) on centers and either supported on or framed into girders. [When supporting a wood plank deck, this includes semi-mill and panel construction, and when supporting (with steel framing) gypsum plank, steel deck, concrete, tile, or similar material, this would include much of the so-called noncombustible construction.]

4-1.3.3* Bar Joist Construction. The term *bar joist construction* refers to construction employing joists consisting of steel truss-shaped members. Wood truss-shaped members which consist of wood top and bottom chord members not exceeding 4 in. (102 mm) in depth with steel tube or bar webs are also defined as bar joists. Bar joist includes noncombustible or combustible roof or floor decks on bar joist construction.

4-1.3.4 Panel Construction. The term *panel construction* as used in this standard includes ceiling panels formed by members capable of trapping heat to aid the operation of sprinklers and limited to a maximum of 300 sq ft (27.9 m^2) in area. Beams spaced more than 7½ ft (2.3 m) apart and framed into girders qualify for panel construction provided the 300 sq ft (27.9 m^2) area limitation is met.

4-1.3.5 Standard Mill Construction. The term *standard mill construction* as used in this standard refers to heavy timber construction as defined in NFPA 220, *Standard on Types of Building Construction.*

4-1.3.6 Semi-Mill Construction. The term *semi-mill construction* as used in this standard refers to a modified standard mill construction, where greater column spacing is used and beams rest on girders.

4-1.3.7 Wood Joist Construction. The term *wood joist construction* refers to solid wood members of rectangular cross section, which may vary from 2 to 4 in. (51 to 102 mm) nominal width and up to 14 in. (356 mm) nominal depth, spaced up to 3 ft (0.9 m) on centers, and spanning up to 40 ft (12 m) between supports, supporting a floor or roof deck. Solid wood members less than 4 in. (102 mm) nominal thickness and up to 14 in. (356 mm) nominal depth, spaced more than 3 ft (0.9 m) on centers are also considered as wood joist construction.

4-1.3.8* Composite Wood Joist Construction. The term *composite wood joist construction* refers to wood beams of I cross section constructed of wood flanges and solid wood web, supporting a floor or roof deck. Composite wood joists may vary in depth up to 48 in. (1.2 m), may be spaced up to 48 in. (1.2 m) on centers, and may span up to 60 ft (18 m) between supports. Joist channels shall be fire-stopped to the full depth of the joists with material equivalent to the web construction so that individual channel areas do not exceed 300 sq ft (27.9 m^2).

4-1.3.9 Wood Truss Construction. The term *wood truss construction* refers to parallel or pitched wood chord members connected by open wood members (webbing), supporting a roof or floor deck. Trusses with steel webbing, similar to bar joist construction, having top and bottom wood chords exceeding 4 in. (102 mm) in depth, shall also be considered wood truss construction.

4-1.3.10 High-Piled Storage. The term *high-piled storage* refers to solid piled, palletized, rack storage, bin box, and shelf storage in excess of 12 ft (3.7 m) in height. See 10-1.2 for availability of information for sprinkler protection of high-piled storage.

4-2 Spacing and Location of Upright and Pendent Sprinklers. (*See also Sections 4-3 and 4-4.*)

4-2.1 Distance Between Sprinklers, on the Branch Lines and Between the Branch Lines.

4-2.1.1 For Light Hazard Occupancies, the distance between sprinklers, either on branch lines or between branch lines, shall not exceed 15 ft (4.6 m).

4-2.1.2* For Ordinary Hazard Occupancies, the distance between sprinklers, either on branch lines or between branch lines, shall not exceed 15 ft (4.6 m).

4-2.1.3 For Extra Hazard Occupancies, the distance between sprinklers, either on branch lines or between branch lines, shall not exceed 12 ft (3.7 m).

4-2.1.4 In areas used for high-piled storage (as defined in 4-1.3.10), the distance between sprinklers shall not exceed 12 ft (3.7 m).

Exception No 1: In bays 25 ft (7.6 m) wide, a spacing of 12 ft 6 in. (3.8 m) between sprinklers is permitted.

Exception No. 2: For systems hydraulically designed for densities below 0.25 gpm per sq ft [(10.2 L/min)/m²)] spacing between sprinklers to 15 ft (4.6 m) is permitted.

4-2.1.5 Distance from Walls.

4-2.1.5.1 The distance from walls to sprinklers shall not exceed one-half of the allowable distance between sprinklers.

Exception: For small rooms, see 4-4.19.

4-2.1.5.2 Sprinklers shall be located a minimum of 4 in. (102 mm) from a wall.

4-2.2* Protection Area Limitations.

4-2.2.1 System Areas. The maximum floor area on any one floor to be protected by sprinklers supplied by any one sprinkler system riser or combined system riser shall be as follows:

Light Hazard — 52,000 sq ft (4831 m^2)

Ordinary Hazard — 52,000 sq ft (4831 m^2)

Extra Hazard — Pipe Schedule — 25,000 sq ft (2323 m^2)

— Hydraulically Calculated — 40,000 sq ft (3716 m^2)

Storage — High-piled storage (as defined in 4-1.3.10) and storage covered by other NFPA standards — 40,000 sq ft (3716 m^2).

Exception: When single systems protect Extra Hazard, high-piled storage, or storage covered by other NFPA standards and Ordinary or Light Hazard areas, the Extra Hazard or storage area coverage shall not exceed the floor area specified for that hazard and the total area coverage shall not exceed 52,000 sq ft (4831 m^2).

4-2.2.2 Light Hazard Occupancy.

4-2.2.2.1 Under smooth ceiling, beam and girder, and bar joist construction (as defined in 4-1.3.1, 4-1.3.2, and 4-1.3.3) the protection area per sprinkler shall not exceed 225 sq ft (20.9 m^2).

Exception: The protection area per sprinkler for pipe schedule systems shall not exceed 200 sq ft (18.6 m^2).

4-2.2.2.2* Under exposed wood joist construction (as defined in 4-1.3.7) the protection area per sprinkler shall not exceed 130 sq ft (12.1 m^2).

4-2.2.2.3 Under exposed composite wood joist and exposed parallel chord wood truss construction (as defined in 4-1.3.8 and 4-1.3.9 respectively) of 16 in. (406 mm) nominal depth or less and exposed pitch chord wood truss construction of any depth, the protection area per sprinkler shall not exceed 130 sq ft (12.1 m^2).

Exception: For composite wood joist construction and exposed parallel wood chord construction with members spaced more than 3 ft (0.9 m) on centers, see 4-2.2.2.4.

4-2.2.2.4 For other types of construction the protection area per sprinkler shall not exceed 168 sq ft (15.6 m^2).

4-2.2.3 Ordinary Hazard Occupancy. For all types of construction the protection area per sprinkler shall not exceed 130 sq ft (12.1 m^2).

4-2.2.4 Extra Hazard Occupancy. The protection area per sprinkler shall not exceed 100 sq ft (9.3 m^2) for any type of building construction. Sprinkler spacing may exceed 100 sq ft (9.3 m^2) but shall not exceed 130 sq ft (12.1 m^2) for densities below 0.25 gpm per sq ft [(10.2 L/min)/m^2].

Exception: The protection area per sprinkler for pipe schedule systems shall not exceed 90 sq ft (8.4 m^2).

4-2.2.5 High-Piled Storage. In areas used for high-piled storage (as defined in 4-1.3.10) or for storage covered by other NFPA standards the protection area per sprinkler shall not exceed 100 sq ft (9.3 m^2).

Exception No. 1: Sprinkler protection areas may exceed 100 sq ft (9.3 m^2) but shall not exceed 130 sq ft (12.1 m^2) in systems hydraulically designed in accordance with NFPA 231, Standard for General Storage, and 231C, Standard for Rack Storage of Materials, for densities below 0.25 gpm per sq ft [(10.2 L/min)/m^2].

Exception No. 2: Where protection areas are specifically indicated in the design criteria of other NFPA standards.

4-2.2.6 Special Conditions. When other NFPA standards have developed more stringent sprinkler system spacing criteria, they shall take precedence when supported by valid fire tests.

4-2.3* Location of Sprinklers and Branch Lines with Respect to Structural Members.

4-2.3.1 Sprinklers may be located under beams, in bays, or both, in combination, but the locations must meet the provisions outlined in Sections 4-2.4 and 4-3.

4-2.3.2 Where there are two sets of joists under a roof or ceiling and there is no flooring over the lower set, sprinklers shall be installed above and below the lower set of joists where there is a clearance of 6 in. (152 mm) or more between the top of the lower joist and bottom of the upper joist. (*See Figure 4-2.3.2.*) Sprinklers may be omitted from below the lower set of joists where at least 18 in. (457 mm) is maintained between sprinkler deflectors and tops of lower joists.

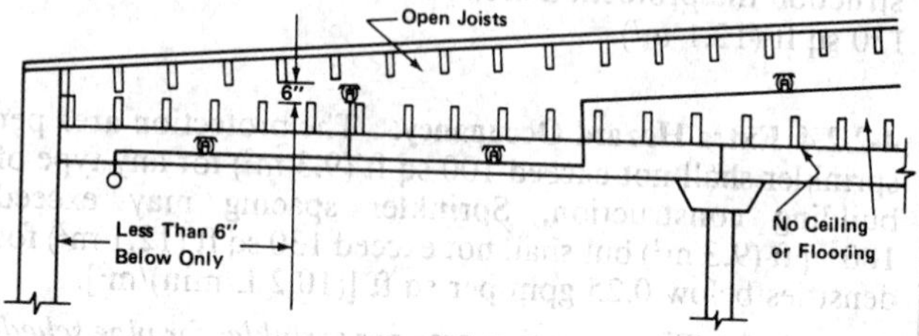
Open Joists
6"
Less Than 6"
Below Only
No Ceiling
or Flooring

For SI Units: 1 in. = 25.4 mm.

Figure 4-2.3.2 Arrangement of Sprinklers under Two Sets of Open Joists — No Sheathing on Lower Joists.

4-2.4 Clearance Between Sprinklers and Structural Members.

4-2.4.1 Trusses.

4-2.4.1.1 Sprinklers installed between the top and bottom chord members shall be located at least 2 ft (0.6 m) laterally from truss members (web or chord) that are more than 4 in. (102 mm) wide, and at least 1 ft (0.3 m) laterally from truss members 4 in. (102 mm) or less in width. For trusses with steel webbing similar to bar joists, clearance from webs shall be in accordance with 4-2.4.5.

Exception: Sprinklers running through or above the trusses may be located on the center line of a truss provided chord members are not more than 8 in. (203 mm) wide, and the deflector is at least 6 in. (152 mm) above the chord member.

4-2.4.1.2 Where sprinklers are located laterally beside the chord members, clearances between the chord members and the sprinkler deflectors shall be in accordance with 4-2.4.6.

4-2.4.2 Girders. When sprinkler lines are located perpendicular to and above girders, sprinklers shall be located at least 3 ft 9 in. (1.14 m) from girders except that they may be located directly above girders with the top flange not more than 8 in. (203 mm) wide, in which case the deflectors shall be at least 6 in. (152 mm) above the top of the girder.

4-2.4.3 When sprinkler deflectors are in accordance with Table 4-2.4.6, the girders may be disregarded in the spacing of the branch lines.

4-2.4.4 Open Web-Type Steel Beams. (*See Figure 4-2.4.4.*) When branch lines are run across and through openings of open web-type steel beams, sprinklers may be spaced "bay and beam" provided:

(a) The distance between sprinklers and between branch lines conforms to 4-2.1,

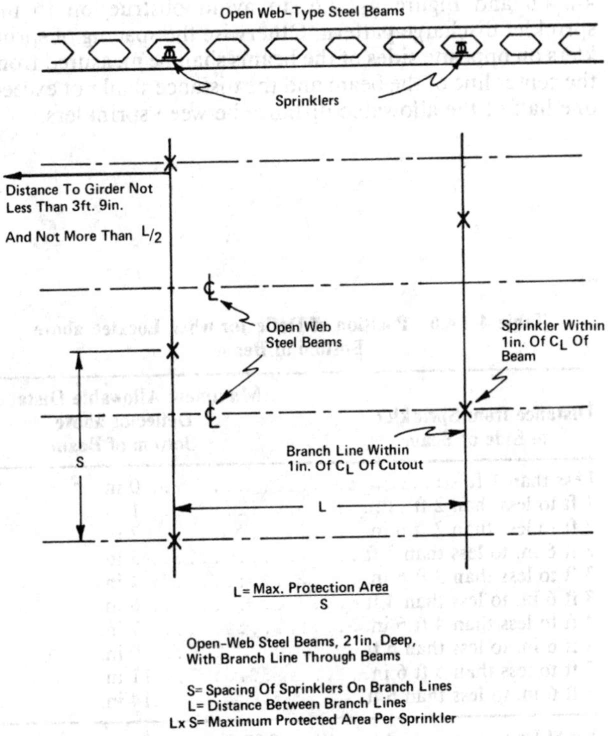
Open Web-Type Steel Beams
Sprinklers
Distance To Girder Not Less Than 3ft. 9in.
And Not More Than L/2
Open Web Steel Beams
Sprinkler Within 1in. Of CL Of Beam
Branch Line Within 1in. Of CL Of Cutout
S
L
L = Max. Protection Area / S
Open-Web Steel Beams, 21in. Deep, With Branch Line Through Beams
S= Spacing Of Sprinklers On Branch Lines
L= Distance Between Branch Lines
Lx S= Maximum Protected Area Per Sprinkler

For SI Units: 1 in. = 25.4 mm.

Figure 4-2.4.4 Location of Branch Lines and Sprinklers.

(b) Sprinklers in the beam openings are located within 1 in. (25 mm) horizontally of the opening center line,

(c) The branch line is located within 1 in. (25 mm) horizontally of the opening center line, and

(d) Sprinklers on alternate lines are staggered.

4-2.4.5 Bar Joists. Sprinklers shall be at least 3 in. (76 mm) laterally from web members of open bar joists which do not exceed ½ in. (13 mm) and at least 6 in. (152 mm) laterally from web members which do not exceed 1 in. (25 mm). When the dimensions of the web member exceed 1 in. (25 mm), see 4-2.4.1.

4-2.4.6* Beams. Deflectors of sprinklers in bays shall be at sufficient distances from the beams, as shown in Table 4-2.4.6 and Figure 4-2.4.6, to avoid obstruction to the sprinkler discharge pattern. Otherwise the spacing of sprinklers on opposite sides of the beams shall be measured from the center line of the beam and the distance shall not exceed one-half of the allowable distance between sprinklers.

Table 4-2.4.6 Position of Deflector when Located above Bottom of Beam

Distance from Sprinkler to Side of Beam	Maximum Allowable Distance Deflector above Bottom of Beam
Less than 1 ft	0 in.
1 ft to less than 2 ft	1 in.
2 ft to less than 2 ft 6 in.	2 in.
2 ft 6 in. to less than 3 ft	3 in.
3 ft to less than 3 ft 6 in.	4 in.
3 ft 6 in. to less than 4 ft	6 in.
4 ft to less than 4 ft 6 in.	7 in.
4 ft 6 in. to less than 5 ft	9 in.
5 ft to less than 5 ft 6 in.	11 in.
5 ft 6 in. to less than 6 ft	14 in.

For SI Units: 1 in. = 25.4 mm; 1 ft = 0.3048 m.

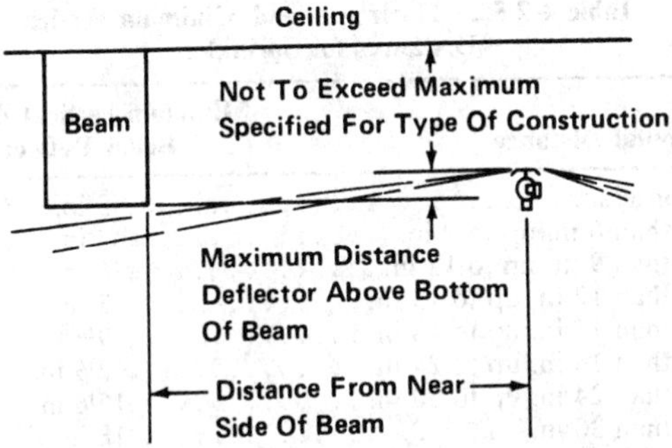
Ceiling
Beam
Not To Exceed Maximum
Specified For Type Of Construction
Maximum Distance
Deflector Above Bottom
Of Beam
Distance From Near
Side Of Beam

Figure 4-2.4.6 Position of Deflector, Upright, or Pendent Sprinkler When Located above Bottom of Beam.

4-2.4.7* Position of Deflectors. Deflectors of sprinklers shall be parallel to ceilings, roofs, or the incline of stairs, but when installed in the peak of a pitched roof they shall be horizontal. Low-pitched roofs having slopes not greater than 1 in. per ft (83 mm/m) may be considered level in the application of this rule, and sprinklers may be installed with deflectors horizontal.

4-2.5 Clear Space Below Sprinklers.

4-2.5.1 A minimum of 18 in. (457 mm) clearance shall be maintained between top of storage and ceiling sprinkler deflectors. For in-rack sprinklers, the clear space shall be in accordance with NFPA 231C, *Standard for Rack Storage of Materials.*

4-2.5.2* The distance from sprinklers to privacy curtains, free-standing partitions, or room dividers shall be sufficient, as shown in Table 4-2.5.2 and Figure 4-2.5.2, to avoid obstruction to the sprinkler discharge pattern.

Table 4-2.5.2 Horizontal and Minimum Vertical Distances for Sprinklers

Horizontal Distance	Minimum Vertical Distance Below Deflector
6 in. or less	3 in.
More than 6 in. up to 9 in.	4 in.
More than 9 in. up to 12 in.	6 in.
More than 12 in. up to 15 in.	8 in.
More than 15 in. up to 18 in.	9½ in.
More than 18 in. up to 24 in.	12½ in.
More than 24 in. up to 30 in.	15½ in.
More than 30 in.	18 in.

For SI Units: 1 in. = 25.4 mm.

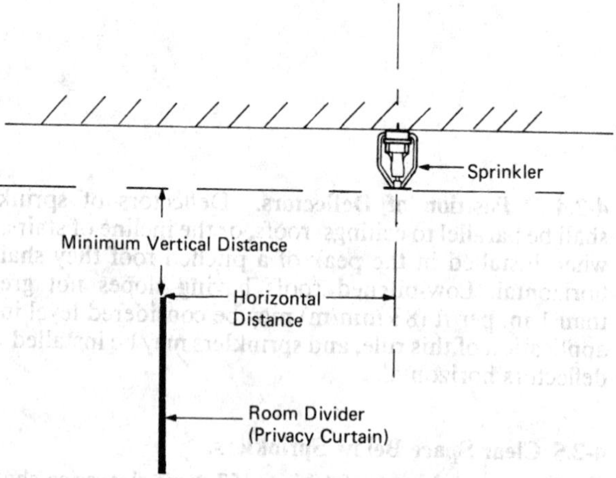
Sprinkler
Minimum Vertical Distance
Horizontal Distance
Room Divider (Privacy Curtain)

Figure 4-2.5.2 Standard Sprinkler Installed Near Privacy Curtains, Free-standing Partitions, or Room Dividers.

4-3 Position of Upright and Pendent Sprinklers.

4-3.1 Smooth Ceiling Construction (*as defined in 4-1.3.1*). Deflectors of sprinklers shall be located 1 to 10 in. (25 to 254 mm) below combustible ceilings or 1 to 12 in. (25 to 305 mm) below noncombustible ceilings. The operating elements of sprinklers shall be located below the ceiling.

Exception No. 1: Deflectors of sprinklers under beams shall be located 1 to 4 in. (25 to 102 mm) below beams, and not more than 14 in. (356 mm) below combustible ceilings or not more than 16 in. (406 mm) below noncombustible ceilings.

Exception No. 2: Special ceiling-type pendent sprinklers (concealed, recessed, and flush-types) may have the operating element above the ceiling and the deflector located nearer to the ceiling when installed in accordance with their listing.

4-3.2 Beam and Girder Construction (*as defined in 4-1.3.2*).

4-3.2.1 Deflectors of sprinklers in bays shall be located 1 to 16 in. (25 to 406 mm) below combustible or noncombustible roof or floor decks.

4-3.2.2 Deflectors of sprinklers under beams shall be located 1 to 4 in. (25 to 102 mm) below beams and not more than 20 in. (508 mm) below combustible or noncombustible roof or floor decks.

4-3.2.3 Deflectors of sprinklers under concrete tee construction with stems spaced less than 7½ ft (2.3 m) but more than 3 ft (0.9 m) on centers shall, regardless of the depth of the tee, be located at or above a plane 1 in. (25 mm) below the level of the bottom of the stems of the tees and comply with Table 4-2.4.6.

4-3.3 Open Bar Joist Construction (*as defined in 4-1.3.3*). Deflectors of sprinklers shall be located 1 to 10 in. (25 to 254 mm) below combustible roof or floor decks or not more than 12 in. (305 mm) below noncombustible roof or floor decks.

4-3.4 Panel Construction (*as defined in 4-1.3.4*).

4-3.4.1 Deflectors of sprinklers in bays formed by members, such as beams framed into girders, resulting in panels up to 300 sq ft (27.9 m^2) shall be located 1 to 18 in. (25 to 457 mm) below combustible or noncombustible roof or floor decks.

4-3.4.2 Deflectors of sprinklers under the members, such as under beams framed into girders, forming panels up to 300 sq ft (27.9 m^2) shall be located 1 to 4 in. (25 to 102 mm) below such members and not more than 22 in. (559 mm) below combustible or noncombustible roof or floor decks.

4-3.5 Wood Joist Construction (*as defined in 4-1.3.7*). In exposed wood joists spaced 3 ft (0.9 m) or less on centers, deflectors of sprinklers shall be located 1 to 6 in. (25 to 152 mm) below the bottom of the joist. If exposed joists are spaced more than 3 ft (0.9 m) on centers, deflectors of sprinklers shall be located in accordance with 4-3.1 or 4-3.2.

4-3.6 Composite Wood Joist Construction (*as defined in 4-1.3.8*). In exposed composite wood joist construction of 16 in. (406 mm) nominal depth or less, deflectors of sprinklers shall be located 1 to 6 in. (25 to 152 mm) below the bottom chord.

4-3.7 Wood Truss Construction (*as defined in 4-1.3.9*). In exposed wood truss construction, sprinklers shall be located within the trusses and shall conform to 4-2.4.1, 4-2.4.5, and 4-3.1.

Exception: For wood truss construction with members 16 in. (406 mm) nominal depth or less, deflectors of sprinklers may be located 1 to 6 in. (25 to 152 mm) below the bottom chord.

4-3.8 Location Under Sheathed or Suspended Ceiling Under Any Type of Construction. The position of sprinklers under sheathed or suspended ceilings with any type of construction shall be the same as for smooth-ceiling construction. (*See 4-3.1.*)

4-4* Locations or Conditions Involving Special Consideration.

4-4.1 Combustible Form Board. When roof or floor decks consist of poured gypsum or concrete on combustible form board supported on steel supports, the position of sprinkler deflectors shall be the same as for noncombustible construction as stated in Section 4-3. When combustible form board is located above suspended ceilings or in concealed spaces, see 4-4.4.1.

4-4.2 Metal Roof Decks. When roof decks are metal with combustible adhesives or vapor seal, the position of sprinklers shall be the same as for combustible construction.

4-4.3 Spaces Under Ground Floors. Sprinklers shall be installed in all spaces below combustible ground floors except that, by permission of the authority having jurisdiction, sprinklers may be omitted when all of the following conditions prevail:

(a) The space is not accessible for storage purposes or entrance of unauthorized persons and is protected against accumulation of wind-borne debris;

(b) The space contains no equipment such as steam pipes, electric wiring, shafting, or conveyors;

(c) The floor over the space is tight;

(d) No combustible or flammable liquids or materials that under fire conditions may convert into combustible or flammable liquids are processed, handled, or stored on the floor above.

4-4.4 Concealed Spaces.

4-4.4.1* All concealed spaces enclosed wholly or partly by exposed combustible construction shall be protected by sprinklers.

Exception No. 1: Spaces formed by studs or joists with less than 6 in. (152 mm) between the inside or near edges of the studs or joists. (See Figure 4-2.3.2.)

Exception No. 2: Spaces formed by bar joists with less than 6 in. (152 mm) between the roof or floor deck and ceiling.

Exception No. 3: Spaces formed by ceilings attached directly to or to within 6 in. (152 mm) of wood joist construction.

Exception No. 4: Spaces formed by ceilings attached directly to the underside of composite wood joist construction, provided the joist channels are fire-stopped into volumes each not exceeding 160 cu ft (4.53 m³) using materials equivalent to the joists.

Exception No. 5: Spaces entirely filled with noncombustible insulation.

Exception No. 6: In wood joist construction and composite wood joist construction with noncombustible insulation filling the space from the ceiling up to the bottom edge of the joist of the roof or floor deck, provided that in composite wood joist construction, the joist channels are fire-stopped into volumes each not exceeding 160 cu ft (4.53 m³) using materials equivalent to the joists.

Exception No. 7: Small spaces over rooms not exceeding 50 sq ft (4.6 m²) in area.

Exception No. 8: When the exposed surfaces have a flame spread rating of 25 or less and the materials have been demonstrated not to propagate fire in the form in which they are installed in the space.

Exception No. 9: When the Btu content of the facing and substrate of insulation material does not exceed 1000 Btu per sq ft (11 356 kJ/m²).

4-4.4.2 Sprinklers in concealed spaces having no access that will allow storage or other use may be installed on the basis of Light Hazard Occupancy.

4-4.4.3 When heat-producing devices such as furnaces or process equipment are located in the joist channels above a ceiling attached directly to the underside of composite wood joist construction that would not otherwise require sprinkler protection of the spaces, the joist channel containing the heat-producing devices shall be sprinklered by installing two sprinklers in each joist channel, one on each side, adjacent to the heat-producing device. The temperature rating of the sprinklers shall be as prescribed in Table 3-11.6.1 and Figure 3-11.6.3(a).

4-4.4.4* In concealed spaces having exposed combustible construction, or containing exposed combustibles, in localized areas, the combustibles shall be protected as follows:

(a) If the exposed combustibles are in the vertical partitions or walls around all or a portion of the enclosure, a single row of sprinklers spaced not over 12 ft (3.7 m) apart nor more than 6 ft (1.8 m) from the inside of the partition may be installed to protect the surface. The first and last sprinklers in such a row shall not be over 5 ft (1.5 m) from the ends of the partitions.

(b) If the exposed combustibles are in the horizontal plane, permission may be given to protect the area of the combustibles on a light hazard spacing and add a row of sprinklers not over 6 ft (1.8 m) outside the outline of the area and not over 12 ft (3.7 m) on center along the outline. When the outline returns to a wall or other obstruction, the last sprinkler shall not be over 6 ft (1.8 m) from a wall or obstruction.

4-4.5 Spacing of Sprinklers Under Pitched Roofs.

4-4.5.1 Branch lines parallel to peaks of pitched roofs and sprinklers on lines perpendicular to peaks shall be spaced throughout the distance measured along the slope. This will place a row of sprinklers either in the peak or one-half the spacing down the slope from the peak.

4-4.5.2 Under saw-toothed roofs, the row of sprinklers at the highest elevation shall not be more than 3 ft (0.9 m) down the slope from the peak.

4-4.5.3 In 4-4.5.1 or 4-4.5.2, sprinklers in or near the peak shall have deflectors located not more than 3 ft (0.9 m) vertically down from the peak. [*See Figures 4-4.5.3(a) and 4-4.5.3(b).*]

Exception: In a steeply pitched roof the distance from the peak to the deflectors may be increased to maintain a horizontal clearance of not less than 2 ft (0.6 m) from other structural members. [See Figure 4-4.5.3(c).]

4-4.6 Spacing of Sprinklers Under Curved Roof Buildings.

4-4.6.1 When roofs are curved down to the floor line, the horizontal distance measured at the floor level from the sidewall or roof construction to the nearest sprinklers shall not be greater than one-half the allowable distance between sprinklers in the same direction.

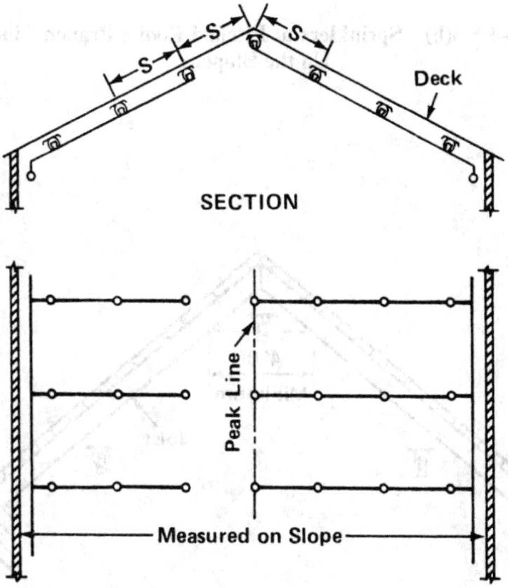
S
S
S
S
Deck
SECTION
Peak Line
Measured on Slope

For SI Units: 1 in. = 25.4 mm; 1 ft = 0.3048 m.

Figure 4-4.5.3(a) Sprinklers at Pitched Roofs; Branch Lines Run Up the Slope.

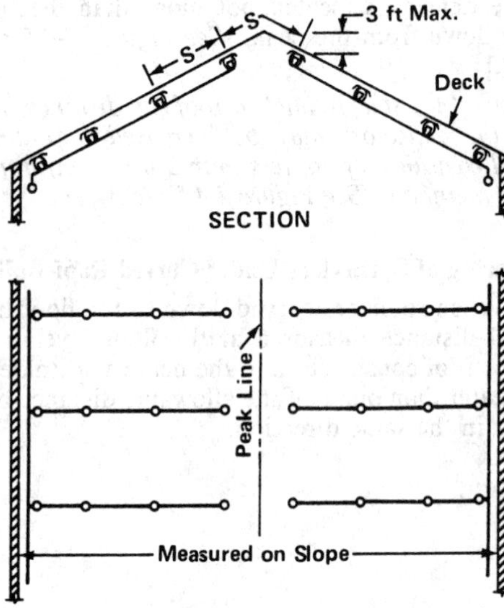
S
S
3 ft Max.
Deck
SECTION
Peak Line
Measured on Slope

For SI Units: 1 in. = 25.4 mm; 1 ft = 0.3048 m.

Figure 4-4.5.3(b) Sprinklers at Pitched Roofs; Branch Lines Run Up the Slope.

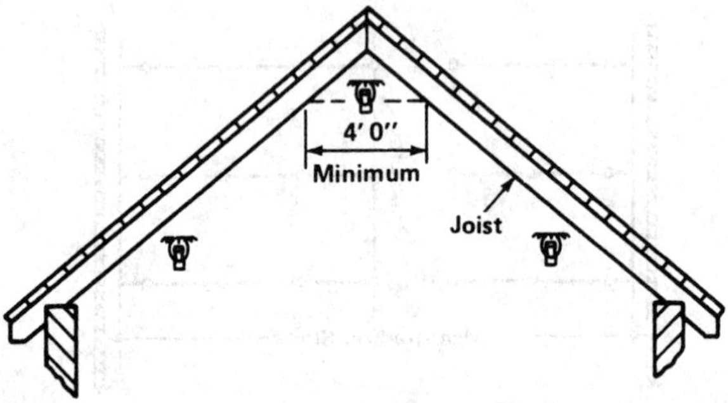
4′ 0″
Minimum
Joist

For SI Units: 1 in. = 25.4 mm; 1 ft = 0.3048 m.

Figure 4-4.5.3(c) Desirable Horizontal Clearance for Sprinklers at Peak of Pitched Roof.

4-4.6.2 Deflectors of sprinklers shall be parallel with the curve of the roof or tilted slightly toward the peak of the roof. Deflectors of sprinklers shall be located as described for beam and girder construction or for the closest comparable type of ceiling construction.

4-4.6.3 When Extra Hazard Occupancy spacing of sprinklers is used under curved ceilings of other than fire-resistive construction, as in aircraft storage or servicing areas, the spacing as projected on the floor shall be not wider than that required for Extra Hazard Occupancies, but in no case shall the spacing on the roof or ceiling be wider than that required for Ordinary Hazard Occupancies.

4-4.7 Elevators, Stairs, and Floor Openings.

4-4.7.1 Vertical Shafts.

4-4.7.1.1 One sprinkler shall be installed at the top of all shafts.

4-4.7.1.2* When vertical shafts have combustible sides, one sprinkler shall be installed at each alternate floor level. When a shaft having combustible surfaces is trapped, an additional sprinkler shall be installed at the top of each trapped section.

4-4.7.1.3 When accessible shafts have noncombustible surfaces, one sprinkler shall be installed near the bottom.

4-4.7.1.4 When vertical openings are not protected by standard enclosures, sprinklers shall be so placed as to fully cover them. This necessitates placing sprinklers close to such openings at each floor level.

4-4.7.2* Stairways.

4-4.7.2.1 Stairways of combustible construction shall be sprinklered underneath, whether risers are open or not.

4-4.7.2.2 Stairways of noncombustible construction with combustible storage beneath shall be sprinklered.

4-4.7.2.3* When moving stairways, staircases, or similar floor openings are unenclosed, the floor openings involved shall be protected by draft stops in combination with closely spaced sprinklers.

The draft stops shall be located immediately adjacent to

the opening, shall be at least 18 in. (457 mm) deep, and shall be of substantially noncombustible material that will stay in place before and during sprinkler operation. Sprinklers shall be spaced not more than 6 ft (1.8 m) apart and placed 6 to 12 in. (152 to 305 mm) from the draft stop on the side away from the opening to form a water curtain. Sprinklers in this water curtain shall be hydraulically designed to provide a discharge of 3 gpm per lineal ft [(37 L/min)/m] of water curtain, with no sprinklers discharging less than 15 gpm (56.8 L/min). The number of sprinklers calculated in this water curtain shall be the number in the length corresponding to the length parallel to the branch lines in the design area determined by 7-4.3.1. The water supply for these sprinklers shall be added to the water supply required for the area of operation in hydraulically designed systems or to the water supply required as determined in accordance with Table 2-2.1.1(a). Supplies shall be balanced to the higher pressure demand in either case. Sprinklers shall be nominal ½ in., 7/16 in., or ⅜ in. orifice. When sprinklers are closer than 6 ft (1.8 m), cross baffles shall be provided in accordance with 4-4.18. When sprinklers in the normal pattern are closer than 6 ft (1.8 m) from the water curtain, it may be preferable to locate the water curtain sprinklers in recessed baffle pockets.

Exception: Closely spaced sprinklers are not required around large openings such as those found in shopping malls, atrium buildings, and similar structures where all adjoining levels and spaces are protected by automatic sprinklers in accordance with this standard, when the openings have all horizontal dimensions between opposite edges of 20 ft (6 m) or greater, and an area of 1000 sq ft (93 m^2) or greater.

4-4.7.2.4* In noncombustible stair shafts, sprinklers shall be installed at the top and under the first landing above the lowest level. When the stair shaft serves two or more separate fire sections, sprinklers shall also be installed at each floor landing.

4-4.8* Building Service Chutes. Building service chutes (linen, rubbish, etc.) shall be protected internally by automatic sprinklers. A sprinkler shall be provided above the top service opening of the chute, above the lowest service opening, and above service openings at alternate levels in buildings over two stories in height. The room or area into which the chute discharges shall also be protected by automatic sprinklers.

4-4.9* Exterior Canopies, Docks, and Platforms.

4-4.9.1 Sprinklers shall be installed under roofs or canopies over outside-loading platforms, docks, or other areas where combustibles are stored or handled.

4-4.9.2 Sprinklers shall be installed under exterior combustible roofs or canopies exceeding 4 ft (1.2 m) in width.

Exception: Sprinklers may be omitted where construction is noncombustible and areas under the roofs or canopies are not used for storage or handling of combustibles.

4-4.9.3 Sprinklers shall be installed under exterior docks and platforms of combustible construction unless such space is closed off and protected against accumulation of debris.

4-4.10* Decks. Sprinklers shall be installed under decks and galleries over 4 ft (1.2 m) wide. Slatting of decks, walkways, or the use of open gratings as a substitute for such sprinklers is not acceptable. Sprinklers installed under open gratings shall be of the listed intermediate level type or shielded from the discharge of overhead sprinklers.

4-4.11 Library Stack Rooms. Sprinklers shall be installed in every aisle and at every tier of stacks with distance between sprinklers along aisles not to exceed 12 ft (3.6 m). [*See Figure 4-4.11(a).*]

Exception No. 1: When vertical shelf dividers are incomplete and allow water distribution to adjacent aisles, sprinklers may be omitted in alternate aisles on each tier. When ventilation openings are also provided in tier floors, sprinklers shall be staggered vertically. [See Figure 4-4.11(b).]

Exception No. 2: Install sprinklers without regard to aisles when there is 18 in. (457 mm) or more clearance between sprinkler deflectors and tops of racks.

4-4.12* Ducts. Sprinklers shall be installed beneath ducts over 4 ft (1.2 m) wide unless ceiling sprinklers can be spaced in accordance with Table 4-2.4.6.

4-4.13 Electrical Equipment. When sprinkler protection is provided in generator and transformer rooms, hoods or shields installed to protect important electrical equipment from water shall be noncombustible.

4-4.14* Open-Grid Ceilings. The following requirements

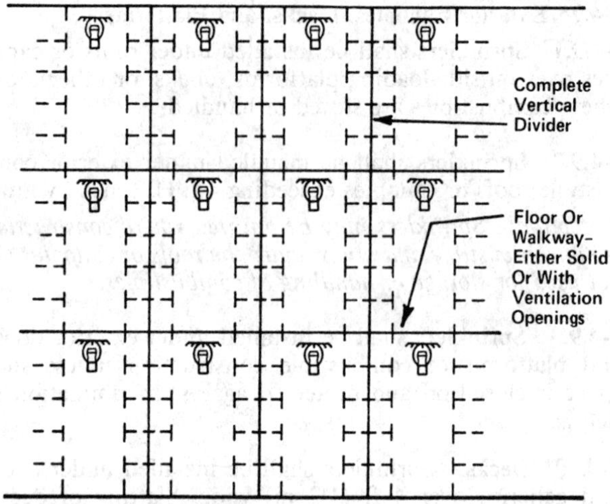
Complete
Vertical
Divider
Floor Or
Walkway-
Either Solid
Or With
Ventilation
Openings

Figure 4-4.11(a) Sprinklers in Multitier Library Bookstacks.

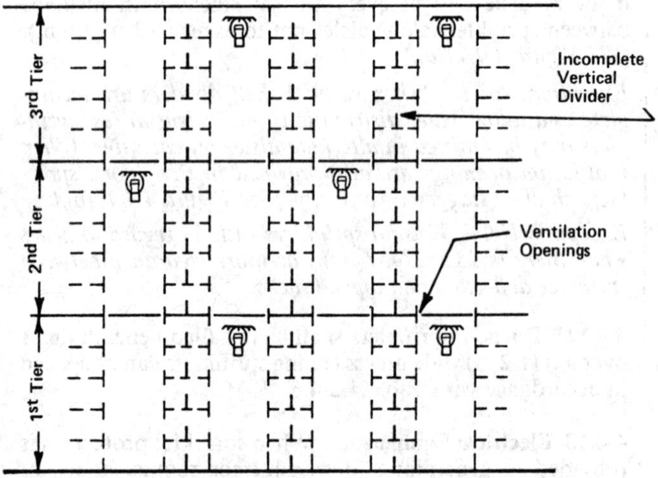
Incomplete
Vertical
Divider
Ventilation
Openings
3rd Tier
2nd Tier
1st Tier

Figure 4-4.11(b) Sprinklers in Multitier Library Bookstacks.

are applicable to open-grid ceilings in which the openings are ¼ in. (6.4 mm) or larger in the least dimension, when the thickness or depth of the material does not exceed the least dimension of the openings, and when such openings constitute at least 70 percent of the area of the ceiling material. Other types of open-grid ceilings shall not be installed beneath sprinklers unless they are listed by a testing laboratory and are installed in accordance with the instructions contained in each package of the ceiling material. Ceilings made of highly flammable material may spread fire faster than sprinklers can control.

(a) In Light Hazard Occupancies when spacing of either standard or old-style sprinklers is not wider than 10 by 10 ft (3 by 3 m), a minimum clearance of at least 18 in. (457 mm) shall be provided between the sprinkler deflectors and the upper surface of the open-grid ceiling. When spacing is wider than 10 by 10 ft (3 by 3 m) but not wider than 10 by 12 ft (3 by 3.7 m), a clearance of at least 24 in. (610 mm) shall be provided from standard sprinklers and at least 36 in. (914 mm) from old-style sprinklers. When spacing is wider than 10 by 12 ft (3 by 3.7 m), a clearance of at least 48 in. (1219 mm) shall be provided.

(b) In Ordinary Hazard Occupancies, open-grid ceilings may be installed beneath sprinklers only where such use is approved by the authority having jurisdiction, and shall be installed beneath standard sprinklers only. When sprinkler spacing is not wider than 10 by 10 ft (3 by 3 m), a minimum clearance of at least 24 in. (610 mm) shall be provided between the sprinkler deflectors and the upper surface of the open-grid ceiling. When spacing is wider than 10 by 10 ft (3 by 3 m), a clearance of at least 36 in. (914 mm) shall be provided.

4-4.15 Drop-out Ceilings.

4-4.15.1 Drop-out ceilings may be installed beneath sprinklers when ceilings are listed for that service and are installed in accordance with their listing. The authority having jurisdiction shall be consulted in all cases.

Exception: Special sprinklers shall not be installed above drop-out ceilings unless specifically listed for this purpose.

4-4.15.2 Drop-out ceilings shall not be considered ceilings within the context of this standard.

4-4.15.3* Piping installed above drop-out ceilings shall not be considered concealed piping. (*See 3-7.4, Exception No. 2.*)

4-4.15.4* Sprinklers shall not be installed beneath drop-out ceilings.

4-4.16 Fur Vaults.

4-4.16.1 Sprinklers in fur storage vaults shall be located centrally over the aisles between racks and shall be spaced not over 5 ft (1.5 m) apart along the aisles.

4-4.16.2 When sprinklers are spaced 5 ft (1.5 m) apart along the sprinkler branch lines, pipe sizes may be in accordance with the following schedule:

1 in.	4 sprinklers	2 in.	20 sprinklers
1¼ in.	6 sprinklers	2½ in.	40 sprinklers
1½ in.	10 sprinklers	3 in.	80 sprinklers

4-4.16.3 Sprinklers shall be listed old-style having orifice sizes selected to provide as closely as possible but not less than 20 gal per min (76 L/min) per sprinkler, for four sprinklers, based on the water pressure available.

NOTE: See NFPA 81, *Standard on Fur Storage, Fumigation and Cleaning.* For tests of sprinkler performance in fur vaults see Fact Finding Report on Automatic Sprinkler Protection for Fur Storage Vaults of Underwriters Laboratories Inc., dated November 25, 1947.

4-4.17 Commercial-type Cooking Equipment and Ventilation.

4-4.17.1 In cooking areas protected by automatic sprinklers, additional sprinklers or automatic spray nozzles shall be provided to protect commercial-type cooking equipment and ventilation systems that are designed to carry away grease-laden vapors unless otherwise protected. (*See NFPA 96, Standard for the Installation of Equipment for the Removal of Smoke and Grease-Laden Vapors from Commercial Cooking Equipment.*)

4-4.17.2 Standard sprinklers or automatic spray nozzles shall be so located as to provide for the protection of exhaust ducts, hood exhaust duct collars, and hood exhaust plenum chambers.

Exception: Sprinklers or automatic spray nozzles in ducts, duct collars, and plenum chambers may be omitted when all cooking equipment is served by listed grease extractors.

4-4.17.3 Exhaust ducts shall have one sprinkler or automatic spray nozzle located at the top of each vertical riser and at the midpoint of each offset. The first sprinkler or automatic spray nozzle in a horizontal duct shall be installed at the duct entrance. Horizontal exhaust ducts shall have such devices located on 10-ft (3-m) centers beginning no more than 5 ft (1.5 m) from the duct entrance. Sprinkler(s) or automatic spray nozzle(s) in exhaust ducts subject to freezing shall be properly protected against freezing by approved means. (*See 3-5.1.*)

Exception: Sprinklers or automatic spray nozzles may be omitted from a vertical riser located outside of a building provided the riser does not expose combustible material or the interior of a building and the horizontal distance between the hood outlet and the vertical riser is at least 25 ft (7.6 m).

4-4.17.4* Each hood exhaust duct collar shall have one sprinkler or automatic spray nozzle located 1 in. minimum to 12 in. maximum (25.4 mm min. to 305 mm max.) above the point of duct collar connection in hood plenum. Hoods that have listed fire dampers located in the duct collar shall be protected with a sprinkler or automatic spray nozzle located on the discharge side of the damper and be so positioned as not to interfere with damper operation.

4-4.17.5 Hood exhaust plenum chambers shall have one sprinkler or automatic spray nozzle centered in each chamber not exceeding 10 ft (3 m) in length. Plenum chambers greater than 10 ft (3 m) in length shall have two sprinklers or automatic spray nozzles evenly spaced with the maximum distance between the two sprinklers not to exceed 10 ft (3 m).

4-4.17.6 Sprinklers or automatic spray nozzles being used in duct, duct collar, and plenum areas shall be of the temperature classification extra high [325 to 375°F (163 to 191°C)] and have orifice sizes no less than ¼ in. (6.4 mm) and no more than ½ in. (13 mm).

Exception: When use of a temperature measuring device indicates temperatures above 300°F (149°C) a sprinkler or automatic spray nozzle of higher classification shall be used.

4-4.17.7 Access must be provided to all sprinklers or automatic spray nozzles for examination and replacement.

4-4.17.8 Cooking Equipment.

4-4.17.8.1 Cooking equipment (such as deep fat fryers, ranges, griddles, and broilers) that may be a source of ignition shall be protected in accordance with the provisions of 4-4.17.1.

4-4.17.8.2 A sprinkler or automatic spray nozzle used for protection of deep fat fryers shall be listed for that application. The position, arrangement, location, and water supply for each sprinkler or automatic spray nozzle shall be in accordance with its listing.

4-4.17.8.3 The operation of any cooking equipment sprinkler or automatic spray nozzle shall automatically shut off all sources of fuel and heat to all equipment requiring protection. Any gas appliance not requiring protection but located under ventilating equipment shall also be shut off. All shutdown devices shall be of the type that requires manual resetting prior to fuel or power being restored.

4-4.17.9* A listed indicating valve shall be installed in the water supply line to the sprinklers and spray nozzles protecting the cooking and ventilating system.

4-4.17.10 An approved line strainer shall be installed in the main water supply preceding sprinklers or automatic spray nozzles having orifices smaller than ⅜ in. (9.5 mm).

4-4.17.11 A system test connection shall be provided to verify proper operation of equipment specified in 4-4.17.8.3.

4-4.17.12 Sprinklers and automatic spray nozzles used for protecting commercial-type cooking equipment and ventilating systems shall be replaced annually.

Exception: When automatic bulb-type sprinklers or spray nozzles are used and annual examination shows no build-up of grease or other material on the sprinklers or spray nozzles.

4-4.18 Baffles. Baffles (*except for in-rack sprinklers, see NFPA 231C, Standard for Rack Storage of Materials*) shall be installed whenever sprinklers are less than 6 ft (1.8 m) apart to prevent the sprinkler first opening from wetting adjacent sprinklers, thus delaying their operation. Baffles shall be located midway between sprinklers and arranged to baffle the actuating elements. Baffles may be of sheet metal about 8 in. (203 mm) wide and 6 in. (152 mm) high. The top of baffles shall extend 2 to 3 in. (51 to 76 mm) above the deflectors of upright sprinklers; and the bottom of baffles shall extend downward to a level at least even with the deflectors of pendent sprinklers.

Exception: Old-style sprinklers protecting fur storage vaults.

4-4.19 Small Rooms. Rooms with smooth ceilings, and having floor areas not exceeding 800 sq ft (74.3 m²), of Light Hazard Occupancy classification.

4-4.19.1* Within small rooms, sprinklers may be located not more than 9 ft (2.7 m) from any single wall; however, sprinkler spacing limitations of 4-2.1.1 and area limitations of 4-2.2.2.1 shall not be exceeded.

4-4.19.2 In hotels, sprinklers may be omitted from bathrooms not exceeding 55 sq ft (5.1 m²) with noncombustible plumbing fixtures and with walls and ceilings surfaced with noncombustible materials.

4-4.19.3 In hotel guest rooms, sprinkler installation may be omitted in clothes closets where the area does not exceed 24 sq ft (2.2 m²), the least dimension does not exceed 3 ft (0.9 m), and the walls and ceilings are surfaced with noncombustible or limited-combustible materials.

4-4.20 Theater Stages. Sprinklers shall be installed under the roof at the ceiling, in spaces under the stage either containing combustible materials or constructed of combustible materials; in all adjacent spaces and dressing rooms, storerooms, and workshops. When proscenium opening protection is required a deluge system shall be provided within 3 ft (0.9 m) of the stage side of the proscenium arch, with open sprinklers spaced up to a maximum of 6 ft (1.8 m) on center and designed to provide a discharge of 3 gpm/lineal ft [(37 L/min)/m] of water curtain, with no sprinkler discharging less than 15 gpm (56.8 L/min).

4-5* Spacing, Location, and Position of Sidewall Sprinklers. (*See 3-11.2.5.*)

4-5.1 Sidewall sprinklers shall only be installed along walls, lintels, or soffits where the distance from the ceiling to the bottom of the lintel or soffit is at least 2 in. (51 mm) greater than the distances from the ceiling to sidewall sprinkler deflector. Sidewall sprinklers shall not be installed back to back without being separated by a lintel or soffit.

4-5.2* Distance Between Sprinklers on Branch Lines.

4-5.2.1 Sidewall sprinklers shall be installed along the length of a single wall of rooms or bays not exceeding the width dimension specified in Table 4-5.2.1.

Exception: Sidewall sprinklers may be installed in Light Hazard Occupancies with smooth ceilings or in bays up to 30 ft (9 m) in width. When sidewall sprinklers are installed on two opposite walls or sides of bays, the spacing shall be as required in Section 4-5 with sprinklers regularly staggered. (See Figure 4-5.2.1.)

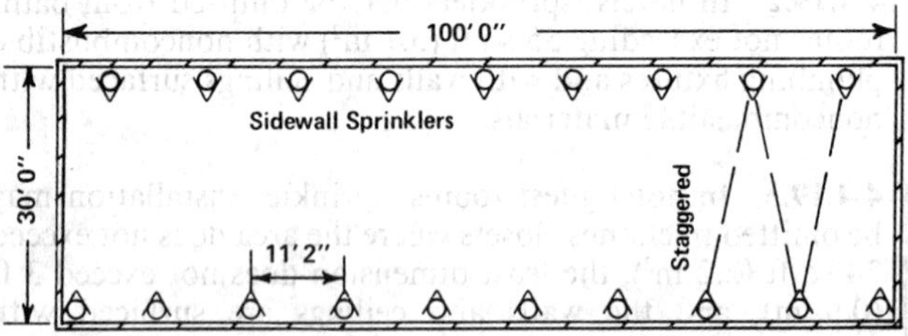
100′ 0″
Sidewall Sprinklers
30′ 0″
Staggered
11′ 2″

For SI Units: 1 in. = 25.4 mm; 1 ft = 0.3048 m.

Figure 4-5.2.1 Spacing of Sidewall Sprinklers under Combustible Smooth Ceilings.

4-5.3 Protection Area Limitations for Light Hazard Occupancy.

4-5.3.1 With noncombustible smooth ceilings the protection area per sprinkler shall not exceed 196 sq ft (18.2 m²).

4-5.3.2 With combustible ceiling construction sheathed with plasterboard, metal, or wood lath and plaster forming

Table 4-5.2.1 Dimensions for Sidewall Sprinkler Installation

	Light Hazard Occupancy			Ordinary Hazard Occupancy	
	Combustible Construction with Combustible Sheathing	Combustible Construction Sheathed with Plaster-board, Metal, or Wood Lath and Plaster	Noncombustible Construction with Noncombustible Sheathing	Combustible Construction with Combustible Sheathing*	Noncombustible Smooth Ceiling
Maximum distance between sprinklers on branch line	14	14	14	10	10
Maximum room width for single branch line along wall (ft)	12	12	14	10	10
Maximum area coverage (ft^2)	120	168	196	80	100

For SI Units: 1 ft = 0.3048 m.

*See 4-5.4.2

a smooth ceiling, the protection area per sprinkler shall not exceed 168 sq ft (15.6 m^2). (*See Table 4-5.2.1.*) When sheathing is combustible, such as wood, fiberboard, or other combustible material, the protection area per sprinkler shall not exceed 120 sq ft (11.1 m^2).

Exception: Noncombustible smooth ceiling spacing is permitted beneath a noncombustible smooth ceiling located beneath any combustible concealed space. (See 4-4.4.1.)

4-5.4 Protection Area Limitations for Ordinary Hazard Occupancy.

4-5.4.1 With noncombustible smooth ceilings the protection area per sprinkler shall not exceed 100 sq ft (9.3 m^2).

4-5.4.2 With combustible ceiling construction sheathed with plasterboard, metal, wood lath and plaster, wood fiberboard, or other combustible material forming a smooth ceiling, the protection area per sprinkler shall not exceed 80 sq ft (7.4 m^2).

Exception: Noncombustible smooth ceiling spacing is permitted beneath a noncombustible smooth ceiling located beneath any combustible concealed space. (See 4-4.4.1.)

4-5.5 Position of Sidewall Sprinklers.

4-5.5.1* Sprinkler deflectors shall be at a distance from walls and ceilings not more than 6 in. (152 mm) or less than 4 in. (102 mm), unless special construction arrangements make a different position advisable for prompt operation and effective distribution.

Exception No. 1: Horizontal sidewall sprinklers may be positioned 6 to 12 in. (152 to 305 mm) below noncombustible ceilings when listed for these positions.

Exception No. 2: Horizontal sidewall sprinklers may be positioned with their deflectors less than 4 in. (102 mm) from the wall on which they are mounted.

4-5.5.2 Where soffits are used for the installation of sidewall sprinklers, they shall not exceed an 8 in. (203 mm) projection from the wall.

Chapter 5 Types of Systems

5-1 Wet-Pipe Systems.

5-1.1* Definition. A system employing automatic sprinklers attached to a piping system containing water and connected to a water supply so that water discharges immediately from sprinklers opened by a fire.

5-1.2 Pressure Gages. An approved pressure gage conforming to 2-9.2.2 shall be installed in each system riser. Pressure gages shall be installed above and below each alarm check valve when such devices are present.

5-1.3 Relief Valves. A gridded wet-pipe system shall be provided with a relief valve not less than ¼ in. (6.4 mm) in size set to operate at pressure not greater than 175 psi (12.1 bars).

Exception No. 1: When the maximum system pressure exceeds 165 psi (11.4 bars), the relief valve shall operate at 10 psi (0.7 bar) in excess of the maximum system pressure.

Exception No. 2: When auxiliary air reservoirs are installed to absorb pressure increases.

5-2 Dry-Pipe Systems.

5-2.1* Definition. A system employing automatic sprinklers attached to a piping system containing air or nitrogen under pressure, the release of which (as from the opening of a sprinkler) permits the water pressure to open a valve known as a dry-pipe valve. The water then flows into the piping system and out the opened sprinklers.

5-2.2 Dry-Pendent Sprinklers. Automatic sprinklers installed in the pendent position shall be of the listed dry-pendent type if installed in an area subject to freezing.

Exception: Pendent sprinklers installed on return bends are permitted when both the sprinklers and the return bends are located in a heated area.

5-2.3* Size of Systems.

5-2.3.1 Volume Limitations. Not more than 750-gal (2839 L) system capacity shall be controlled by one dry-pipe valve. Gridded dry-pipe systems shall not be installed.

Exception: Piping volume may exceed 750 gal (2839 L) for nongridded systems if the system design is such that water is delivered to the system test connection in not more than 60 seconds, starting at the normal air pressure on the system and at the time of fully opened inspection test connection.

5-2.4 Quick-Opening Devices.

5-2.4.1 Dry-pipe valves shall be provided with a listed quick-opening device when system capacity exceeds 500 gal (1893 L).

Exception: A quick-opening device shall not be required if the requirements of 5-2.3.1 Exception can be met without such a device.

5-2.4.2* The quick-opening device shall be located as close as practical to the dry-pipe valve. To protect the restriction orifice and other operating parts of the quick-opening device against submergence, the connection to the riser shall be above the point at which water (priming water and back drainage) is expected when the dry-pipe valve and quick-opening device are set, except where design features of the particular quick-opening device make these requirements unnecessary.

5-2.4.3 A soft disc globe or angle valve shall be installed in the connection between the dry-pipe sprinkler riser and the quick-opening device.

5-2.4.4 A check valve shall be installed between the quick-opening device and the intermediate chamber of the dry-pipe valve. If the quick-opening device requires pressure feedback from the intermediate chamber, a valve of the type that will clearly indicate whether it is opened or closed may be installed in place of that check valve. This valve shall be constructed so that it may be locked or sealed in the open position.

5-2.4.5 An approved antiflooding device shall be installed in the connection between the dry-pipe sprinkler riser and the quick-opening device, unless the particular quick-opening device has built-in antiflooding design features.

5-2.5* Location and Protection of Dry-Pipe Valve.

5-2.5.1 The dry-pipe valve and supply pipe shall be protected against freezing and mechanical injury.

5-2.5.2 Valve rooms shall be lighted and heated. The

source of heat shall be of a permanently installed type. Heat tape shall not be used in lieu of heated valve enclosures to protect the dry-pipe valve and supply pipe against freezing.

5-2.5.3 The supply for the sprinkler in the dry-pipe valve enclosure shall be from the dry side of the system.

5-2.5.4 Protection against accumulation of water above the clapper shall be provided for a low differential dry-pipe valve. This may be an automatic high water level signaling device or an automatic drain device.

5-2.6* Cold Storage Rooms.

5-2.6.1 Fittings for Inspection Purposes.

5-2.6.1.1 Fittings for inspection purposes shall be provided whenever a cross main connects to a riser or feed main. This may be accomplished by a blind flange on a fitting (tee or cross) in the riser or cross main or a flanged removable section 24 in. (610 mm) long in the feed main as shown in Figure 5-2.6.1(A). Such fittings in conjunction with the flushing connections specified in 3-3.2 would permit examination of the entire lengths of the cross mains. Branch lines may be examined by backing the pipe out of fittings.

5-2.6.1.2 Whenever feed mains change direction, facilities shall be provided for direct observation of every length of feed main within the refrigerated area. This may be accomplished by means of 2-in. (51-mm) capped nipples or blind flanges on fittings.

5-2.6.1.3 Fittings for inspection purposes shall be provided whenever a riser or feed main passes through a wall or floor from a warm room to a cold room. This may be accomplished at floor penetrations by a tee with a blind flange in the cold room and at wall penetrations by a 24-in. (610-mm) flanged removable section in the warm room as shown in Figure 5-2.6.1(B).

5-2.6.2 A local low air-pressure alarm shall be installed on sprinkler systems supplying freezer sections.

5-2.6.3 Piping in cold storage rooms shall be installed with pitch, as outlined in 3-6.1.3.

5-2.6.4 The air supply for dry-pipe systems in cold storage plants shall be taken from the freezers of lowest temperature

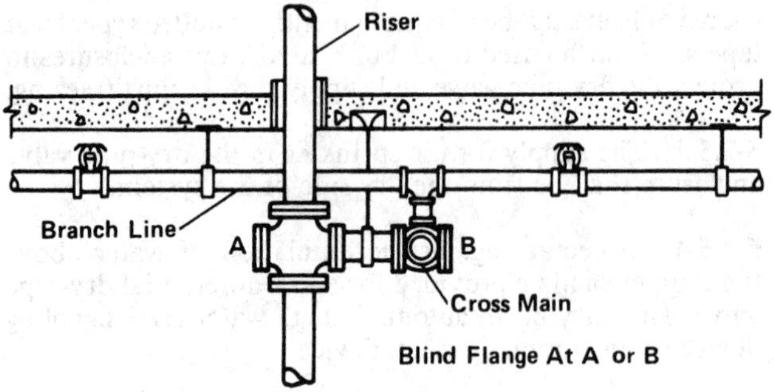
Riser
Branch Line
A
B
Cross Main
Blind Flange At A or B

(a) Elevation At Riser And Cross Main

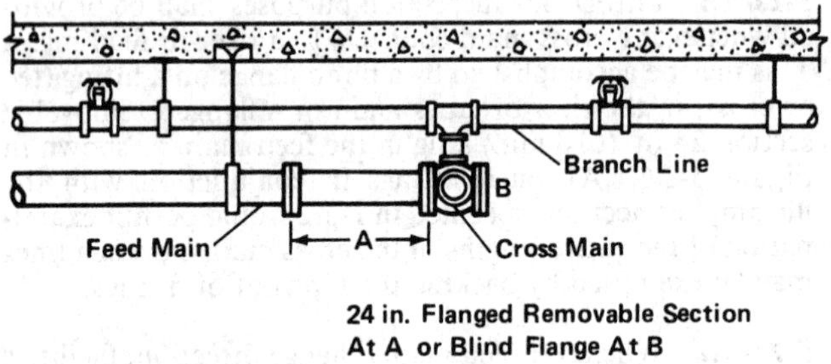
Branch Line
B
Feed Main
A
Cross Main
24 in. Flanged Removable Section
At A or Blind Flange At B

(b) Elevation At Feed Main And Cross Main

For SI Units: 1 in. = 25.4 mm.

Figure 5-2.6.1(A) Fittings to Facilitate Examination of Feed Mains, Risers, and Cross Mains in Freezing Areas.

or through a chemical dehydrator. Compressed nitrogen gas from cylinders may be used in place of air in dry-pipe systems to eliminate introducing moisture.

5-2.7 Air Pressure and Supply.

5-2.7.1 Maintenance of Air Pressure. Air or nitrogen pressure shall be maintained on dry-pipe systems throughout the year.

5-2.7.2* Air Supply. The compressed air supply shall be

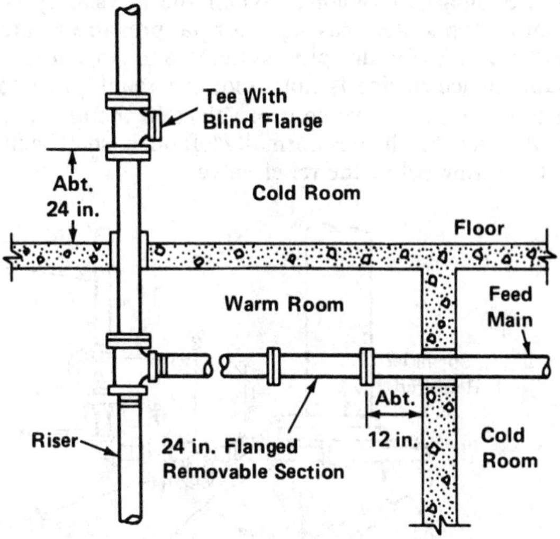
Tee With
Blind Flange
Abt.
24 in.
Cold Room
Floor
Warm Room
Feed
Main
Abt.
12 in.
Riser
24 in. Flanged
Removable Section
Cold
Room

For SI Units: 1 in. = 25.4 mm.

Figure 5-2.6.1(B) Fittings in Feed Main or Riser Passing through Wall or Floor from Warm Room to Cold Room.

from a source available at all times and having a capacity capable of restoring normal air pressure in the system within 30 minutes, except for low differential dry-pipe systems where this time may be 60 minutes. Where low differential dry-pipe valves are used, the air supply shall be maintained automatically.

5-2.7.3 Air Filling Connection. The connection pipe from the air compressor shall not be less than ½ in. (13 mm) and shall enter the system above the priming water level of the dry-pipe valve. A check valve shall be installed in this air line and a shutoff valve of renewable disc type shall be installed on the supply side of this check valve and shall remain closed unless filling the system.

5-2.7.4 Relief Valve. An approved relief valve shall be provided between the compressor and controlling valve, set to relieve at a pressure 5 psi (0.3 bars) in excess of maximum air pressure that should be carried in the system.

5-2.7.5 Shop Air Supply. When the air supply is taken from a shop system having a normal pressure greater than that required for dry-pipe systems and an automatic air maintenance device is not used, the relief valve shall be installed between two control valves in the air line, and a small air cock, which is normally left open, shall be installed in the fitting below the relief valve.

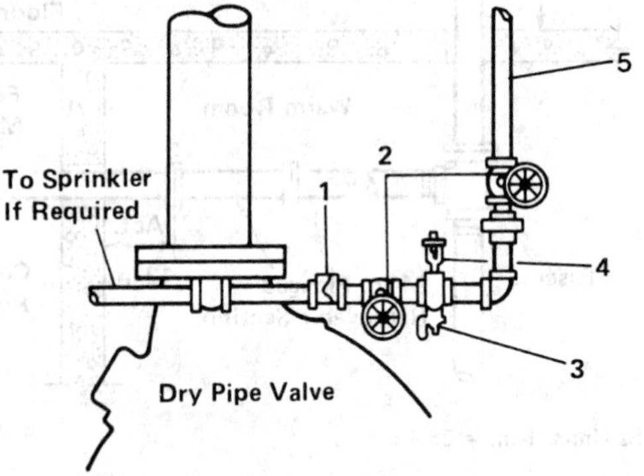
To Sprinkler
If Required
Dry Pipe Valve
1
2
3
4
5

1. Check Valve
2. Control Valve (Renewable Disc Type)
3. Small Air Cock (Normally Open)
4. Relief Valve
5. Air Supply

Figure 5-2.7.5 Air Supply from Shop System.

5-2.7.6 Automatic Air Compressor. When a dry-pipe system is supplied by an automatic air compressor or plant air system, any device or apparatus used for automatic maintenance of air pressure shall be of a type specifically approved for such service and capable of maintaining the required air pressure on the dry-pipe system. Automatic air supply to more than one dry-pipe system shall be connected to enable individual maintenance of air pressure in each system. A check valve or other positive backflow prevention device shall be installed in the air supply to each system to prevent air or water flow from one system to another.

5-2.7.7 Air Pressure to Be Carried. The air pressure to be carried shall be in accordance with the instruction sheet furnished with the dry-pipe valve, when available, or 20 psi (1.4 bars) in excess of the calculated trip pressure of the dry-pipe valve, based on the highest normal water pressure of the system supply. The permitted rate of air leakage shall be as specified in 1-11.3.2.

5-2.7.8 When used, nitrogen shall be introduced through a pressure regulator set to maintain system pressure in accordance with 5-2.7.7.

5-2.8 Pressure Gages. Approved pressure gages conforming to 2-9.2.2 shall be connected:

(a) On the water side and air side of the dry-pipe valve,

(b) At the air pump supplying the air receiver,

(c) At the air receiver,

(d) In each independent pipe from air supply to dry-pipe system, and

(e) At exhausters and accelerators.

5-3 Preaction and Deluge Systems.

5-3.1 Definitions.

Preaction System. A system employing automatic sprinklers attached to a piping system containing air that may or may not be under pressure, with a supplemental fire detection system installed in the same areas as the sprinklers. Actuation of the fire detection system (as from a fire) opens a valve that permits water to flow into the sprinkler piping system and to be discharged from any sprinklers that may be open.

Deluge System. A system employing open sprinklers attached to a piping system connected to a water supply through a valve that is opened by the operation of a fire detection system installed in the same areas as the sprinklers. When this valve opens water flows into the piping system and discharges from all sprinklers attached thereto.

5-3.2* Description. Preaction and deluge systems are normally without water in the system piping. The water supply is controlled by an automatic valve operated by means of fire detection devices and provided with manual means for operation that are independent of the sprinklers. Systems may have equipment of the types described in (a) through (f) below. (*See 5-3.6.2.*)

(a) Automatic sprinklers with both sprinkler piping and fire detection devices automatically supervised.

(b) Automatic sprinklers with sprinkler piping and fire detection devices not automatically supervised.

(c) Open sprinklers with only fire detection devices automatically supervised.

(d) Open sprinklers with fire detection devices not automatically supervised.

(e) Combination of open and automatic sprinklers with fire detection devices automatically supervised.

(f) Combination of open and automatic sprinklers with fire detection devices not automatically supervised.

5-3.3* General.

5-3.3.1 A supply of spare fusible elements for heat-responsive devices, not less than two of each temperature rating, shall be maintained on the premises for replacement purposes.

5-3.3.2 When hydraulic release systems are used, it is possible to water column the deluge valve or deluge-valve actuator if the heat-actuated devices (fixed temperature or rate-of-rise) are located at extreme heights above the valve. Refer to the manufacturer for height limitations of a specific deluge valve or deluge-valve actuator.

5-3.3.3 All new preaction or deluge systems shall be tested hydrostatically as specified in 1-11.2.1. In testing deluge systems, plugs shall be installed in fittings and replaced with open sprinklers after the test is completed, or automatic sprinklers may be installed and the operating parts removed after the test is completed.

5-3.4 Location and Protection of Preaction and Deluge Systems.

5-3.4.1 The preaction and deluge system water control valves and supply pipes shall be protected against freezing and mechanical injury.

5-3.4.2 Valve rooms shall be lighted and heated. The source of heat shall be of a permanently installed type.

5-3.4.3 Heat tape shall not be used in lieu of heated valve enclosure rooms to protect preaction and deluge valves and supply pipe against freezing.

5-3.5 Location and Spacing of Fire Detection Devices.

Spacing of fire detection devices other than automatic sprinklers shall be in accordance with their listing by testing laboratories or in accordance with manufacturer's specifications. When automatic sprinklers are used as detectors, the distance between detectors and the area per detector shall not exceed the maximum permitted for suppression sprinklers as specified in 4-2.1 and 4-2.2; they shall be positioned in accordance with Section 4-3, but need not conform with the clearance requirements of 4-2.4. (*See NFPA 72E, Standard on Automatic Fire Detectors.*)

5-3.6 Preaction Systems.

5-3.6.1 All components of pneumatic, hydraulic, or electrical preaction systems shall be compatible.

5-3.6.2 Size of Systems. Not more than 1,000 closed sprinklers shall be controlled by any one preaction valve.

5-3.6.3 Supervision. Sprinkler piping and fire detection devices shall be automatically supervised when there are more than 20 sprinklers on the system.

5-3.6.4 For pipe schedules see Chapter 7 and Sections 8-2, 8-3, 8-4, and 8-5.

5-3.6.5 Pendent Sprinklers. Automatic sprinklers on preaction systems installed in the pendent position shall be of the listed dry-pendent type if installed in an area subject to freezing.

Exception: Pendent sprinklers installed on return bends are permitted when both the sprinklers and the return bends are located in a heated area.

5-3.7* Deluge Systems. The fire detection devices or systems shall be automatically supervised when there are more than 20 sprinklers on the system.

5-3.8 Devices for Test Purposes and Testing Apparatus.

5-3.8.1 When fire detection devices installed in circuits are located where not readily accessible, an additional fire detection device shall be provided on each circuit for test purposes at an accessible location and shall be connected to the circuit at a point that will assure a proper test of the circuit.

5-3.8.2 Testing apparatus capable of producing the heat or impulse necessary to operate any normal fire detection device shall be furnished to the owner of the property with each installation. Where explosive vapors or materials are present, hot water, steam, or other methods of testing not involving an ignition source shall be used.

5-3.8.3 Pressure Gages. Approved pressure gages conforming to 2-9.2.2 shall be installed as follows:

(a) Above and below preaction valve and below deluge valve.

(b) On air supply to preaction and deluge valves.

5-4 Combined Dry-Pipe and Preaction Systems.

5-4.1 General.

5-4.1.1* Definition. A combined dry-pipe and preaction sprinkler system is one employing automatic sprinklers attached to a piping system containing air under pressure with a supplemental fire detection system installed in the same areas as the sprinklers; operation of the fire detection system, as from a fire, actuates tripping devices that open dry-pipe valves simultaneously and without loss of air pressure in the system. Operation of the fire detection system also opens approved air exhaust valves at the end of the feed main, which facilitates the filling of the system with water, which usually precedes the opening of sprinklers. The fire detection system also serves as an automatic fire alarm system.

5-4.1.2 Combined automatic dry-pipe and preaction systems shall be so constructed that failure of the fire detection system shall not prevent the system from functioning as a conventional automatic dry-pipe system.

5-4.1.3 Combined automatic dry-pipe and preaction systems shall be so constructed that failure of the dry-pipe system of automatic sprinklers shall not prevent the fire detection system from properly functioning as an automatic fire alarm system.

5-4.1.4 Provisions shall be made for the manual operation of the fire detection system at locations requiring not more than 200 ft (61.0 m) of travel.

5-4.1.5 Except as indicated in 5-2.2, automatic sprinklers installed in the pendent position shall be of the approved dry-pendent type.

5-4.2 Dry-Pipe Valves in Combined Systems.

5-4.2.1 Where the system consists of more than 600 sprinklers or has more than 275 sprinklers in any fire area, the entire system shall be controlled through two 6-in. (152-mm) dry-pipe valves connected in parallel and shall feed into a common feed main. These valves shall be checked against each other. (*See Figure 5-4.2.*)

5-4.2.2 Each dry-pipe valve shall be provided with an approved tripping device actuated by the fire detection system. Dry-pipe valves shall be cross connected through a 1-in. (25.4-mm) pipe connection to permit simultaneous tripping of both dry-pipe valves. This 1-in. (25.4-mm) pipe connection shall be equipped with a gate valve so that either dry-pipe valve can be shut off and worked on while the other remains in service.

5-4.2.3 The check valves between the dry-pipe valves and the common feed main shall be equipped with ½-in. (13-mm) bypasses so that a loss of air from leakage in the trimmings of a dry-pipe valve will not cause the valve to trip until the pressure in the feed main is reduced to the tripping point. A gate valve shall be installed in each of these bypasses so that either dry-pipe valve can be completely isolated from the main riser or feed main and from the other.

5-4.2.4 Each combined dry-pipe and preaction system shall be provided with approved quick-opening devices at the dry-pipe valves.

5-4.3* Air Exhaust Valves. One or more approved air exhaust valves of 2-in. (51-mm) or larger size controlled by operation of a fire detection system shall be installed at the end of the common feed main. (*See Figure A-5-4.3.*) These air exhaust valves shall have soft-seated globe or angle valves in their intakes; also, approved strainers shall be installed between these globe valves and the air exhaust valves.

5-4.4 Subdivision of System Using Check Valves.

5-4.4.1 Where more than 275 sprinklers are required in a

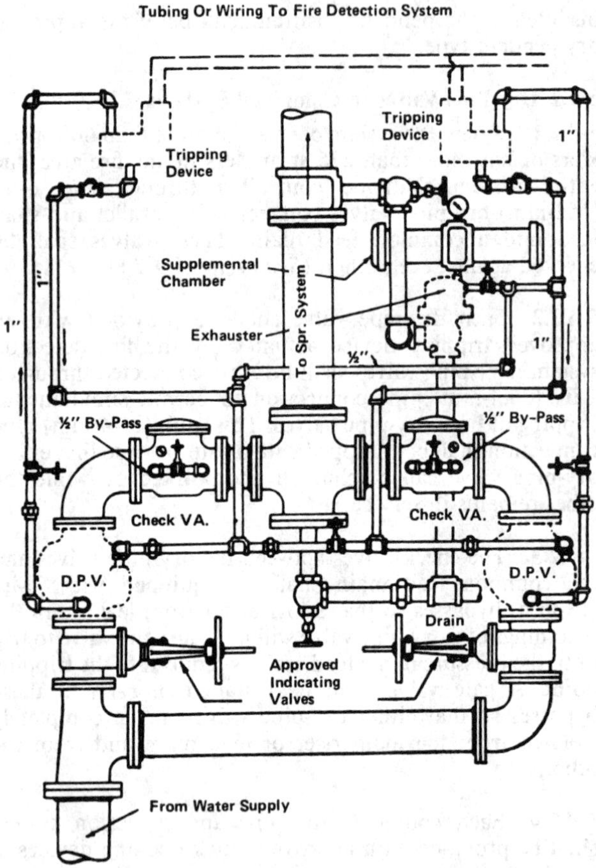
Tubing Or Wiring To Fire Detection System
Tripping Device
Tripping Device
1"
Supplemental Chamber
To Spr. System
1"
1"
Exhauster
1"
½"
½" By-Pass
½" By-Pass
Check VA.
Check VA.
D.P.V.
D.P.V.
Drain
Approved Indicating Valves
From Water Supply

For SI Units: 1 in. = 25.4 mm.

Figure 5-4.2 Header for Combined Dry-Pipe and Preaction Sprinkler System, Standard Trimmings not Shown.

single fire area, the system shall be divided into sections of 275 sprinklers or less by means of check valves. If the system is installed in more than one fire area or story, not more than 600 sprinklers shall be supplied through any one check valve. Each section shall have a 1¼-in. (33-mm) drain on the system side of each check valve supplemented by a drum drip.

5-4.4.2 Section drain lines and drum drips shall be located in heated areas or inside of thermostatically controlled electrically heated cabinets of sufficient size to enclose drain valves and drum drips for each section. Drum drips shall also be provided for all low points except that heated cabinets need not be required for systems of 20 sprinklers or less.

5-4.4.3 Air exhaust valves at the end of a feed main and associated check valves shall be protected against freezing.

5-4.5 Time Limitation. The sprinkler system shall be so constructed and the number of sprinkler heads controlled shall be so limited that water shall reach the farthest sprinkler within a period of time not exceeding 1 minute for each 400 ft (122 m) of common feed main from the time the heat-responsive system operates. Maximum time permitted shall not exceed 3 minutes.

5-4.6 System Test Connection. The end section shall have a system test connection as required for dry-pipe systems.

5-5 Antifreeze Systems.

5-5.1 Definition. An antifreeze system is one employing automatic sprinklers attached to a piping system containing an antifreeze solution and connected to a water supply. The antifreeze solution, followed by water, discharges immediately from sprinklers opened by a fire.

5-5.2* Where Used. The use of antifreeze solutions shall be in conformity with any state or local health regulations.

5-5.3 Antifreeze Solutions.

5-5.3.1 When sprinkler systems are supplied by public water connections the use of antifreeze solutions other than water solutions of pure glycerine (C.P. or U.S.P. 96.5 percent grade) or propylene glycol shall not be permitted. Suitable glycerine-water and propylene glycol-water mixtures are shown in Table 5-5.3.1.

5-5.3.2 If public water is not connected to sprinklers, the commercially available materials indicated in Table 5-5.3.2 are suitable for use in antifreeze solutions.

5-5.3.3* An antifreeze solution shall be prepared with a freezing point below the expected minimum temperature

Table 5-5.3.1 Antifreeze Solutions to be Used if Public Water is Connected to Sprinklers

Material	Solution (by Volume)	Specific Gravity at 60°F (15.6°C)	Freezing Point °F	Freezing Point °C
Glycerine	50% Water	1.133	−15	−26.1
C.P. or U.S.P. Grade*	40% Water	1.151	−22	−30.0
	30% Water	1.165	−40	−40.0
Hydrometer Scale 1.000 to 1.200				
Propylene Glycol	70% Water	1.027	+9	−12.8
	60% Water	1.034	−6	−21.1
	50% Water	1.041	−26	−32.2
	40% Water	1.045	−60	−51.1
Hydrometer Scale 1.000 to 1.200 (Subdivisions 0.002)				

*C.P. —Chemically Pure.
U.S.P.—United States Pharmacopoeia 96.5%.

Table 5-5.3.2 Antifreeze Solutions to be Used if Public Water is not Connected to Sprinklers

Material	Solution (by Volume)	Specific Gravity at 60°F (15.6°C)	Freezing Point °F	Freezing Point °C
Glycerine	If glycerine is used, see Table 5-5.3.1			
Diethylene Glycol	50% Water	1.078	−13	−25.0
	45% Water	1.081	−27	−32.8
	40% Water	1.086	−42	−41.1
Hydrometer Scale 1.000 to 1.120 (Subdivisions 0.002)				
Ethylene Glycol	61% Water	1.056	−10	−23.3
	56% Water	1.063	−20	−28.9
	51% Water	1.069	−30	−34.4
	47% Water	1.073	−40	−40.0
Hydrometer Scale 1.000 to 1.120 (Subdivisions 0.002)				
Propylene Glycol	If propylene glycol is used, see Table 5-5.3.1			
Calcium Chloride 80% "Flake"	Lb $CaCl_2$ per gal of Water			
*Fire Protection Grade**	2.83	1.183	0	−17.8
Add corrosion inhibitor	3.38	1.212	−10	−23.3
of sodium bichromate	3.89	1.237	−20	−28.9
¼ oz per gal water	4.37	1.258	−30	−34.4
	4.73	1.274	−40	−40.0
	4.93	1.283	−50	−45.6

*Free from magnesium chloride and other impurities.

for the locality. The specific gravity of the prepared solution shall be checked by a hydrometer with suitable scale. [*See Figures 5-5.3.3(a) and (b).*]

5-5.4* Arrangement of Supply Piping and Valves. All permitted antifreeze solutions are heavier than water. At the point of contact (interface) the heavier liquid will be below the lighter liquid in order to prevent diffusion of water into the unheated areas. In most cases, this necessitates the use of a 5-ft (1.5-m) drop pipe or U-loop as illustrated in Figure 5-5.4. The preferred arrangement is to have the sprinklers below the interface between the water and the antifreeze solution.

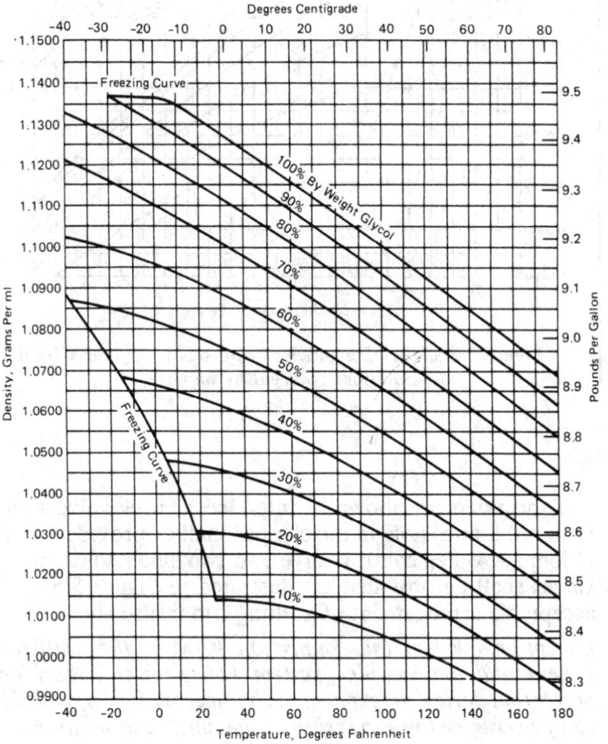
Degrees Centigrade
-40 -30 -20 -10 0 10 20 30 40 50 60 70 80
Freezing Curve
100% By Weight Glycol
90%
80%
70%
60%
50%
40%
30%
20%
10%
Freezing Curve
Density, Grams Per ml
1.1500 1.1400 1.1300 1.1200 1.1100 1.1000 1.0900 1.0800 1.0700 1.0600 1.0500 1.0400 1.0300 1.0200 1.0100 1.0000 0.9900
Pounds Per Gallon
9.5 9.4 9.3 9.2 9.1 9.0 8.9 8.8 8.7 8.6 8.5 8.4 8.3
-40 -20 0 20 40 60 80 100 120 140 160 180
Temperature, Degrees Fahrenheit

Figure 5-5.3.3(a) Densities of Aqueous Ethylene Glycol Solutions (percent by weight).

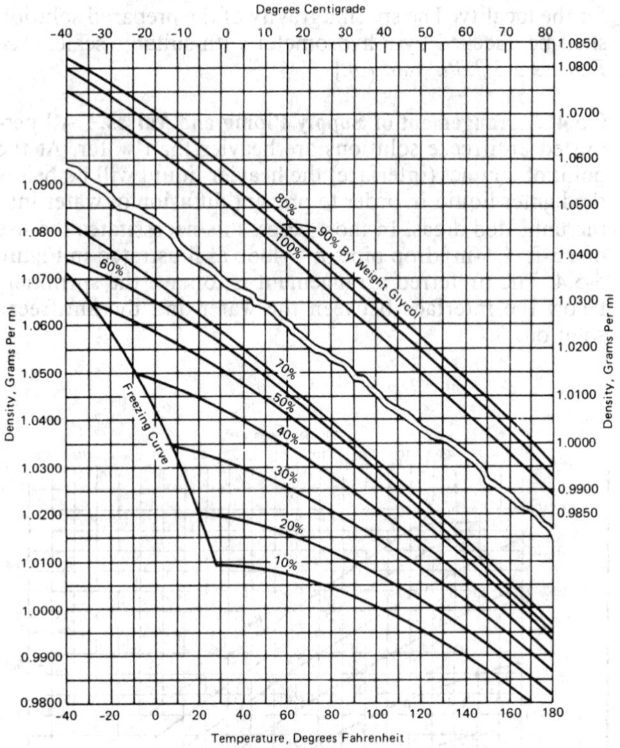

Degrees Centigrade
-40 -30 -20 -10 0 10 20 30 40 50 60 70 80
Temperature, Degrees Fahrenheit
-40 -20 0 20 40 60 80 100 120 140 160 180
Density, Grams Per ml
1.0900 1.0800 1.0700 1.0600 1.0500 1.0400 1.0300 1.0200 1.0100 1.0000 0.9900 0.9800
1.0850 1.0800 1.0700 1.0600 1.0500 1.0400 1.0300 1.0200 1.0100 1.0000 0.9900 0.9850
80%
90% By Weight Glycol
100%
60%
70%
50%
40%
30%
20%
10%
Freezing Curve

Figure 5-5.3.3(b) Densities of Aqueous Propylene Glycol Solutions (percent by weight).

If sprinklers are above the interface, a check valve with a 1/32-in. (0.8-mm) hole in the clapper shall be provided in the U-loop. A water control valve and two small solution test valves shall be provided as illustrated in Figure 5-5.4. An acceptable arrangement of a filling cup is also shown.

Exception: When the connection between the antifreeze system and the wet-pipe system incorporates a backflow prevention device, an expansion chamber shall be provided to compensate for the expansion of the antifreeze solution.

5-5.5* Testing. Before freezing weather each year, the solution in the entire system shall be emptied into convenient containers and brought to the proper specific gravity by adding concentrated liquid as needed. The resulting solution may be used to refill the system.

5-6 Automatic Sprinkler Systems with Nonfire Protection Connections.

5-6.1 Circulating Closed-Loop Systems.

5-6.1.1 Definition. A circulating closed loop is one with nonfire protection connections to automatic sprinkler systems in a closed-loop piping arrangement for the purpose of utilizing sprinkler piping to conduct water for heating or cooling. Water is not removed or used from the system, but only circulated through the piping system.

5-6.1.2 System Components.

5-6.1.2.1 Basic Principle. A circulating closed-loop system is primarily a sprinkler system, and all provisions of this standard such as control valves, area limitation of a system, alarms, fire department connections, sprinkler spacing, etc., are to be satisfied.

Exception: Items as specifically detailed within 5-6.1.

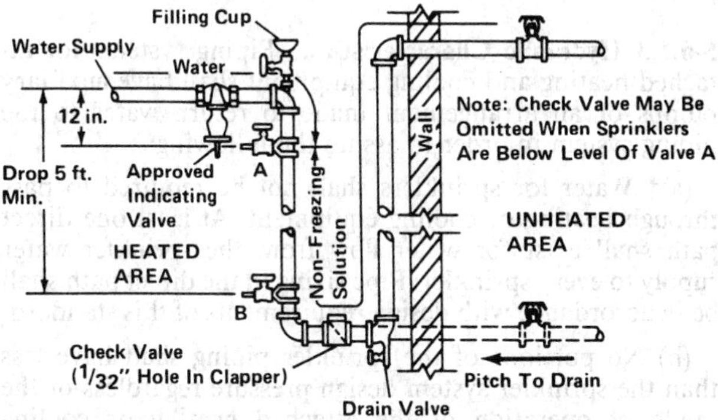
Filling Cup
Water Supply
Water
12 in.
Drop 5 ft. Min.
Approved Indicating Valve
A
HEATED AREA
B
Non-Freezing Solution
Wall
Note: Check Valve May Be Omitted When Sprinklers Are Below Level Of Valve A
UNHEATED AREA
Check Valve (1/32" Hole In Clapper)
Pitch To Drain
Drain Valve

NOTE: The 1/32-in. (0.8-mm) hole in the check valve clapper is needed to allow for expansion of the solution during a temperature rise and thus prevent damage to sprinkler heads.

For SI Units: 1 in. = 25.4 mm; 1 ft = 0.3048 m.

Figure 5-5.4 Arrangement of Supply Piping and Valves.

5-6.1.2.2 Piping, fittings, valves, and pipe hangers shall meet requirements specified in Chapter 3.

5-6.1.2.3 A dielectric fitting shall be installed in the junction where dissimilar piping materials are joined, e.g., copper to steel.

Exception: Dielectric fittings are not required in the junction where sprinklers are connected to piping.

5-6.1.2.4 It is not required that other auxiliary devices be listed for sprinkler service; however, these devices, such as pumps, circulating pumps, heat exchangers, radiators, and luminaires shall be pressure rated at 175 or 300 psi (12.1 or 20.7 bars) (rupture pressure of 5 X rated water working pressure), to match the required rating of sprinkler system components.

5-6.1.2.5 Auxiliary devices shall incorporate materials of construction and be so constructed that they will maintain their physical integrity under fire conditions to avoid impairment to the fire protection system.

5-6.1.2.6 Auxiliary devices where hung from the building structure shall be supported independently from the sprinkler portion of the system, following recognized engineering practices.

5-6.1.3 Hydraulic Characteristics. Piping systems for attached heating and cooling equipment shall have auxiliary pumps or an arrangement made to return water to the piping system in order to assure the following:

(a)* Water for sprinklers shall not be required to pass through heating or cooling equipment. At least one direct path shall exist for water flow from the sprinkler water supply to every sprinkler. Pipe sizing in the direct path shall be in accordance with design requirements of this standard.

(b) No portions of the sprinkler piping shall have less than the sprinkler system design pressure regardless of the mode of operation of the attached heating or cooling equipment.

(c) There shall be no loss or outflow of water from the system due to or resulting from the operation of heating or cooling equipment.

(d) Shutoff valves and a means of drainage shall be provided on piping to heating or cooling equipment at all points of connection to sprinkler piping and shall be installed in such a manner as to make possible repair or removal of any auxiliary component without impairing the serviceability and response to the sprinkler system. All auxiliary components, including the strainer, shall be installed on the auxiliary equipment side of the shutoff valves.

5-6.1.4 Water Temperature.

5-6.1.4.1 Maximum. In no case shall maximum water temperature flowing through the sprinkler portion of the system exceed 120°F (49°C). Protective control devices listed for this purpose shall be installed to shut down heating or cooling systems when temperature of water flowing through the sprinkler portion of the system exceeds 120°F (49°C). When water temperature exceeds 100°F (37.8°C), intermediate or higher temperature rated sprinklers shall be used.

5-6.1.4.2 Minimum. Precaution shall be taken to ensure that temperatures below 40°F (4°C) will not be permitted.

5-6.1.5 Obstruction to Discharge. Automatic sprinklers shall not be obstructed by auxiliary devices, piping, insulation, etc., from detecting fire or from proper distribution of water.

5-6.1.6 Valve Supervision. Position of all valves controlling sprinkler system (post indicator, main gate, sectional control) shall be supervised open by one of the following methods:

(a) Central station, proprietary, or remote station alarm service.

(b) Local alarm service, which will cause the sounding of an audible signal at a constantly attended point.

5-6.1.7 Signs. Caution signs shall be attached to all controlling sprinkler valves. The caution sign shall be worded as follows:

"This valve controls fire protection equipment. Do not close until after fire has been extinguished. Use auxiliary valves when necessary to shut supply to auxiliary equipment. CAUTION: Automatic alarm will be sounded if this valve is closed."

5-6.1.8 Water Additives. Materials added to water shall

not adversely affect the fire-fighting properties of the water and shall be in conformity with any state or local health regulations. Due care and caution shall be given to the use of additives that may remove or suspend scale from older piping systems. When additives are necessary for proper system operation, due care shall be taken to ensure that additives are replenished after alarm testing or whenever water is removed from the system.

5-6.1.9 Waterflow Detection. The supply of water from sprinkler piping through auxiliary devices, circulatory piping, and pumps shall not under any condition or operation, transient or static, cause false sprinkler waterflow signals.

5-6.1.9.1 A sprinkler waterflow signal shall not be impaired when water is discharged through an opened sprinkler or through the system test connection while auxiliary equipment is in any mode of operation (on, off, transient, stable).

5-6.1.10* Working Plans. Working plans shall be prepared and submitted in accordance with Section 1-9. Special symbols shall be used and explained for auxiliary piping, pumps, heat exchangers, valves, strainers, and the like, clearly distinguishing those devices and piping runs from those of the sprinkler system. Model number, type, and manufacturer's name shall be identified for each piece of auxiliary equipment.

5-6.1.11 Testing.

5-6.1.11.1 All sprinkler system and auxiliary system components shall be hydrostatically tested in accordance with 1-11.3.

5-6.1.11.2 Sprinkler system discharge tests shall be conducted using system test connections described in 3-4.1. Pressure gages shall be installed at critical points and readings taken under various modes of auxiliary equipment operation. Waterflow alarm signals shall be responsive to discharge of water through system test pipes while auxiliary equipment is in each of the possible modes of operation.

5-6.1.12 Contractor's Material and Test Certificate. Additional information shall be appended to the Contractor's Material and Test Certificate as shown in Figures 1-10.1(a) and (b), as follows:

(a) Certification that all auxiliary devices, such as heat pumps, circulating pumps, heat exchangers, radiators, and luminaires have a pressure rating of 175 or 300 psi (12.1 or 20.7 bars).

(b) All components of sprinkler system and auxiliary system have been pressure tested as a composite system in accordance with 1-11.2, Hydrostatic Tests.

(c) Waterflow tests have been conducted and waterflow alarms have operated while auxiliary equipment is in each of the possible modes of operation.

(d) With auxiliary equipment tested in each possible mode of operation and with no flow from sprinklers or test connection, waterflow alarm signals did not operate.

(e) Excess temperature controls for shutting down the auxiliary system have been properly field tested.

Chapter 6 Outside Sprinklers for Protection Against Exposure Fires

6-1 Water Supply and Control.

6-1.1 Water Supply.

6-1.1.1* Sprinklers installed for protection against exposure fires shall be supplied from a standard water supply as outlined in Chapter 2.

Exception: When approved, other supplies such as manual valves or pumps, or fire department connections, may be used.

6-1.1.2 When automatic systems of sprinklers are installed, water supplies shall be from an automatic source.

6-1.1.3 When the water supply feeds other fire protection appliances, it shall be capable of furnishing total demand for such appliances as well as the outside sprinkler demand.

6-1.1.4 When fire department connections are used for water supply, they shall be so located that they will not be affected by the exposing fire.

6-1.2 Control.

6-1.2.1 Each system of outside sprinklers shall have an independent control valve. When more than one system is required, the division between systems shall be vertical and not horizontal.

Exception: When more than six lines are installed, the systems shall be divided horizontally with independent risers.

6-1.2.2 Manually controlled open sprinklers shall be used only where constant supervision is present.

6-1.2.3 Sprinklers may be of the open or closed type. Closed sprinklers in areas subject to freezing shall be on dry-pipe systems conforming to Section 5-2 or antifreeze systems conforming to Section 5-5.

6-1.2.4* Automatic systems of open sprinklers shall be controlled by the operation of fire detection devices designed for the specific application.

6-2 System Components.

6-2.1* Valves.

6-2.1.1 Control valves shall be of the listed indicating type and shall be distinctively marked by letters not less than ½ in. (13 mm) high to clearly explain their use.

6-2.1.2 Drain Valve. Each system of outside sprinklers shall have a separate drain valve installed on the system side of each control valve. Drain valves shall be in accordance with 3-6.2, except that in no case shall valves be smaller than 1 in. (25.4 mm).

6-2.1.3 Check Valves. When sprinklers run on two adjacent sides of a building, protecting against two separate and distinct exposures, with separate control valves for each side, the end lines shall be connected with check valves located so that one sprinkler around the corner will operate. The intermediate pipe between the two check valves shall be arranged to drain. As an alternate solution, an additional sprinkler shall be installed on each system located around the corner from the system involved.

6-2.1.4 When one exposure affects two sides of the protected structure, the system shall not be subdivided between the two sides, but rather shall be arranged to operate as a single system.

6-2.2 Pipe and Fittings. Approved corrosion-resistant pipe and fittings shall be used for the equipment as far back as the control valve on the water supply.

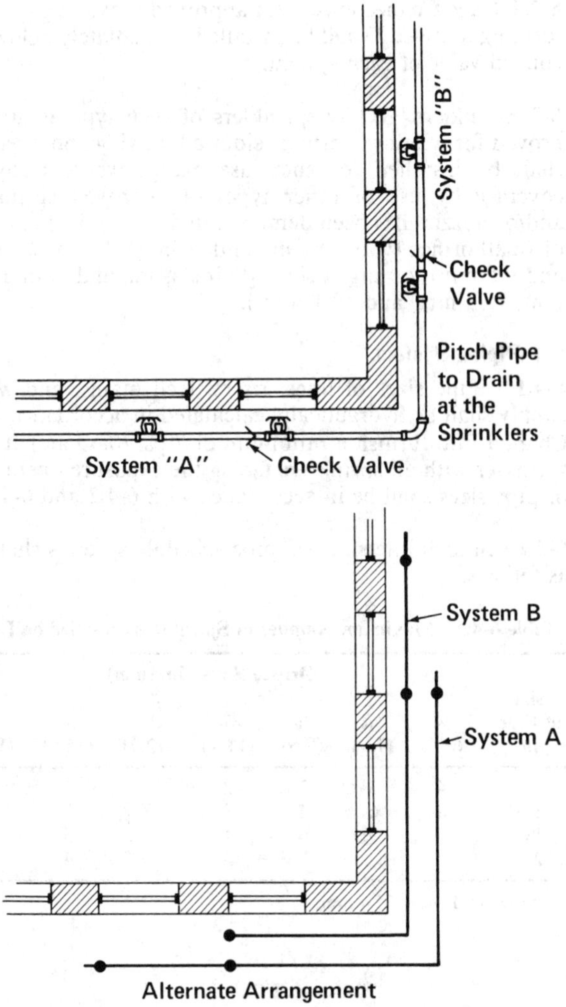
System "B"
Check
Valve
Pitch Pipe
to Drain
at the
Sprinklers
System "A"
Check Valve
System B
System A
Alternate Arrangement

Figure 6-2.1.3 Arrangement of Check Valves.

6-2.3 Strainers. An approved strainer shall be provided in the riser or feed main, which supplies sprinklers having orifices smaller than 3/8 in. (9.5 mm).

6-2.4 Gage Connections. An approved pressure gage conforming to 2-9.2.2 shall be installed immediately below the control valve of each system.

6-3 Sprinklers.[1] Only sprinklers of such type as are approved for window, cornice, sidewall, or ridge pole service shall be installed for such use except where adequate coverage by use of other types of approved sprinklers and/or nozzles has been demonstrated. Sprinklers may be of small orifice [1/4 in., 5/16 in., and 3/8 in. (6.4 mm, 7.9 mm, and 9.5 mm)] or large orifice [1/2 in., 5/8 in., and 3/4 in. (12.7 mm, 15.9 mm, and 19.1 mm)].

6-4 Piping System.

6-4.1* Pipe sizes of lines, risers, feed mains, and water supply shall be hydraulically calculated in accordance with Chapter 7 to furnish a minimum of 7 psi (0.5 bars) at any sprinkler with all sprinklers facing the exposure operating, or pipe sizes shall be in accordance with 6-4.2 and 6-4.3.

6-4.2 Branch line sizes on pipe schedule systems shall be as follows:

Table 6-4.2 Maximum Number of Sprinklers Supplied on Line

Size of Pipe In.	Orifice Size—In. (mm) 1/4 (6.4)	5/16 (7.9)	3/8 (9.5)	7/16 (11.1)	1/2 (12.7)	5/8 (15.9)	3/4 (19.1)
1	4	3	2	2	1	1	1
1 1/4	8	6	4	3	2	2	1
1 1/2		9	6	4	3	3	2
2				5	4	4	3

For SI Units: 1 in. = 25.4 mm.

[1]For additional information on outside sprinklers see Appendix B-6-1.

6-4.3 Risers and feed main sizes on pipe schedule systems shall be as follows for central feed risers:

Table 6-4.3 Maximum Number of Sprinklers— Riser or Feed Mains

	Number of Sprinklers		
Pipe Size	⅜ in. (9.5 mm) or smaller orifice	½ in. (12.7 mm) orifice	¾ in. (19.1 mm) orifice
1½	6	3	2
2	10	5	4
2½	18	9	7
3	32	16	12
3½	48	24	17
4	65	33	24
5	120	60	43
6		100	70

For SI Units: 1 in. = 25.4 mm.

6-5 Testing and Flushing.

6-5.1 Tests.

6-5.1.1 All piping shall be tested hydrostatically as specified in 1-11.2.

6-5.1.2 Operating tests shall be made of the system when completed, except where such tests may risk water damage.

6-5.2 Flushing. Flushing shall be conducted in accordance with 1-11.1.

Chapter 7 Hydraulically Designed Sprinkler Systems

7-1 General.

7-1.1 Definition.

7-1.1.1 A hydraulically designed sprinkler system is one in which pipe sizes are selected on a pressure loss basis to provide a prescribed density, in gallons per minute per square foot [(L/min)/m²], distributed with a reasonable degree of uniformity over a specified area. This permits the selection of pipe sizes in accordance with the characteristics of the water supply available. The stipulated design density and area of application will vary with occupancy hazard.

7-1.1.2* The design basis for such a system or addition to an existing system supersedes the rules in the sprinkler standard governing pipe schedules, except that all systems continue to be limited by area, and pipe sizes shall be no less than 1 in. (25.4 mm) nominal for ferrous piping and ¾ in. (19 mm) nominal for copper tubing. The size of pipe, number of sprinklers per branch line, and number of branch lines per cross main are otherwise limited only by the available water supply. However, sprinkler spacing and all other rules covered in this and other applicable standards shall be observed.

7-1.2* Nameplate Data. The installer shall properly identify a hydraulically designed automatic sprinkler system by a permanently attached nameplate indicating the location(s) and the basis of design(s) [discharge density(ies) over designed area(s) of discharge, including gallons per minute and residual pressure demand at base of riser] and hose stream demand supplied by the sprinkler piping. Such nameplates shall be placed at the controlling alarm, dry-pipe, or preaction valve, for the system containing the hydraulically designed layout(s).

7-2 Information Required.

7-2.1 Basic Design Information. Basic design criteria for hydraulically designed sprinkler systems shall be obtained from this or other applicable standards. Where no standards exist, the authority having jurisdiction shall be consulted.

7-2.2 Sprinkler System Requirements. The following information shall be included when applicable:

(a) Area of water application, sq ft

(b) Minimum rate of water application (density), gpm/sq ft

(c) Area per sprinkler, sq ft

(d) Allowance for inside hose and outside hydrants, gpm

(e) Allowance for in-rack sprinklers, gpm.

7-2.3* Water Supply Information. The following information shall be included: waterflow data with existing or proposed water supply, dead-end or circulating:

(a) Location and elevation of static and residual test gage with relation to the riser reference point

(b) Flow location

(c) Static pressure, psi

(d) Residual pressure, psi

(e) Flow, gpm

(f) Date

(g) Time

(h) Test conducted by or information supplied by . . .

7-2.4 Information Required on the Drawings.

7-2.4.1 In addition to the requirements of Section 1-9, the drawings shall also contain the information mentioned in the remainder of 7-2.4.

7-2.4.2 Hydraulic Reference Points. Reference points may be shown by a number and/or letter designation and shall correspond with comparable reference points shown on the hydraulic calculation sheets.

7-2.4.3 Sprinklers. Description of sprinklers used.

7-2.4.4 System Design Criteria. The minimum rate of water application (density), the design area of water application, in-rack sprinkler demand, and the water required for hose streams both inside and outside shall be included.

7-2.4.5 Actual Calculated Requirements. The total quantity of water and the pressure required shall be noted at a common reference point for each system.

7-2.4.6 Elevation Data. Relative elevations of sprinklers, junction points, and supply or reference points shall be noted.

7-3 Data Sheets and Abbreviations.

7-3.1 General. Hydraulic calculations shall be prepared on form sheets that include a summary sheet, detailed work sheets, and a graph sheet. (*See copy of typical forms, Figures A-7-3.3 and A-7-3.4.*)

7-3.2 Summary Sheet. The summary sheet shall contain the following information, when applicable:

(a) Date

(b) Location

(c) Name of owner and occupant

(d) Building number or other identification

(e) Description of hazard

(f) Name and address of contractor or designer

(g) Name of approving agency

(h) System design requirements

1. Design area of water application, sq ft

2. Minimum rate of water application (density), gpm per sq ft

3. Area per sprinkler, sq ft

(i) Total water requirements as calculated including allowance for inside hose and outside hydrants

(j) Water supply information.

7-3.3* Detailed Work Sheets. Detailed work sheets (*for sample work sheet, refer to Figure A-7-3.3*) or computer printout sheets shall contain the following information:

(a) Sheet number

(b) Sprinkler description and discharge constant (K)

(c) Hydraulic reference points

(d) Flow in gpm

(e) Pipe size

(f) Pipe lengths, center to center of fittings

(g) Equivalent pipe lengths for fitting and devices

(h) Friction loss in psi per ft of pipe

(i) Total friction loss between reference points

(j) In-rack sprinkler demand

(k) Elevation head in psi between reference points

(l) Required pressure in psi at each reference point

(m) Velocity pressure and normal pressure if included in calculations

(n) Notes to indicate starting points, reference to other sheets, or to clarify data shown

(o)* Diagram to accompany gridded system calculations to indicate flow quantities and directions for lines with sprinklers operating in the remote area. [*See Figure A-7-3.3(o).*]

7-3.4* Graph Sheet. Water supply curves and system requirements, plus hose and in-rack sprinkler demand when applicable, shall be plotted on semi-logarithmic graph paper ($Q^{1.85}$) so as to present a graphic summary of the complete hydraulic calculation.

7-3.5 Abbreviations and Symbols. The following standard abbreviations and symbols shall be used on the calculation form:

Symbol or Abbreviation	Item
p	Pressure in psi
gpm	U.S. Gallons per minute
q	Flow increment in gpm to be added at a specific location
Q	Summation of flow in gpm at a specific location
P_t	Total pressure in psi at a point in a pipe
P_f	Pressure loss due to friction between points indicated in location column
P_e	Pressure due to elevation difference between indicated points. This can be a plus value or a minus value. Where minus, the (−) shall be used; where plus, no sign need be indicated
P_v	Velocity pressure in psi at a point in a pipe
P_n	Normal pressure in psi at a point in a pipe
E	90° Ell
EE	45° Ell
Lt.E	Long Turn Elbow
Cr	Cross
T	Tee — flow turned 90 degrees
GV	Gate Valve
BV	Butterfly Valve
Del V	Deluge Valve
ALV	Alarm Valve
CV	Swing Check Valve
WCV	Butterfly (Wafer) Check Valve
St	Strainer
psi	pounds per square inch
v	Velocity of water in pipe in feet per second

7-4 Calculation.

7-4.1 Formulas.

7-4.1.1 Friction Loss Formula. Pipe friction losses shall be determined on the basis of the Hazen-Williams formula.

$$p = \frac{4.52\, Q^{1.85}}{C^{1.85}\, d^{4.87}}$$

where p is the frictional resistance in pounds pressure per square inch per foot of pipe, Q is the gallons per minute flowing, and d is the actual internal diameter of pipe in inches with C as the friction loss coefficient.

$$\text{For SI Units: } P_m = 6.05 \times \frac{Q_m^{1.85}}{C^{1.85}\, d_m^{4.87}} \times 10^{5}$$

P_m is the frictional resistance in bars per meter of pipe, Q_m is the flow in L/min, and d_m is the actual internal diameter in mm with C as the friction loss coefficient.

7-4.1.2 Velocity Pressure Formula. Velocity pressure shall be determined on the basis of the formula

$$P_v = 0.001\,123\, Q^2/D^4$$

P_v = velocity pressure psi.

where:

Q = flow in gpm.

D = the inside diameter in inches.

For SI units: 1 in. = 25.4 mm; 1 gal = 3.785 L; 1 psi = 0.0689 bar.

7-4.1.3 Normal pressure P_n shall be determined on the basis of the formula

$$P_n = P_t - P_v$$

where:

P_t = total pressure in psi (bars)

P_v = velocity pressure in psi (bars)

7-4.1.4 Hydraulic Junction Points. Pressures at hydraulic junction points shall balance within 0.5 psi (0.03 bar). The highest pressure at the junction point, and the total flows as adjusted, shall be carried into the calculations.

7-4.2 Equivalent Pipe Lengths of Valves and Fittings.

7-4.2.1 Table 7-4.2 shall be used to determine the equivalent length of pipe for fittings and devices unless manufacturer's test data indicate that other factors are appropriate. For saddle-type fittings having friction loss greater than that shown in Table 7-4.2, the increased friction loss shall be included in hydraulic calculations.

7-4.2.2 Use Table 7-4.2 with Hazen-Williams C = 120 only. For other values of C, the values in Table 7-4.2 shall be multiplied by the factors indicated below:

Value of C	100	130	140	150
Multiplying Factor	0.713	1.16	1.33	1.51

(This is based upon the friction loss through the fitting being independent of the C factor available to the piping.)

7-4.2.3 Specific friction loss values or equivalent pipe lengths for alarm valves, dry-pipe valves, deluge valves, strainers, and other devices shall be made available to the authority having jurisdiction.

7-4.3* Calculation Procedure.

7-4.3.1* For all systems the design area shall be the hydraulically most demanding based on the criteria of 2-2.1.3. When the design is based on area/density method, the calculation shall be a rectangular area having a dimension parallel to the branch lines at least 1.2 times the square root of the area of sprinkler operation used. This may include sprinklers on both sides of the cross main. Any fractional sprinkler shall be carried to the next higher whole sprinkler. When the design is based on the room design method, the calculation shall be based on the room that is the hydraulically most demanding.

Exception No. 1: Where the design area under consideration consists of a corridor protected by one row of sprinklers, the maximum number of sprinklers that need be calculated is 5, unless openings from the corridor are unprotected. (See 2-2.3.)

Exception No. 2: In systems having branch lines with an insufficient number of sprinklers to fulfill the $1.2\sqrt{A}$ *requirement, the design area shall be extended to include sprinklers on adjacent branch lines supplied by the same cross main.*

Exception No. 3: Where the design is based on the criteria of 2-2.3, including the Exceptions to that section, the above dimensional requirements do not apply.

Exception No. 4: Where the design area under consideration consists of a building service chute supplied by a separate riser, the maximum number of sprinklers that need be calculated is 3.

Exception No. 5: Residential sprinkler designs shall be in accordance with 7-4.4.

Table 7-4.2 Equivalent Pipe Length Chart

Fittings and Valves	Fittings and Valves Expressed in Equivalent Feet of Pipe.													
	¾ in.	1 in.	1¼ in.	1½ in.	2 in.	2½ in.	3 in.	3½ in.	4 in.	5 in.	6 in.	8 in.	10 in.	12 in.
45° Elbow	1	1	1	2	2	3	3	3	4	5	7	9	11	13
90° Standard Elbow	2	2	3	4	5	6	7	8	10	12	14	18	22	27
90° Long Turn Elbow	1	2	2	2	3	4	5	5	6	8	9	13	16	18
Tee or Cross (Flow Turned 90°)	3	5	6	8	10	12	15	17	20	25	30	35	50	60
Butterfly Valve	—	—	—	—	6	7	10	—	12	9	10	12	19	21
Gate Valve	—	—	—	—	1	1	1	1	2	2	3	4	5	6
Swing Check*	—	5	7	9	11	14	16	19	22	27	32	45	55	65

For SI Units: 1 ft = 0.3048 m.

*Due to the variations in design of swing check valves, the pipe equivalents indicated in the above chart are considered average.

NOTE: This table applies to all types of pipe listed in Table 7-4.3.1.4.

Exception No. 6: Designs for ESFR sprinklers shall be in accordance with Chapter 9.

7-4.3.1.1* For gridded systems, the designer shall verify that the hydraulically most demanding area is being used. A minimum of two additional sets of calculations shall be submitted to demonstrate peaking of demand area friction loss when compared to areas immediately adjacent on either side along the same branch lines.

Exception: Computer programs that show the peaking of the demand area friction loss shall be acceptable based on a single set of calculations.

7-4.3.1.2 System piping shall be hydraulically designed using design densities and areas of operation in accordance with Table 2-2.1.1(b) as required for the occupancies involved.

(a)* The density shall be calculated on the basis of floor area. The area covered by any sprinkler for use in hydraulic design and calculations shall be determined as follows:

1. Along Branch Lines. Determine distance to next sprinkler (or to wall in case of end sprinkler on branch line) upstream and downstream. Choose larger of either twice (1) the distance to the wall, or (2) distance to the next sprinkler. Call this "S."

2. Between Branch Lines. Determine the perpendicular distance to sprinklers on branch lines (or to wall in case of the last branch line) on each side of the branch line on which the subject sprinkler is positioned. Choose the larger of (1) the larger distance to the sprinklers on the next branch line, or (2) in the case of the last branch line, twice the distance to the wall. Call this "L."

Exception: For sidewall sprinklers, L will be the distance to the wall opposite the sprinklers, or in the case where sprinklers are provided on two sides, half the distance between the two sides.

3. Design Area for Sprinkler = S × L.

Exception: This does not apply to small rooms. (See 4-4.19.)

(b)* When sprinklers are installed above and below a ceiling or in a case where more than two areas are supplied from a common set of branch lines, the branch lines and supplies shall be calculated to supply the largest water demand.

(c) When sprinklers are installed above and below temporary obstructions such as overhead doors, the branch lines and the supply shall be calculated to supply the sprinklers both above and below the temporary obstruction.

7-4.3.1.3* Each sprinkler in the design area and the remainder of the hydraulically designed system shall discharge at a flow rate at least equal to the stipulated minimum water application rate (density). Begin calculations at the hydraulically most remote sprinkler. Discharge at each sprinkler shall be based on the calculated pressure at that sprinkler.

7-4.3.1.4 Calculate pipe friction loss in accordance with the Hazen-Williams formula with C values from Table 7-4.3.1.4.

(a) Include pipe, fittings, and devices such as valves, meters, and strainers, and calculate elevation changes that affect the sprinkler discharge.

(b) Calculate the loss for a tee or a cross where flow direction change occurs based on the equivalent pipe length of the piping segment in which the fitting is included. The tee at the top of a riser nipple shall be included in the branch line; the tee at the base of a riser nipple shall be included in the riser nipple; and the tee or cross at a cross main–feed main junction shall be included in the cross main. Do not include fitting loss for straight through flow in a tee or cross.

(c) Calculate the loss of reducing elbows based on the equivalent feet value of the smallest outlet. Use the equivalent feet value for the *standard elbow* on any abrupt 90-degree turn, such as the screw-type pattern. Use the equivalent feet value for the *long-turn elbow* on any sweeping 90-degree turn, such as a flanged, welded, or mechanical joint-elbow type. (*See Table 7-4.2.*)

(d) Friction loss shall be excluded for the fitting directly connected to a sprinkler.

(e) Losses through a pressure-reducing valve shall be included based on the normal inlet pressure condition. Pressure loss data from the manufacturer's literature shall be used.

7-4.3.1.5* Orifice plates or sprinklers of different orifice sizes shall not be used for balancing the system, except for special use such as exposure protection, small rooms or

Table 7-4.3.1.4 Hazen-Williams C Values

Pipe or Tube	C Value*
Unlined Cast or Ductile Iron	100
Black Steel (Dry Systems including Preaction)	100
Black Steel (Wet Systems including Deluge)	120
Galvanized (all)	120
Plastic (listed)—All	150
Cement Lined Cast or Ductile Iron	140
Copper Tube or Stainless Steel	150

*The authority having jurisdiction may recommend other C values.

enclosures, or directional discharge. (*See 4-4.19 for definition of small rooms.*)

7-4.3.1.6 Sprinkler discharge in closets, washrooms, and similar small compartments requiring only one sprinkler may be omitted from hydraulic calculations within the area of application. [Sprinklers in these small compartments shall, however, be capable of discharging minimum densities in accordance with Table 2-2.1.1(b).]

Exception: This shall not apply when areas of application are less than 1500 sq ft (140 m²).

7-4.3.1.7 Where sprinklers are provided above and below permanent obstructions such as wide ducts, tables, etc., the water supply for one of the levels of sprinklers may be omitted from the hydraulic ceiling design calculations within the area of application. In any case, the most hydraulically demanding arrangement shall be calculated.

7-4.3.1.8* Velocity pressure (P_v) may or may not be included in the calculations at the discretion of the designer. If velocity pressures are used, they shall be used on both branch lines and cross mains where applicable.

7-4.3.2 Minimum operating pressure of any sprinkler shall be 7 psi (0.5 bar).

Exception: When higher minimum operating pressure for the desired application is specified in the listing of the sprinkler, it shall govern.

7-4.4 Dwelling Units. When residential sprinklers are used, design shall comply with this section.

7-4.4.1 Design Discharge. The system shall provide a discharge of not less than 18 gal/min (68 L/min) to any operating sprinkler and not less than 13 gal/min (49 L/min) per sprinkler to all operating sprinklers in the design area. Other discharge rates may be used in accordance with flow rates indicated in individual residential sprinkler listings.

7-4.4.2* Number of Design Sprinklers. The number of design sprinklers shall include all sprinklers within a compartment to a maximum of 4 sprinklers. When a compartment contains less than 4 sprinklers, the number of design sprinklers shall include all sprinklers in that compartment plus sprinklers in adjoining compartments to a total of 4 sprinklers. Adjoining corridors, if used in the calculations, shall be considered adjoining compartments solely for the purposes of these calculations. In all cases the design area shall include the 4 most hydraulically demanding sprinklers. (*See Figure A-7-4.4.2.*)

7-4.4.3 The definition of compartment for use in 7-4.4.2 to determine the number of design sprinklers is a space completely enclosed by walls and a ceiling. The compartment enclosure may have openings to an adjoining space if the openings have a minimum lintel depth of 8 in. (203 mm) from the ceiling.

7-4.4.4 Water Demand. The water demand for the dwelling unit shall be determined by multiplying the design discharge of 7-4.4.1 by the number of design sprinklers specified in 7-4.4.2.

7-4.4.5 Other Areas. When areas such as attics, basements, or other types of occupancies are outside of dwelling units but within the same structure, these areas shall be protected in accordance with all sections of this standard including appropriate water supply requirements of Table 2-2.1.1(b).

Chapter 8* Pipe Schedule Systems

8-1* General. The pipe schedule sizing provisions shall not apply to hydraulically designed systems. Sprinkler systems having sprinklers with orifices other than ½ in.

(13 mm) nominal, or piping material other than that covered in Table 3-1.1.1, shall be hydraulically designed. (*See Chapter 7.*)

Exception: Exposure protection systems designed in accordance with Chapter 6.

8-1.1 The number of automatic sprinklers on a given pipe size on one floor shall not exceed the number given in Sections 8-2, 8-3, or 8-4 for a given occupancy.

8-1.2 Size of Risers. Each system riser shall be sized to supply all sprinklers on the riser on any one floor as determined by the standard schedules of pipe sizes in Sections 8-2, 8-3, or 8-4.

8-1.3 Slatted Floors, Large Floor Openings, Mezzanines, and Large Platforms. Buildings having slatted floors, or large unprotected floor openings without approved stops, shall be treated as one area with reference to the pipe sizes, and the feed mains or risers shall be of the size required for the total number of sprinklers.

8-2 Schedule for Light Hazard Occupancies.

8-2.1 Branch lines shall not exceed 8 sprinklers on either side of a cross main.

Exception: When more than 8 sprinklers on a branch line are necessary, lines may be increased to 9 sprinklers by making the two end lengths 1 in. (25.4 mm) and 1¼ in. (33 mm) respectively, and the sizes thereafter standard. Ten sprinklers may be placed on a branch line making the two end lengths 1 in. (25.4 mm) and 1¼ in. (33 mm), respectively, and feeding the tenth sprinkler by a 2½ in. (64 mm) pipe.

8-2.2 Pipe sizes shall be in accordance with Table 8-2.2.

Exception: Each area requiring more sprinklers than the number specified for 3½ in. (89 mm) pipe in Table 8-2.2 and without subdividing partitions (not necessarily fire walls) shall be supplied by mains or risers sized for Ordinary Hazard Occupancies.

8-2.3 When sprinklers are installed above and below ceilings [*see Figures 8-2.3(a), (b), and (c)*] and such sprinklers are supplied from a common set of branch lines or separate branch lines from a common cross main, such branch lines shall not exceed 8 sprinklers above and 8 sprinklers below any ceiling on either side of the cross main. Pipe sizing up to and including 2½ in. (64 mm), shall be as shown in Table 8-2.3 utilizing the greatest number of sprinklers to be found on any two adjacent levels.

8-2.3.1* When the total number of sprinklers above and below a ceiling exceeds the number specified in Table 8-2.3 for 2½-in. (64-mm) pipe, the pipe supplying such sprinklers shall be increased to 3 in. (76 mm) and sized thereafter according to the schedule shown in Table 8-2.2 for the number of sprinklers above or below a ceiling, whichever is larger.

Table 8-2.2 Light Hazard Pipe Schedules

Steel		Copper	
1 in.	2 sprinklers	1 in.	2 sprinklers
1¼ in.	3 sprinklers	1¼ in.	3 sprinklers
1½ in.	5 sprinklers	1½ in.	5 sprinklers
2 in.	10 sprinklers	2 in.	12 sprinklers
2½ in.	30 sprinklers	2½ in.	40 sprinklers
3 in.	60 sprinklers	3 in.	65 sprinklers
3½ in.	100 sprinklers	3½ in.	115 sprinklers
4 in.	See 4-2.2.1	4 in.	See 4-2.2.1

Table 8-2.3 Number of Sprinklers Above and Below a Ceiling

Steel		Copper	
1 in.	2 sprinklers	1 in.	2 sprinklers
1¼ in.	4 sprinklers	1¼ in.	4 sprinklers
1½ in.	7 sprinklers	1½ in.	7 sprinklers
2 in.	15 sprinklers	2 in.	18 sprinklers
2½ in.	50 sprinklers	2½ in.	65 sprinklers

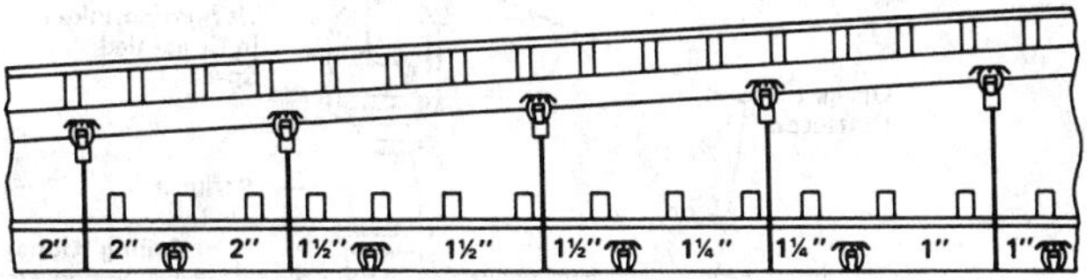
2"
2"
2"
1½"
1½"
1½"
1¼"
1¼"
1"
1"

For SI Units: 1 in. = 25.4 mm.

Figure 8-2.3(a) Arrangement of Branch Lines Supplying Sprinklers Above and Below a Ceiling.

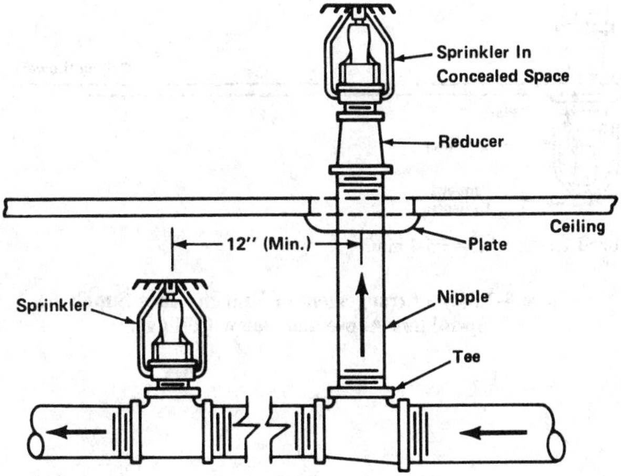
Sprinkler In Concealed Space
Reducer
Ceiling
12" (Min.)
Plate
Sprinkler
Nipple
Tee

For SI Units: 1 in. = 25.4 mm.

Figure 8-2.3(b) Sprinkler on Riser Nipple from Branch Line in Lower Fire Area.

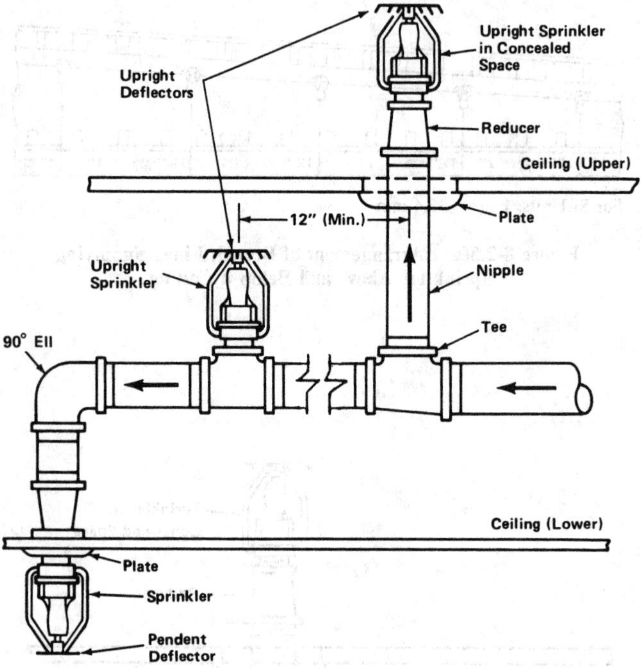
Upright Sprinkler in Concealed Space
Upright Deflectors
Reducer
Ceiling (Upper)
Plate
12" (Min.)
Upright Sprinkler
Nipple
Tee
90° Ell
Ceiling (Lower)
Plate
Sprinkler
Pendent Deflector

For SI Units: 1 in. = 25.4 mm.

Figure 8-2.3(c) Arrangement of Branch Lines Supplying Sprinklers Above and Below Ceilings.

8-3 Schedule for Ordinary Hazard Occupancies.

8-3.1 Branch lines shall not exceed 8 sprinklers on either side of a cross main.

Exception: When more than 8 sprinklers on a branch line are necessary, lines may be increased to 9 sprinklers by making the two end lengths 1 in. (25.4 mm) and 1¼ in. (33 mm), respectively, and the sizes thereafter standard. Ten sprinklers may be placed on a branch line making the two end lengths 1 in. (25.4 mm) and 1¼ in. (33 mm) respectively, and feeding the tenth sprinkler by a 2½ in. (64 mm) pipe.

8-3.2 Pipe sizes shall be in accordance with Table 8-3.2(a).

Table 8-3.2(a) Ordinary Hazard Pipe Schedule

Steel		Copper	
1 in.	2 sprinklers	1 in.	2 sprinklers
1¼ in.	3 sprinklers	1¼ in.	3 sprinklers
1½ in.	5 sprinklers	1½ in.	5 sprinklers
2 in.	10 sprinklers	2 in.	12 sprinklers
2½ in.	20 sprinklers	2½ in.	25 sprinklers
3 in.	40 sprinklers	3 in.	45 sprinklers
3½ in.	65 sprinklers	3½ in.	75 sprinklers
4 in.	100 sprinklers	4 in.	115 sprinklers
5 in.	160 sprinklers	5 in.	180 sprinklers
6 in.	275 sprinklers	6 in.	300 sprinklers
8 in.	See 4-2.2.1 and 4-2.2.1 Exception	8 in.	See 4-2.2.1 and 4-2.2.1 Exception

Exception: When the distance between sprinklers on the branch line exceeds 12 ft (3.7 m), or the distance between the branch lines exceeds 12 ft (3.7 m), the number of sprinklers for a given pipe size shall be in accordance with Table 8-3.2(b).

Table 8-3.2(b) Number of Sprinklers—Greater than 12 ft Separations

Steel		Copper	
2½ in.	15 sprinklers	2½ in.	20 sprinklers
3 in.	30 sprinklers	3 in.	35 sprinklers
3½ in.	60 sprinklers	3½ in.	65 sprinklers

For other pipe and tube sizes, see Table 8-3.2(a).

8-3.3 When sprinklers are installed above and below ceilings and such sprinklers are supplied from a common set of branch lines or separate branch lines supplied by a common cross main, such branch lines shall not exceed 8 sprinklers above and 8 sprinklers below any ceiling on either side of the cross main. Pipe sizing up to and including 3 in. (76 mm) shall be as shown in Table 8-3.3 [*see Figures 8-2.3(a), (b), and (c)*] utilizing the greatest number of sprinklers to be found on any two adjacent levels.

Table 8-3.3 Number of Sprinklers Above and Below a Ceiling

Steel		Copper	
1 in.	2 sprinklers	1 in.	2 sprinklers
1¼ in.	4 sprinklers	1¼ in.	4 sprinklers
1½ in.	7 sprinklers	1½ in.	7 sprinklers
2 in.	15 sprinklers	2 in.	18 sprinklers
2½ in.	30 sprinklers	2½ in.	40 sprinklers
3 in.	60 sprinklers	3 in.	65 sprinklers

8-3.3.1* When the total number of sprinklers above and below a ceiling exceeds the number specified in Table 8-3.3 for 3-in. (76-mm) pipe, the pipe supplying such sprinklers shall be increased to 3½ in. (89 mm) and sized thereafter according to the schedule shown in Table 8-2.2 or Table 8-3.2(a) for the number of sprinklers above or below a ceiling, whichever is larger.

Exception: When the distance between the sprinklers protecting the occupied area exceeds 12 ft (3.7 m) or the distance between the branch lines exceeds 12 ft (3.7 m), the branch lines shall be sized in accordance with either Table 8-3.2(b), taking into consideration the sprinklers protecting the occupied area only, or paragraph 8-3.3, whichever requires the greater size of pipe.

8-4 Schedule for Extra Hazard Occupancies. Branch lines shall not exceed 6 sprinklers on either side of a cross main. The number of sprinklers for a given pipe size shall be in accordance with Table 8-4.

Table 8-4 Extra Hazard Pipe Schedule

Steel		Copper	
1 in.	1 sprinkler	1 in.	1 sprinkler
1¼ in.	2 sprinklers	1¼ in.	2 sprinklers
1½ in.	5 sprinklers	1½ in.	5 sprinklers
2 in.	8 sprinklers	2 in.	8 sprinklers
2½ in.	15 sprinklers	2½ in.	20 sprinklers
3 in.	27 sprinklers	3 in.	30 sprinklers
3½ in.	40 sprinklers	3½ in.	45 sprinklers
4 in.	55 sprinklers	4 in.	65 sprinklers
5 in.	90 sprinklers	5 in.	100 sprinklers
6 in.	150 sprinklers	6 in.	170 sprinklers
8 in.	See 4-2.2.1	8 in.	See 4-2.2.1

8-5 Deluge Systems. Open sprinkler and deluge systems shall be hydraulically calculated according to applicable standards.

Exception: Open sprinklers for exposure protection installed in conformance with Chapter 6.

Chapter 9 Large-Drop and Early Suppression Fast Response (ESFR) Sprinklers

9-1 General.

9-1.1 Applications. This chapter provides requirements for the installation of large-drop and early suppression fast response (ESFR) sprinklers. Listed sprinklers other than large-drop and ESFR sprinklers are not covered by this chapter.

9-2 Large-Drop Sprinklers.

9-2.1* Definition. Large-Drop Sprinkler. A listed large-drop sprinkler is characterized by a K factor between 11.0 and 11.5, and proven ability to meet prescribed penetration, cooling, and distribution criteria prescribed in the large-drop sprinkler examination requirements. The deflector/discharge characteristics of the large-drop sprinkler generate large drops of such size and velocity as to enable effective penetration of the high-velocity fire plume.

9-2.2* Applicability.

9-2.2.1* Large-drop sprinklers are suitable for use with the hazards listed in Table A-9-2.4 and may be used in other specific hazard classifications and configurations only when proven by large-scale fire testing.

9-2.2.2 Requirements of this standard shall apply, except those portions dealing with subjects specifically addressed in this chapter.

9-2.3 Installation.

9-2.3.1 Operating Pressure.

9-2.3.1.1 Large-drop sprinkler systems shall be designed such that the minimum operating pressure is not less than

25 psi (1.7 bar), unless large-scale testing proves a lesser pressure to be adequate for a particular hazard.

9-2.3.1.2 For design purposes, 95 psi (6.5 bar) shall be the maximum discharge pressure used at the starting point of the hydraulic calculations.

9-2.3.2 Type of System.

9-2.3.2.1 Large-drop sprinkler systems shall be limited to wet-pipe or preaction systems.

9-2.3.2.2 Galvanized steel or copper pipe and fittings shall be used in preaction systems to avoid scale accumulation.

9-2.3.3 System Design.

9-2.3.3.1 Pipe shall be sized by hydraulic calculation.

9-2.3.3.2* The nominal diameter of branch line pipes (including riser nipples) shall be not less than 1¼ in. (33 mm) or greater than 2 in. (51 mm), except starter pieces, which may be 2½ in. (64 mm).

Exception: When branch lines are larger than 2 in. (51 mm), the sprinkler shall be supplied by a riser nipple to elevate the sprinkler 13 in. (330 mm) for 2½-in. (64-mm) pipe and 15 in. (380 mm) for 3-in. (76-mm) pipe. These dimensions are measured from the center line of the pipe to the deflector. In lieu of this, sprinklers may be offset horizontally a minimum of 12 in. (305 mm).

9-2.3.4 Temperature Rating. Sprinkler temperature ratings shall be the same as those used in large-scale fire testing to determine the protection requirements for the hazard involved.

Exception: Sprinklers of intermediate and high temperature ratings shall be installed in specific locations as required by 3-11.6.3.

9-2.3.5* Spacing.

9-2.3.5.1* The area of coverage shall be limited to a minimum of 80 sq ft (7.4 m^2) and a maximum of 130 sq ft (12.18 m^2).

9-2.3.5.2 The distance between branch lines and between sprinklers on the branch lines shall be limited to not more than 12 ft (3.7 m) nor less than 8 ft (2.4 m).

Exception: Under open wood joist construction, the maximum distance shall be limited to 10 ft (3.0 m).

9-2.3.6 Clear Space Below Sprinklers. At least 36 in. (914 mm) shall be maintained between sprinkler deflectors and the top of storage.

9-2.3.7* Distance Below Ceiling. Sprinklers shall be positioned so that the tops of deflectors are in conformance with Table 9-2.3.7.

Table 9-2.3.7 Minimum and Maximum Distance of Deflectors Below Ceiling for Various Construction Types

Construction Type[1]	Minimum Distance, In. (mm)	Maximum Distance, In. (mm)
Smooth ceiling and bar joist	6 (152)	8 (203)
Beam and girder	6 (152)	12 (305)
Panel up to 300 sq ft (27.9 m^2)	6 (152)	14 (358)
Open wood joist	1 (25) below bottom of joists	6 (152) below bottom of joists

[1]See Chapter 4 for definitions of construction types.

9-2.3.8 Location of Sprinklers in Beam and Girder and Panel Construction.

9-2.3.8.1 Under beam and girder construction and under panel construction, the branch lines may run across the beams, but sprinklers shall be located in the bays and not under the beams.

9-2.3.8.2 The maximum distance of deflector above the bottom of beams shall be limited to the values specified in Chapter 4.

9-2.3.9* Obstructions in Piping.

9-2.3.9.1 Screens located in the inlet piping directly connected to rivers, lakes, ponds, reservoirs, uncovered tanks, and similar sources (*see NFPA 24, Standard for the Installation of Private Fire Service Mains and Their Appurtenances*) shall be cleaned and serviced at least annually and immediately after any work has been performed on nearby underground mains.

9-2.3.9.2* Visual and/or flushing investigations shall be conducted of all systems for foreign material, at intervals not exceeding five years.

9-2.3.10* Obstructions to Distribution.

9-2.3.10.1 Obstructions Located at the Ceiling. When sprinkler deflectors are located above the bottom of beams, girders, ducts, fluorescent lighting fixtures, or other obstructions located at the ceiling, the sprinklers shall be positioned so that the maximum distance from the bottom of the obstruction to the deflectors does not exceed the value specified in Chapter 4.

9-2.3.10.2 Obstructions Located Below the Sprinklers.

9-2.3.10.2.1 Sprinklers shall be positioned with respect to fluorescent lighting fixtures, ducts, and obstructions more than 24 in. (610 mm) wide and located entirely below the sprinklers so that the minimum horizontal distance from the near side of the obstruction to the center of the sprinkler is not less than the value specified in Table 9-2.3.10.2.1. (*See Figure 9-2.3.10.2.1.*)

9-2.3.10.2.2 When the bottom of the obstruction is located 24 in. (610 mm) or more below the sprinkler deflectors:

(a) Sprinklers shall be positioned so that the obstruction is centered between adjacent sprinklers. (*See Figure 9-2.3.10.2.2.*)

Table 9-2.3.10.2.1 Position of Sprinklers in Relation to Obstructions Located Entirely Below the Sprinklers

Distance of Deflector Above Bottom of Obstruction	Minimum Distance to Side of Obstruction, ft (m)
Less than 6 in. (152 mm)	1½ (0.5)
6 in. (152 mm) to less than 12 in. (305 mm)	3 (0.9)
12 in. (305 mm) to less than 18 in. (457 mm)	4 (1.2)
18 in. (457 mm) to less than 24 in. (610 mm)	5 (1.5)

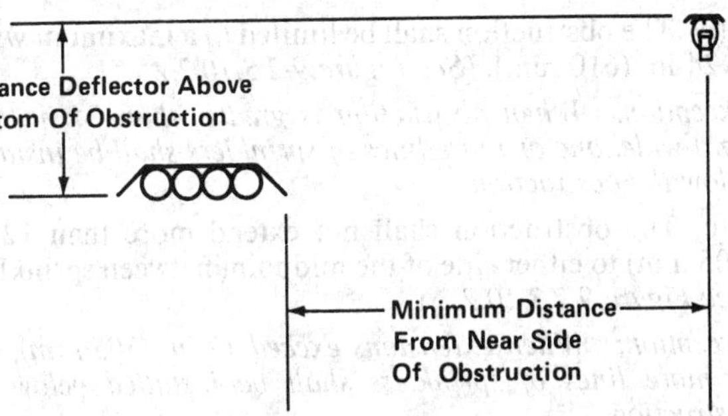
Distance Deflector Above
Bottom Of Obstruction
Minimum Distance
From Near Side
Of Obstruction

Figure 9-2.3.10.2.1 Position of Sprinklers in Relation to Obstructions Located Entirely below the Sprinklers. (To be used with Table 9-2.3.10.2.1)

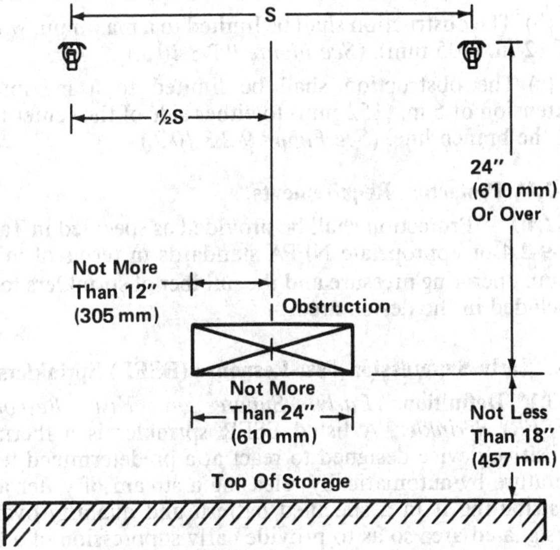
S
½S
24"
(610 mm)
Or Over
Not More
Than 12"
(305 mm)
Obstruction
Not More
Than 24"
(610 mm)
Not Less
Than 18"
(457 mm)
Top Of Storage

Figure 9-2.3.10.2.2 Position of Sprinklers in Relation to Obstructions Located 24 in. (610 mm) or more below Deflectors.

(b) The obstruction shall be limited to a maximum width of 24 in. (610 mm). (*See Figure 9-2.3.10.2.2.*)

Exception: When obstruction is greater than 24 in. (610 mm) wide, one or more lines of sprinklers shall be installed below the obstruction.

(c) The obstruction shall not extend more than 12 in. (305 mm) to either side of the midpoint between sprinklers. (*See Figure 9-2.3.10.2.2.*)

Exception: When extensions exceed 12 in. (305 mm), one or more lines of sprinklers shall be installed below the obstruction.

(d) At least 18 in. (457 mm) clearance shall be maintained between the top of storage and the bottom of the obstruction. (*See Figure 9-2.3.10.2.2.*)

9-2.3.10.3 Obstructions Parallel to and Directly Below Branch Lines. In the special case of an obstruction running parallel to and directly below a branch line:

(a) The sprinkler shall be located at least 36 in. (914 mm) above the top of the obstruction. (*See Figure 9-2.3.10.3.*)

(b) The obstruction shall be limited to a maximum width of 12 in. (305 mm). (*See Figure 9-2.3.10.3.*)

(c) The obstruction shall be limited to a maximum extension of 6 in. (152 mm) to either side of the center line of the branch line. (*See Figure 9-2.3.10.3.*)

9-2.4* Protection Requirements.

9-2.4.1* Protection shall be provided as specified in Table A-9-2.4 or appropriate NFPA standards in terms of minimum operating pressure and the number of sprinklers to be included in the design area.

9-3 Early Suppression Fast Response (ESFR) Sprinklers.

9-3.1* Definition. *Early Suppression Fast Response (ESFR) Sprinkler.* A listed ESFR sprinkler is a thermosensitive device designed to react at a predetermined temperature by automatically releasing a stream of water and distributing it in a specified pattern and quantity over a designated area so as to provide early suppression of a fire when installed on the appropriate sprinkler piping.

9-3.2 Applicability.

9-3.2.1 ESFR sprinklers are suitable for use with the

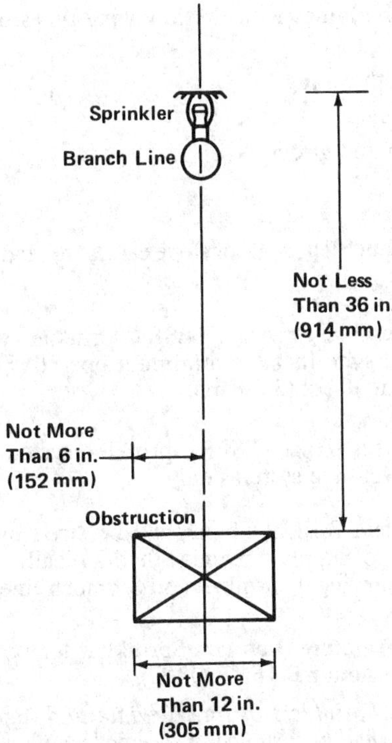
Sprinkler
Branch Line
Not Less
Than 36 in.
(914 mm)
Not More
Than 6 in.
(152 mm)
Obstruction
Not More
Than 12 in.
(305 mm)

Figure 9-2.3.10.3 Position of Sprinklers in Relation to Obstructions Running Parallel to and Directly below Branch Lines.

hazards listed in Table A-9-3.4.1 and may be used in other specific hazard classifications and configurations only when proven by large-scale or other suitable fire testing.

9-3.2.2 Requirements of this standard shall apply, except those portions dealing with subjects specifically addressed in this chapter.

9-3.3 Installation.

9-3.3.1 Construction.

9-3.3.1.1 Roof Construction. ESFR sprinklers are suitable for use in buildings with the following types of roof construction:

(a) Smooth ceiling,
(b) Bar joist,
(c) Beam and girder,
(d) Panel.

9-3.3.1.2 Roof Slope. Roof slope cannot exceed ¼ in. per ft (21 mm/m).

9-3.3.2 Operating Pressure. ESFR sprinkler systems shall be designed such that the minimum operating pressure is not less than 50 psi (3.4 bars).

9-3.3.3 System Type. ESFR sprinkler systems shall be limited to wet-pipe systems only.

9-3.3.4 System Design. Pipe shall be sized by hydraulic calculation to supply the most hydraulically remote 12 sprinklers, flowing 4 sprinklers on 3 branch lines.

9-3.3.5 Temperature Rating. Sprinkler temperature ratings shall be nominal 165°F (74°C).

Exception: Sprinklers of intermediate and high temperature ratings shall be installed in specific locations as required by 3-11.6.3.

9-3.3.6* Spacing.

9-3.3.6.1 The protection area per sprinkler shall be limited to a minimum of 80 sq ft (7.4 m^2) and a maximum of 100 sq ft (9.3 m^2).

9-3.3.6.2 The distance between branch lines and between sprinklers on the branch lines shall be limited to not more than 12 ft (3.7 m) nor less than 8 ft (2.4 m).

9-3.3.7 Distances.

9-3.3.7.1 Clear Space Below Sprinklers. At least 36 in. (914 mm) shall be maintained between sprinkler deflectors and the top of storage.

9-3.3.7.2 Distances Below Ceiling. Sprinklers shall be positioned so that deflectors are a maximum 14 in. (356 mm) and a minimum 6 in. (152 mm) below the ceiling.

9-3.3.8 Location of Sprinklers in Beam and Girder and Panel Construction. Under beam and girder construction and under panel construction, the branch lines may run across the beams, but sprinklers shall be located in the bays and not under the beams.

9-3.3.9 Obstruction in Piping.

9-3.3.9.1 Screens located in the inlet piping directly connected to rivers, lakes, ponds, reservoirs, uncovered tanks, and similar sources (*see NFPA 24, Standard for Installation of Private Fire Service Mains and Their Appurtenances*) shall be cleaned and serviced at least annually and after any work has been performed on fire protection water supply.

9-3.3.9.2 Visual and/or flushing investigations shall be conducted of all systems for foreign material at intervals not exceeding five years.

9-3.3.10 Obstruction to Distribution.

9-3.3.10.1 Obstructions Located at or Near the Ceiling. When sprinkler deflectors are located above the bottom of beams, girders, ducts, fluorescent lighting fixtures, or other obstructions located at the ceiling, the sprinklers shall be positioned so that the maximum distance from the bottom of the obstruction to the deflector does not exceed the value specified in Chapter 4.

9-3.3.10.2 Obstructions Located Entirely Below the Sprinklers.

9-3.3.10.2.1 Sprinklers shall be positioned with respect to any fluorescent lighting fixtures, ducts, or any other obstruction more than 12 in. (305 mm) wide and located entirely below the sprinklers so that the minimum horizontal distance from the near side of the obstruction to the center of the sprinkler is not less than the value specified in Table 9-3.3.10.2.1. (*See Figure 9-2.3.10.2.1.*)

9-3.3.10.2.2 When the bottom of obstructions more than 12 in. (305 mm) wide is located below the sprinkler deflectors such that the deflector distances above obstructions specified in Table 9-3.3.10.2.1 are exceeded, install additional sprinklers beneath obstructions, and include such sprinklers in the water demand.

Exception No. 1: Obstructions up to 12 in. (305 mm) wide and located below a single sprinkler, but not below two or more adjacent sprinklers (including diagonally).

Table 9-3.3.10.2.1 Position of Sprinklers in Relation to Obstructions Located Entirely Below the Sprinklers

Distance of Deflector Above Bottom of Obstruction	Minimum Distance to Side of Obstruction, ft (m)
Less than 6 in. (152 mm)	1½ (0.5)
6 in. (152 mm) to less than 12 in. (305 mm)	3 (0.9)
12 in. (305 mm) to less than 18 in. (457 mm)	4 (1.2)
18 in. (457 mm) to less than 24 in. (610 mm)	5 (1.5)
24 in. (610 mm) to less than 30 in. (660 mm)	6 (1.8)

Exception No. 2: Continuous obstructions, such as utility piping or ductwork, up to 12 in. (305 mm) wide, offset by at least 24 in. (610 mm) from both the center line of sprinklers and the center line of any flue spaces for rack storage.

9-3.4 Protection Requirements.

9-3.4.1* Occupancies. ESFR sprinklers may be used to protect the occupancies indicated in Table A-9-3.4.1. ESFR sprinklers cannot be used to protect rack storage with solid shelves or with solid, five-sided, open-top containers.

9-3.4.2 Hose Streams. Small hose stations shall be provided. Hose stream water demand is not required to be added to total water demand.

9-3.4.3 Water Supply Duration. Water supply duration shall be at least 60 minutes.

Chapter 10 Referenced Publications

10-1 The following documents or portions thereof are referenced within this standard and shall be considered part of the requirements of this document. The edition indicated for each reference shall be the current edition as of the date of the NFPA issuance of this document.

10-1.1 NFPA Publications. National Fire Protection Association, Batterymarch Park, Quincy, MA 02269.

NFPA 13A-1987, *Recommended Practice for the Inspection, Testing and Maintenance of Sprinkler Systems*

NFPA 13D-1989, *Standard for the Installation of Sprinkler Systems for One- and Two-Family Dwellings and Mobile Homes*

NFPA 14-1986, *Standard for the Installation of Standpipe and Hose Systems*

NFPA 20-1987, *Standard for the Installation of Centrifugal Fire Pumps*

NFPA 22-1987, *Standard for Water Tanks for Private Fire Protection*

NFPA 24-1987, *Standard for the Installation of Private Fire Service Mains and Their Appurtenances*

NFPA 51B-1984, *Standard for Fire Prevention in Use of Cutting and Welding Processes*

NFPA 71-1987, *Standard for the Installation, Maintenance, and Use of Signaling Systems for Central Station Service*

NFPA 72A-1987, *Standard for the Installation, Maintenance, and Use of Local Protective Signaling Systems for Guard's Tour, Fire Alarm, and Supervisory Service*

NFPA 72B-1986, *Standard for the Installation, Maintenance, and Use of Auxiliary Protective Signaling Systems for Fire Alarm Service*

NFPA 72C-1986, *Standard for the Installation, Maintenance, and Use of Remote Station Protective Signaling Systems*

NFPA 72D-1986, *Standard for the Installation, Maintenance, and Use of Proprietary Protective Signaling Systems*

NFPA 72E-1987, *Standard on Automatic Fire Detectors*

NFPA 81-1986, *Standard for Fur Storage, Fumigation and Cleaning*

NFPA 96-1987, *Standard for the Installation of Equipment for the Removal of Smoke and Grease-Laden Vapors from Commercial Cooking Equipment*

NFPA 220-1985, *Standard on Types of Building Construction*

NFPA 231-1987, *Standard for General Storage*

NFPA 231C-1986, *Standard for Rack Storage of Materials*

NFPA 1963-1985, *Standard for Screw Threads and Gaskets for Fire Hose Connections.*

10-1.2 The following additional NFPA codes and standards contain specific sprinkler design criteria. (*See 2-2.1.1 Exception No. 4 and A-2-1.*)

NFPA 15-1985, *Standard for Water Spray Fixed Systems for Fire Protection*

NFPA 16-1986, *Standard on Deluge Foam-Water Sprinkler and Foam-Water Spray Systems*

NFPA 40-1988, *Standard for the Storage and Handling of Cellulose Nitrate Motion Picture Film*

NFPA 43A-1980, *Code for the Storage of Liquid and Solid Oxidizing Materials*

NFPA 45-1986, *Standard on Fire Protection for Laboratories Using Chemicals*

NFPA *101®*-1988, *Life Safety Code®*

NFPA 214-1988, *Standard on Water-Cooling Towers*

NFPA 231-1987, *Standard for General Storage*

NFPA 231C-1986, *Standard for Rack Storage of Materials*

NFPA 231D-1986, *Standard for Storage of Rubber Tires*

NFPA 231F-1987, *Standard for Storage of Roll Paper*

NFPA 307-1985, *Standard for Construction and Fire Protection of Marine Terminals, Piers, and Wharves*

NFPA 409-1985, *Standard on Aircraft Hangars*

NFPA 423-1983, *Standard for Construction and Protection of Aircraft Engine Test Facilities.*

10-1.3 Other Codes and Standards.

10-1.3.1 ANSI Publications. American National Standards Institute, Inc., 1450 Broadway, New York, New York 10018.

ANSI B1.20.1-1983, *Pipe Threads, General Purpose*

ANSI B16.1-1975, *Cast Iron Pipe Flanges and Flanged Fittings, Class 25, 125, 250 and 800*

ANSI B16.3-1985, *Malleable Iron Threaded Fittings, Class 150 and 300*

ANSI B16.4-1985, *Cast Iron Threaded Fittings, Classes 125 and 250*

ANSI B16.5-1981, *Pipe Flanges and Flanged Fittings*

ANSI B16.9-1986, *Factory-Made Wrought Steel Buttwelding Fittings*

ANSI B16.11-1980, *Forged Steel Fittings, Socket-Welding and Threaded*

ANSI B16.18-1984, *Cast Copper Alloy Solder Joint Pressure Fittings*

ANSI B16.22-1980, *Wrought Copper and Copper Alloy Solder Joint Pressure Fittings*

ANSI B16.25-1986, *Buttwelding Ends*

ANSI B36.10M-1985, *Welded and Seamless Wrought Steel Pipe.*

10-1.3.2 ASTM Publications. American Society for Testing and Materials, 1916 Race Street, Philadelphia, PA 19105.

ASTM A53-1987, *Standard Specification for Welded Pipe, Steel, Black and Hot-Dipped, Zinc-Coated and Seamless Steel Pipe*

ASTM A234-1987, *Standard Specification for Piping Fittings of Wrought-Carbon Steel and Alloy Steel for Moderate and Elevated Temperatures*

ASTM A795-1985, *Specification for Black and Hot-Dipped Zinc-Coated (Galvanized) Welded and Seamless Steel Pipe for Fire Protection Use*

ASTM B32-1987, *Standard Specification for Solder Metal, 95-5 (Tin-Antimony-Grade 95TA)*

ASTM B75-1986, *Standard Specification for Seamless Copper Tube*

ASTM B88-1986, *Standard Specification for Seamless Copper Water Tube*

ASTM B251-1987, *Standard Specification for General Requirements for Wrought Seamless Copper and Copper-Alloy Tube*

ASTM E380-1986, *Standard for Metric Practice.*

10-1.3.3 AWS Publications. American Welding Society, 2501 N.W. 7th Street, Miami, FL 33125.

AWS A5.8-1981, *Specification for Brazing Filler Metal*

AWS D10.9-1980, *Specification for Qualification of Welding Procedures and Welders for Piping and Tubing.*

Appendix A

This Appendix is not a part of the requirements of this NFPA document, but is included for information purposes only.

A-1-3 A sprinkler system is considered to have a single system riser control valve.

A-1-5.1 Impairments. Before shutting off a section of the fire service system to make sprinkler system connections, notify the authority having jurisdiction, plan the work carefully, and assemble all materials to enable completion in the shortest possible time. Work started on connections should be rushed to completion without interruption, and protection restored as promptly as possible. During the impairment, provide emergency hose lines, additional fire pails and extinguishers, and maintain extra watch service in the areas affected.

When changes involve shutting off water from any considerable number of sprinklers for more than a few hours, temporary water supply connections should be made to sprinkler systems so that reasonable protection can be maintained. In adding to old systems or revamping them, protection should be restored each night so far as possible. The members of the private fire brigade as well as public fire department should be notified as to conditions.

A-1-7.1 Occupancy examples in the listings as shown in the various hazard classifications are intended to represent the norm for those occupancy types. Unusual or abnormal fuel loadings or combustible characteristics and susceptibility for changes in these characteristics, for a particular occupancy, are considerations that should be weighed in the selection and classification.

The Light Hazard classification is intended to encompass residential occupancies; however, this is not intended to preclude the use of listed residential sprinklers in residential occupancies or residential portions of other occupancies.

A-1-7.2.1 Light Hazard Occupancies include occupancies having conditions similar to:

Churches
Clubs
Eaves and overhangs, if combustible construction with no combustibles beneath

Educational
Hospitals
Institutional
Libraries, except large stack rooms
Museums
Nursing or Convalescent Homes
Office, including Data Processing
Residential
Restaurant seating areas
Theaters and Auditoriums excluding stages
 and prosceniums
Unused attics.

A-1-7.3.1 Ordinary Hazard Occupancies (Group 1) include occupancies having conditions similar to:

Automobile parking garages
Bakeries
Beverage manufacturing
Canneries
Dairy products manufacturing and processing
Electronic plants
Glass and glass products manufacturing
Laundries
Restaurant service areas.

A-1-7.3.2 Ordinary Hazard Occupancies (Group 2) include occupancies having conditions similar to:

Cereal Mills
Chemical Plants — Ordinary
Cold Storage warehouses
Confectionery products
Distilleries
Horse Stables
Leather goods manufacturing
Libraries — large stack room areas
Machine shops
Metal working
Mercantiles
Printing and publishing
Textile manufacturing
Tobacco products manufacturing
Wood product assembly.

A-1-7.3.3 Ordinary Hazard Occupancies (Group 3) include occupancies having conditions similar to:

Feed Mills

Paper and pulp mills
Paper process plants
Piers and wharves
Repair garages
Tire manufacturing
Warehouses (having moderate to higher combustibility of content, such as paper, household furniture, paint, general storage, whiskey, etc.)[1]
Wood machining.

When hazards in those buildings or portions of buildings of this occupancy group are severe, the authority having jurisdiction should be consulted for special rulings regarding water supplies, types of equipment, pipe sizes, types of sprinklers, and sprinkler spacing.

A-1-7.4 New installations protecting Extra Hazard Occupancies should be hydraulically designed where standards giving design criteria are available.

A-1-7.4.1 Extra Hazard Occupancies (Group 1) include occupancies having conditions similar to:

Combustible Hydraulic Fluid use areas
Die Casting
Metal Extruding
Plywood and particle board manufacturing
Printing [using inks with below 100°F (37.8°C) flash points]
Rubber reclaiming, compounding, drying, milling, vulcanizing
Saw Mills
Textile picking, opening, blending, garnetting, carding, combining of cotton, synthetics, wool shoddy, or burlap
Upholstering with plastic foams.

Extra Hazard Occupancies (Group 2) include occupancies having conditions similar to:

Asphalt saturating
Flammable liquids spraying
Flow coating
Mobile Home or Modular Building assemblies (where

---

[1] For high-piled storage as defined in 4-1.3.10, see Appendix C for separately published NFPA standards relating to water supply requirements, particularly NFPA 231, *Standard for General Storage*, and NFPA 231C, *Standard for Rack Storage of Materials*.

finished enclosure is present and has combustible interiors)
Open oil quenching
Solvent cleaning
Varnish and paint dipping.

A-1-8 Sprinkler Systems in Buildings Subject to Flood. When sprinkler systems are installed in buildings subject to recurring floods, the location of control valves, alarm devices, dry-pipe valves, pumps, compressors, power and fuel supplies should be such that system operation will be uninterrupted by high water.

A-1-8.1.2 Under special conditions used equipment may be reused by the original owner, subject to the approval of the authority having jurisdiction. Second-hand alarm valves, retarding chambers, circuit closers, water-motor alarms, dry-pipe valves, quick-opening devices, and other devices may be used as replacement equipment in existing systems subject to the approval of the authority having jurisdiction.

A-1-9 Preliminary layouts should be submitted for review to the authority having jurisdiction before any equipment is installed or remodeled in order to avoid error or subsequent misunderstanding. Any material deviation from approved plans will require permission of the authority having jurisdiction.

Preliminary layouts should show:

(a) Name of owner and occupant

(b) Location, including street address

(c) Point of compass

(d) Construction and occupancy of each building

NOTE: Date on special hazards should be submitted as they may require special rulings.

(e) Building height in feet

(f) If it is proposed to use a city main as a supply, whether the main is dead-end or circulating, size of the main and pressure in psi; and if dead-end, direction and distance to nearest circulating main

(g) Distance from nearest pumping station or reservoir

(h) In cases where reliable up-to-date information is not

available, a waterflow test of the city main should be conducted in accordance with B-2-1.1. (The preliminary plan should specify who conducted the test, date and time, the location of the hydrants where flow was taken, and where static and residual pressure readings were recorded; the size of main supplying these hydrants, and the results of the test, giving size and number of open hydrant butts flowed; also data covering minimum pressure in the connection with the city main should be included.)

(i) Data covering waterworks systems in small towns in order to expedite the review of plans

(j) Fire walls, fire doors, unprotected window openings, large unprotected floor openings, and blind spaces

(k) Distance to and construction and occupancy of exposing buildings — e.g., lumber yards, brick mercantiles, fire-resistive office buildings, etc.

(l) Spacing of sprinklers, number of sprinklers in each story or fire area and total number of sprinklers, number of sprinklers on each riser and on each system by floors, total area protected by each system on each floor, total number of sprinklers on each dry-pipe system or preaction or deluge system and if extension to present equipment, number of sprinklers on riser per floor, sprinklers already installed

(m) Capacities of dry-pipe systems with the bulk pipe included (*see Table A-5-2.3*), and if an extension is made to an existing dry-pipe system. The total capacity of the existing and also extended portion of the system

(n) Weight or class, size, and material of any proposed underground pipe

(o) Whether property is located in a flood area requiring consideration in the design of sprinkler system

(p) Name and address of party submitting the layout.

A-1-11.1 Underground mains and lead-in connections to system risers should be flushed through hydrants at dead ends of the system or through accessible aboveground flushing outlets allowing the water to run until clear. If water is supplied from more than one source or from a looped system, divisional valves should be closed to produce a high-velocity flow through each single line. The flows specified in Table 1-11.1 will produce a velocity of at least 10 ft/sec (3 m/s), which is necessary for cleaning the pipe and for lifting foreign material to an aboveground flushing outlet.

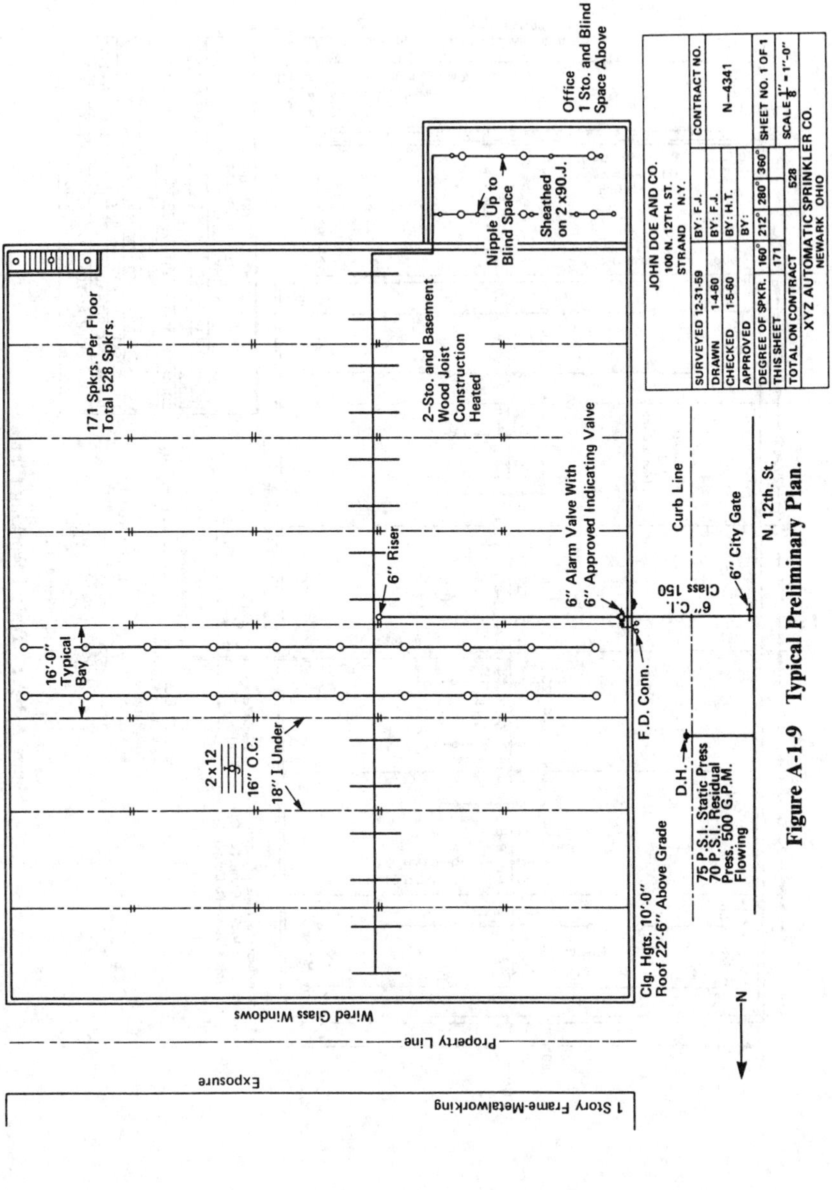
171 Spkrs. Per Floor
Total 528 Spkrs.
Office
1 Sto. and Blind
Space Above
Nipple Up to
Blind Space
Sheathed
on 2 x90.J.
2-Sto. and Basement
Wood Joist
Construction
Heated
JOHN DOE AND CO.
100 N. 12TH. ST.
STRAND N.Y.
SURVEYED 12-31-59
BY: F.J.
CONTRACT NO.
DRAWN 1-4-60
BY: F.J.
CHECKED 1-5-60
BY: H.T.
N–4341
APPROVED
BY:
DEGREE OF SPKR. 160° 212° 280° 360°
SHEET NO. 1 OF 1
THIS SHEET 171
TOTAL ON CONTRACT 528
SCALE 1/8" = 1'-0"
XYZ AUTOMATIC SPRINKLER CO.
NEWARK OHIO
6" Riser
6" Alarm Valve With
6" Approved Indicating Valve
Curb Line
6" C.I.
Class 150
6" City Gate
N. 12th. St.
16'-0"
Typical
Bay
2 x 12
16" O.C.
18" I Under
F.D. Conn.
D.H.
75 P.S.I. Static Press
70 P.S.I. Residual
Press. 500 G.P.M.
Flowing
Clg. Hgts. 10'-0"
Roof 22'-6" Above Grade
Wired Glass Windows
Property Line
Exposure
1 Story Frame-Metalworking
N

Figure A-1-9 Typical Preliminary Plan.

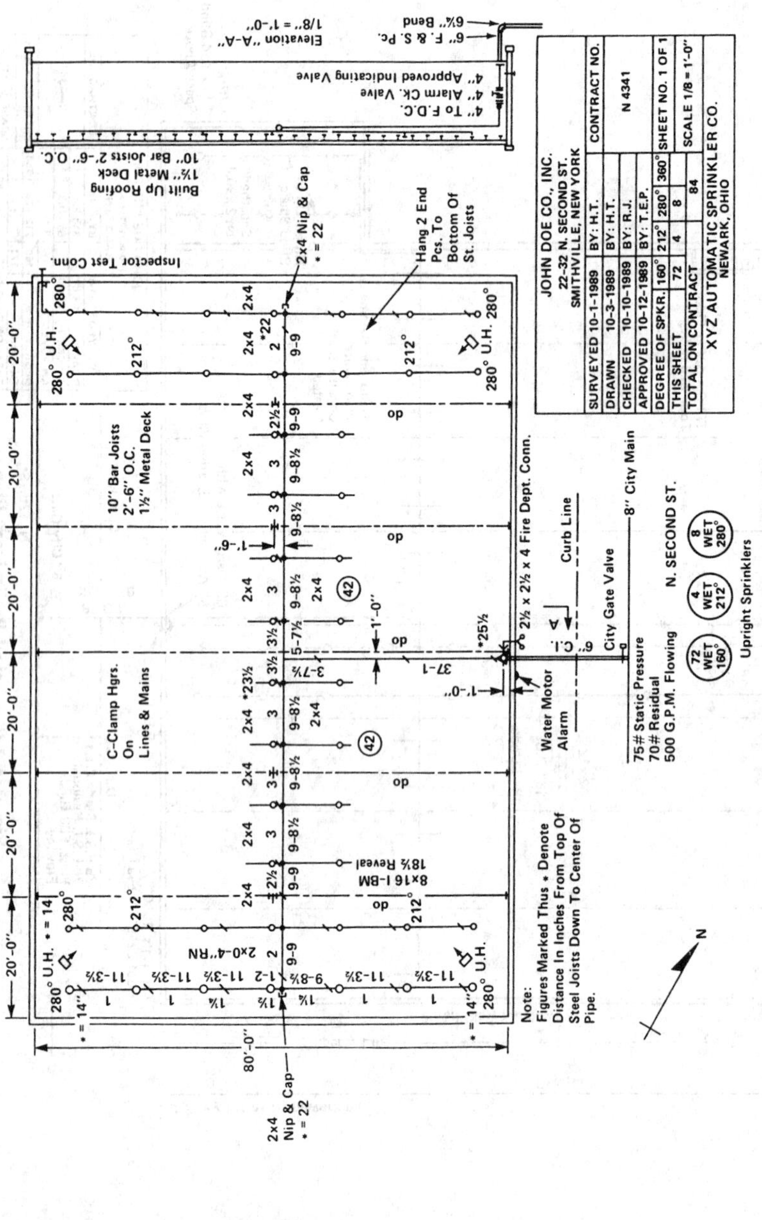
Elevation "A-A"
1/8" = 1'-0"
6" F. & S. Pc.
6¾" Bend
Built Up Roofing
1½" Metal Deck
10" Bar Joists 2'-6" O.C.
4" To F.D.C.
4" Alarm Ck. Valve
4" Approved Indicating Valve
Inspector Test Conn.
2x4 Nip & Cap
* = 22
Hang 2 End Pcs. To Bottom Of St. Joists
10" Bar Joists 2'-6" O.C. 1½" Metal Deck
C-Clamp Hgrs. On Lines & Mains
8x16 I-BM 18½ Reveal
2½ x 2½ x 4 Fire Dept. Conn.
Water Motor Alarm
Curb Line
City Gate Valve
8" City Main
N. SECOND ST.
75# Static Pressure
70# Residual
500 G.P.M. Flowing
72 WET 160°
4 WET 212°
8 WET 280°
Upright Sprinklers
80'-0"
20'-0"
Note: Figures Marked Thus * Denote Distance In Inches From Top Of Steel Joists Down To Center Of Pipe.
N
JOHN DOE CO., INC.
22-32 N. SECOND ST.
SMITHVILLE, NEW YORK
CONTRACT NO.
N 4341
SURVEYED 10-1-1989 BY: H.T.
DRAWN 10-3-1989 BY: H.T.
CHECKED 10-10-1989 BY: R.J.
APPROVED 10-12-1989 BY: T.E.P.
DEGREE OF SPKR. 160° 212° 280° 360°
THIS SHEET 72 4 8
TOTAL ON CONTRACT 84
SHEET NO. 1 OF 1
SCALE 1/8 = 1'-0"
XYZ AUTOMATIC SPRINKLER CO.
NEWARK, OHIO

Figure A-1-9.2 Typical Working Plans.

A-1-11.2.1 Example. A sprinkler system has for its water supply a connection to a public water service main. A 100 psi (6.9 bar) rated pump is installed in the connection. With a maximum normal public water supply of 70 psi (4.8 bars) at the low elevation point of the individual system or portion of the system being tested and a 120 psi (8.3 bars) pump (churn) pressure, the hydrostatic test pressure is 70 + 120 + 50 or 240 psi (16.5 bars).

Systems that have been modified or repaired to any appreciable extent should be hydrostatically tested at not less than 50 psi (3.4 bars) in excess of normal static pressure for 2 hours.

To reduce the possibility of serious water damage in case of a break, pressure may be maintained by a small pump, the main controlling gate meanwhile being kept shut during the test.

Polybutylene pipe will undergo expansion during initial pressurization. In this case a reduction in gage pressure may not necessarily indicate a leak. The pressure reduction should not exceed the manufacturer's specifications and listing criteria.

A-1-11.2.2 Valves isolating the section to be tested may not be "drop tight." When such leakage is suspected, test blanks of the type recommended in 1-11.2.5 should be used in a manner that includes the valve in the section being tested.

A-2-1 Water supplies should have adequate pressure, capacity, and reliability.

The water supply needed for various occupancies, including Extra Hazard Occupancies, is determined by evaluating the number of sprinklers that may be expected to operate from any one fire plus quantities needed simultaneously for hose streams.

Determination of the water supply needed for Extra Hazard Occupancies will require special consideration of four factors: (1) area of sprinkler operation, (2) density of discharge, (3) required time of discharge, and (4) amount of water needed simultaneously for hose streams.

When the occupancy presents a possibility of intense fires requiring extra heavy discharge, this may be obtained by an increase in the pressure and volume of the water supply, by a closer spacing of sprinklers, by the use of larger pipe sizing, or by a combination of these methods. In such cases, consideration should be given to hydraulically designed systems. (*See Chapter 7.*)

When separately published standards on various subjects contain specific provisions for water supplies, these should be consulted. (*See Chapter 10 for availability of standards.*)

A-2-2 The water supply requirement for sprinkler protection is determined by the number of sprinklers expected to operate in the event of fire. The primary factors affecting the number of sprinklers that might open are:

1. Occupancy
2. Combustibility of contents
3. Area shielded from proper distribution of water
4. Height of stock piles
5. Combustibility of construction (ceilings and blind spaces)
6. Ceiling heights and draft conditions
7. Horizontal and vertical cutoffs
8. Wet or dry sprinkler system
9. High water pressure
10. Housekeeping
11. Temperature rating of sprinklers
12. Waterflow alarm and response thereto.

A-2-2.2 For occupancies with the potential for fast-spreading fire due to the presence of lint, combustible residue, combustible hydraulic fluids under high pressure with ignition sources nearby, etc., the minimum area of operation should encompass the entire area likely to be involved in such a fire.

A-2-2.3 Corridors are rooms and should be considered as such. This section allows for calculation of the sprinklers in the largest room, so long as the calculation produces the greatest hydraulic demand among selection of rooms and communicating spaces. For example, in a case where the largest room has four sprinklers and a smaller room has two sprinklers but communicates through unprotected openings with three other rooms, each having two sprinklers, the smaller room and group of communicating spaces should also be calculated. Another example in which the room

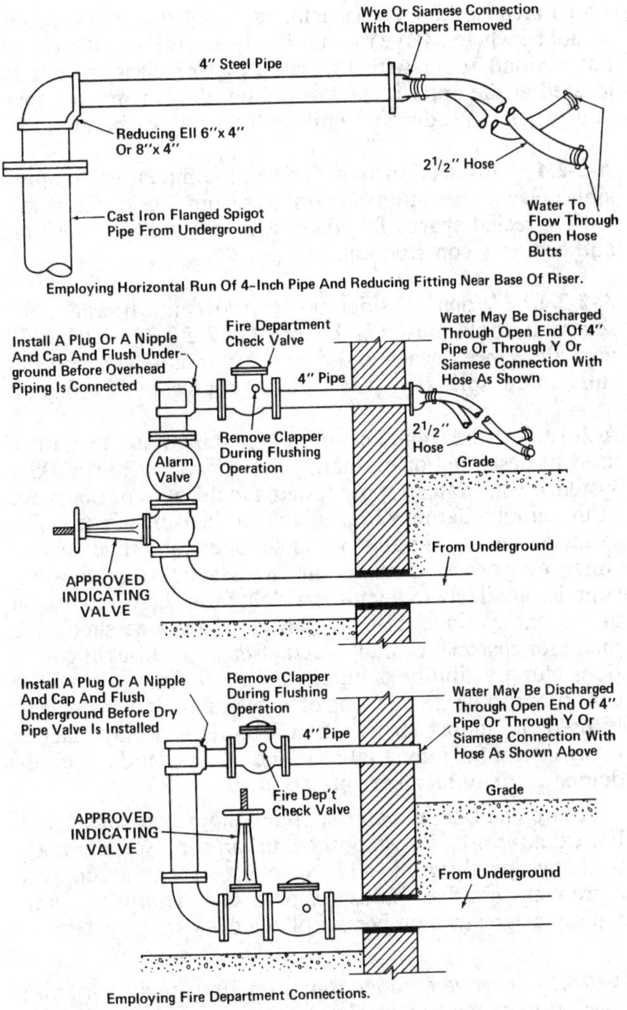
Wye Or Siamese Connection With Clappers Removed
4" Steel Pipe
Reducing Ell 6"x 4" Or 8"x 4"
2 1/2" Hose
Cast Iron Flanged Spigot Pipe From Underground
Water To Flow Through Open Hose Butts
Employing Horizontal Run Of 4-Inch Pipe And Reducing Fitting Near Base Of Riser.
Install A Plug Or A Nipple And Cap And Flush Underground Before Overhead Piping Is Connected
Fire Department Check Valve
4" Pipe
Water May Be Discharged Through Open End Of 4" Pipe Or Through Y Or Siamese Connection With Hose As Shown
Remove Clapper During Flushing Operation
Alarm Valve
2 1/2" Hose
Grade
From Underground
APPROVED INDICATING VALVE
Install A Plug Or A Nipple And Cap And Flush Underground Before Dry Pipe Valve Is Installed
Remove Clapper During Flushing Operation
4" Pipe
Water May Be Discharged Through Open End Of 4" Pipe Or Through Y Or Siamese Connection With Hose As Shown Above
Fire Dep't Check Valve
Grade
APPROVED INDICATING VALVE
From Underground
Employing Fire Department Connections.

Figure A-1-11.1 Methods of Flushing Water Supply Connections.

which creates the greatest demand is not the largest room would be where a large room is located near the system riser but a small room with the same hazard classification is located at the opposite end of the building or on an upper floor so as to produce a significantly higher demand.

A-2-2.4 This section is included to compensate for possible delay in operation of sprinklers from fires in combustible concealed spaces found in wood frame, brick veneer, and ordinary construction.

A-2-2.4.1 When considering the 100 gpm allowance for several hose stations, it is the intent of 2-2.3.3 to apply a 50 gpm allowance to each of the two most remote area connections to the sprinkler system, for an aggregate of 100 gpm.

A-2-3.1.1 Care should be taken in making water tests to be used in designing or evaluating the capability of sprinkler systems. The water supply tested should be representative of the supply that may be available at the time of a fire. For example, testing of public water supplies should be done at times of normal demand on the system. Public water supplies are likely to fluctuate widely from season to season and even within a 24-hour period. Allowance should be made for seasonal or daily fluctuations, for drought conditions, for possibility of interruption by flood, or for ice conditions in winter. Testing of water supplies also normally used for industrial use should be done while water is being drawn for industrial use. The range of industrial-use demand should be taken into account.

Future changes in water supplies should be considered. For example a large, established, urban supply is not likely to change greatly within a few years. However, the supply in a growing suburban industrial park may deteriorate quite rapidly as greater numbers of plants draw more water.

A-2-3.2 In private underground piping systems for buildings of other than Light Hazard Occupancy, any dead-end pipe supplying both sprinklers and hydrants should not be less than 8 in. (203 mm) in size. Also see NFPA 24, *Standard for the Installation of Private Fire Service Mains and Their Appurtenances.*

A-2-5.1 An automatically controlled vertical turbine pump taking suction from a reservoir, pond, lake, river, or well complies with 2-5.1.

A-2-5.2 See sections dealing with sprinkler equipment supervisory and waterflow alarm services in NFPA 71, *Standard for the Installation, Maintenance, and Use of Signaling Systems for Central Station Service*; NFPA 72A, *Standard for the Installation, Maintenance, and Use of Local Protective Signaling Systems for Guard's Tour Fire Alarm, and Supervisory Service*; NFPA 72B, *Standard for the Installation, Maintenance, and Use of Auxiliary Protective Signaling Systems for Fire Alarm Service*; NFPA 72C, *Standard for the Installation, Maintenance, and Use of Remote Station Protective Signaling Systems*; or NFPA 72D, *Standard for the Installation, Maintenance, and Use of Proprietary Protective Signaling Systems.*

A-2-6.3 The air pressure to be carried and the proper proportion of air in the tank may be determined from the following formulas, in which,

P = Air pressure carried in pressure tank
A = Proportion of air in tank
H = Height of highest sprinkler above tank bottom

When tank is placed above highest sprinkler

$$P = \frac{30}{A} - 15.$$

A = ⅓ then P = 90 − 15 = 75 lb per sq in.
A = ½ then P = 60 − 15 = 45 lb per sq in.
A = ⅔ then P = 45 − 15 = 30 lb per sq in.

When tank is below level of the highest sprinkler

$$P = \frac{30}{A} - 15 + \frac{0.434H}{A}$$

A = ⅓ then P = 75 + 1.30H.
A = ½ then P = 45 + 0.87H.
A = ⅔ then P = 30 + 0.65H.

The respective air pressures above are calculated to ensure that the last water will leave the tank at a pressure of 15 psi (1.03 bars) when the base of the tank is on a level with the highest sprinkler, or at such additional pressure as is equivalent to a head corresponding to the distance between the base of the tank and the highest sprinkler when the latter is above the tank.

The final pressure required at the pressure tank for

systems designed from Table 2-2.1.1(b) will normally be higher than the 15 psi (1.03 bars) anticipated in the previous paragraph. The following formula should be used to determine the tank pressure and ratio of air to water in hydraulically designed systems.

$$P_i = \frac{P_f + 15}{A} - 15$$

where
P_i = Tank pressure
P_f = Pressure required from hydraulic calculations
A = Proportion of air

Example: Hydraulic calculations indicate 75 psi is required to supply the system. What tank pressure will be required?

$$P_i = \frac{75 + 15}{.5} - 15$$

$$P_i = 180 - 15 = 165 \text{ psi}$$

For SI Units: 1 ft = 0.3048 m; 1 psi = 0.0689 bar.

In this case the tank would be filled with 50 percent air and 50 percent water and the tank pressure would be 165 psi (11.4 bars). If the pressure is too high, the amount of air carried in the tank will have to be increased.

Location of Pressure Tanks. Pressure tanks should be located above the top level of sprinklers but may be located in the basement or elsewhere.

A-2-7.1 The fire department connection should be located not less than 18 in. (457 mm) and not more than 5 ft (1.5 m) above the level of the adjacent grade or access level.

A-2-7.2 For hydraulically designed sprinkler systems, the size of the fire department connection should be sufficient to supply the sprinkler water demand developed from Table 2-2.1.1(b).

A-2-7.3 Fire department connections should be located and arranged so that hose lines can be readily and conveniently attached without interference from nearby objects including buildings, fences, posts, or other fire department connections. When a hydrant is not available, other water supply sources such as a natural body of water, a tank, or reservoir should be utilized. The water authority should be consulted when a nonpotable water supply is proposed as a suction source for the fire department.

A-2-8.2 When the system riser is close to an outside wall, underground fittings of proper length should be used in order to avoid pipe joints located in or under the wall. When the connection passes through the foundation wall below grade, a 1- to 3-in. (25- to 76-mm) clearance should be provided around the pipe and the clear space filled with asphalt mastic or similar flexible waterproofing material. (*Also see Appendix B-3-1.*)

A-2-9.1

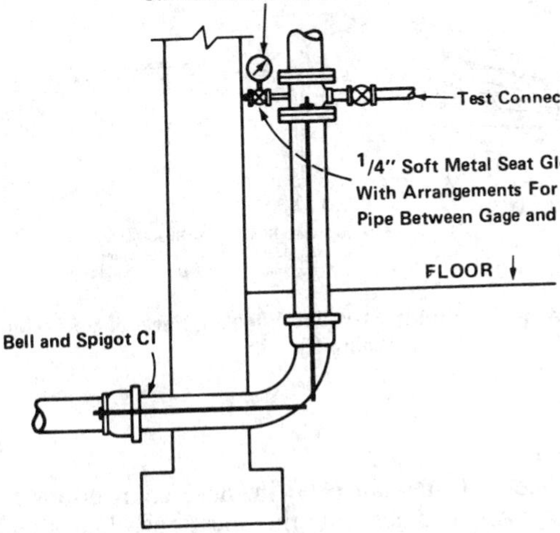
Pressure Gage to be
Standard Size and Make
Test Connection or Drain
1/4" Soft Metal Seat Globe Valve
With Arrangements For Draining
Pipe Between Gage and Valve
FLOOR
Bell and Spigot CI

Figure A-2-9.1 Test Connection on Water Supply with Outside Control. (Also applicable to an interior riser.)

A-3-1.1.5 The investigation of pipe and tube other than that described in Table 3-1.1.1 should involve consideration of many factors:

(a) Pressure rating.

(b) Beam strength (hangers).

(c) Unsupported vertical stability.

(d) Movement during sprinkler operation (affecting water distribution).

(e) Corrosion (internal and external; chemical and electrolytic).

(f) Resistance to failure when exposed to elevated temperatures.

(g) Methods of joining (strength, permanence, fire hazard).

(h) Physical characteristics related to integrity during earthquakes.

A-3-3.2 See page 74 for Figures A-3-3.2 (a) and (b). Also see NFPA 13A, *Recommended Practice for the Inspection, Testing and Maintenance of Sprinkler Systems.*

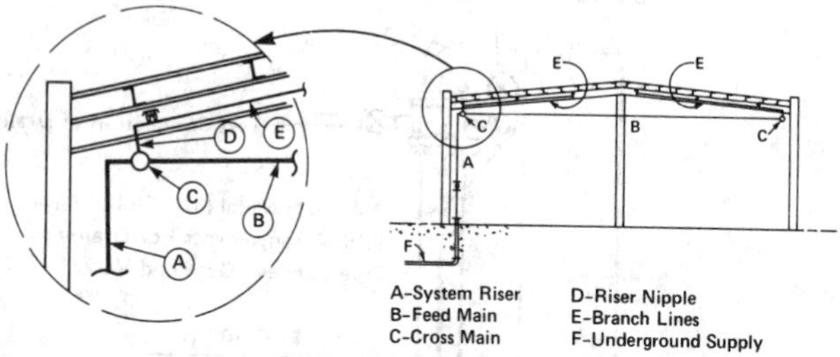
D
E
C
B
A
E
E
C
B
C
A
F
A-System Riser
B-Feed Main
C-Cross Main
D-Riser Nipple
E-Branch Lines
F-Underground Supply

Figure A-3-2 Building Elevation Showing Parts of Sprinkler Piping System.

A-3-3.7 One and one-half (1½) in. hose connections for use in storage occupancies and other locations where standpipe systems are not required are covered by this standard. When Class II standpipe systems are required see the appropriate provisions of NFPA 14, *Standard for the Installation of Standpipe and Hose Systems*, with respect to hose stations and water supply for hose connections from sprinkler systems.

A-3-3.8 Combined automatic sprinkler and standpipe risers should not be interconnected by sprinkler system piping.

A-3-4.1.1 This test connection should be in the upper story, and the connection should preferably be piped from

Table A-3-1.1.2 Steel Pipe Dimensions

Nominal Pipe Size	Outside Diameter		Schedule 10[1] Inside Diameter		Schedule 10[1] Wall Thickness		Schedule 30 Inside Diameter		Schedule 30 Wall Thickness		Schedule 40 Inside Diameter		Schedule 40 Wall Thickness	
in.	in.	(mm)	in.	(mm)	in.	(mm)	in.	(mm)	in.	(mm)	in.	(mm)	in.	(mm)
1	1.315	(33.4)	1.097	(27.9)	0.109	(2.8)	—	—	—	—	1.049	(26.6)	0.133	(3.4)
1¼	1.660	(42.2)	1.442	(36.6)	0.109	(2.8)	—	—	—	—	1.380	(35.1)	0.140	(3.6)
1½	1.900	(48.3)	1.682	(42.7)	0.109	(2.8)	—	—	—	—	1.610	(40.9)	0.145	(3.7)
2	2.375	(60.3)	2.157	(54.8)	0.109	(2.8)	—	—	—	—	2.067	(52.5)	0.154	(3.9)
2½	2.875	(73.0)	2.635	(66.9)	0.120	(3.0)	—	—	—	—	2.469	(62.7)	0.203	(5.2)
3	3.500	(88.9)	3.260	(82.8)	0.120	(3.0)	—	—	—	—	3.068	(77.9)	0.216	(5.5)
3½	4.000	(101.6)	3.760	(95.5)	0.120	(3.0)	—	—	—	—	3.548	(90.1)	0.226	(5.7)
4	4.500	(114.3)	4.260	(108.2)	0.120	(3.0)	—	—	—	—	4.026	(102.3)	0.237	(6.0)
5	5.563	(141.3)	5.295	(134.5)	0.134	(3.4)	—	—	—	—	5.047	(128.2)	0.258	(6.6)
6	6.625	(168.3)	6.357	(161.5)	0.134[2]	(3.4)	—	—	—	—	6.065	(154.1)	0.280	(7.1)
8	8.625	(219.1)	8.249	(209.5)	0.188[2]	(4.8)	8.071	(205.0)	0.277	(7.0)	—	—	—	—
10	10.75	(273.1)	10.37	(263.4)	0.188[2]	(4.8)	10.14	(257.6)	0.307	(7.8)	—	—	—	—

NOTE 1: Schedule 10 defined to 5 in. (127 mm) nominal pipe size by ASTM A135.
NOTE 2: Wall thickness specified in 3-1.1.2.

Table A-3-1.1.4 Copper Tube Dimensions

Nominal Tube Size	Outside Diameter		Type K Inside Diameter		Type K Wall Thickness		Type L Inside Diameter		Type L Wall Thickness		Type M Inside Diameter		Type M Wall Thickness	
in.	in.	(mm)	in.	(mm)	in.	(mm)	in.	(mm)	in.	(mm)	in.	(mm)	in.	(mm)
¾	0.875	(22.2)	0.745	(18.9)	0.065	(1.7)	0.785	(19.9)	0.045	(1.1)	0.811	(20.6)	0.032	(0.8)
1	1.125	(28.6)	0.995	(25.3)	0.065	(1.7)	1.025	(26.0)	0.050	(1.3)	1.055	(26.8)	0.035	(0.9)
1¼	1.375	(34.9)	1.245	(31.6)	0.065	(1.7)	1.265	(32.1)	0.055	(1.4)	1.291	(32.8)	0.042	(1.1)
1½	1.625	(41.3)	1.481	(37.6)	0.072	(1.8)	1.505	(38.2)	0.060	(1.5)	1.527	(38.8)	0.049	(1.2)
2	2.125	(54.0)	1.959	(49.8)	0.083	(2.1)	1.985	(50.4)	0.070	(1.8)	2.009	(51.0)	0.058	(1.5)
2½	2.625	(66.7)	2.435	(61.8)	0.095	(2.4)	2.465	(62.6)	0.080	(2.0)	2.495	(63.4)	0.065	(1.7)
3	3.125	(79.4)	2.907	(73.8)	0.109	(2.8)	2.945	(74.8)	0.090	(2.3)	2.981	(75.7)	0.072	(1.8)
3½	3.625	(92.1)	3.385	(86.0)	0.120	(3.0)	3.425	(87.0)	0.100	(2.5)	3.459	(87.9)	0.083	(2.1)
4	4.125	(104.8)	3.857	(98.0)	0.134	(3.4)	3.905	(99.2)	0.110	(2.8)	3.935	(99.9)	0.095	(2.4)
5	5.125	(130.2)	4.805	(122.0)	0.160	(4.1)	4.875	(123.8)	0.125	(3.2)	4.907	(124.6)	0.109	(2.8)
6	6.125	(155.6)	5.741	(145.8)	0.192	(4.9)	5.845	(148.5)	0.140	(3.6)	5.881	(149.4)	0.122	(3.1)
8	8.125	(206.4)	7.583	(192.6)	0.271	(6.9)	7.725	(196.2)	0.200	(5.1)	7.785	(197.7)	0.170	(4.3)
10	10.13	(257.3)	9.449	(240.0)	0.338	(8.6)	9.625	(244.5)	0.250	(6.4)	9.701	(246.4)	0.212	(5.4)

the end of the most remote branch line. The discharge should be at a point where it can be readily observed. In locations where it is not practical to terminate the test connection outside the building, the test connection may terminate into a drain capable of accepting full flow under system pressure. (*See A-3-6.4.1.*) In this event, the test connection should be made using an approved sight test connection containing a smooth bore corrosion-resistant orifice giving a flow equivalent to one sprinkler simulating the least flow from an individual sprinkler in the system. [*See Figures A-3-4.1.1(a) and A-3-4.1.1(b).*] The test valve should be located at an accessible point, and preferably not over 7 ft (2.1 m) above the floor. The control valve on the test connection should be located at a point not exposed to freezing.

A-3-5 Protection of Piping Against Damage Due to Impact. Sprinkler piping should be located so as to minimize the possibility of damage due to impact by mobile material handling equipment and other vehicles. For example, risers adjacent to structural columns and out of vehicle travel routes are generally safe, as are feed mains and cross mains shielded by heavy structural members such as girders.

A-3-5.1.2 In areas subject to freezing climates, when piping extends through an exterior wall, as for fire department connections, system test connection, or drains, a minimum of 4 ft (1.2 m) of pipe should be maintained between the wall and the section of piping containing water.

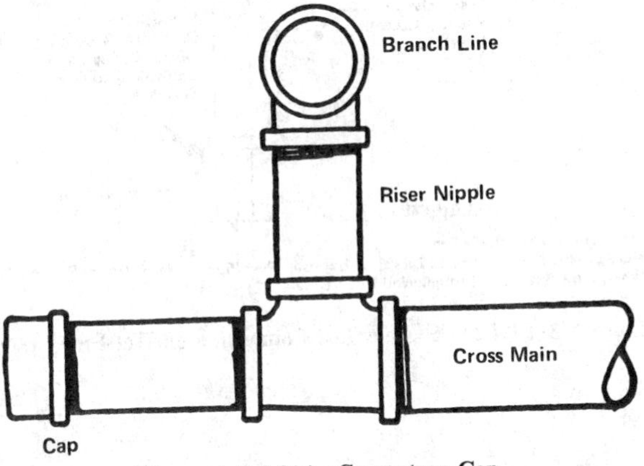
Branch Line
Riser Nipple
Cross Main
Cap

Figure A-3-3.2(a) Screw-type Cap.

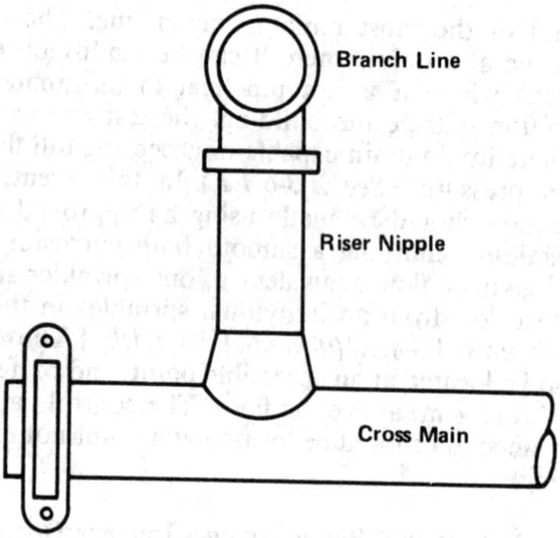
Branch Line
Riser Nipple
Cross Main

Figure A-3-3.2(b) Groove-type Cap.

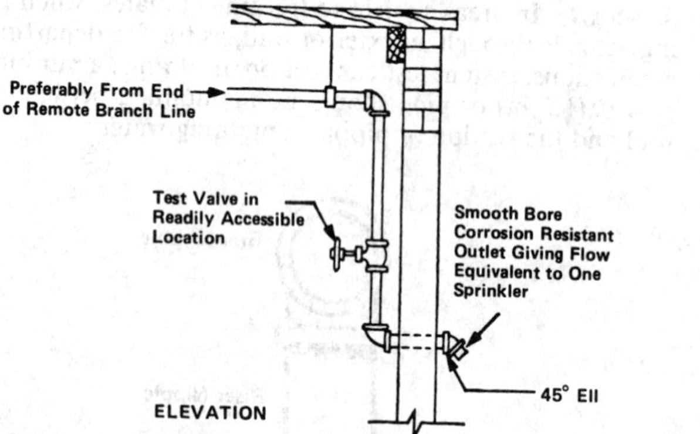
Preferably From End of Remote Branch Line
Test Valve in Readily Accessible Location
Smooth Bore Corrosion Resistant Outlet Giving Flow Equivalent to One Sprinkler
45° Ell
ELEVATION

For SI Units: 1 ft = 0.3048 m.
NOTE: Not Less Than 4ft (1.2 m) of Exposed Test Pipe in Warm Room Beyond Valve When Pipe Extends Through Wall to Outside.

Figure A-3-4.1.1(a) System Test Connection on Wet-Pipe System.

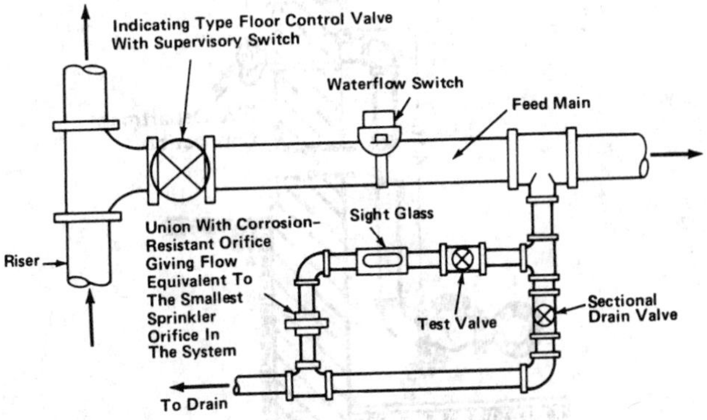
Indicating Type Floor Control Valve
With Supervisory Switch
Waterflow Switch
Feed Main
Riser
Union With Corrosion-Resistant Orifice Giving Flow Equivalent To The Smallest Sprinkler Orifice In The System
Sight Glass
Test Valve
Sectional Drain Valve
To Drain

Figure A-3-4.1.1(b) Floor Control Valve.

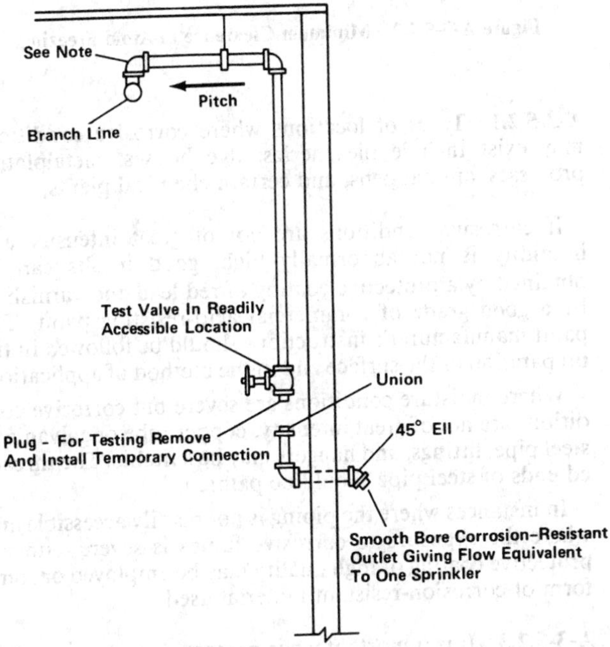
See Note
Pitch
Branch Line
Test Valve In Readily Accessible Location
Union
Plug - For Testing Remove And Install Temporary Connection
45° Ell
Smooth Bore Corrosion-Resistant Outlet Giving Flow Equivalent To One Sprinkler

NOTE: To minimize condensation of water in the drop to the test connection, provide a nipple-up off of the branch line.

Figure A-3-4.2 System Test Connection on Dry-Pipe System.

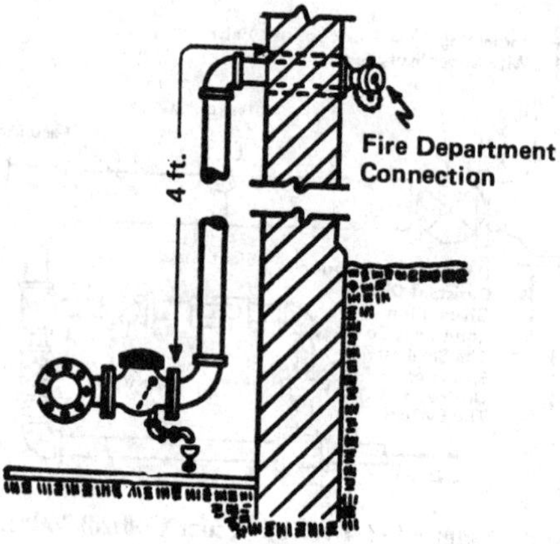
4 ft.
Fire Department
Connection

For SI Units: 1 ft=0.3048 m.

Figure A-3-5.1.2 Minimum Clearance to Avoid Freezing.

A-3-5.2.1 Types of locations where corrosive conditions may exist include bleacheries, dye houses, metalplating processes, animal pens, and certain chemical plants.

If corrosive conditions are not of great intensity and humidity is not abnormally high, good results can be obtained by a protective coating of red lead and varnish or by a good grade of commercial acid-resisting paint. The paint manufacturer's instructions should be followed in the preparation of the surface and in the method of application.

Where moisture conditions are severe but corrosive conditions are not of great intensity, copper tube or galvanized steel pipe, fittings, and hangers may be suitable. The threaded ends of steel pipe should be painted.

In instances where the piping is not readily accessible and where the exposure to corrosive fumes is severe, either a protective coating of high quality may be employed or some form of corrosion-resistant material used.

A-3-5.2.3 It is important when protected steel pipe (galvanized, dipped and wrapped, coated, etc.) is used that particular care is taken to see that all exposed threads, wrench marks, or abrasions that have penetrated through the protection be repaired, sealed, and/or properly coated.

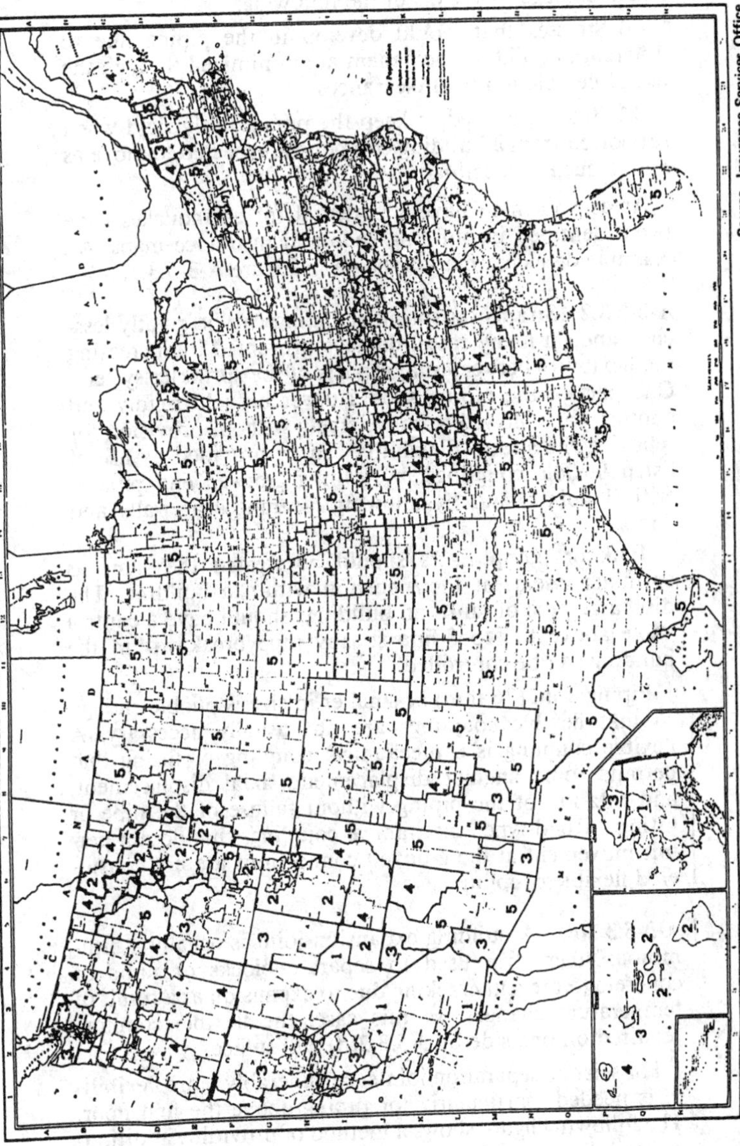

Source—Insurance Services Office

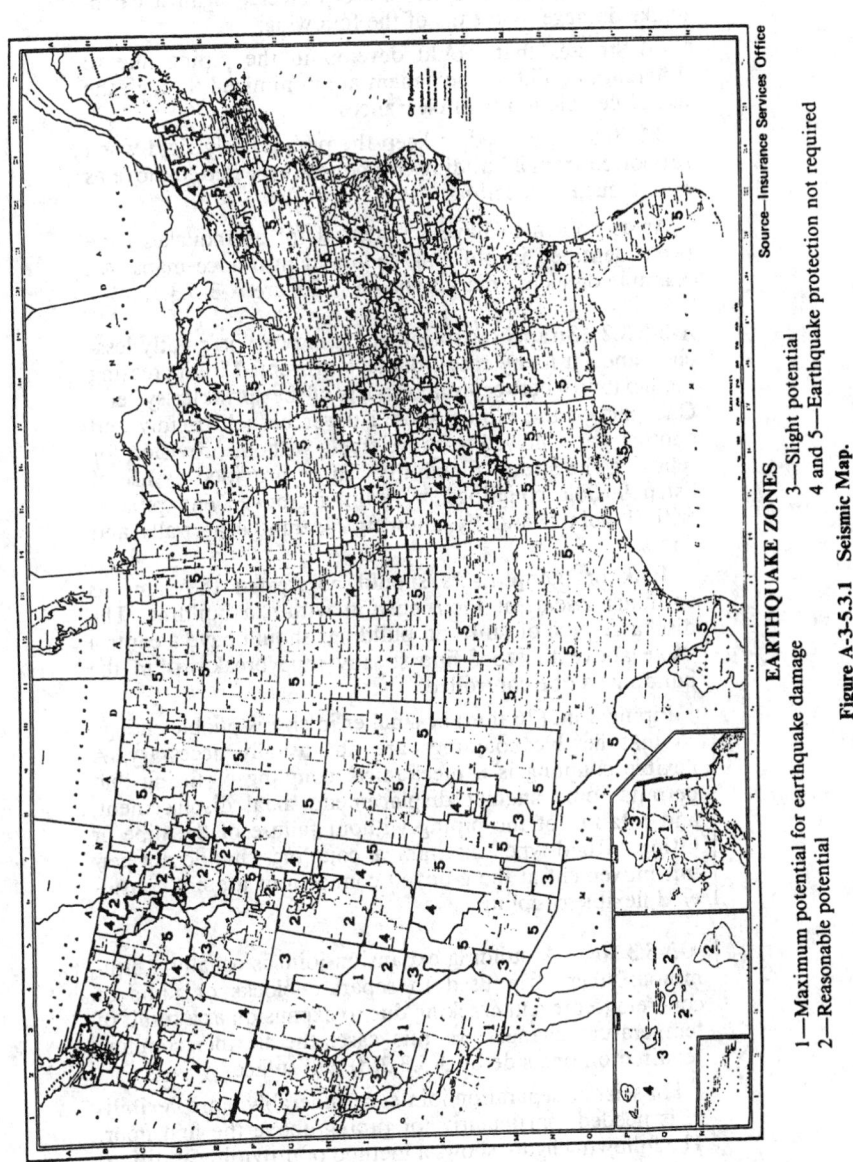

EARTHQUAKE ZONES

1—Maximum potential for earthquake damage
2—Reasonable potential
3—Slight potential
4 and 5—Earthquake protection not required

Figure A-3-5.3.1 Seismic Map.

A-3-5.3.1 Sprinkler systems are protected against earthquake damage by means of the following:

(a) Stresses that would develop in the piping due to differential building movement are minimized through the use of flexible joints or clearances.

(b) Bracing is used to keep the piping fairly rigid when supported from a building component expected to move as a unit, such as a ceiling.

Areas known to have a potential for earthquakes have been identified in building code and insurance maps. An example of such a map is shown in Figure A-3-5.3.1.

A-3-5.3.2 Strains on sprinkler piping can be greatly lessened and, in many cases, damage prevented by increasing the flexibility between major parts of the sprinkler system. One part of the piping should never be held rigidly and another part allowed to move freely without provision for relieving the strain. Flexibility can be provided by use of listed flexible couplings, by joining grooved end pipe at critical points, and by allowing clearances at walls and floors.

Tank or pump risers should be treated the same as sprinkler risers for their portion within a building. The discharge pipe of tanks on buildings should have a control valve above the roof line so any pipe break within the building can be controlled.

Piping 3 in. (76 mm) or smaller in size is pliable enough so that flexible couplings are not usually necessary. A flexible coupling is a mechanical coupling or fitting that permits some angular displacement, axial displacement, and rotation of the piping without failure of the pipe or fitting. "Rigid-type" mechanical couplings that do not permit movement at the grooved connections are not considered flexible couplings.

A-3-5.3.2(d) A building expansion joint is usually a bituminous fiber strip used to separate blocks or units of concrete to prevent cracking due to expansion as a result of temperature changes. In this case, the flexible coupling required on one side by 3-5.3.2(d) will suffice.

For seismic separation joints, considerably more flexibility is needed, particularly for piping above the first floor. The following figure shows a method of providing additional flexibility through the use of swing joints.

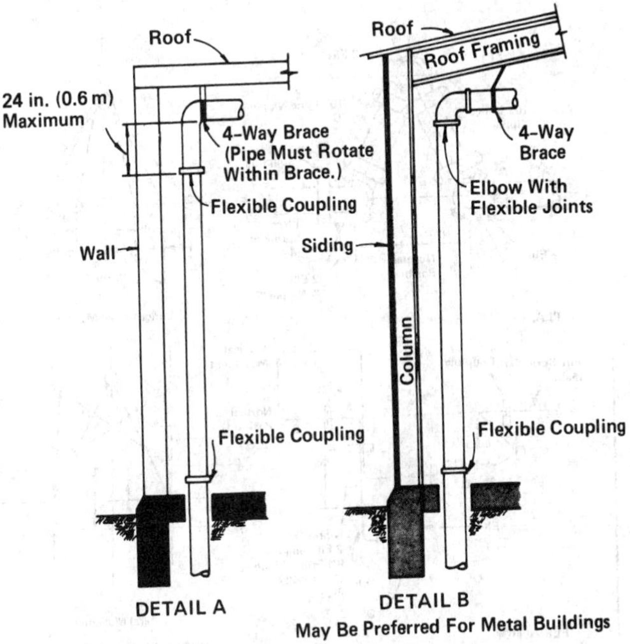
Roof
24 in. (0.6 m) Maximum
4-Way Brace (Pipe Must Rotate Within Brace.)
Flexible Coupling
Wall
Flexible Coupling
DETAIL A
Roof
Roof Framing
4-Way Brace
Elbow With Flexible Joints
Siding
Column
Flexible Coupling
DETAIL B
May Be Preferred For Metal Buildings

Note to Detail A: The four-way brace should be attached above the upper flexible coupling required for the riser, and preferably to the roof structure if suitable. The brace should not be attached directly to a plywood or metal deck.

Figure A-3-5.3.2(a) Riser Details.

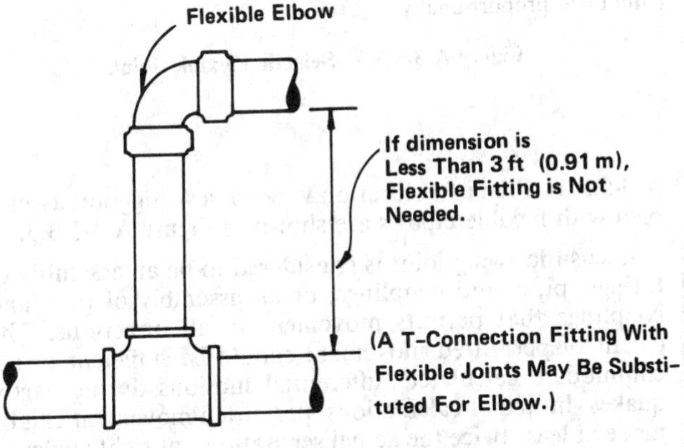
Flexible Elbow
If dimension is Less Than 3 ft (0.91 m), Flexible Fitting is Not Needed.
(A T-Connection Fitting With Flexible Joints May Be Substituted For Elbow.)

Figure A-3-5.3.2(b) Detail at Short Riser.

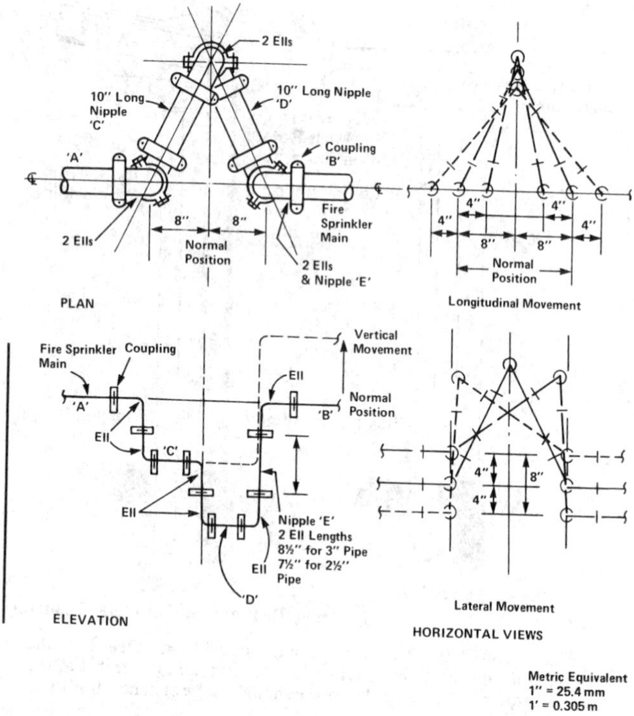
2 Ells
10" Long Nipple 'C'
10" Long Nipple 'D'
'A'
Coupling 'B'
Fire Sprinkler Main
2 Ells
8"
8"
Normal Position
2 Ells & Nipple 'E'
PLAN
4"
4"
4"
4"
8"
8"
Normal Position
Longitudinal Movement
Fire Sprinkler Main
Coupling
Vertical Movement
Ell
'A'
'B'
Normal Position
Ell
'C'
Ell
Nipple 'E'
2 Ell Lengths
8½" for 3" Pipe
7½" for 2½" Pipe
Ell
'D'
4"
8"
4"
Lateral Movement
ELEVATION
HORIZONTAL VIEWS
Metric Equivalent
1" = 25.4 mm
1' = 0.305 m

NOTE: The figure illustrates an 8-in. separation crossed by pipes up to 4 in. in nominal diameter. For other separation distances and pipe sizes, lengths and distances should be modified proportionally.

Figure A-3-5.3.3 Seismic Flexible Joint.

A-3-5.3.3 Plan and elevation views of a swing joint assembled with flexible elbows are shown in Figure A-3-5.3.3.

A seismic swing joint is considered to be an assembly of fittings, pipe, and couplings, or an assembly of pipe and couplings that permits movement in all directions. The extent of permitted movement should be sufficient to accommodate calculated differential motions during earthquakes. In lieu of calculations, permitted movement can be made at least twice the actual separations, at right angles to the separation as well as parallel to it.

A-3-5.3.4 While clearances are necessary around the sprinkler piping to prevent breakage due to building movement, suitable provision should also be made to prevent passage of water, smoke, or fire.

Drains, fire department connections, and other auxiliary piping connected to risers should not be cemented into walls or floors; similarly, pipes that pass horizontally through walls or foundations should not be cemented solidly or strains will accumulate at such points.

When risers or lengths of pipe extend through suspended ceilings, they should not be fastened to the ceiling framing members.

A-3-5.3.5.1 Sway Bracing.

Location of Bracing. [*See Figure A-3-5.3.5.1(a).*]

Two-way braces are either longitudinal or lateral depending on their orientation with the axis of the piping. [*See Figures A-3-5.3.5.1(a), (b), (c), and (d)*]. The simplest form of two-way brace is a piece of steel pipe or angle. Because the brace must act in both compression and tension, it is necessary to size the brace to prevent buckling.

An important aspect of sway bracing is its location.

In Building 1, the relatively heavy main will pull on the branch lines when shaking occurs. If the branch lines are held rigidly to the roof or floor above, the fittings can fracture due to the induced stresses.

Bracing should be on the main as indicated at Location B. With shaking in the direction of the arrows, the light branch lines will be held at the fittings. When a branch line can pound against a piece of equipment, such as a space heater or a structural member, a lateral brace should be installed on the branch line to help prevent rupture.

A four-way brace is indicated at Location A. [*Also see Figure A-3-5.3.2(a).*] This keeps the riser and main lined up and also prevents the main from shifting.

In Building 1, the branch lines are flexible in a direction parallel to the main, regardless of building movement. The heavy main cannot shift under the roof or floor, and it also steadies the branch lines.

While the main is braced, the flexible couplings on the riser allow the sprinkler system to move with the floor or roof above, relative to the floor below.

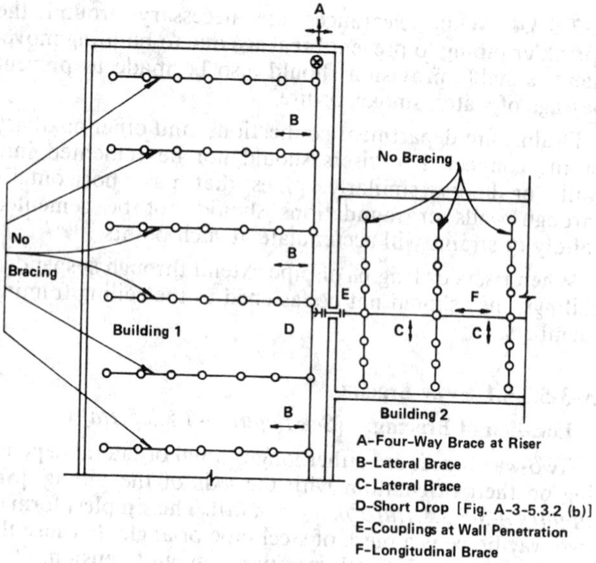
A
B
B
B
No Bracing
No
Bracing
Building 1
D
E
F
C
C
Building 2
A-Four-Way Brace at Riser
B-Lateral Brace
C-Lateral Brace
D-Short Drop [Fig. A-3-5.3.2 (b)]
E-Couplings at Wall Penetration
F-Longitudinal Brace

Figure A-3-5.3.5.1(a) Earthquake Protection for Sprinkler Piping.

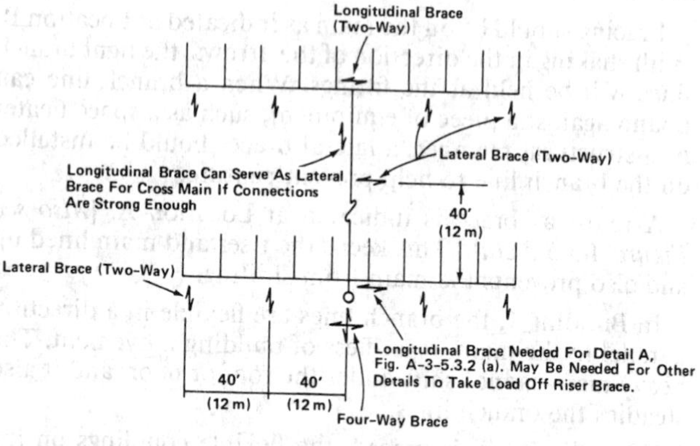
Longitudinal Brace (Two-Way)
Lateral Brace (Two-Way)
Longitudinal Brace Can Serve As Lateral Brace For Cross Main If Connections Are Strong Enough
40′ (12 m)
Lateral Brace (Two-Way)
Longitudinal Brace Needed For Detail A, Fig. A-3-5.3.2 (a). May Be Needed For Other Details To Take Load Off Riser Brace.
40′
40′
(12 m)
(12 m)
Four-Way Brace

Figure A-3-5.3.5.1(b) Typical Location of Bracing on a Pipe Schedule System.

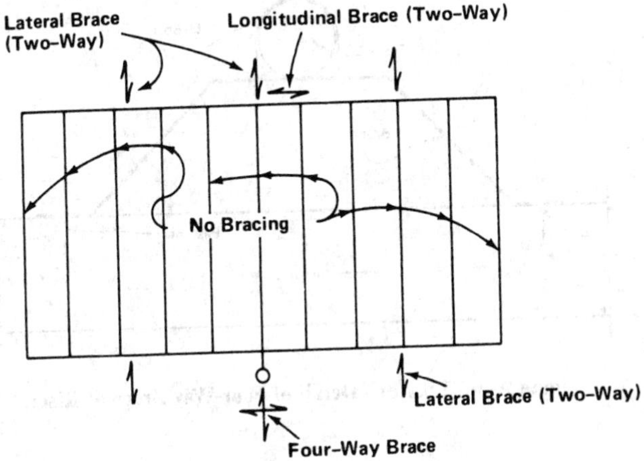
Lateral Brace
(Two-Way)
Longitudinal Brace (Two-Way)
No Bracing
Lateral Brace (Two-Way)
Four-Way Brace

Figure A-3-5.3.5.1(c) Typical Location of Bracing on a Gridded System.

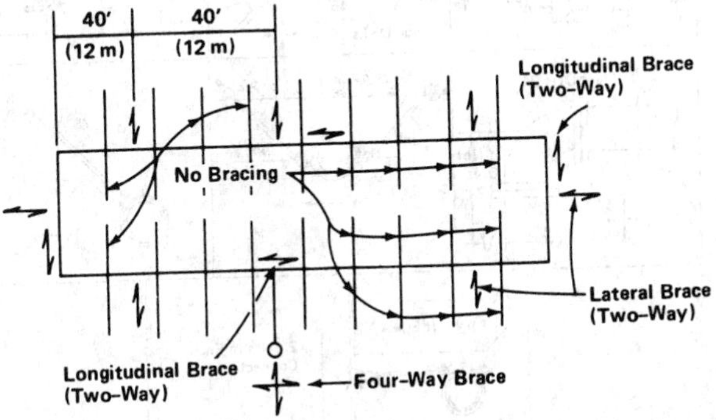
40′
(12 m)
40′
(12 m)
Longitudinal Brace
(Two-Way)
No Bracing
Lateral Brace
(Two-Way)
Longitudinal Brace
(Two-Way)
Four-Way Brace

Figure A-3-5.3.5.1(d) Typical Location of Bracing on a Looped System.

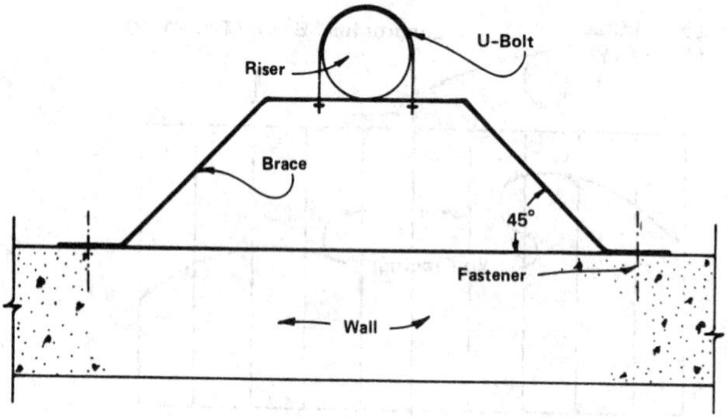
U-Bolt
Riser
Brace
45°
Fastener
Wall

Figure A-3-5.3.5.1(e) Detail of Four-Way Brace at Riser.

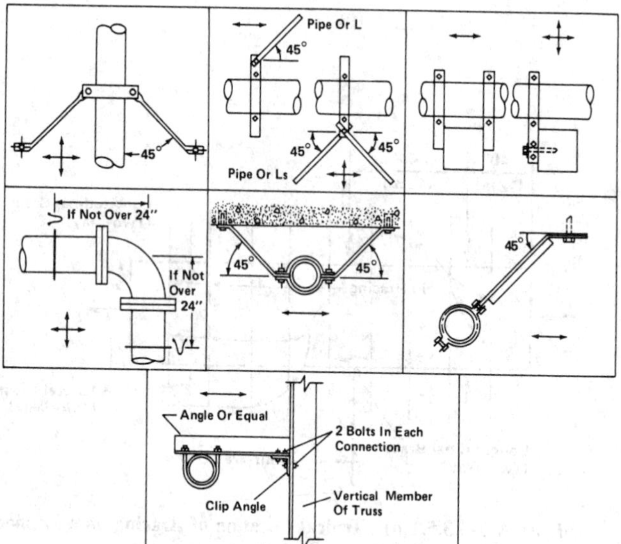
45°
Pipe Or L
45°
45°
45°
Pipe Or Ls
If Not Over 24"
If Not Over 24"
45°
45°
45°
Angle Or Equal
2 Bolts In Each Connection
Clip Angle
Vertical Member Of Truss

Figure A-3-5.3.5.1(f) Acceptable Types of Sway Bracing.

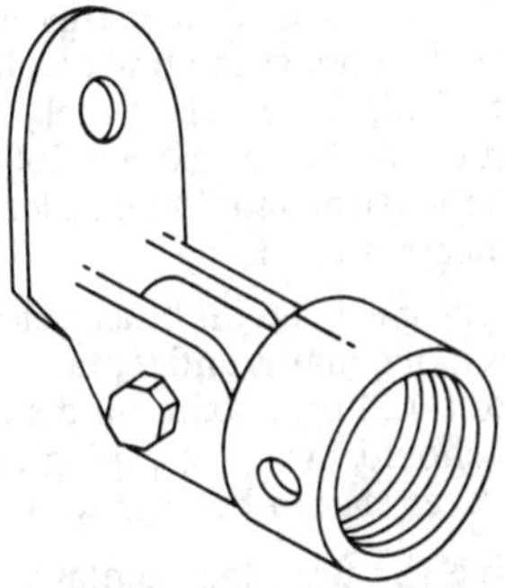

Figure A-3-5.3.5.1(g) Special Fitting.

Figures A-3-5.3.5.1(b), (c), and (d) show typical locations of sway bracing for pipe schedule, gridded, and looped sprinkler systems.

Listed devices permitting connection of braces to both the pipe and the building structure are available and are recommended. However, alternate means of attachment capable of handling the expected loads are acceptable.

Connection of the brace to the pipe can be made with a pipe clamp or U-bolt. One bolt of the pipe clamp can pass through a flattened end of pipe or one leg of an angle. (The other leg and filet of the angle can be cut away.) Pipe rings should be avoided because they result in a loose fit. Once the pipe is able to vibrate within a loose fitting, the bolts in the ring assembly can be fractured.

The brace can be attached to the structural system directly through a leg of an angle or a flattened portion of pipe. Where dimensions are tight or some play must be allowed, a special fitting can be used. [*See Figure A-3-5.3.5.1(b)*]. This threads on an end of pipe. Rotation of the flat around the bolt allows play in the angle of the brace without sacrificing snugness.

Some adjustment can be provided in a pipe brace by use of a left-hand/right-hand coupling. For all threaded connections, holes or other means should be provided to permit indication that sufficient thread is engaged.

To properly size and space braces, it is necessary to employ the following steps:

(a) Based on the distance of mains from the structural members that will support the braces, choose brace shapes and sizes from Table 3-5.3.5.1(2) such that the maximum slenderness ratios *l/r* do not exceed 200. The angle of the braces from the vertical should be at least 30 degrees, and preferably 45 degrees or more.

(b) Tentatively space lateral braces at 40 ft (12 m) maximum distances along mains and tentatively space longitudinal braces at 80 ft (24 m) maximum distances along mains. Lateral braces should meet the piping at right angles, and longitudinal braces should be aligned with the piping.

(c) Determine the total load tentatively applied to each brace in accordance with the examples shown in Figure A-3-5.3.5.1(h) and the following:

1. For the loads on lateral braces on cross mains, add one-half the weight of branch to one-half the weight of the portion of the cross main within the zone of influence of the brace. [*See examples 1, 3, 6, and 7 in Figure A-3-5.3.5.1(h).*]

2. For the loads on longitudinal braces on cross mains, consider only one-half the weight of the cross mains and feed mains within the zone of influence. [*See examples 2, 3, 5, and 8 in Figure A-3-5.3.5.1(h).*]

3. For the four-way brace at the riser, add the longitudinal and lateral loads within the zone of influence of the brace. [*See examples 2, 3, 4, 5, 7, and 8 in Figure A-3-5.3.5.1(h).*]

Use the information on weights of water-filled piping contained within Table A-3-5.3.5.1.

(d) If the total expected loads are less than the maximums permitted in Table 3-5.3.5.1(2) for the particular brace and orientation, go on to step (e). If not, add additional braces to reduce the zones of influence of overloaded braces.

(e) Check that fasteners connecting the braces to structural supporting members are adequate to support the expected loads on the braces in accordance with Table 3-5.3.5.1(3). If not, again add additional braces or additional means of support.

A-3-5.3.5.3 The four-way brace provided at the riser may also provide longitudinal and lateral bracing for adjacent mains.

A-3-6.1.1 All piping should be arranged where practicable to drain to the main drain valve.

Table A-3-5.3.5.1
Piping Weights for Determining Horizontal Load

Schedule 40 Pipe	Weight of Water-Filled Pipe (lb per ft)	½ Weight of Water-Filled Pipe (lb per ft)
1	2.05	1.03
1¼	2.93	1.47
1½	3.61	1.81
2	5.13	2.57
2½	7.89	3.95
3	10.82	5.41
3½	13.48	6.74
4	16.40	8.20
5	23.47	11.74
6	31.69	15.85
8*	47.70	23.85
Schedule 10 Pipe		
1	1.81	0.91
1¼	2.52	1.26
1½	3.04	1.52
2	4.22	2.11
2½	5.89	2.95
3	7.94	3.97
3½	9.78	4.89
4	11.78	5.89
5	17.30	8.65
6	23.03	11.52
8	40.08	20.04

*Schedule 30

A-3-6.3.2.3 An example of a suitable location would be a valve located approximately 7 ft (2 m) above the floor level to which a hose could be connected to discharge the water in an acceptable manner.

A-3-6.3.3.3 The size of tie-in drain lines should be increased as necessary to provide efficient removal of trapped water. Consideration should be given to the volume of water trapped, elevation head available, and the time required to discharge water. Water or condensation or both that remains after initial drain down should not be permitted to collect since freezing may cause failure of the drain/system piping.

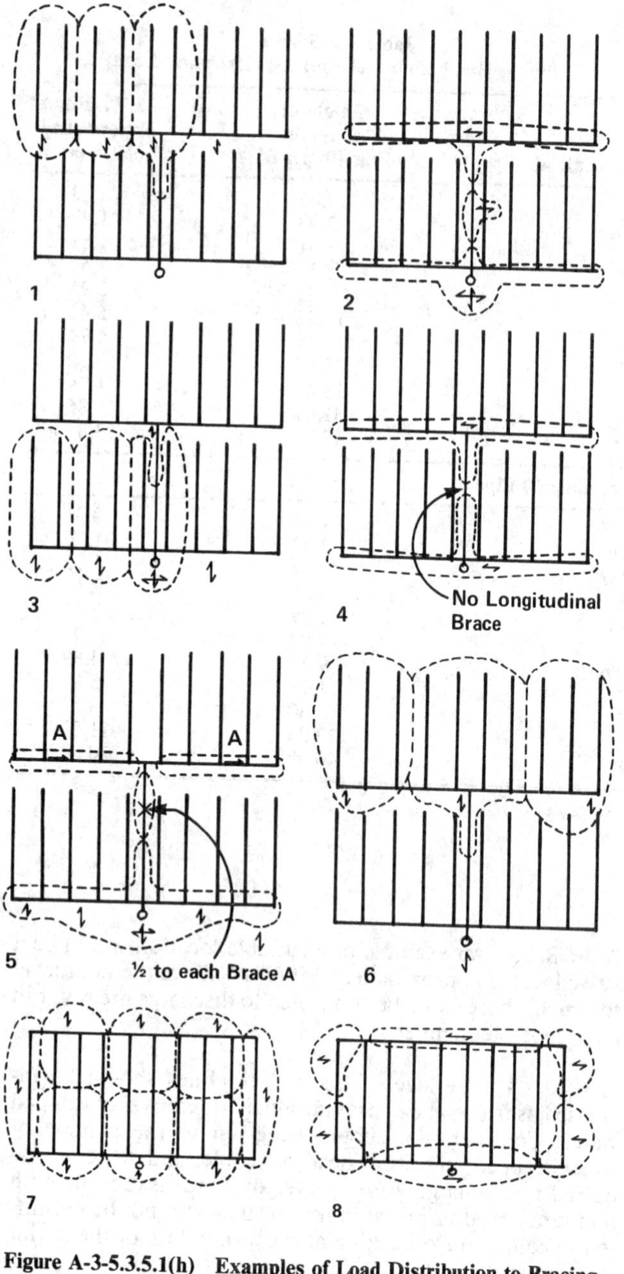
1
2
3
4
No Longitudinal Brace
A
A
5
½ to each Brace A
6
7
8

Figure A-3-5.3.5.1(h) Examples of Load Distribution to Bracing.

A-3-6.4.1 When possible, the main sprinkler riser drain should discharge outside the building at a point free from the possibility of causing water damage. When it is not possible to discharge outside the building wall, the drain should be piped to a sump, which in turn should discharge by gravity or be pumped to a waste water drain or sewer. The main sprinkler riser drain connection should be of a size sufficient to carry off water from the fully open drain valve while it is discharging under normal water system pressures. When this is not possible, a supplementary drain of equal size should be provided for test purposes with free discharge, located at or above grade.

A-3-6.4.5 When exterior ambient temperatures are subject to freezing [32°F (0°C) or less], at least 4 ft (1.2 m) of pipe should be installed beyond the valve, in a warm room.

A-3-7.1.2 Some steel piping material having lesser wall thickness than specified in 3-7.1.2 has been listed for use in sprinkler systems when joined with threaded connections. The service life of such products may be significantly less than that of Schedule 40 steel pipe and it should be determined if this service life will be sufficient for the application intended.

All such threads should be checked by the installer using working ring gages conforming to the Basic Dimensions of Ring Gages for USA (American) Standard Taper Pipe Threads, NPT, as per ANSI/ASME B1.20.1, Table 8.

A-3-7.2.2 As used in this standard, *shop* in the term *shop welded* means either:

(a) At the sprinkler contractor's or fabricator's premise.

(b) An approved welding area at the building site.

A-3-7.2.6(a) Listed, shaped, contoured nipples meet the definition of fabricated fittings.

A-3-7.4 The fire hazard of the brazing process should be suitably safeguarded.

Self-cleaning fluxes should not be used. Continued corrosive action after the soldering process is completed could result in leaks from the seats of sprinklers.

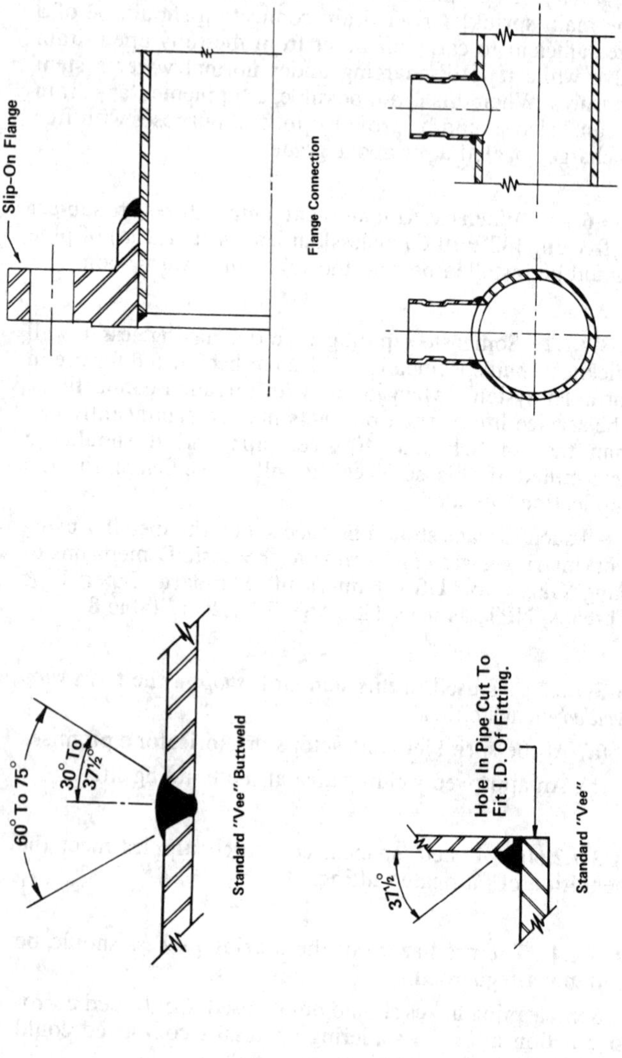
Slip-On Flange
Flange Connection
60° To 75°
30° To 37½°
Standard "Vee" Buttweld
Hole In Pipe Cut To Fit I.D. Of Fitting.
37½°
Standard "Vee"

Figure A-3-7.2(a) Acceptable Weld Joints.

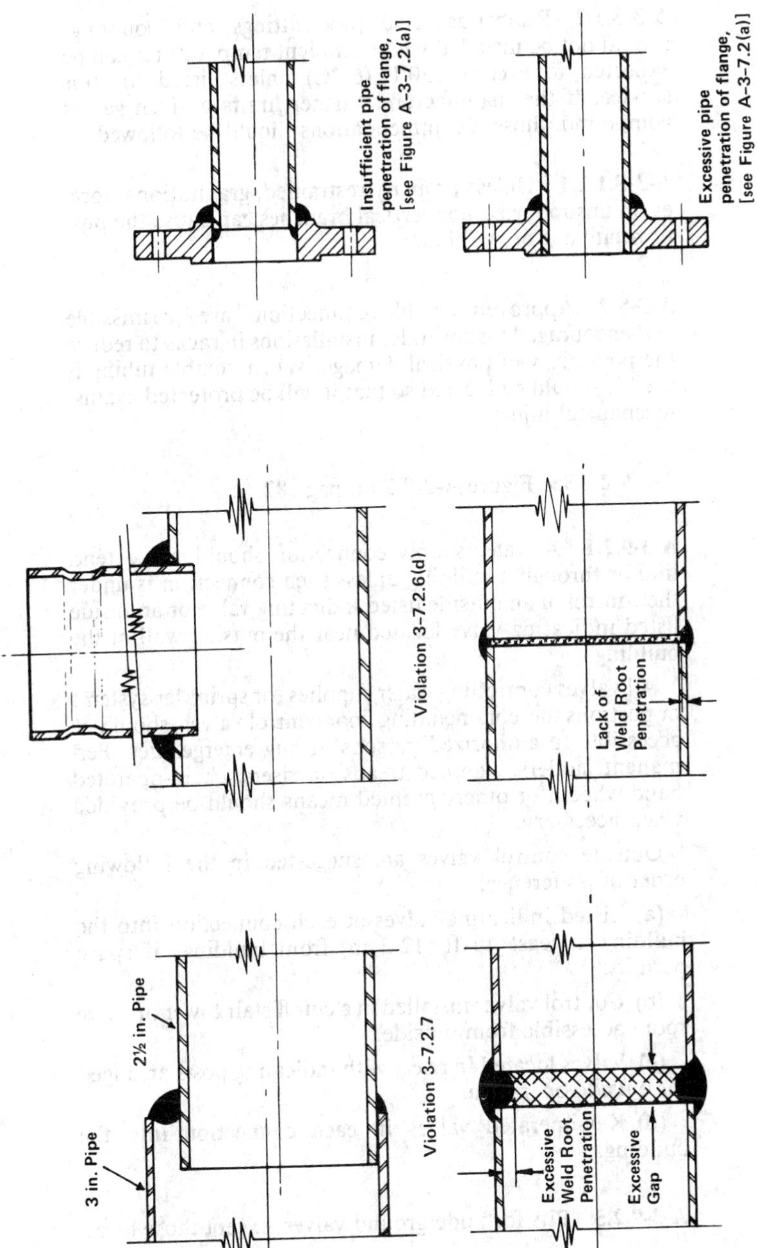
3 in. Pipe
2½ in. Pipe
Violation 3-7.2.7
Excessive Weld Root Penetration
Excessive Gap
Violation 3-7.2.6(d)
Lack of Weld Root Penetration
Insufficient pipe penetration of flange, [see Figure A-3-7.2(a)]
Excessive pipe penetration of flange, [see Figure A-3-7.2(a)]

Figure A-3-7.2(b) Unacceptable Weld Joints.

A-3-8.1.2 Rubber-gasketed pipe fittings and couplings should not be installed where ambient temperatures can be expected to exceed 150°F (66°C) unless listed for this service. If the manufacturer further limits a given gasket compound, those recommendations should be followed.

A-3-8.1.2.1 Unless properly restrained, gravitational forces on unsupported nonvertical branches can cause the pipe to rotate out of position.

A-3-8.2 Approved flexible connections are permissible and encouraged for sprinkler installations in racks to reduce the possibility of physical damage. When flexible tubing is used it should be located so that it will be protected against mechanical injury.

A-3-9.2 See Figure A-3-9.2 on page 82.

A-3-9.2.1 A water supply connection should not extend into or through a building unless such connection is under the control of an outside listed indicating valve or an inside listed indicating valve located near the outside wall of the building.

All valves controlling water supplies for sprinkler systems or portions thereof, including floor control valves, should be accessible to authorized persons during emergencies. Permanent ladders, clamped treads on risers, chain-operated hand wheels, or other accepted means should be provided when necessary.

Outside control valves are suggested in the following order of preference:

(a) Listed indicating valves at each connection into the building at least 40 ft (12.2 m) from buildings if space permits.

(b) Control valves installed in a cutoff stair tower or valve room accessible from outside.

(c) Valves located in risers with indicating posts arranged for outside operation.

(d) Key-operated valves in each connection into the building.

A-3-9.2.5 Pits for underground valves, except those locat-

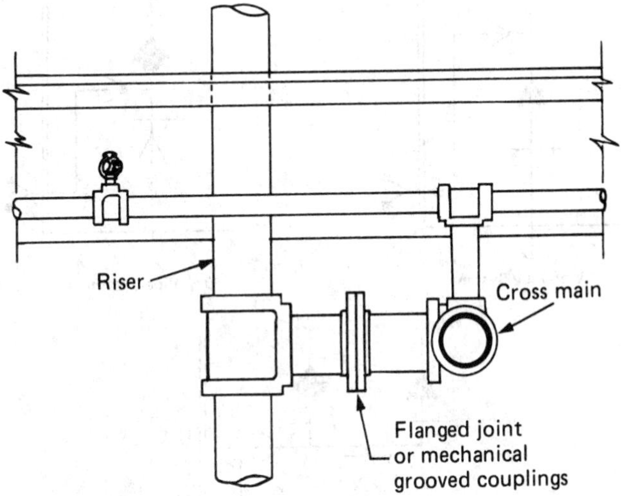
Riser
Cross main
Flanged joint
or mechanical
grooved couplings

Figure A-3-8.1.5 One Arrangement of Flanged Joint at Sprinkler Riser.

ed at the base of a tank riser, are described in NFPA 24, *Standard for Installation of Private Fire Service Mains and Their Appurtenances.* For pits protecting valves located at the base of a tank riser, refer to NFPA 22, *Standard for Water Tanks for Private Fire Protection.*

A-3-9.2.6 When a system having only one dry-pipe valve is supplied with city water.and fire department connection it will be satisfactory to install the main check valve in water supply connection immediately inside of the building; in case there is no outside control, the system indicating valve should be placed at the wall flange ahead of all fittings.

A-3-9.4 All control, drain, and test connections should be provided with identification signs.

A-3-10.1 Branch line hangers under metal decking may be attached by drilling or punching vertical members and

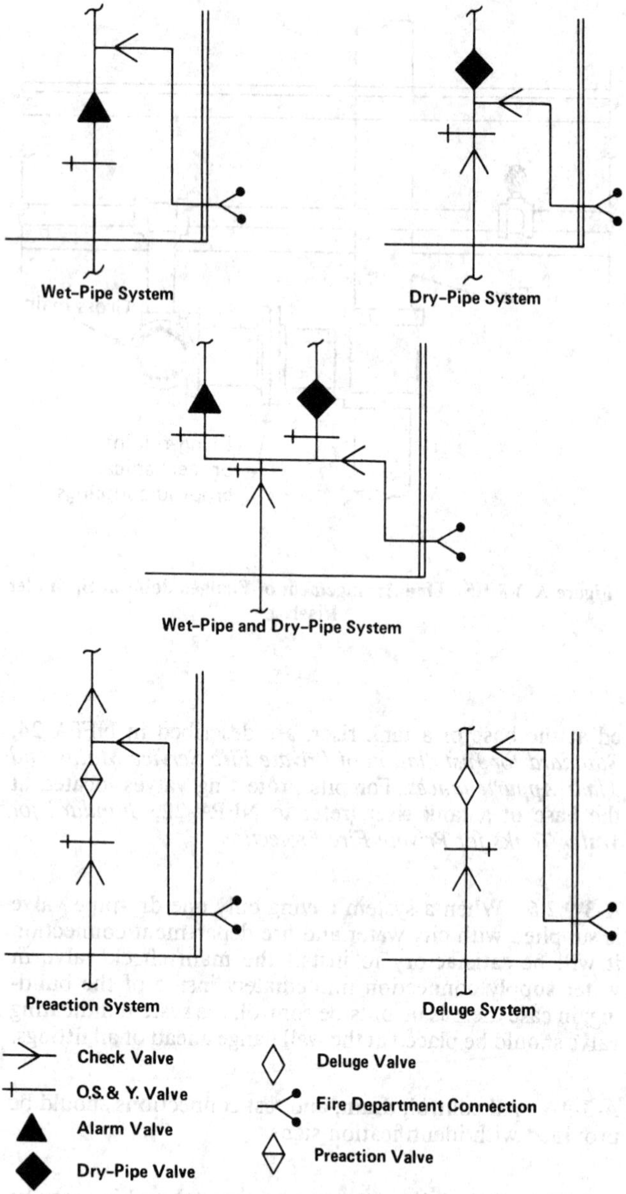
Wet-Pipe System
Dry-Pipe System
Wet-Pipe and Dry-Pipe System
Preaction System
Deluge System
Check Valve
O.S.& Y. Valve
Alarm Valve
Dry-Pipe Valve
Deluge Valve
Fire Department Connection
Preaction Valve

Figure A-3-9.2 Examples of Acceptable Valve Arrangements.

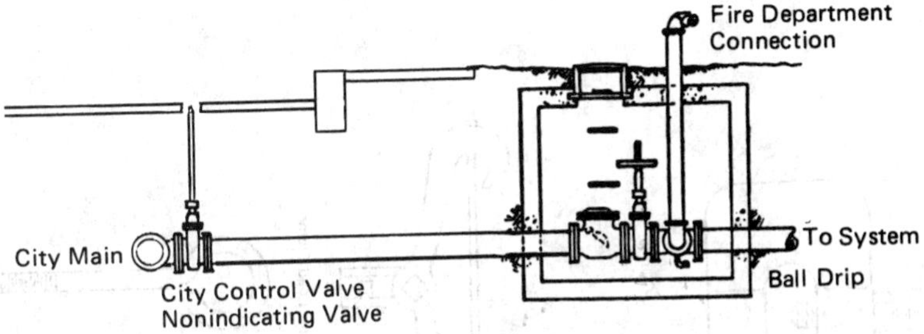
Fire Department Connection
To System
Ball Drip
City Main
City Control Valve
Nonindicating Valve

Figure A-3-9.2.5 Pit for Gate Valve, Check Valve, and Fire Department Connection.

using through bolts. The distance from the bottom of the bolt hole to the bottom of the vertical member should be not less than ⅜ in. (9.5 mm).

To take care of the thrust in a steeply pitched roof branch line, a clamp should be installed on the pipe just above the lowest hanger.

A-3-10.1.3 The rules covering the hanging of sprinkler piping take into consideration the weight of water-filled pipe plus a safety factor. No allowance has been made for the hanging of nonsystem components from sprinkler piping.

A-3-10.1.7 Table 3-10.1.7(a) assumes that the load from 15 ft (5 m) of water-filled pipe, plus 250 lb (114 kg), is located at the midpoint of the span of the trapeze member, with a maximum allowable bending stress of 15 KSI (111 kg). If the load is applied at other than the midpoint, for the purpose of sizing the trapeze member, an equivalent length of trapeze may be used, derived from the formula

$L = \frac{4ab}{a + b}$ where "L" is the equivalent length, "a" is the distance from one support to the load, and "b" is the distance from the other support to the load.

When multiple mains are to be supported or multiple trapeze hangers are provided in parallel, the required or available section modulus may be added.

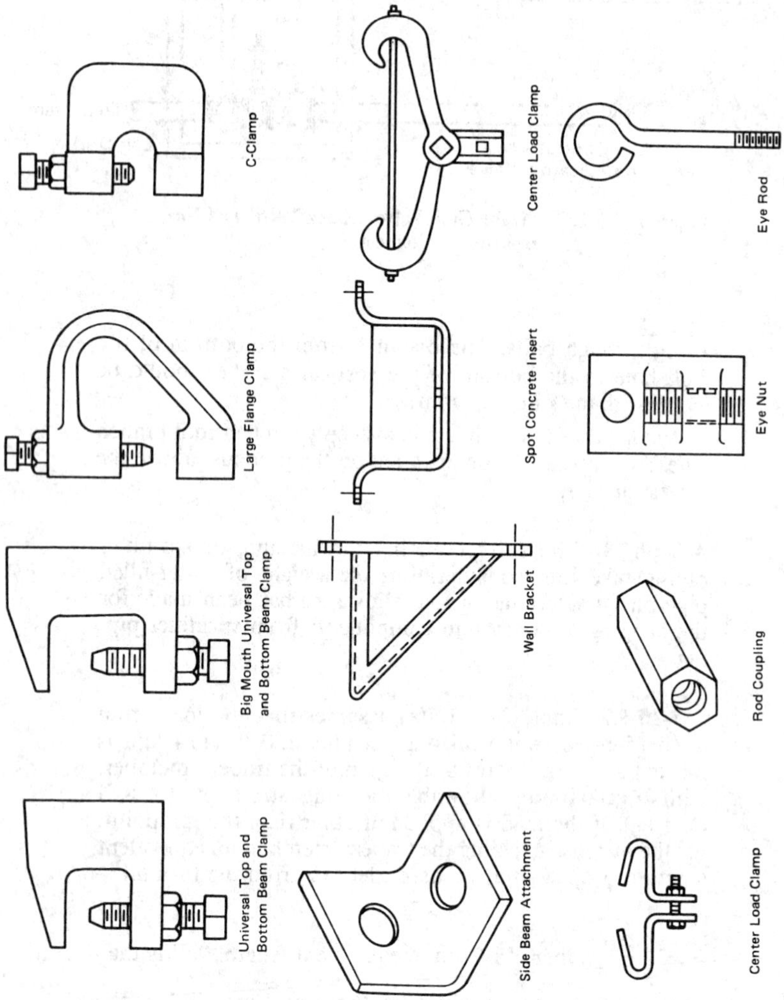
C-Clamp
Large Flange Clamp
Big Mouth Universal Top and Bottom Beam Clamp
Universal Top and Bottom Beam Clamp
Center Load Clamp
Spot Concrete Insert
Wall Bracket
Side Beam Attachment
Eye Rod
Eye Nut
Rod Coupling
Center Load Clamp

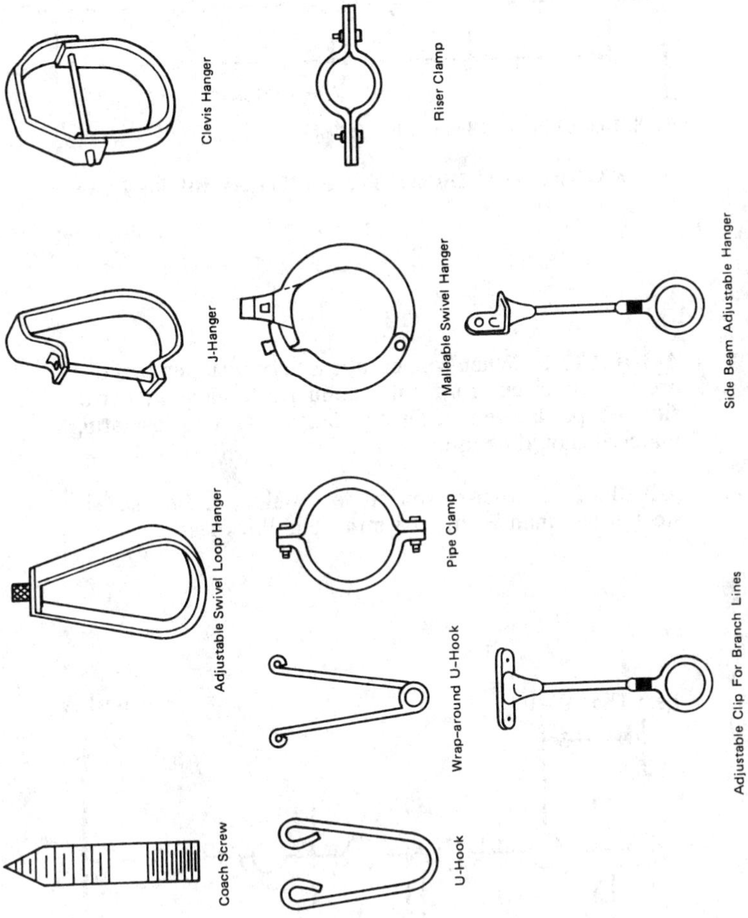
Coach Screw
Adjustable Swivel Loop Hanger
J-Hanger
Clevis Hanger
U-Hook
Wrap-around U-Hook
Pipe Clamp
Malleable Swivel Hanger
Riser Clamp
Adjustable Clip For Branch Lines
Side Beam Adjustable Hanger

Figure A-3-10.1 Common Types of Acceptable Hangers.

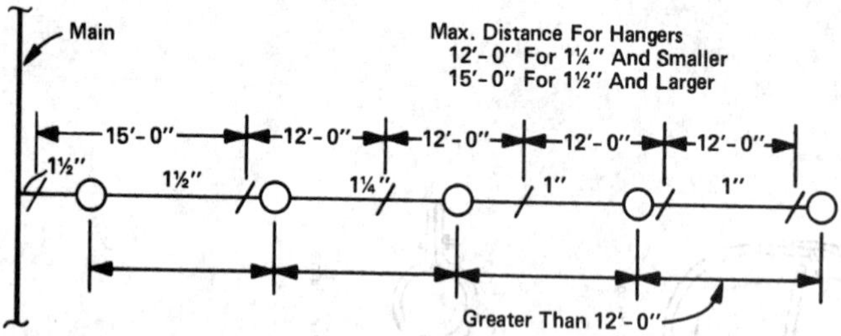
Main
Max. Distance For Hangers
12′-0″ For 1¼″ And Smaller
15′-0″ For 1½″ And Larger
15′-0″
12′-0″
12′-0″
12′-0″
12′-0″
1½″
1½″
1¼″
1″
1″
Greater Than 12′-0″

For SI Units: 1 in. = 25.4 mm; 1 ft = 0.3048 m.

Figure A-3-10.1.11.1 Distance Between Hangers with Steel Pipe.

A-3-10.1.11.2 When copper tube is to be installed in moist areas or other environments conducive to galvanic corrosion, copper hangers or ferrous hangers with an insulating material should be used.

A-3-10.3.1 Powder-driven studs should not be used in steel of less than 3⁄16 in. (4.8 mm) total thickness.

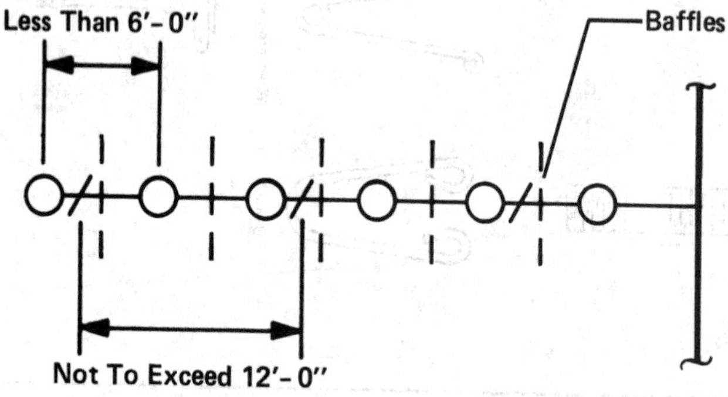
Less Than 6′-0″
Baffles
Not To Exceed 12′-0″

For SI Units: 1 in. = 25.4 mm; 1 ft = 0.3048 m.

Figure A-3-10.5.2 Distance Between Hangers.

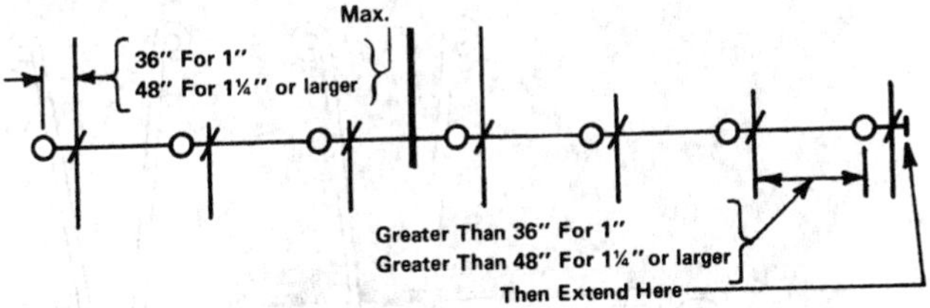
Max.
36" For 1"
48" For 1¼" or larger
Greater Than 36" For 1"
Greater Than 48" For 1¼" or larger
Then Extend Here

For SI Units: 1 in. = 25.4 mm; 1 ft = 0.3048 m.

Figure A-3-10.5.5 Distance from Sprinkler to Hanger.

NOTE: For pendent sprinklers below a ceiling and exposed to maximum pressure greater than 100 psi, see Figure A-3-10.5.5 Exception.

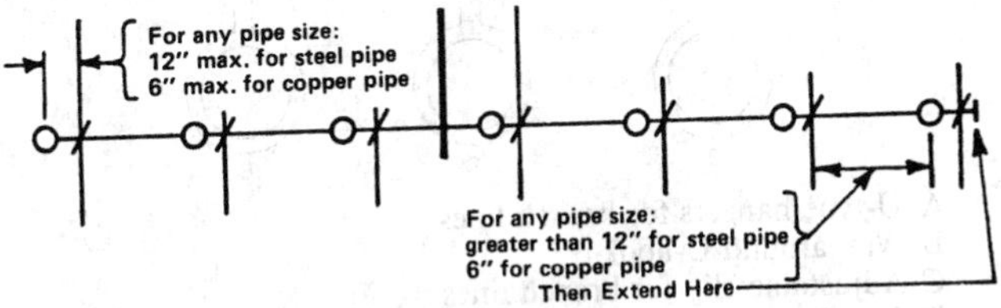
For any pipe size:
12" max. for steel pipe
6" max. for copper pipe
For any pipe size:
greater than 12" for steel pipe
6" for copper pipe
Then Extend Here

For SI Units: 1 in. = 25.4 mm; 1 ft = 0.3048 m.

Figure A-3-10.5.5 Exception. Distance from sprinkler to hanger where maximum pressure exceeds 100 psi (6.9 bars) and a branch line above a ceiling supplies pendent sprinklers below the ceiling.

NOTE 1: The pendent sprinkler may be installed either directly in the fitting at the end of the line, or in a fitting at the bottom of a drop nipple.

NOTE 2: Hanger closest to sprinkler shall be of a type that clamps to and prevents upward movement of the pipe.

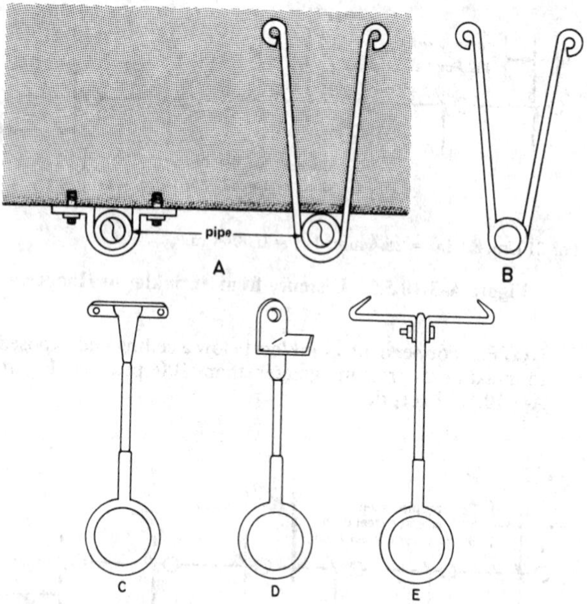
pipe
A
B
C
D
E

A U-type hangers for branch lines
B Wraparound U-hook
C Adjustable clip for branch lines
D Side beam adjustable hanger
E Adjustable coach screw clip for branch lines

Figure A-3-10.5.5(a) Examples of Acceptable Hangers for End of Line (or Armover) Pendent Sprinklers.

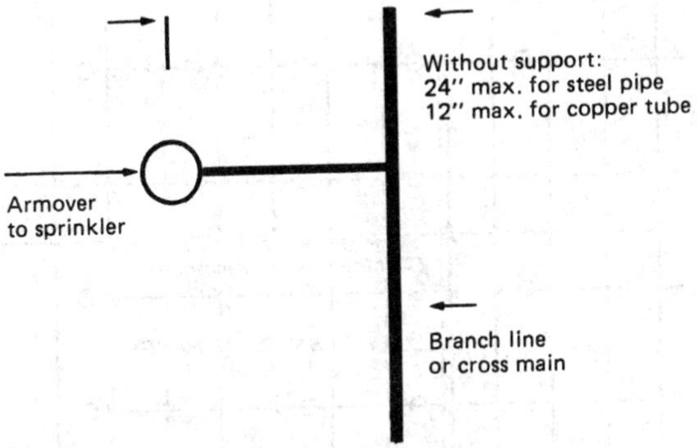
Without support:
24" max. for steel pipe
12" max. for copper tube
Armover
to sprinkler
Branch line
or cross main

For SI Units: 1 in. = 25.4 mm; 1 ft = 0.3048 m.

Figure A-3-10.5.6 Maximum Length for Unsupported Armover.

NOTE: For a pendent sprinkler below a ceiling and exposed to maximum pressure greater than 100 psi, see Figure A-3-10.5.6 Exception.

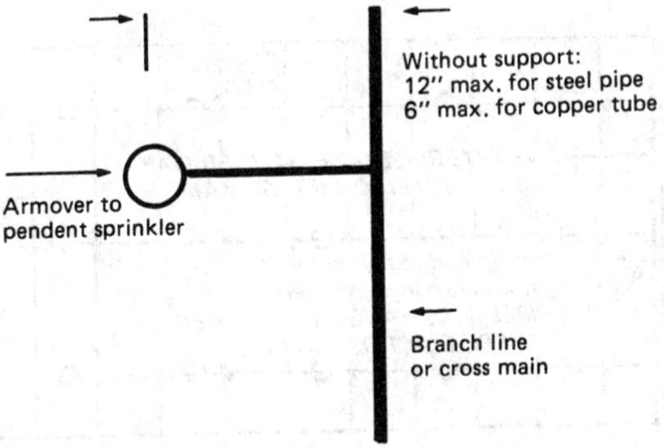
Without support:
12" max. for steel pipe
6" max. for copper tube
Armover to
pendent sprinkler
Branch line
or cross main

For SI Units: 1 in. = 25.4 mm; 1 ft = 0.3048 m.

Figure A-3-10.5.6 Exception. Maximum length of unsupported armover when the maximum pressure exceeds 100 psi (6.9 bars) and a branch line above a ceiling supplies pendent sprinklers below the ceiling.

NOTE: The pendent sprinkler may be installed either directly in the fitting at the end of the armover or in a fitting at the bottom of a drop nipple.

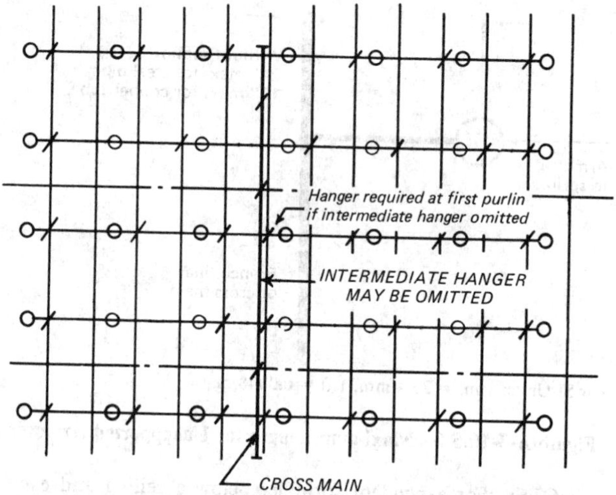
Hanger required at first purlin if intermediate hanger omitted
INTERMEDIATE HANGER MAY BE OMITTED
CROSS MAIN

Figure A-3-10.6.1(a) Hangers on Cross Main.

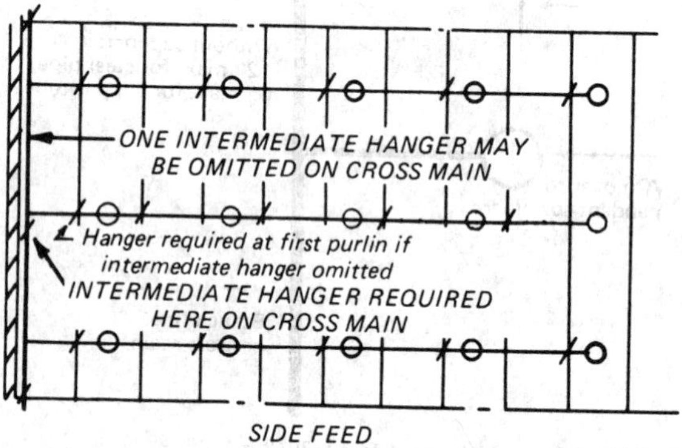
ONE INTERMEDIATE HANGER MAY BE OMITTED ON CROSS MAIN
Hanger required at first purlin if intermediate hanger omitted
INTERMEDIATE HANGER REQUIRED HERE ON CROSS MAIN
SIDE FEED

Figure A-3-10.6.1(b) Hanger Omission on Side Feed System.

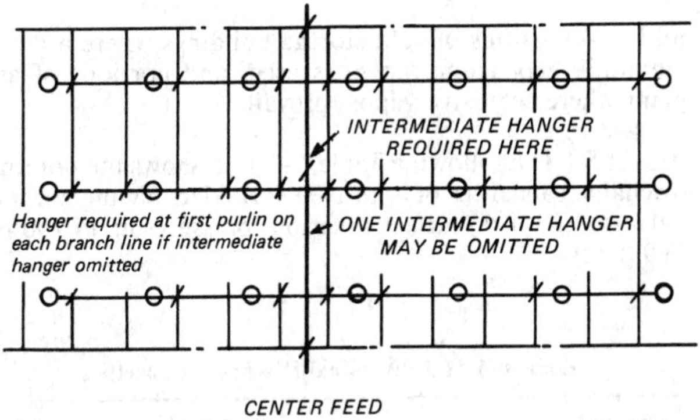
INTERMEDIATE HANGER
REQUIRED HERE
Hanger required at first purlin on
each branch line if intermediate
hanger omitted
ONE INTERMEDIATE HANGER
MAY BE OMITTED
CENTER FEED

Figure A-3-10.6.1(c) Hangers on Cross Main — Center Feed System.

A-3-11.1(h) and (i) Under certain ambient conditions, wet-pipe systems having dry-pendent (or upright) sprinklers may freeze due to heat loss by conduction. Therefore, due consideration should be given to the amount of heat maintained in the heated space, the length of the nipple in the heated space, and other relevant factors.

A-3-11.2.1 Upright sprinklers should be installed with the frame parallel to the branch line pipe to reduce to minimum the obstruction of the discharge pattern.

A-3-11.2.9.1 The response and water distribution pattern of listed residential sprinklers have been shown by extensive fire testing to provide better control than conventional sprinklers in residential occupancies. These sprinklers are intended to prevent flashover in the room of fire origin, thus improving the chance for occupants to escape or be evacuated.

A-3-11.4.1 Examples of such locations are paper mills, packing houses, tanneries, alkali plants, organic fertilizer plants, foundries, forge shops, fumigation, pickle and vinegar works, stables, storage battery rooms, electroplating rooms, galvanizing rooms, steam rooms of all descriptions, including moist vapor dry kilns, salt storage rooms, locomotive sheds or houses, driveways, areas exposed to outside weather such as piers and wharves exposed to salt air, areas under sidewalks, around bleaching equipment in flour mills, all portions of cold storage buildings where a direct ammonia expansion system is used, and portions of any plant where corrosive vapors prevail.

A-3-11.5 The following Table A-3-11.5 shows the nominal discharge capacities of approved sprinklers having a nominal ½-in. (13-mm) orifice at various pressures up to 100 psi (6.9 bars).

Table A-3-11.5 Nominal Discharge Capacities

Pressure at Sprinkler psi	Discharge gpm	Pressure at Sprinkler psi	Discharge gpm
10	18	35	34
15	22	50	41
20	25	75	50
25	28	100	58

For SI Units: 1 gpm = 3.785 L/min; 1 psi = 0.0689 bar.

A-3-11.6 Information regarding the highest temperature that may be encountered in any location in a particular installation may be obtained by use of a thermometer that will register the highest temperature encountered, which should be hung for several days in the questionable location, with the plant in operation.

When an occupancy hazard normally may be expected to produce a fast-developing fire or a rapid rate of heat release, the use of sprinklers of high temperature classification, as a means of limiting the total number of sprinklers that might open in a fire, is recommended. Since the number of sprinklers that might be expected to open will be reduced where the water pressure effective in first operating sprinklers is at least 75 psi (5.2 bars) without the disadvantage of a potential increase in fire damage, this alternative should be given first consideration.

NOTE: Fire tests have shown that the number of sprinklers that might be expected to open, particularly under conditions where fast-developing fires may be expected, can be limited by the use of sprinklers of High Temperature Classification. This may be of advantage in reducing the number of sprinklers that would otherwise open outside the area directly involved in a fire and decrease the overall water demand. However, some increase in fire damage and fire temperatures may be expected when sprinklers of Intermediate or High Temperature Classification are used.

Some occupancies employ high-temperature fumigation processes requiring consideration in the selection of sprinkler temperature ratings.

A-3-11.7 For equipment aboard vessels or in isolated locations, a greater number of sprinklers should be provided to permit equipment to be put back into service promptly after a fire. When a great number of sprinklers are likely to be opened by a flash fire, a greater number of sprinklers should be provided.

A-3-11.8 Sprinklers under open gratings should be provided with shields. Shields over automatic sprinklers should not be less, in least dimension, than four times the distance between the shield and fusible element, except special sprinklers incorporating a built-in shield need not comply with this recommendation if listed for the particular application.

A-3-11.9.1 When painting sprinkler piping or painting in areas near sprinklers, the sprinklers may be protected by covering them with a bag that should be removed immediately after the painting has been finished.

A-3-11.9.2 Painting of sprinklers may retard the thermal response of the heat-responsive element, may interfere with the free movement of parts, and may render the sprinkler inoperative. Moreover, painting may invite the application of subsequent coatings, thus increasing the possibility of a malfunction of the sprinkler.

A-3-12.2 Central station, auxiliary, remote station, or proprietary protective signaling systems are a highly desirable supplement to local alarms, especially from a safety to life standpoint. (*See 3-12.6.*)

Identification Signs. Approved identification signs should be provided for outside alarm devices. The sign should be located near the device in a conspicuous position and should be worded as follows:

SPRINKLER FIRE ALARM — WHEN BELL RINGS CALL FIRE DEPARTMENT OR POLICE. (*See Figure A-3-12.2.*)

SPRINKLER
FIRE-ALARM
WHEN BELL RINGS
CALL
FIRE DEP'T OR POLICE

Figure A-3-12.2 Identification Sign.

A-3-12.3.3 A mechanical alarm (water motor gong) may also be required.

A-3-12.3.4 The surge of water when the valve trips may seriously damage the device.

A-3-12.4.1 Audible alarms are normally located on the outside of the building. Listed electric gongs, bells, horns, or sirens inside the building or a combination inside and outside are sometimes advisable.

A-3-12.4.2 All alarm apparatus should be so located and installed that all parts are accessible for inspection, removal, and repair, and should be substantially supported.

A-3-12.5 Water-motor-operated devices should be located as near as practicable to the alarm valve, dry-pipe valve, or other waterflow detecting device. The total length of the pipe to these devices should not exceed 75 ft (22.9 m) nor should the water-motor-operated device be located over 20 ft (6.1 m) above the alarm device or dry-pipe valve.

A-3-12.7.2 Switches that will silence electric alarm sounding devices by interruption of electrical current are not desirable; however, if such means are provided, then the electrical alarm sounding device circuit should be arranged so that when the sounding device is electrically silenced, that fact shall be indicated by means of a conspicuous light located in the vicinity of the riser or alarm control panel. This light shall remain in operation during the entire period of the electrical circuit interruption.

A-4-1.1 The installation requirements are specific for the normal arrangement of structural members. There will be arrangements of structural members not specifically detailed by the requirements. By applying the basic principles, layouts for such construction can vary from specific illustrations, provided the maximum specified for the spacing of sprinklers (Section 4-2) and position of sprinklers (Section 4-3) are not exceeded.

All needless ceiling sheathing, hollow siding, tops of high shelving, partitions, or decks should be removed. Sheathing of paper and similar light flammable materials is particularly objectionable.

A-4-1.1.1 This standard contemplates full sprinkler protection for all areas. Other NFPA standards that mandate sprinkler installation may not require sprinklers in certain areas. The requirements of this standard should be used insofar as they are applicable. The authority having jurisdiction should be consulted in each case.

A-4-1.2 Installation of sprinklers throughout the premises is necessary for protection of life and property. In some cases partial sprinkler installations covering hazardous sections and other areas are specified in codes or standards or are required by authorities having jurisdiction for minimum protection to property or to provide opportunity for safe exit from the building.

When buildings or portions of buildings are of combustible construction or contain combustible material, standard fire barriers should be provided to separate the areas that are sprinkler protected from adjoining unsprinklered areas. All openings should be protected in accordance with applicable standards and no sprinkler piping should be placed in an unsprinklered area unless the area is permitted to be unsprinklered by this standard.

Water supplies for partial systems should be adequate and designed with due consideration to the fact that in a partial system more sprinklers may be opened in a fire that originates in an unprotected area and spreads to the sprinklered area than would be the case in a completely protected building. Fire originating in a nonsprinklered area may overpower the partial sprinkler system.

When sprinklers are installed in corridors only, sprinklers should be spaced up to the maximum of 15 ft (4.5 m) along the corridor, with one sprinkler opposite the center of any door or pair of adjacent doors opening onto the corridor, and with an additional sprinkler spaced inside each adjacent room above the door opening. When the sprinkler in the adjacent room provides full protection for that space, an additional sprinkler is not required in the corridor adjacent to the door.

A-4-1.3.3 See Figures A-4-1.3.3(a) and (b) for examples of bar joist construction.

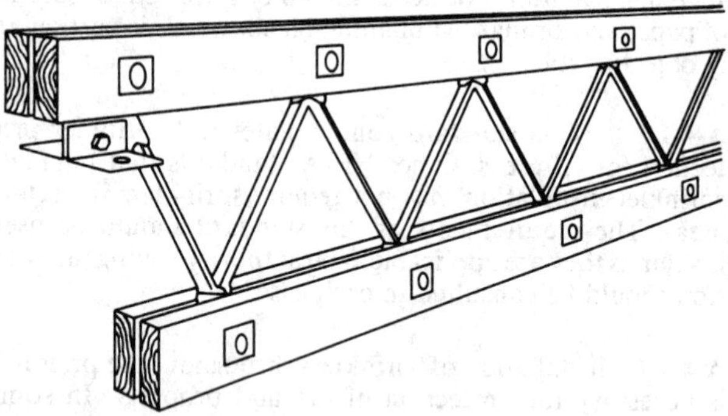

Figure A-4-1.3.3(a) Wood Bar Joist Construction.

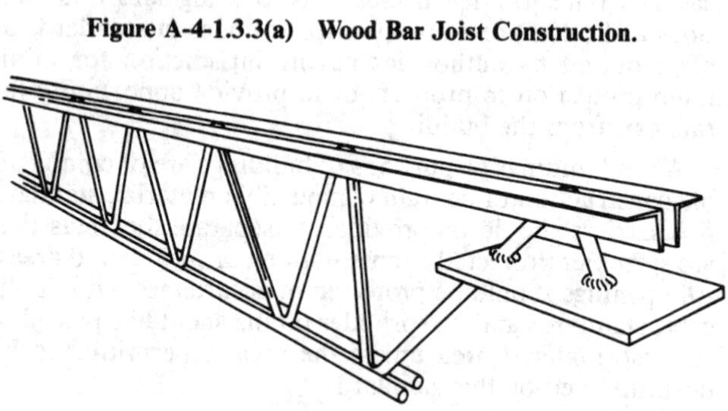

Figure A-4-1.3.3(b) Open-Web Bar Joist Construction.

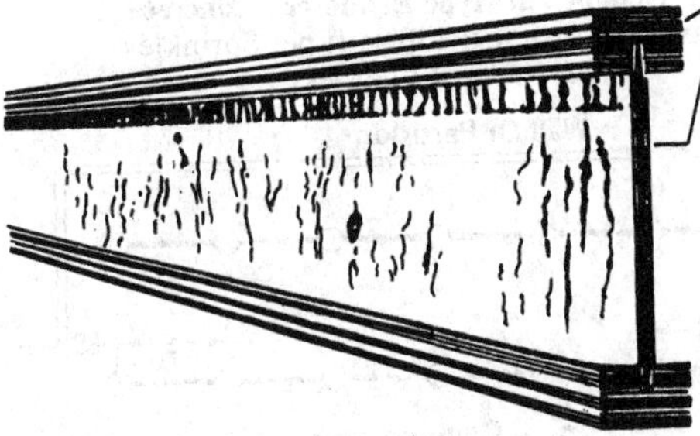
Wood

Figure A-4-1.3.8 Typical Composite Wood Joist Construction.

A-4-2.1.2 For examples of sprinkler layouts under smooth ceiling construction, refer to Figures A-4-2.1.2(a) and (b).

A-4-2.2 The protection area per sprinkler should be determined as follows:

1. Along Branch Lines. Determine distance to next sprinkler (or to wall in case of end sprinkler on branch line) upstream and downstream. Choose the larger of either twice the distance to the wall or distance to the next sprinkler. Call this "S".

2. Between Branch Lines. Determine perpendicular distance to sprinkler on branch lines (or to wall in the case of the branch line) on each side of the branch line on which the subject sprinkler is positioned. Choose the larger of (1) the larger distance to the sprinklers on the next branch line, or (2) in the case of the last branch line, twice the distance to the wall. Call this "L".

3. Protection area of the sprinkler = S × L.

4. This does not apply to any sprinkler located more than 7.5 ft (2.3 m) from any single wall in a small room. (*See 4-4.19.*)

A-4-2.3 The arrangement of branch lines depends upon such construction features as the distance between girders or trusses, columns of mushroom-type reinforced concrete, and beams of standard mill construction. Each space or bay should usually be treated as a unit, installing the same number of branch lines uniformly in each space. When single branch lines will suffice, they should be placed midway in each bay or space. The arrangement of branch

Flat Slab or Pan-Type Reinforced Concrete
Maximum Spacing: 130 sq ft per Sprinkler
L × S = 130 or less

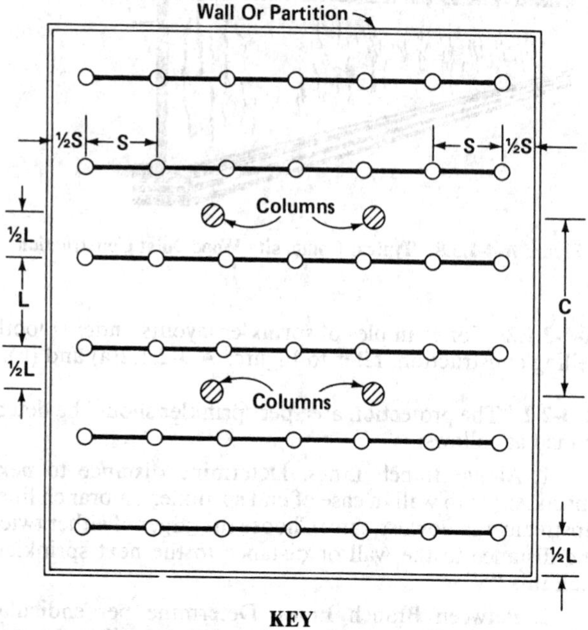
Wall Or Partition
½S
S
S
½S
Columns
½L
L
½L
C
Columns
½L

KEY

C = Column spacing.
L = Distance between branch lines, limit 15 ft.
S = Distance between sprinklers on branch lines, limit 15 ft.

Examples

C	L	S (Max)	C	L	S (Max)
21 ft 8 in.	10 ft 10 in.	12 ft 0 in.	21 ft 6 in.	10 ft 9 in.	12 ft 1 in.
24 ft 2 in.	12 ft 1 in.	10 ft 9 in.			

For SI Units: 1 in. = 25.4 mm; 1 ft = 0.3048 m; 1 ft² = 0.0929 m².

Figure A-4-2.1.2(a) Layout of Sprinklers under Smooth Ceiling Construction — Ordinary Hazard Occupancy.

Continuous Smooth Bays with Beams Supported on Columns
Maximum Spacing: 130 sq ft per Sprinkler
L × S = 130 or less

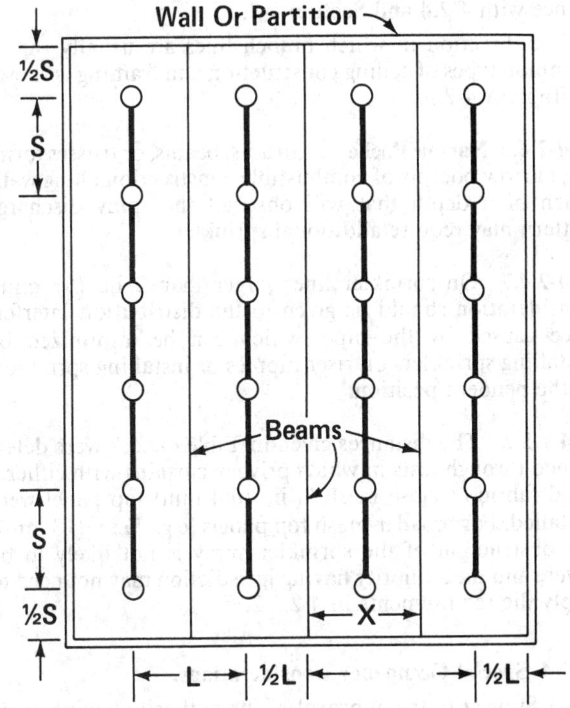

Wall Or Partition
½S
S
Beams
S
½S
X
L
½L
½L

KEY

L = Distance between branch lines, limit 15 ft.
S = Distance between sprinklers on branch lines, limit 15 ft.
X = Width of bay.

Examples

X	L	S (Max)	X	L	S (Max)
10 ft 10 in.	10 ft 10 in.	12 ft 0 in.	10 ft 9 in.	10 ft 9 in.	12 ft 1 in.
12 ft 1 in.	12 ft 1 in.	10 ft 9 in.			

For SI Units: 1 in. = 25.4 mm; 1 ft = 0.3048 m; 1 ft^2 = 0.0929 m^2.

Figure A-4-2.1.2(b) Layout of Sprinklers under Smooth Ceiling Construction — Ordinary Hazard Occupancy.

lines also depends upon the structural members available and suitable for the attachment of hangers, and upon the need for properly locating sprinkler deflectors in accordance with 4-2.4 and Section 4-3.

The direction in which branch lines are usually run in common types of ceiling construction and framing is shown in Table A-4-2.3.

A-4-2.4.6 Narrow Pocket. Girders, beams, or trusses forming narrow pockets of combustible construction along walls when of a depth that will obstruct the spray discharge pattern may require additional sprinklers.

A-4-2.4.7 On sprinkler lines larger than 2 in. (51 mm), consideration should be given to the distribution interference caused by the pipe, which can be minimized by installing sprinklers on riser nipples or installing sprinklers in the pendent position.

A-4-2.5.2 The distances given in Table 4-2.5.2 were determined through tests in which privacy curtains with either a solid fabric or close mesh ¼ in. (6.4 mm) top panel were installed. For broader-mesh top panels [e.g., ½ in. (13 mm)] the obstruction of the sprinkler spray is not likely to be severe and the authority having jurisdiction may not need to apply the requirements in 4-2.5.2.

A-4-4 Special Occupancy Considerations.

(a) Subject to the approval of the authority having jurisdiction, sprinklers may be omitted in rooms or areas where they are considered undesirable because of the nature of the contents, or in rooms or areas of noncombustible construction with wholly noncombustible contents and that are not exposed by other areas. Sprinklers should not be omitted from any room merely because it is damp or of fire-resistive construction.

(b) It is not advisable to install sprinklers when the application of water, or of flame and water, to a room or area's contents may constitute a serious life or fire hazard, as in the manufacture or storage of quantities of aluminum powder, calcium carbide, calcium phosphide, metallic sodium and potassium, quicklime, magnesium powder, and sodium peroxide. The manufacture and storage of such materials should be confined to specially cut-off, unsprinklered rooms, or buildings of fire-resistive construction.

Joists Above Girders or Framed into Girders;
Branch Lines Uniformly Spaced Between Girders
Maximum Spacing: 130 sq ft per Sprinkler
$L \times S = 130$ or less

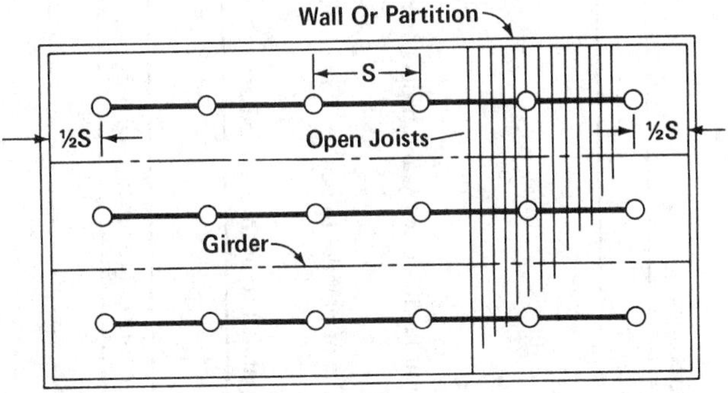
Wall Or Partition
S
½S
Open Joists
½S
Girder

KEY

L = Distance between branch lines, limit 15 ft.
S = Distance between sprinklers on branch lines, limit 15 ft.
Y = Maximum distance between girders.

Examples

Y	L	S (Max)	Y	L	S (Max)
10 ft 9 in.	10 ft 9 in.	12 ft 1 in.	10 ft 10 in. 12 ft 1 in.	10 ft 10 in. 12 ft 1 in.	12 ft 0 in. 10 ft 9 in.

For SI Units: 1 in. = 25.4 mm; 1 ft = 0.3048 m; 1 ft² = 0.0929 m².

Figure A-4-2.2.2.2 Layout of Sprinklers under Open Wood Joist Construction — Light and Ordinary Hazard Occupancies.

A-4-4.4.1 Exceptions No. 1, 2, and 3 do not require sprinkler protection because it is not physically practical to install sprinklers in these spaces. To prevent the possibility of uncontrolled fire spread, consideration should be given in these unsprinklered concealed space situations by using other means such as Exceptions No. 5, 8, and 9.

A-4-4.4.4 When there is a limited amount of combustibles available to burn and a limited prospect of fire propagation, sprinklers may not be required.

Table A-4-2.3 Common Branch Line Run Directions

Type of Ceiling	Location of Branch Lines
Smooth Continuous:	
Concrete mushroom	Either direction
Concrete pan-type or flat	Either direction
Sheathed (ceiling attached to bottom of beams, wood joists, or bar joists):	
Girders beneath sheathing	Across the beam or joists
No girders beneath sheathing	Whichever direction facilitates easy and proper hanging
Bays more than 7½ ft (2.3 m) wide:	
Formed by beams supported on columns	Parallel to beams
Formed by beams supported on girders or trusses	Either across beams or parallel to beams in the bays above girders or trusses
Supported directly on girders	Parallel to girders
Supported directly on trusses	Either direction, parallel to or through trusses
Beam and Girder:	
Wood or steel beams spaced 3 to 7½ ft (0.9 to 2.3 m) apart	Across beams
Open Bar Joist	Across the joists or trusses (either through or under them)
Open Joist (wood, steel, or concrete)	Across joists

A-4-4.7.1.2 When practicable, sprinklers should be staggered at the alternate floor levels, particularly when only one sprinkler is installed at each floor level.

A-4-4.7.2 Floor or wall openings tending to create vertical or horizontal drafts, or other structural conditions that would delay the prompt operation of automatic sprinklers by preventing the banking up of the heated air from the fire, should be properly stopped in order to permit control of fire at any point by local sprinklers.

A-4-4.8 The installation of sprinklers at floor levels should be so arranged as to protect the sprinklers from mechanical injury, from falling materials, and not cause obstruction within the chute. This can usually be accomplished by recessing the sprinkler in the wall of the chute or by providing a protective deflector canopy over the sprinkler. Sprinklers should be placed so that there will be minimum

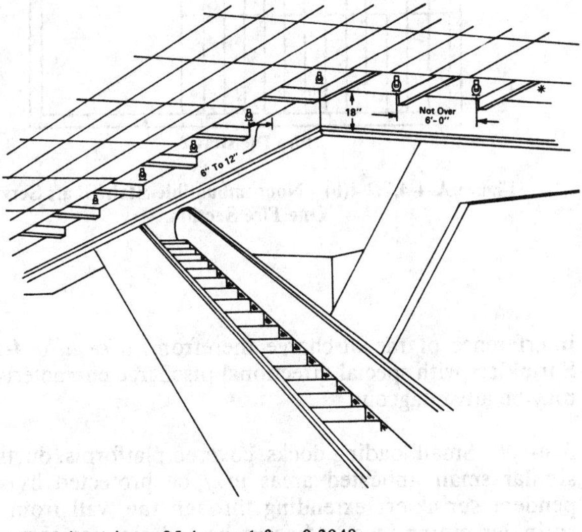
18"
Not Over 6'- 0"
6" To 12"
*

For SI Units: 1 in. = 25.4 mm; 1 ft = 0.3048 m.
*Baffle (*see 4-4.18*).

Figure A-4-4.7.2.3 Sprinklers Around Escalators.

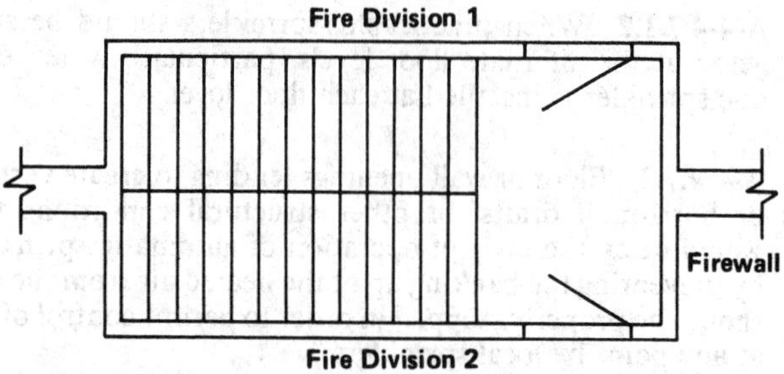
Fire Division 1
Firewall
Fire Division 2

Figure A-4-4.7.2.4(a) Noncombustible Stair Shaft Serving Two Fire Sections.

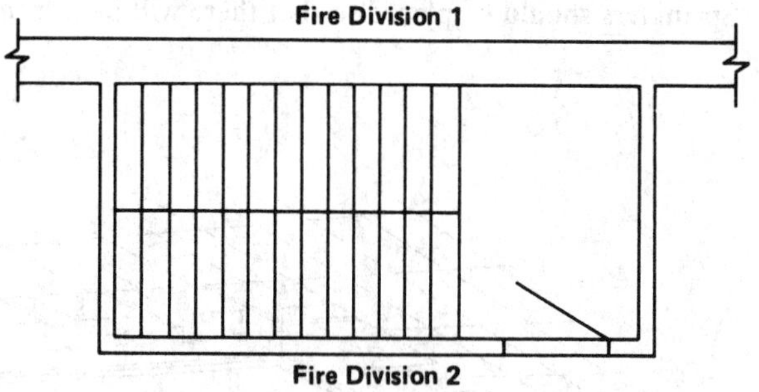
Fire Division 1
Fire Division 2

Figure A-4-4.7.2.4(b) Noncombustible Stair Shaft Serving One Fire Section.

interference of the discharge therefrom. (*See also 4-1.2.*) Sprinklers with special directional discharge characteristics may be advantageous.

A-4-4.9 Small loading docks, covered platforms, ducts, or similar small unheated areas may be protected by dry-pendent sprinklers extending through the wall from wet sprinkler piping in an adjacent heated area, as shown in Figure A-4-4.9.

Where possible, the dry-pendent sprinkler should extend down at a 45-degree angle. The width of the area to be

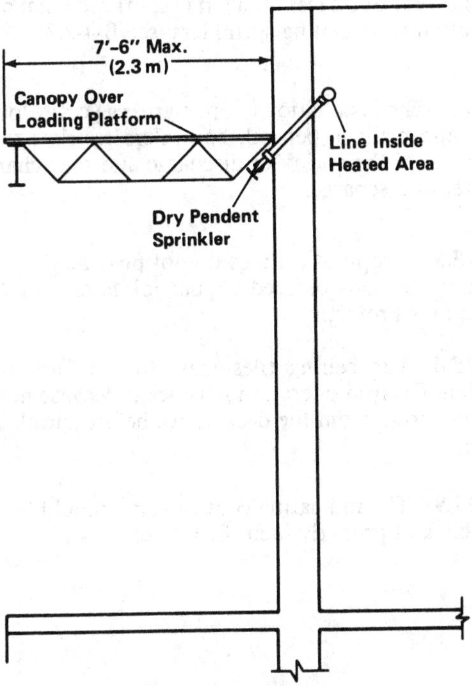
7'-6" Max.
(2.3 m)
Canopy Over
Loading Platform
Line Inside
Heated Area
Dry Pendent
Sprinkler

Figure A-4-4.9 Dry-Pendent Sprinklers for Protection of Covered Platforms, Shipping Docks, and Similar Areas.

protected should not exceed 7½ ft (2.3 m). Sprinklers should be spaced not over 12 ft (3.7 m) apart.

A-4-4.10 Frequently, additional sprinkler equipment can be avoided by reducing the width of decks or galleries and providing proper clearances. Slatting of decks or walkways or the use of open grating as a substitute for automatic sprinklers thereunder is not acceptable. The use of cloth or paper dust tops for rooms forms obstruction to water distribution. If employed, the area below should be sprinklered.

A-4-4.12 For ducts less than 4 ft (1.2 m) wide that obstruct distribution from ceiling sprinklers, see B-4-2.3.

A-4-4.14 The installation of open-grid egg crate, louver, or honeycomb ceilings beneath sprinklers restricts the sideways travel of the sprinkler discharge and may change the character of discharge.

A-4-4.15.3 Drop-out ceilings do not provide the required protection for soft-soldered copper joints or other piping that requires protection.

A-4-4.15.4 The ceiling tiles may drop before sprinkler operation. Delayed operation may occur because heat must then bank down from the deck above before sprinklers will operate.

A-4-4.17.9 The indicating control valve should be readily accessible and properly identified. (*See 3-9.4.*)

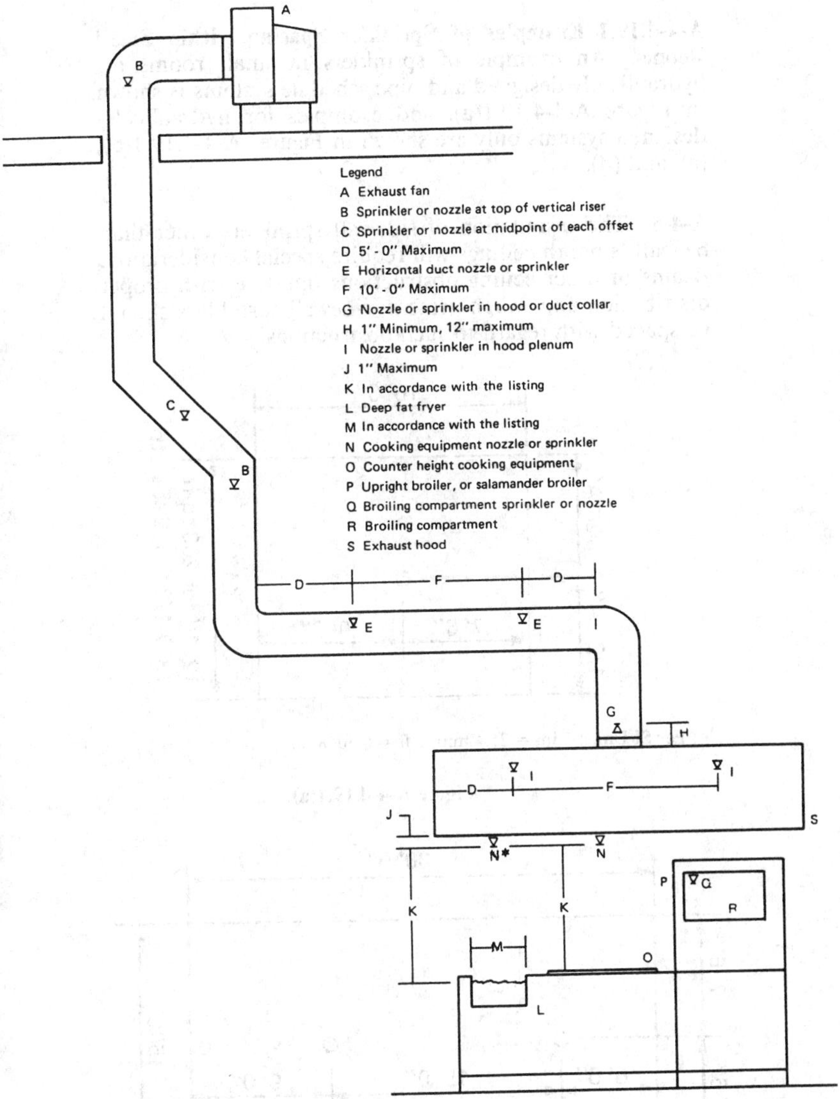
Legend
A Exhaust fan
B Sprinkler or nozzle at top of vertical riser
C Sprinkler or nozzle at midpoint of each offset
D 5' - 0" Maximum
E Horizontal duct nozzle or sprinkler
F 10' - 0" Maximum
G Nozzle or sprinkler in hood or duct collar
H 1" Minimum, 12" maximum
I Nozzle or sprinkler in hood plenum
J 1" Maximum
K In accordance with the listing
L Deep fat fryer
M In accordance with the listing
N Cooking equipment nozzle or sprinkler
O Counter height cooking equipment
P Upright broiler, or salamander broiler
Q Broiling compartment sprinkler or nozzle
R Broiling compartment
S Exhaust hood
N*

*Listed for deep fat fryer protection.

Figure A-4-4.17.4 Typical Installation Showing Automatic Sprinklers or Automatic Spray Nozzles Being Used for the Protection of Commercial Cooking Equipment and Ventilation Systems.

A-4-4.19.1 Examples of Sprinkler Spacing within Small Rooms. An example of sprinklers in small rooms for hydraulically designed and pipe schedule systems is shown in Figure A-4-4.19.1(a), and examples for hydraulically designed systems only are shown in Figures A-4-4.19.1(b), (c), and (d).

A-4-5 The installation of sidewall sprinklers other than beneath smooth ceilings will require special consideration. Beams or other ceiling obstructions interfere with proper distribution and, when present, sidewall sprinklers should be spaced with regard to such obstructions.

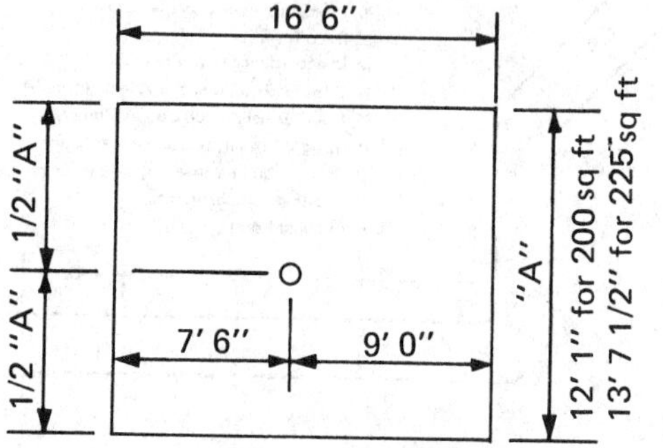
16′ 6″
1/2 "A"
1/2 "A"
7′ 6″
9′ 0″
"A"
12′ 1″ for 200 sq ft
13′ 7 1/2″ for 225 sq ft

For SI Units: 1 in. = 25.4 mm; 1 ft = 0.3048 m.

Figure A-4-4.19.1(a).

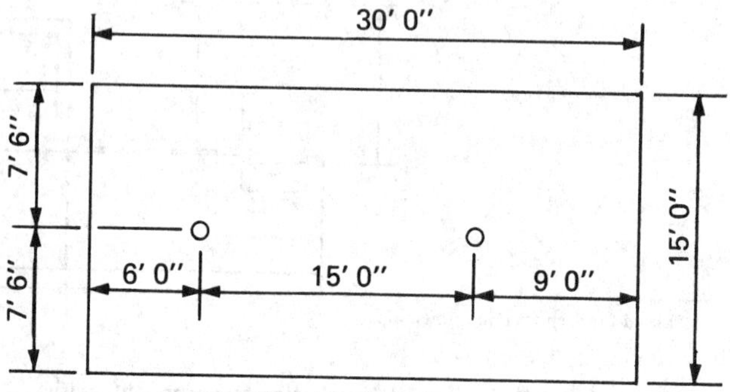
30′ 0″
7′ 6″
7′ 6″
6′ 0″
15′ 0″
9′ 0″
15′ 0″

For SI Units: 1 in. = 25.4 mm; 1 ft = 0.3048 m.

Figure A-4-4.19.1(c).

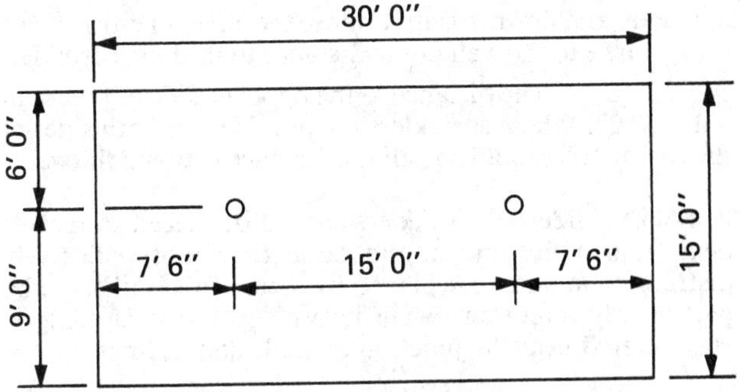
30′ 0″
6′ 0″
9′ 0″
7′ 6″
15′ 0″
7′ 6″
15′ 0″

For SI Units: 1 in. = 25.4 mm; 1 ft = 0.3048 m.

Figure A-4-4.19.1(b).

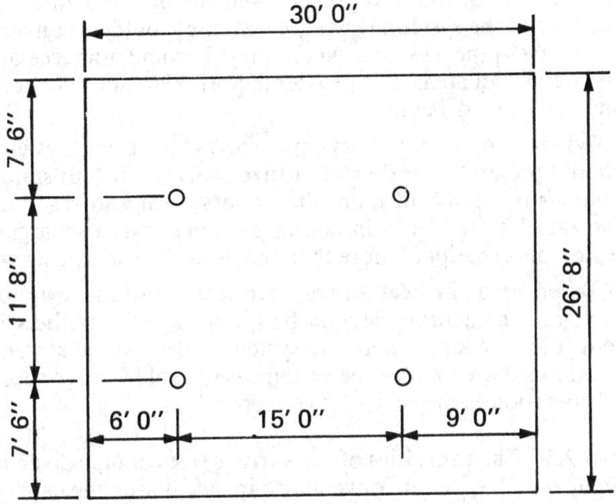
30′ 0″
7′ 6″
11′ 8″
7′ 6″
6′ 0″
15′ 0″
9′ 0″
26′ 8″

For SI Units: 1 in. = 25.4 mm; 1 ft = 0.3048 m.

Figure A-4-4.19.1(d).

A-4-5.2 The protection area per sprinkler should be determined using the S × L = Protection Area rule as follows:

1. "S" — Determine distance to the next sprinkler (or to the wall, in case of an end sprinkler on a branch line)

upstream and downstream. Choose the larger of either twice the distance to the wall or the distance to the next sprinkler.

2. "L" — The distance to the opposite side of the room will be "L". Where sprinklers are provided on both sides of the room, "L" should be half the distance between the walls.

A-4-5.5.1 Sidewall sprinklers should be placed to receive heat from a fire and at the same time most effectively distribute the water discharged by them. This is likely to be particularly important when heavy decorative molding is encountered near the junction of walls and ceilings.

A-5-1.1 A dry-pipe, preaction, or deluge system may be supplied from a larger wet-pipe system, provided the water supply is adequate.

A-5-2.1 A dry-pipe system should be installed only where heat is not adequate to prevent freezing of water in all or sections of the system. Dry-pipe systems should be converted to wet-pipe systems when they become unnecessary because adequate heat is provided. Sprinklers should not be shut off in cold weather.

When two or more dry-pipe valves are used, systems should preferably be divided horizontally to prevent simultaneous operation of more than one system and resultant increased time delay in filling systems and discharging water, plus receipt of more than one waterflow alarm signal.

When adequate heat is present in sections of the dry-pipe system, consideration should be given to dividing the system into a separate wet-pipe system and dry-pipe system. Minimized use of dry-pipe systems is desirable where speed of operation is of particular concern.

A-5-2.3 The capacities of the various sizes of pipe given in Table A-5-2.3 are for convenience in calculating the capacity of a system.

A-5-2.4.2 In the case of dry-pipe valves having relatively small priming chambers and in which the normal quantity of priming water fills, or nearly fills, the entire priming chamber, the objective contemplated by this rule will be met by requiring connection of the quick-opening device at a point on the riser above the dry-pipe valve, which will provide a capacity measure between the normal priming level of the air chamber and the connection of 1½, 2, and 3 gal (5.7, 7.6, and 11.4 L) for 4-, 5-, and 6-in. (102-, 127-, and

Table A-5-2.3 Capacity of One Foot of Pipe (Based on actual internal pipe diameters)

Nominal Diameter	Gal Sch 40	Sch 10	Nominal Diameter	Gal Sch 40	Sch 10
¾ in.	0.028	—	3 in.	0.383	0.433
1 in.	0.045	0.049	3½ in.	0.513	0.576
1¼ in.	0.078	0.085	4 in.	0.660	0.740
1½ in.	0.106	0.115	5 in.	1.040	1.144
2 in.	0.174	0.190	6 in.	1.501	1.649[1]
2½ in.	0.248	0.283	8 in.	2.66[3]	2.776[2]

For SI Units: 1 in. = 25.4 mm; 1 ft = 0.3048 m; 1 gal = 3.785 L.

[1]0.134 Wall Pipe
[2]0.188 Wall Pipe
[3]Schedule 30

152-mm) risers, respectively. Making the connection 24 in. (610 mm) above the normal priming water level will ordinarily provide this capacity.

A-5-2.5 The dry-pipe valve should be located in an accessible place near the sprinkler system it controls.

When exposed to cold, the dry-pipe valve should be located in an approved valve room or enclosure and, where this is not possible, in an underground pit acceptable to the authority having jurisdiction. The room should be of sufficient size to give at least 2½ ft (0.8 m) of free space at the sides and in front of, above and below, the dry-pipe valve or valves, and this room, if feasible, should not be built until the valve is in position.

Size of enclosure should be governed by the number and arrangement of dry-pipe valves, so as to give ready access to these devices.

A-5-2.6 Careful installation and maintenance, and some special arrangements of piping and devices as outlined in this section, are needed to avoid the formation of ice and frost inside piping in cold storage rooms that will be maintained at or below 32°F (0°C). Conditions are particularly favorable to condensation where pipes enter cold rooms from rooms having temperatures above freezing.

Whenever the opportunity offers, fittings such as those specified in 5-2.6.1 and illustrated in Figures 5-2.6.1(A) and

5-2.6.1(B), as well as flushing connections specified in 3-3.2, should be provided in existing systems.

When possible, risers should be located in stair towers or other locations outside of refrigerated areas. This would reduce the probabilities of ice or frost formation within the riser (supply) pipe.

Cross mains should be connected to risers or feed mains with flanges. In general, flanged fittings should be installed at points that would allow easy dismantling of the system. Split ring or other easily removable types of hangers will facilitate the dismantling.

Because it is not practical to allow water to flow into sprinkler piping in spaces that may be constantly subject to freezing, or where temperatures must be maintained at or below 40°F (4.4°C), it is important that means be provided at the time of system installation to conduct trip tests on dry-pipe valves which service such systems. NFPA 13A contains guidance in this matter.

A-5-2.7.2 The compressor should draw its air supply from a place where the air is dry and not too warm. Moisture from condensation may cause trouble in the system.

A-5-3.2 Preaction and deluge systems may also have outside sprinklers for protection against exposure fire.

A-5-3.3 Conditions of occupancy or special hazards may require quick application of large quantities of water and in such cases deluge systems may be needed.

Fire detection devices should be selected to assure operation, yet guard against premature operation of sprinklers, based on normal room temperatures and draft conditions.

In locations where ambient temperature at the ceiling is high, from heat sources other than fire conditions, heat-responsive devices that operate at higher than ordinary temperature and are capable of withstanding the normal high temperature for long periods of time should be selected.

When corrosive conditions exist, materials or protective coatings that resist corrosion should be used.

To help avoid ice formation in piping due to accidental tripping of dry-pipe valves in cold storage rooms, a deluge automatic water control valve may be used on the supply side of the dry-pipe valve. When this combination is employed:

(a) Dry systems may be manifolded to a deluge valve, the protected area not exceeding 40,000 sq ft (3716 m^2). The distance between valves should be as short as possible to minimize water hammer.

(b) The dry-pipe valves should be pressurized to 50 psi (3.4 bars) to reduce the possibility of dry-pipe valve operation from water hammer.

A-5-3.7 Deluge systems are usually applied to severe conditions of occupancy. In designing piping systems the pipe sizes should be calculated in accordance with the standard for hydraulically designed sprinkler systems as given in Chapter 7.

When 8-in. (203-mm) piping is employed to reduce friction losses in a system operated by fire detection devices, a 6-in. (152-mm) preaction or deluge valve and 6-in. (152-mm) gate valve between taper reducers may be used.

A-5-4.1.1 When Installed. Combined dry-pipe and preaction systems may be installed when wet-pipe systems are impractical. They are intended for use in but not limited to structures where a number of dry-pipe valves would be required if a dry-pipe system were installed.

A-5-5.2 Antifreeze solutions may be used for maintaining automatic sprinkler protection in small unheated areas. Antifreeze solutions are recommended only for systems not exceeding 40 gallons (151 L).

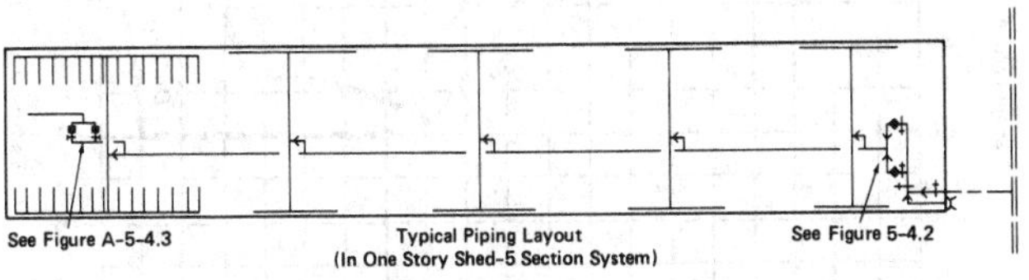
See Figure A-5-4.3
Typical Piping Layout
(In One Story Shed-5 Section System)
See Figure 5-4.2

Figure A-5-4.1.1 Typical Piping Layout for Combined Dry-Pipe and Preaction Sprinkler System.

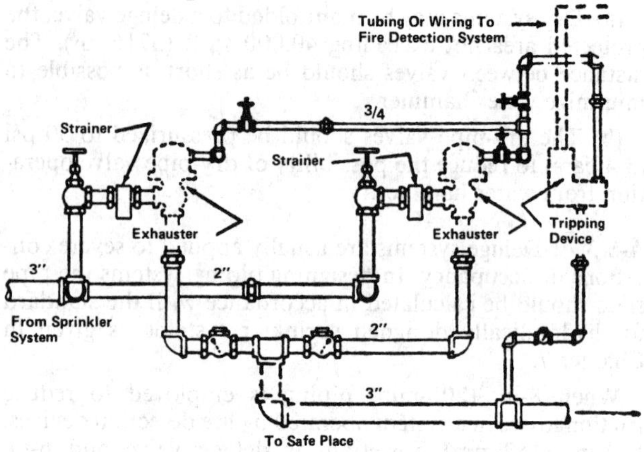

Tubing Or Wiring To
Fire Detection System
3/4
Strainer
Strainer
Exhauster
Exhauster
Tripping
Device
3"
2"
From Sprinkler
System
2"
3"
To Safe Place

For SI Units: 1 in. = 25.4 mm.

Figure A-5-4.3 Arrangement of Air Exhaust Valves for Combined Dry-Pipe and Preaction Sprinkler System.

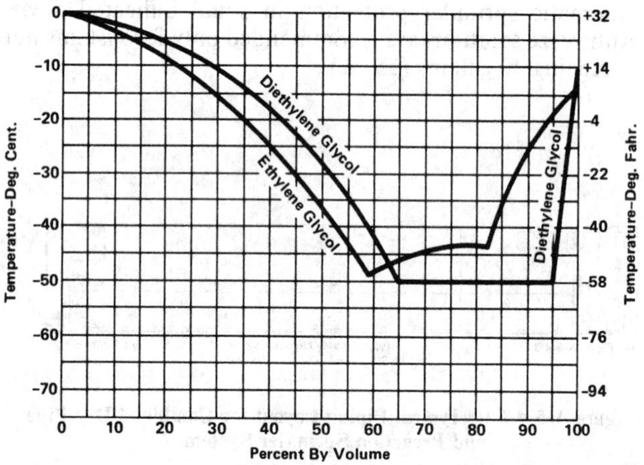

Temperature–Deg. Cent.
0
-10
-20
-30
-40
-50
-60
-70
Temperature–Deg. Fahr.
+32
+14
-4
-22
-40
-58
-76
-94
Diethylene Glycol
Ethylene Glycol
Diethylene Glycol
0
10
20
30
40
50
60
70
80
90
100
Percent By Volume

Figure A-5-5.3.3 Freezing Points of Water Solutions of Ethylene Glycol and Diethylene Glycol.

Because of the cost of refilling the system or replenishing small leaks, it is advisable to use small dry valves where more than 40 gallons (151 L) are to be supplied.

Propylene glycol or other suitable material may be used as a substitute for priming water, to prevent evaporation of the priming fluid, and thus reduce ice formation within the system.

A-5-5.3.3 Beyond certain limits, increased proportion of antifreeze does not lower the freezing point of solution. (*See Figure A-5-5.3.3.*) Glycerine, diethylene glycol, ethylene glycol, and propylene glycol should never be used without mixing with water in proper proportions, because these materials tend to thicken near 32°F (0°C).

A-5-5.4 To avoid leakage, the materials and workmanship should be excellent, the threads clean and sharp, and the joints tight. Use only metal-faced valves.

A-5-5.5 Tests should be made by drawing a sample of the solution from valve B two or three times during the freezing season, especially if it has been necessary to drain the building sprinkler system for repairs, changes, etc. A small hydrometer should be used so that a small sample will be sufficient. When water appears at valve B or when the test sample indicates that the solution has become weakened, empty the entire system and recharge as previously described.

A-5-6.1.3(a) Outlets should be provided at critical points on sprinkler system piping to accommodate attachment of pressure gages for test purposes.

A-6-1.1.1 The water supply should be capable of furnishing the total demand for all exposure sprinklers operating simultaneously for protection against the exposure fire under consideration for a duration of not less than 60 minutes.

A-6-1.2.4 Spacing between approved fire detection devices should not exceed 30 ft (9.1 m) on buildings of less than three stories in height, and not exceed 40 ft (12.1 m) on buildings three or more stories in height. On buildings in excess of eight stories in height, there shall be at least one line of fire detectors for each eight stories with fire detectors staggered. One line of fire detectors should be located close up under the cornice, eave, or outside parapet.

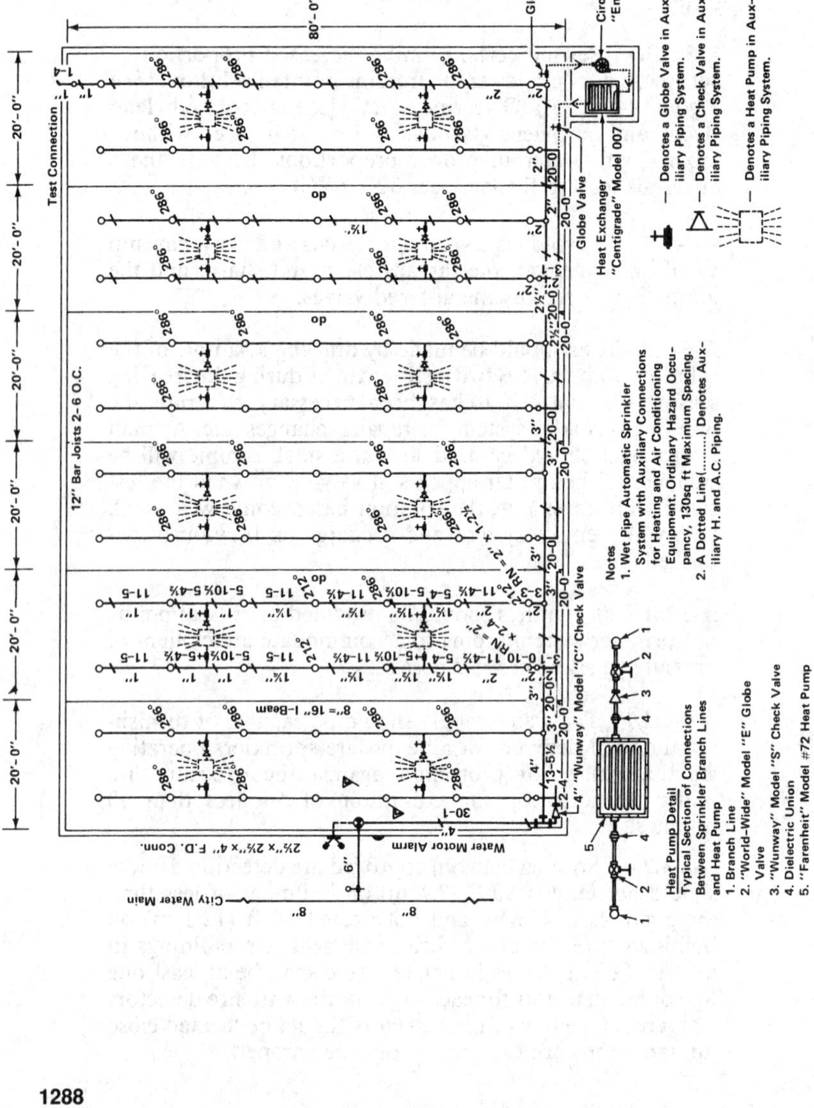
Test Connection
12" Bar Joists 2-6 O.C.
8" = 16" I-Beam
80'-0"
20'-0"
Globe Valve
Circulating Pump "Empellor" Model PS-1
Heat Exchanger "Centigrade" Model 007
4" "Wunway" Model "C" Check Valve
Water Motor Alarm
2½" x 2½" x 4" F.D. Conn.
City Water Main
— Denotes a Globe Valve in Auxiliary Piping System.
— Denotes a Check Valve in Auxiliary Piping System.
— Denotes a Heat Pump in Auxiliary Piping System.
Notes
1. Wet Pipe Automatic Sprinkler System with Auxiliary Connections for Heating and Air Conditioning Equipment. Ordinary Hazard Occupancy, 130sq ft Maximum Spacing.
2. A Dotted Line(.........) Denotes Auxiliary H. and A.C. Piping.
Heat Pump Detail
Typical Section of Connections Between Sprinkler Branch Lines and Heat Pump
1. Branch Line
2. "World-Wide" Model "E" Globe Valve
3. "Wunway" Model "S" Check Valve
4. Dielectric Union
5. "Farenheit" Model #72 Heat Pump

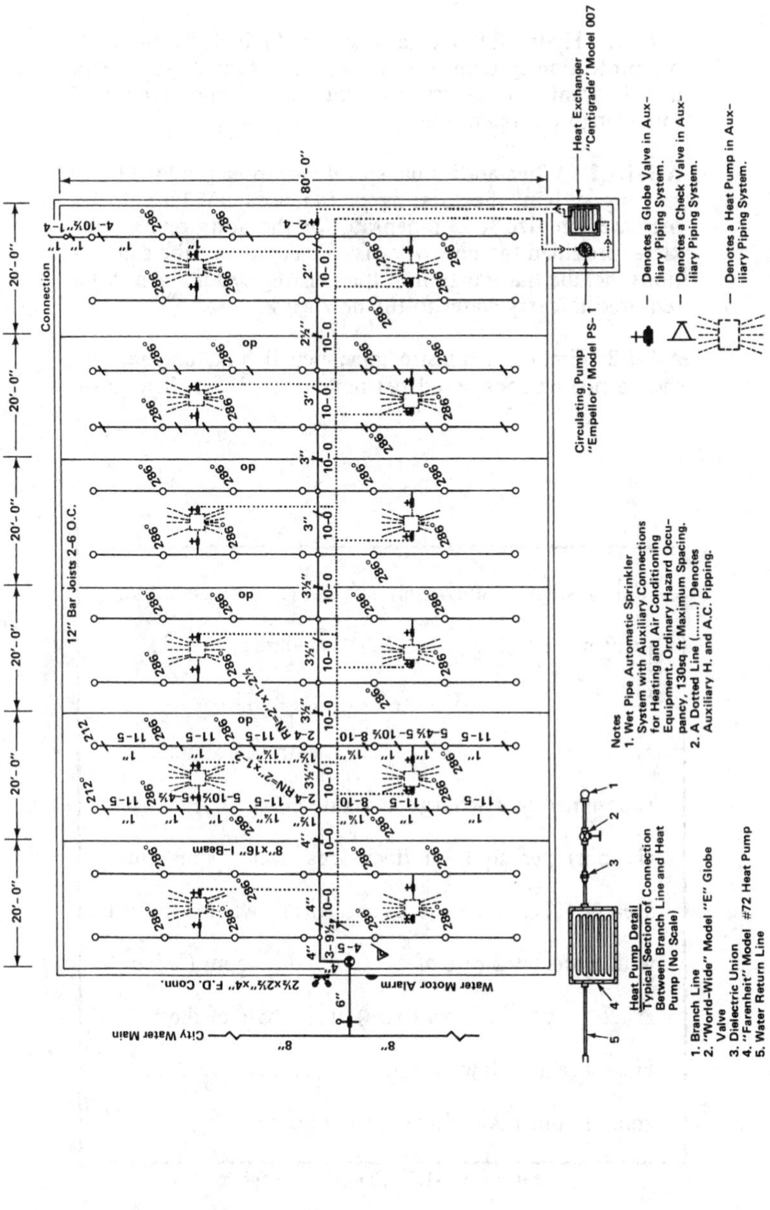

20'-0"
20'-0"
20'-0"
20'-0"
20'-0"
20'-0"
Connection
12" Bar Joists 2-6 O.C.
8"x16" I-Beam
80'-0"
City Water Main
8"
8"
6"
Water Motor Alarm
2½x2½"x4" F.D. Conn.
Heat Exchanger "Centigrade" Model 007
Circulating Pump "Empellor" Model PS- 1
Heat Pump Detail
Typical Section of Connection Between Branch Line and Heat Pump (No Scale)
1. Branch Line
2. "World-Wide" Model "E" Globe Valve
3. Dielectric Union
4. "Farenheit" Model #72 Heat Pump
5. Water Return Line
Notes
1. Wet Pipe Automatic Sprinkler System with Auxiliary Connections for Heating and Air Conditioning Equipment. Ordinary Hazard Occupancy, 130sq ft Maximum Spacing.
2. A Dotted Line (........) Denotes Auxiliary H. and A.C. Pipping.
— Denotes a Globe Valve in Auxiliary Piping System.
— Denotes a Check Valve in Auxiliary Piping System.
— Denotes a Heat Pump in Auxiliary Piping System.

Figures A-5-6.1.10(a) and (b) Working Plans for Circulating Closed-Loop Systems.

A-6-2.1 Valves should be so located as to be easily accessible.

A-6-4.1 Hydraulic calculations should include all other fire protection systems or devices, such as inside sprinklers and hydrants, to determine that there is no danger of impairing their operation.

A-7-1.1.2 When additional sprinkler piping is added to an existing system, the existing piping does not have to be increased in size to compensate for the additional sprinklers, provided the new work is calculated and the calculations include that portion of the existing system as may be required to carry water to the new work.

A-7-1.2 Embossed plastic tape, pencil, ink, crayon, etc. should not be considered permanent markings. The pres-

This system as shown on .... company
print no. .... dated ....
for ....
at .... contract no. ....
is designed to discharge at a rate of .... gpm
(L/min) per sq ft of floor area over a maximum
area of .... sq ft (m^2) when supplied
with water at a rate of .... gpm (L/min)
at .... psi (bars) at the base of the riser.
Hose stream allowance of ....
gpm (L/min) is included in the above.

Figure A-7-1.2 Sample Nameplate.

sure values should be rounded to the nearest psi (0.1 bar) and discharge flow to the nearest 5 gpm (20 L/min) increment. The nameplate should be secured to the riser with durable wire, chain, or equivalent.

A-7-2.3 Designers should consult with the authority having jurisdiction on the water supply to be used in system calculations prior to system design and calculation.

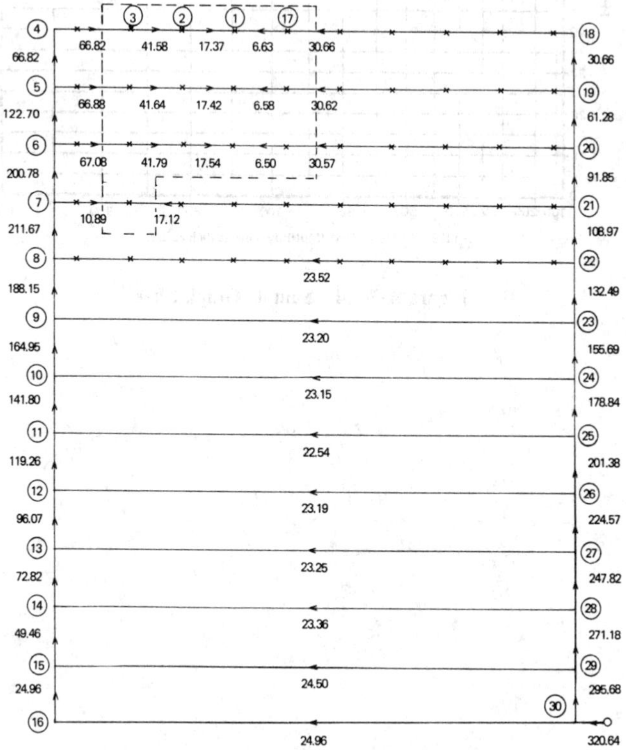
3
2
1
17
4
66.82
41.58
17.37
6.63
30.66
18
66.82
30.66
5
66.88
41.64
17.42
6.58
30.62
19
122.70
61.28
6
67.08
41.79
17.54
6.50
30.57
20
200.78
91.85
7
10.89
17.12
21
211.67
108.97
8
23.52
22
188.15
132.49
9
23.20
23
164.95
155.69
10
23.15
24
141.80
178.84
11
22.54
25
119.26
201.38
12
23.19
26
96.07
224.57
13
23.25
27
72.82
247.82
14
23.36
28
49.46
271.18
15
24.50
29
24.96
295.68
30
16
24.96
320.64

Figure A-7-3.3(o) Flow Quantities and Direction.

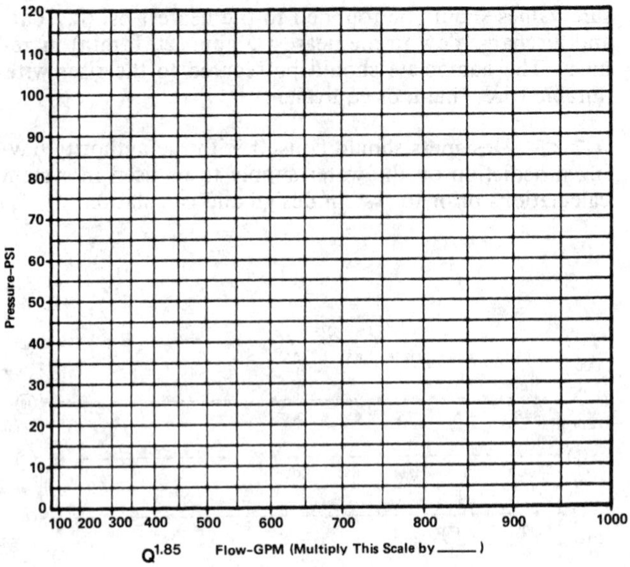
Pressure–PSI
120
110
100
90
80
70
60
50
40
30
20
10
0
100 200 300 400 500 600 700 800 900 1000
$Q^{1.85}$
Flow-GPM (Multiply This Scale by ______)

Figure A-7-3.4 Sample Graph Sheet.

(Figure No. A-7-3.3 appears on the following pages.)

Contract No. ____________________ Sheet No. __________ of __________

Name & Location ____

Nozzle Type & Location	Flow in GPM (L/min)	Pipe Size in.	Fitting & Devices	Pipe Eqiv. Length	Friction Loss psi/ft. (bars/m)	Req. Psi. (bars)	Normal Pressure	Notes
	q			lgth.		Pt	Pt	
				ftg.		Pf	Pv	
	Q			tot.		Pe	Pn	
	q			lgth.		Pt	Pt	
				ftg.		Pf	Pv	
	Q			tot.		Pe	Pn	
	q			lgth.		Pt	Pt	
				ftg.		Pf	Pv	
	Q			tot.		Pe	Pn	
	q			lgth.		Pt	Pt	
				ftg.		Pf	Pv	
	Q			tot.		Pe	Pn	
	q			lgth.		Pt	Pt	
				ftg.		Pf	Pv	
	Q			tot.		Pe	Pn	
	q			lgth.		Pt	Pt	
				ftg.		Pf	Pv	
	Q			tot.		Pe	Pn	
	q			lgth.		Pt	Pt	
				ftg.		Pf	Pv	
	Q			tot.		Pe	Pn	
	q			lgth.		Pt	Pt	
				ftg.		Pf	Pv	
	Q			tot.		Pe	Pn	

q	lgth.	Pt	Pt
	ftg.	Pf	Pv
Q	tot.	Pe	Pn
q	lgth.	Pt	Pt
	ftg.	Pf	Pv
Q	tot.	Pe	Pn
q	lgth.	Pt	Pt
	ftg.	Pf	Pv
Q	tot.	Pe	Pn
q	lgth.	Pt	Pt
	ftg.	Pf	Pv
Q	tot.	Pe	Pn
q	lgth.	Pt	Pt
	ftg.	Pf	Pv
Q	tot.	Pe	Pn
q	lgth.	Pt	Pt
	ftg.	Pf	Pv
Q	tot.	Pe	Pn
q	lgth.	Pt	Pt
	ftg.	Pf	Pv
Q	tot.	Pe	Pn
q	lgth.	Pt	Pt
	ftg.	Pf	Pv
Q	tot.	Pe	Pn
q	lgth.	Pt	Pt
	ftg.	Pf	Pv
Q	tot.	Pe	Pn
q	lgth.	Pt	Pt
	ftg.	Pf	Pv
Q	tot.	Pe	Pn

Figure A-7-3.3 Sample Work Sheet.

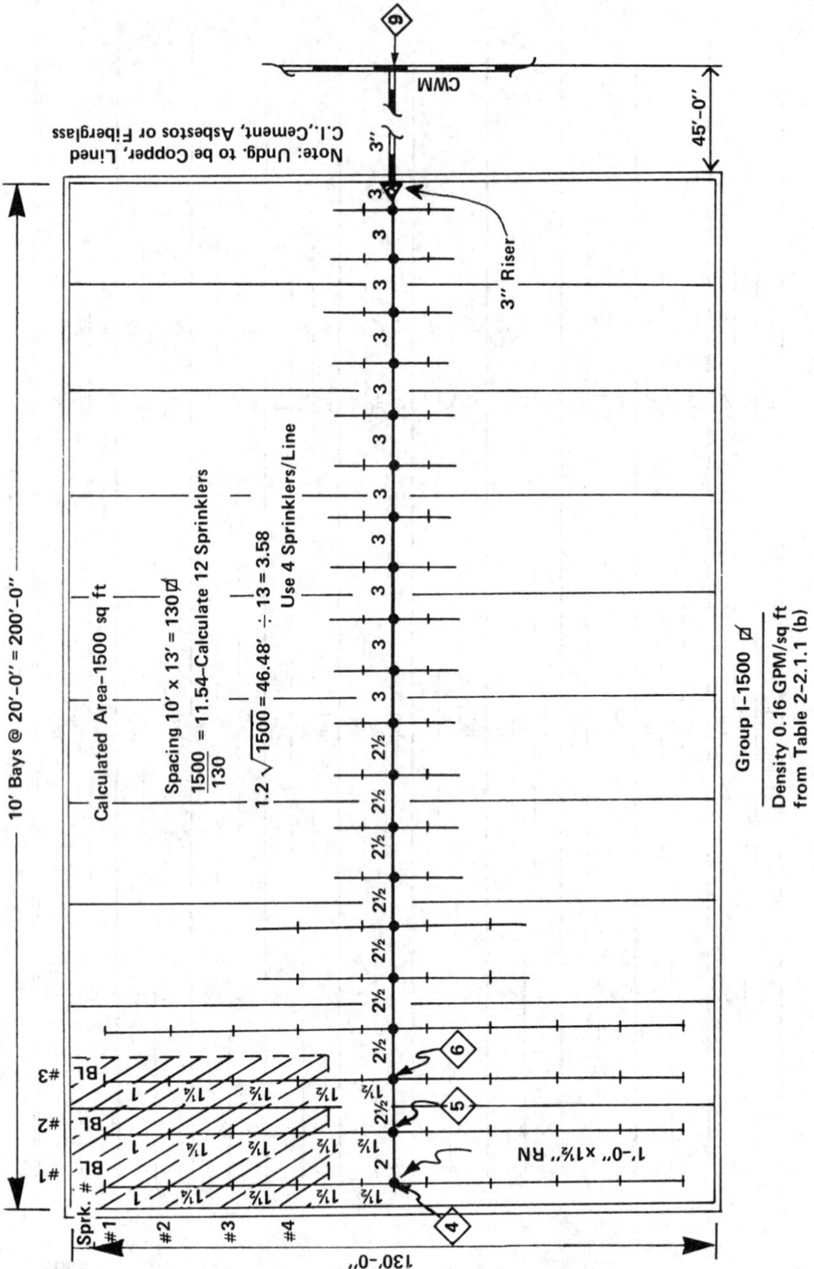
10' Bays @ 20'-0" = 200'-0"
Calculated Area–1500 sq ft
Spacing 10' × 13' = 130 ⌀
1500/130 = 11.54–Calculate 12 Sprinklers
1.2 √1500 = 46.48' ÷ 13 = 3.58
Use 4 Sprinklers/Line
Note: Undg. to be Copper, Lined C.I., Cement, Asbestos or Fiberglass
CWM
3"
45'-0"
3" Riser
Group I–1500 ⌀
Density 0.16 GPM/sq ft from Table 2-2.1.1 (b)
1'-0" × 1½" RN
130'-0"
Sprk. #
#1
#2
#3
#4
BL #1
BL #2
BL #3
4
5
6
9

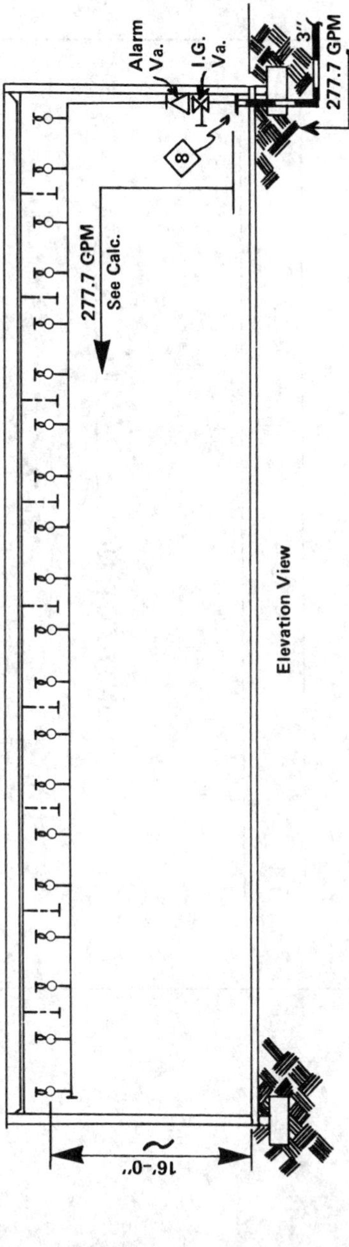
Alarm Va.
I.G. Va.
3"
277.7 GPM
8
277.7 GPM
See Calc.
Elevation View
16'-0"

◇ — Denotes Reference Step.

For SI Units: 1 in. = 25.4 mm; 1 ft = 0.3048 m.

Figure A-7-4.3(a) Hydraulic Calculation Example.

HYDRAULIC CALCULATIONS

FOR

ABC COMPANY

CONTRACT NO. 4001

DATE 1-7-75

DESIGN DATA—

OCCUPANCY CLASSIFICATION ORD. GR. 1

DENSITY 0.16 GPM/SQ. FT.

AREA OF APPLICATION 1500 SQ. FT.

COVERAGE PER SPRINKLER 130 SQ. FT.

NO. OF SPRINKLERS CALCULATED 12

TOTAL WATER REQUIRED 650 GPM.
INCLUDING HOSE STREAMS.

NAME OF CONTRACTOR ______

NAME OF DESIGNER ______

AUTHORITY HAVING JURISDICTION ______

Figure A-7-4.3(b) Calculation Coversheet.

CONTRACT NAME *GROUP I 1500 ⊄* SHEET *2* OF *3*

STEP NO.	NOZZLE IDENT. AND LOCATION	FLOW IN G.P.M.	PIPE SIZE	PIPE FITTINGS AND DEVICES	EQUIV. PIPE LENGTH	FRICTION LOSS P.S.I./FOOT	PRESSURE SUMMARY	NORMAL PRESSURE	D=0.16 GPM/⊄ NOTES K=5.65	REF. STEP
1	1 BL-1	q	1		L 13.0	C=120	Pt 13.6	Pt	q=130X.16=20.8	
					F		Pe	Pv		
		Q 20.8			T 13.0	.140	Pf 1.8	Pn		
2	2	q 22.2	1 1/4		L 13.0		Pt 15.4	Pt	$q=5.65\sqrt{15.4}$	
					F		Pe	Pv		
		Q 43.0			T 13.0	.141	Pf 1.8	Pn		
3	3	q 23.4	1 1/2		L 13.0		Pt 17.2	Pt	$q=5.65\sqrt{17.2}$	
					F		Pe	Pv		
		Q 66.4			T 13.0	.149	Pf 1.9	Pn		
4	4 DN RN	q 24.7	1 1/2	2T-16	L 20.5		Pt 19.1	Pt	$q=5.65\sqrt{19.1}$	4
					F 16.0		Pe	Pv		
		Q 91.1			T 36.5	.267	Pf 9.7	Pn		
5	CM TO BL-2	q	2		L 10.0		Pt 28.8	Pt	$K=\frac{91.1}{\sqrt{28.8}}$	5
					F		Pe	Pv		
		Q 91.1			T 10.0	.079	Pf .8	Pn	K= 16.98	

6		BL-2 CM	q 92.4	$2\frac{1}{2}$		L 10.0		Pt 29.6	Pt		
		TO				F		Pe	Pv	$q=16.98\sqrt{29.6}$	6
		BL-3	Q 183.5			T 10.0	.122	Pf 1.2	Pn		
7		BL-3	q 94.2	$2\frac{1}{2}$		L 70.0		Pt 30.8	Pt		
		CM				F		Pe	Pv	$q=16.98\sqrt{30.8}$	
			Q 277.7			T 70.0	.262	Pf 18.3	Pn		
8		CM			E 5	L 119.0		Pt 49.1	Pt		
		TO	q	3	AV 15	F		Pe 6.5	Pv	Pe=15 x .433	8
		F/S	Q 277.7		GV 1	T 140.0	.091	Pf 12.7	Pn		
9		THRU UNDER-			E 5	L 50.0	C=150	Pt 68.3	Pt	COPPER	
		GROUND TO	q	3	GV 1	F 32.0	TYPE "M"	Pe	Pv	21 X 1.51 = 32	9
		CITY MAIN	Q 277.7		T 15	T 82.2	.069	Pf 5.7	Pn		
						L		Pt 74.0	Pt		
			q			F		Pe	Pv		
			Q			T		Pf	Pn		
						L		Pt	Pt		
			q			F		Pe	Pv		
			Q			T		Pf	Pn		
								Pt			

Figure A-7-4.3(c) Hydraulic Calculations.

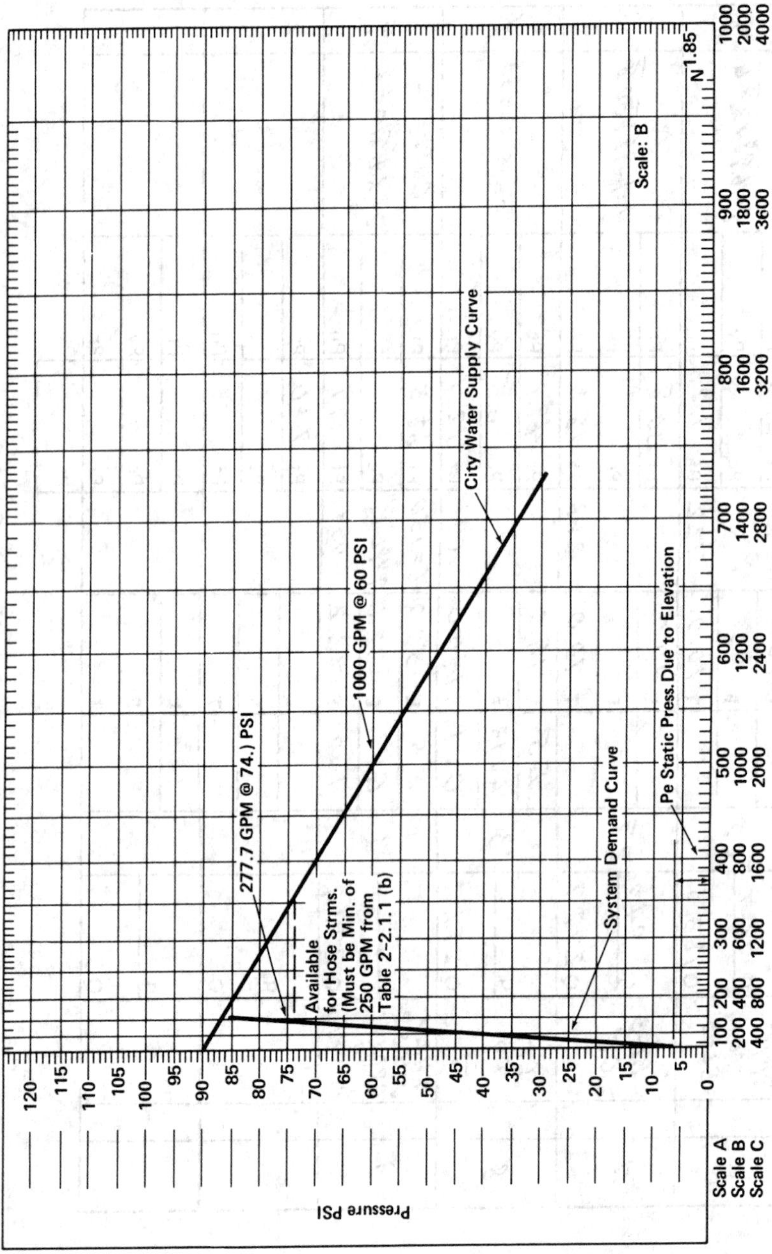
Pressure PSI
Scale A
Scale B
Scale C
120
115
110
105
100
95
90
85
80
75
70
65
60
55
50
45
40
35
30
25
20
15
10
5
0
100 200 300 400 500 600 700 800 900 1000
200 400 600 800 1000 1200 1400 1600 1800 2000
400 800 1200 1600 2000 2400 2800 3200 3600 4000
Water Flow GPM
$N^{1.85}$
Scale: B
City Water Supply Curve
1000 GPM @ 60 PSI
277.7 GPM @ 74.) PSI
Available for Hose Strms. (Must be Min. of 250 GPM from Table 2-2.1.1 (b)
System Demand Curve
Pe Static Press. Due to Elevation

Figure A-7-4.3(d) Hydraulic Graph.

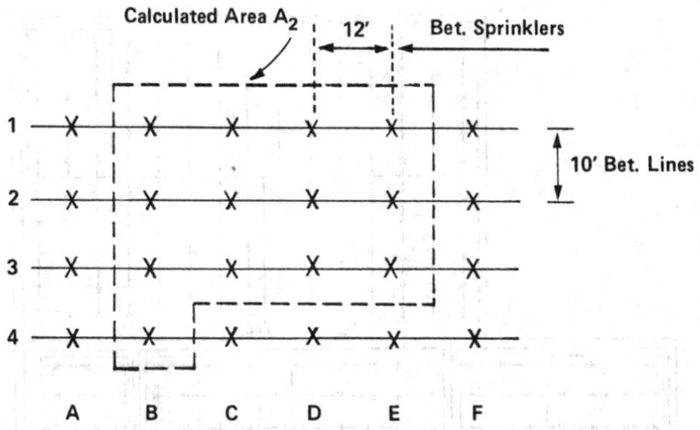
Calculated Area A_2
12′
Bet. Sprinklers
10′ Bet. Lines
1
2
3
4
A
B
C
D
E
F

Figure A-7-4.3.1(a) Example of Determining the Number of Sprinklers to Be Calculated.

NOTE 1: For gridded systems, the extra sprinkler (or sprinklers) on branch line 4 may be placed in any adjacent location from B to E at the designer's option.

NOTE 2: For tree and looped systems, the extra sprinkler on line 4 should be placed closest to the cross main.

Figure A-7-4.3.1(a) Example:

Assume a remote area of 1,500 sq ft with sprinkler coverage of 120 sq ft

$$\text{Total sprinklers to calculate} = \frac{\text{Design Area}}{\text{Area per Sprinkler}}$$

$$= \frac{1500}{120} = 12.5, \text{ calculate } 13$$

$$\text{Number of sprinklers on branch line} = \frac{1.2\sqrt{A}}{S}$$

Where A = Design Area

S = Distance Between Sprinklers on Branch Line

Number of sprinklers on branch line $= \frac{1.2\sqrt{1500}}{12} = 3.87$, calculate 4

For SI Units: 1 ft = 0.3048 m; 1 sq ft = 0.0929 m^2.

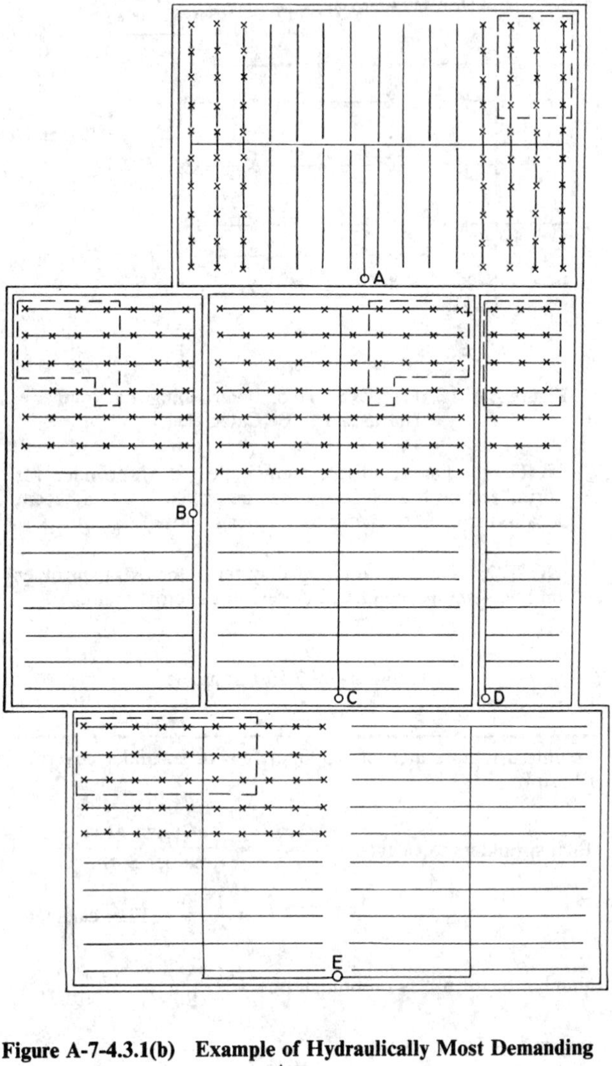
A
B
C
D
E

Figure A-7-4.3.1(b) Example of Hydraulically Most Demanding Area.

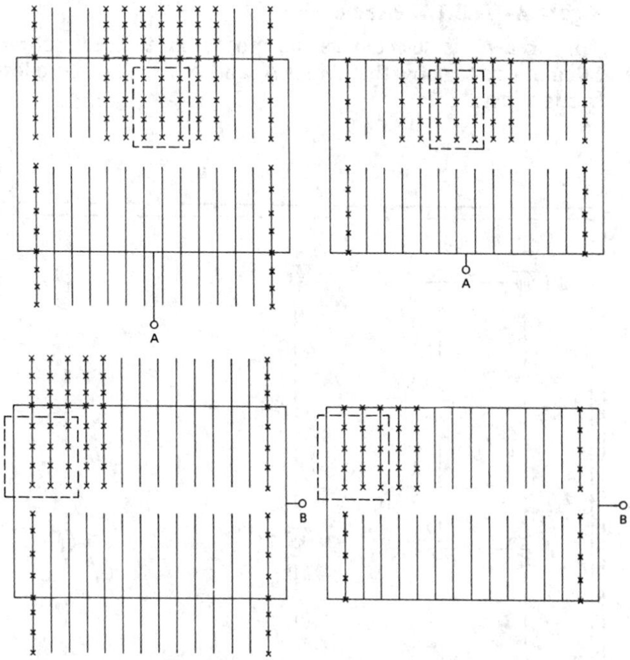
A
A
B
B

Figure A-7-4.3.1(c) Example of Hydraulically Most Demanding Area.

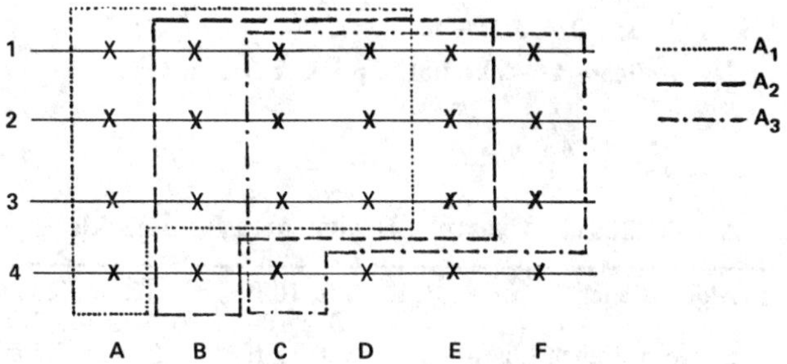
1
2
3
4
A
B
C
D
E
F
A_1
A_2
A_3

Figure A-7-4.3.1.1 Example of Determining the Most Remote Area for a Gridded System.

Figure A-7-4.3.1.1 Example:

If Area A_2 is selected as the most remote area, submit calculations to show that Areas A_1 and A_3 are subject to less friction loss.

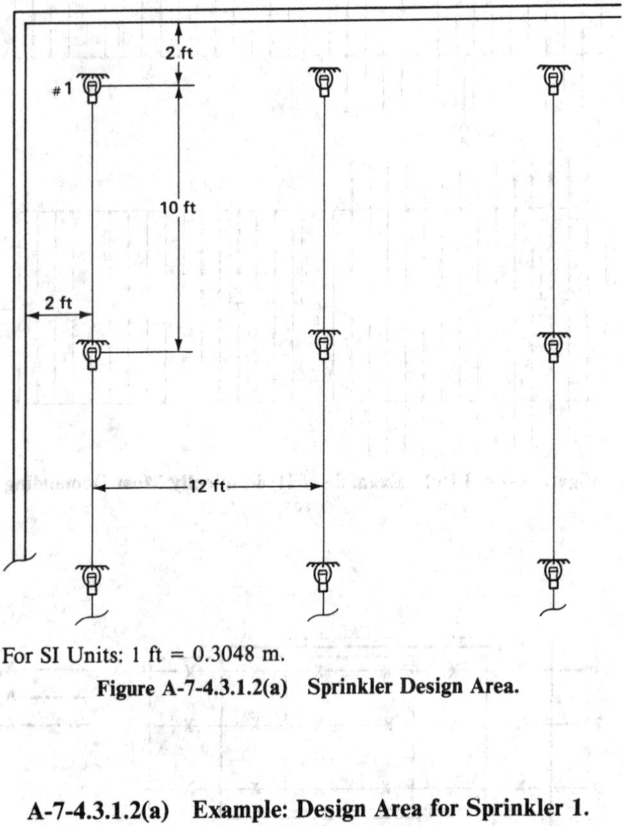
2 ft
#1
10 ft
2 ft
12 ft

For SI Units: 1 ft = 0.3048 m.

Figure A-7-4.3.1.2(a) Sprinkler Design Area.

A-7-4.3.1.2(a) Example: Design Area for Sprinkler 1.

1. Along Branch Lines—	2 ft, 10 ft S = 10	(0.6 m, 3.0 m) (S = 3.0)
2. Between Branch Lines—	2 ft, 12 ft L = 12	(0.6 m, 3.7 m) (L = 3.7)
3. Design Area—	10 × 12 = 120 sq ft	(3.0 × 3.7) = 11.1 m^2

For SI Units: 1 ft = 0.3048 m; 1 sq ft = 0.0929 m^2.

A-7-4.3.1.2(b) This subsection contemplates a ceiling constructed so as to reasonably assure that a fire on one side of the ceiling will operate sprinklers on one side only. When a ceiling is sufficiently open or of such construction that operation of sprinklers above and below the ceiling may be anticipated, the operation of such additional sprinklers should be considered in the calculations.

A-7-4.3.1.3 When it is not obvious by comparison that the design area selected is the hydraulically most remote, additional calculations should be submitted. The most remote area, distance-wise, is not necessarily the hydraulically most remote area.

A-7-4.3.1.5 The use of sprinklers with differing orifice sizes in situations where different protection areas are needed is not considered balancing. An example would be a room that could be protected with sprinklers having differing orifice size in closet, foyer, and room areas. However, this procedure introduces difficulties when restoring a system to service after operation since it is not always clear which sprinklers go where.

A-7-4.3.1.8 When velocity pressure is included in the calculations, the following assumptions are to be used:

(a) At any flowing outlet along a pipe, except the end outlet, only the normal pressure (P_n) can act on the outlet. At the end outlet the total pressure (P_t) can act. The following are to be considered end outlets:

1. The last flowing sprinkler on a dead-end branch line.

2. The last flowing branch line on a dead-end cross main.

3. Any sprinkler where a flow split occurs on a gridded branch line.

4. Any branch line where a flow split occurs on a loop system.

(b) At any flowing outlet along a pipe except the end outlet, the pressure acting to cause flow from the outlet is equal to the total pressure (P_t) minus the velocity presssure (P_v) on the upstream side.

(c) To find the normal pressure (P_n) at any flowing outlet except the end outlet, assume a flow from the outlet in question and determine the velocity pressure (P_v) for the total flow on the upstream side. Because normal pressure (P_n) equals total pressure (P_t) minus velocity pressure, the value of the normal pressure (P_n) so found should result in an outlet flow approximately equal to the assumed flow. If not, a new value should be assumed and the calculations repeated.

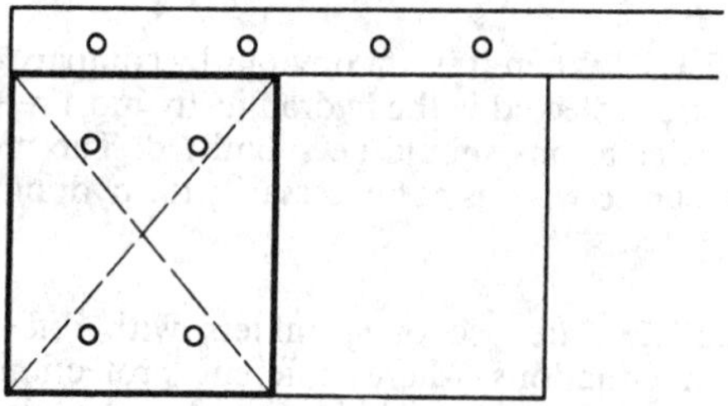

(a)

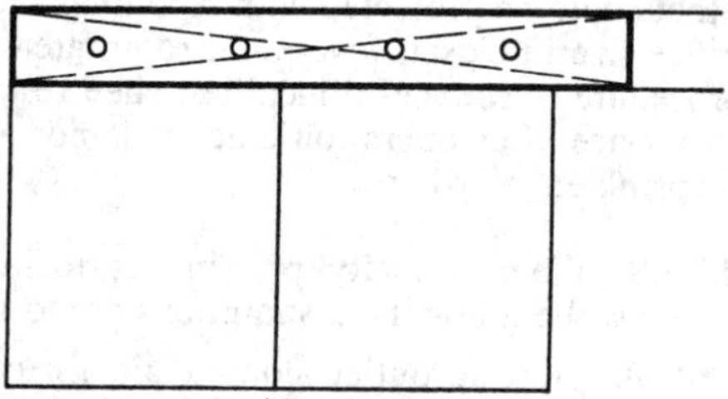

(b)

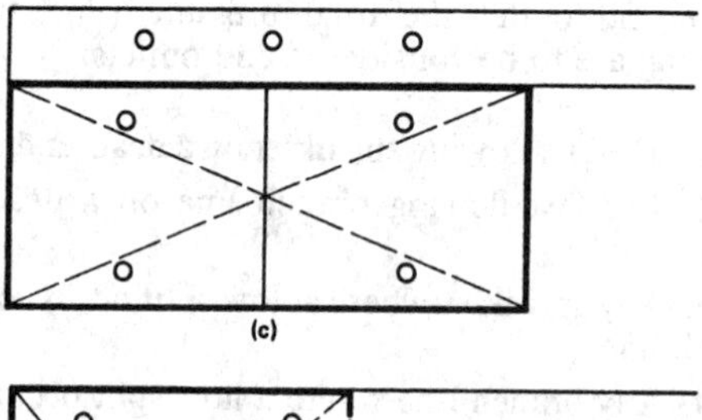

(c)

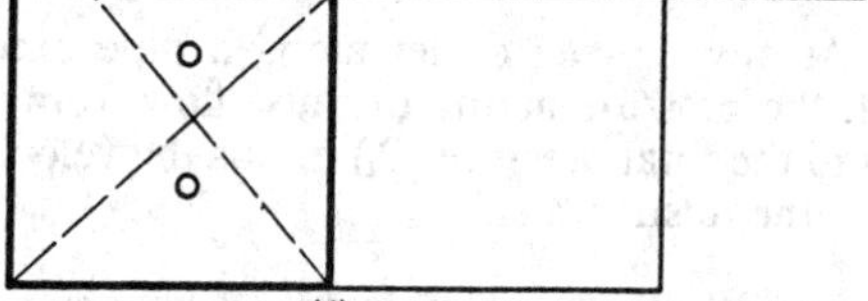

(d)

Calculate Area Indicated By Heavy Outline and X
O Indicates Sprinklers

Figure A-7-4.4.2 Examples of Design Area for Dwelling Units.

A-8 Long Runs of Pipe. When the construction or conditions introduce unusually long runs of pipe or many angles in risers or feed mains, an increase in pipe size over that called for in the schedules may be required to compensate for increased friction losses.

A-8-1 The demonstrated effectiveness of pipe schedule systems is limited to their use with ½-in. (13-mm) orifice sprinklers. The use of other size orifices requires hydraulic calculations to prove their ability to deliver the required amount of water within the available water supply.

A-8-2.3.1 For example, a 2½-in. (64-mm) steel pipe, which is permitted to supply 30 sprinklers, may supply a total of 50 sprinklers where not more than 30 sprinklers are above or below a ceiling.

A-8-3.3.1 For example, a 3-in. (76-mm) steel pipe, which is permitted to supply 40 sprinklers in an Ordinary Hazard area, may supply a total of 60 sprinklers when not more than 40 sprinklers protect the occupied area.

A-9-2.1 Large-drop sprinkler development began with the idea that a sprinkler that would produce a high proportion of large drops would be more effective against high-challenge fires than standard nominal ½-in. and 17/32-in. sprinklers. Large drops are better able to fight their way through the strong updraft generated by a severe fire. The general philosophy behind this idea was to create an offensive weapon for direct attack against the burning fuel, but with as little diminution of defensive capability as possible. As originally conceived, it was supposed that the large drops were the predominant reason for increased effectiveness. It later became evident, however, that other factors such as distribution and pressure play an equal (and possibly more important) role. A consideration of all characteristics indicated that the desired sprinkler would provide high penetration, adequate cooling, reasonable distribution, low skipping potential, and increased discharge capacity.

A-9-2.2 Large-drop sprinklers were developed for use against severe fire challenges requiring sprinkler discharges of 55 gal/min (208 L/min) per sprinkler or more. The sprinklers were designed to deliver a heavy discharge through the strong updrafts generated by high-challenge fires. They depend primarily on direct attack of the burning fuel to gain rapid control of the fire, and to a lesser extent on prewetting and cooling.

Large-drop sprinklers will provide excellent protection against high-challenge fires, but careful design and close adherence to the rules given in Chapter 9 are required. This is especially important because experimental findings indicate that the characteristics of large-drop sprinklers are not the same as those attributed to standard sprinklers.

A-9-2.2.1 Fire tests have not been conducted with large-drop sprinklers over Ordinary and Extra Hazard Occupancies. Therefore, the protection requirements remain unknown.

At a given pressure, large-drop sprinklers will discharge approximately 100 percent and 40 percent more water than standard (½-in.) and large orifice (17/32-in.) sprinklers, respectively.

Large-drop sprinklers were designed to cope with high-challenge fires where high levels of penetration and cooling are required. Since both characteristics fall off sharply at low pressures, large-drop sprinklers cannot be used effectively to compensate for weak water supplies by taking advantage of the increased discharge capacity.

A-9-2.3.3.2 This test data was developed with 2-in. (51-mm) diameter pipe maximum. Riser nipples are required when branch lines exceed 2 in. (51 mm) in diameter.

A-9-2.3.5 It is important that sprinklers in the immediate vicinity of the fire center not skip, and this requirement imposes certain restrictions on the spacing.

A-9-2.3.5.1 Tests involving areas of coverage over 100 sq ft (9.3 m^2) are limited in number, and the use of areas of coverage over 100 sq ft (9.3 m^2) should be carefully considered.

A-9-2.3.7 If all other factors are held constant, the operating time of the first sprinkler will vary exponentially with the distance between the ceiling and deflector. At distances greater than 7 in. (178 mm), for other than open wood joist construction, the delayed operating time will permit the fire to gain headway, with the result that substantially more sprinklers operate. At distances less than 7 in. (178 mm), other effects come into play. Changes in distribution, penetration, and cooling nullify the advantage gained by faster operation. The net result is again increased fire damage accompanied by an increase in the number of sprinklers operated. The optimum clearance between deflectors and ceiling is, therefore, 7 in. (178 mm). For open wood joist construction the optimum clearance between deflectors and the bottom of joists is 3½ in. (89 mm).

A-9-2.3.9 The plugging of a single sprinkler in the vicinity of the fire origin can cause a significant increase in the number of operating sprinklers as well as an increase in fire damage. Therefore, it is essential that the sprinkler piping be kept free of obstructing material.

Fouling or plugging of piping or heads may be prevented by several methods: sound installation practices, including the provision of screens or strainers when necessary; avoidance of dry-pipe systems with their history of plugging; and a high level of maintenance.

A-9-2.3.9.2 Investigations should be conducted more frequently when justified by local conditions.

A-9-2.3.10 To a great extent, large-drop sprinklers rely on direct attack to gain rapid control of both the burning fuel and ceiling temperatures. Therefore, interference with the discharge pattern and obstructions to the distribution should be avoided.

A-9-2.4 Large scale fire testing has shown that large-drop sprinkler systems designed per the rules of Chapter 9 to provide the minimum operating pressures for the number of design sprinklers for the specific hazards of Table A-9-2.4 will adequately control the fire.

A-9-2.4.1 In testing where discharge density and all other conditions (except pressure and spacing) remained constant, sprinkler demand area, steel temperatures, and fire damage all exhibited a marked increase as the spacing was decreased. The importance of these findings cannot be overemphasized. They state clearly that the term density has no meaning when applied to large-drop sprinklers and it (density) cannot be used as a design parameter.

Table A-9-2.4 Pressure and Number of Design Sprinklers for Various Hazards (Note 6) for Large-Drop Sprinklers

Minimum Operating Pressure (Note 1), psi (bar)	25 (1.7)	50 (3.4)	75 (5.2)
Hazard (Note 2)		Number Design Sprinklers	
Palletized Storage			
Class I, II, and III commodities up to 25 ft (7.6 m) with maximum 10 ft (3.0 m) clearance to ceiling	15	Note 3	Note 3
Class IV commodities up to 20 ft (6.1 m) with maximum 10 ft (3.0 m) clearance to ceiling	20	15	Note 3
Unexpanded plastics up to 20 ft (6.1 m) with maximum 10 ft (3.0 m) clearance to ceiling	25	15	Note 3
Idle wood pallets up to 20 ft (6.1 m) with maximum 10 ft (3.0 m) clearance to ceiling	15	Note 3	Note 3
Solid-Piled Storage			
Class I, II, and III commodities up to 20 ft (6.1 m) with maximum 10 ft (3.0 m) clearance to ceiling	15	Note 3	Note 3
Class IV commodities and unexpanded plastics up to 20 ft (6.1 m) with maximum 10 ft (3.0 m) clearance to ceiling	Does Not Apply	15	Note 3
Double-Row Rack Storage with Minimum 5½ ft (1.7 m) Aisle Width (Note 4)			
Class I and II commodities up to 25 ft (7.6 m) with maximum 5 ft (1.5 m) clearance to ceiling	20	Note 3	Note 3
Class I, II, and III commodities up to 20 ft (6.1 m) with maximum 10 ft (3.0 m) clearance to ceiling	15	Note 3	Note 3
Class IV commodities up to 20 ft (6.1 m) with maximum 10 ft (3.0 m) clearance to ceiling	Does Not Apply	20	15
Unexpanded plastics up to 20 ft (6.1 m) with maximum 10 ft (3.0 m) clearance to ceiling	Does Not Apply	30	20
Unexpanded plastics up to 20 ft (6.1 m) with maximum 10 ft (3.0 m) clearance to ceiling (Note 7)	Does Not Apply	20	Note 3

Class IV commodities and unexpanded plastics up to 20 ft (6.1 m) with maximum 5 ft (1.5 m) clearance to ceiling	Does Not Apply	15	Note 3
On-End Storage of Roll Paper (Note 5)			
Heavyweight paper, in closed array, banded in open array, or banded or unbanded in a standard array, up to 26 ft (7.9 m) with a maximum 34 ft (10.4 m) clearance to ceiling	Does Not Apply	15	Note 3
Any grade of paper, EXCEPT LIGHTWEIGHT paper, with stacks in closed array, or banded or unbanded standard array up to 20 ft (6.1 m) with maximum 10 ft (3.0 m) clearance to ceiling	Does Not Apply	15	Note 3
Medium weight paper completely wrapped (sides and ends) in one or more layers of heavyweight paper, or lightweight paper in two or more layers of heavyweight paper with stacks in closed array, banded in open array, or banded or unbanded in a standard array, up to 26 ft (7.9 m) with maximum 34 ft (10.4 m) clearance to ceiling	Does Not Apply	15	Note 3
Record Storage			
Paper records and/or computer tapes in multitier steel shelving up to 5 ft (1.5 m) in width and with aisles 30 in. (76 cm) or wider, without catwalks in the aisles, up to 15 ft (4.6 m) with maximum 5 ft (1.5 m) clearance to ceiling	15	Note 3	Note 3
Same as above, but with catwalks of expanded metal or metal grid with minimum 50 percent open area, in the aisles	Does Not Apply	15	Note 3

Notes:

1. Open Wood Joist Construction. Testing with open wood joist construction showed that each joist channel should be fully firestopped to its full depth at intervals not exceeding 20 ft (6.1 m). In unfirestopped open wood joist construction, or if firestops are installed at intervals exceeding 20 ft (6.1 m), the minimum operating pressures should be increased by 40 percent.
2. Building steel required no special protection for the occupancies listed.
3. The higher pressure will successfully control the fire, but the required number of design sprinklers should not be reduced from that required for the lower pressure.
4. In addition to the transverse flue spaces required by NFPA 231C, minimum 6 in. (152 mm) longitudinal flue spaces were maintained.
5. See NFPA 231F for definitions.
6. Unless otherwise specified the sprinklers used in the tests were high temperature rating.
7. Based on tests using sprinklers of ordinary temperature rating.

In testing the effect of discharge pressure, series of tests were run with two different fuel types. Although the relationship of decreased number of operated sprinklers with increased pressure held, the associated curves did not parallel each other. Therefore, it is not possible to extrapolate the protection requirements from one hazard to a higher hazard, nor is it possible to develop a curve from one test point. However, the protection requirements developed for a particular hazard (through large-scale fire tests) may be applied safely to hazards known to be less severe, provided that the less severe hazards are arranged in the same configuration.

A-9-3.1 It is important to realize that the effectiveness of these highly tested and engineered sprinklers depends on the combination of fast response and the quality and uniformity of the sprinkler discharge. It should also be realized that ESFR sprinklers cannot be relied upon to provide fire "control," let alone suppression, if they are used outside the guidelines specified in Section 9-3.

A-9-3.3.6 Limitations on spacing and distances between sprinklers are based on testing that shows that ESFR sprinklers cannot distribute water sufficiently to achieve suppression when these limitations are exceeded.

Table A-9-3.4.1 Protectible Occupancies for ESFR Sprinklers

Type of Storage	Commodity	Maximum Height of Storage	Maximum Height of the Building
Single-, double-, and multiple-row and portable rack storage (no open-top containers or solid shelves), and solid-piled or palletized storage.	Cartoned unexpanded plastics Class I through IV commodities. Cartoned polyurethane (*not* polystyrene) foamed-in-place packaging (encapsulated or nonencapsulated)	25	30
Roll paper on end, open/standard/closed array, banded or unbanded	Heavyweight paper	20	30
Roll paper on end, open/standard/closed array, banded or unbanded	Mediumweight paper	20	30
Aerosol storage	To be determined		

Appendix B

This Appendix is not a part of the requirements of this NFPA document, but is included for information purposes only.

B-1 The following appendix contains useful and explanatory information about subjects related to the installation of sprinkler systems but not covered in the test.

B-2 Water Supplies.

B-2-1 Testing of Water Supply.

B-2-1.1 To determine the value of public water as a supply for automatic sprinkler systems, it is generally necessary to make a flow test to determine how much water can be discharged at a residual pressure at a rate sufficient to give the required residual pressure under the roof (with the volume flow hydraulically translated to the base of the riser) — i.e., a pressure head represented by the height of the building plus the required residual pressure.

B-2-1.2 The proper method of conducting this test is to use two hydrants in the vicinity of the property. The static pressure should be measured on the hydrant in front of or nearest to the property and the water allowed to flow from the hydrant next nearest the property, preferably the one farthest from the source of supply if the main is fed only one way. The residual pressure will be that indicated at the hydrant where water is not flowing.

B-2-1.3 Referring to Figure B-2, the method of conducting the flow tests is as follows:

1. Attach gage to hydrant (A) and obtain static pressure.

2. Either attach second gage to hydrant (B) or use pitot tube at outlet. Have hydrant (B) opened wide and read pressure at both hydrants.

3. Use the pressure at (B) to compute the gallons flowing and read the gage on (A) to determine the residual pressure or that which will be available on the top line of sprinklers in the property.

B-2-1.4 Water pressure in pounds for a given height in feet equals height multiplied by 0.434.

B-2-1.5 In making flow tests, whether from hydrants or from nozzles attached to hose, always measure the size

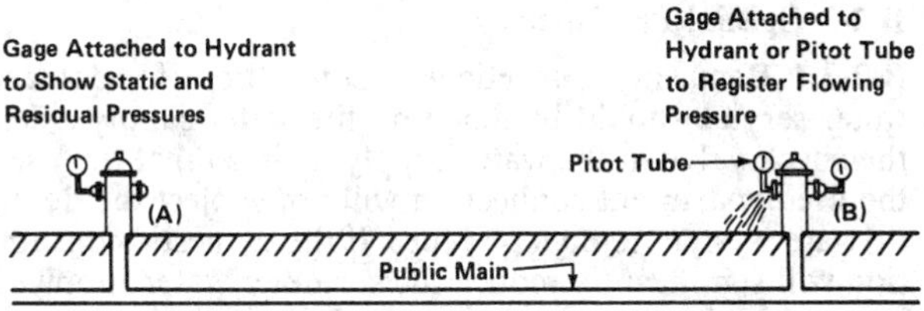
Gage Attached to Hydrant
to Show Static and
Residual Pressures
Gage Attached to
Hydrant or Pitot Tube
to Register Flowing
Pressure
Pitot Tube
(A)
(B)
Public Main

Figure B-2 Method of Conducting Flow Tests.

of the orifice. While hydrant outlets are usually 2½ in. (64 mm) they are sometimes smaller and occasionally larger. The UL play pipe is 1⅛ in. (29 mm) and 1¾ in. (44 mm) with tip removed, but occasionally nozzles will be 1 in. (25 mm) or 1¼ in. (33 mm), and with the tip removed the opening may be only 1½ in. (38 mm).

B-2-1.6 The pitot tube should be held approximately one-half the diameter of the hydrant or nozzle opening away from the opening. It should be held in the center of the stream, except that in using hydrant outlets the stream should be explored to get the average pressure.

B-2-2 Interconnection of Water Supplies.

B-2-2.1 All main water supplies should be connected with the sprinkler system at the base of the riser, except that where a gravity or pressure tank or both constitute the only automatic source of water supply, permission may be given to connect the tank or tanks with the sprinkler system at the top of the riser.

B-2-2.2 Where a gravity tank and a pressure tank are connected to a common riser, approved means should be provided to prevent residual air pressure in the pressure tank (after water has been drained from it) from holding the gravity tank check valve closed, a condition known as air lock. Under normal conditions, air lock may be conveniently prevented in new equipment by connecting the gravity tank and pressure tank discharge pipes 45 ft (13.7 m) or more below the bottom of the gravity tank and placing the gravity tank check valve at the level of this connection.

B-2-3 Special Provisions.

B-2-3.1 Domestic Connections. Connections for domestic water service should be made on the water supply side of the check valve in the water supply main so that the use of the fire department connection will not subject the domestic water system to high pressure. If the domestic consumption will significantly reduce the sprinkler water supply, an increase in the size of the pipe supplying both the domestic and sprinkler water may be justified. Circulation of water in sprinkler pipes is objectionable, owing to increased corrosion, deposits of sediment, and condensation drip from pipes.

Aboveground domestic connections to sprinkler system piping should be metallic pipe or suitably protected. Nonmetallic aboveground domestic pipe connections may fail during a fire, diverting water from the sprinklers.

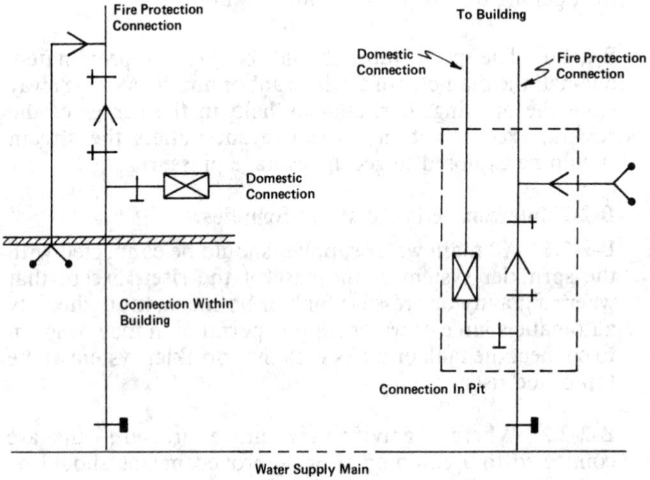
Fire Protection Connection
Domestic Connection
Connection Within Building
To Building
Domestic Connection
Fire Protection Connection
Connection In Pit
Water Supply Main

Figure B-2-3.1 Connection for Domestic Water.

B-2-3.2 Water Hammer. When connections are made from water mains subject to severe water hammer [especially when pressure is in excess of 100 psi (6.9 bars)], it may be desirable to provide either a relief valve, properly connected to a drain, or an air chamber in the connection. If an air chamber is used, it should be located close to where the pipe comes through the wall and on the supply side of all other valves and so located as to take the full force of water hammer. Air chambers should have a capacity of not less than 4 cu ft (0.12 m^3), should be controlled by an approved indicating valve, and should be provided with a drain at the bottom and an air vent with control valve and plug to permit inspection.

B-2-3.3 Penstocks, Flumes, etc. Water supply connections from penstocks, flumes, rivers, or lakes should be arranged to avoid mud and sediment, and should be provided with approved double removable screens or approved strainers installed in an approved manner.

B-3 System Components.

B-3-1 Sleeves for Pipe Risers. (*See Figure B-3-1.*)

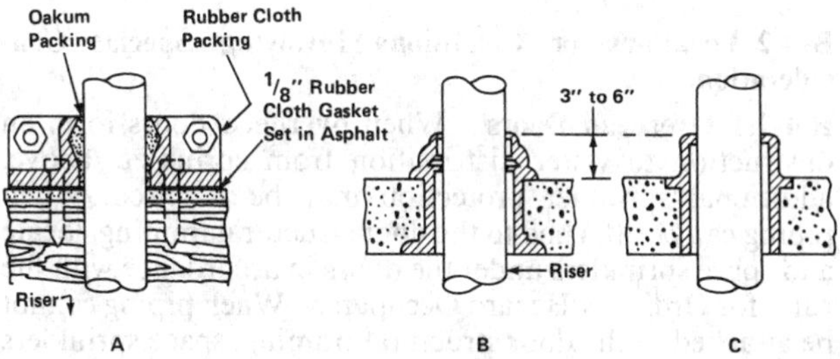
Oakum Packing
Rubber Cloth Packing
1/8" Rubber Cloth Gasket Set in Asphalt
3" to 6"
Riser
Riser
A
B
C

A–For Wood or Concrete Floors; B and C–For Concrete Floors.

For SI Units: 1 in. = 25.4 mm.

Figure B-3-1 Watertight Riser Sleeves.

B-3-1.1 Sprinkler piping passing through floors of concrete or waterproof construction should have properly designed substantial thimbles or sleeves projecting 3 to 6 in. (76 to 152 mm) above the floor to prevent possible floor leakage, except in areas subject to earthquakes. (*See A-3-5.3.1.*) The space between the pipe and sleeve should be caulked with oakum or equivalent material. If floors are of cinder concrete, thimbles or sleeves should extend all the way through to protect the piping against corrosion.

B-3-1.2 Ordinary floors through which pipes pass should be made reasonably tight around the risers, except in areas subject to earthquakes. (*See A-3-5.3.1.*)

B-3-1.3 The time required to remove water from a trapped section of the system is important. In extreme cases the time required to drain the system may allow water to freeze.

B-4 Spacing, Location, and Position of Sprinklers.

B-4-1.1 Cutting holes through partitions, either solid or slatted, to allow sprinklers on one side thereof to distribute water to the other side is not effective.

B-4-1.2 When wood cornices on masonry buildings face an exposure they should be replaced with a parapet, or the projecting woodwork should be cut away and metal flashing extended to cover the exposed edge of planking, or suitable sprinkler protection should be provided.

B-4-2 Locations or Conditions Involving Special Consideration.

B-4-2.1 Overhead Doors. When overhead doors form an obstruction to water distribution from sprinklers above, additional sprinkler protection may be required. When piping can be attached to the door structural framing, locate and space sprinklers under the doors in accordance with the rules for Ordinary Hazard Occupancy. When piping cannot be attached to the door structural framing, space sprinklers not more than 12 ft (3.1 m) apart around the perimeter of the three accessible sides of the doors and at least 12 in. (305 mm) in from the edges of the doors. Deflectors should not be more than 10 in. (254 mm) below the doors in the open position. Sidewall sprinklers may be used when their distribution would be more effective than that from standard sprinklers. When doors are predominantly glass construction and when those doors, in an open position, will merely be over a traffic aisle, sprinkler protection is not necessarily required.

B-4-2.2 Tables.

B-4-2.2.1 Sprinklers should be installed under cutting,

pressing, sewing machine, and other work tables over 4 ft (1.2 m) wide. Sprinklers may be omitted under tables less than 5½ ft (1.7 m) but wider than 4 ft (1.2 m) if the tables are of temporary or semipermanent nature, as determined by the authority having jurisdiction, and tight vertical partitions of galvanized iron or other noncombustible material are provided not more than 10 ft (3.0 m) apart.

B-4-2.2.2 Partitions should be the full width of the table, extend from the underside of the table to the floor and from the front edge to back edge of the table; should be substantially fastened to the underside of the table and to the floor; and should be reinforced with angle or channel iron uprights.

B-4-2.2.3 The outer edges of each partition should be smoothly finished (rounded if of metal) so as to prevent injury to employees.

B-4-2.2.4 Instructions should be obtained relative to the installation of "stops" under tables of unusual construction.

B-4-2.3 Obstructions. Timbers, uprights, hangers, piping, lighting fixtures, ducts, etc., are likely to interfere with the proper distribution of water from sprinklers. Therefore, sprinklers should be so located or spaced that any interference is held to a minimum. The required clearance between such members and sprinklers is dependent upon the size of the obstruction to water distribution. The clearances should not be less than those specified between sprinklers and truss members in 4-2.4.1 and 4-2.4.5. (*See also 4-2.4.6.*)

B-4-2.4 Enclosures.

B-4-2.4.1 Sprinklers should be installed in enclosed equipment where combustible materials are processed or where combustible wastes or deposits may accumulate. Examples of such locations may include ovens, driers, dust collectors, conveyors, large ducts, spray booths, paper machine hoods, paper machine economizers, parts of textile preparatory machines, and similar enclosures.

B-4-2.4.2 Sprinklers should be installed in small enclosed structures of combustible construction or containing combustible material. Examples of such locations may include penthouses, passageways, small offices, stock rooms, closets, vaults, or similar enclosures.

B-4-2.4.3 For small enclosures, pipes may be run outside the enclosures and sprinklers installed in approved dome-shaped covers about 10 in. (254 mm) in diameter. Where sprinklers can be nippled into the enclosure without forming an obstruction this should be done and dome-shaped covers omitted.

B-4-2.4.4 Sprinkler piping may be run above hoods over paper machines and similar equipment where dripping of condensation from sprinkler piping must be avoided and the sprinklers nippled through. The lower sprinklers under the hoods should be located outside of the line of the cylinders or rolls.

B-4-2.4.5 When enclosures are subject to freezing temperatures, special types of sprinkler protection should be provided. Manually operated systems should not be used.

B-4-2.4.6 The provision of other approved extinguishing systems does not permit the omission of sprinklers except in special situations, such as high value records or museum displays in vaults, commercial-type cooking equipment, or computer or other electrical equipment enclosures. The authority having jurisdiction should be consulted.

B-4-2.4.7 Safe deposit or other vaults of fire-resistive construction will not ordinarily require sprinkler protection when used for the storage of records, files, and other documents, when stored in metal cabinets.

B-4-2.4.8 Stock Fixtures. Sprinklers should be installed in all stock fixtures that exceed 5 ft (1.5 m) in width, also in those that are less than 5 ft (1.5 m) but more than 2½ ft (0.8 m) in width unless bulkheaded with tight partitions. Sprinklers should be installed in any compartments that are larger than 5 ft (1.5 m) deep, 8 ft (2.4 m) long, and 3 ft (0.9 m) high.

B-4-2.4.9 Lighting fixtures of the pendent or surface-mounted type may offer obstruction to discharge from sprinklers unless the clearances specified in Table 4-2.4.6 are provided.

B-5 Types of Systems.

B-5-1 Preaction and Deluge Systems — Valves.

B-5-1.1 In hazardous locations, an approved indicating-type valve or manual means for operation of preaction or deluge valve should be installed in a location where access to the control valves is not likely to be prevented under fire emergency conditions.

B-5-1.2 With deluge systems, the deluge valve should be located as close as possible to the hazard protected, outside any fire or explosion hazard area.

B-5-2 Filling with Antifreeze Solutions. With the water supply valve closed and the system drained, fill the piping through the filling cup, using a suitable antifreeze solution of the proper concentration. Vent the air at the end sprinklers. Back out all sprinklers slightly until the liquid appears so that the piping will be completely filled and all air expelled. If the filling cup is not above the highest sprinklers, the piping may be filled through valve B by means of a small pump or through a filling cup installed at the highest branch sprinkler line. If the last-named method is used, the drop pipe should be filled through the filling cup shown in Figure 5-5.4. Then tighten the sprinkler heads and open valve A until the 12-in. (305-mm) section of pipe above this valve is empty and the level of the antifreeze solution in the drop pipe is at valve A. Close valve A. Close the filling connection valve and slowly open the supply valve wide.

B-5-3 Dry-Pipe Systems.

B-5-3.1 Eight-Inch Systems. Where an 8-in. (203-mm) riser is employed in connection with a dry-pipe system, a 6-in. (152-mm) dry-pipe valve and a 6-in. (152-mm) gate valve between taper reducers may be used.

B-5-3.2 Dry-Pipe System Serving Several Remote Unheated Areas. Where a single dry-pipe valve is used to supply piping and sprinklers located in several small unheated areas that are remote from each other, the dry-pipe valve and riser may be sized according to the number of sprinklers in the largest area. (*Also see 5-2.3.1.*)

B-6 Outside Sprinklers.

B-6-1 Type.

B-6-1.1 Small orifice sprinklers will normally be used where exposure is light or moderate, the area of coverage is small, or where one horizontal line of window sprinklers is installed at each floor level.

B-6-1.2 Large orifice sprinklers should be used where exposure is severe, or where one horizontal line of sprinklers is used to protect windows at more than one floor level.

B-6-2 Window Sprinklers.

B-6-2.1 When the exposure hazard is light or moderate, and only one horizontal line of sprinklers is installed, the sprinklers should have 3/8-in. (9.5-mm) orifices. Where conditions require more than one line of sprinklers, the sprinklers should have orifices as shown in the following table:

Table B-6-2.1

	2 Lines	3 Lines	4 Lines	5 Lines	6 Lines
Top line	3/8 in.	3/8 in.	3/8 in.	3/8 in.	3/8 in.
Next below	5/16 in.	5/16 in.	3/8 in.	3/8 in.	3/8 in.
Next below		1/4 in.	5/16 in.	5/16 in.	5/16 in.
Next below			1/4 in.	5/16 in.	5/16 in.
Next below				1/4 in.	1/4 in.
Next below					1/4 in.

For SI Units: 1 in. = 25.4 mm.

B-6-2.2 When there are more than six horizontal rows of windows, sprinklers over the first story may be omitted. Sprinklers may also be omitted over the second story windows if a field test indicates wetting of all surfaces.

B-6-2.3 Large orifice sprinklers may be used for protecting windows in two or three stories from one line of sprinklers. This will be determined by window and wall construction, such that all parts of the windows and frames will be thoroughly wetted by a single line of sprinklers.

B-6-2.4 For buildings not over three stories in height, one line of sprinklers will often be sufficient, located at the top story windows. For buildings more than three stories in height, a line of sprinklers may be used in every other story beginning at the top. With an odd number of stories, the lowest line can protect the first three stories. When several lines are used, the orifice should be decreased one size for each successive line below the top. In no case should an orifice less than 1/2 in. (13 mm) be used.

B-6-2.5 For windows not exceeding 5 ft (1.5 m) wide protected by small orifice sprinklers, one sprinkler should be placed at the center near the top, so located that water discharged therefrom will wet the upper part of the window and, by running down over the sash and glass, wet the entire window. This may ordinarily be accomplished by placing one sprinkler in the center with the deflector about on a line with the top of the upper sash and 7, 8, and 9 in. (178, 203, and 229 mm) in front of the glass, with windows 3, 4, and 5 ft (0.9, 1.2, and 1.5 m) wide, respectively. When windows are over 5 ft (1.5 m) wide, or where mullions interfere, two or more sprinklers should be used.

B-6-2.6 When windows are 3 ft (0.9 m) or less in width, an orifice a size smaller than that required by B-6-2.1 may be used, but in no case may the orifice be smaller than 1/4 in. (6.4 mm).

B-6-2.7 For windows up to 5 ft (1.5 m) wide protected by large orifice sprinklers, use one 1/2-in. (13-mm) sprinkler at the center of each window. For windows from 5 to 7 ft (1.5 to 2.1 m) wide, use a 5/8-in. (16-mm) sprinkler at the center of each window. For windows from 7 to 9 1/2 ft (2.1 to 2.9 m) wide, use one 3/4-in. (19-mm) sprinkler at the center of each window. For windows from 9 1/2 to 12 ft (2.9 to 3.7 m) wide, use two 1/2-in (13-mm) sprinklers at each window.

B-6-2.8 Large orifice wide-deflector sprinklers should be placed with deflectors 2 in. (51 mm) below the top of the sash and 12 to 15 in. (305 to 380 mm) out from the glass. When the face of the glass is close to the exterior wall, cantilever brackets or similar type hangers may be used to maintain the window sprinklers 12 to 15 in. (305 to 380 mm) out from the glass.

B-6-3 Cornice Sprinklers.

B-6-3.1 The discharge orifice should be at least 3/8 in. (9.5 mm) in diameter except, when the exposure is severe, 1/2-in. or 5/8-in. (13-mm or 16-mm) cornice sprinklers should be installed.

B-6-3.2 Sprinklers should not be more than 8 ft (2.4 m) apart, except as noted in B-6-3.6. Projecting beams or other obstructions may make additional sprinklers necessary.

B-6-3.3 For cornices with bays up to 8 ft (2.4 m) wide,

sprinklers should be placed in the center of each bay. For cornices with bays from 8 to 10 ft (2.4 to 3.0 m) wide, sprinkler orifices should be increased one size.

B-6-3.4 Cornice sprinklers should be located with deflectors approximately 8 in. (203 mm) below the roof plank.

B-6-3.5 When wood cornices are 30 in. (762 mm) or less above the windows, cornice sprinklers may be supplied by the same pipe used for window sprinklers.

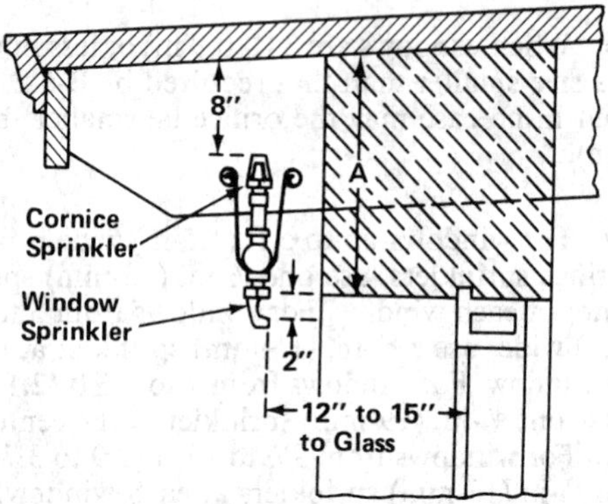
8"
A
Cornice Sprinkler
Window Sprinkler
2"
12" to 15" to Glass

For SI Units: 1 in. = 25.4 mm.

Figure B-6-3.5 Location of Window and Cornice Sprinklers.

B-6-3.6 Where the overhang of the cornice is not over 1 ft (0.3 m), window sprinklers should be used and be spaced as follows:

3/8-in. and 1/2-in. sprinklers	Not more than 5 ft apart
5/8-in. sprinklers.	Not more than 7 ft apart
3/4-in. sprinklers.	Not more than 9 ft apart

For SI Units: 1 in. = 25.4 mm; 1 ft = 0.3048 m.

B-6-3.7 The window sprinklers should be placed above the pipe near the outer edge of the cornice with deflectors not more than 3 in. (76 mm) down from the cornice and at such an angle as to throw the water upward and inward.

B-6-3.8 With an overhang of more than 1 ft (0.3 m), cornice sprinklers should be used.

B-7 Sprinkler System Performance Criteria.

B-7-1 Sprinkler system performance criteria have been based on test data. The factors of safety are generally small and are not definitive, and can depend on expected (but not guaranteed) inherent characteristics of the sprinkler systems involved. These inherent factors of safety consist of the following:

(a) The flow-declining pressure characteristic of sprinkler systems whereby the initial operating sprinklers discharge at a higher flow than with all sprinklers operating within the designated area.

(b) The flow-declining pressure characteristic of water supplies. This is particularly steep where fire pumps are the water source. This characteristic similarly produces higher than design discharge at the initially operating sprinklers.

The user of these standards may elect an additional factor of safety if the inherent factors are not considered adequate.

B-7-1.1 Performance specified sprinkler systems as opposed to scheduled systems can be designed to take advantage of multiple loops or gridded configurations. This results in minimum line losses at expanded sprinkler spacing, in contrast to the older *tree-type* configurations, where advantage cannot be taken of two-way type flows.

Where the water supply characteristics are relatively flat with pressures being only slightly above the required sprinkler pressure at the spacing selected, gridded systems with piping designed for minimal economic line losses can all but eliminate the inherent flow-declining pressure characteristic generally assumed to exist in sprinkler systems. In contrast, the economic design of a *tree-type* system would likely favor a system design with closer sprinkler spacing and greater line losses, demonstrating the inherent flow-declining pressure characteristic of the piping system.

Elements that enter into the design of sprinkler systems include:

1. Selection of density and area of application.
2. Geometry of the area of application (remote area).
3. Permitted pressure range at sprinklers.
4. Determination of the water supply available.

5. Ability to predict expected performance from calculated performance.

6. Future upgrading of system performance.

7. Size of sprinkler systems.

In developing sprinkler specifications, each of these elements needs to be considered individually. The most conservative design will be based on the application of the most stringent conditions for each of the elements.

B-7-1.2 Selection of Density and Area of Application. Specifications for density and area of application are developed from NFPA and other standards. It is desirable to specify densities rounded upward to the nearest 0.005 gpm/sq ft.

Prudent design should consider reasonable-to-expect variations in occupancy. This would include not only variations in types of occupancy, but, in the case of warehousing, the anticipated future range of materials to be stored, clearances, types of arrays, packaging, pile height, and pile stability, as well as other factors.

Design also considers some degree of adversity at the time of a fire. To take this into account, the density and/or area of application may be increased. Another way is to use a dual performance specification where, in addition to the normal primary specifications, a secondary density and area of application is specified. The objective of such a selection is to control the declining pressure-flow characteristic of the sprinkler system beyond the primary design flow.

A case can be made for designing feed and cross mains to lower velocities than branch lines to achieve the same result as specifying a second density and area of application.

B-7-1.3 Geometry of the Area of Application (Remote Area). It is expected that over any portion of the sprinkler system equivalent in size to the area of application, the system will achieve the minimum specified density for each sprinkler within that area.

Where a system is computer-designed, ideally the program should verify the entire system by shifting the area of application the equivalent of one sprinkler at a time so as to cover all portions of the system. Such a complete computer verification of performance of the system is most desirable, but unfortunately not all available computer verification programs currently do this.

The selection of the proper Hazen-Williams coefficient is important. New unlined steel pipe has a Hazen-Williams coefficient close to 140. However, it quickly deteriorates to 130, and after a few years of use, to 120. Hence, the basis for normal design is a Hazen-Williams coefficient of 120 for steel-piped wet systems. A Hazen-Williams coefficient of 100 is generally used for dry-pipe systems because of the increased tendency for deposits and corrosion in these systems. However, it should be realized that a new system will have fewer line losses than calculated, and the distribution pattern will be affected accordingly.

Conservatism can also be built into systems by intentionally designing to a lower Hazen-Williams coefficient than those indicated.

B-7-1.4 Ability to Predict Expected Performance from Calculated Performance. Ability to accurately predict the performance of a complex array of sprinklers on piping is basically a function of the pipe line velocity. The greater the velocity the greater is the impact on difficult-to-assess pressure losses. These pressure losses are presently determined by empirical means that lose validity as velocities increase. This is especially true for fittings with unequal and more than two flowing ports.

The inclusion of velocity pressures in hydraulic calculations improves the predictability of the actual sprinkler system performance. Calculations should come as close as practicable to predicting actual performance. Conservatism in design should be arrived at intentionally by known and deliberate means. It should not be left to chance.

B-7-1.5 Future Upgrading of System Performance. It may be desirable in some cases to build into the system the capability to achieve a higher level of sprinkler performance than needed at present. If this is to be a consideration in conservatism, consideration needs to be given to maintaining sprinkler operating pressures on the lower side of the optimum operating range, and/or by designing for low pipe line velocities, particularly on feed and cross mains, to facilitate future reinforcement.

Appendix C Referenced Publications

C-1 The following documents or portions thereof are referenced within this standard for informational purposes only and thus are not considered part of the requirements of this document. The edition indicated for each reference should be the current edition as of the date of the NFPA issuance of this document.

C-1.1 NFPA Publications. National Fire Protection Association, Batterymarch Park, Quincy, MA 02269.

NFPA 13A-1987, *Recommended Practice for the Inspection, Testing and Maintenance of Sprinkler Systems*

NFPA 231C-1986, *Standard for Rack Storage of Materials*

NFPA 231F-1987, *Standard for the Storage of Roll Paper.*

C-2 The following NFPA Recommended Practices contain specific sprinkler design criteria on various subjects. (*See 2-2.1.1 Exception No. 4 and A-2-1.*)

NFPA 16A-1988, *Recommended Practice for the Installation of Closed-Head Foam-Water Sprinkler Systems*

NFPA 231E-1989, *Recommended Practice for the Storage of Baled Cotton.*

UNIFORM BUILDING CODE STANDARD NO. 38-2

STANDPIPE SYSTEMS

Installation Standard of the International Conference of Building Officials

See Sections 3801 (b) and (d) and 3805 (a), Uniform Building Code

Scope

Sec. 38.201. This standard applies to the design, installation, testing and maintenance of standpipe systems required by the Uniform Building Code.

Definitions

Sec. 38.202. Certain terms in this standard are defined as follows:

FIRE DEPARTMENT INLET CONNECTION is a connection through which the fire department can pump water into a standpipe system, or sprinkler system.

STANDPIPE SYSTEM is a wet or dry system of piping, valves, outlets and related equipment designed to provide water at specified pressures and installed exclusively for the fighting of fires, including the following:

Class I is a standpipe system equipped with $2^1/_2$-inch outlets.

Class II is a standpipe system directly connected to a water supply and equipped with $1^1/_2$-inch outlets and hose.

Class III is a standpipe system directly connected to a water supply and equipped with $2^1/_2$-inch outlets or $2^1/_2$-inch and $1^1/_2$-inch outlets when a $1^1/_2$-inch hose is required. Hose connections for Class III systems may be made through $2^1/_2$-inch hose valves with easily removable $2^1/_2$-inch by $1^1/_2$-inch reducers.

Required Water Supplies

Sec. 38.203. (a) **Source.** The source of the water supply for standpipe systems shall be reliable and capable of meeting the requirements of this section. The source shall be capable of providing the required supply for not less than 30 minutes.

(b) **Minimum Water Supply.** The minimum water supply for standpipe systems shall be as follows:

Class I systems shall receive from their source a supply sufficient to provide 500 GPM for a single standpipe and 250 GPM for each additional standpipe. The total supply need not exceed 2500 GPM. The supply system shall be capable of maintaining a residual pressure of 100 psi at each topmost outlet with 500 GPM flowing from the most remote standpipe and 250 GPM flowing from each additional standpipe up to a maximum of 2500 GPM flowing. If available, fire apparatus of adequate capacity are acceptable in meeting the supply requirements for Class I service.

Class II systems shall receive from their source a supply sufficient to provide a minimum of 100 GPM. The supply system shall be capable of maintaining a residual pressure of 65 psi at the topmost outlet with 100 GPM flowing.

Class III systems shall receive from their source a supply sufficient to provide 500 GPM for a single standpipe and 250 GPM for each additional standpipe. The total supply need not exceed 2500 GPM. The supply system shall be capable of maintaining a residual pressure of 100 psi at each topmost outlet with 500 GPM flowing from the most remote standpipe and 250 GPM flowing from each additional standpipe up to a maximum of 2500 GPM flowing.

(c) **Water Supply for Combined Standpipe and Sprinkler Risers.** Standpipe piping may be used to supply water for automatic fire sprinkler systems. For fully sprinklered buildings, the water supply required for sprinklers need not be added to the standpipe demand as specified in this section. The standpipe supply required in a fully sprinklered building need not exceed 1500 GPM in a Light Hazard Occupancy building and 2000 GPM in an Ordinary Hazard building unless required by the authority having jurisdiction.

Standpipe and Supply Piping Design

Sec. 38.204. All standpipe systems shall be hydraulically designed in accordance with the hydraulic design methods prescribed by U.B.C. Standard No. 38-1 for the minimum flow specified in Section 38.203.

Height Limit

Sec. 38.205. Buildings shall be zoned so that standpipe system risers do not exceed 275 feet in height unless control of the nozzle pressure under both flow and static conditions is attained at each standpipe outlet by the installation of a listed pressure-regulating device and provided further that all of the following three limitations are met:

1. The pressure on the listed pressure-regulating device inlet side is not in excess of the rated working pressure of the listed pressure-regulating device and the remaining portions of the standpipe system are rated for not less than the maximum system pressure.
2. The hose valve outlet pressure is limited to a maximum of 125 psi by the listed pressure-regulating device.
3. The zone height does not exceed 400 feet.

System Zoning Requirements

Sec. 38.206. Provisions to sustain a positive pressure to all zones in multiple-zoned systems is required. When fire pumps are required, separate fire pumps shall be required to serve each zone.

Fire pumps which individually serve separate zones and which are located at the same level may be installed in series.

Direct supply piping from the higher-zone fire pump to the higher-zone system piping shall be provided when the fire pump for the higher zone is on the same level as the fire pump serving the lower zone. If the higher-zone system has more than one vertical riser, two direct supply lines to the higher zone shall be provided. The size of the direct supply piping to the higher zone shall be not less than the size of the largest standpipe riser served.

Lower-zone standpipe piping used to supply a zone above shall be not less than the size of the largest standpipe riser of the higher-zone system which is being supplied. The two zones shall be connected by a minimum of two supply pipes of which one shall be capable of automatically providing water to the higher zone from the lower zone. A secondary method of supply is required when a residual pressure of 100 psi cannot be provided.

Fire Department Inlet Connections

Sec. 38.207. Each Class I or III standpipe system shall be equipped with one or more fire department inlet connections. Fire department inlet connection locations shall be subject to the approval of the fire department, and the connections shall be equipped with approved caps which the fire department can easily remove to make connection. Fire department inlet connections shall be protected against mechanical damage and shall be visible and accessible. Installation of a shutoff valve in the fire department inlet connection is prohibited.

The piping between the outside fire department inlet connection point and the connection to the system riser shall be provided with an approved check valve. The piping between the check valve and the outside inlet connection point shall be equipped with a listed automatic drain valve.

> **EXCEPTION:** An approved check valve is not required for Class I standpipe systems without permanently connected water supply.

Fire department inlet connections shall be identified by an approved sign which specifies the type of system served. The sign shall read "Standpipe" for those connections serving a standpipe system only and shall read "Standpipe and Auto. Spkr." for those connections serving both a standpipe and automatic sprinkler system.

In buildings which have multiple zones, each zone shall be provided with separate inlet connections. Where the fire department inlet connection does not serve the entire building, the portions served shall be suitably identified.

A means for the removal of debris from a dry standpipe system shall be provided.

Gravity Tanks and Pressure Tanks

Sec. 38.208. (a) **Tank System Connections.** Except for tanks used to supply standpipes connected in several buildings or sections of a building, gravity tanks and pressure tanks shall be connected to the top of the standpipe system served. Gravity tanks and pressure tanks shall be connected to the base of the standpipe systems when such tanks serve standpipe systems in several buildings or sections of a building. An interconnection at the top of the risers of a standpipe system serving an individual building shall be provided when the standpipe system is tank supplied. Tank-to-standpipe connecting piping shall be not less than the size of the standpipe served.

(b) **Avoiding Air Lock.** When gravity tanks and pressure tanks are connected to a common riser, a method of preventing an air lock of the gravity tank check valve shall be provided. For additional information, see U.B.C Standard No. 38-1.

Piping, Valves and Fittings

Sec. 38.209. (a) **Supply Piping.** Supply piping shall be of a size capable of providing the flow rates and pressures specified within this standard.

(b) **Indicator, Isolation and Check Valve.** Check valves and indicating-type valves shall be installed as near as practical to all water supplies. Unless otherwise permitted by the building official and subject to concurrence by the fire department, a listed indicator post designed for use with an underground valve or an approved integral indicator post and valve shall be provided for the control of the water supply from a public water supply to a standpipe system and suitable identification of the system being controlled shall be provided.

Isolation valves shall be installed in standpipe systems to prevent the loss of water supply to the remaining portion of a system by the failure of individual system risers.

The valves required by this subsection shall be listed and shall be rated for the maximum anticipated system pressure.

(c) **Pressure Ratings of Fittings.** Fittings used in standpipe systems shall be rated for not less than the maximum anticipated system pressure.

(d) **Pipe, Tube, and Fitting Specifications.** Pipe, tube and fittings used in standpipe systems shall conform with the applicable requirements specified in Section 38.104 (c) of U.B.C. Standard No. 38-1.

(e) **Threaded Joints, Welded Joints or Flexible Couplings.** Piping shall be connected by means of threaded or flanged fittings, flexible couplings or other approved means.

Welding of joints may be approved provided such welding is done in the shop of an approved fabricator and approved welding fittings are utilized.

(f) **Piping System Support.** Hangers and piping shall be designed for lateral load in accordance with Section 2336 of the Uniform Building Code or shall be designed and detailed in accordance with nationally recognized standards.

(g) **Pressure Gauges.** A pressure gauge of an approved type shall be provided at the discharge pipe from fire pumps, the supply connection of the public waterworks and at the top of each standpipe riser. When pressure tanks are provided, a pressure gauge at the tank and the air pump shall also be provided. A valve for draining each gauge shall be provided. Where several standpipes are interconnected at the top, a single gauge properly located may be substituted for the gauges at the top of each standpipe.

(h) **Corrosion and Temperature Protection.** Provisions to protect systems from detrimental corrosive or temperature effects shall be provided.

Fire Department Outlets

Sec. 38.210. Fire department outlets shall be installed in such a manner as to be easily accessible for use by the fire department. A wrench clearance on all sides of the outlet shall be provided to ensure that a 12-inch-long wrench can be used to connect hose to the outlet.

Outlets shall be provided with a listed hose valve protected by a cap with attachment chain.

Outlet Pressure Limitation

Sec. 38.211. Outlet residual pressures in excess of 125 pounds per square inch shall be reduced to not more than 125 pounds per square inch at the required flow by the installation of a listed pressure-reducing device. Unless otherwise permitted by the fire department, pressure-reducing devices shall not be of the type which can be adjusted for pressures above 125 pounds per square inch. When adjustable devices are permitted and the outlet residual pressure may exceed 150 pounds per square inch, signs denoting that fact shall be posted at the outlet.

Hose, Reels, Racks, and Cabinets

Sec. 38.212 (a) **Hose Cabinets.** Hose cabinets housing the standpipe system outlet shall be of sufficient size and design to accommodate the required equipment to be housed therein. Adequate clearance to allow for the operation of the hose valves shall be provided. Cabinet doors may be secured by a latching device, and the latching device may be protected by an approved-type cover. A permanent label specifying the instructions for operating the equipment housed within the hose cabinet shall be provided.

(b) **Hose for 1$^1/_2$-inch Outlets.** 1$^1/_2$-inch outlets shall be provided with a listed hose valve equipped with listed lined hose not less than 1$^1/_2$ inches in diameter. Such hose shall be equipped with a listed variable fog nozzle.

(c) **Hose Rack or Reels.** A listed hose reel or rack shall be provided for hose required by Section 38.212 (b). Hose reels or racks shall be appropriately protected against mechanical injury.

Installation

Sec. 38.213. (a) **General.** Standpipe systems required by the Uniform Building Code shall be installed in locations required by the Uniform Building Code and in conformance with the approved plans and this standard. Details of the installation shall be in accordance with nationally recognized standards for the installation of standpipe systems.

(b) **Workmanship.** Standpipe systems shall be installed in a workmanlike manner conforming to generally accepted standard practice for the trades involved and in accordance with this standard.

(c) **Systems Tests.** 1. **Hydrostatic tests required.** Standpipe systems including the supply piping thereto with design pressures not exceeding 150 psi shall be hydrostatically tested at not less than 200 psi for a duration of not less than two hours. For systems with design pressures exceeding 150 psi, the hydrostatic test shall be not less than 50 psi above the system design pressure for not less than a two-hour duration.

Leakage shall not be permitted for the portion of the system piping contained within a building or structure.

2. **Functional flow test required.** Standpipe systems shall be flow tested to demonstrate the capability of providing the required flow.

3. **Flushing of the system.** Underground portions of the systems shall be flushed prior to connection and acceptance testing. The flushing shall be continued until all materials have been removed.

(d) **Contractor's Certification.** The installing contractor shall furnish written certification to the building official that the system was installed, flushed and tested in accordance with the Building Code, this standard, and approved plans and calculations. The certification shall indicate, as a minimum:

1. The address of the property.
2. The contractor's name, address and license number (if applicable).
3. Listed and approved materials and devices installed.
4. Description of system tests conducted and dates of flushing and testing.
5. Deviations from approved plans and calculations along with revised plans and calculations (if necessary).
6. Certification that special procedures, such as connections and welding, conform to nationally accepted standards.
7. Certification that the system is complete and in service.
8. Approved signage has been provided and attached as appropriate.
9. Hose threads of fire department connections and test connections match hose of responding fire department.
10. Name, title and dated signature of contractor representative authorized for certification.

UNIFORM BUILDING CODE STANDARD NO. 38-3

INSTALLATION OF SPRINKLER SYSTEMS IN GROUP R OCCUPANCIES FOUR STORIES OR LESS

See Sections 3801 (b) and (d), 4204 (a), 4205, 5207 (a) and 5208 (a), Uniform Building Code

Part I

Adoption of NFPA Standard

Sec. 38.301. Except for the limitations, deletions, modifications and amendments set forth in Section 38.302 of this standard, the installation of sprinkler systems in Group R Occupancies required by the Uniform Building Code shall be in accordance with the Standard for the Installation of Sprinkler Systems in Residential Occupancies, NFPA 13R-1989, published by the National Fire Protection Association, copyright © 1989, Batterymarch Park, Quincy, Massachusetts 02269, as if set out at length herein, or U.B.C. Standard No. 38-1.

Amendments

Sec. 38.302. The National Fire Protection Association standard adopted by Section 38.101 applies to the selection, installation, acceptance inspection and acceptance testing of sprinkler systems in residential occupancies four stories or less, except as follows:

1. Sec. 1-3 is amended as follows:

The definition of "authority having jurisdiction" is revised as follows:

The **"authority having jurisdiction"** is the building official.

The definitions of "approved" and "listed" shall be as set forth in the Uniform Building Code.

The definitions of "should" and "standard" are deleted.

The definition of "residential occupancies" is revised as follows:

RESIDENTIAL OCCUPANCIES are Group R Occupancies.

The definitions of "acceptance" and "building official" are added as follows:

ACCEPTANCE is acceptance by the building official.

BUILDING OFFICIAL is the officer or other designated authority charged with the administration and enforcement of this standard, or the officer's or other designated authority's duly authorized representative.

2. Sec. 1-6.2.1 is revised by changing the reference to "NFPA 13" to "U.B.C. Standard No. 38-1."

3. Sec. 2-1.3.2 is revised by changing the reference to "NFPA 13" to "U.B.C. Standard No. 38-1."

4. Sec. 2-3.2 is revised by changing the reference to "NFPA 20 and 22" to "nationally recognized standards" and changing the reference to "NFPA 13" to "U.B.C. Standard No. 38-1."

5. Sec. 2-3.3.2 is revised by changing the reference to "NFPA 13" to "U.B.C. Standard No. 38-1."

6. Sec. 2-4.4 is revised by changing the reference to "NFPA 13" to "U.B.C. Standard No. 38-1."

7. Sec. 2-5.2 is revised by changing the reference to "NFPA 13" to "U.B.C. Standard No. 38-1."

8. Sec. 2-5.3 is revised by changing the reference to "NFPA 13" to "U.B.C. Standard No. 38-1."

9. Sec. 2-6 is revised by changing the reference to "NFPA 220" to "the Building Code."

10. Secs. 2-7.1 and 2-7.2 are added as follows:

2-7.1. A sprinkler system installed under this standard shall be maintained in accordance with the Fire Code.

2-7.2. The installer of the system shall provide the owner with written instructions and information relating to the care and maintenance of the sprinkler system, with special attention given to the sprinkler system devices.

11. Chapter 3 is deleted in its entirety.

Part II

Reproduced with permission from the Standard for the Installation of Sprinkler Systems in Residential Occupancies up to Four Stories in Height, NFPA 13R, copyright © 1989, National Fire Protection Association, Batterymarch Park, Quincy, Massachusetts 02269. Persons desiring to reprint in whole or part any portion of the Standard for Installation of Sprinkler Systems in Residential Occupancies up to Four Stories in Height, NFPA 13R-1989, must secure permission from the National Fire Protection Association. The following standard is not necessarily the latest revision used by NFPA. If the reader desires to compare with that version, the same is available from NFPA.

Contents

NFPA 13R

Standard for the Installation of Sprinkler Systems in Residential Occupancies up to Four Stories in Height

1989 Edition

NOTICE: An asterisk (*) following the number or letter designating a paragraph indicates explanatory material on that paragraph in Appendix A.

Information on referenced publications can be found in Chapter 3 and Appendix B.

Preface

It is intended that this standard provide a method for those individuals wishing to install a sprinkler system for life safety and property protection. It is not the purpose of this standard to require the installation of an automatic sprinkler system. This standard assumes that one or more smoke detectors will be installed in accordance with NFPA 74, *Standard for the Installation, Maintenance, and Use of Household Fire Warning Equipment.*

Chapter 1 General Information

1-1* Scope. This standard deals with the design and installation of automatic sprinkler systems for protection against fire hazards in residential occupancies up to four stories in height.

1-2* Purpose. The purpose of this standard is to provide design and installation requirements for a sprinkler system to aid in the detection and control of fires in residential occupancies and thus provide improved protection against injury, life loss, and property damage. A sprinkler system designed and installed in accordance with this standard is expected to prevent flashover (total involvement) in the room of fire origin, when sprinklered, and to improve the chance for occupants to escape or be evacuated.

Nothing in this standard is intended to restrict new technologies or alternate arrangements, providing that the level of safety prescribed by the standard is not lowered.

1-3 Definitions.

Approved. Acceptable to the "authority having jurisdiction."

NOTE: The National Fire Protection Association does not approve, inspect or certify any installations, procedures, equipment, or materials nor does it approve or evaluate testing laboratories. In determining the acceptability of installations or procedures, equipment or materials, the authority having jurisdiction may base acceptance on compliance with NFPA or other appropriate standards. In the absence of such standards, said authority may require evidence of proper installation, procedure or use. The authority having jurisdiction may also refer to the listings or labeling practices of an organization concerned with product evaluations which is in a position to determine compliance with appropriate standards for the current production of listed items.

Authority Having Jurisdiction. The "authority having jurisdiction" is the organization, office or individual responsible for "approving" equipment, an installation or a procedure.

NOTE: The phrase "authority having jurisdiction" is used in NFPA documents in a broad manner since jurisdictions and "approval" agencies vary as do their responsibilities. Where public safety is primary, the "authority having jurisdiction" may be a federal, state, local or other regional department or individual such as a fire chief, fire marshal, chief of a fire prevention bureau, labor department, health department, building official, electrical inspector, or others having statutory authority. For insurance purposes, an insurance inspection department, rating bureau, or other insurance company representative may be the "authority having jurisdiction." In many circumstances the property owner or his designated agent assumes the role of the "authority having jurisdiction"; at government installations, the commanding officer or departmental official may be the "authority having jurisdiction."

Check Valve. A valve that allows flow in one direction only.

Control Valve. An indicating valve employed to control (shut) a supply of water to a sprinkler system.

Design Discharge. Rate of water discharged by an automatic sprinkler, expressed in gallons per minute.

Dry System. A system employing automatic sprinklers that are attached to a piping system containing air under atmospheric or higher pressures. Loss of pressure from the opening of a sprinkler or detection of a fire condition causes the release of water into the piping system and out the opened sprinkler.

Dwelling Unit. One or more rooms arranged for the use of one or more individuals living together as in a single housekeeping unit, normally having cooking, living, sanitary, and sleeping facilities.

Labeled. Equipment or materials to which has been attached a label, symbol or other identifying mark of an organization acceptable to the "authority having jurisdiction" and concerned with product evaluation, that maintains periodic inspection of production of labeled equipment or materials and by whose labeling the manufacturer indicates compliance with appropriate standards or performance in a specified manner.

Listed. Equipment or materials included in a list published by an organization acceptable to the "authority having jurisdiction" and concerned with product evaluation, that maintains periodic inspection of production of listed equipment or materials and whose listing states either that the equipment or material meets appropriate standards or has been tested and found suitable for use in a specified manner.

NOTE: The means for identifying listed equipment may vary for each organization concerned with product evaluation, some of which do not recognize equipment as listed unless it is also labeled. The "authority having jurisdiction" should utilize the system employed by the listing organization to identify a listed product.

Multipurpose Piping Systems. Piping systems within residential occupancies intended to serve both domestic and fire protection needs.

Residential Occupancies. Residential occupancies as included in the scope of this standard include the following, as defined in NFPA *101®*, *Life Safety Code®*:

(1) Apartment buildings.

(2) Lodging and rooming houses.

(3) Board and care facilities (slow evacuation type with 16 or less occupants and prompt evacuation type).

(4) Hotels, motels, and dormitories.

Residential Sprinkler. An automatic sprinkler that has been specifically listed for use in residential occupancies.

Shall. Indicates a mandatory requirement.

Should. Indicates a recommendation or that which is advised but not required.

Sprinkler—Automatic. A fire suppression device that operates automatically when its heat-actuated element is heated to or above its thermal rating, allowing water to discharge over a specific area.

Sprinkler System. An integrated system of piping connected to a water supply, with listed sprinklers that will automatically initiate water discharge over a fire area. When required, the sprinkler system also includes a control valve and a device for actuating an alarm when the system operates.

Standard. A document containing only mandatory provisions using the word "shall" to indicate requirements. Explanatory material may be included only in the form of "fine print" notes, in footnotes, or in an appendix.

Waterflow Alarm. A sounding device activated by a waterflow detector or alarm check valve.

Waterflow Detector. An electric signaling indicator or alarm check valve actuated by water flow in one direction only.

Wet System. A system employing automatic sprinklers that are attached to a piping system containing water and connected to a water supply, so that water discharges immediately from sprinklers opened by a fire.

1-4 Units. Metric units of measurement in this standard are in accordance with the modernized metric system known as the International System of Units (SI). Two units (liter and bar), outside of but recognized by SI, are commonly used in international fire protection. These units are listed, with conversion factors, in Table 1-4.

1-4.1 If a value for measurement as given in this standard is followed by an equivalent value in other units, the first stated is to be regarded as the requirement. A given equivalent value may be approximate.

1-4.2 The conversion procedure for the SI units has been to multiply the quantity by the conversion factor and then round the result to the appropriate number of significant digits.

Table 1-4

Name of Unit	Unit Symbol	Conversion Factor
liter	L	1 gal = 3.785 L
pascal	Pa	1 psi = 6894.757 Pa
bar	bar	1 psi = 0.0689 bar
bar	bar	1 bar = 105 Pa

For additional conversions and information see ASTM E380, *Standard for Metric Practice.*

1-5 Piping.

1-5.1 Pipe or tube used in sprinkler systems shall be of the materials in Table 1-5.1 or in accordance with 1-5.2 through 1-5.5. The chemical properties, physical properties, and dimensions of the materials listed in Table 1-5.1 shall be at least equivalent to the standards cited in the table and designed to withstand a working pressure of not less than 175 psi (12.1 bars).

1-5.2 Other types of pipe or tube may be used, but only those listed for this service.

1-5.3 Whenever the word pipe is used in this standard, it shall be understood to also mean tube.

1-5.4 Pipe joined with mechanical grooved fittings shall be joined by a listed combination of fittings, gaskets, and grooves. When grooves are cut or rolled on the pipe they shall be dimensionally compatible with the fittings.

Exception: Steel pipe with wall thicknesses less than Schedule 30 [in sizes 8 in. (203 mm) and larger] or Schedule 40 [in

Table 1-5.1

Materials and Dimensions	Standard
Specification for Black and Hot-Dipped Zinc-Coated (Galvanized) Welded and Seamless Steel Pipe for Fire Protection Use	ASTM A795
Specification for Welded and Seamless Steel Pipe	ASTM A53
Wrought-Steel Pipe	ANSI B36.10M
Specification for Electric-Resistance Welded Steel Pipe	ASTM A135
Copper Tube (Drawn, Seamless) Specification for Seamless Copper Tube	ASTM B88
Specification for General Requirements for Wrought Seamless Copper and Copper-Alloy Tube	ASTM B251
Brazing Filler Metal (Classification BCuP-3 or BCuP-4)	AWS A5.8
Specification for Solder Metal, 95-5 (Tin-Antimony-Grade 95TA)	ASTM B32

sizes less than 8 in. (203 mm)] shall not be joined by fittings used with pipe having cut grooves.

1-5.5 Fittings used in sprinkler systems shall be of the materials listed in Table 1-5.5 or in accordance with 1-5.7. The chemical properties, physical properties, and dimensions of the materials listed in Table 1-5.5 shall be at least equivalent to the standards cited in the table. Fittings used in sprinkler systems shall be designed to withstand the working pressures involved, but not less than 175 psi (12.1 bars) cold water pressure.

1-5.6 Joints for the connection of copper tube shall be brazed.

Exception: Soldered joints (95-5 solder metal) may be used for wet-pipe copper tube systems.

1-5.7 Other types of fittings may be used, but only those listed for this service.

Table 1-5.5

Materials and Dimensions	Standard
Cast Iron	
Cast Iron Threaded Fittings, Class 125 and 250	ANSI B16.4
Cast Iron Pipe Flanges and Flanged Fittings	ANSI B16.1
Malleable Iron	
Malleable Iron Threaded Fittings, Class 150 and 300	ANSI B16.3
Steel	
Factory-made Threaded Fittings Class 150 and 300	ANSI B16.9
Buttwelding Ends for Pipe, Valves, Flanges, and Fittings	ANSI B16.25
Spec. for Piping Fittings of Wrought Carbon Steel and Alloy Steel for Moderate and Elevated Temperatures	ASTM A234
Pipe Flanges and Flanged Fittings, Steel Nickel Alloy and Other Special Alloys	ANSI B16.5
Forged Steel Fittings, Socket Welded and Threaded	ANSI B16.11
Copper	
Wrought Copper and Copper Alloy Solder-Joint Pressure Fittings	ANSI B16.22
Cast Copper Alloy Solder-Joint Pressure Fittings	ANSI B16.18

1-6 System Types.

1-6.1 Wet-Pipe Systems. A wet-pipe system shall be used when all piping is installed in areas not subject to freezing.

1-6.2 Provision shall be made to protect piping from freezing in unheated areas by use of one of the following acceptable methods:

(a) Antifreeze system.

(b) Dry-pipe system.

Exception: Listed standard dry-pendent, dry upright, or dry sidewall sprinklers may be extended into unheated areas not intended for living purposes.

1-6.2.1 Antifreeze solutions shall be installed in accordance with 5-5.3 of NFPA 13, *Standard for the Installation of Sprinkler Systems.*

Chapter 2 Working Plans, Design, Installation, Acceptance Tests, and Maintenance

2-1 Working Plans and Acceptance Tests.

2-1.1 Working Plans.

2-1.1.1 Working plans shall be submitted for approval to the authority having jurisdiction before any equipment is installed or remodeled. Deviations from approved plans will require permission of the authority having jurisdiction.

2-1.1.2 Working plans shall be drawn to an indicated scale, on sheets of uniform size, with a plan of each floor, made so that they can be easily duplicated, and shall show the following data:

(a) Name of owner and occupant.

(b) Location, including street address.

(c) Point of compass.

(d) Ceiling construction.

(e) Full height cross section.

(f) Location of fire walls.

(g) Location of partitions.

(h) Occupancy of each area or room.

(i) Location and size of concealed spaces, attics, closets, and bathrooms.

(j) Any small enclosures in which no sprinklers are to be installed.

(k) Size of city main in street, pressure and whether dead-end or circulating and, if dead-end, direction and distance to nearest circulating main, city main test results including elevation of test hydrant.

(l) Make, manufacturer, type, heat-response element, temperature rating, and nominal orifice size of sprinkler.

(m) Temperature rating and location of high-temperature sprinklers.

(n) Number of sprinklers on each riser, per floor.

(o) Kind and location of alarm bells.

(p) Type of pipe and fittings.

(q) Type of protection for nonmetallic pipe.

(r) Nominal pipe size with lengths shown to scale.

NOTE: Where typical branch lines prevail, it will be necessary to size only one line.

(s) Location and size of riser nipples.

(t) Type of fittings and joints and location of all welds and bends.

(u) Types and locations of hangers, sleeves, braces, and methods of securing sprinklers, where applicable.

(v) All control valves, check valves, drain pipes, and test connections.

(w) Underground pipe size, length, location, weight, material, point of connection to city main; the type of valves, meters, and valve pits; and the depth at which the top of the pipe is laid below grade.

(x) For hydraulically designed systems, the material to be included on the hydraulic data nameplate.

(y) Name and address of contractor.

2-1.2 Approval of Sprinkler Systems.

2-1.2.1 The installer shall perform all required acceptance tests (*see 2-1.3*), complete the Contractor's Material and Test Certificate(s) (*see Figure 2-1.2.1*), and forward the certificate(s) to the authority having jurisdiction, prior to asking for approval of the installation.

2-1.2.2 When the authority having jurisdiction desires to be present during the conducting of acceptance tests, the installer shall give advance notification of the time and date the testing will be performed.

2-1.3 Acceptance Tests.

2-1.3.1 Flushing of Underground Connections.

2-1.3.1.1 Underground mains and lead-in connections to system risers shall be flushed before connection is made to sprinkler piping, in order to remove foreign materials that may have entered the underground piping during the course of the installation. For all systems, the flushing operation shall be continued until water is clear.

2-1.3.1.2 Underground mains and lead-in connections shall be flushed at the hydraulically calculated water demand rate of the system.

2-1.3.1.3 To avoid property damage, provision shall be made for the disposal of water issuing from test outlets.

2-1.3.2* All systems shall be tested for leakage at 50 psi (3.4 bars) above maximum system design pressure.

Exception: When a fire department connection is provided, hydrostatic pressure tests shall be provided in accordance with NFPA 13, Standard for the Installation of Sprinkler Systems.

2-2 Design and Installation.

2-2.1 Devices and Materials.

2-2.1.1* Only new sprinklers shall be employed in the installation of sprinkler systems.

2-2.1.2 Only listed or approved devices and materials as indicated in this standard shall be used in sprinkler systems.

2-2.1.3 Sprinkler systems shall be designed for a maximum working pressure of 175 psi (12.1 bars).

Exception: Higher design pressures may be used when all system components are rated for pressures higher than 175 psi (12.1 bars).

2-3 Water Supply.

2-3.1 General Provisions. Every automatic sprinkler system shall have at least one automatic water supply. When stored water is used as the sole source of supply, the minimum quantity shall equal the water demand rate times 30 minutes. (*See 2-5.1.3.*)

2-3.2* Water Supply Sources. The following water supply sources are acceptable:

(a) A connection to a reliable water works system with or without a booster pump, as required.

(b) An elevated tank.

CONTRACTOR'S MATERIAL & TEST CERTIFICATE FOR ABOVEGROUND PIPING

PROCEDURE

Upon completion of work, inspection and tests shall be made by the contractor's representative and witnessed by an owner's representative. All defects shall be corrected and system left in service before contractor's personnel finally leave the job.

A certificate shall be filled out and signed by both representatives. Copies shall be prepared for approving authorities, owners, and contractor. It is understood the owner's representative's signature in no way prejudices any claim against contractor for faulty material, poor workmanship, or failure to comply with approving authority's requirements or local ordinances.

PROPERTY NAME	DATE
PROPERTY ADDRESS	

PLANS	ACCEPTED BY APPROVING AUTHORITIES (NAMES)		
	ADDRESS		
	INSTALLATION CONFORMS TO ACCEPTED PLANS	☐ YES	☐ NO
	EQUIPMENT USED IS APPROVED	☐ YES	☐ NO
	IF NO, EXPLAIN DEVIATIONS		
INSTRUCTIONS	HAS PERSON IN CHARGE OF FIRE EQUIPMENT BEEN INSTRUCTED AS TO LOCATION OF CONTROL VALVES AND CARE AND MAINTENANCE OF THIS NEW EQUIPMENT?	☐ YES	☐ NO
	IF NO, EXPLAIN		
	HAVE COPIES OF THE FOLLOWING BEEN LEFT ON THE PREMISES:	☐ YES	☐ NO
	1. SYSTEM COMPONENTS INSTRUCTIONS	☐ YES	☐ NO
	2. CARE AND MAINTENANCE INSTRUCTIONS	☐ YES	☐ NO
	3. NFPA 13A	☐ YES	☐ NO
LOCATION OF SYSTEM	SUPPLIES BUILDINGS		

SPRINKLERS

MAKE	MODEL	YEAR OF MANUFACTURE	ORIFICE SIZE	QUANTITY	TEMPERATURE RATING

PIPE AND FITTINGS

Type of Pipe ______________________

Type of Fittings ______________________

ALARM VALVE OR FLOW INDICATOR

ALARM DEVICE			MAXIMUM TIME TO OPERATE THROUGH TEST CONNECTION	
TYPE	MAKE	MODEL	MIN.	SEC.

DRY PIPE OPERATING TEST

DRY VALVE			Q.O.D.		
MAKE	MODEL	SERIAL NO.	MAKE	MODEL	SERIAL NO.

	TIME TO TRIP THRU TEST CONNECTION*		WATER PRESSURE	AIR PRESSURE	TRIP POINT AIR PRESSURE	TIME WATER REACHED TEST OUTLET*		ALARM OPERATED PROPERLY	
	MIN.	SEC.	PSI	PSI	PSI	MIN.	SEC.	YES	NO
Without Q.O.D.									
With Q.O.D.									

IF NO, EXPLAIN

* MEASURED FROM TIME INSPECTOR'S TEST CONNECTION IS OPENED.

85A (10-88) PRINTED IN U.S.A. (OVER)

Figure 2-1.2.1 Contractor's Material and Test Certificate for Aboveground Piping.

DELUGE & PREACTION VALVES

OPERATION ☐ PNEUMATIC ☐ ELECTRIC ☐ HYDRAULIC

PIPING SUPERVISED ☐ YES ☐ NO | DETECTING MEDIA SUPERVISED ☐ YES ☐ NO

DOES VALVE OPERATE FROM THE MANUAL TRIP AND/OR REMOTE CONTROL STATIONS ☐ YES ☐ NO

IS THERE AN ACCESSIBLE FACILITY IN EACH CIRCUIT FOR TESTING ☐ YES ☐ NO | IF NO, EXPLAIN

MAKE	MODEL	DOES EACH CIRCUIT OPERATE SUPERVISION LOSS ALARM		DOES EACH CIRCUIT OPERATE VALVE RELEASE		MAXIMUM TIME TO OPERATE RELEASE	
		YES	NO	YES	NO	MIN.	SEC.

TEST DESCRIPTION

HYDROSTATIC: Hydrostatic tests shall be made at not less than 50 psi (3.4 bars) above design pressure for two hours. Differential dry-pipe valve clappers shall be left open during test to prevent damage. All aboveground piping leakage shall be stopped. Systems with fire department connections shall be hydrostatically tested in accordance with NFPA 13, paragraph 1-11.2.

PNEUMATIC: Establish 40 psi (2.7 bars) air pressure and measure drop which shall not exceed 1-1/2 psi (0.1 bars) in 24 hours. Test pressure tanks at normal water level and air pressure and measure air pressure drop which shall not exceed 1-1/2 psi (0.1 bars) in 24 hours.

TESTS

ALL PIPING HYDROSTATICALLY TESTED AT ______ PSI FOR ______ HRS. | IF NO, STATE REASON

DRY PIPING PNEUMATICALLY TESTED ☐ YES ☐ NO

EQUIPMENT OPERATES PROPERLY ☐ YES ☐ NO

DO YOU CERTIFY AS THE SPRINKLER CONTRACTOR THAT ADDITIVES AND CORROSIVE CHEMICALS, SODIUM SILICATE OR DERIVATIVES OF SODIUM SILICATE, BRINE, OR OTHER CORROSIVE CHEMICALS WERE NOT USED FOR TESTING SYSTEMS OR STOPPING LEAKS? ☐ YES ☐ NO

DRAIN TEST | READING OF GAGE LOCATED NEAR WATER SUPPLY TEST CONNECTION: ______ PSI | RESIDUAL PRESSURE WITH VALVE IN TEST CONNECTION OPEN WIDE ______ PSI

UNDERGROUND MAINS AND LEAD IN CONNECTIONS TO SYSTEM RISERS FLUSHED BEFORE CONNECTION MADE TO SPRINKLER PIPING.

VERIFIED BY COPY OF THE U FORM NO. 85B ☐ YES ☐ NO | OTHER EXPLAIN

FLUSHED BY INSTALLER OF UNDERGROUND SPRINKLER PIPING ☐ YES ☐ NO

BLANK TESTING GASKETS

NUMBER USED	LOCATIONS	NUMBER REMOVED

WELDING

WELDED PIPING ☐ YES ☐ NO

IF YES . . .

DO YOU CERTIFY AS THE SPRINKLER CONTRACTOR THAT WELDING PROCEDURES COMPLY WITH THE REQUIREMENTS OF AT LEAST AWS D10.9, LEVEL AR-3 ☐ YES ☐ NO

DO YOU CERTIFY THAT THE WELDING WAS PERFORMED BY WELDERS QUALIFIED IN COMPLIANCE WITH THE REQUIREMENTS OF AT LEAST AWS D10.9, LEVEL AR-3 ☐ YES ☐ NO

DO YOU CERTIFY THAT WELDING WAS CARRIED OUT IN COMPLIANCE WITH A DOCUMENTED QUALITY CONTROL PROCEDURE TO INSURE THAT ALL DISCS ARE RETRIEVED, THAT OPENINGS IN PIPING ARE SMOOTH, THAT SLAG AND OTHER WELDING RESIDUE ARE REMOVED, AND THAT THE INTERNAL DIAMETERS OF PIPING ARE NOT PENETRATED ☐ YES ☐ NO

CUTOUTS (DISCS)

DO YOU CERTIFY THAT YOU HAVE A CONTROL FEATURE TO ENSURE THAT ALL CUTOUTS (DISCS) ARE RETRIEVED? ☐ YES ☐ NO

HYDRAULIC DATA NAMEPLATE

NAME PLATE PROVIDED ☐ YES ☐ NO | IF NO, EXPLAIN

REMARKS

DATE LEFT IN SERVICE WITH ALL CONTROL VALVES OPEN:

SIGNATURES

NAME OF SPRINKLER CONTRACTOR

TESTS WITNESSED BY

FOR PROPERTY OWNER (SIGNED)	TITLE	DATE
FOR SPRINKLER CONTRACTOR (SIGNED)	TITLE	DATE

ADDITIONAL EXPLANATION AND NOTES

85A BACK

gure 2-1.2.1 (Continued) **Contractor's Material and Test Certificate for Aboveground Piping.**

(c) A pressure tank installed in accordance with NFPA 13, *Standard for the Installation of Sprinkler Systems,* and NFPA 22, *Standard for Water Tanks for Private Fire Protection.*

(d) A stored water source with an automatically operated pump, installed in accordance with NFPA 20, *Standard for the Installation of Centrifugal Fire Pumps.*

2-3.3 Multipurpose Piping System.

2-3.3.1* A common supply main to the building, serving both sprinklers and domestic uses, shall be acceptable when the domestic design demand is added to the sprinkler system demand.

Exception: Domestic design demand need not be added if provision is made to prevent flow on the domestic water system upon operation of sprinklers.

2-3.3.2 Sprinkler systems with nonfire protection connections shall comply with Section 5-6 of NFPA 13, *Standard for the Installation of Sprinkler Systems.*

2-4 System Components.

2-4.1 Valve and Drains.

2-4.1.1 When a common supply main is used to supply both domestic and sprinkler systems, a single listed control valve shall be provided to shut off both the domestic and sprinkler systems, and a separate shutoff valve shall be provided for the domestic system only. [*See Figure A-2-3.2(a).*]

Exception: The sprinkler system piping may have a separate control valve when supervised by one of the following methods:

(a) Central station, proprietary, or remote station alarm service,

(b) Local alarm service that will cause the sounding of an audible signal at a constantly attended point, or

(c) Locking the valves open.

2-4.1.2 Each sprinkler system shall have a 1-in. (25.4-mm) or larger drain and test connection with valve on the system side of the control valve.

2-4.1.3 Additional ½-in. (13-mm) drains shall be installed for each trapped portion of a dry system that is subject to freezing temperatures.

2-4.2 At least one 1½ in. (38 mm) or 2½ in. (64 mm) fire department connection shall be provided when the sprinkler system has 20 sprinklers or more.

2-4.3 Pressure Gages. Pressure gages shall be provided to indicate pressures on the supply and system sides of main check valves and dry-pipe valves, and to indicate pressure on water supply pressure tanks.

2-4.4 Piping Support. Piping hanging and bracing methods shall comply with NFPA 13, *Standard for the Installation of Sprinkler Systems.*

2-4.5 Sprinklers.

2-4.5.1 Listed residential sprinklers shall be used inside dwelling units. The basis of such a listing shall consist of tests to establish the ability of the sprinklers to control residential fires under standardized fire test conditions. The standardized room fires shall be based on a residential array of furnishings and finishes.

Exception No. 1: Residential sprinklers shall not be used in dry systems unless specifically listed for that purpose.

Exception No. 2: Other types of listed sprinklers may be installed in accordance with their listing in dwelling units meeting the definition of a compartment (as defined in 2-5.1.2.2) provided no more than four sprinklers are located in the dwelling unit and at least one smoke detector is provided in each sleeping room.

2-4.5.2 Ordinary temperature rated sprinklers [135 to 170°F (57 to 77°C)] shall be installed where maximum ambient ceiling temperatures do not exceed 100°F (38°C).

2-4.5.3 Intermediate temperature rated residential sprinklers [175 to 225°F (79 to 107°C)] shall be installed where maximum ambient ceiling temperatures are between 101 and 150°F (38 and 66°C).

2-4.5.4 The following practices shall be observed when installing residential sprinklers, unless maximum expected ambient temperatures are otherwise determined.

(a) Sprinklers under glass or plastic skylights exposed to direct rays of the sun shall be of intermediate temperature classification.

(b) Sprinklers in an unventilated concealed space under an uninsulated roof, or in an unventilated attic, shall be of intermediate temperature classification.

2-4.5.5 When residential sprinklers are installed within a compartment, as defined in 2-5.1.2.2, all sprinklers shall be from the same manufacturer and have the same heat-response element, including temperature rating.

Exception: Different temperature ratings are permitted when required by 2-4.5.4.

2-4.5.6 Standard sprinklers shall be used in areas outside the dwelling unit.

Exception No. 1: Residential sprinklers may be used in adjoining corridors or lobbies with flat, smooth ceilings and a height not exceeding 10 ft (3.0 m).

Exception No. 2: Quick-response sprinklers may be used in accordance with 2-5.2, Exception No. 1.

2-4.5.7 Operated or damaged sprinklers shall be replaced with sprinklers having the same performance characteristics as original equipment.

2-4.5.8 When nonmetallic ceiling plates (escutcheons) are used, they shall be listed. Escutcheon plates used to create a recessed or flush-type sprinkler shall be part of a listed sprinkler assembly.

2-4.5.9 Painting and Ornamental Finishes.

2-4.5.9.1 Sprinkler frames may be factory painted or enameled as ornamental finish in accordance with 2-4.5.9.2; otherwise, sprinklers shall not be painted and any sprinklers that have been painted, except those with factory applied coatings, shall be replaced with new listed sprinklers.

2-4.5.9.2* Ornamental finishes shall not be applied to sprinklers by anyone other than the sprinkler manufacturer, and only sprinklers listed with such finishes shall be used.

2-4.6 Alarms. Local waterflow alarms shall be provided on all sprinkler systems and shall be connected to the building fire alarm system, when provided.

2-5 System Design.

2-5.1 Design Criteria—Inside Dwelling Unit.

2-5.1.1 Design Discharge. The system shall provide a discharge of not less than 18 gpm (68 L/min) to any single operating sprinkler and not less than 13 gpm (49 L/min) per sprinkler to the number of design sprinklers, but not less than the listing of the sprinkler(s).

Exception: Design discharge for sprinklers installed in accordance with Exception No. 2 of 2-4.5.1 shall be in accordance with sprinkler listing criteria.

2-5.1.2* Number of Design Sprinklers.

2-5.1.2.1 The number of design sprinklers shall include all sprinklers within a compartment to a maximum of four sprinklers.

2-5.1.2.2 The definition of compartment for use in 2-5.1.2.1 to determine the number of design sprinklers is a space that is completely enclosed by walls and a ceiling. The compartment enclosure may have openings to an adjoining space if the openings have a minimum lintel depth of 8 in. (203 mm) from the ceiling.

2-5.1.3 Water Demand. The water demand for the system shall be determined by multiplying the design discharge of 2-5.1.1 by the number of design sprinklers of 2-5.1.2.

2-5.1.4 Sprinkler Coverage.

2-5.1.4.1 Residential sprinklers shall be spaced so that the maximum area protected by a single sprinkler does not exceed 144 sq ft (13.4 m^2).

2-5.1.4.2 The maximum distance between sprinklers shall not exceed 12 ft (3.7 m) and the maximum distance to a wall or partition shall not exceed 6 ft (1.8 m).

2-5.1.4.3 The minimum distance between sprinklers within a compartment shall be 8 ft (2.4 m).

2-5.1.5 The minimum operating pressure of any sprinkler shall be in accordance with the listing information of the sprinkler and shall provide the minimum flow rates specified in 2-5.1.1.

2-5.1.6 Application rates, design areas, areas of coverage, and minimum design pressures other than those specified in 2-5.1.1, 2-5.1.2, 2-5.1.4, and 2-5.1.5 may be used with special sprinklers that have been listed for such specific residential installation conditions.

2-5.1.7 Position of Residential Sprinklers.

2-5.1.7.1 Pendent and upright sprinklers shall be positioned so that the deflectors are within 1 to 4 in. (25.4 to 102 mm) from the ceiling.

Exception: Special residential sprinklers shall be installed in accordance with the listing limitations.

2-5.1.7.2 Sidewall sprinklers shall be positioned so that the deflectors are within 4 to 6 in. (102 to 152 mm) from the ceiling.

Exception: Special residential sprinklers shall be installed in accordance with the listing limitations.

2-5.1.7.3* Sprinklers shall be positioned so that the response time and discharge are not unduly affected by obstructions such as ceiling slope, beams, or light fixtures.

2-5.2 Design Criteria—Outside Dwelling Unit. The design discharge, number of design sprinklers, water demand of the system, sprinkler coverage, and position of sprinklers for areas to be sprinklered outside the dwelling unit shall comply with specifications in NFPA 13, *Standard for the Installation of Sprinkler Systems.*

Exception No. 1: When compartmented into areas of 500 sq ft (46 m^2) or less by 30-minute fire-rated construction, and the area is protected by standard or quick-response sprinklers not exceeding 130 sq ft (12 m^2) per sprinkler, the system demand may be limited to the number of sprinklers in the compartment area, but not less than a total of four sprinklers. Openings from the compartments need not be protected provided such openings are provided with a lintel at least 8 in. (203 mm) in depth and the total area of such openings does not exceed 50 sq ft (4.6 m^2) for each compartment. Discharge density shall be appropriate for the hazard classification as determined by NFPA 13.

Exception No. 2: Lobbies, in other than hotels and motels, foyers, corridors, and halls outside the dwelling unit, with flat, smooth ceilings and not exceeding 10 ft (3.0 m) in height, may be protected with residential sprinklers, with a maximum system demand of four sprinklers.

2-5.3 Pipe Sizing. Piping shall be sized in accordance with hydraulic calculation procedures to comply with NFPA 13, *Standard for the Installation of Sprinkler Systems.*

2-6 Location of Sprinklers. Sprinklers shall be installed in all areas.

Exception No. 1: Sprinklers may be omitted from bathrooms not exceeding 55 sq ft (5.1 m²) with noncombustible plumbing fixtures.

Exception No. 2: Sprinklers may be omitted from small clothes closets where the least dimension does not exceed 3 ft (0.9 m) and the area does not exceed 24 sq ft (2.2 m²) and the walls and ceiling are surfaced with noncombustible or limited combustible materials as defined by NFPA 220, Standard on Types of Building Construction.

Exception No. 3: Sprinklers may be omitted from open attached: porches, balconies, corridors, and stairs.

Exception No. 4: Sprinklers may be omitted from attics, penthouse equipment rooms, crawl spaces, floor/ceiling spaces, elevator shafts, and other concealed spaces that are not used or intended for living purposes or storage.

2-7* Maintenance. The owner is responsible for the condition of a sprinkler system and shall keep the system in normal operating condition.

Chapter 3 Referenced Publications

3-1 The following documents or portions thereof are referenced within this standard and shall be considered part of the requirements of this document. The edition indicated for each reference is the current edition as of the date of the NFPA issuance of this document.

3-1.1 NFPA Publications. National Fire Protection Association, Batterymarch Park, Quincy, MA 02269.

NFPA 13-1989, *Standard for the Installation of Sprinkler Systems*

NFPA 20-1987, *Standard for the Installation of Centrifugal Fire Pumps*

NFPA 22-1987, *Standard for Water Tanks for Private Fire Protection*

NFPA 74-1989, *Standard for the Installation, Maintenance, and Use of Household Fire Warning Equipment*

NFPA *101*®-1988, *Life Safety Code*®

NFPA 220-1985, *Standard on Types of Building Construction.*

3-1.2 Other Publications.

3-1.2.1 ANSI Publications. American National Standards Institute, Inc., 1430 Broadway, New York, NY 10018.

ANSI B16.1-1975, *Cast Iron Pipe Flanges and Flanged Fittings, Class 25, 125, 250 and 800*

ANSI B16.3-1985, *Malleable Iron Threaded Fittings, Class 150 and 300*

ANSI B16.4-1985, *Cast Iron Threaded Fittings, Classes 125 and 250*

ANSI B16.5-1981, *Pipe Flanges and Flanged Fittings*

ANSI B16.9-1986, *Factory-Made Wrought Steel Buttwelding Fittings*

ANSI B16.11-1980, *Forged Steel Fittings, Socket-Welding and Threaded*

ANSI B16.18-1984, *Cast Copper Alloy Solder Joint Pressure Fittings*

ANSI B16.22-1980, *Wrought Copper and Copper Alloy Solder Joint Pressure Fittings*

ANSI B16.25-1986, *Buttwelding Ends*

ANSI B36.10M-1985, *Welded and Seamless Wrought Steel Pipe.*

3-1.2.2 ASTM Publications. American Society for Testing and Materials, 1916 Race Street, Philadelphia, PA 19103.

ASTM A53-1987, *Standard Specification for Pipe, Steel, Black and Hot-Dipped, Zinc-Coated Welded and Seamless Steel Pipe*

ASTM A135-1986, *Standard Specification for Electric-Resistance-Welded Steel Pipe*

ASTM A234-1987, *Standard Specification for Piping Fittings of Wrought-Carbon Steel and Alloy Steel for Moderate and Elevated Temperatures*

ASTM A795-1985, *Specification for Black and Hot-Dipped Zinc-Coated (Galvanized) Welded and Seamless Steel Pipe for Fire Protection Use*

ASTM B32-1987, *Standard Specification for Solder Metal, 95-5 (Tin-Antimony-Grade 95TA)*

ASTM B88-1986, *Standard Specification for Seamless Copper Water Tube*

ASTM B251-1987, *Standard Specification for General Requirements for Wrought Seamless Copper and Copper-Alloy Tube*

ASTM E380-1986, *Standard for Metric Practice.*

3-1.2.3 AWS Publication. American Welding Society, 2501 N.W. 7th Street, Miami, FL 33125.

AWS A5.8-1981, *Specification for Brazing Filler Metal.*

Appendix A

This Appendix is not a part of the requirements of this NFPA document, but is included for information purposes only.

A-1-1 NFPA 13R is appropriate for use only in residential occupancies, as an option to NFPA 13, *Standard for the Installation of Sprinkler Systems,* as defined in this standard, up to four stories in height. Residential portions of any other building may be protected with residential sprinklers in accordance with 3-11.2.9 of NFPA 13, *Standard for the Installation of Sprinkler Systems.* Other portions of such sections should be protected in accordance with NFPA 13.

The criteria in this standard are based on full-scale fire tests of rooms containing typical furnishings found in residential living rooms, kitchens, and bedrooms. The furnishings were arranged as typically found in dwelling units in a manner similar to that shown in Figures A-1-1(a), (b), and (c). Sixty full-scale fire tests were conducted in a two-story dwelling in Los Angeles, California, and 16 tests were conducted in a 14-ft (4.3-m) wide mobile home in Charlotte, North Carolina. Sprinkler systems designed and installed according to this standard are expected to prevent flashover within the compartment of origin if sprinklers are installed in the compartment. A sprinkler system designed and installed according to this standard may not, however, be expected to control a fire involving unusually higher average fuel loads than typical for dwelling units [10 psi (0.7 bar)], configurations of fuels other than those with typical residential occupancies, or conditions where the interior finish has an unusually high flame spread rating (greater than 225).

To be effective, sprinkler systems installed in accordance with this standard must have the sprinklers closest to the fire open before the fire exceeds the ability of the sprinkler discharge to extinguish or control that fire. Conditions that allow the fire to grow beyond that point before sprinkler activation or that interfere with the quality of water distribution can produce conditions beyond the capabilities of the sprinkler system described in this standard. Unusually high ceilings or ceiling configurations that tend to divert the rising hot gases from sprinkler locations or change the sprinkler discharge pattern from its standard pattern can produce fire conditions that cannot be extinguished or controlled by the systems described in this standard.

A-1-2 Levels of Protection. Various levels of sprinkler protection are available to provide life safety and property protection. The standard is designed to provide a high, but not absolute, level of life safety and a lesser level of property protection. Greater protection to both life and property could be achieved by sprinklering all areas in accordance with NFPA 13, *Standard for the Installation of Sprinkler Systems*, which permits the use of residential sprinklers in residential areas.

This standard recommends, but does not require, sprinklering of all areas in the building; it permits sprinklers to be omitted in certain areas. These areas are the ones shown by NFPA statistics to be ones where the incidence of life loss from fires in residential occupancies is low. Such an approach provides a reasonable degree of fire safety to life. (*See Table A-1-2 for Deaths and Injuries in Multifamily Residential Buildings.*)

It should be recognized that the omission of sprinklers from certain areas could result in the development of untenable conditions in adjacent spaces. Where evacuation times may be delayed, additional sprinkler protection and other fire protection features, such as detection and compartmentation, may be necessary.

A-2-1.3.2 Testing of a system can be accomplished by filling the system with water and checking visually for leakage at each joint or coupling.

Fire department connections are not required for all systems covered by this standard, but may be installed at the discretion of the owner. In these cases, hydrostatic tests in accordance with NFPA 13, *Standard for the Installation of Sprinkler Systems*, are required.

Dry systems should also be tested by placing the system under air pressure. Any leak that results in a drop in system pressure greater than 2 psi (0.14 bar) in 24 hours should be corrected. Check for leaks using soapy water brushed on each joint or coupling. Leaks will be shown by the presence of bubbles. This test should be made prior to concealing of piping.

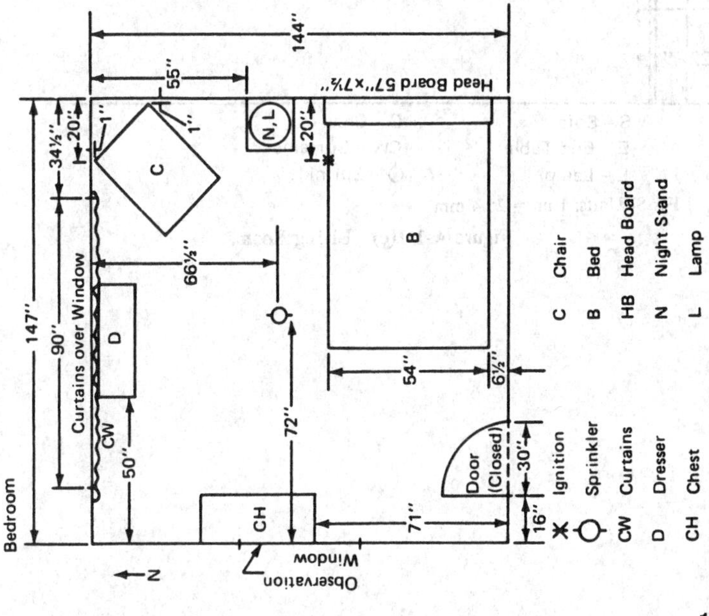
Bedroom
N
Observation Window
147″
90″
Curtains over Window
34½″
20″
1″
1″
55″
144″
Head Board 57″×7½″
N,L
20″
C
CW
D
50″
66½″
B
CH
72″
71″
54″
6½″
Door (Closed)
30″
16″
✱ Ignition
Sprinkler
CW Curtains
D Dresser
CH Chest
C Chair
B Bed
HB Head Board
N Night Stand
L Lamp

For SI Units: 1 in. = 25.4 mm.

Figure A-1-1(a) Bedroom.

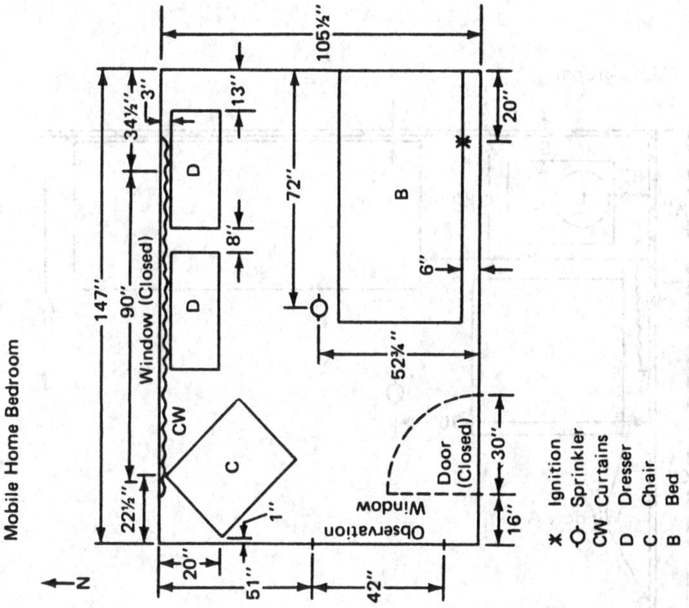
Mobile Home Bedroom
N
147″
90″
Window (Closed)
34½″
3″
22½″
CW
C
1″
D
D
13″
8″
72″
105½″
B
6″
20″
52¾″
Observation Window
Door (Closed)
30″
16″
20″
51″
42″
✱ Ignition
Sprinkler
CW Curtains
D Dresser
C Chair
B Bed

For SI Units: 1 in. = 25.4 mm.

Figure A-1-1(b) Mobile Home Bedroom.

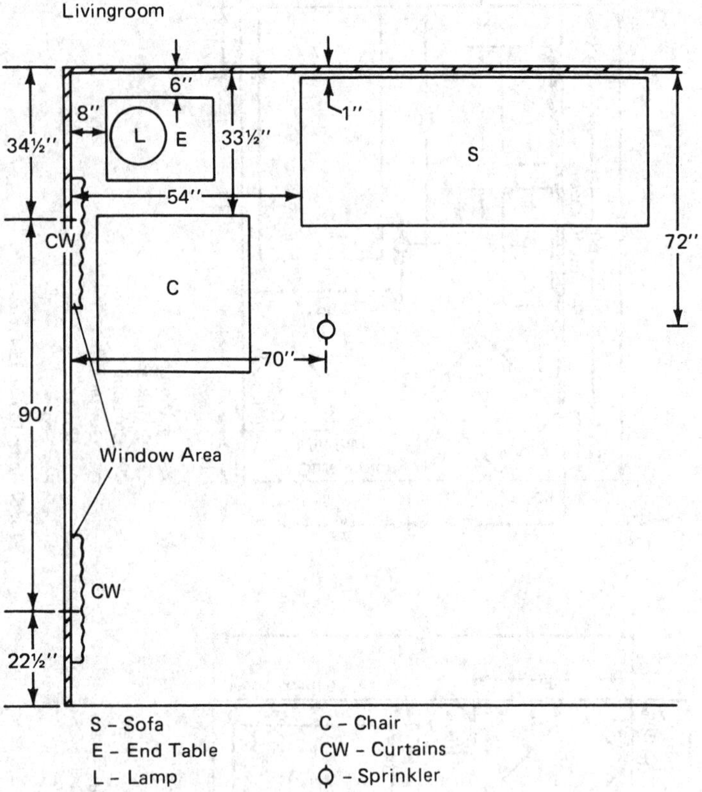
Livingroom
6″
1″
8″
L
E
34½″
33½″
S
54″
72″
CW
C
70″
90″
Window Area
CW
22½″
S - Sofa
C - Chair
E - End Table
CW - Curtains
L - Lamp
- Sprinkler

For SI Units: 1 in. = 25.4 mm.

Figure A-1-1(c) Living Room.

Table A-1-2
Annual Averages of Deaths and Injuries in Apartments
1980-1984

Fires–123,000	Civilian Deaths–930		Civilian Injuries–5,470
	Percentages by Area of Origin		
Area of Origin (901 Code)	**Civilian Deaths (Used for Ranking)**	**Fires**	**Civilian Injuries**
Living room, den, lounge (14)	38.5	11.3	23.2
Bedroom (21-22)	28.7	17.4	27.1
Kitchen (24)	9.8	35.3	27.2
Hallway corridor (101)	4.3	3.2	3.4
Interior stairway (03)	3.2	1.0	1.1
Structural Area (70-79)	3.1	8.1	3.5
[Balcony, porch (72)]	(1.2)	(1.3)	(0.7)
[Unspecified (79)]	(1.0)	(0.5)	(0.2)
[Ceiling/Roof assembly (74)]	(0.3)	(0.7)	(0.3)
Lobby (05)	1.3	0.6	0.7
Dining room (23)	1.2	0.8	1.0
Closet (42)	1.2	1.9	1.9
Balcony, porch (72)	1.2	1.3	0.7
Other known single area	4.1	17.8	8.8
[Bathroom (25)]	(0.6)	(2.1)	(1.3)
Multiple areas (97)	1.6	0.7	0.9
Unclassified, not applicable (98-99)	1.8	0.6	0.5
Total:	100.0	100.0	100.0

A-2-2.1.1 At least three spare sprinklers of each type, temperature rating, and orifice size used in the system should be kept on the premises. When fused sprinklers are replaced by the owner, fire department, or others, care should be taken to assure that the replacement sprinkler has the same operating characteristics.

A-2-3.2 Connection for fire protection to city mains is often subject to local regulation concerning metering and backflow prevention requirements. Preferred and acceptable water supply arrangements are shown in Figures A-2-3.2(a), (b), and (c). When a meter must be used between the city water main and the sprinkler system supply, an acceptable arrangement is shown in Figure A-2-3.2(c). Under these circumstances, the flow characteristics of the meter must be included in the hydraulic calculation of the system. When a tank is used for both domestic and fire protection purposes, a low water alarm acuated when the water level falls below 110 percent of the minimum quantity specified in 2-3.1 should be provided.

A-2-3.3.1 The tables on the following page can be used to determine a domestic design demand. Using Table A-2-3.3.1(a), determine the total number of water supply fixture units downstream of any point in the piping serving both sprinkler and domestic needs. Using Table A-2-3.3.1(b), determine the appropriate total flow allowance, and add this flow to the sprinkler demand at the total pressure required for the sprinkler system at that point.

A-2-4.5.9.2 Decorative painting of a residential sprinkler is not to be confused with the temperature identification colors as referenced in 3-11.6 of NFPA 13, *Standard for the Installation of Sprinkler Systems.*

A-2-5.1.2 It is intended that the design area is to include up to four adjacent sprinklers producing the greatest water demand within the compartment.

A-2-5.1.7.3 Fire testing has indicated the need to wet walls in the area protected by residential sprinklers at a level closer to the ceiling than that accomplished by standard sprinkler distribution. Where beams, light fixtures, sloped ceilings, and other obstructions occur, additional residential sprinklers may be necessary to achieve proper response and distribution, and a greater water supply may be necessary.

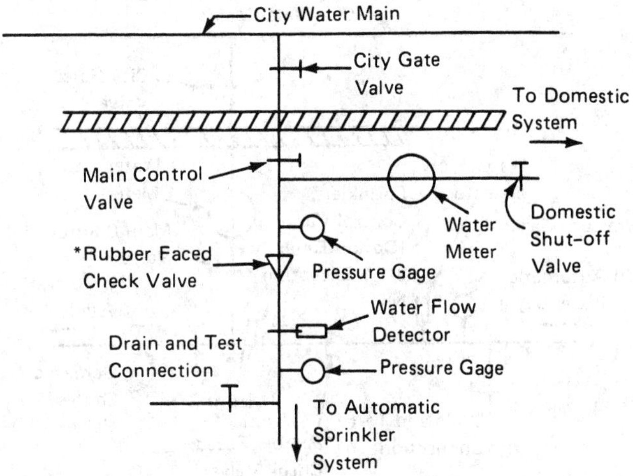
City Water Main
City Gate Valve
To Domestic System
Main Control Valve
Water Meter
Domestic Shut-off Valve
*Rubber Faced Check Valve
Pressure Gage
Water Flow Detector
Drain and Test Connection
Pressure Gage
To Automatic Sprinkler System

Figure A-2-3.2(a) Preferable Arrangement.

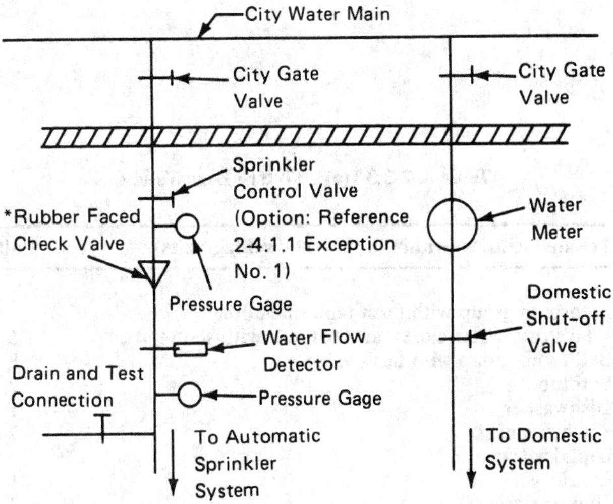
City Water Main
City Gate Valve
City Gate Valve
Sprinkler Control Valve (Option: Reference 2-4.1.1 Exception No. 1)
*Rubber Faced Check Valve
Water Meter
Pressure Gage
Domestic Shut-off Valve
Water Flow Detector
Drain and Test Connection
Pressure Gage
To Automatic Sprinkler System
To Domestic System

Figure A-2-3.2(b) Acceptable Arrangement with Valve Supervision. (*See 2-4.1.1 Exception.*)

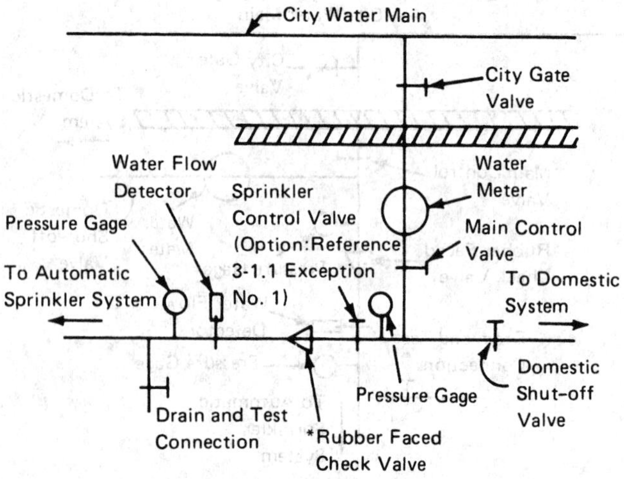
City Water Main
City Gate Valve
Water Meter
Main Control Valve
To Domestic System
Domestic Shut-off Valve
Water Flow Detector
Sprinkler Control Valve (Option:Reference 3-1.1 Exception No. 1)
Pressure Gage
To Automatic Sprinkler System
Drain and Test Connection
*Rubber Faced Check Valve
Pressure Gage

*Rubber Faced Check Valves Optional.

Figure A-2-3.2(c) Acceptable Arrangement with Valve Supervision. (*See 2-4.1.1 Exception.*)

Table A-2-3.3.1(a) Fixture Load Values

Private facilities (within individual dwelling units)	Unit
Bathroom group with flush tank (including lavatory, water closet, and bathtub with shower)	6
Bathroom group with flush valve	8
Bathtub	2
Dishwasher	1
Kitchen sink	2
Laundry trays	3
Lavatory	1
Shower stall	2
Washing machine	2
Water closet with flush valve	6
Water closet with flush tank	3

Table A-2-3.3.1(a) Fixture Load Values *(Continued)*

Public Facilities	
Bathtub	4
Drinking fountain	0
Kitchen sink	4
Lavatory	2
Service sink	3
Shower head	4
Urinal with 1 in. flush valve	10
Urinal with ¾ in. flush valve	5
Urinal with flush tank	3
Washing machine (8 lb)	3
Washing machine (16 lb)	4
Water closet with flush valve	10
Water closet with flush tank	5

Table A-2-3.3.1(b) Total Estimated Domestic Demand

Total Fixture Load Units [from Table A-2-3.3.1(a)]	Total Demand in Gallons Per Minute For Systems with Predominantly Flush Tanks	For Systems with Predominantly Flush Valves
1	3 gpm	
2	5	
5	10	15 gpm
10	15	25
20	20	35
35	25	45
50	30	50
70	35	60
100	45	70
150	55	80
200	65	90
250	75	100
350	100	125
500	125	150
750	175	175
1000	200	200
1500	275	275
2000	325	325
3500	500	500

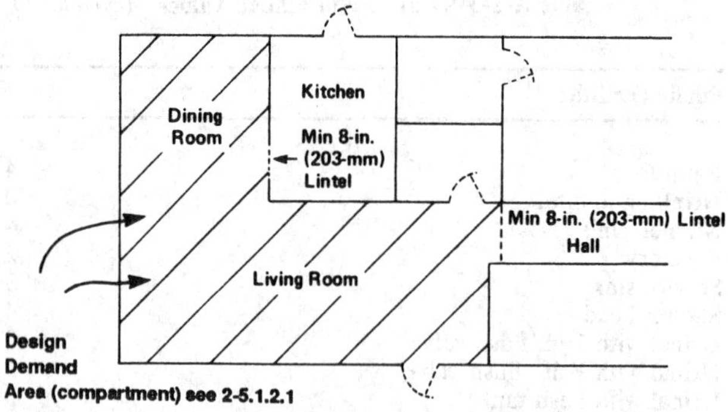
Kitchen
Dining Room
Min 8-in. (203-mm) Lintel
Min 8-in. (203-mm) Lintel
Hall
Living Room
Design Demand Area (compartment) see 2-5.1.2.1

Figure A-2-5.1.2(a) Sprinkler Design Areas for Typical Residential Occupancy.

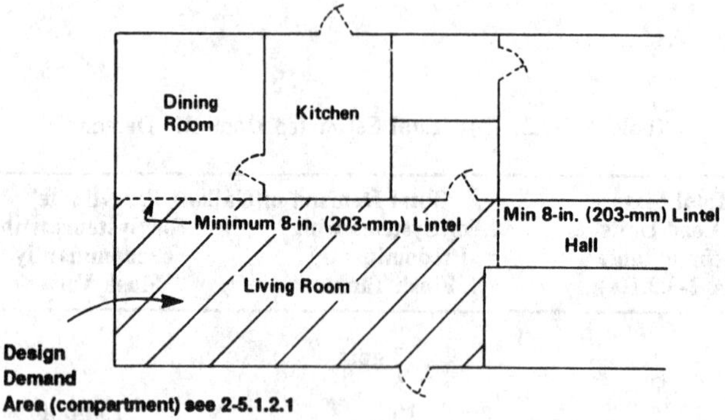
Dining Room
Kitchen
Minimum 8-in. (203-mm) Lintel
Min 8-in. (203-mm) Lintel
Hall
Living Room
Design Demand Area (compartment) see 2-5.1.2.1

Figure A-2-5.1.2(b) Sprinkler Design Areas for Typical Residential Occupancy.

Table A-2-5.1.7.3 and Figure A-2-5.1.7.3 provide guidance for location of sprinklers near ceiling obstructions.

A-2-7 The responsibility for properly maintaining a sprinkler system is the obligation of the owner or manager, who should understand the sprinkler system operation. A minimum monthly maintenance program should include the following:

(a) Visual inspection of all sprinklers to ensure against obstruction of spray.

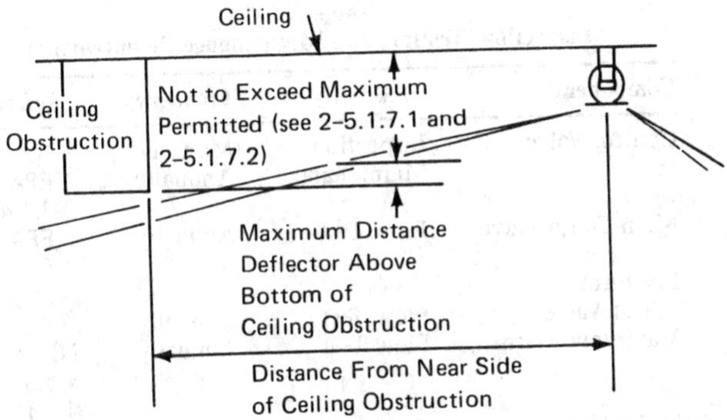
Ceiling
Ceiling
Obstruction
Not to Exceed Maximum
Permitted (see 2-5.1.7.1 and
2-5.1.7.2)
Maximum Distance
Deflector Above
Bottom of
Ceiling Obstruction
Distance From Near Side
of Ceiling Obstruction

Figure A-2-5.1.7.3 Position of Deflector, Upright or Pendent, When Located Above Bottom of Ceiling Obstruction.

(b) Inspection of all valves to assure that they are open.

(c) Testing of all waterflow devices.

(d) Testing of the alarm system, if installed.

NOTE: When it appears likely that the test will result in a response of the fire department, notification to the fire department should be made prior to the test.

Table A-2-5.1.7.3 Maximum Distance from Sprinkler Deflector to Bottom of Ceiling Obstruction

Distance from Sprinkler to Side of Ceiling Obstruction	Maximum Distance from Sprinkler Deflector to Bottom of Ceiling Obstruction
Less than 6 in.	Not permitted
6 in. to less than 1 ft	0 in.
1 ft to less than 2 ft	1 in.
2 ft to less than 2 ft 6 in.	2 in.
2 ft 6 in. to less than 3 ft	3 in.
3 ft to less than 3 ft 6 in.	4 in.
3 ft 6 in. to less than 4 ft	6 in.
4 ft to less than 4 ft 6 in.	7 in.
4 ft 6 in. to less than 5 ft	9 in.
5 ft to less than 5 ft 6 in.	11 in.
5 ft 6 in. to less than 6 ft	14 in.

For SI Units: 1 in. = 25.4 mm; 1 ft = 0.3048 m.

Table A-2-7
Inspection, Testing, and Maintenance Requirements

Component	Activity	Frequency	Reference
Control Valve	Inspection	Monthly	
	Maintenance	Annually	NFPA 13A, 2-7.1.4
Main Drain Valve	Flow Test	Annually	NFPA 13A, 2-6.1
Inspectors' Test Valve	Flow Test	Annually	
Waterflow Alarm	Flow Test	Annually	NFPA 13A, 4-5.3, 4-7.1
Sprinklers	Test	50 Yrs.	NFPA 13A, 3-3.3
Sprinklers, Res/QR	Test	20 Yrs.	NFPA 13A, 3-3.4
Pump	Flow Test	Annually	NFPA 13A, 2-4.2.5
Antifreeze Solutions	Test	Annually	NFPA 13A, 4-7.3

(e) Operation of pumps, where employed, should be operated. See NFPA 20, *Standard for the Installation of Centrifugal Fire Pumps.*

(f) Checking of the pressure of air used with dry systems.

(g) Checking of water level in tanks.

(h) Care should be taken to see that sprinklers are not painted either at the time of installation or during subsequent redecoration. When painting sprinkler piping or painting in areas next to sprinklers, the sprinklers may be protected by covering with a bag, which should be removed immediately after painting is finished.

For further information see NFPA 13A, *Recommended Practice for the Inspection, Testing and Maintenance of Sprinkler Systems.*

Appendix B Referenced Publications

B-1 The following documents or portions thereof are referenced within this standard for informational purposes only and thus are not considered part of the requirements of this document. The edition indicated for each reference is the current edition as of the date of the NFPA issuance of this document.

B-1.1 NFPA Publications. National Fire Protection Association, Batterymarch Park, Quincy, MA 02269.

NFPA 13-1989, *Standard for the Installation of Sprinkler Systems*

NFPA 13A-1987, *Recommended Practice for the Inspection, Testing and Maintenance of Sprinkler Systems*

NFPA 20-1987, *Standard for the Installation of Centrifugal Fire Pumps.*

UNIFORM BUILDING CODE STANDARD NO. 42-1

TEST METHOD FOR SURFACE-BURNING CHARACTERISTICS OF BUILDING MATERIALS

Based on Standard Test Method E 84-84 of the American Society for Testing and Materials. Extracted, with permission, from the Annual Book of ASTM Standards, copyright American Society for Testing and Materials, 1916 Race Street, Philadelphia, PA 19103.

See Sections 401 (b), 407, 415, 417, 1701 (b), 1713 (c), 1713 (e) 2, 1713 (f), 1714 (b), 1714 (c), 3901 (a), 3903 (d), 4201 (a) 1, 4201 (b) and 4202 (b), Uniform Building Code; Section 416, Table No. 5-A and Appendix B—Section 2127, Uniform Mechanical Code; and Sections 202 and 211, Uniform Sign Code

Scope

Sec. 42.101. This method for surface-burning characteristics of building materials is applicable to any type of building material that, by its own structural quality or the manner in which it is applied, is capable of supporting itself in position or may be supported in the test furnace to a thickness comparable to its recommended use.

The purpose of the test is to determine the comparative burning characteristics of the material under test by evaluating the flame spread over its surface when exposed to a test fire and to thus establish a basis on which surface-burning characteristics of different materials may be compared, without specific considerations of all the end-use parameters that might affect the surface-burning characteristics.

Smoke density as well as the flame-spread rate are recorded in this test. However, there is not necessarily a relationship between these measurements.

It is the intent of this method to register performance during the period of exposure, and not to determine suitability for use after the test exposure

This standard shall be used to measure and describe the properties of materials, products, or assemblies in response to heat and flame under controlled laboratory conditions and is not to describe or appraise the fire hazard or fire risk of materials, products, or assemblies under actual fire conditions. However, results of this test may be used as elements of a fire risk assessment which takes into account all of the factors which are pertinent to an assessment of the fire hazard of a particular end use.

This method is intended to provide only comparative measurements of surface flame-spread and smoke-density measurements with that of Select grade red oak and asbestos-cement board surfaces under the specific fire exposure conditions described herein.

The test exposes a nominal 24-foot-long by 20-inch-wide specimen to a controlled air flow and flaming fire exposure adjusted to spread the flame along the entire length of the select grade red oak specimen in 5½ minutes.

The test method does not provide for the following:

Measurement of heat transmission through the tested surface.

The effect of aggravated flame-spread behavior of an assembly resulting from the proximity of combustible walls and ceilings.

Classifying or defining a material as noncombustible, by means of a flame-spread index by itself.

Fire Test Chamber

Sec. 42.102. The fire test chamber, Figures Nos. 42-1-1 and 42-1-2, shall consist of a horizontal duct having an inside width of 17¾ ± ¼ inch measured at ledge location along side walls and 17⅝ ± ⅜ inch at all other points; a depth of 12 ± ½ inch measured from the bottom of the test chamber to the ledge of the inner walls on which the sample is supported (including the ⅛-inch thickness of asbestos fabric gasketing tape); and a length of 25 feet. The sides and base of the duct are to be lined with insulating masonry as illustrated in Figure No. 42-1-2 consisting of A. P. Green, G-26 refractory firebrick. The operation and calibration of this equipment is based on the use of A. P. Green Refractories. One side is to be provided with a double window with the inside pane flush mounted (see Figure No. 42-1-2) pressure tight as described in Section 42.104. Exposed inside glass shall be 2¾ ± ⅜ by 11 plus 1 minus 2 inch. The center line of the exposed area of the inside glass shall be in the upper half of the furnace wall, with the upper edge not less than 2.5 inches below the furnace ledge. The window shall be located such that not less than 12 inches of the specimen width can be observed. Multiple windows shall be located along the tunnel so that the entire length of the test sample may be observed from outside the fire chamber.

The ledges shall be fabricated of structural material capable of withstanding the abuse of continuous testing, level with respect to length and width of the chamber and each other and maintained in a state of repair commensurate with the frequency, volume and severity of testing occurring at any time.

To provide air turbulance for proper combustion, turbulence baffling is to be provided as necessary by positioning six A. P. Green, G-26, refractory firebricks (long dimension vertical 4½-inch dimension along the wall) along the sidewalls of the chamber at distances of 7, 12 and 20, ±0.5 feet on the window side and 4½, 9½ and 16, ±0.5 feet on the opposite side.

The top shall consist of a removeable noncombustible (metal and mineral composite) structure, insulated with nominal 2-inch-thick mineral composition material as shown in Figure No. 42-1-2 and of a size necessary to completely cover the fire test chamber and the test samples. The mineral composition material shall have physical characteristics comparable to the following;

Maximum effective temperature—1200°F.
Bulk density—12.5 ± 1.5 lb./ft.^{3}
Thermal conductivity—0.45—0.65 Btu in./h. ft.^{2} °F. at 300-700°F.

The entire lid assembly shall be protected with flat sections of high density (nominal 110 lb./ft.^{3}) ¼-inch asbestos-cement board maintained in an unwarped and uncracked condition through continued replacement. When in place, the top is to be completely sealed against the leakage of air into the fire test chamber during the test.

One end of the test chamber, designated as the "fire end," shall be provided with two gas burners delivering flames upward against the surface of the test sample. The burners are to be spaced 12 inches from the fire end of the test chamber sample and 7½ ± ½ inch below the under surface of the test sample. The air intake shutter is to be located 54 ± 5 inches upstream of the burner, as measured from the burners' center line to the outside surface of the shutter. Gas to the burners shall be provided through a single inlet pipe, distributed to each port burner through a tee section. The outlet shall be a ¾-inch elbow. The plane of the port shall be parallel to the furnace floor, such that the gas is directed upward toward the specimen. Each part shall be positioned transversely approximately 4 ± ½ inch on each side of the center line of the furnace so that the flame is evenly distributed over the width of the exposed sample surface. See Figure No. 42-1-2. The controls used to assure constant flow of gas to the burners during periods of use are to consist of a pressure regulator, a gas meter calibrated to read in increments of not more than 0.1 ft.^{3}, a manometer to indicate gas pressure in inches of water, a quick-acting gas shutoff valve, a gas-metering valve and an orifice plate in combination with a water manometer to assist in maintaining uniform gas-flow conditions. An air intake fitted with a vertically sliding shutter extending the entire width of the test chamber is to be provided at the fire end. The shutter is to be positioned so as to provide an air-inlet port 3 ± 1/16 inch high measured from the floor level of the test chamber at the air-intake point.

The other end of the test chamber, designated as the "vent end," is to be fitted with a gradual rectangular-to-round transition piece, not less than 20 inches in length with a minimum cross-sectional area of 200 square inches at any point. The transition piece shall in turn be fitted to a 16-inch-diameter flue pipe. The movement of air is to be by induced draft system, and the draft-inducing system is to have a total draft capacity of at least 0.15-inch water column with the sample in place, the shutter at the fire end open to normal 3 ± 1/16 inch, and the damper in the wide-open position. A draft gage tap to indicate static pressure shall be inserted through the top at the midwidth of the tunnel, 1 ±0.5 inch below the ceiling, 15 ± 0.5 inch downstream from the inlet shutter.

A light source shall be mounted on a horizontal section of the 16-inch-diameter horizontal vent pipe at a point where it will be preceded by a straight run of pipe (at least 12 diameters or 16 feet and not more than 30 diameters or 40 feet), from the vent end of the chamber, with the light beam directed upward along the vertical axis of the vent pipe. The vent pipe is to be insulated with at least 2 inches of high-temperature mineral composition material from the vent end of the chamber to the photometer location. A photoelectric cell of which the output is directly proportional to the amount of light received is to be mounted over the light source and connected to a recording device for indicating changes in the attenuation of incident light by passing smoke, particulate and other effluent. The distance between the light source lens and the photocell lens shall be 36 ± 4 inches. The cylindrical light beam shall pass through 3-inch-diameter openings at the top and bottom of the 16-inch-diameter duct, with the resultant light beam centered on the photocell.

Linearity of the photometer system shall be verified periodically by interrupting the light beam with calibrated neutral density filters. The filters shall cover the full range of the recording instrument. Transmittance values measured by the photometer, using neutral density filters, shall be within ±3 percent of the calibrated value for each filter.

An automatically controlled damper to regulate the draft pressure shall be installed in the vent pipe downstream of the smoke-indicating attachment. The damper shall be provided with a manual override.

Other manual or automatic draft regulation devices, or both, may be incorporated to maintain fan characterization and air-flow control throughout test periods.

A No. 18 AWG thermocouple, with 3/8 ± 1/8 inch of the junction exposed in the air, shall be inserted through the floor of the test chamber so that the tip is 1 ± 1/32 inch below the top surface of the asbestos gasketing tape and 23 feet ± 1/2 inch from the center line of the burner ports at the center of its width.

A No. 18 AWG thermocouple embedded 1/8 inch below the floor surface of the test chamber is to be mounted in refractory or portland cement carefully dried to avoid cracking at distances of 13 feet ± 1/2 inch and 23 1/4 feet ± 1/2 inch from the center line of the burner ports.

The room in which the test chamber is located is to have provision for a free inflow of air during test to maintain the room at atmospheric pressure during the entire test run.

Test Specimens

Sec. 42.103. The test specimen shall be at least 2 inches wider (nominally 20 1/4 ± 3/4 inch) than the interior width of the tunnel and total 24 feet ± 1/2 inch in length. The specimen may consist of a continuous, unbroken length or of sections joined end-to-end. A 14- ± 1/8-inch length of uncoated 16-gage (0.053- to 0.060-inch) steel sheet shall be placed on specimen mounting ledge in front of and under the specimen in the upstream end of the tunnel. Specimens shall truly represent the materials for which classification is desired. Properties adequate for identification of the materials or ingredients, or both, of which the test specimen is made are to be determined and recorded.

The test specimen shall be conditioned to a constant weight at a temperature of 73.4 ± 5°F. and at a relative humidity of 50 ± 5 percent.

Calibration of Test Equipment

Sec. 42.104. A ¼-inch asbestos-cement board shall be placed on the ledge of the furnace chamber. The removable top of the test chamber shall be placed in position.

With the ¼-inch asbestos-cement board in position on top of the ledge of the furnace chamber, and with the removable top in place, the draft is to be established so as to produce a 0.15-inch water-column reading on the draft manometer, with the fire-end shutter open 3 ± ¹⁄₁₆ inch by manually setting the damper as a characterization of fan performance. The fire-end shutter shall be closed and sealed without changing the damper position. The manometer reading shall increase to at least 0.375-inch water column, indicating that no excessive air leakage exists.

In addition, a supplemental leakage test is to be conducted periodically with the fire shutter and exhaust duct beyond the differential manometer tube sealed, by placing a smoke bomb in the chamber. The bomb shall be ignited and the chamber pressurized to 0.375 ± 0.15-inch water column. All points of leakage observed in the form of escaping smoke particles shall be sealed.

A draft reading shall be established within the range 0.055- to 0.100-inch water column. The required draft gage reading shall be maintained by the automatic damper. Record the air velocity at seven points, 23 feet from the center line of the burner ports, 6 ± ¼ inch below the plane of the specimen mounting ledge. Determine these seven points by dividing the width of the tunnel into seven equal sections and recording the velocity at the geometrical center of each section. During the measurement of velocity, remove the turbulence bricks and exposed 23-foot thermocouple and place 24-inch-long straightening vanes between 16 and 18 feet from the burner. The straightening vanes shall divide the furnace cross section into nine uniform sections. Determine the velocity with furnace air temperature at 73.4 ± 5°F. using a velocity transducer. The velocity, determined as the arithmetic average of the seven readings, shall be 240 ± 5 feet per minute.

Maintain the air supply at a temperature of 73.4 ± 5°F. and a relative humidity of 50 ± 5 percent.

The fire test chamber shall be supplied with natural (city) or methane (bottled) gas fuel of uniform quality with a heating value of nominally 1000 Btu/ft^3. The gas supply is to be initially adjusted at approximately 5000 Btu/min. The gas pressure, the pressure differential across the orifice plate and the volume of gas used shall be recorded in each test. Unless otherwise corrected for, when bottled methane is employed, a length of coiled copper tubing is to be inserted into the gas line between the supply and metering connection to compensate for possible errors in the flow indicated due to reductions in gas temperature associated with the pressure drop and expansion across the regulator. With the draft and gas supply adjusted as indicated in this section, the test flame is to extend downstream to a distance of 4½ feet over the specimen surface, with negligible upstream coverage.

The test chamber shall be preheated with the ¼-inch asbestos-cement board and the removable top in place and with the fuel supply adjusted to the required flow. The preheating shall be continued until the temperature indicated by the floor thermocouple at 23¼ feet reaches 150 ± 5°F. During the preheat test, the temperatures indicated by the thermocouple at the vent end of the test chamber shall be recorded at 15-second intervals and compared to the preheat temperature shown in the time-temperature curve, Figure No. 42-1-3. The preheating is for the purpose of establishing the conditions that will exist following the successive tests and to indicate the control of the heat input into the test chamber. If the appreciable variation from the temperatures shown in the representative preheat curve is observed, because of variation in the characteristics of the gas used, adjustments in the fuel supply may be made prior to proceeding with the red oak calibration tests.

The furnace shall be allowed to cool after each test. When the floor thermocouple at 13 feet shows a temperature of 105 ± 5°F., the next specimen shall be placed in position for test.

With the test equipment adjusted and conditioned as described in this section, a test or series of tests shall be made, using nominal 23/32-inch Select grade red oak flooring as the sample, conditioned to 6 to 8 percent moisture content as determined by the 221°F. oven-dry method in accordance with approved nationally recognized standards. Observations shall be made at distance intervals of not more than 2 feet and time intervals of not more than 30 seconds and the time recorded when the flame reaches the end of the specimen, that is, 19½ feet from the end of the ignition fire. The end of the ignition fire shall be considered as being 4½ feet from the burners. The flame shall reach the end point in five and one-half minutes ± 15 seconds. The temperature measured by the thermocouple near the vent end shall be automatically recorded at least every 15 seconds. The photoelectric cell output shall be automatically recorded immediately prior to the test and at least every 15 seconds during the test.

The results of tests of Select grade red oak flooring in which the flame spreads 19½ feet from the end of the igniting flame in five and one-half minutes shall be considered as representing a classification of 100. Plot the flame spread distance, temperature, and change in photoelectric cell readings separately on suitable coordinate paper. Figures Nos. 42-1-4, 42-1-5 and 42-1-6 are representative curves for red oak flame spread distance, time-temperature development, and smoke density, respectively. Flame-spread distance shall be determined as the observed distance minus 4½ feet.

Following the calibration tests for red oak, a similar test(s) is to be conducted on samples of ¼-inch asbestos-cement board. The results are to be considered as representing a classification of zero. The temperature readings shall be plotted separately on coordinate paper. Figure No. 42-1-7 is a representative curve for fuel contribution of asbestos-cement board.

Test Procedure

Sec. 42.105. With the furnace draft operating, the test specimen shall be placed on the test chamber ledges which have been completely covered with nominal ⅛-inch-thick by 1½-inch-wide woven asbestos tape. The removable top shall be placed in position over the specimen.

The completely mounted specimen is to remain in position in the chamber with the furnace draft operating for 120 ± 15 seconds prior to application of the test flame.

The igniting flame shall be lighted and adjusted. The distance and time of maximum flame front travel is to be observed and recorded. The test shall to be continued for a 10-minute period unless the sample is completely consumed in the fire area before that time, in which case the test is to be ended after no further progressive burning is evident and the photoelectric cell reading has returned to the base line.

The photoelectric cell output shall be recorded immmediately prior to the test and at least every 15 seconds during test.

The gas pressure, the pressure differential across the orifice plate and the volume of gas used shall be recorded in each test.

When the test is ended, the gas supply shall be shut off, smoldering and other conditions within the test duct are to be observed and the sample removed for further examination.

The temperature, flame-spread distance and change in photoelectric cell readings shall be plotted separately on the same coordinate paper as used for those graphs required in Section 42.104 for use in determining the flame-spread and smoke-developed indexes as outlined in Section 42.106. Flame front advancement shall be recorded at the time of occurrence or at least every 30 seconds if no advancement is noted. Flame-spread distance shall be determined as the observed distance minus 4½ feet.

Interpretation of Results

Sec. 42.106. The flame-spread index (FSI) shall be determined as follows:

In plotting the flame-spread distance-time relationship, all progressive flaming as previously recorded shall be included at the time of occurrence. A straight line shall be used to connect successive points. The total area (A_T) under the flame-spread distance-time plot shall be determined by ignoring any flame front recession. For example, in Figure No. 42-1-8 the flame spreads 10 feet in 2½ minutes and then recedes. The area is calculated as if the flame had spread to 10 feet in 2½ minutes and then remained at 10 feet for the remainder of the test or until the flame front again passed 10 feet. This is shown by the dashed line in Figure No. 42-1-8. The area (A_T) used for calculating the flame-spread index is the sum of areas A_1 and A_2 in Figure No. 42-1-8.

If this total area (A_T) is less than or equal to 97.5 ft·min., the flame-spread index shall be 0.515 times the total area ($FSI = 0.515\,A_T$).

If the total area (A_T) is greater than 97.5 ft·min., the flame-spread index shall be 4900, divided by the difference of 195 minus the total area (A_T). [$FSI = 4900/(195 - A_T)$].

The test results for smoke shall be plotted, using the same coordinates as in Section 42.104. The area under the curve shall be divided by the area under the curve for red oak, and multiplied by 100, to establish a numerical index by which the performance of the material may be compared with that of asbestos-cement board and Select grade red oak flooring, which have been arbitrarily established as 0 and 100, respectively.

Analysis of Products of Combustion

Sec. 42.107. Samples for combustion product analysis, when analysis is requested, shall be taken downstream from the photometer, or shall consist of not more than 1 percent of the total flow. It should be noted that analysis of the products of combustion is not required in this method.

Report

Sec. 42.108. The report shall include the following:

1. Description of the material being tested,
2. Test results as calculated in Section 42.106,
3. Details of the method used in placing the specimen in the test chamber,
4. Observations of the burning characteristics of the specimen during test exposure, such as delamination, sagging, shrinkage, fallout, etc., and
5. Graphical plots of flame-spread and smoke-developed data.

FIGURE NO. 42-1-1
DETAILS OF TEST FURNACE

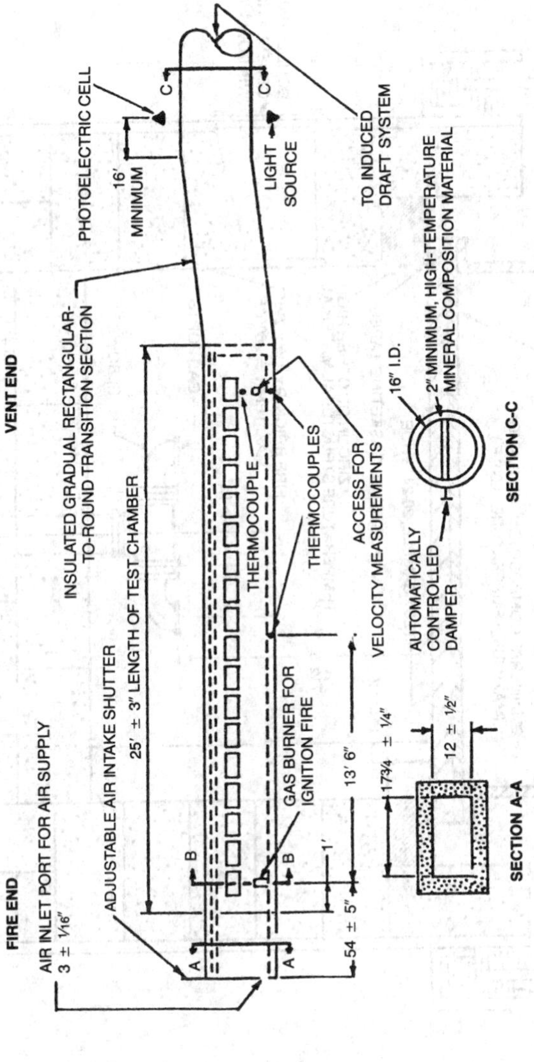
FIRE END
VENT END
AIR INLET PORT FOR AIR SUPPLY
3 ± 1⁄16″
ADJUSTABLE AIR INTAKE SHUTTER
25′ ± 3″ LENGTH OF TEST CHAMBER
INSULATED GRADUAL RECTANGULAR-TO-ROUND TRANSITION SECTION
PHOTOELECTRIC CELL
16′ MINIMUM
A
B
C
GAS BURNER FOR IGNITION FIRE
THERMOCOUPLE
THERMOCOUPLES
LIGHT SOURCE
54 ± 5″
1′
13′ 6″
ACCESS FOR VELOCITY MEASUREMENTS
TO INDUCED DRAFT SYSTEM
17¾ ± ¼″
12 ± ½″
SECTION A-A
AUTOMATICALLY CONTROLLED DAMPER
16″ I.D.
2″ MINIMUM, HIGH-TEMPERATURE MINERAL COMPOSITION MATERIAL
SECTION C-C

FIGURE NO. 42-1-2
SECTION B-B

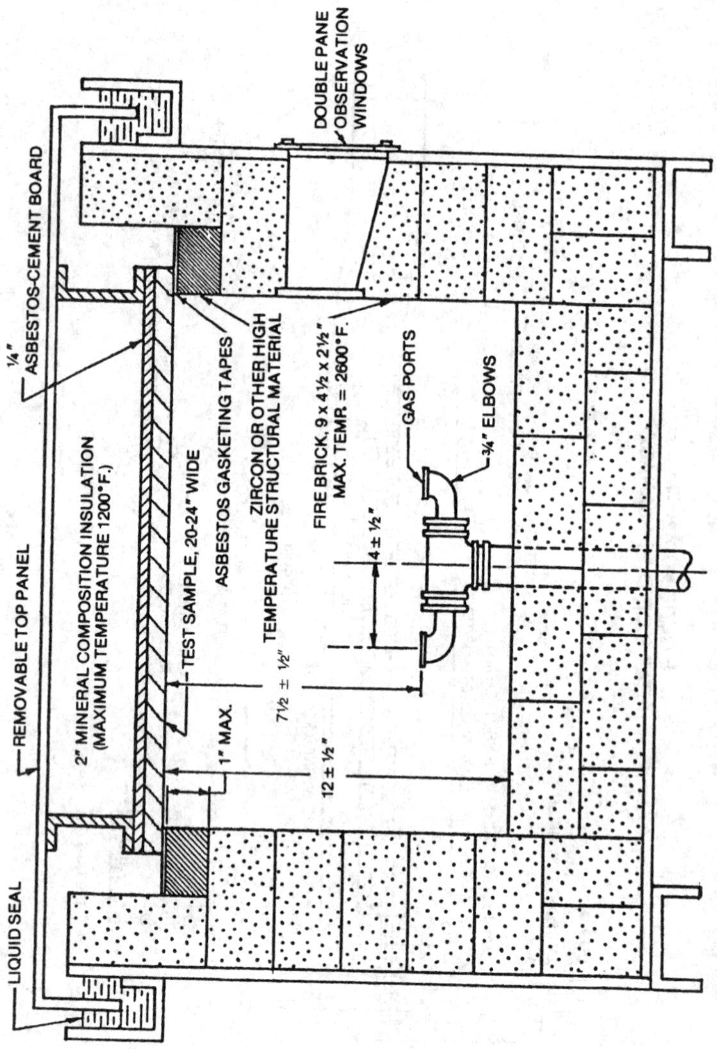
DOUBLE PANE OBSERVATION WINDOWS
1/4" ASBESTOS-CEMENT BOARD
REMOVABLE TOP PANEL
2" MINERAL COMPOSITION INSULATION (MAXIMUM TEMPERATURE 1200°F.)
TEST SAMPLE, 20-24" WIDE
ASBESTOS GASKETING TAPES
ZIRCON OR OTHER HIGH TEMPERATURE STRUCTURAL MATERIAL
FIRE BRICK, 9 x 4½ x 2½" MAX. TEMP. = 2600°F.
GAS PORTS
3/4" ELBOWS
4 ± ½"
7½ ± ½"
1" MAX.
12 ± ½"
LIQUID SEAL

FIGURE NO. 42-1-3
TIME TEMPERATURE FOR PREHEAT TEMPERATURE

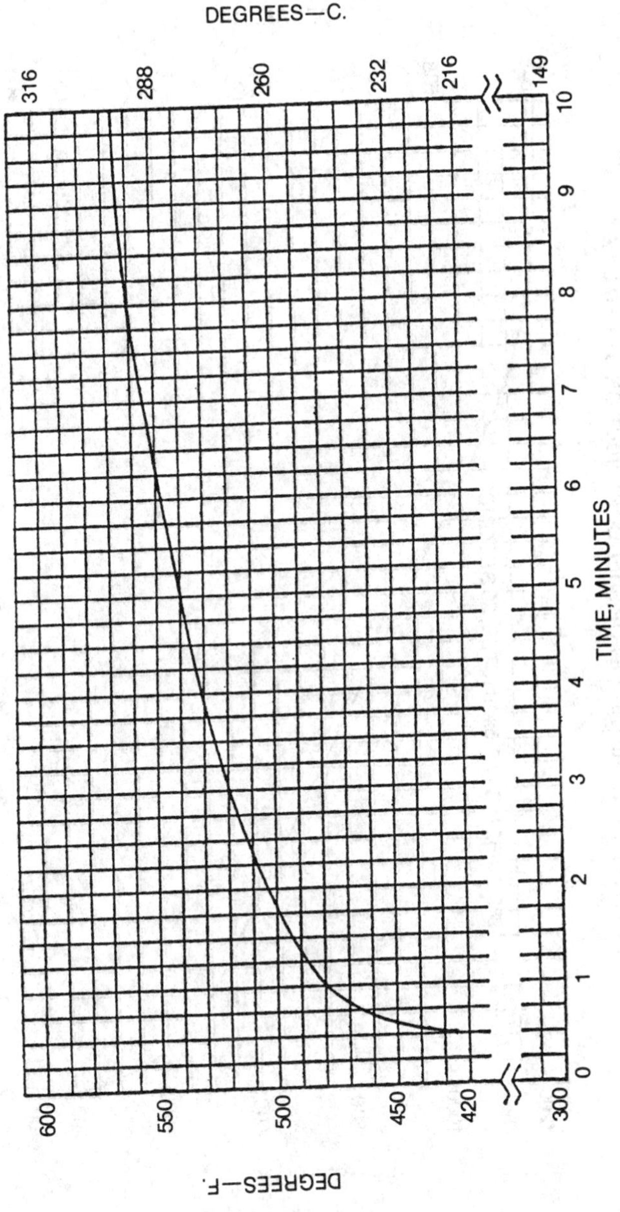
DEGREES—C.
316
288
260
232
216
149
DEGREES—F.
600
550
500
450
420
300
TIME, MINUTES
0
1
2
3
4
5
6
7
8
9
10

FIGURE NO. 42-1-5
TIME TEMPERATURE CURVE FOR FUEL CONTRIBUTION OF RED OAK

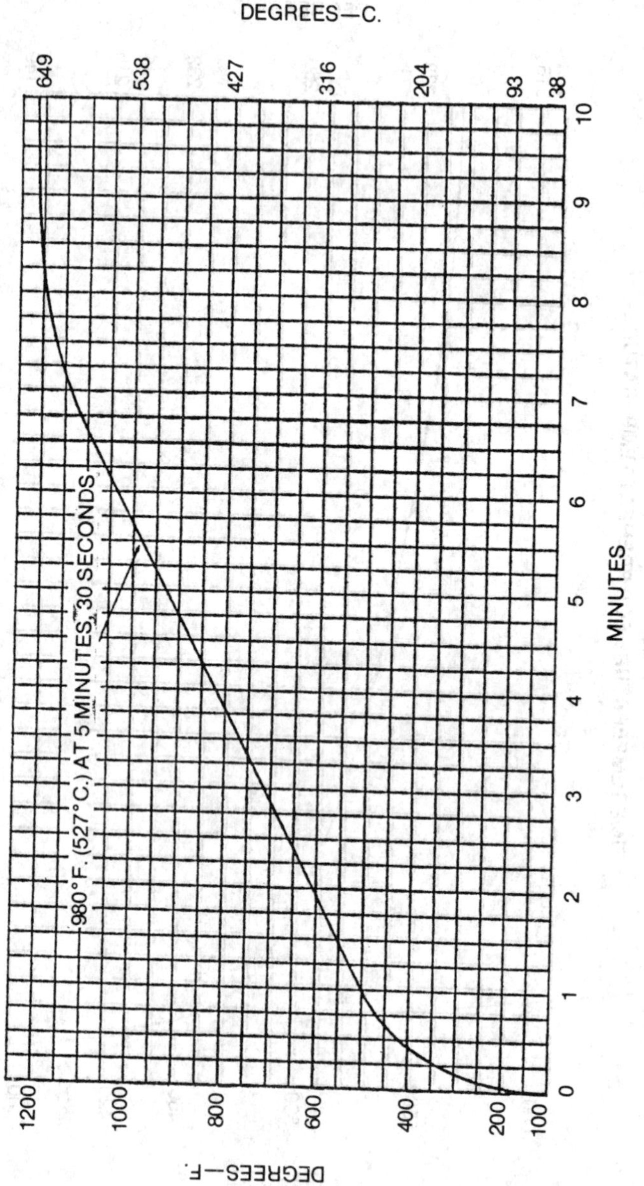
DEGREES—C.
649
538
427
316
204
93
38
980°F. (527°C.) AT 5 MINUTES, 30 SECONDS
1200
1000
800
600
400
200
100
DEGREES—F.
0
1
2
3
4
5
6
7
8
9
10
MINUTES

FIGURE NO. 42-1-6
SMOKE DENSITY—RED OAK

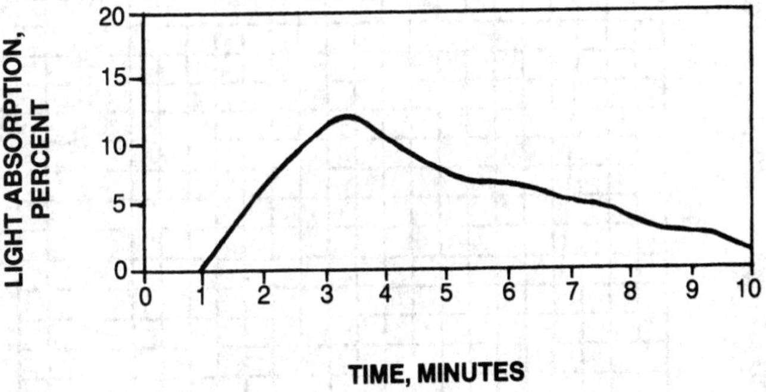
LIGHT ABSORPTION, PERCENT
20
15
10
5
0
0
1
2
3
4
5
6
7
8
9
10
TIME, MINUTES

FIGURE NO. 42-1-7
TIME TEMPERATURE CURVE FOR FUEL CONTRIBUTION OF
ASBESTOS-CEMENT BOARD

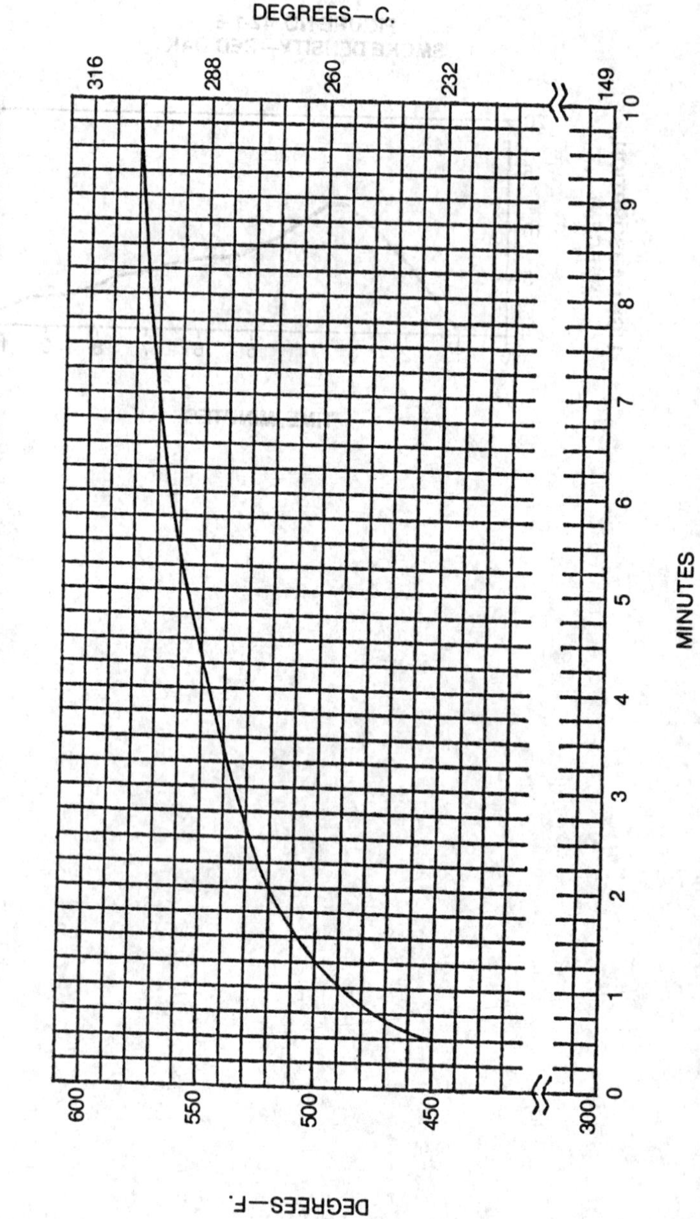
DEGREES—C.
316
288
260
232
149
DEGREES—F.
600
550
500
450
300
MINUTES
0
1
2
3
4
5
6
7
8
9
10

FIGURE NO. 42-1-8
EXAMPLE OF TIME-DISTANCE RELATIONSHIP WITH FLAME FRONT RECESSION
(Total Area, $A_T = A_1 + A_2$)

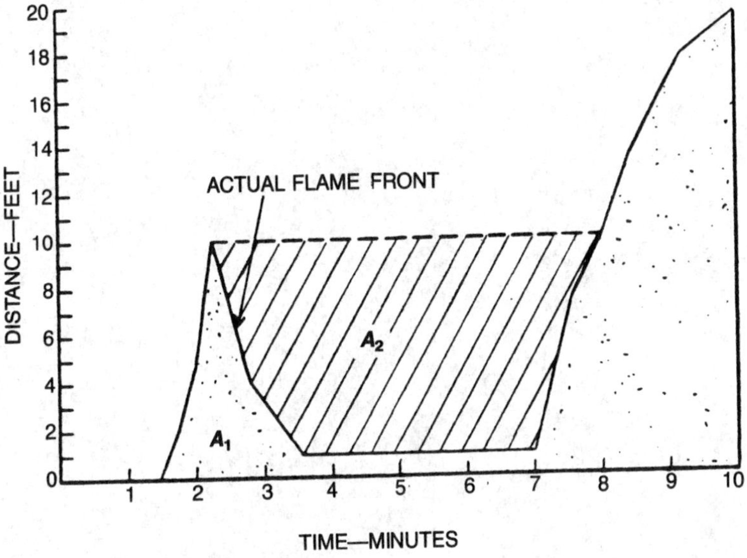
20
18
16
14
12
10
8
6
4
2
0
DISTANCE—FEET
ACTUAL FLAME FRONT
A1
A2
1
2
3
4
5
6
7
8
9
10
TIME—MINUTES

UNIFORM BUILDING CODE STANDARD NO. 42-2

STANDARD TEST METHOD FOR EVALUATING ROOM FIRE GROWTH CONTRIBUTION OF TEXTILE WALL COVERING

Test Method of the International Conference of Building Officials

See Sections 4201 (b) and 4205, Uniform Building Code

Scope

Sec. 42.201. This standard describes a method for determining the contribution of textile wall covering to room fire growth during specified fire exposure conditions. This method is not intended to evaluate the fire endurance of assemblies, nor is it able to evaluate the effect of fires originating within the wall assembly. The method is not intended for the evaluation of floor or ceiling finishes.

This method is to be used to evaluate the flammability characteristics of textile wall coverings when such materials constitute the exposed interior surfaces of buildings. This test method does not apply to fabric covered less than ceiling height, freestanding, prefabricated panel furniture systems or demountable, relocatable, full-height partitions used in open building interiors. Freestanding panel furniture systems include all freestanding panels that provide visual and/or acoustical separation and are intended to be used to divide space and may support components to form complete work stations. Demountable, relocatable, full-height partitions include demountable, relocatable, full-height partitions that fill the space between the finished floor and the finished ceiling.

This method is to be used to evaluate the flammability characteristics of textile wall coverings when required by the Uniform Building Code.

Significance and Use

Sec. 42.202. This fire test measures certain fire performance characteristics of textile wall covering materials in an enclosure under specified fire exposure conditions. It determines the extent to which the textile wall covering materials may contribute to fire growth in a room and the potential for fire spread beyond the room under the particular conditions simulated. The test indicates the maximum extent of fire growth in a room, the rate of heat release, and if they occur, the time to flashover and the time to flame extension beyond the doorway following flashover. It does not measure the fire growth in, or the contribution of, the room contents. Time to flashover is defined herein as either the time when the radiant flux onto the floor reaches 20 kW/m^2 or the temperature of the upper air reaches 600°C. A crumpled single sheet of newspaper shall be placed on the floor 3 feet out from the center of the rear wall. The spontaneous ignition of this newspaper provides the visual indication of flashover.

The potential for spread of fire to other objects in the room, remote from the ignition source, is evaluated by measurements of:

1. The total heat flux incident on the center of the floor.
2. A characteristic upper-level gas temperature in the room.
3. Instantaneous net peak rate of heat release.

The potential for the spread of fire to objects outside the room of origin is evaluated by the measurement of the total heat release of the fire.

Measurements of the rate of production of carbon monoxide and carbon dioxide are taken. Where carbon dioxide is "scrubbed" and therefore not measured, refer to Section 42.214 for alternate calculation method for rate of heat release.

The overall performance of the test specimen is to be visually documented by full-color photographic records. Video taping of the complete fire test may be done as an alternative to the photographic record. Such records will show when each area of the test specimen becomes involved in the fire.

Summary of Method

Sec. 42.203. The test method has two types of protocols. One is a "screening test" protocol and the second is the "fully lined test" protocol. The "screening test" protocol utilizes a corner test exposure of relatively small specimens mounted on the walls of the test compartment. The "fully lined test" protocol involves the same test in a compartment having three fully lined walls.

This method uses a gas burner to produce a diffusion flame to expose the walls in the corner of an 8- by 12- by 8-foot-high room. The burner produces a prescribed rate of heat output of 40 kW for five minutes followed by 150 kW for ten minutes, for a total exposure period of 15 minutes. The contribution of the textile wall covering to fire growth is measured via constant monitoring of the incident heat flux on the center of the floor, the temperature of the gases in the upper part of the room, the rate of heat release and the time to flashover. The test is conducted with natural ventilation to the room provided through a single doorway 30 by 80 inches in width and height. The combustion products are collected in a hood feeding into a plenum connected to an exhaust duct in which measurements are made of the gas velocity, temperature, and concentrations of selected gases.

Ignition Source

Sec. 42.204. The ignition source for the test shall be a gas burner with a nominal 12- by 12-inch porous top surface of a refractory material. See Figure No. 42-2. A burner may be constructed with a 1-inch-thick porous ceramic-fiberboard over a 6-inch plenum, or, alternatively, a minimum 4-inch layer of Ottawa sand can be used to provide the horizontal surface through which the gas is supplied.

The top surface of the burner through which the gas is applied shall be 12 inches above the floor, and the burner enclosure shall be located such that the edge of the diffusion surface is located 2 inches from both walls in the left corner of the room opposite from the door. See Figure No. 42-2-2.

The gas supply to the burner (see Figure No. 2) shall be of C.P. grade propane (99 percent purity). The burner shall be capable of producing a gross heat output of 40 ± 1 kW for five minutes followed by a 150 ± 5 kW for ten minutes. The flow rate shall be metered throughout the test. Flow rates may be calculated using propane's gross heat of combustion as 2480 Btu/feet^3 at 68°F. and 14.70 psia. The burner design shall permit switching from 40 kW to 150 kW within ten seconds. Burner controls should be provided for automatic shutoff of the gas supply if flameout occurs. Two arrangements for gas supply that have been used are shown in Figure No. 42-2-2.

The burner shall be ignited by a pilot burner or a remotely controlled spark igniter.

Compartment Geometry and Construction

Sec. 42.205. The interior dimensions of the floor of the fire room, when the specimens are in place, shall measure 8 feet ± 1 inch by 12 feet ± 1 inch. The finished ceiling shall be 8 feet ± 0.5 inches above the floor. There shall be four walls at right angles defining the compartment.

There shall be a 30 ± 0.25 by 80 ± 0.25-inch doorway in the center of one of the 8- by 8-foot walls, and no other wall, floor or ceiling openings that allow ventilation.

The inside surface of the wall containing the door shall be of calcium-silicate board of 46 lb./ft.^{3} density and 0.5 inch in nominal thickness or 0.5-inch gypsum wallboard. The door frame shall be constructed to remain unchanged during the test period to a tolerance of ± 1 percent in height and width.

The test compartment may be framed or a concrete block structure. If self-supporting panels are tested, a separate exterior frame or block compartment may not be required.

The floor, ceiling and walls of the test compartment shall be covered by calcium silicate board or by gypsum wallboard.

Specimen Mounting

Sec. 42.206. Test specimens shall be mounted on a framing or support system comparable to that intended for their actual use, using backing materials, insulation or air gaps as appropriate to the intended application and representing a typical value of thermal resistance for the wall system. Where a manufacturer specifies use of an adhesive, specimens shall be mounted using the adhesive and application rate as recommended by the manufacturer and comparable to actual field installations. The adhesive utilized shall be the same as that intended for actual use.

Where a textile wall covering has a distinct directionality, the sample shall be mounted such that the machine direction is vertical unless the manufacturer indicates a different method of mounting will be used in actual installations.

For the screening test protocol, specimens shall be mounted on the left side and rear walls (as viewed from the room door) and as illustrated in Figure No. 42-2-3. Vertically mounted portions of test specimens shall extend 2 feet from the room corner on the left side and rear walls. Horizontally mounted specimens on the rear and left sidewalls shall extend 2 feet down from the ceiling and be installed for the full 8-foot width of the rear wall and the full 12-foot length of the left sidewall.

In the fully lined room protocol test, specimens shall be mounted to fully cover both 8- by 12-foot walls and the 8- by 8-foot wall, which does not have a door in it.

Fire Room Environment

Sec. 42.207. (a) **General.** The test building in which the fire room is located shall have vents for the discharge of the combustion products and have provisions for fresh air intake so that no oxygen-deficient air shall be introduced into the fire room during the test. Prior to the start of the test, the ambient air at the midheight entrance to the compartment shall have a velocity in any direction of less than 100 ft./min. The building shall be of adequate size so that there shall be no smoke accumulation in the building below the level of the top of the fire compartment.

(b) **Ambient Conditions in Test Building.** The ambient temperature in the test building at locations around the fire compartment shall be above 40°F. and the relative humidity shall be less than 75 percent for the duration of the test.

(c) **Ambient Conditions in Fire Room.** If test samples are installed within the test room two or more hours prior to test, the following ambient conditions shall be maintained:

1. The ambient temperature in the fire room measured by one of the thermocouples in Section 42.208 shall be from 65° to 75°F.
2. The ambient relative humidity in the fire room shall be within the range of 50 ± 5 percent.

(d) **Specimen Conditioning.** Prior to testing, mounted specimens shall be conditioned for a minimum of seven days and until the sample reaches a rate of weight change of less than 0.1 percent per day at a temperature of 70° ± 5°F. and at a relative humidity of 50 ± 5 percent.

Instrumentation

Sec. 42.208. The following are minimum requirements for instrumentation for this test:

1. **Total heat flux gauge.** A. **Location.** A gauge shall be mounted a maximum of 2 inches above the floor surface, facing upward in the geometric center of the test room (see Figure No. 42-2-4).

B. **Specification.** The gauge shall be of the Gardon type, with a flat black surface, and a 180 degree view angle. In operation, it shall be maintained at a constant temperature (within ± 5 percent °F.) above the dew point by water supplied at a temperature from 120° to 150°F. This will normally require a flow rate of at least 0.1 gal./min. The full-scale output range shall be 50 kW/m^2 for the gauge.

2. **Gas temperature thermocouples** A. **Specification.** Bare chromel-alumel thermocouples 20 mil in diameter shall be used at each required location. The thermocouple wire, within 0.5 inches of the bead, should be run along expected isotherms to minimize conduction errors. The insulation between the chromel and alumel wires shall be stable to at least 2000°F. or the wires shall be separated. Metal-clad thermocouples with ceramic-powder filling shall be used.

B. **Location in doorway.** A thermocouple shall be located in the interior plane of the door opening on the door center line, 4 inches down from the top. (See Figure No. 42-2-5.)

C. **Locations for room.** Thermocouples shall be located 4 inches below the ceiling at the center of the ceiling, the center of each of the four ceiling quadrants and directly over the center of the ignition burner. The thermocouples shall be mounted on supports or penetrate through the ceiling with their junctions 4 inches away from a solid surface. (See Figure No. 42-2-5.) Any ceiling penetration shall be just large enough to permit passage of the thermocouples. Spackling compound or ceramic fiber insulation shall be used to backfill the holes around the thermocouple wires.

D. **Location in canopy hood and duct system.** One pair of thermocouples shall be placed 11 feet downstream of the entrance to the horizontal duct. The pair of thermocouples shall straddle the center of the duct and be separated 2 inches from each other. (See Figure No. 42-2-6.)

3. **Canopy hood and exhaust duct.** A. **Location and design.** A hood shall be installed immediately adjacent to the door of the fire room. The bottom of the hood shall be level with the top surface of the room. The face dimensions of the hood shall be at least 8 by 8 feet and the depth shall be 3.5 feet. The hood shall feed into a plenum having a 3- by 3-foot cross section. The plenum shall have a minimum height of 3 feet and a maximum height of 6 feet. The exhaust duct connected to the plenum shall be 16 inches in diameter, horizontal, and shall have a circular aperture of 12 inches at its entrance. (See Figures Nos. 42-2-6 and 42-2-7.)

B. The hood shall have sufficient draft to collect all of the combustion products leaving the room. (This draft should be capable of moving up to 7000 standard feet^3/minimum equivalent to 16,000 acfm at 750°F. during the test.) Provisions shall be made so that the draft can operate at either 1000 or 7000 standard feet^3/minimum. Mixing vanes may also be required in the duct if concentration gradients are found to exist.

C. An alternative exhaust system design may be used if it has been shown to produce equivalent results. (Equivalency may be shown by meeting the requirements of Section 42.209.)

4. **Duct gas velocity.** A. **Specification.** A bidirectional probe or an equivalent measuring system shall be used to measure gas velocity in the duct. The probe shown in Figure No. 42-2-8 consists of a short stainless steel cylinder 1.75 inches long and 0.875 inch inside diameter with a solid diaphragm in the center. The pressure taps on either side of the diaphragm support the probe. The axis of the probe shall be along the center line of the duct 11 feet downstream from the entrance. The taps shall be connected to a pressure transducer that shall be able to resolve pressure differences of 0.001 inch H_2O. Capacitance transducers have been found to be most stable for this application.

5. **Oxygen-depletion measurements.** A. **Determination of rate of heat release.** A stainless steel gas sampling tube shall be located 13 feet downstream from the entrance to the

duct at the geometric center of the duct ± ½ inch to obtain a continuously flowing sample for determining the oxygen concentration of the exhaust gas as a function of time. A suitable filter and cold trap shall be placed in the line ahead of the analyzer to remove particulates and water. The oxygen analyzer shall be of the paramagnetic or polarographic type and shall be capable of measuring the oxygen concentration in the range from 21 percent down to 15 percent with a relative accuracy of ± 2 percent in this concentration range. The signal from the oxygen analyzer shall be within 5 percent of its final value in 30 seconds after introducing a step change in composition of the gas stream flowing past the inlet to the sampling tube.

B. **Duct carbon dioxide concentration: specification.** The gas-sampling tube described in Section 42.208 may be used to provide a continuous sample for the measurement of the carbon dioxide concentration using an analyzer with a range of 0 to 20 percent, with a maximum relative error of 2 percent of full scale. The total system response time between the sampling inlet and the meter shall be no greater than 30 seconds.

C. **Duct carbon monoxide concentration: specification.** The gas-sampling tube defined in Section 42.208 shall provide a continuous sample for the measurement of the carbon monoxide concentration using an analyzer with a range from 0 to 10 percent with a maximum relative error of 2 percent of full scale. The signal from the analyzer shall be within 5 percent of its final value in 30 seconds after introducing a step change in composition of the gas stream flowing past the inlet to the sampling tube.

6. **Photographic records.** Photographic or video equipment shall be used to record the fire spread in the room and the fire projection from the door of the room. The location of the camera shall avoid interference with the air inflow. The interior wall surfaces of the test room, adjacent to the corner in which the burner is located, shall be clearly marked with a 12-inch grid. A clock shall appear in all photographic records, giving time to the nearest 1 second or 0.01 minimum from the start of the test. This clock shall be accurately synchronized with all other measurements, or other provision shall be made to correlate the photo record with time. Color slides shall be taken at 30-second intervals for the duration of the test or a continuous video recording shall be made.

Calibration and Documentation of Ignition Source and Test Equipment

Section 42.209. A calibration test shall have been performed prior to and within 30 days of any fire test. The calibration test, to last for 15 minutes, shall use the standard ignition source with inert wall and ceiling materials (calcium silicate board of 46 pounds/feet^3 density, 0.50 inch in thickness). The following data shall be reported:

1. The output as a function of time, after the burner is activated, of all instruments normally used for the standard fire test.
2. The maximum extension of the burner flame, as recorded by still photographs taken at 30-second intervals or continuous video recording.
3. The temperature and velocity profiles across the duct cross section at the location of the bidirectional probe. These profiles shall be used to determine the factor, *k*, in Equation 12 of Section 42.213.
4. The total rate of heat production as determined both by the oxygen consumption calculation and by independent measurement of the volumetric flow rate and weight loss of propane supply shall agree to within 5 percent. A net heat of combustion is 2349 Btu/feet^3 for propane at 68°F. and 14.70 psia value shall be used in this calculation.

Procedure

Section 42.210. The screening test protocol and the fully lined test protocol, except for specimen mounting, follow the same test procedure. Where indicated by Section 42.211, the fully lined test protocol shall be followed.

Establish an initial volumetric flow rate of 1000 feet^3/minimum through the duct and increase the volume flow rate to 7000 feet^3/minimum when the oxygen content falls below 14 percent.

Turn on all sampling and recording devices, and establish steady-state baseline readings for at least 3 minutes.

Ignite the gas burner and simultaneously start the clock and increase gas flow rate to provide a rate of heat release of 40 ± 1 kW by the burner. Continue the exposure at the 40 ± 1 kW level for five minutes. Within ten seconds following the five-minute exposure, increase the gas flow to provide a rate of heat release by the burner of 150 ± 5 kW exposure for ten minutes.

Take 35mm color photographs at 30-second intervals or provide a continuous video recording to document the growth of the fire.

Provide a continuous voice or written record of the fire, which will give times of all significant events, such as time of ignition, flames out the doorway, flashover, etc.

The ignition burner shall be shut off at 15 minutes after start of the test and the test terminated at that time, unless safety considerations dictate an earlier termination.

Document damage after the test, using words, pictures and drawings.

Acceptance Criteria

Section 42.211. Textile wall coverings shall be considered as demonstrating satisfactory performance if, during the screening test protocol, the following conditions are met:

Flame shall not spread to the ceiling during the 40 kW exposure.

During the 150 kW exposure, the following criteria shall be met:

1. Flame shall not spread to the outer extremity of the sample on the 8- by 12-foot wall.
2. The specimen shall not burn to the outer extremity of the 2-foot-wide samples mounted vertically in the corner of the room.
3. Burning droplets shall not be formed and drop to the floor which are judged to be capable of igniting the textile wall covering or which persist in burning for 30 seconds or more.
4. Flashover shall not occur. Flashover may be judged to occur when heat flux at floor level exceeds 20 kW/m^2, upper-level air temperatures within the room exceed 1100°F. or flames project out the room door opening.
5. The maximum instantaneous net peak rate of heat release shall not exceed 300 kW. Textile wall coverings in the screening test protocol developing a maximum, instantaneous net peak rate of heat release of 300 kW may or may not cause flashover in a fully lined room. A fully lined room test protocol shall be used to judge acceptability of such products. The maximum instantaneous net peak rate of heat release shall be derived by taking the measured maximum rate of heat release and subtracting the burner output.

Textile wall coverings which fail to meet the criteria of Section 42.211 may be judged to perform satisfactorily when tested following the fully lined test protocol and when meeting the following criteria:

A. Flame shall not spread to the ceiling during the 40 kW exposure.

During the 150 kW exposure, the following criteria shall be met:

(i) Flame shall not spread to the outer extremities of the samples on the 8- by 12-foot walls.

(ii) Flashover shall not occur. Flashover shall be judged to have occured when heat flux at floor level exceeds 20 kW/m^2, upper-level air temperatures exceed 1100°F. or flames project out the room door opening.

Report

Sec. 42.212. The report shall include the following:

1. **Materials:**

A. **Material description.** The name, thickness, density and size of the material to be listed, along with other identifying characteristics or labels.

B. Materials mounting and conditioning.

C. Layout of specimens and attachments in test room (include appropriate drawings).

D. Relative humidity and temperature of the room and the test building prior to and during the test.

2. **Burner gas flow.** The fuel gas flow to the ignition burner and its calculated rate of heat output.

3. **Time history of the total heat flux to floor.** The total incident heat flux at the center of the floor for the heat flux gauge as a function of time starting three minutes prior to the test.

4. **Time history of the gas temperature.** The temperature of gases in the room, the doorway, and in the exhaust duct for each thermocouple as a function of time starting three minutes prior to the test.

5. **Time history of the total rate of heat production of the fire.** The total of heat production shall be calculated from the measured oxygen and carbon monoxide concentrations (refer to Section 42.214) or measured oxygen, carbon monoxide and carbon dioxide concentrations (refer to Section 42.213) and the temperature and volumetric flow rate of the gas in the duct. The calculations shall be based on the method shown in either Section 42.213 or Section 42.214.

6. **Time history of the fire growth.** A transcription of the visual, photographic, audio and written records of the fire test. The records shall indicate the time of ignition of the wall finish, the approximate location of the flame front most distant from the ignition source, at intervals not exceeding 15 seconds during the fire test, the time of flashover, and the time at which flames extend outside the doorway. In addition, still photographs taken at intervals not exceeding 30 seconds or continuous video recordings shall be supplied. Drawings and photographs or video recordings showing the extent of the damage of the materials after the test shall also be supplied.

7. **Discussion of performance.** Complete discussion of sample performances related to acceptance criteria within Section 42.211.

Calculation of the Total Rate of Heat and Carbon Monoxide or Carbon Dioxide Production

Sec. 42.213. The total rate of heat production is as follows:

$$\dot{Q} = E\phi X^{\circ}_{O_2} V_A \qquad (1)$$

WHERE:

E = heat release per volume of oxygen consumed, 467 Btu/ft.^{3} or 17.4 MJ/m^3,

ϕ = fraction of the oxygen consumed,

XO_2 = ambient molar concentration of oxygen (0.21) and

V_A = volume flow rate of air into the system corrected to 20°C., including that which enters the room and that which passes directly into the exhaust duct.

The oxygen depletion is as follows:

$$\phi = [M^{\circ}_{O_2} - M_{O_2}]/M^{\circ}_{O_2} \qquad (2)$$

WHERE:

$M^{\circ}_{O_2}$ = is the molar flow rate of oxygen into the system, and

M_{O_2} = is the molar flow rate of oxygen in the exhaust duct.

The concentrations of oxygen and carbon dioxide in the analyzers are given as follows:

$$X_{O_2} = M_{O_2}/(M^{\circ}_{N_2} + M_{O_2} + M_{CO_2}) \quad (3)$$

$$X_{CO_2} = M_{CO_2}/(M^{\circ}_{N_2} + M_{O_2} + M_{CO_2}) \quad (4)$$

WHERE:

$M^{\circ}_{N_2}$ = is the molar flow rate of nitrogen into the system, and

M_{CO_2} = is the molar flow rate of carbon dioxide in the exhaust duct. It is assumed that all of the water is trapped out and that the only gases passing through the analyzers are nitrogen, oxygen, and carbon dioxide. Combining Equations 3 and 4 as follows:

$$M_{CO_2} = (X_{CO_2}/X_{O_2})M_{O_2}$$

and noting that

$$X^{\circ}_{O_2} = M^{\circ}_{O_2}/(M^{\circ}_{N_2} + M^{\circ}_{O_2})$$

Equation 3 can be solved for M_{O_2} as follows:

$$M_{O_2} = [M^{\circ}_{O_2}((X_{O_2}/X^{\circ}_{O_2}) - X_{O_2})/(1 - X_{O_2} - X_{CO_2})] \quad (5)$$

which, when substituted into Equation 2, yields:

$$\phi = [X^{\circ}_{O_2} - X_{O_2}/(1 - X_{CO_2})]/[X^{\circ}_{O_2}(1 - X_{O_2}/(1 - X_{CO_2}))] \quad (6)$$

The volume flow rate in the exhaust duct is as follows:

$$V_S = (1 - \phi)V_A + \alpha\phi V_A \quad (7)$$

where V_S is referred to standard conditions (68°F.) and α is the expansion factor, due to chemical reaction, of the air that is depleted of its oxygen.

$$\alpha = X^{\circ}_{N_2} + bX^{\circ}_{O_2} = 0.79 + 0.21b \quad (8)$$

where b is the ratio of the moles of combustion products formed to the moles of oxygen consumed. The value of α ranges from 1.000 for carbon to 1.175 for cellulose with the plastics having values in between. In order to reduce the error incurred when unknown products are burning, α is taken to have an intermediate value of 1.084, which is exact for propane, the burner gas. From Equation 7, the volume flow rate of air entering the system is as follows:

$$V_A = V_S/(1 + (\alpha - 1)\phi) \tag{9}$$

Setting $\alpha = 1.084$, $E = 467$ Btu/ft.^{3} and $X°_{O_2} = 0.21$, Equation 1 becomes

$$\dot{Q} = [E\phi X°_{O_2} V_S/1 + (\alpha - 1)\phi] \tag{10}$$

$$= [98.1\phi V_s/(1 + 0.084\phi)]\text{Btu/min}$$

if V_S is measured as cfm referred to 68°F. Setting $E = 17.4\ MJ/m^3$

$$\dot{Q} = [3.65\phi V_S/(1 + 0.084\phi)]\text{MW} \tag{11}$$

where V_S is measured as cubic meters per second. The oxygen depletion, ϕ, is obtained from equation 6 and V_6 is determined from the flow measurement in the exhaust duct.

When the velocity is measured with a bidirectional probe and the Reynolds number correction is taken into account, the volumetric flow rate is m_3/sec in the duct under standard conditions is as follows:

$$V_S = 0.926kA\ \left(\frac{2\Delta p}{\rho_0}\frac{T_0}{T}\right)\ 1/2 = 20.1kA\sqrt{\Delta p/T} \tag{12}$$

WHERE:

0.926 = a suitable calibration factor for air velocities in excess of 3 ft./sec. (0.914 m/sec.) in a 16-inch duct,

k = ratio of the average duct gas mass flow per unit area, as determined by measuring the velocity and temperature profiles across the stack, and the velocity and temperature at the center line where the bidirectional probe is located during the test,

A = cross-sectional area of the duct at the location of the probe, m^2,

Δp = is the differential pressure measured with the probe in Pa,

ρO = is the density of air in kg/m^3 and at the reference temperature T_o, K and

T = is the duct gas temperature in K.

The volumetric flow rate can be expressed in cubic feet per minute (scfm) at 60°F. using common engineering units as follows:

$$V_S = 8.38 \text{ by } 10^4 kA[\Delta p/(t + 459)]^{1/2} \text{ standard ft}^3\text{/min} \tag{13}$$

WHERE:

A = is given in ft.^{2} and inches of water,

Δp = is given in ft.^{2} and inches of water, and

t = is the duct gas temperature in °F.

The volume flow rate of CO in m³/sec through the duct may be calculated as follows:

$$V_{CO} = [0.79\ V_S X_{CO}/(1 + 0.084\phi)(1 - X_{O_2} - X_{CO_2} - X_{CO})] \tag{14}$$

WHERE:

X_{CO} = is the concentration of carbon monoxide measured in the analyzer. This can be calculated as follows:

$$\frac{V_{CO}}{V_A} = \frac{M_{CO}}{M_{Air}} = \frac{M_{CO}}{M_{O_2}}\ \frac{M_{O_2}}{M^o_{O_2}}\ \frac{M^o_{O_2}}{M_A} \tag{15}$$

$$= \frac{X_{CO}}{X_{O_2}}\ \frac{M_{O_2}}{M^o_{O_2}}\ X^o_{O_2}$$

where M_{CO} and M_A are the molar flow rates of carbon dioxide in the duct and of the air into the system including that flowing into the room and that entering the exhaust duct directly. The ratio of the CO and O_2 concentration in the duct are the same as in the analyzer so that

$$\frac{M_{CO}}{M_{O_2}} = \frac{X_{CO}}{X_{O_2}} \tag{16}$$

When CO is present in the sampling line, Equation 5 becomes

$$M_{O_2} = M^o_{O_2}\ \frac{\dfrac{X_{O_2}}{X^o_{O_2}} - X_{O_2}}{1 - X_{O_2} - X_{CO_2} - X_{CO}} \tag{17}$$

Equation 14 is obtained by combining Equations 15, 16 and 17, letting

$$1 - X^o_{O_2} = 0.79, \text{ and letting } V_A = \frac{S}{1 - 0.084\phi}$$

Alternate Calculation of the Total Rate of Heat Release When Carbon Monoxide is Measured and Carbon Dioxide is Removed From the Gas Sampling Train

Sec. 42.214. When CO is not measured, but is removed from the sample line, and CO is measured, ϕ and Q are calculated as follows:

$$\phi = \frac{X^o_{O_2} - (X_{O_2}/1 - X_{CO})}{X^o_{O_2}(X_{O_2}/1 - X_{CO})} \tag{18}$$

$$\dot{Q} = [\phi - ((E'' - E')/E')((1 - \phi)/2)(X_{CO}/X_{O_2})]E'X^{\circ}_{O_2}V_A(MW) \quad (19)$$

WHERE:

$E'' = 23.4\ MJ/m^3$

$E' = 17.4\ MJ/m^3$, and

$V_A = m^3/sec.$,

referred to a 68°F. base. Thus Q becomes

$$\dot{Q} = [\phi - 0.345((1 - \phi)/2)(X_{CO}/X_{O_2})]17.4X^{\circ}_{O_2}V_A(MW) \quad (20)$$

When Equations 18 through 20 are used to calculate the rate of heat release, the carbon dioxide must be removed from the sample streams flowing through the oxygen and carbon monoxide analyzers. The removal of carbon dioxide can be accomplished by passing the sample stream through a filter of either ascarite or an aqueous solution of sodium hydroxide.

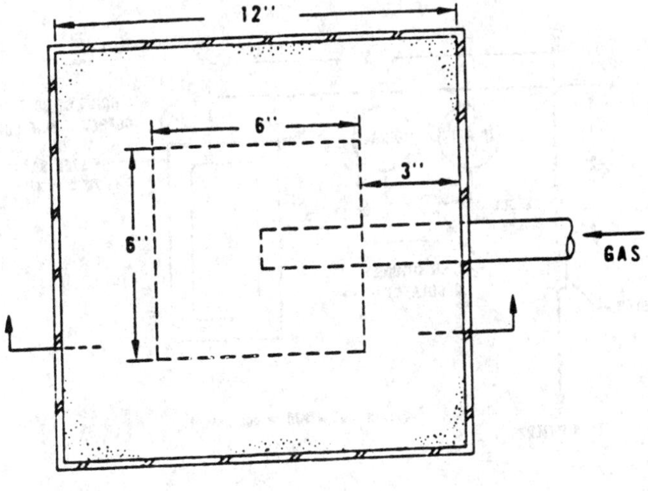
12"
6"
3"
6"
GAS

FIGURE NO. 42-2-1—GAS BURNER

(Continued)

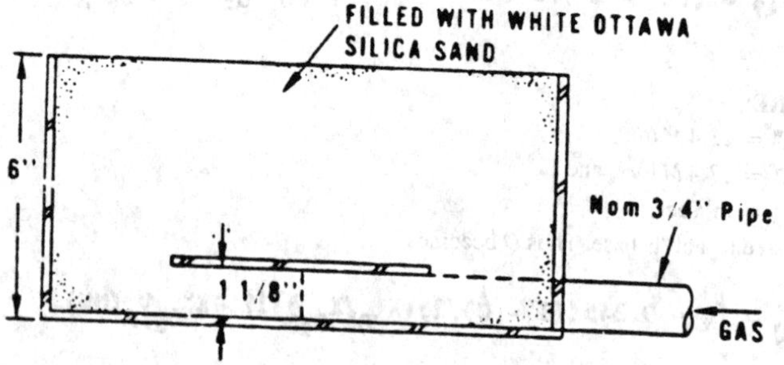
FILLED WITH WHITE OTTAWA SILICA SAND
6"
Nom 3/4" Pipe
1 1/8"
GAS

FIGURE NO. 42-2-1—GAS BURNER—(Continued)

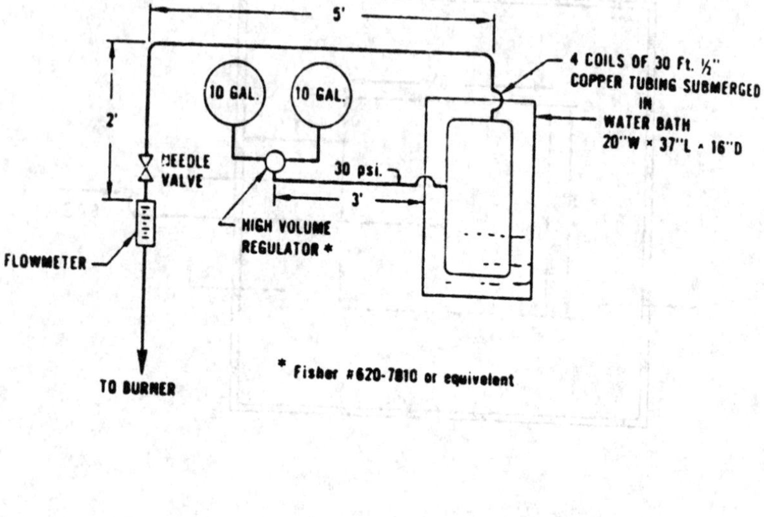
5'
2'
10 GAL.
10 GAL.
4 COILS OF 30 Ft. ½" COPPER TUBING SUBMERGED IN
WATER BATH 20"W × 37"L × 16"D
NEEDLE VALVE
30 psi.
3'
HIGH VOLUME REGULATOR *
FLOWMETER
TO BURNER
* Fisher #620-7810 or equivalent

FIGURE NO. 42-2-2A—TYPICAL GAS FLOW REGULATION SYSTEM

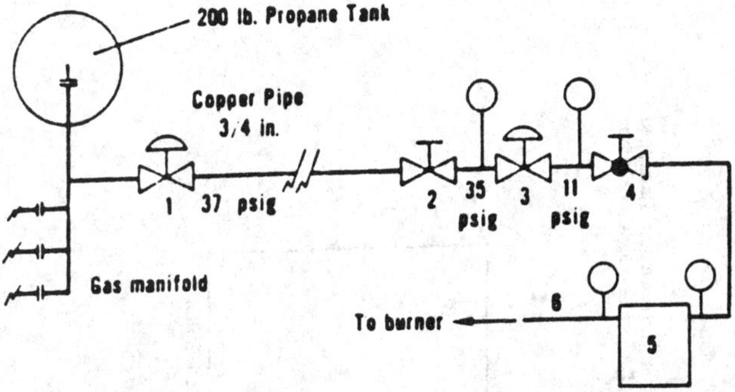
200 lb. Propane Tank
Copper Pipe
3/4 in.
1
37 psig
2
35
psig
3
11
psig
4
Gas manifold
6
To burner
5

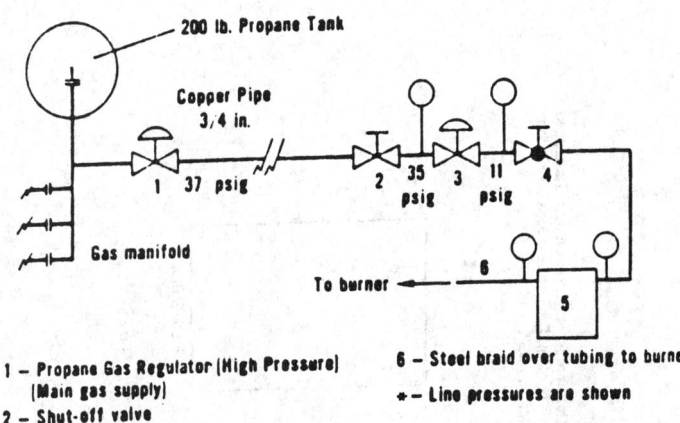

1 – Propane Gas Regulator (High Pressure) (Main gas supply)

2 – Shut-off valve

3 – Regulator (Low Pressure)

4 – Adjustable valve for flow impendance

5 – Volume meter

6 – Steel braid over tubing to burner

* – Line pressures are shown

FIGURE NO. 42-2-2B—TYPICAL GAS FLOW REGULATION SYSTEM

FIGURE NO. 42-2-3

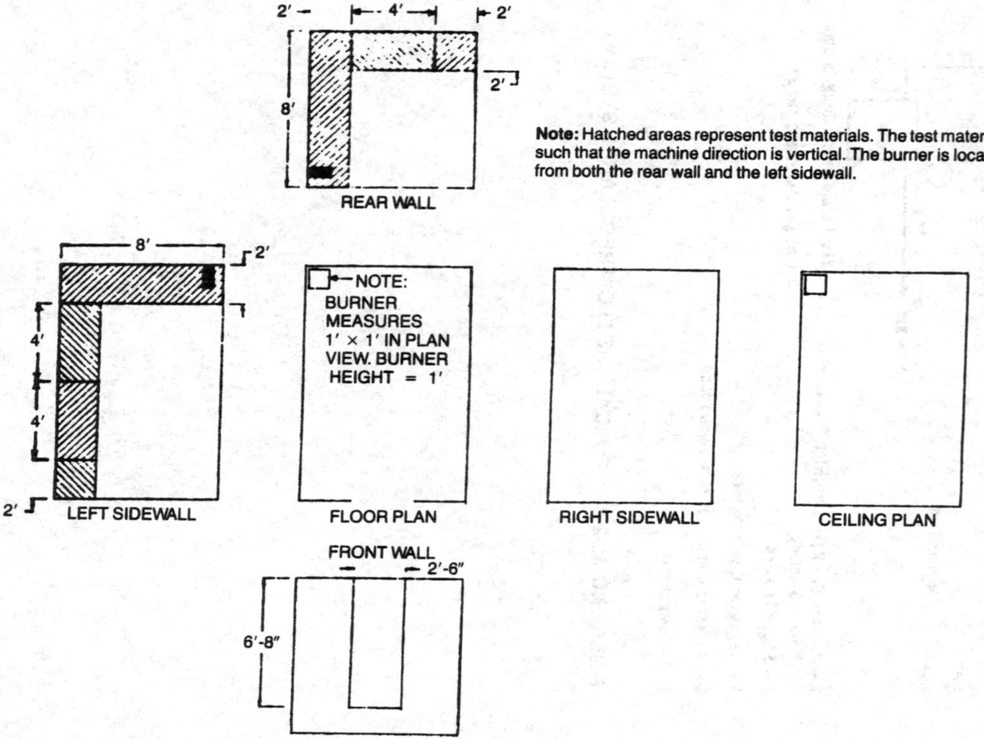
2′
4′
2′
2′
8′
REAR WALL
8′
2′
4′
4′
2′
LEFT SIDEWALL
NOTE:
BURNER
MEASURES
1′ × 1′ IN PLAN
VIEW. BURNER
HEIGHT = 1′
FLOOR PLAN
RIGHT SIDEWALL
CEILING PLAN
FRONT WALL
2′-6″
6′-8″

Note: Hatched areas represent test materials. The test material is applied such that the machine direction is vertical. The burner is located 2 inches from both the rear wall and the left sidewall.

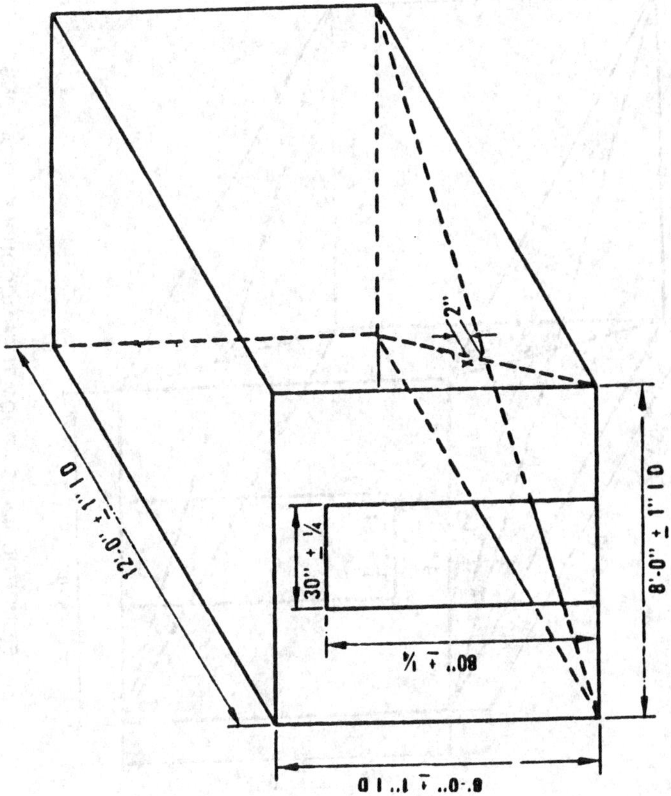
12'-0" ± 1" I D
30" ± 1/4
80" ± 1/4
8'-0" ± 1" I D
6'-0" ± 1" I D
2"
x

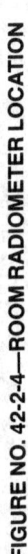

FIGURE NO. 42-2-4—ROOM RADIOMETER LOCATION

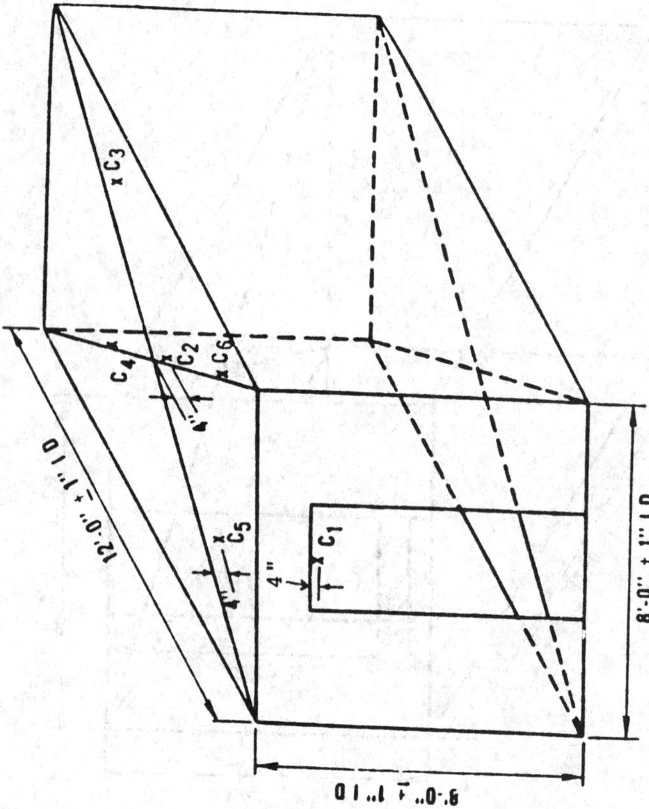
x C3
C4
C2
C6
4"
C5
4"
C1
4"
12'-0" ± 1" I D
8'-0" ± 1" I D
9'-0" ± 1" I D

FIGURE NO. 42-2-5—ROOM THERMOCOUPLE LOCATIONS

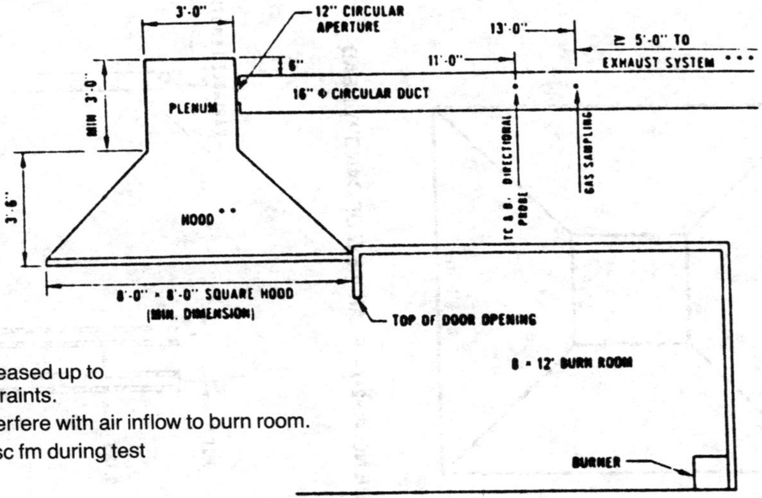
3'-0"
12" CIRCULAR APERTURE
13'-0"
≥ 5'-0" TO EXHAUST SYSTEM ***
6"
11'-0"
16" Φ CIRCULAR DUCT
PLENUM
MIN 3'-0"
TC & B.D. DIRECTIONAL PROBE
GAS SAMPLING
3'-6"
HOOD **
8'-0" × 8'-0" SQUARE HOOD
(MIN. DIMENSION)
TOP OF DOOR OPENING
8 × 12' BURN ROOM
BURNER

*Height of plenum may be increased up to 6 ft. to adjust to building constraints.

**Support for hood must not interfere with air inflow to burn room.

***Capable of exhausting 7000 sc fm during test

FIGURE NO. 42-2-6—CANOPY HOOD AND EXHAUST DUCT

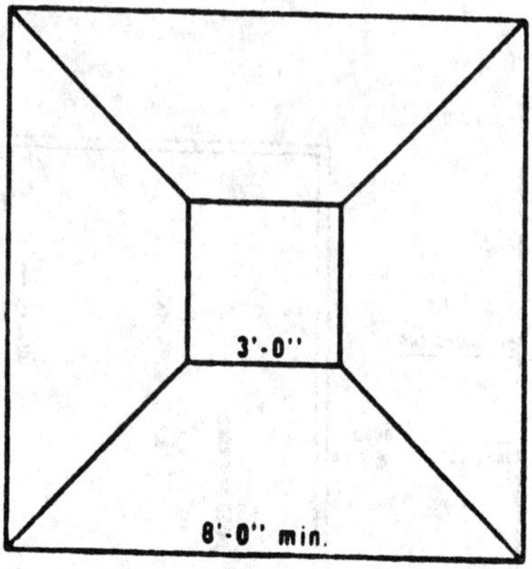
3'-0''
8'-0'' min.

FIGURE NO. 42-2-7—PLAN VIEW OF CANOPY HEAD

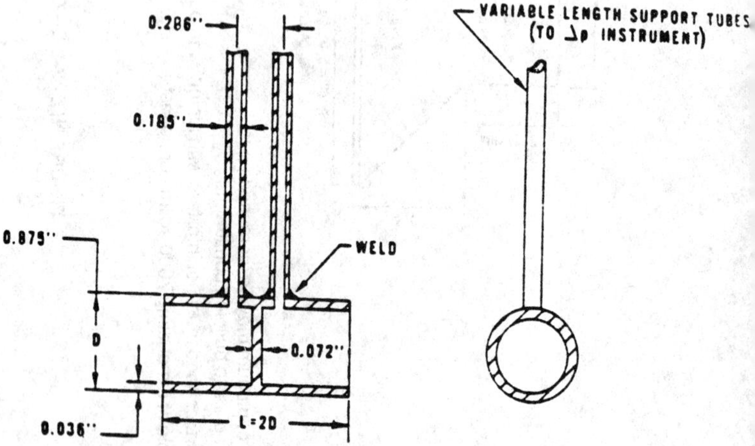
0.286''
0.185''
0.875''
WELD
D
0.072''
0.036''
L=2D
VARIABLE LENGTH SUPPORT TUBES
(TO Δp INSTRUMENT)

FIGURE NO. 42-2-8—BIDIRECTIONAL PROBE

UNIFORM BUILDING CODE STANDARD NO. 43-1

FIRE TESTS OF BUILDING CONSTRUCTION AND MATERIALS

Based on Standard Methods E 119-83 of the American Society for Testing and Materials. Extracted, with permission, from the Annual Book of ASTM Standards, copyright American Society for Testing and Materials, 1916 Race Street, Philadelphia, PA 19103.

See Sections 1701 (b), 1704 (b), 1707, 1713 (e) 2, 3901 (a), 3903 (d), 4301 (a), 4302 (b), 4304 (d), 4304 (e), 4304 (f) 4, 4305 (b), 4305 (c) and Table No. 43-A, Uniform Building Code

Scope

Sec. 43.101. This standard for fire tests is applicable to assemblies of masonry units and to composite assemblies of structural materials for buildings, including bearing and other walls and partitions, columns, girders, beams, slabs, and composite slab and beam assemblies for floors and roofs. They are also applicable to other assemblies and structural units that constitute permanent integral parts of a finished building.

It is the intent that classifications shall register performance during the period of exposure and shall not be construed as having determined suitability for use after fire exposure.

Control of Fire Tests

Time-Temperature Curve

Sec. 43.102. The conduct of fire tests of materials and construction shall be controlled by the standard time-temperature curve shown in Figure No. 43-1-1. The points on the curve that determine its character are:

1000°F.	at 5 minutes
1300°F.	at 10 minutes
1550°F.	at 30 minutes
1700°F.	at 1 hour
1850°F.	at 2 hours
2000°F.	at 4 hours
2300°F.	at 8 hours or over

Furnace Temperatures

Sec. 43.103. The temperature fixed by the curve shall be deemed to be the average temperature obtained from the readings of not less than nine thermocouples for a floor, roof, wall or partition and not less than eight thermocouples for a structural column symmetrically disposed and distributed to show the temperature near all parts of the sample, the thermocouples being enclosed in protection tubes of such materials and dimensions that the time constant of the protected thermocouple assembly lies within the range from 5.0 to 7.2 minutes. The exposed length of the pyrometer tube and thermocouple in the furnace chamber shall be not less than 12 inches. Other types of protecting tubes or pyrometers may be used that, under test conditions, give the same indications as the above standard within the limit of accuracy that applies for furnace-temperature measurements. For floors and columns, the junction of the thermocouples shall be placed 12 inches away from the exposed face of the sample at the beginning of the test and, during the test, shall not touch the sample as a result of its deflection. In the case of walls and partitions, the thermocouples shall be placed 6 inches away from the exposed face of the sample at the beginning of the test, and shall not touch the sample during the test in the event of deflection.

The temperatures shall be read at intervals not exceeding five minutes during the first two hours, and thereafter the intervals may be increased to not more than 10 minutes.

The accuracy of the furnace control shall be such that the area under the time-temperature curve, obtained by averaging the results from the pyrometer readings, is within 10 percent of the corresponding area under the standard time-temperature curve shown in Figure No. 43-1-1 for fire tests of one hour or less duration, within 7.5 percent for those over one hour and not more than two hours, and within 5 percent for tests exceeding two hours in duration.

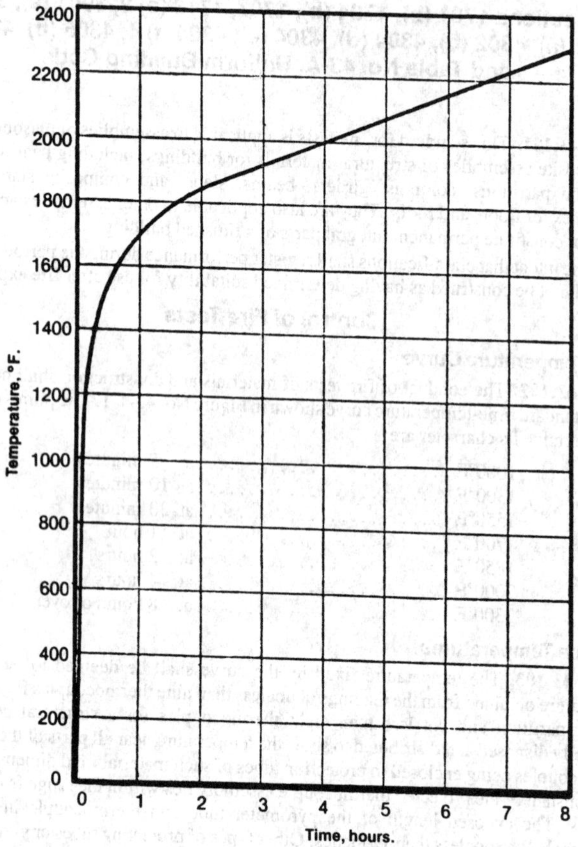
2400
2200
2000
1800
1600
1400
1200
1000
800
600
400
200
0
Temperature, °F.
0
1
2
3
4
5
6
7
8
Time, hours.

FIGURE NO. 43-1-1

Temperatures of Unexposed Surfaces of Floors, Walls and Partitions

Sec. 43.104. Temperatures at unexposed surfaces shall be measured with thermocouples or thermometers placed under flexible, dry, felted asbestos pads 6 inches square, 0.4 inch in thickness and weighing not less than one nor more than 1.4 pounds per square foot. The pads shall be sufficiently soft so that, without breaking, they may be shaped to contact over the whole surface against which they are placed. The wire leads of the thermocouple or the stem of the thermometer shall have an immersion under the pad and be in contact with the unexposed surface for not less than 3½ inches. The hot junction of the thermocouple or the bulb of the thermometer shall be placed approximately under the center of the pad. The outside diameter of protecting or insulating tubes, and of thermometer stems, shall be not more than 5/16 inch. The pad shall be held firmly against the surface and shall fit closely about the thermocouples or thermometer stems. Thermometers shall be of the partial-immersion type with a length of stem between the end of the bulb and the immersion mark of 3 inches. The wires for the thermocouple in the length covered by the pad shall be not heavier than No. 18 B. & S. gage (0.04 inch) and shall be electrically insulated with heat-resistant and moisture-resistant coatings.

Temperature readings shall be taken at not less than nine points on the surface; five of these shall be symmetrically disposed, one to be approximately at the center of the specimens and four at approximately the center of quarter sections. The other four should be located at the discretion of the testing agency to obtain representative information on the performance of the construction under tests. None of the thermocouples shall be located nearer to the edges of the test specimen than one and one-half times the thickness of the construction or 12 inches. An exception can be made in those cases where there is an element of the construction that is not otherwise represented in the remainder of the test specimen. None of the thermocouples shall be located opposite or on top of beams, girders, pilasters or other structural members if temperatures at such points will obviously be lower than at more representative locations. None of the thermocouples shall be located opposite or on top of fasteners such as screws, nails or staples that will be obviously higher or lower in temperature than at more representative locations if the aggregate area of any part of such fasteners projected to the unexposed surface is less than 0.8 percent of the area within any 5-inch square. Such fasteners shall not extend through the assembly.

Temperature readings shall be taken at intervals not exceeding 15 minutes until a reading exceeding 212°F. has been obtained at any one point. Thereafter the readings may be taken more frequently at the discretion of the testing body, but the intervals need not be less than five minutes.

Where the conditions of acceptance place a limitation on the rise of temperature of the unexposed surface, the temperature end point of the fire-endurance period shall be determined by the average of the measurements taken at individual points; except that if a temperature rise 30 percent in excess of the specified limit occurs at any one of these points, the remainder shall be ignored and the fire-endurance period judged as ended.

Classification as Determined by Test

Report of Results

Sec. 43.105. Results shall be reported in accordance with the performance in the tests prescribed in this standard. They shall be expressed in time periods of resistance to the nearest integral minute. Reports shall include observations of significant details of the behavior of the material or construction during the test and after the furnace fire is cut off, including information on deformation, spalling, cracking, burning of the specimen or its component parts, continuance of flaming and production of smoke.

Reports of tests involving wall, floor, beam or ceiling constructions in which restraint is provided against expansion, contraction or rotation of the construction shall describe the method used to provide this restraint.

Reports of tests in which other than maximum load conditions are imposed shall fully define the conditions of loading used in the test and shall be designated in the title of the report of the test as a restricted load condition.

When the indicated resistance period is one-half hour or over, and determined by the average or maximum temperature rise on the unexposed surface or within the test sample, or by failure under load, a correction shall be applied for variation of the furnace exposure from that prescribed where it will affect the classification by multiplying the indicated period by two thirds of the difference in area between the curve of average furnace temperature and the standard curve for the first three fourths of the period and dividing the product by the area between the standard curve and a base line of 68°F. for the same part of the indicated period, the latter area increased by 54 Fahrenheit-hours (3240 Fahrenheit-minutes), to compensate for the thermal lag of the furnace thermocouples during the first part of the test. For fire exposure in the test higher than standard, the indicated resistance period shall be increased by the amount of the correction and be similarly decreased for fire exposure below standard.

NOTE: The correction can be expressed by the following formula:

$$C = \frac{2I\ (A - A_s)}{3\ (A_s + L)}$$

WHERE:

C = correction in the same units as I.

I = indicated fire-resistance period.

A = area under the curve of indicated average furnace temperature for the first three fourths of the indicated period.

A_s = area under the standard furnace curve for the same part of the indicated period.

L = lag correction in the same units as A and A_s[54 Fahrenheit-hours (3240 Fahrenheit-minutes)].

Walls and partitions of nonsymmetrical construction shall be tested with both faces exposed to the furnace and the report shall indicate the fire-endurance classification applicable to each side. Subject to the approval of the building official based on data submitted by the applicant justifying a single side test only, unsymmetrical wall assemblies may be tested with the least fire-resistive side exposed in the furnace.

Test Specimen

Sec. 43.106. The test sample shall be truly representative of the construction for which classification is desired, as to materials, workmanship, and details such as dimensions of parts, and shall be built under conditions representative of those obtained as practically applied in building construction and operation. The physical properties of the materials and ingredients used in the test sample shall be determined and recorded.

The size and dimensions of the test sample specified herein are intended to apply for rating constructions of dimensions within the usual general range employed in buildings. If the conditions of use limit the construction to smaller dimensions, a proportionate reduction may be made in the dimensions of the samples for a test qualifying them for such restricted use.

When it is desired to include a built-up roof covering, the test specimen shall have a roof covering of 3-ply, 15-pound-type felt not in excess of 120 pounds per square (100 square feet) of hot-mopping asphalt without gravel surfacing. Tests of assemblies with this covering do not preclude the field use of other built-up roof coverings.

Fire Test Procedures

Fire-endurance Test

Sec. 43.107. The fire-endurance test on the sample with its applied load, if any, shall be continued until failure occurs, or until the sample has withstood the test conditions for a period equal to that herein specified in the conditions of acceptance for the given type of construction.

For the purpose of obtaining additional performance data, the test may be continued beyond the time the fire-endurance classification is determined.

Hose Stream Test

Sec. 43.108. (a) **General.** Where required by the conditions of acceptance, a duplicate sample shall be subjected to a fire-exposure test for a period equal to one half of that indicated as the resistance period in the fire-endurance test, but not for more than one hour, immediately after which the sample shall be subjected to the impact, erosion and cooling effects of a hose stream directed first at the middle and then at all parts of the exposed face, changes in direction being made slowly.

(b) **Exemption.** The hose stream test shall not be required in the case of constructions having a resistance period, indicated in the fire-endurance test, of less than one hour.

(c) **Optional Program.** The submitter may elect, with the advice and consent of the testing body, to have the hose stream test made on the sample subjected to the fire-endurance test and immediately following the expiration of the fire-endurance test.

(d) **Stream Equipment and Details.** The stream shall be delivered through a 2½-inch hose discharging through a National Standard Playpipe of corresponding size equipped with a 1⅛-inch discharge tip of the standard-taper smooth-bore pattern without shoulder at the orifice. The water pressure and duration of application shall be as prescribed in Table No. 43-1-A.

TABLE NO. 43-1-A—CONDITIONS FOR HOSE STREAM TEST

RESISTANCE PERIOD	WATER PRESSURE AT BASE OF NOZZLE (Pounds per Square Inch)	DURATION OF APPLICATION (Minutes per 100 Square Feet) EXPOSED AREA
8 hours and over	45	6
4 hours and over if less than 8 hours	45	5
2 hours and over if less than 4 hours	30	2½
1½ hours and over if less than 2 hours	30	1½
1 hour and over if less than 1½ hours	30	1
Less than 1 hour, if desired	30	1

(e) **Nozzle Distance.** The nozzle orifice shall be 20 feet from the center of the exposed surface of the test sample if the nozzle is so located that when directed at the center its axis is normal to the surface of the test sample. If otherwise located, its distance from the center shall be less than 20 feet by an amount equal to 1 foot for each 10 degrees of deviation from the normal.

Time of Testing

Sec. 43.109. The material or construction shall not be tested until a large proportion of its final strength has been attained and, if it contains moisture, until the excess has been removed to achieve an air-dry condition in accordance with the requirements given in this section. Protect the testing equipment and sample undergoing the fire test from any condition of wind or weather that might lead to abnormal results. The ambient air temperature at the beginning of the test shall be within the range of 50° to 90°F. The velocity of air across the unexposed surface of the sample, measured just before the test begins, shall not exceed 4.4 feet as determined by an anemometer placed at right angles to the unexposed surface. If mechanical ventilation is employed during the test, an airstream shall not be directed across the surface of the specimen.

Prior to fire test, condition constructions with the objective of providing, within a reasonable time, a moisture condition within the specimen approximately representative of that likely to exist in similar construction in buildings. For purposes of standardization, this condition is to be considered as that which would be established at equilibrium resulting from drying in an ambient atmosphere of 50 percent relative humidity at 73°F. However, with some constructions, it may be difficult or impossible to achieve such uniformity within a reasonable period of time. Accordingly, where this is the case, specimens may be tested when the dampest portion of the structure, the portion at 6 inches depth below the surface of massive constructions, has achieved a moisture content corresponding to drying to equilibrium with air in the range of 50 to 75 percent relative humidity at 73° ± 5°F. In the event that specimens dried in a heated building fail to meet these requirements after a 12-month conditioning period, or in the event that the nature of the construction is such that it is evident that drying of the specimen interior will be prevented by hermetic sealing, these requirements may be waived, except as to attainment of a large portion of final strength, and the specimen tested in the condition in which it then exists.

If during the conditioning of the specimen it appears desirable or is necessary to use accelerated drying techniques, it is the responsibility of the laboratory conducting the test to avoid procedures which will significantly alter the structural or fire-endurance characteristics of the specimen or both from those produced as the result of drying in accordance with procedures given in this section.

Within 72 hours prior to the fire test, information on the actual moisture content and distribution within the specimen shall be obtained. Include this information in the test report.

Tests of Bearing Walls and Partitions

Size of Sample

Sec. 43.110. The area exposed to fire shall be not less than 100 square feet, with neither dimension less than 9 feet. The test specimen shall not be restrained on its vertical edges.

Loading

Sec. 43.111. Throughout the fire endurance and fire and hose stream tests, apply a constant superimposed load to simulate a maximum load condition. The applied load shall be as nearly as practicable the maximum load allowed by design under design criteria set forth in the Building Code. The tests may also be conducted by applying to the specimen a load less than the maximum. Such tests shall be identified in the test report as having been conducted under restricted load conditions. The applied load, and the applied expressed as a percentage of the maximum allowable design load, shall be included in the report. A double-wall assembly shall be loaded during the test to simulate field-use conditions, with either side loaded separately or both sides together (Note: The method used shall be reported).

The choice depends on the intended use and whether the load on the exposed side, after it has failed, will be transferred to the unexposed side. If, in the intended use, the load from the structure above is supported by both walls as a unit and would be or is transferred to the unexposed side in case of collapse of the exposed side, both walls shall be loaded in the test by a single unit. If in the intended use the load from the structure above each wall is supported by each wall separately, the walls shall be loaded separately in the test by separate load sources. If the intended use of the construction system being tested involved situations of both loading conditions described above, the walls shall be loaded separately in the test by separate load sources. In tests conducted with the walls loaded separately, the condition of acceptance requiring the walls to maintain the applied load shall be based on the time at which the first of either of the walls fails to sustain the load.

Conditions of Acceptance

Sec. 43.112. The test shall be regarded as successful if the following conditions are met:

1. The wall or partition shall have sustained the applied load during the fire-endurance test without passage of flame or gases hot enough to ignite cotton waste, for a period equal to that for which classification is desired.

2. The wall or partition shall have sustained the applied load during the fire and hose stream test as specified in Section 43.108, without passage of flame, of gases hot enough to ignite cotton waste, or of the hose stream. The assembly shall be considered to have failed the hose stream test if an opening develops that permits a projection of water from the stream beyond the unexposed surface during the time of the hose stream test.

3. Transmission of heat through the wall or partition during the fire-endurance test shall not have been such as to raise the temperature on its unexposed surface more than 250°F. above its initial temperature.

Tests of Nonbearing Walls and Partitions

Size of Sample

Sec. 43.113. The area exposed to fire shall be not less than 100 square feet, with neither dimension less than 9 feet. The test specimen shall be restrained on all four edges.

Conditions of Acceptance

Sec. 43.114. The test shall be regarded as successful if the following conditions are met:

1. The wall or partition shall have withstood the fire-endurance test without passage of flame or gases hot enough to ignite cotton waste, for a period equal to that for which classification is desired.

2. The wall or partition shall have withstood the fire and hose stream test as specified in Section 43.108, without passage of flame, of gases hot enough to ignite cotton waste, or of the hose stream. The assembly shall be considered to have failed the hose stream test if an opening develops that permits a projection of water from the stream beyond the unexposed surface during the time of the hose stream test.

3. Transmission of heat through the wall or partition during the fire-endurance test shall not have been such as to raise the temperature on its unexposed surface more than 250°F. above its initial temperature.

Tests of Columns

Size of Sample

Sec. 43.115. The length of the column exposed to fire shall, when practicable, approximate the maximum clear length contemplated by the design, and for building columns shall be not less than 9 feet. The contemplated details of connections, and their protection if any, shall be applied according to the methods of acceptable field practice.

Loading

Sec. 43.116. During the fire endurance test the column shall be exposed to fire on all sides and shall be loaded in a manner calculated to develop theoretically, as nearly as practicable, the working stresses contemplated by the design. Provision shall be made for transmitting the load to the exposed portion of the column without unduly increasing the effective column length.

If the submitter and the building official jointly so decide, the column may be subjected to one and three-fourths times its designed working load before the fire-endurance test is undertaken. The fact that such a test has been made shall not be construed as having had a deleterious effect on the fire-endurance test performance.

Condition of Acceptance

Sec. 43.117. The test shall be regarded as successful if the column sustains the applied load during the fire-endurance test for a period equal to that for which classification is desired.

Alternate Test of Protection for Structural Steel Columns

Application

Sec. 43.118. This test procedure does not require column loading at any time and may be used at the discretion of the testing laboratory to evaluate steel column protections that are not required by design to carry any of the column load.

Size and Character of Sample

Sec. 43.119. The size of the steel column used shall be such as to provide a test specimen that is truly representative of the design, materials and workmanship for which classification is desired. The protection shall be applied according to the methods of acceptable field practice. The length of the protected column shall be at least 8 feet. The column shall be vertical during application of the protection and during the fire exposure.

The applied protection shall be restrained against longitudinal temperature expansion greater than that of the steel column by rigid steel plates or reinforced concrete attached to the ends of the steel column before the protection is applied. The size of the plates or amount of concrete shall be adequate to provide direct bearing for the entire transverse area of the protection.

The ends of the specimen, including the means for restraint, shall be given sufficient thermal insulation to prevent appreciable direct heat transfer from the furnace.

Temperature Measurement

Sec. 43.120. The temperature of the steel in the column shall be measured by at least three thermocouples located at each of four levels. The upper and lower levels shall be 2 feet from the ends of the steel column, and the other two intermediate levels shall be equally spaced. The thermocouples at each level shall be so placed as to measure significant temperatures of the component elements of the steel section.

Exposure to Fire

Sec. 43.121. During the fire-endurance test the specimen shall be exposed to fire on all sides for its full length.

Conditions of Acceptance

Sec. 43.122. The test shall be regarded as successful if the transmission of heat through the protection during the period of fire exposure for which classification is desired does not raise the average (arithmetical) temperature of the steel at any one of the four levels above 1000°F., or does not raise the temperature above 1200°F. at any one of the measured points.

Tests of Floors and Roofs

Application

Sec. 43.123. This procedure is applicable to floor and roof assemblies with or without attached, furred or suspended ceilings and requires application of fire exposure to the underside of the specimen under test.

Two fire-endurance classifications shall be developed for assemblies restrained against thermal expansion, a restrained assembly classification based upon the conditions of acceptance specified in Section 43.127 and an unrestrained assembly classification based upon the conditions of acceptance specified in Section 43.128.

One fire-endurance classification shall be developed from tests of assemblies not restrained against thermal expansion based upon the conditions of acceptance specified in Section 43.128, Items 1 and 2.

Individual unrestrained classifications may be developed for beams tested in accordance with this test method using the conditions of acceptance specified in Section 43.136.

Size and Characteristics of Specimen

Sec. 43.124. The area exposed to fire shall be not less than 180 square feet with neither dimension less than 12 feet. Structural members, if a part of the construction under test, shall lie within the combustion chamber and have a side clearance of not less than 8 inches from its walls.

The specimen shall be installed in accordance with recommended fabrication procedures for the type of construction and shall be representative of the design for which classification is desired. Where a restrained classification is desired, specimens representing forms of construction in which restraint to thermal expansion occurs shall be reasonably restrained in the furnace.

Loading

Sec. 43.125. Throughout the fire-endurance test apply a superimposed load to the specimen. This load, together with the weight of the specimen, shall be as nearly as practicable the maximum theoretical dead and live loads permitted by the Uniform Building Code. A fire endurance test may be conducted applying a restricted load condition to the specimen which shall be identified for a specific load condition other than the maximum allowed load condition.

Temperature Measurement

Sec. 43.126. For specimens employing structural members (beams, open-web steel joists, etc.) spaced at more than 4 feet on centers, measure the temperature of the steel in these structural members by thermocouples at three or more sections spaced along the length of the members with one section preferably located at midspan, except that in cases where the cover thickness is not uniform along the specimen length, at least one of the sections at which temperatures are measured shall include the point of minimum cover.

For specimens employing structural members (beams, open-web steel joists, etc.) spaced at 4 feet on center or less, measure the temperature of the steel in these structural members by four thermocouples placed on each member, except that no more than four members shall be so instrumented. Place the thermocouples at significant locations, such as at midspan, over joints in the ceiling, and over light fixtures, etc.

For steel structural members there shall be four thermocouples at each section, except that where only four thermocouples are required on a member, the thermocouples may be distributed along the member at significant locations as provided for in the preceding paragraph. Locate two on the bottom of the bottom flange or chord, one on the web at the center, and one on the top flange or chord. The recommended thermocouple distribution at each section is shown in Figure No. 43-1-2.

For reinforced or prestressed concrete structural members, locate thermocouples on each of the tension reinforcing elements, unless there are more than eight such elements, in which case place thermocouples on eight elements selected in such a manner as to obtain representative temperatures of all the elements.

For steel floor or roof units locate four thermocouples on each section (a section to comprise the width of one unit), one on the bottom plane of the unit at an edge joint, one on the bottom plane of the unit remote from the edge, one on the side wall of the unit, and one on the top plane of the unit. The thermocouples should be applied, where practicable, to the surface of the units remote from fire and spaced across the width of the unit. No more than four nor less than two sections need be so instrumented in each representative span. Locate the groups of four thermocouples in representative locations. Typical thermocouple locations for a unit section are shown in Figure No. 43-1-3.

Conditions of Acceptance—Restrained Assembly

Sec. 43.127. In obtaining a restrained assembly classification, the following conditions shall be met:

1. The specimen shall have sustained the applied load during the classification period without developing unexposed surface conditions which will ignite cotton waste.

2. Transmission of heat through the specimen during the classification period shall not have been such as to raise the average temperature on its unexposed surface more than 250°F. above its initial temperature.

3. For specimens employing steel structural members (beams, open-web steel joists, etc.) spaced more than 4 feet on centers, the assembly shall achieve a fire-endurance classification on the basis of the temperature criteria specified in Section 43.128, Item No. 3, for assembly classifications up to and including one hour. For classifications greater than one hour, the above temperature criteria shall apply for a period of one half the classification of the assembly or one hour, whichever is the greater.

4. For specimens employing steel structural members (beam, open-web steel joists, etc.) spaced 4 feet or less on centers, the assembly shall achieve a fire-endurance classification on the basis of the temperature criteria specified in Section 43.128, Item No. 4, for assembly classifications up to and including one hour. For classifications greater than one hour, the above temperature criteria shall apply for a period of one half the classification of the assembly or one hour, whichever is the greater.

5. For specimens employing conventionally designed concrete beams, spaced more than 4 feet on centers, the assembly shall achieve a fire-endurance classification on the basis of the temperature criteria specified in Section 43.128, Item No. 5, for assembly classifications up to and including one hour. For classifications greater than one hour, the above temperature criteria shall apply for a period of one half the classification of the assembly or one hour, whichever is the greater.

Conditions of Acceptance—Unrestrained Assembly

Sec. 43.128. In obtaining an unrestrained assembly classification, the following conditions shall be met:

1. The specimen shall have sustained the applied load during the classification period

without developing unexposed surface conditions which will ignite cotton waste.

2. The transmission of heat through the specimen during the classification period shall not have been such as to raise the average temperature on its unexposed surface more than 250°F. above its initial temperature.

3. For specimens employing steel structural members (beams, open-web steel joists, etc.), spaced more than 4 feet on centers, the temperature of the steel shall not have exceeded 1300°F. at any location during the classification period nor shall the average temperature recorded by four thermocouples at any section have exceeded 1100°F. during the classification period.

4. For specimens employing steel structural members (beams, open-web steel joists, etc.), spaced 4 feet or less on center, the average temperature recorded by all joist or beam thermocouples shall not have exceeded 1100°F. during the classification period.

5. For specimens employing conventionally designed concrete structural members (excluding cast-in-place concrete roof or floor slabs having spans equal to or less than those tested), the average temperature of the tension steel at any section shall not have exceeded 800°F. for cold-drawn prestressing steel or 1100°F. for reinforcing steel during the classification period.

6. For specimens employing steel floor or roof units intended for use in spans greater than those tested, the average temperature recorded by all thermocouples located on any one span of the floor or roof units shall not have exceeded 1100°F. during the classification period.

Report of Results

Sec. 43.129. The fire-endurance classification of a restrained assembly shall be reported as that developed by applying the conditions of acceptance specified in Section 43.127.

The fire-endurance classification of an unrestrained assembly shall be reported as that developed by applying the conditions of acceptance specified in Section 43.128 to a specimen tested in accordance with this test procedure.

Tests of Loaded Restrained Beams

Application

Sec. 43.130. An individual classification of a restrained beam may be obtained by this procedure and based upon the conditions of acceptance specified in Section 43.133. The fire-endurance classification so derived shall be applicable to the beam when used with a floor or roof construction which has a comparable or greater capacity for heat dissipation from the beam than the floor or roof with which it was tested. The fire-endurance classification developed by this method shall not be applicable to sizes of beams smaller than those tested.

Size and Characteristics of Specimen

Sec. 43.131. Install the test specimen in accordance with recommended fabrication procedures for the type of construction. It shall be representative of the design for which classification is desired. The length of beam exposed to the fire shall be not less than 12 feet and the member shall be tested in its normal horizontal position. A section of a representative floor or roof construction not more than 7 feet wide, symmetrically located with reference to the beam, may be included with the test specimen and exposed to the fire from below. Restrain the beam including that part of the floor or roof element forming the complete beam as designed (such as composite steel or concrete construction) against longitudinal thermal expansion in a manner simulating the restraint in the construction represented. Do not support or restrain the perimeter of the floor or roof element of the specimen, except that part which forms part of a beam as designed.

Loading

Sec. 43.132. Throughout the fire-endurance tests apply a superimposed load to the specimen. This load, together with the weight of the specimen, shall be as nearly as practicable the maximum theoretical dead and live loads permitted by the Uniform Building Code.

Conditions of Acceptance

Sec. 43.133. The following conditions shall be met:

1. The specimen shall have sustained the applied load during the classification period.
2. The specimen shall have achieved a fire-endurance classification on the basis of the temperature criteria specified in Section 43.128, Item 3 or 4, of one half the classification of the assembly or one hour, whichever is the greater.

Alternative Classification Procedure for Loaded Beams

Application

Sec. 43.134. Individual unrestrained classifications may be developed for beams tested as part of a floor or roof assembly as described in Sections 43.123 through 43.126 (except for the fourth paragraph of Section 43.123) or for restrained beams tested in accordance with the procedure described in Sections 43.130 through 43.132. The fire-endurance classification so derived shall be applicable to beams when used with a floor or roof construction which has a comparable or greater capacity for heat dissipation from the beam than the floor or roof with which it was tested. The fire-endurance classification developed by this method shall not be applicable to sizes of beams smaller than those tested.

Temperature Measurement

Sec. 43.135. Measure the temperature of the steel in structural members by thermocouples at three or more sections spaced along the length of the members with one section preferably located at midspan, except that in cases where the cover thickness is not uniform along the specimen length, at least one of the sections at which temperatures are measured shall include the point of minimum cover.

For steel beams, there shall be four thermocouples at each section; locate two on the bottom of the bottom flange, one on the web at the center, and one on the bottom of the top flange.

For reinforced or prestressed concrete structural members, locate thermocouples on each of the tension reinforcing elements unless there are more than eight such elements, in which case place thermocouples on eight elements selected in such a manner as to obtain representative temperatures of all the elements.

Conditions of Acceptance

Sec. 43.136. In obtaining an unrestrained beam classification the following conditions shall be met:

1. The specimen shall have sustained the applied load during the classification period.
2. For steel beams the temperature of the steel shall not have exceeded 1300°F. at any location during the classification period nor shall the average temperature recorded by four thermocouples at any section have exceeded 1100°F. during this period.
3. For conventionally designed concrete beams, the average temperature of the tension steel at any section shall not have exceeded 800°F. for cold-drawn prestressing steel or 1100°F. for reinforcing steel during the classification period.

Alternate Test of Protection for Solid Structural Steel Beams and Girders

Application

Sec. 43.137. Where the loading required in Section 43.125 is not feasible, this alternate test procedure may be used to evaluate the protection of steel beams and girders without application of design load, provided that the protection is not required by design to function structurally in resisting applied loads. The conditions of acceptance of this alternate test are not applicable to tests made under design load as provided under tests for floors and roofs in Sections 43.124, 43.127 and 43.128.

Size and Character of Sample

Sec. 43.138. The size of the steel beam or girder shall be such as to provide a test specimen that is truly representative of the design, materials and workmanship for which classification is desired. The protection shall be applied according to the methods of acceptable field practice and the projection below the ceiling, if any, shall be representative of the conditions of intended use. The length of beam or girder exposed to the fire shall be not less than 12 feet and the member shall be tested in horizontal position. A section of a representative floor construction not less than 5 feet wide, symmetrically located with reference to the beam or girder and extending its full length, shall be included in the test assembly and exposed to fire from below. The rating of performance shall not be applicable to sizes smaller than those tested.

The applied protection shall be restrained against longitudinal expansion greater than that of the steel beam or girder by rigid steel plates or reinforced concrete attached to the ends of the member before the protection is applied. The ends of the member, including the means for restraint, shall be given sufficient thermal insulation to prevent appreciable direct heat transfer from the furnace to the unexposed ends of the member or from the ends of the member to the outside of the furnace.

Temperature Measurement

Sec. 43.139. The temperature of the steel in the beam or girder shall be measured with not less than four thermocouples at each of four sections equally spaced along the length of the beam and symmetrically disposed and not nearer than 2 feet from the inside face of the furnace. The thermocouples at each section shall be symmetrically placed so as to measure significant temperatures of the component elements of the steel section.

Conditions of Acceptance

Sec. 43.140. The test shall be regarded as successful if the transmission of heat through the protection during the period of fire exposure for which classification is desired does not raise the average (arithmetical) temperature of the steel at any one of the four sections above 1000°F., or does not raise the temperature above 1200°F. at any one of the measured points.

Determining Conditions of Restraint for Floor and Roof Assemblies and for Individual Beams

General

Sec. 43.141. Construction tested in accordance with this standard shall be classified as restrained or unrestrained.

A restrained condition in fire tests, as used in this standard, is one in which expansion at the supports of a load-carrying element resulting from the effects of the fire is resisted by forces external to the element. An unrestrained condition is one in which the load-carrying element is free to expand and rotate at its supports.

For the purpose of this section, restraint in buildings is defined as follows: Floor and roof assemblies and individual beams in buildings shall be considered restrained when the surrounding or supporting structure is capable of resisting the thermal expansion throughout the range of anticipated elevated temperatures. Construction not complying with this definition is assumed to be free to rotate and expand and shall be considered as unrestrained.

Restraint may be provided by the lateral stiffness of supports for floor and roof assemblies and intermediate beams forming part of the assembly. In order to develop restraint, connections must adequately transfer thermal thrusts to such supports. The rigidity of adjoining panels or structures shall be considered in assessing the capability of a structure to resist thermal expansion.

Performance of Protective Membranes in Wall, Partition, Floor or Roof Assemblies

Application

Sec. 43.142. When the thermal protection afforded by membrane elements in wall, partition, floor or roof assemblies is to be determined, the nonstructural performance of protective membranes shall be obtained by the following procedure. The performance of protective membranes as determined by this procedure is not a substitute for the fire-endurance classification determined by Sections 43.110 through 43.141 of this standard.

Size and Character of Sample

Sec. 43.143. The sample shall conform to the provisions specified in Section 43.106. The size of the sample shall also conform to the provisions specified in Section 43.110 for bearing walls and partitions, Section 43.113 for nonbearing walls and partitions, or Section 43.124 for floors or roofs.

Temperature Performance of Protective Membranes

Sec. 43.144. The temperature performance of protective membranes shall be measured with thermocouples, the measuring junctions of which are in intimate contact with the exposed surface of the elements being protected. The diameter of the wires used to form the thermo-junction shall not be greater than the thickness of sheet metal framing or panel members to which they are attached and in no case greater than No. 18 B. & S. gage (0.040 inch). The lead shall be electrically insulated with heat-resistant and moisture-resistant coatings.

For each class of elements being protected, temperature readings shall be taken at not less than five representative points. Thermocouples shall not be located nearer to the edges of the test assembly than 12 inches. An exception may be made in those cases when there is an element or feature of the construction that is not otherwise represented in the test assembly. Thermocouples shall not be located opposite, on top of or adjacent to fasteners such as screws, nails or staples when such locations are excluded for thermocouple placement on the unexposed surface of the test assembly as specified in the second paragraph of Section 43.104.

Thermocouples shall be located to obtain representative information on the temperature of the interface between the exposed membrane and the substrate or element being protected.

Temperature readings shall be taken at intervals not exceeding 5 minutes, but the intervals need not be less than 2 minutes.

Conditions of Performance

Sec. 43.145. Unless otherwise specified, the performance of protective membranes shall be determined as the time at which the following conditions occur:

1. The average temperature rise of any set of thermocouples for each class of element being produced is more than 250°F. above the initial temperature, or

2. The temperature rise of any one thermocouple of the set for each class of element being protected is more than 325°F. above the initial temperature.

Report of Results

Sec. 43.146. The protective membrane performance for each class of element being protected shall be reported to the nearest integral minute.

The test report shall identify each class of elements being protected and shall show the location of each thermocouple.

The test report shall show the time-temperature data recorded for each thermocouple and the average temperature for the set of thermocouples on each element being protected.

The test report shall state any visual observations recorded that are pertinent to the performance of the protective membrane.

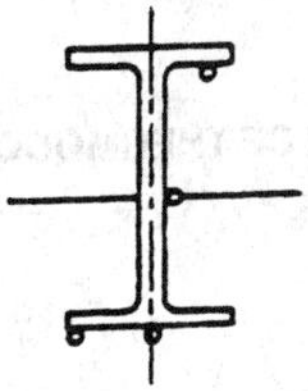

SECTION A

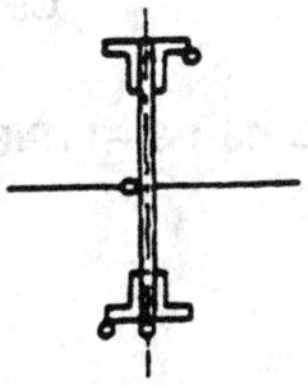

SECTION B

FIGURE NO. 43-1-2—RECOMMENDED THERMOCOUPLE DISTRIBUTION

FLUTED UNIT

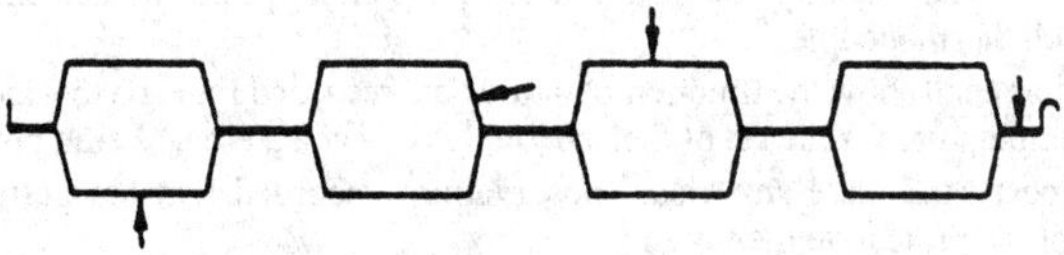

CELLULAR UNIT

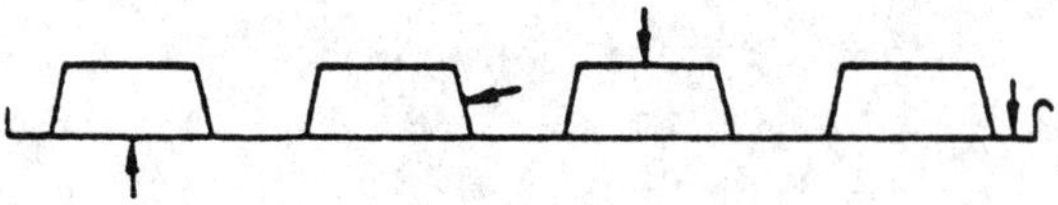

CELLULAR UNIT

FIGURE NO. 43-1-3—TYPICAL LOCATION OF THERMOCOUPLES

UNIFORM BUILDING CODE STANDARD NO. 43-2

FIRE TESTS OF DOOR ASSEMBLIES

See Sections 503 (d), 802 (b) 2, 3305 (h), 3309 (c), 4301 (a), 4305 (i), and 4306 (e) and (j), Uniform Building Code

Part I

Based on Underwriters Laboratories Inc. Standard 10B-1988, Fire Tests of Door Assemblies

Scope

Sec. 43.201. These methods of fire test are applicable for door assemblies of various materials and types of construction, for use in wall openings to retard the passage of fire.

Tests made in conformity with these test methods will register performance during the test exposure; but such tests shall not be construed as determining suitability for use after exposure to fire.

Time-Temperature Curve

Sec. 43.202. The fire exposure of door assemblies shall be controlled to conform to the applicable portion of the standard time-temperature curve shown in Figure No. 43-1-1 of U.B.C. Standard No. 43-1. The points on the curve that determine its character are:

1000°F	at 5 minutes
1300°F	at 10 minutes
1462°F	at 20 minutes
1550°F	at 30 minutes
1638°F	at 45 minutes
1700°F	at 1 hour
1792°F	at 1 1/2 hours
1850°F	at 2 hours
1925°F	at 3 hours

Furnace Temperatures

Sec. 43.203. (a) **Test Exposure.** The temperatures of the test exposure shall be deemed to be the average temperature obtained from the readings of not less than nine thermocouples symmetrically disposed and distributed to show the temperature near all parts of the test assembly. The thermocouples shall be protected by sealed porcelain tubes having 3/4-inch outside diameter and 1/8-inch wall thickness; or, as an alternate, in the case of base metal thermocouples shall be protected by 1/2-inch wrought steel or wrought-iron pipe of standard weight. The junction of the thermocouples shall be 6 inches from the exposed face of the test assembly or from the masonry in which the assembly is installed during the entire test exposure.

(b) **Reading Intervals.** The temperatures shall be read at intervals not exceeding five minutes during the first two hours, and thereafter the intervals may be increased to not more than 10 minutes.

(c) **Accuracy of Control.** The accuracy of furnace control shall be such that the area under the time-temperature curve, obtained by averaging the results from the thermocouple readings, is within 10 percent of the corresponding area under the standard time-temperature curve for fire tests of one hour or less duration, within 7.5 percent of those over one hour and not more than two hours and within 5 percent for tests exceeding two hours in duration.

Unexposed Surface Temperatures

Sec. 43.204. If unexposed surface temperatures are recorded other than for single-layer metal doors, they shall be determined in the following manner:

1. Unexposed surface temperatures shall be taken at not less than three points with at least one thermocouple in each 16-square-foot area of the door.

Thermocouples shall not be located over reinforcements extending through the door, over vision panels or nearer than 12 inches from the edge of the door.

2. Unexposed surface temperatures shall be measured with thermocouples placed under flexible, over-dry, felted asbestos pads, $6^1/_8$ inches square, 0.40 ± 0.05 inch thick and weighing not less than 1.0 pound or more than 1.4 pounds per square foot. The pads shall be held firmly against the surface of the door and shall fit closely about the thermocouples. The thermocouple leads shall be positioned under the pad for a distance of not less than $3^1/_2$ inches with the hot junction under the center of the pad. The thermocouple leads under the pads shall not be heavier than No. 18 AWG (0.04 inch) and shall be electrically insulated with heat-resistant and moisture-resistant coatings.

3. Unexposed-surface temperatures shall be read at the same intervals as those for furnace temperatures in Section 43.203 (b).

Test Assemblies

Sec. 43.205. (a) **Construction and Size.** The construction and size of the test door assembly, consisting of single doors or doors in pairs, special purpose doors (such as dutch doors, double egress doors, etc.) or multisection doors shall be representative of that for which classification or rating is desired.

(b) **Sills.** A floor structure shall be provided as part of the opening to be protected except where such sill interferes with the operation of the door. The sill shall be of noncombustible material and project into the furnace to a distance approximately twice the thickness of the test door or to the limit of the frame, whichever is greater.

Mounting

Sec. 43.206. (a) **Side to Be Exposed.** Swinging doors shall be mounted so as to open into the furnace chamber.

Sliding and rolling doors, except passenger-elevator shaft doors, shall be mounted on the exposed side of the opening in the wall closing the furnace chamber.

Horizontal slide-type elevator shaft doors shall be mounted on the unexposed side of the opening in the wall closing the furnace chamber.

Access-type doors and chute-type doors and frame assemblies shall be mounted so as to have one assembly open into the furnace chamber and another assembly open away from the furnace chamber.

Dumbwaiter and service-counter doors and frame assemblies shall be mounted on the exposed side of the opening in the wall.

(b) **Frames.** Door frames shall be evaluated when mounted so as to have the doors open either away from, or into, the furnace chamber at the discretion of the testing agency, to obtain representative information on the performance of the construction under test.

(c) **Hardware.** Surface-mounted hardware (fire-exit devices) for use on fire doors shall be evaluated by being installed on one door assembly swinging into the furnace chamber and another door assembly swinging away from the furnace chamber.

(d) **Anchors.** Door frame wall anchors, when used, shall be acceptable for the wall or partition construction.

(e) **Fit.** The mounting of all doors shall be such that they fit snugly within the frame, against the wall surfaces, or in guides, but such mounting shall not prevent free and easy operation of the test door.

(f) **Clearances.** Clearances for swinging doors shall be as follows: With a minus $^1/_{16}$-inch tolerance—$^1/_8$ inch along the top, $^1/_8$ inch along the hinge and latch jambs, $^1/_8$ inch along the meeting edge of doors in pairs, and $^3/_8$ inch at the bottom edge of a single swing door, and $^1/_4$ inch at the bottom of a pair of doors.

Clearances for horizontal sliding doors not mounted within guides shall be as follows: With a minus 1/8-inch tolerance—1/2 inch between door and wall surfaces, 3/8 inch between door and floor structure, and 1/4 inch between the meeting edges of center-parting doors. A maximum lap of 4 inches of the door over the wall opening at sides and top shall be provided.

Clearances for vertical sliding doors moving within guides shall be as follows: With a minus 1/8-inch tolerance—1/2 inch between door and wall surfaces along top and/or bottom door edges with guides mounted directly to the wall surface and 3/16 inch between meeting edges of biparting doors or 3/16 inch between door and floor structure or sill.

Clearances for horizontal slide-type elevator doors shall be as follows: With a minus 1/8-inch tolerance—3/8 inch between door and wall surfaces, 3/8 inch between multisection door panels and 3/8 inch from the bottom of the panel to the sill. Multisection door panels shall overlap 3/4 inch. Door panels shall lap the wall opening 3/4 inch at sides and top.

Conduct of Test

Sec. 43.207. (a) **Time of Testing.** Masonry settings shall have sufficient strength to retain the assembly securely in position throughout the fire and hose stream tests.

(b) **Fire-endurance Test.** The pressure in the furnace chamber shall be maintained as nearly equal to the atmospheric pressure as possible.

The test shall be continued until the exposure period of the desired classification or rating is reached unless the conditions of acceptance specified in Section 43.209 are exceeded in a shorter period.

(c) **Hose Stream Test.** Immediately following the fire-endurance test, the test assembly shall be subjected to the impact, erosion and cooling effects of a hose stream directed first at the middle and then at all parts of the exposed surface, changes in direction being made slowly.

The hose stream shall be delivered through a 21/2-inch hose discharging through a National Standard playpipe of corresponding size equipped with a 11/8-inch discharge tip of standard-taper smoothbore pattern without shoulder at the orifice. The water pressure at the base of the nozzle and the duration of application in seconds per square foot of exposed area shall be as set forth in Table No. 43-2-A.

The tip of the nozzle shall be located 20 feet from and on a line normal to the center of the test door. If impossible to be so located, the nozzle may be on a line deviating not to exceed 30 degrees from the line normal to the center of the test door.

When so located, the distance from the center shall be less than 20 feet by an amount equal to 1 foot for each 10 degrees of deviation from the normal.

Report

Sec. 43.208. Results shall be reported in accordance with the performance in the tests prescribed in these test methods. The report shall show the performance under an exposure period chosen from the following: 20 minutes, 30 minutes, three-fourths hour, one hour, one and one-half hours, or three hours. The report shall include the temperature measurements of the furnace and, if determined, of the unexposed side of the test assembly. It shall also contain a record of all observations having a bearing on the performance of the test assembly including:

1. Any flaming on the unexposed surface of the door leaf.

2. The amount of movement of any portion of the edges of the door adjacent to the door frame from the original position.

3. The materials and construction of the door and frame and the details of the installation, hardware, hangers, guides, trim, finish and clearance or lap shall also be recorded or appropriately referenced to provide positive identification or duplication in all respects.

4. It shall also contain pressure measurements relative to the elevation of the top of the door.

Conditions of Acceptance

Sec. 43.209. (a) **General.** A door assembly shall be considered as meeting the requirements for acceptable performance when it remains in the opening during the fire-endurance test and hose stream test within the following limitations:

1. The movement of swinging doors shall not permit any portion of the edges to move from the original position more than the thickness of the door, during the first half of the classification period or more than $1^1/_2$ times the thickness during the entire classification period.

2. An assembly consisting of a pair of swinging doors shall not separate more than $^3/_4$ inch or a distance equal to the throw of the latch bolt at the latch location.

3. An assembly consisting of a single swinging door shall not separate more than $^1/_2$ inch at the latch location.

4. The lap edges of passenger (horizontal slide-type) elevator doors, including the lap edges of multisection doors, shall not move from the wall or adjacent panel surfaces sufficiently to develop a separation of more than $2^7/_8$ inches during the entire classification period, or immediately following the hose stream test. The meeting edges of center-parting elevator door assemblies, for a fire and hose stream exposure of $1^1/_2$ hours or less, shall not move apart more than $1^1/_4$ inches as measured in any horizontal plane during the entire classification period or immediately following the hose stream test.

5. Doors mounted in guides shall not release from guides and guides shall not loosen from fastenings.

6. The test assembly shall have withstood the fire-endurance test and the hose stream test without developing openings anywhere through the assembly; except that dislodging of small portions of glass by the hose stream and within the limits specified in these requirements shall remain in place.

7. An opening is defined as a through hole in the assembly that can be seen from the unexposed side when viewed from the direction perpendicular to the plan of the assembly at the location of the suspected opening.

(b) **Specific, All Doors.** 1. No flaming shall occur on the unexposed surface of a door assembly during the first 30 minutes of the classification period.

2. After 30 minutes, some intermittent light flames (approximately 6 inches long), for periods not exceeding five-minute intervals, may occur along the edges of doors.

3. Light flaming may occur during the last 15 minutes of the classification period on the unexposed surface area of the door, provided it is contained within a distance of $1^1/_2$ inches from a vertical door edge and within 3 inches from the top edge of the door and within 3 inches from the top edge of the frame of a vision panel.

4. When hardware is to be evaluated for use on fire doors, it shall hold the door closed in accordance with the conditions of acceptance for the intended door assembly classification

period and, in addition, the latch bolt shall remain projected and shall be intact after the test. The hardware need not be operable after test.

(c) **Swinging Doors.** The movement of swinging doors shall not result in any portion of the edges adjacent to the door frame moving from the original position in a direction perpendicular to the plane of the door more than the thickness of the door during the first half of the classification period, or more than one and one-half times the door thickness during the entire classification period or as a result of the hose stream test.

The movement of swinging doors mounted in pairs shall not result in any portion of the meeting edges moving more than the thickness of the door away from the adjacent door edge in a direction perpendicular to the plane of the doors during the entire classification period or as a result of the hose stream test.

An assembly consisting of a pair of swinging doors incorporating an astragal shall not separate in a direction parallel to the plane of the doors more than 3/4 inch or a distance equal to the throw of a latch bolt at the latch location.

An assembly consisting of a pair of swinging doors, without an overlapping astragal, for a fire and hose stream exposure of one and one-half hours or less, shall not separate along the meeting edges more than 3/8 inch, including the initial clearance between doors.

An assembly consisting of a single swinging door shall not separate more than 1/2 inch at the latch location.

Door frames to be evaluated with doors shall remain securely fastened to the wall on all sides and shall not permit through openings between frame and doors or between frame and adjacent wall.

(d) **Sliding Doors.** Doors mounted on the face of the wall shall not move from the wall sufficiently to develop a separation of more than 27/8 inches during the entire classification period or as a result of the hose stream test.

Doors mounted in guides shall not release from the guides, and the guides shall not loosen from fastenings.

The bottom bar of rolling steel doors shall not separate from the floor structure more than 3/4 inch during the entire classification period or as a result of the hose stream test.

The meeting edge of center-parting horizontal sliding doors and biparting vertical sliding doors shall not separate more than the door thickness in a direction perpendicular to the plane of the doors. The meeting edges of center-parting horizontal sliding doors and biparting vertical sliding doors without an overlapping astragal, for a fire and hose stream exposure of one and one-half hours or less, shall not separate in a direction parallel to the plane of the doors more than 3/8 inch along the meeting edges, including the initial clearance between doors.

The meeting edges of center-parting horizontal sliding doors incorporating an astragal shall not separate in a direction parallel to the plane of the doors more than 3/4 inch nor a distance equal to the throw of the latch bolt along the meeting edges.

The bottom edge of service-counter doors or single-slide dumbwaiter doors shall not separate from the sill more than 3/8 inch.

A resilient astragal, if provided, shall not deteriorate sufficiently to result in through openings during the fire-endurance test, but small portions may be dislodged during the hose stream test.

TABLE NO. 43-2-A—WATER PRESSURE AT BASE OF NOZZLE AND DURATION OF APPLICATION

DESIRED RATING	WATER PRESSURE AT BASE OF NOZZLE (Pounds per Square Inch)	DURATION OF APPLICATION Seconds Per Square Foot Of Exposed Area
3 hr.	45	3
1½ hour and over, if less than 3 hr.	30	1.5
1 hr. and over, if less than 1½ hr.	30	0.9
Less than 1 hr.	30	0.6

Part II—Test Standard for Smoke- and Draft-control Assemblies of the International Conference of Building Officials

Smoke- and Draft-Control Door Assemblies

Sec. 43.210. (a) **Fire-endurance Test.** The method of test for 20-minute smoke- and draft-control assemblies shall be as required for swinging doors under Part I of this standard. The fire-endurance test for these door assemblies shall be for an exposure period of not less than 20 minutes except that the hose stream test required by Section 43.207 (c) need not be applied.

(b) **Conditions of Acceptance.** A smoke- and draft-control door assembly shall be considered as meeting the requirements for acceptable performance when it remains in the opening during the fire-endurance test and complies with the following:

1. Flaming shall not occur on the unexposed surface of the door assembly during the fire-endurance test.

2. The movement shall not result in any portion of the edges adjacent to the door frame moving from the original position in a direction perpendicular to the plane of the door equivalent to the thickness of the door.

3. Neither the unexposed surface of the door nor the door itself shall emit excessive amounts of smoke during the fire test.

4. Smoke- and draft-control door assemblies shall be provided with a gasket so installed as to provide a seal where the door meets the stop on both sides and across the top. The gasketing need not be installed on the test assembly.

UNIFORM BUILDING CODE STANDARD NO. 43-3

TINCLAD FIRE DOORS

Based on Tinclad Fire Doors Standard ANSI/UL 10 A—1979 (R 1985)

See Sections 4301 (a) 1 and 4306 (e), Uniform Building Code

Part I—General

Scope

Sec. 43.301. This standard covers the design and construction of tin clad fire doors which have shown by fire tests to possess sufficient fire-retardant values to warrant classification as three, one and one-half or three-fourths-hour assemblies, when tested in accordance with the Standard Specification for Fire Tests of Door Assemblies. Doors complying with these requirements are classified in two temperature-rise groups:

1. Temperature rise on the unexposed side at the end of 30 minutes 250°F. maximum.

2. Temperature rise on the unexposed side at the end of 30 minutes in excess of 650°F.

Requirements

Sec. 43.302. A door conforming to these specifications consists essentially of a core made up of layers of boards nailed to each other, encased in terne or zinc-coated steel in the form of sections jointed together at their edges and nailed through the seams to the core.

Sizes and Ratings

Sec. 43.303. The sizes and ratings for three-ply and two-ply doors are given in Table No. 43-3-A.

Doors exceeding the sizes in Table No. 43-3-A have not been subjected to standard fire tests, and certificates on such doors indicate that the units conform to construction requirements of this standard except for size.

It should be noted that Table No. 43-3-A pertains to maximum size of opening. Doors limited in size by these two tables fall into two categories: (1) swinging doors intended to be installed within an opening, and (2) all sliding doors and those swinging doors intended for surface mounting outside of the opening. Swinging doors in the first category are limited in size to the maximum dimensions specified for the opening. Doors in the second category must be larger than the maximum opening dimensions to provide the minimum 4-inch lap at each side and the top of the door. Doors exceeding these two basic dimension considerations are termed "Oversize," the design and construction of which are not necessarily fully covered in these requirements.

Part II—Materials

Lumber

Sec. 43.304. (a) **Species and Condition.** The following soft woods may be used, provided only one kind of lumber is used in the assembly of a single core:

Cedars—All classes	Redwood
Cypress—All classes	Sitka Spruce
Douglas Fir	Tupelo Gum
Eastern Spruce	Yellow Poplar
Northern White Pine	Western White Pine

Other kinds of lumber may be added to the foregoing list, provided the kind of wood to be used has properties equivalent to the above species with respect to low resin content, light weight, resistance to fungus and decay, and ability to withstand nailing without splitting or splintering.

Lumber shall have a moisture content of 19 percent or less at the time of manufacturing door cores. Tests for moisture content shall be made using the oven drying or the electrical meter method in accordance with approved methods for tests for moisture content of wood.

Stocks of lumber shall be stored under cover in the premises of the fire-door manufacturer for at least one month before being used in the manufacture of fire-door cores and, while in storage, shall be piled in such a manner that the air has free access to all surfaces of each board. Kiln drying will be accepted for the 30-day drying period.

(b) **Size.** The boards shall be nominal 1-inch lumber, surfaced on two sides and matched. They shall be without beading, beveling, painting or other treatment.

The actual thickness of the boards shall be not less than ¾ inch.

The boards shall be not less than 4 inches nor more than 8 inches in nominal width.

The nominal width (or stock width) is greater than the actual width over the tongue and groove.

(c) **Grading.** The boards shall be free from wane (bark), decay, knots or other holes, loose knots, unsound knots or knots exceeding 2½ inches in any dimension.

Lumber of a No. 2 Common or Construction grade or better will generally meet these requirements. However, because some pieces of No. 2 grade could be unacceptable, the kind of lumber used and its condition shall be judged from characteristic properties of the wood as commmonly known. These characteristics include:

1. **Decay**—Destruction of the wood substance due to the action of wood destroying fungi. NOTE: "Dote" and "rot" are synonymous with "decay" and are any form of decay which may be evident either as a dark red discoloration, not found in the sound wood, or the presence of white or red rotten spots.
2. **Advanced (typical decay)**—The older stage of decay in which the destruction is readily recognized because the wood has become punky, soft and spongy, stringy, ring shaped, pitted or crumbly.
3. **Incipient decay**—The early stage of decay which has not proceeded far enough to soften or otherwise perceptibly impair the hardness of the wood.
4. **Knot**—That portion of a branch which has become incorporated in the body of a tree.
5. **Loose knot**—A knot which is not firmly held in place by growth or position.
6. **Tight knot**—A knot so fixed by growth or position that it will firmly retain its place in the wood piece.
7. **Hollow knot**—A hollow knot is an apparently sound knot except it contains a hole over ¼ inch in diameter or a void area behind the knot.
8. **Check**—A separation along the grain, the greater part of which occurs across the rings of annual growth.
9. **Wane** — The lack of wood from any cause, or bark on the surface of lumber.

To permit judging of the several characteristics of knots, such are to be measured across their lines of growth for oval and circular knots. For spike knots the measurement is to be parallel to the lines of growth. In all cases the measured distance is to be the visible portion of the knot and is normally darker or lighter than the coloring of the board.

The following characteristics are to be judged as unacceptable:

1. Oval, circular or spike knots exceeding 2½ inches in any direction.
2. Loose knots, open knots or any knot over 1 inch in any direction located on the tongue or lip.
3. Loose knots, open knots, through holes and surface pits (deeper than 1/16 inch) in the central portion of the boards.
4. Hollow and decayed knots.
5. Checks, advanced (typical) and incipient decay.
6. Warpage which would prevent the boards from being nailed flat or which would affect the flatness of the nailed core.
7. Cluster knots or knots in groups (less than 5/8 inch apart).

Tight knots on the lips or tongue of a board may be judged acceptable if due to manufacturing they have been chipped, but only to the extent that (1) the dimensions of the damage do not exceed 3/8 inch in length and 3/16 inch in diameter, and (2) the lip or tongue with a chip cannot be easily broken, such as upon exerting direct hand pressure.

Metal Coverings

Sec. 43.305. (a) **General.** The terne or zinc-coated steel sections shall have straight edges and square corners. A deviation of 1/32 inch per foot from square shall be accepted, provided the door manufacturer is able to obtain true, straight joints and to avoid patching the rows of sheets in the covering.

(b) **Terne-coated Sheet Steel.** Prime terne plate only shall be used. For the purpose of these requirements, "terne" shall be understood as indicating an alloy of tin and lead in the proportion of 80 percent lead and 20 percent tin, hot-dipped applied. The terne coating shall be uniformly applied on both sides of sheet steel having an uncoated thickness of not less than 0.010 inch. The terne coating shall not crack, peel or flake when formed.

The sheet steel shall be coated with not less than 0.55 ounce per square foot average of terne coating (total both sides) by triple spot test and not less than 0.40 oz./sq. ft. of terne coating (total both sides) by the single spot test, with not less than 40 percent of the coating on any side, base the single spot test requirement. The weight of terne coating shall be determined by approved nationally recognized methods.

A determination for percent tin shall be made on a portion of the solution containing the stripped terne coating, using standard laboratory analytical methods. The amount of tin in the coating shall be not less than 20 percent.

A determination for percent lead may be made on a portion of the solution containing the stripped terne coating, using standard laboratory analytical methods, or the percent of lead in coating may be determined by subtracting the percent of tin from 100 percent.

(c) **Zinc-coated (Galvanized) Sheet Steel.** Zinc-coated sheet steel shall have an uncoated thickness of not less than 0.010 inch. The zinc coating shall not crack or flake when formed.

Finished doors shall be painted with a good grade of corrosion-resisting paint before shipment. Before painting, zinc surfaces shall be thoroughly cleaned and pretreated to provide for adherence of the paint coating.

The protective coating of zinc shall be as applied to hot-dipped mill galvanized sheet steel, with not less than 40 percent of the zinc on any side, based on the single spot requirement. The weight of zinc coating, minimum 0.5 oz./ft.^{2} shall be determined by approved nationally recognized methods.

Nails

Sec. 43.306. Core nails shall be cut nails of the clinch type or duck bill point type power-driven nails that clinch. For three-ply cores the nails shall be not less than 2⅞ inches nor more than 3 inches long. For two-ply cores the nails shall be not less than 1¹¹⁄₁₆ inches nor more than 2 inches long. The shank diameters of duck bill point nails shall be 0.130—0.140 inch for three-ply doors and 0.100—0.110 inch for two-ply doors.

Nails for applying the metal covering shall be wire nails with flat heads. The shank of the nails shall be not less than 0.091 inch nor more than 0.109 inch in diameter. The nails for three-ply cores shall be 2 inches long, and for two-ply cores shall be not less than 1¼ inches nor more than 1½ inches long.

Part III—Construction

Assembly of Boards

Sec. 43.307. The details for the assembly of boards are shown in Figures Nos. 43-3-1 and 43-3-2.

Only one stock width of board shall be used in any one core, except that the edge board and the stock board immediately adjacent to the edge board may differ in width from the remaining stock boards. Edge boards shall finish not less than 3 inches in width and the exposed edges shall not be tongued or grooved.

Boards shall be not less than 1 foot in length, with ends cut square. Not more than two pieces shall be used in any continuous strip in any outside layer of a two-ply or three-ply core, nor more than three pieces in any middle layer strip of a three-ply core. At least alternate strips in outside layers shall be full-length boards.

If glass panels are provided and the panel opening is of such a size that the distance between the opening and the edges of the door is less than 2 feet, all boards bordering the vertical edges of the opening may be laid vertically and all boards bordering the horizontal edges of the opening may be laid horizontally.

If glass panels are provided, the boards in the normally vertical layers bordering the sides of the panel opening shall be continuous from top to bottom of the door, and boards in the normally horizontal layer bordering the top or bottom of the panel opening shall be continuous from side to side of the door. The distance between the panel opening and the side of the door shall be not less than 7 inches. See Figure No. 43-3-2.

Outside layers in a three-ply core and one layer of a two-ply core shall be vertical, and the other layer horizontal. The several boards in each layer and the ends of pieces of boards in strips shall make tight joints at edges and ends of boards.

The top edge for a sliding door designed to close by gravity shall conform to an incline of ¾ inch per foot. The minimum face width of the top horizontal board of a core having the top edge inclined shall be not less than 3 inches. See Figures Nos. 43-3-3, 43-3-4 and 43-3-5.

Nailing of Cores

Sec. 43.308. (a) **General.** The boards shall be nailed so that the several layers are fastened tightly together, with the points of the nails turning back and clinching thoroughly in the face of the core and with no portion of the nails projecting beyond the surfaces of the core. See Figure No. 43-3-6.

(b) **Two-ply and Three-ply Cores of Boards 3 to 4 Inches (Inclusive) Stock Width.** The details for nailing of boards 3 to 4 inches, inclusive, stock width are shown in Figure No. 43-3-3.

Horizontal rows of nails shall be about the center of each horizontal layer board. Vertical rows of nails shall be about the center of each vertical layer of board. Nails in horizontal and vertical rows shall be spaced not more than five times the face width of each board. Rows of nails at edges of core shall be about 1½ inches from each edge. Nails in vertical edge rows shall be placed not more than the face width of each board and shall be about the center of each horizontal board. Nails in horizontal edge rows shall be spaced not more than the face width of each board and shall be about the center of each vertical board.

(c) **Two-ply and Three-ply Cores of Boards 4½ to 8 Inches (Inclusive) Stock Width.** The details for nailing of boards 4½ to 8 inches, inclusive, stock width are shown in Figure No. 43-3-4.

Horizontal rows of nails shall be about 1 inch from each edge of each horizontal layer board (two horizontal rows of nails through each horizontal board). Vertical rows of nails shall be about 1 inch from each edge of each vertical layer board (two vertical rows of nails through each vertical board). Nails in horizontal and vertical rows shall be spaced not more than twice the face width of each board.

Rows of nails at edges of core shall be about 1½ inches from each edge. Nails in vertical-edge rows shall be spaced not more than the face width of each board and shall be about the center of each horizontal board. Nails in horizontal edge rows shall be spaced not more than the face width of each board and shall be about the center of each vertical board, except that the nails in the top edge row of a core having the top edge inclined shall be spaced not more than 4½ inches.

(d) **Three-ply Cores Only of Boards 4½ to 8 Inches (Inclusive) Stock Width.** The details for nailing of boards 4½ to 8 inches, inclusive, stock width for three-ply core only are shown in Figure 43-3-5.

Horizontal rows of nails shall be about the center of each horizontal layer board. Vertical rows of nails shall be about 1 inch from each edge of each vertical layer board (two vertical rows of nails through each vertical board). Nails in horizontal rows shall be spaced not more than the face width of each board. Nails in vertical rows shall be spaced not more than twice the face width of each board.

Rows of nails at edges of core shall be about 1½ inches from each edge. Nails in vertical edge rows shall be spaced not more than the face width of each board and shall be about the center of each horizontal board. Nails in horizontal edge rows shall be spaced about 1 inch from each edge of each vertical board, except that each vertical edge board shall have only one nail, which should be placed about the center of the board.

Finished Cores

Sec. 43.309. A finished three-ply core shall be not less than 2¼ inches nor more than 2⅝ inches in thickness, and a finished two-ply core shall be not less than 1½ inches nor more than 1¾ inches in thickness.

EXCEPTION: A finished three-ply core door which is less than 2¼ inches thick may be marked in accordance with the schedule for two-ply doors.

The cores shall have true corners. All edges shall be finished smooth and square, excepting that meeting edges of swinging doors may be beveled ¼ inch (not rabbeted).

Sizes of Steel Sections

Sec. 43.310. Coated steel sections shall be not larger than the 14- by 20-inch size. Corner sections shall be not over 14 inches wide and of any length that will avoid joints with edge sections coming under miter fold. Edge sections (excepting "cap" sections) shall be of the same width as corner sections and of any convenient length. Cap sections shall be of any convenient length and equal in width to thickness of core plus $3^1/_2$ inches.

Forming of Steel Sections

Sec. 43.311. Turned edges of coated steel sections shall be parallel to cut edges. Turned up portions of all sections shall be of uniform width.

Faces sections, excepting the face sections used in the row forming the closure, shall have one vertical edge turned $^5/_8$ inch and the other vertical edge doubled under $1^3/_{16}$ inches and the doubled edge then turned up $^5/_8$ inch from cut edge as shown in Figure No. 43-3-7, Section A-B.

Face sections, excepting face sections forming top horizontal seams, shall have both horizontal seams, shall have both horizontal edges turned $^5/_8$ inch to lock with edge and other face sections shown in Figure No. 43-3-7, Section C-D.

Face sections forming top horizontal seams, excepting seams formed with a cap, shall have the lower horizontal edge turned $^5/_8$ inch to lock with other face sections, and the other horizontal edge doubled under $1^3/_{16}$ inches and the doubled edge then turned up $^5/_8$ inch from cut edge.

Face sections forming top horizontal seams with a cap shall have both horizontal edges turned up $^5/_8$ inch to lock with cap and other face sections.

Corner sections shall have all edges turned $^5/_8$ inch so as to lock with edge and face sections as shown in Figure No. 43-3-8.

Edge sections, excepting cap sections, shall have all edges turned $^5/_8$ inch so as to lock with corner, face and other edge sections as shown in Figure No. 43-3-9.

Cap sections shall have edges forming seams with other cap sections turned $^5/_8$ inch. Cap sections shall have edges forming top horizontal seams with face and edge sections double under $1^3/_{16}$ inches and the portion next to the cut edge turned down $^5/_8$ inch so as to lap the edge and face sections as shown in Figure No. 43-3-10.

Application of Steel Sections

Sec. 43.312. The sections shall fit the core as flatly and tightly as practicable. Any air space created as the result of bulging shall not exceed $^3/_{16}$ inch.

The sections shall be locked together not less than $^1/_2$ inch. Both faces of the core shall be covered with sections laid with their longer sides vertical, except that the sections in one vertical row on each face of the core may be laid horizontally.

Vertical seams formed with face sections shall be hook seams with the upper section having a fold for covering the heads of the nails in the seam as shown in Figure No. 43-3-11.

Horizontal seams formed with face sections, excepting top horizontal seams, shall be hook seams as shown in Figure No. 43-3-12. Top horizontal seams, excepting seams formed with a cap, shall have a fold for covering the heads of the nails in the seam as shown in Figure No. 43-3-11. Top horizontal seams formed with a cap shall be lock seams with the locking portion of the cap having a fold for covering the heads of the nails in the seam as shown in Figure No. 43-3-10.

The upper ends of vertical seams shall be covered by the doubled edges of the top horizontal seams.

Each bottom corner of the core shall be covered with a section bent over the edges of the core and lapped an equal distance on both faces of the core, making a miter fold (without cutting) on each face, the folds on a door for use at an opening in an exterior wall being arranged to shed water as shown in Figure No. 43-3-8.

Each upper corner shall be covered the same as bottom corners if a cap is not used for covering the top edge of the core.

The bottom edge and the vertical edges of the core shall be covered with sections bent over edges of the core and lapped an equal distance on both faces. The sections shall be joined to each other and to the corners with hook seams, the seams being made so as to shed water when the door is for use at an opening in an exterior wall as shown in Figures Nos. 43-3-7 and 43-3-9.

The top edge of the core shall be covered the same as the bottom and vertical edges if a cap is not used. The top edge of a core shall be covered with a cap when the door is for use at an opening in an exterior wall or when the door has a segmental head. The cap shall be formed of sections joined to each other with hook seams as shown in Figure No. 43-3-13.

If glass panels are provided and band or angle iron reinforcement for glass grooves is used, the vertical edges of the panel openings shall be covered with terne or zinc-coated steel secured to the face sections by vertical seams. The covering at the horizontal edges of the opening shall be cap seams as shown in Figure No. 43-3-14.

Nailing of Steel Sections

Sec. 43.313. The nails shall pass straight into the core and as near as possible through the center of the lock in the seams as shown in Figures Nos. 43-3-10, 43-3-11 and 43-3-12.

Full-sized face sections shall be held to the core by 18 nails in the seams, with nails near but not in the corners, and with four nails along each short side and five along each long side of each section.

Face sections smaller than 14- by 20-inch size shall be held to the core by nails in the seams placed near but not in the corners, with at least two nails along each side and with nails spaced not over 3 inches apart in horizontal seams and not over 4 inches apart in vertical seams.

Vertical seams formed with face sections shall have nails through two thicknesses of each section as shown in Figure No. 43-3-11.

Horizontal seams formed with face sections except top horizontal seams, shall have nails through two thicknesses of lower sections and one thickness of upper section forming the seams as shown in Figure No. 43-3-12. Top horizontal seams, except seams made with a cap, shall have nails through two thicknesses of each section forming the seams as shown in Figure No. 43-3-11. Top horizontal seams formed with a cap shall have nails through one thickness of each plate forming the seams as shown in Figure No. 43-3-10.

Each corner section shall be held to the core with two nails on each side near the edge of the core as shown in Figure No. 43-3-8.

If glass panels are provided and band or angle-iron reinforcement for glass grooves is used, nails securing seams between face sections and strips covering edges of panel opening shall be spaced at intervals not exceeding 3 inches in horizontal seams and 4 inches in vertical seams, with one nail near but not in each corner.

Protection of Nailheads

Sec. 43.314. Heads of nails in vertical seams formed with face sections shall be covered by the doubled edges of face sections as shown in Figure No. 43-3-11. Heads of nails in horizontal seams formed with face sections, except top horizontal seams, shall be covered by the face sections as shown in Figure No. 43-3-12. Heads of nails in top horizontal seams formed with face sections shall be covered by the doubled edges of face sections or cap as shown in Figures Nos. 43-3-10 and 43-3-11. Heads of nails in corner sections shall be covered by the miter fold as shown in Figure No. 43-3-8.

Astragals

Sec. 43.315. Swinging doors to be mounted in pairs shall be provided with at least one astragal extending the full height of the doors. Sliding doors to be mounted in pairs shall be provided with only one astragal extending to within 4 inches of the top and bottom of the doors. Astragals shall be of steel not less than $\frac{3}{16}$ inch thick and 3 inches wide. The astragal shall be fastened to the door, when installed, by not less than $\frac{1}{4}$-inch carriage or stove bolts spaced at intervals not exceeding 12 inches. Top bolts shall be not over 5 inches from the end of the astragal and bottom bolts not over 3 inches. Bolts shall pass through astragal and be secured by nuts on the opposite side of the door. Washers shall be used under nuts. Bolt holes in astragal and door shall be so located that astragal will extend at least $\frac{3}{4}$ inch beyond the edge of the door to which it is attached.

In case the astragal is to be attached in the field, the bolt holes in the astragal shall be drilled by the manufacturer to ensure proper spacings, fit, etc. In such case it will not be necessary to drill the door for the bolts.

Glass Panels

Sec. 43.316. (a) General. The construction details for any one of the following types of glass panel construction shall not be used in or combined with any of the other types described.

(b) **Reinforcements for Grooves.** In all doors provided with grooves constructed of angles, the opening shall be reinforced either by means of a band-iron strip not less than $\frac{1}{8}$ inch in thickness and equal in width to the thickness of the core or by means of $\frac{1}{8}$- by $1\frac{3}{8}$- by $\frac{7}{8}$-inch angles bolted together through the door. See Figures Nos. 43-3-14, 43-3-15 and 43-3-16.

The band-iron strip shall be secured to the inner edges of the panel opening by not less than two wood screws and shall be provided with threaded holes for receiving the bolts which secure the angles forming the glass grooves.

The $\frac{1}{8}$- and $1\frac{3}{8}$- by $\frac{7}{8}$-inch angles shall be bolted together through the door by $\frac{3}{16}$-inch stove bolts spaced at intervals not exceeding 12 inches and not more than 2 inches from each end. They shall be provided with threaded holes for receiving the bolts which secure angles forming the glass groove.

(c) **Glass Grooves Constructed of Angles.** The angles used in forming the glass grooves shall be not less than $\frac{1}{8}$ inch in thickness and shall be of such other dimensions as to provide a groove not less than $\frac{3}{4}$ inch deep by $\frac{3}{8}$ inch wide as shown by Figures Nos. 43-3-14, 43-3-15 and 43-3-16.

Rivets or screws used to secure the groove angles to the reinforcement shall be spaced at intervals not exceeding 12 inches and not more than 2 inches from each end.

(d) **Grooves Constructed of Formed Sheet Metal.** Grooves of this type shall be formed of a single piece of galvanized or terne-coated sheet steel having an uncoated thickness of not less than 0.020 inch as shown by Figures Nos. 43-3-17, 43-3-18 and 43-3-19 and shall be not less than $\frac{3}{4}$ inch deep by $\frac{3}{8}$ inch wide.

The edges of this formed strip shall be secured to the face sections of the door by vertical seams at the vertical edges of the opening as shown by Figure No. 43-3-19, Section B-B, and by cap seams at the horizontal edges of the opening as shown by Figure No. 43-3-19, Section D-D.

The edges of this formed strip shall be secured to the face plates of the door by vertical seams at the vertical edges of the opening as shown by Figure No. 43-3-19, Section B-B, and by cap seams at the horizontal edges of the opening as shown by Figure No. 43-3-19, Section D-D.

In the case of glass openings employing only one light, the sheet-metal glass groove may be constructed as shown by Figure No. 43-3-19, Section A-A. In this type of glass groove the reinforcing strip shall be ⅛-inch band iron and shall either be continuous for the full length of the groove or consist of individual reinforcing strips not less than 1 inch long for each screw securing the removable molding. The reinforcing strip shall be secured to the fixed part of the glass groove by rivets or screws, independent of the screws fastening the removable molding. Rivets or screws used to secure the reinforcing strip or the removable molding shall be spaced at intervals not exceeding 12 inches and not more than 2 inches from each end.

Nails securing seams between molding strips and face sections shall be spaced at intervals not exceeding 3 inches in horizontal seams and 4 inches in vertical seams, with one nail near but not in each corner.

(e) **Muntins.** Muntins may be of any of the constructions shown by Figures Nos. 43-3-12 through 43-3-19. In all cases, fixed parts of muntins shall be firmly secured to glass moldings at ends and at intersections with each other. Rivets, screws, welds or clips may be employed. Rivets, screws, etc., shall be spaced at intervals not exceeding 12 inches.

When muntins are formed of sheet metal, the reinforcing plate shall be ⅛-inch band iron which may be either continuous for the full length of the muntin or may consist of individual reinforcing strips not less than 1 inch long for each screw securing the removable part of the muntin.

(f) **Screws and Rivets.** Screw sizes shall be: $\frac{3}{16}$ inch (10-24) spaced 10 inches on centers; ⅛ inch (either 6-32 or 8-32) spaced 8 inches on centers. Rivets shall be not less than ⅛ inch in diameter.

(g) **Glass Sizes.** Individual lights in doors bearing the marking "Rating: ¾-Hr. (C) or (E)" shall not exceed 1296 square inches in exposed area or 54 inches in either dimension.

Area of exposed glass light per door leaf in doors bearing the marking "Rating: 1½-Hr. (B), Temp. Rise—30 Min.—250°F. Max." shall not exceed 100 square inches, neither length nor width to exceed 12 inches.

Glass lights shall not be used in doors bearing the marking "Rating: 3-Hr. (A) or 1½-Hr. (D)."

Splicing of Doors Made in Sections

Sec. 43.317. If doors are made in sections to be assembled as a single unit in the field, each section shall be constructed and marked in accordance with the requirements for a completed door.

Sections less than 10 feet in height (not more than two) shall be joined together vertically by attaching to each face of the completed door a strip of galvanized sheet steel having a minimum thickness of not less than 0.056 inch, not less than 6 inches in width and of a length corresponding to the height of the door. The splice metal sections shall be attached to each section of the door by not less than ¼-inch through bolts spaced on not more than 12-inch centers and at not to exceed 3 inches from the top and bottom edges of the door. Through bolts shall extend through both splice plates and the door body and shall thread into nuts.

Sections over 10 feet in height (not more than two) may be joined together vertically by attaching to each face of the completed door not more than two strips of sheet steel having a minimum thickness of 0.12 inch, painted on both sides, or galvanized sheet steel having a minimum thickness of 0.126 inch not less than 6 inches in width and of a length corresponding to the height of the door. The meeting edges of such splice sections on one side of the door section shall be at least 2 feet higher or lower than those on the opposite side.

On three-ply doors, 2- by 2- by 3/16-inch angles or 2 1/2- by 5/8- by 3/16-inch channels shall be attached horizontally across the width of the door at not to exceed 18 inches from the bottom edge and the lowest corner of the top edge by not less than 3/8-inch through bolts spaced on not more than 18-inch centers and at not more than 6 inches from each edge of the assembled door. On two-ply doors, 2- by 1 1/2- by 3/16-inch angles or 1 1/2- by 5/8- by 3/16-inch channels shall be attached in a like manner.

Angle- and channel-iron reinforcements and both splice plates may be shipped separately but through bolts shall be secured to them before shipment. Both sections of the door shall be drilled at the factory to receive through bolts for attachment of splice metal sections and angle- and channel-iron reinforcements.

Wickets

Sec. 43.318. Doors or door sections shall not be provided with wickets or openings for same.

Applied Metals

Sec. 43.319. Doors or door sections shall not be provided with kick plates or metals applied over the standard construction.

Part IV—Marking

Marking

Sec. 43.320. (a) **Content.** Each door shall be marked with:

1. The manufacturer's or vendor's name or identifying symbol.
2. The words "Tinclad Fire Door."
3. The appropriate hourly rating and temperature rise for the classification and any glass panels.

If a door has been provided with edge notches to clear conveyor rails, for example, it becomes ineligible to carry the marking outlined in Section 43.320 (a) 3; but it shall be otherwise identified with the following statement:

"This door(s) violates one of the fundamental principles of wall opening protection in that it (they) does not provide for a continuous lap of the door over the edge of the opening to oppose the passage of flame and therefore cannot be provided with an hourly classification."

If a manufacturer produces doors at more than one factory, each door shall have a distinctive marking to identify it as the product of a particular factory.

(b) **Application.** Markings shall be permanent to the degree afforded by a lithographed metal plate, a pressure-sensitive label, or stamping. All markings on one door shall be grouped in one location.

TABLE NO. 43-3-A—SIZES AND RATINGS

TYPE, METHOD OF OPERATION AND MAXIMUM SIZE OF OPENING	RATING AND CLASS OF OPENING	MAXIMUM EXPOSED GLASS AREA
Three-ply Swinging single 6′0″ x 12′0″ Swinging in pairs 10′0″ x 12′0″ Sliding single and Center-parting 120 square feet with maximum dimension 12′0″ Vertically sliding 80 square feet with maximum dimension 10′0″	3-Hr. (A)[1] 1½-Hr. (B)[1] ¾-Hr. (C)[2] 1½-Hr. (D)[1] ¾-Hr. (E)[2]	None 100 square inches per door 1296 square inches per light None 1296 square inches per light
Two-ply Swinging single 6′0″ x 10′0″ Swinging in pairs 10′0″ x 10′0″ Sliding single and 80 square feet with maximum dimension 10′0″	1½-Hr. (B)[1] ¾-Hr. (C)[2] 1½-Hr. (D)[1] ¾-Hr. (E)[2]	100 square inches per door 1296 square inches per light None 1296 square inches per light

[1]Three-Hr. (A), 1½-Hr. (B) and 1½-Hr. (D) doors have a temperature rise of 250°F. maximum at 30 minutes.

[2]Three-fourths-Hr. (C) and ¾-Hr. (E) doors with large glass lights may permit a temperature rise in excess of 650°F. on the unexposed side at 30 minutes.

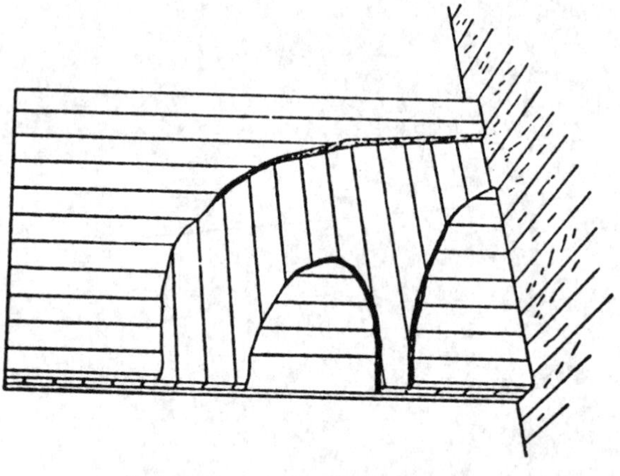

FIGURE NO. 43-3-1
ASSEMBLY OF BOARDS
IN THREE-PLY CORE

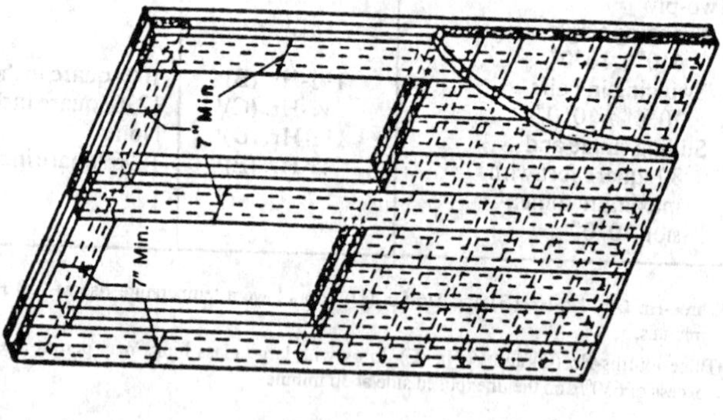
7" Min.
7" Min.

FIGURE NO. 43-3-2
ASSEMBLY OF BOARDS
IN THREE-PLY CORE
WITH GLASS OPENINGS

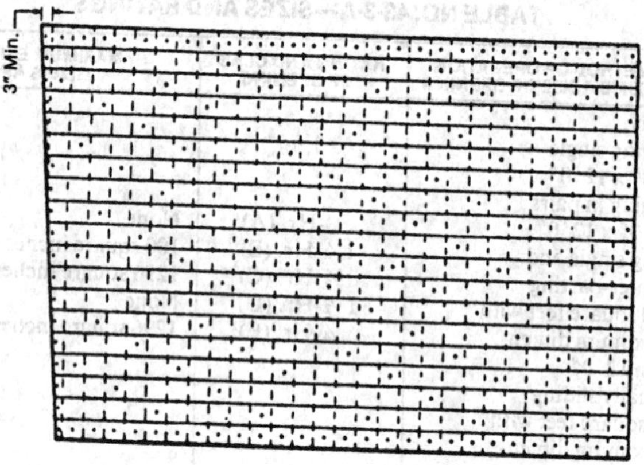
3" Min.

FIGURE NO. 43-3-3
NAILING FOR 3- TO 4-INCH STOCK

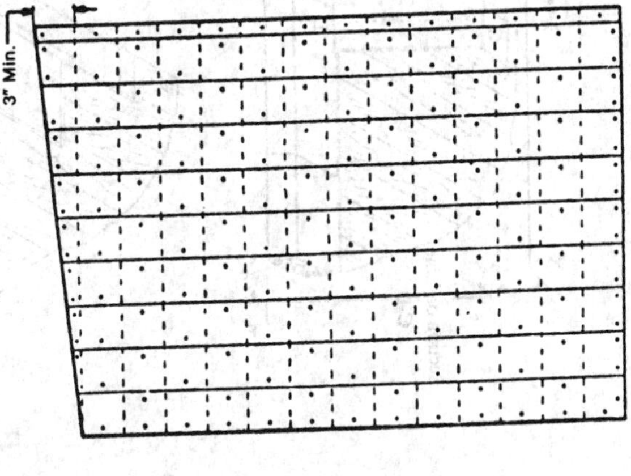
3" Min.

FIGURE NO. 43-3-4
NAILING FOR 4½- TO 8-INCH STOCK

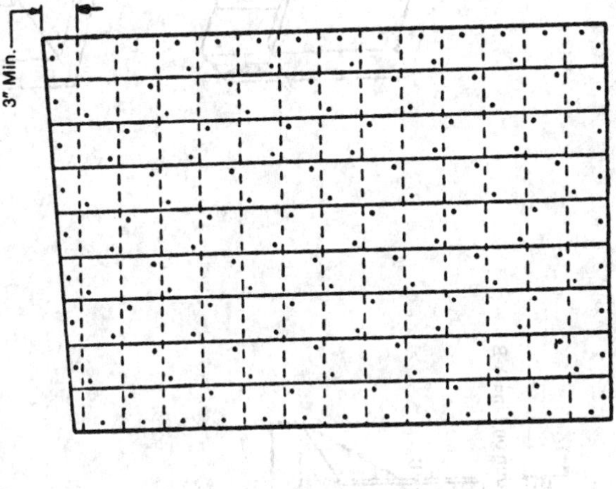
3" Min.

FIGURE NO. 43-3-5
NAILING FOR THREE-PLY CORES
ONLY 4½- TO 8-INCH STOCK

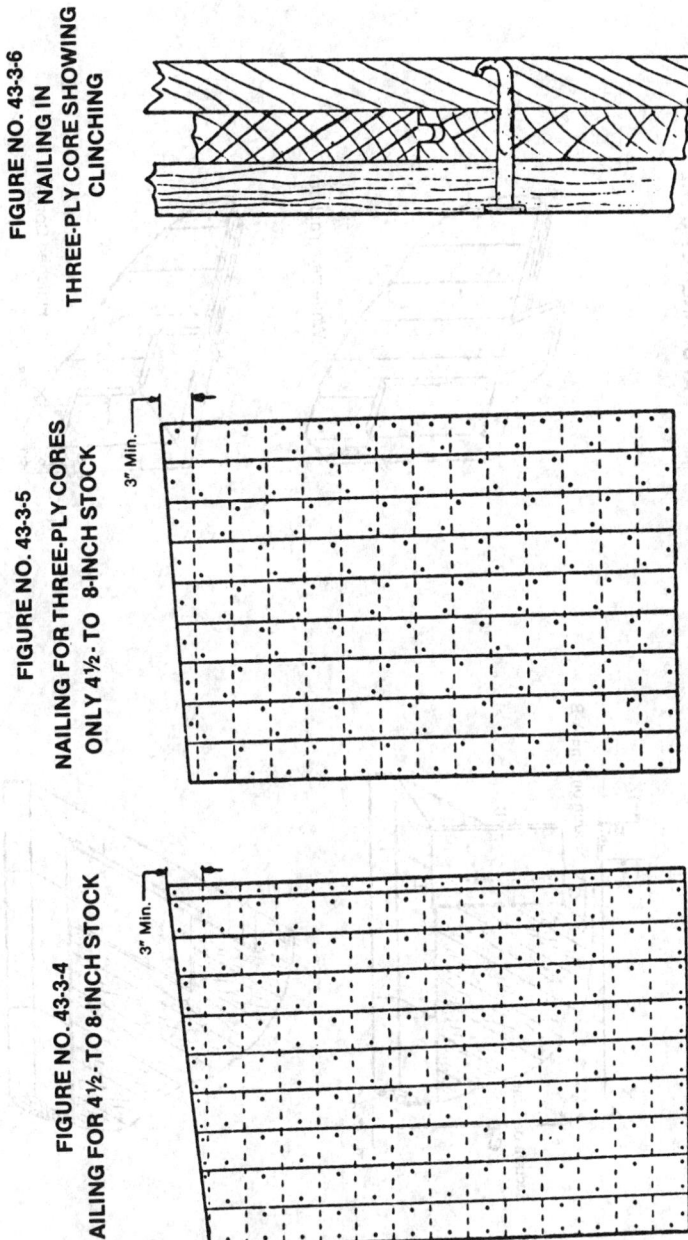

FIGURE NO. 43-3-6
NAILING IN
THREE-PLY CORE SHOWING
CLINCHING

FIGURE NO. 43-3-7
APPLICATION OF METAL SECTIONS ON FACE OF CORE

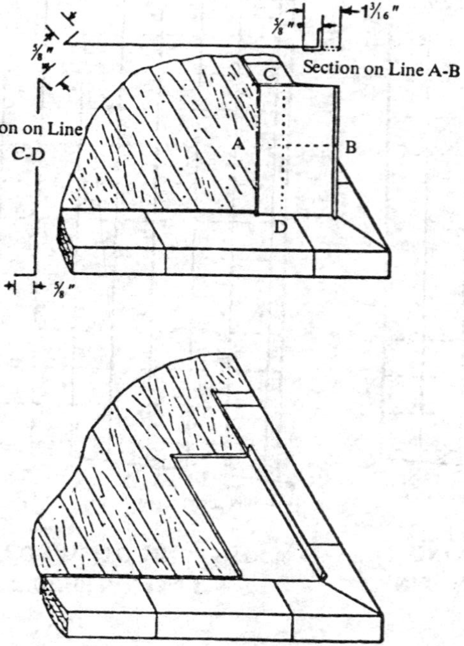
1$\frac{3}{16}$"
$\frac{5}{8}$"
Section on Line A-B
Section on Line
C-D
$\frac{5}{8}$"
$\frac{5}{8}$"
A
B
C
D

FIGURE NO. 43-3-8
APPLICATION OF METAL SECTIONS
AT CORNER OF CORE

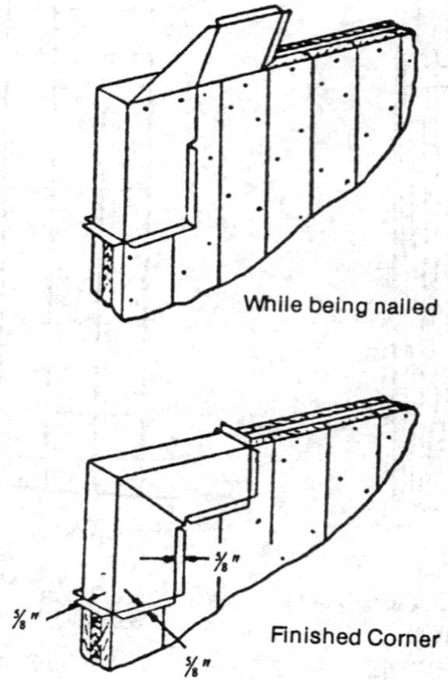
While being nailed
$\frac{5}{8}$"
$\frac{5}{8}$"
$\frac{5}{8}$"
Finished Corner

FIGURE NO. 43-3-9
APPLICATION OF METAL SECTIONS
AT EDGES OF CORE

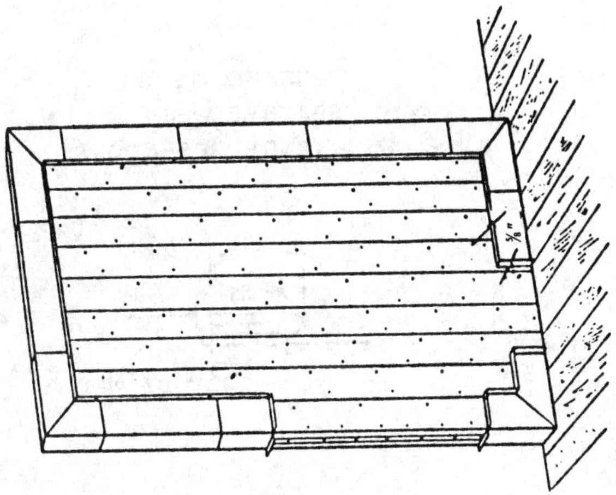
3/8"

FIGURE NO. 43-3-10
APPLICATION OF CAP
METAL SECTIONS AT TOP EDGE OF CORE

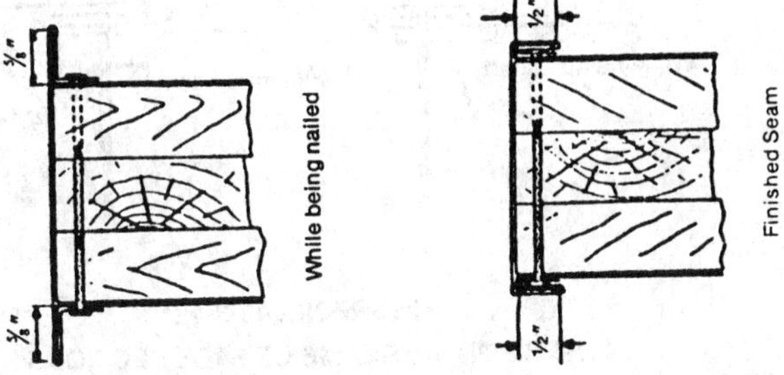
3/8"
3/8"
While being nailed
1/2"
1/2"
Finished Seam

FIGURE NO. 43-3-11
VERTICAL SEAMS OF FACE SECTIONS
(TOP VIEW)

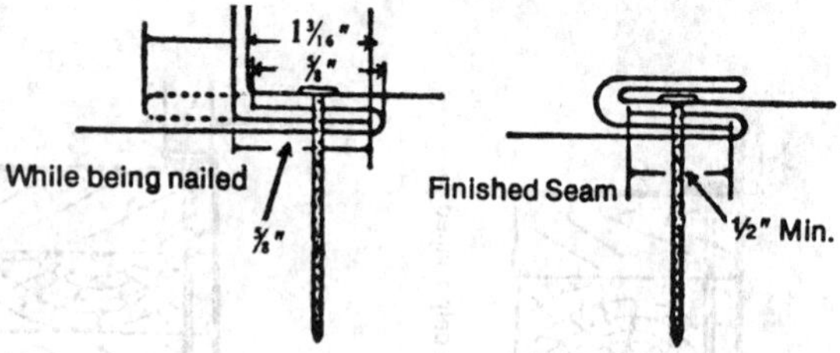
1 3/16"
5/8"
While being nailed
5/8"
Finished Seam
1/2" Min.

FIGURE NO. 43-3-12
HORIZONTAL SEAMS OF FACE SECTIONS
(SIDE VIEW)

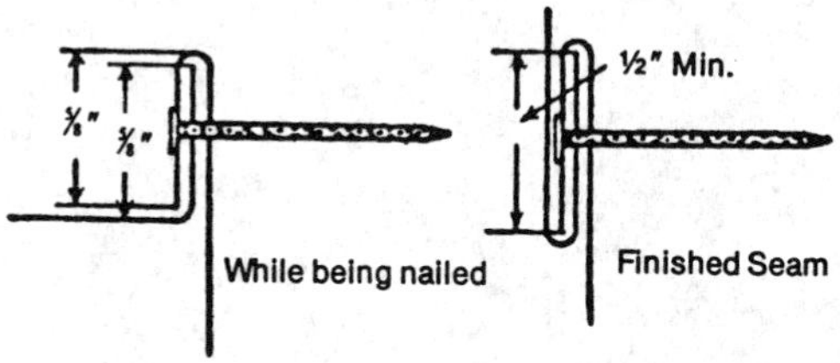
7/8"
5/8"
While being nailed
1/2" Min.
Finished Seam

FIGURE NO. 43-3-13
SEAMS BETWEEN
CORNER AND EDGE SECTIONS

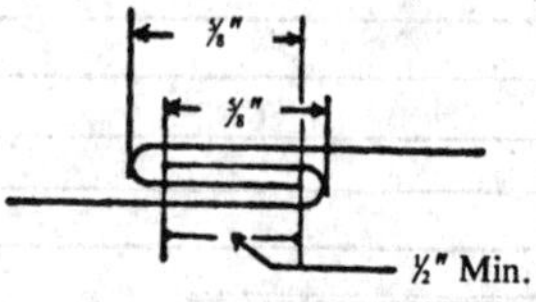
7/8"
5/8"
1/2" Min.

FIGURE NO. 43-3-14
GLASS OPENING DETAILS

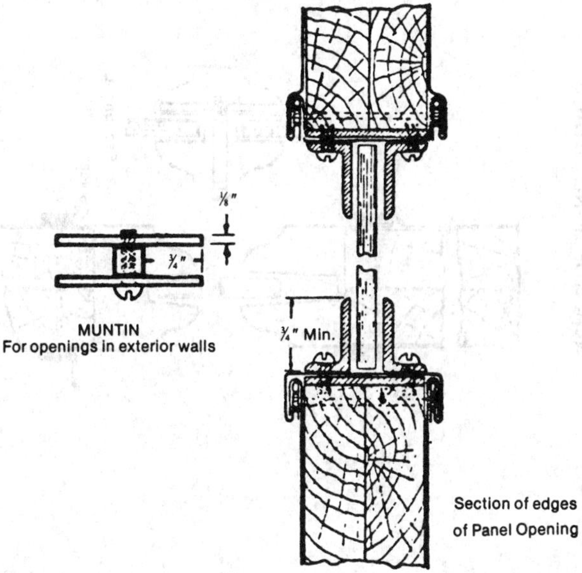
⅛"
¾"
MUNTIN
For openings in exterior walls
¾" Min.
Section of edges
of Panel Opening

FIGURE NO. 43-3-15
GLASS OPENING DETAILS

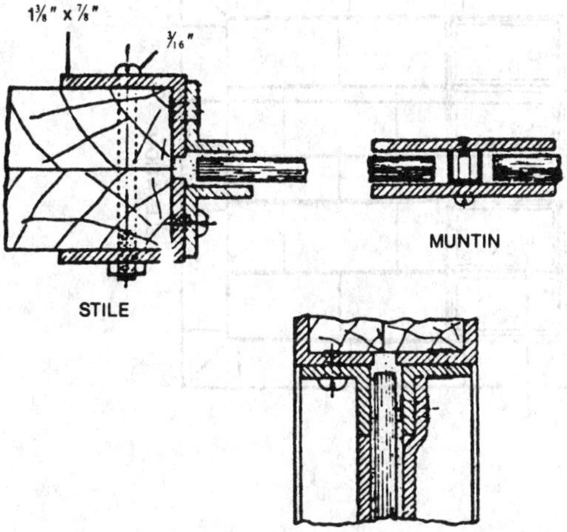
1⅜" x ⅞"
³⁄₁₆"
STILE
MUNTIN

FIGURE NO. 43-3-16
GLASS OPENING DETAILS

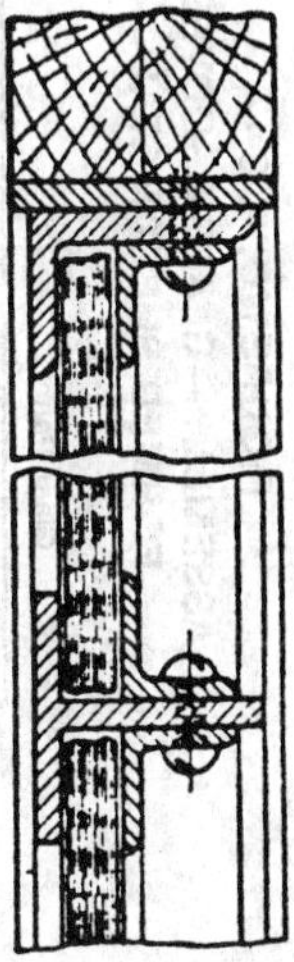

FIGURE NO. 43-3-17
ASSEMBLY—GLASS GROOVES,
FORMED SHEET METAL

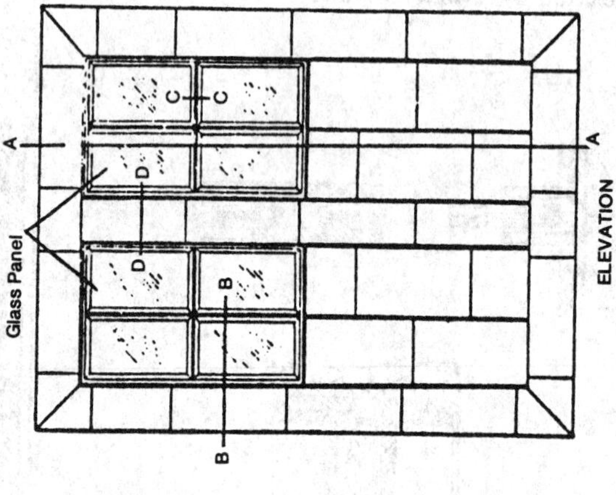
Glass Panel
A
A
B
B
C
C
D
D
ELEVATION

FIGURE NO. 43-3-18
GLASS OPENING DETAILS

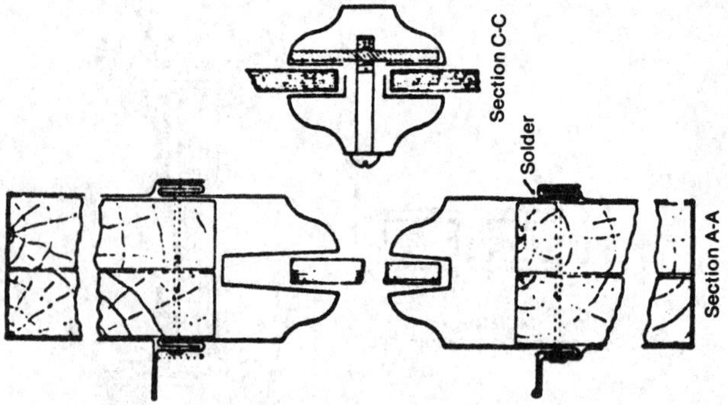
Solder
Section A-A
Section C-C

FIGURE NO. 43-3-19—GLASS OPENING DETAILS

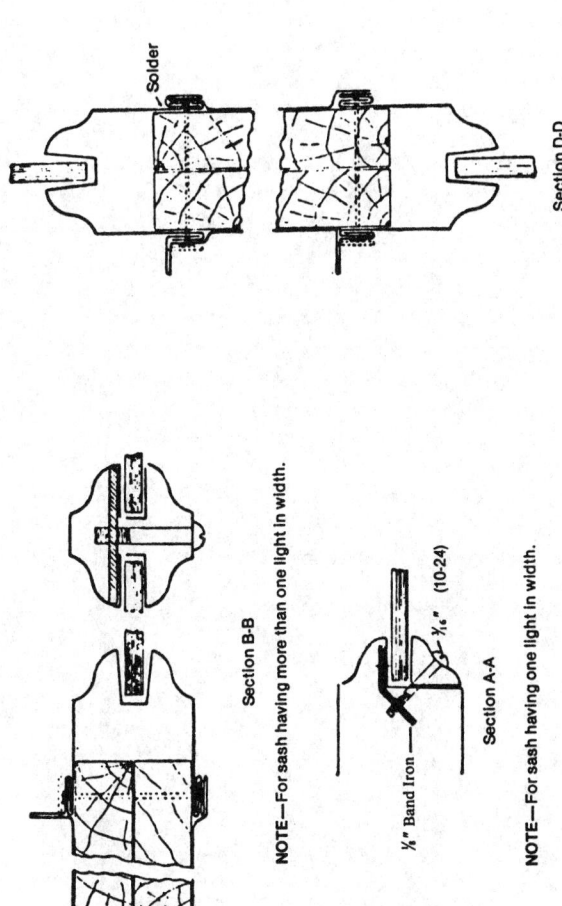

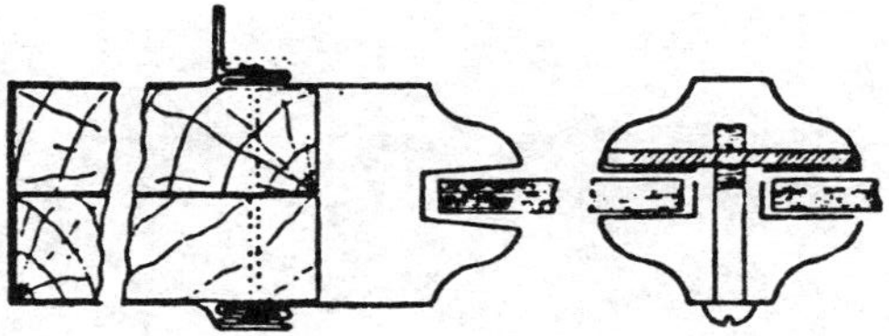

Section B-B

NOTE—For sash having more than one light in width.

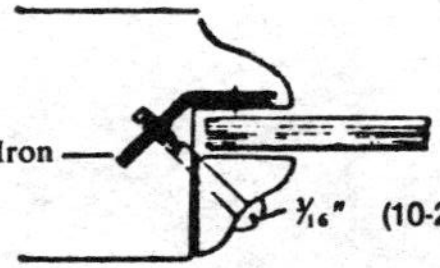
⅛" Band Iron
$\frac{3}{16}$" (10-24)

Section A-A

NOTE—For sash having one light in width.

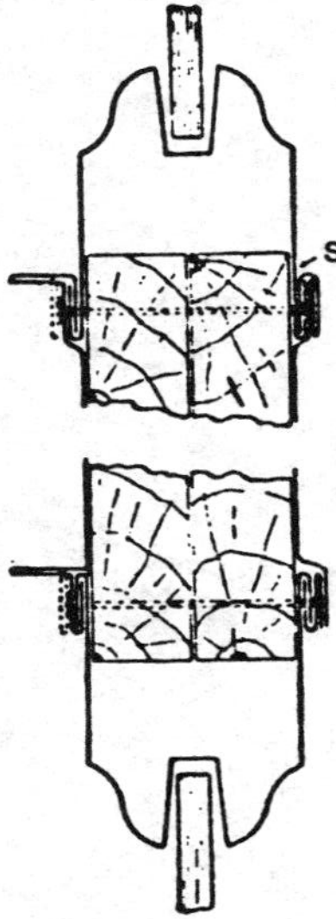
Solder

Section D-D

UNIFORM BUILDING CODE STANDARD NO. 43-4

FIRE TESTS OF WINDOW ASSEMBLIES

Based on Standard Methods E 163-76 of the American Society for Testing and Materials. Extracted, with permission, from the Annual Book of ASTM Standards, copyright American Society for Testing and Materials, 1916 Race Street, Philadelphia, PA 19103.

See Sections 4301 (a) and 4306 (e) and (i), Uniform Building Code

Scope

Sec. 43.401. These methods of fire tests are applicable to window assemblies, including glass block and other light-transmitting assemblies, for use in wall openings to retard the passage of fire. Test methods in this standard are intended to evaluate the ability of a window or other light-transmitting assembly to remain in an opening during a predetermined test exposure of 45-minute duration.

Tests made in conformity with these test methods will register performance during the test exposure and develop data to determine the suitability of window assemblies for use in wall openings where fire protection is required. Such tests shall not be construed as determining suitability of window assemblies for continued use after fire exposure.

Control of Fire Tests

Sec. 43.402. (a) **Time-temperature Curve.** The fire exposure of window assemblies shall be controlled to conform to the standard time-temperature curve shown in Figure No. 43-1-1.

(b) **Furnace Temperatures.** The temperatures of the test exposure shall be the average temperature obtained from the readings of not less than nine thermocouples symmetrically disposed and distributed to show the temperature near all parts of the test assembly. The thermocouples shall be protected by sealed porcelain tubes having ¾-inch outside diameter and ⅛-inch wall thickness or, as an alternate, in the case of base metal thermocouples, protected by sealed ½-inch wrought-steel or wrought-iron pipe of standard weight. The exposed length of the thermocouple protection tube in the furnace chamber shall be not less than 12 inches. The junction of the thermocouples shall be 6 inches from the exposed face of the test assembly or from the masonry in which the assembly is installed during the entire test exposure.

The temperature shall be read at intervals not exceeding five minutes.

The furnace shall be controlled so that the maximum temperature at individual points shall not exceed 1650°F.* and the area under the time-temperature curve, obtained by averaging the results from the temperature readings, is within 10 percent of the corresponding area under the standard time-temperature curve.

Test Assemblies

Sec. 43.403. (a) **Construction and Size.** The design, construction, material, workmanship and hardware of the test window assembly shall be representative of that for which approval is desired. A record of materials and construction details adequate for identification shall be made.

The area of the test assembly shall be not less than 100 square feet, with neither dimension less than 9 feet. If the conditions of use limit the construction to smaller

***NOTE:** In case the temperature at any point does exceed 1650°F., the performance of the glass in that area shall be disregarded.

dimensions a proportionate reduction may be made in the dimensions of the test assembly for tests qualifying them for such restricted use.

(b) **Mounting.** The test assembly shall be installed in the manner in which it is to be used. It shall be mounted so that the latches and fasteners other than hinges shall be on the unexposed side, and the mounting shall not prevent the free and easy operation of all openable components such as ventilators and sash.

Conduct of Tests: Time of Testing

Sec. 43.404. Masonry settings shall be allowed to season at least seven days and reinforced concrete settings at least 28 days, before fire tests are made.

Fire-endurance Test

Sec. 43.405. The pressure in the furnace chamber shall be maintained as nearly equal to the atmospheric pressure as possible.

The test shall be continued for 45 minutes unless the conditions of acceptance specified in Section 43.401 are exceeded in a shorter period.

Hose Stream Test

Sec. 43.406. Immediately following the fire-endurance test and within one and one-half minutes, the fire exposed side of the test assembly shall be subjected to the impact, erosion and cooling effects of the hose stream.

The hose stream shall be delivered through a 2½-inch hose discharging through a National Standard Playpipe of corresponding size equipped with a 1⅛-inch discharge tip of the standard-taper smooth-bore pattern without shoulder at the orifice.

The tip of the nozzle shall be located 20 feet from and on a line normal to the center of the test assembly. If impossible to be so located, the nozzle may be on a line deviating not to exceed 30 degrees from the line normal to the center of the test assembly. When so located, the distance from the plane of the surface of the test assembly shall be less than 20 feet by an amount equal to 1 foot for each 10 degrees of deviation from the normal.

The hose stream shall be directed around the periphery of the test assembly starting upward from a lower corner. When the circuit is about 1 foot from the starting point, the hose stream shall be applied in paths about 1 foot apart up and down the assembly across the entire width and then back and forth horizontally across the entire height.

The water pressure at the base of the nozzle shall be 30 psi and the hose stream shall be applied $\frac{9}{10}$ second for each square foot of area of the test assembly.

Conditions of Acceptance

Sec. 43.407. (a) **Window Assemblies.** A window assembly shall be considered as meeting the requirements for acceptable performance when it remains in the opening during the fire-endurance and hose stream tests within the following limitations:

1. The window assembly shall not be loosened from its fastenings.

2. Movement at the perimeter of openable components, from the initial closed position, shall not exceed the thickness of the frame member at any point.

3. At least 70 percent of the edges of each individual glass light shall remain in position through the hose stream test. The dislodging of small fragments from the central areas of individual lights shall be disregarded.

(b) **Glass Block Assemblies.** A glass block assembly shall be considered as meeting the requirements for acceptable performance when it remains in the opening during the fire-endurance and hose stream tests within the following limitations:

1. The glass block assembly shall not be loosened from the frame.
2. At least 70 percent of the glass blocks shall not develop through openings.

UNIFORM BUILDING CODE STANDARD NO. 43-6

FIRE TESTS OF THROUGH-PENETRATION FIRE STOPS

Based on Standard Methods E 814-82 of the American Society for Testing and Materials. Extracted, with permission, from the Annual Book of ASTM Standards, copyright American Society for Testing and Materials, 1916 Race Street, Philadelphia, PA 19103.

See Section 4308, Uniform Building Code

Part I—General

Scope

Sec. 43.601. This method is applicable to penetration fire stops as defined in the Uniform Building Code. Part I of this standard is applicable to both through-penetration and membrane-penetration fire stops. Part II contains additional criteria applicable to through-penetration fire stops.

In addition to evaluating the fire-resistive characteristics of penetration fire stops, this test method considers the resistance of penetration fire stops to an external force stimulated by a hose stream. However, this method shall not be construed as determining the performance of the fire stop during actual fire conditions when subjected to forces such as failure of support systems and falling debris.

Significance and Use

Sec. 43.602. This method is used to determine the performance of a penetration fire stop with respect to exposure to a standard temperature-time fire test and hose stream test. The performance of a penetration fire stop is dependent upon the specific assembly of materials tested, including the number, type and size of penetrations and the floors or walls in which it is installed.

Definitions

Sec. 43.603. For the the purpose of this standard, certain terms are defined as follows:

TEST ASSEMBLY is the wall or floor into which the test sample is mounted or installed.

TEST SAMPLE is the fire stop being tested.

Control of Fire Tests

Sec. 43.604. (a) **Temperature-Time Curve.** The fire environment within the furnace shall be in accordance with the standard temperature-time curve shown in U.B.C. Standard No. 43-1, Figure No. 43-1-1. The points on the curve that determine its character are set forth in Section 43.102.

(b) **Furnace Temperatures.** The temperature fixed by the curve shall be the average temperature obtained from the readings of thermocouples symmetrically disposed and distributed within the test furnace to show the temperature near all parts of the assembly. Use a minimum of three thermocouples, with not fewer than five thermocouples per 100 square feet of floor surface, and not fewer than nine thermocouples per 100 square feet of wall specimen surface.

Enclose the thermocouples in sealed protection tubes of such materials and dimensions that the time constant of the protected thermocouple assembly lies within the range from 300 to 400 seconds. The exposed length of the pyrometer tube and thermocouple in the furnace chamber shall be not less than 12 inches. Other types of protection tubes of pyrometers may be used, provided that temperature measurements obtained in accordance with Figure No. 43-1-1 are within the limit of accuracy that applies for furnace temperature measurements.

For floors, place the junction of the thermocouples 12 inches away from the exposed face of the assembly. In the case of walls, place the thermocouples 6.0 inches away from the exposed face.

Read the temperature at intervals not exceeding 5 minutes during the first 120 minutes. Thereafter, the intervals may be increased to not more than 10 minutes.

The accuracy of the furnace control shall be such that the area under the temperature-time curve, obtained by averaging the results from the pyrometer or thermoelectric device readings, is within 10 percent of the corresponding area under the standard temperature-time curve shown in Figure No. 43-1-1 for fire tests of 60 minutes or less duration; within 7.5 percent for those over 60 minutes and not more that 120 minutes; and within 5 percent for tests exceeding 120 minutes in duration.

(c) **Unexposed Surface Temperatures.** Measure temperatures on the unexposed surface of the test sample and assembly with thermocouples placed under flexible pads.

The pads shall be of suitable inorganic material and shall exhibit the following properties:

1. **Length and width:** 2.00 ± 0.04 inch.
2. **Thickness:** 0.40 ± 0.05 inch.
3. **Density:** 31.2 ± 0.6 pounds/cubic feet.
4. **Thermal conductivity (k) at 150°F.:** 0.380 ± 0.027 Btu × inches/hour × square feet °F.

The pads shall be sufficiently soft so that, without breaking, they may be shaped to contact over the whole surface against which they are placed.

The pads shall be held firmly against the surface; they shall fit closely about the thermocouples. The thermocouple junction shall be located under the center of the pads. The thermocouple leads under the pads shall be not heavier that No. 18 B. & S. gauge and shall be electrically insulated with heat-resistant moisture-resistant coverings.

Read temperatures at intervals not exceeding 15 minutes until a reading exceeding 212°F. has been obtained at any one point. Thereafter, the readings may be taken more frequently, but the intervals need not be less than 5 minutes.

For specific locations of thermocouples, see Part II.

Additional temperature measurements may be made at the discretion of the testing agency to obtain representative information on the performance of the test sample.

(d) **Differential Pressure.** Measure the pressure differential between the exposed and unexposed surfaces of the test assembly required in Section 43.607 (b) at three points 0.78 inch from the surface and locate as follows:

1. **Walls**—At the center and quarter points on the vertical center line.
2. **Floors**—At the center and quarter points along the longitudinal center line.

The pressure-measuring probe tips shall be as shown in Figure No. 43-6-2, manufactured from stainless steel or other suitable material.

Measure the pressure by means of a manometer or equivalent transducer. The manometer or transducer shall be capable of reading 0.01-inch H_2O increments.

Test Sample

Sec. 43.605. The construction of the test sample shall be of sufficient size and include all conduits, pipes, cables (jacket types, sizes, conductor types, percent fills), required supports or other penetrating items so as to produce a representative penetration fire stop for which evaluation is desired. Penetration fire stops shall be installed and tested in each representative construction for which ratings are desired.

The periphery of the test sample shall not be closer than one and one-half times the thickness of the test assembly or a minimum of 12 inches to the furnace edge, whichever is greater.

The distance between test sample periphery and furnace edge may be reduced if the testing agency demonstrates and reports that the edge effects do not affect the results.

Protecting and Conditioning

Sec. 43.606. Prior to fire test, condition the floor or wall assembly and test samples to provide, within a reasonable time, a moisture condition approximately representative of that likely to exist in similar construction in buildings. This moisture condition is considered as that which would be established at equilibrium resulting from drying in an ambient atmosphere of 50 percent relative humidity at 73°F. However, with some assemblies and test samples it may be difficult or impossible to achieve the equilibrium moisture condition within a reasonable period of time. Therefore, floor or wall assemblies and test samples may be tested when their dampest portion has achieved a moisture content corresponding to drying to equilibrium with air in the range from 50 to 75 percent relative humidity at 73 ± 5°C. If the assembly or test sample dried in a heated building fails to meet these requirements after a 12-month conditioning period, or if the nature of the construction is such that drying of the assembly or test sample interior will be prevented by hermetic sealing, these requirements may be waived, except as to attainment of the required strength as described in Section 43.607 (a), and the assembly or test sample may be tested in the condition in which it then exists.

Protect the testing equipment, sample and assembly undergoing the fire test from any condition of wind or weather that might lead to abnormal results. The ambient air temperature at the beginning of the test shall be within the range from 50 to 90°F. The velocity of air across the unexposed surface measured just before the test begins shall not exceed 4.4 feet/seconds as determined by an anomometer placed at right angles to the unexposed surface. If mechanical ventilation is employed during the test, an airstream shall not be directed across the surface of the sample.

Conduct of Tests

Sec. 43.607. (a) **Time of Testing.** The test sample shall not be tested until the test assembly has developed sufficient strength to retain the test sample securely in position.

(b) **Fire Test.** After the first 10 minutes, the test sample shall be subject to a minimum positive pressure differential of 0.01 inch of water.

Continue the test until the desired evaluation period is reached or until the rating criteria are satisfied.

(c) **Hose Stream Test.** Subject a duplicate test sample to a fire exposure test for a period equal to one half of that indicated as the resistance period in the fire test, but not more than 60 minutes, immediately after which subject the sample to the impact, erosion and cooling effects of a hose stream as described in Table No. 43-6-A directed first at the middle and then at all parts of the exposed face, with changes in direction being made slowly.

The test sponsor may elect, with the advice and consent of the testing body, to have the hose stream test made on the sample subjected to the fire test and immediately following the fire test.

The stream shall be delivered through a 2 1/2-inch hose and discharged through a National Standard Playpipe of corresponding size equipped with a 1 1/8-inch discharge tip of the standard-taper, smooth-bore pattern without a shoulder at the orifice. The water pressure shall be 30 ± 2 psi as measured at the base of the nozzle.

The nozzle orifice shall be 20 feet from the center of the exposed surface of the test sample if the nozzle is so located that when directed at the center its axis is normal to the surface of the test sample. If otherwise located, its distance from the center shall be less than 20 feet by an amount equal to 1 foot for each 10 degrees of deviation from the normal.

Report

Sec. 43.608. Results expressed as F and T ratings, as appropriate, shall be reported in accordance with the performance in the tests prescribed in this method. They shall be expressed in hours and minutes to the nearest integral minute. Reports shall include the following:

1. The assembly, materials and penetrating items of the tested penetration fire stop, clearly identified and described. Drawings depicting geometry, exact size (length, width, thickness) and location of penetration fire stops within the test assembly.
2. The relative humidities of the test assembly and test sample materials, if applicable.
3. The furnace and the unexposed side temperatures for the duration of the standard fire test.
4. The measurement of differential pressure between the exposed and unexposed test assembly surfaces during the fire test.
5. Observations of significant details of the behavior of the test sample during the test and after the furnace fire is extinguished. These shall include cracks, deformation, flaming and smoke issuance. Also, these include continued burning within the test sample after termination of the fire test.

When the indicated, penetration fire-stop rating period is 60 minutes or over, a correction shall be applied for variation of the furnace exposure from that prescribed, where it will affect the rating, by multiplying the indicated period by two thirds of the difference in area between the curve of average furnace temperature and the standard curve for the first three fourths of the period and dividing the product by the area between the standard curve above a base line of 68°F. for the same part of the indicated period, the latter areas increased by 54°F. × hours (3240°F. × minutes), to compensate for the thermal lag of the furnace thermocouples during the first part of the test. For fire exposure in the test higher than standard, the indicated rating period shall be increased by the amount of the correction and be similarly decreased for fire exposure below surface. The correction can be expressed as follows:

$$C = \frac{2I(A - A_s)}{3(A_s + L)}$$

WHERE:

C = correction in the same units as I.

I = indicated fire-resistance period.

A = area under the curve of indicated average furnace temperature for the first three fourths of the indicated period.

A_s = area under the standard furnace curve for the same part of the indicated period.

L = lag correction in the same units as A and A_s (54°F. × hours; 3240°F. × minutes).

Part II—Through-penetration Fire Stops

Scope

Sec. 43.609. This part of this standard contains specific criteria for testing and rating through-penetration fire stops.

Two ratings are established for each through-penetration fire stop. An F rating is based upon flame occurrence on the unexposed surface, while the T rating is based upon the temperature rise on the unexposed side of the through-penetration fire stop.

Unexposed Surface and Penetration Temperatures

Sec. 43.610. Measurements shall be made at the locations on the unexposed surface of the test sample and floor or wall assembly as shown in Figure No. 43-6-1 and as described in the following:

Measure temperatures of each type and size of penetrating item with at least one thermocouple located 1 inch from the unexposed surface of the test sample. Where a thermal protection assembly is used to wrap around the penetrating items on the unexposed side, an additional thermocouple shall be located on the penetrating items 1 inch from the end of the thermal-protection assembly. The thermocouple bead shall be held firmly against the penetrating item. The thermocouple leads shall not be heavier than No. 22 B. & S. gauge and shall be electrically insulated with heat-resistant and moisture-resistant coverings. The pads as described in Part I shall be held firmly against the penetrating item and shall fit closely about the thermocouples.

Installation of Penetrating Items

Sec. 43.611. Penetrating items shall be installed so that they extend a minimum of 12 inches on the exposed side and a minimum of 36 inches on the unexposed side. The extended portion of the penetrating items on the unexposed side shall be supported in the same manner as methods employed in field installation. When the end use of the penetrating items precludes the minimum projections specified, the penetrating items shall be installed in the end-use configuration.

Each end of the individual penetrating items shall be covered and sealed by suitable means to prevent excessive transfer of gases through the items between the furnace and the laboratory environment.

Rating Criteria

Sec. 43.612. (a) **F Rating.** A through-penetration fire stop shall be considered as meeting the requirements for an F rating when it remains in the test assembly during the fire test and hose stream test within the following limitations:

1. The through-penetration fire stop shall have withstood the fire test for the rating period without permitting the passage of flame through openings or the occurrence of flaming on any element of the unexposed side of the test sample.

2. The transmission of heat through the test assembly shall not have been such as to raise the temperature of the thermocouple located on the unexposed surface of the test assembly at Point E in Figure No. 43-6-1 by more than 325°F. above its initial temperature.

3. During the hose stream test, the test sample shall not develop any opening that would permit a projection of water from the stream beyond the unexposed side.

(b) **T Rating.** A through-penetration fire stop shall be considered as meeting the requirements for a T rating when it remains in the test assembly during the fire test and hose stream test so as to meet the requirements for an F rating and it performs within the following limitations:

1. The transmission of heat through the test sample during the rating period shall not have been such as to raise the temperature of any thermocouple on the unexposed surface of the test sample or any penetrating item more than 325°F. above its initial temperature.

Report

Sec. 43.613. In addition to the information required in Section 43.608, the following shall be included in the report:

1. The F and T ratings for each through-penetration fire stop in the time period of resistance.

TABLE NO. 43-6-A—HOSE STREAM TEST PRESSURE AND DURATION

RESISTANCE PERIOD	DURATION OF APPLICATION (Seconds Per Sq. Ft. of Exposed Area[1])
120 minutes and over	1.5
90 minutes and over if less than 120 minutes	0.9
Less than 90 minutes	0.6

[1]The exposed area shall be calculated using the area of the wall or floor assembly in which the penetration fire stop is mounted.

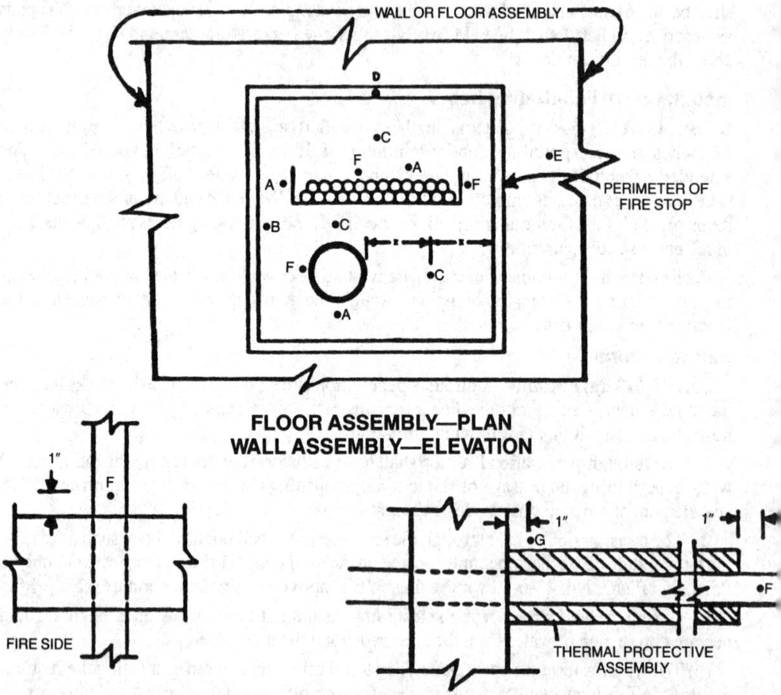
WALL OR FLOOR ASSEMBLY
D
C
F
A
E
A
F
PERIMETER OF FIRE STOP
B
C
F
C
A
FLOOR ASSEMBLY—PLAN
WALL ASSEMBLY—ELEVATION
1"
F
FIRE SIDE
1"
G
1"
F
THERMAL PROTECTIVE ASSEMBLY

FLOOR ASSEMBLY—SECTIONAL VIEW WALL ASSEMBLY—ELEVATION

FIGURE NO. 43-6-1—TEMPERATURE MEASUREMENT LOCATIONS

Legend: A—At a point on the surface of the fire stop 1 in. from one through-penetrating item for each type of penetrating item employed in te field of the fire stop. If the grouping of penetrating items through the test sample prohibits placement of the thermocouple pad, the thermocouple shall not be required.

B—At a point on the fire stop surface at the periphery of the fire stop.

(Continued)

C—At a minimum of three points on the fire stop surface approximately equidistant from a penetrating item or group of penetrating items in the field of the fire stop and the periphery.

D—At one point on any frame that is installed about the perimeter of the opening.

E—At one point on the unexposed surface of the wall or floor that is a maximum of 12 inches from any opening.

F—At one point on each type of through-penetrating item, 1 inch beyond thermal protection assembly.

G—All surface of thermal protection assembly, 1 inch beyond test sample.

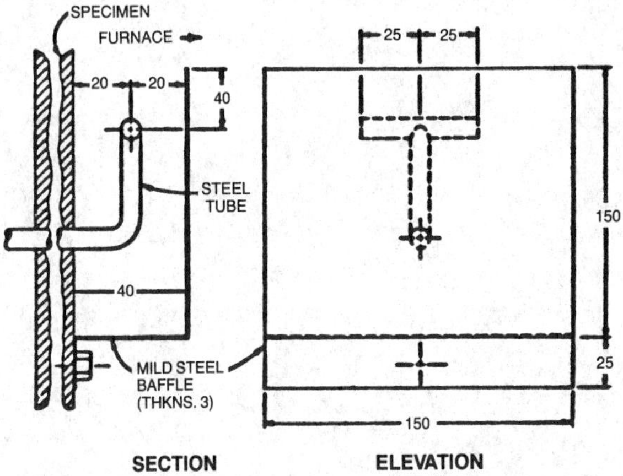
SPECIMEN
FURNACE
20
20
40
STEEL TUBE
40
MILD STEEL BAFFLE (THKNS. 3)
25
25
150
25
150
SECTION
ELEVATION

FIGURE NO. 43-6-2—STATIC PRESSURE-MEASURING DEVICE DIMENSIONS IN MILLIMETERS

UNIFORM BUILDING CODE STANDARD NO. 43-7

FIRE DAMPERS AND CEILING DAMPERS

Test Standard of the International Conference of Building Officials

See Sections 503 (c), 1701 (b), 1706 (b), 4301 (a), 4306 (e) and (j), Uniform Building Code, and Sections 406 and 1006, Uniform Mechanical Code

Scope

Sec. 43.701. These requirements and methods of test apply to fire damper and ceiling damper assemblies of various materials and types of construction. As used in this standard, the term "damper assembly" applies to both fire dampers and ceiling dampers.

Tests made in conformity with these test methods will register performance during the fire test exposure; but such tests shall not be construed as determining suitability for use after exposure to fire.

Instructions

Sec. 43.702. (a) **General.** Installation shall be in accordance with the manufacturer's listing. Instructions with illustrations where appropriate shall be included for mounting in the ceiling, wall, door or floor and for joining with duct material.

(b) **Attachments.** The instructions for fire dampers shall require the use of sleeves with perimeter mounting angles attached to the sleeve on both sides of the wall or floor opening. The connecting ducts shall not be shown as continuous but shall be shown to terminate at the sleeve. The minimum thickness of sleeves shall be 0.055 inch (No. 16 gage) for dampers with dimensions not exceeding 24 inches in height nor 36 inches in width, and 0.068 inch (No. 14 gage) for larger sizes.

EXCEPTIONS: 1. Sleeves in thicknesses less than required by Section 43.702 (b) may be indicated in installation instructions when the damper and sleeve have been tested and listed in combination and provided that S-type slip joints are indicated as the means of connection between the sleeve and duct, and provided that the sleeve thickness is not less than the duct thickness required by the Uniform Mechanical Code.

2. The installation instructions for fire dampers tested and listed with integral frame and sleeve of sufficient length to permit direct attachment of perimeter mounting angles on each side of the wall or floor opening are not required to indicate the use of sleeves, provided the gauges of the damper frame conform to the requirements for sleeves.

Construction

Sec. 43.703. (a) **General.** Fire dampers shall be constructed so as to provide an effective barrier to air flow when in the closed position. In fire dampers intended for installation in ducts, the vertical through openings at the sides of the blades for operating clearance shall not exceed 3/8 inch, horizontal through openings for operating clearance shall not exceed 1/32 inch. Fire dampers intended for installation in walls or floors outside of ducts shall have no vertical or horizontal through openings.

NOTE: A through opening in a fire damper is a visible opening in the face of the damper when viewed on a plane perpendicular to the mounting plane.

(b) **Binders, Adhesives, Sealants and Finishes.** Nonmetallic or organic materials used as binders, adhesives, insulation sealants or finishes may be used if the product otherwise conforms to these requirements.

(c) **Corrosion Resistances.** Component springs and bearings used in the assembly of ceiling or fire dampers shall be of material having resistance to atmospheric corrosion equivalent to brass or bronze.

Component springs used in the assembly of a fire or ceiling damper shall be of material having spring properties equivalent to stainless steel conforming to A313.

Steel parts used in the assembly shall be provided with corrosion protection equivalent to one of the following:

1. Employing stainless steel having resistance to corrosion at least equal to one of the 300 series of stainless steels.

2. Coating of zinc capable of withstanding not less than two dips in a standard copper sulfate solution.

3. Coating of cadmium not less than 0.00050 inch thick.

4. Two coats of good quality finish of the alkyd-resin type or other type outdoor paint. The suitability of the paint may be determined by consideration of its composition or by corrosion tests.

Coated or uncoated metals used in the assembly of fire dampers shall not be used in combination such as to cause detrimental galvanic action which will adversely affect the function of any part of the assembly formed from such material.

(d) **Fusible Link or Responsive Device.** A fusible link, other temperature-responsive device, smoke or particles of combustion-responsive device shall be of an approved type.

The load on a fusible link shall not exceed the listed design load of the fusible link.

Performance

Sec. 43.704. The performance of fire and ceiling dampers shall meet the applicable requirements when tested as described herein. If any indications are observed during the tests that the product will not continue to meet the requirements in normal usage so as to assure continued safe performance, such supplementary tests shall be conducted as deemed necessary to assure safe service. Table No. 43-7-A indicates the tests applicable to the specific types of fire dampers.

TABLE NO. 43-7-A— TEST FOR FIRE DAMPERS AND CEILING DAMPERS

TESTS	FIRE DAMPERS IN OR OUTSIDE DUCTS THROUGH WALLS OR FLOORS		CEILING DAMPERS IN OPENINGS THROUGH FIRE-RESISTING CEILINGS	
	Gravity-operated	Spring-operated	Gravity-operated	Spring-operated
(1) Closing Reliability	X	X	X	X
(2) Dust Loading	X	X	X	X
(3) Salt-spray Exposure	X	X	X	X
(4) Spring Closing Force	—	X	—	X
(5) Fire Endurance	X	X	X	X
(6) Hose Stream	X	X	—	—

X = Test applicable.
— = Test not applicable.

Closing Reliability Test

Sec. 43.705. (a) **Performance.** A damper assembly shall close and latch automatically (if a latch is provided) from the open position during each of 250 operations and shall throughout this test show no evidence of undue wear, distortion, displacement or rupture of its parts.

(b) **Selecting and Positioning Samples.** Samples representative of the largest and smallest size, style and arrangement of damper assembly shall be subjected to this test. Damper assemblies intended for horizontal installation shall be tested in a horizontal plane and not depend on installation in an inclined position for proper operation.

Dust Loading Test

Sec. 43.706. (a) **Performance.** A damper assembly shall close and latch automatically (if latch is provided) from the open position following exposure for seven hours to an air-blown circulating grain-dust air mixture. The grain dust shall pass through a 100-mesh screen.

(b) **Selecting and Positioning Sample.** Samples representative of each style and arrangement of damper assembly supported in the position of its intended use shall be tested in a specially constructed test chamber approximately 5 by 7 1/2 by 5 feet high, provided with observation windows and with auxiliary equipment to produce a circulating grain-dust-air mixture. Nozzles shall be provided to direct the dust-air mixture toward the sample, and the dust particles shall be allowed to accumulate on the various parts of the damper assembly.

Salt-spray Exposure Test

Sec. 43.707. (a) **Performance.** A damper assembly shall close and latch automatically (if a latch is provided) following exposure for a period of five days to salt spray when tested in accordance with this section.

(b) **Selecting and Preparing Sample.** A representative sample of each style and arrangement of damper assembly shall be used for the salt-spray exposure test. Prior to test, all grease or oil shall be removed from the test sample, using organic solvents.

(c) **Positioning of Sample.** The test sample shall be installed in the test chamber with the damper open and supported in the position of its intended use and exposed to the salt spray for a period of five days (120 hours). The temperature of the sample and the test chamber shall be maintained at 95°F. plus 2°F. or minus 3°F. throughout the test period.

(d) **Test Equipment.** The apparatus to be used for salt-spray (fog) testing shall consist of a fog chamber having a salt solution reservoir, a supply of suitably conditioned compressed air, a dispersion tower for producing a salt fog, specimen supports, provision for heating the chamber, and necessary means of control. The dispersion tower shall be located in the center of the chamber and shall be supplied with salt solution and with warmed, humidified air at a pressure of 17 to 19 pounds per square inch so as to disperse the salt solution in the form of a fine mist or fog throughout the interior of the chamber.

(e) **Salt Solution.** The salt solution shall consist of 20 percent by weight of common salt (sodium chloride) and distilled water. The pH value of this solution as collected after spraying in the test apparatus shall be between 6.5 and 7.2 and the specific gravity between 1.126 and 1.157 at 95°F.

(f) **Efficiency.** At the conclusion of the salt-spray exposure, the test sample shall be removed from the chamber and allowed to dry for 24 hours at room temperature. It shall then be placed in its normal mounting position and on release shall close and latch automatically (if latch is provided).

Spring Closing Force Test

Sec. 43.708. (a) **Performance.** A spring-operated damper assembly shall employ a spring or springs capable of exerting a force of two and one-half times that required to close and automatically latch (if a latch is provided) the damper.

(b) **Selecting and Positioning Sample.** A sample representative of each size, style and arrangement of damper assembly shall be subjected to this test. All springs shall be disconnected and the damper assembly placed in the intended operating position.

(c) **Measuring Force.** The force required to close and latch the damper shall be measured by appropriate means at each of a series of positions assumed by the damper from wide open to closed (latched). Force as measured shall be applied through, and at the point of connection of the spring or springs, to the damper blade or operating arm.

(d) **Efficiency.** Three samples of each spring employed for closing and latching shall be tested for force exerted over the range of extension or compression required for the motion involved in the assembly. The force available from the action of the spring or springs shall be two and one-half times that required for the closing and latching of the damper at any position of travel from wide open to latched.

Zinc Coatings

Sec. 43.709. (a) **Performance.** A protective coating of zinc shall be such that a sample of finished galvanized steel parts will not show a fixed deposit of copper after two one-minute immersions in a standard copper sulfate solution, as described below.

(b) **Test Equipment.** The apparatus consists of a large glass beaker; a chemical, all-glass, mercury thermometer; a watch or clock with a second hand; a standard solution of copper sulfate; a number of clean, dry cheesecloths; and a solvent (carbon tetrachloride or chloroform). It is essential that running tap water be available.

(c) **Copper Sulfate Solution.** The standard solution of copper sulfate which is to be used in this test is to be made up from distilled water and crystals of chemically pure copper sulfate. In a copper bottle or other suitable container made of copper, a sufficient number of the crystals is to be dissolved in hot distilled water to obtain a solution which has a specific gravity slightly higher than 1.186 after the solution has been cooled to a temperature of 65.0°F. Any free acid which may be present in the solution is to be neutralized by the addition of approximately one gram of cupric oxide (CuO) or one gram of cupric hydroxide [$Cu\ (OH)_2$] per liter of solution. The solution is then to be diluted with distilled water to obtain a specific gravity of exactly 1.186 at a temperature of 65.0°F. The solution is then to be filtered.

(d) **Selection of Specimen.** Several 6-inch-long specimen are to be cut and any grease, paraffin or the like is to be removed by washing the specimen in carbon tetrachloride or chloroform. Each specimen is then to be examined for evidence of damage to the zinc coating, and one which is not damaged is to be selected for use in the test.

(e) **Preparation of Specimen.** The selected specimen is to be rinsed in water and dried with a piece of clean cheesecloth. The surface of the zinc must be perfectly clean before the specimen is immersed in the solution of copper sulfate. Due care must be taken to avoid any contact between the hands or any foreign material and the cleaned surface.

(f) **Immersion of Specimen.** A glass beaker having a diameter equal to at least twice the width of the specimen is to be filled with the standard solution of copper sulfate. The temperature of the solution is to be maintained at 65.0°F. ±2.0°F. The specimen is to be immersed in the solution and supported on end in the center of the beaker so that not less than 2 1/2 inches of its length are immersed. The specimen is to remain in the solution for 60 seconds, during which time it is not to be moved nor the solution stirred.

(g) **Examination of Specimen.** At the end of the 60-second period the specimen is to be removed from the beaker, rinsed immediately in running tap water, rubbed with clean cheesecloth until any loosely adhering deposits of copper are removed, and is then to be dried with a piece of clean cheesecloth. Again, care is to be taken to avoid contact of the test surface with any foreign objects or the hands. If any part of the surface which was immersed has a bright deposit of firmly adhering metallic copper, an estimate is to be made quickly of the ratio of the area of the covered surface to the area of the total immersed surface, the portion of the specimen within 1/2 inch of the cut end or edges being disregarded.

(h) **Number of Immersions.** The immersion, washing and wiping operation just described is to be repeated successively, using the same portion of the standard solution of copper sulfate, until a bright, firmly adhering deposit of metallic copper remains on the specimen. The specimen is to be subjected to at least one more than the minimum number of such operations required for acceptable performance.

(i) **Other Specimens.** A fixed deposit of metallic copper generally occurs first at the thinnest points in the zinc coating or at those points in the zinc coating where the zinc adheres to the steel less firmly than in others. The area occupied by the fixed deposit increases upon successive dips until the entire zinc coating has disappeared. After the dips have been completed on any one specimen, the portion of the solution of copper sulfate used is to be discarded. A fresh portion of the standard solution is to be employed for each of any succeeding specimens.

(j) **Test Results.** The results are to be expressed as an estimate of the percentage of the total immersed surface (excepting the area of the 1/2-inch portion at the cut end or edges) which shows a fixed deposit of copper after each dip, i.e., after the specimen has been dipped, washed, rubbed, dried and then examined. Failure is to be recorded for any part from which a specimen shows a fixed deposit of copper as the result of a number of dips equal to or less than the required number stated in Section 43.709 (a).

Cadmium Coatings

Sec. 43.710. (a) **Minimum Thickness.** The thickness of a cadmium coating on the steel parts shall be not less than 0.00050 inch when determined by the chromic-acid dropping test, conducted as described in this section.

(b) **Chromic-acid Solution.** The solution to be used for the chromic-acid dropping test is to be made from distilled water and is to contain 200 grams per liter of chemically pure chromic acid, CrO_3, and 50 grams per liter of chemically pure concentrated sulfuric acid, H_2SO_4 (The latter is equivalent to 27 milliliters per liter of chemically pure concentrated sulfuric acid, specific gravity 1.84, containing 96 percent of H_2SO_4.)

(c) **Test Equipment.** The test solution is to be contained in a glass vessel such as a separatory funnel with the outlet equipped with a stopcock and a capillary tube of approximately 0.025-inch inside bore and 5.5 inches long. The lower end of the capillary tube is tapered to form a tip, the drops from which are about 0.05 milliliter each. To preserve an effectively constant level, a small glass tube is inserted in the top of the funnel through a rubber stopper and its position is to be adjusted so that, when the stopcock is open, the rate of dropping is 100 ± 5 drops per minute. If desired, an additional stopcock may be used in place of the glass tube to control the rate of dropping.

(d) **Solution Temperature.** The sample and the test solution should be kept in the test room long enough to acquire the temperature of the room, which should be noted and recorded. The test is to be conducted at a room temperature between 65° and 95°F.

(e) **Preparation of Sample.** Each sample is to be thoroughly cleaned before testing. All grease and other nonmetallic coatings are to be removed completely by means of suitable solvents. Samples are then to be thoroughly rinsed in water and dried with clean cheesecloth. Care should be exercised to avoid contact of the cleaned surface with the hands or any foreign material.

(f) **Positioning Sample.** The sample to be tested is to be supported from 0.7 to 1 inch below the orifice so that the drops of solution strike the point to be tested and run off quickly. The surface to be tested should be inclined about 45 degrees from horizontal.

(g) **Testing.** After cleaning, the sample to be tested is to be put in place under the orifice. The stopcock is to be opened and the time in seconds is to be measured with a stop watch until the dropping solution dissolves off the protective metallic coating, exposing the base metal. The end point is the first appearance of the base metal recognizable by the change in color at that point.

(h) **Number of Tests.** Each sample of a test lot is to be subjected to the test at three or more points, excluding cut edges and threaded surfaces.

(i) **Test Results.** If the time required for dissolving off the cadmium coating in the test is not less than that given in the following table, corresponding to the room temperature, the thickness of the coating is considered to comply with the requirement of Section 43.710 (a).

TEMPERATURE IN DEGREES FAHRENHEIT	TIME IN SECONDS
65	12
70	11
75	11
80	10
85	10
90	10
95	9

Fire-endurance Tests

Sec. 43.711. (a) **Test Assemblies.** The construction, materials and size of the test fire damper assembly, consisting of single dampers or single dampers installed in a multiple assembly, shall be representative of that for which the damper assembly is to be classified or rated. The size and dimensions of the test specimen and the exposure specified herein are intended to apply for rating of fire damper assemblies within the usual range employed in buildings. The testing agency may, at its discretion, require changes in the proposed installation when, in its judgment, such changes are necessary to obtain representative information on the performance of the construction under test or when the proposed installation is not representative of those applied in building construction.

(b) **Test Installation, Fire Dampers in Ducts, Walls or Floors.** Each test fire damper assembly shall be installed on a large-scale furnace in its intended position. If the conditions of use limit the fire damper assembly to smaller dimensions, a proportionate reduction may be made in the dimensions of the fire damper test specimen for a test qualifying them for such restricted use. Such test fire damper assembly shall be installed on a half-scale (or larger) furnace in its intended position.

Fire dampers intended for use in ducts shall be installed in a sleeve extending not more than 3 inches into the furnace. Fire dampers intended for installation in partitions or walls outside of ducts shall be installed in a frame. For a single fire damper, a sample damper shall be installed with the upstream side facing the furnace. An additional sample shall be installed with the downstream side facing the furnace. If multiple assemblies are tested at one time, the upstream sides of half the individual dampers and the downstream sides of the other half of the dampers shall face the furnace.

1. **Wall or floor clearances.** Clearances between the fire damper assembly installed in their sleeves and the wall or floor opening shall be such that the lap of the mounting angles on the wall or floor assembly is not less than 1 inch. The installation of the test fire dampers assembly shall otherwise be made in accordance with the manufacturer's installation instructions.

2. **Masonry or concrete settings.** Masonry settings shall be allowed to season at least three days before fire test. Concrete settings shall be allowed to season at least 28 days before fire test.

(c) **Test Installation, Ceiling Dampers in Fire-resisting Ceilings.** Test specimen ceiling dampers shall be installed in a fire-resisting ceiling-floor assembly on a horizontal large-scale furnace. The area of the ceiling exposed to fire shall be not less than 180 square feet, with neither dimension less than 12 feet. Fire exposure shall be to the underside of the construction.

The ceiling-floor assembly shall be representative of the type of construction (combustible, noncombustible) and the fire-endurance time period for which classification is desired, as to materials, workmanship and details such as dimensions of parts, and shall be representative of those applied in building construction and operation.

The number and area of individual fire dampers installed in each 100 square feet of ceiling area shall be representative of that for which the damper assembly is to be classified or rated.

Test specimen ceiling dampers in fire-resisting ceilings shall be mounted in the bottom of the air duct section over the air outlet or in the throat of the air duct outlet drop with support from the construction above. Subject to the provisions of Section 43.711 (a), the installation shall be made in accordance with the manufacturer's proposed installation instructions. Insulation around the duct, if any, or insulation around the air outlet duct drop shall be in accordance with the fire damper manufacturer's proposed installation instructions.

The thermocouples, their placement and temperature readings shall conform to "Fire Tests of Building Construction and Materials." Thermocouples shall be placed on structural elements (beams, girders, joists and trusses) as specified.

(d) **Alternate Test Installation, Ceiling Dampers in Fire-resisting Ceilings.** Test specimen ceiling dampers shall be installed in a fire-resisting ceiling assembly on a horizontal small-scale furnace in its intended position. The net ceiling area exposed to fire shall be not less than 40 square feet, with no dimension less than 5 feet.

1. **Representative assembly.** The assembly shall be representative of an assembly which has been tested in the horizontal large-scale furnace and for which a detailed test report containing temperature readings on the unexposed surface and structural framing members has been issued.

2. **Area.** The area of the ceiling damper shall be the maximum area for which the fire damper is to be classified.

3. **Installing test specimen.** The test specimen ceiling damper shall be installed in a representative ceiling-floor or ceiling-roof assembly as indicated in Section 43.711 (b) 1. The minimum width of exposed ceiling area on two sides of the test specimen shall be not less than 12 inches with a minimum width of exposed ceiling area on the opposite sides of not less than 6 inches. The test specimen ceiling damper shall be mounted in the bottom of a representative duct system over the air outlet or in the throat of the air duct outlet drop with support from the constructions above. Subject to the provisions of Section 43.711 (a), the installation shall be made in accordance with the manufacturer's instructions. Insulation around the duct, if any, or insulation around the air outlet duct drop shall be in accordance with the ceiling damper manufacturer's proposed installation instructions.

4. **Thermocouple placement.** Temperature readings shall be taken on the unexposed surface, in the plenum space, on the underside of the floor or roof deck and on structural members when structural members are contained in the construction. Thermocouples, their placement, and temperature readings shall conform to "Fire Tests of Building Construction and Materials."

(e) **Exposure Period.** The fire test shall be continued until the exposure period for which the damper assembly is to be rated is reached, or until the assembly fails to conform with the conditions of acceptance specified in Section 43.713. The exposure period for which the assembly is to be rated shall be determined by test as being either 45 minutes, one hour, one and one half hours, two hours or three hours.

Hose Stream Test

Sec. 43.712. (a) **Application.** Immediately following the fire exposure portion of the test for fire dampers, the fire damper test assembly shall be subjected to the impact, erosion and cooling effects of a hose stream directed first at the middle and then at all parts of the exposed surface of the damper assembly, with changes in direction of the hose stream being made slowly.

(b) **Time.** The hose stream shall be delivered through a $2^1/_2$-inch hose discharging through a national standard playpipe of corresponding size equipped with a $1^1/_8$-inch discharge tip of the standard-taper smoothbore pattern without shoulder at the orifice. The water pressure at the base of the nozzle and duration of application in minutes per 100 square feet of exposed area of the damper assembly shall be as given in Table No. 43-7-B.

TABLE NO. 43-7-B—HOSE STREAM TEST

FIRE EXPOSURE PERIOD	WATER PRESSURE AT BASE OF NOZZLE psi	DURATION OF APPLICATION, MINUTES PER 100 SQUARE FEET EXPOSED AREA
3-Hour	45	5
1 1/2-Hour and over if less than 3-Hour	30	2 1/2
1-Hour and over if less than 1 1/2-Hour	30	1 1/2

(c) **Distance.** The tip of the nozzle shall be located 20 feet from and on a line normal to the center of the test assembly. If impossible to be so located, the nozzle may be on a line deviating not more than 30 degrees from the line normal to the center of the assembly. When so located, the distance from the center shall be less than 20 feet by an amount equal to 1 foot for each 10 degrees of deviation from the normal.

Conditions of Acceptance

Sec. 43.713. (a) **Fire Dampers in Duct Systems Passing through Walls or Floors.** Fire dampers in duct systems passing through walls or floors shall be as follows:

1. A damper shall remain in the opening during the fire-endurance test for the fire exposure period for which it is to be rated and for the hose stream test.

2. All dampers in the test assembly shall close and latch automatically (if a latch is provided) during the first 60 seconds of the fire-endurance portion of the test or before the furnace temperature at the fusible element location reaches 285°F., whichever occurs first. (The temperature on the standard time-temperature curve at one minute is 285°F.)

3. During the fire and hose stream test, the movement or warping of any part of the damper assembly shall not result in a visible through opening when viewed on a plane perpendicular to the mounting plane.

4. During the fire-endurance and hose stream test, movement or warping of any part of the damper assembly shall not result in through openings between individual parts greater than 3/4 inch during the fire-endurance portion of the test, and greater than 1 inch during the hose stream portion of the test.

5. Through openings at the sides of multiblade dampers provided for operating clearances shall not increase in width during the fire-endurance and hose stream tests.

6. Latching mechanisms, blade shafts in their bearings, interlocking-type damper blades with relation to their guides, and blade guides shall remain engaged and secure during the fire-endurance and hose stream test.

(b) **Fire Dampers in Doors, Walls or Floors outside of Ducts.** Fire dampers in doors, walls or floors outside of ducts shall be as follows:

1. A damper assembly shall remain in the opening during the fire-endurance test for the fire-exposure period for which it is to be rated and for the hose stream test.

2. All dampers in the test assembly shall close and latch automatically (if a latch is provided) during the first 60 seconds of the fire-endurance portion of the test or before the furnace temperature at the fusible element location reaches 285°F., whichever occurs first. (The temperature on the standard time-temperature curve at one minute is 285°F.)

3. During the fire-endurance and hose stream test, the movement or warping of any part of the damper assembly shall not result in a visible through opening when viewed on a plane perpendicular to the mounting plane.

4. During the fire-endurance test, movement or warping of any part of the damper assembly shall not result in visible through openings between individual parts, at the sides or around the blades as viewed in any direction.

5. During the hose stream test, the movement or warping of any part of the damper assembly shall not result in through openings between individual parts as viewed in any direction greater than the width of blade lap on each other or on blade stops during the first one half of the classification but shall in no case exceed one and one-half times the width of the blade lap on each other or on the blade stops.

6. Latching mechanisms, blade shafts in their bearings, interlocking-type damper blades with relation to their guides, and blade guides shall remain engaged and secure during the fire exposure and hose stream test.

(c) **Ceiling Dampers in Fire-resisting Ceilings.** The ceiling-floor assembly tested in the horizontal large-scale furnace, may be rated for fire endurance in accordance with conditions of acceptance set forth in U.B.C. Standard No. 43-1.

(d) **Ceiling Dampers in Fire-resisting Ceilings, Alternate Test Method.** Classification of fire damper assemblies for use in fire-resisting ceilings tested in the horizontal small-scale furnace shall be in accordance with the following:

1. The ceiling damper assembly, or assemblies, in its frame shall remain in the ceiling opening during the fire-endurance test for the fire-exposure period for which it is to be rated. Openings in the ceiling assembly shall not result in greater distortion or warping of components or larger through openings than in the ceiling-floor assembly tested without openings.

2. Transmission of heat through the ceiling-floor assembly during the fire-endurance test shall not have been such as to raise the average temperature on its unexposed surface more than 250°F. above its initial temperature nor more than 325°F. at any point.

3. The average temperature of three thermocouples on the bottom surface of the wood members (2 by 10 joist at 16 inches on center shall be employed) shall not exceed 600°F. at 30 minutes or 1200°F. at 55 minutes.

4. The average temperature on any section of structural steel or reinforcing steel shall not exceed 1100°F. and the maximum temperature at any point shall not exceed 1300°F.

5. The average temperature shall not exceed 800°F. on cold-drawn prestressing steel.

Marking

Sec. 43.714. (a) **Label.** Fire and ceiling damper assemblies shall bear a label issued by an approved listing agency or a label showing the fire-protection rating of the assembly. The label shall be of metal attached to the assembly by welding or brazing or shall be a metallized label attached to the assembly with contact adhesive.

(b) **Label Markings.** The markings on the label shall include the following:

1. Name and address of the listee.
2. Model number or type.
3. Symbol, serial or issue number issued by the listing agency.
4. Rating of three, one and one-half, one or three-fourths hour indicating duration of exposure to fire.
5. The words "duct," "wall," "floor" or "ceiling" following the hourly rating designating the location for which the assembly is designed.

UNIFORM BUILDING CODE STANDARD NO. 43-8

THICKNESS AND DENSITY DETERMINATION FOR SPRAY-APPLIED FIREPROOFING

Test Standard of the International Conference of Building Officials

See Sections 301 (c), 306 (a), 4301 (a) and 4303 (e), Uniform Building Code

Scope

Sec. 43.801. These methods cover procedures for obtaining the thickness and density for sprayed fibrous and cementitious fire-resistive materials. In addition, provisions for field inspection procedures by an approved agency on a random sample basis are included.

Application

Sec. 43.802. These test methods require that the application of the field-applied, sprayed, fire-resistive material be in accordance with the manufacturer's published instructions. The apparatus, materials and procedure used to apply the fire-resistive material shall be the same as the procedure used to prepare the test specimens which were subjected to the fire tests set forth in U.B.C. Standard No. 43-1.

Test Methods for Thickness

Sec. 43.803. (a) **General.** The following tests based on samplings as described in this standard shall be conducted by an approved agency.

(b) **Substrate Condition.** The condition of the substrate on each floor shall be inspected prior to application of the spray-applied fireproofing material. The substrate shall be prepared in accordance with the manufacturer's instructions and shall be free of dirt, grease, oil, loose scale, loose paint or primer and other materials which may prevent adequate adhesion.

(c) **Thickness Measurement and Acceptance Criteria.** The thickness of the spray-applied fireproofing shall be measured by either of the following methods:

1. A steel rule graduated in at least $\frac{1}{16}$-inch increments, a depth gage consisting of a movable needle or pin and a disc perpendicular to the needle as shown in Figure No. 1.

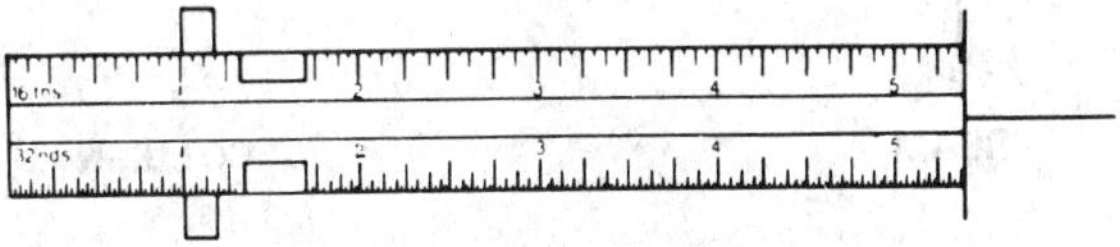

FIGURE NO. 1—THICKNESS GAGE

The pin shall be of sufficient length to penetrate the material to be measured. The disc shall be perpendicular to the needle at all times and shall have a friction device to grip the pin unless purposely moved. The disc shall have a diameter of $1\frac{1}{8}$ inches to permit complete contact with the surface of the specimen to be measured. In materials not readily penetrated by the depth gage, other suitable approved measuring devices may be used.

The thicknesses shall be determined by inserting the penetrating pin of the depth gage perpendicular to and through the sprayed fire-resistive material to the substrate. When the point of the pin touches the substrate the disc shall be moved against the fire-resistive material with sufficient force on the disc to register the average plane of the surface. The gage shall be withdrawn to read the thickness in $\frac{1}{16}$-inch increments as shown by the position of the sliding clip indicator. The acceptance of measurements with a minus tolerance greater than $\frac{1}{8}$ inch shall not be permitted. Measurements greater than $\frac{1}{8}$ inch above the required shall not be used to determine the thickness average.

2. As an alternate to the method described above, the thickness of the spray- applied fireproofing may be measured by a fixed probe with a $1\frac{1}{8}$-inch-diameter disc set to the required thickness. If any measurement is less than that required, the thickness shall be increased or measurements shall be taken as required in Method 1.

Where thickness is less than that required, the condition shall be corrected. The location of any uncorrected areas shall be reported to the building official.

(d) **Thickness Determination for Structural Frame Members.** Twenty-five percent of the structural frame, columns and beams as defined in Section 1702 of the Uniform Building Code in each story shall be inspected for thickness determination. Five measurements at a single cross section shall be made and averaged on structural frame beams, and six measurements shall be made and averaged at a single cross section on columns as shown in Figure No. 2.

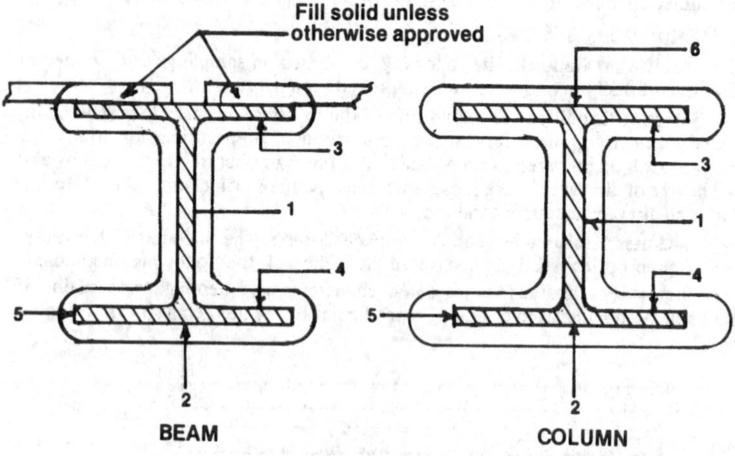
Fill solid unless otherwise approved
6
3
1
4
5
2
3
1
4
5
2
BEAM
COLUMN

FIGURE NO. 2

Where open flutes or valley of steel deck sections occur over beams, they shall be filled solid unless the flutes were unfilled in the fire-tested assembly.

(e) **Thickness Determination for Beams Other than Structural Frame.** Ten percent of beams (other than structural frame members) on each floor shall be selected at random and shall be measured for thickness as required for structural frame members in Section 43.803 (d).

(f) **Thickness Determination for Floor Sections.** Ten floor thickness measurements for each prescribed thickness shall be made on a random basis for each 10,000 square feet. At each area selected a rectangle having an area of 144 square inches and a minimum width of 6 inches where possible shall be laid out and a thickness measurement shall be taken at the center and at each corner. The five measurements shall be averaged and shall be reported as a single measurement of the area. The average thickness as determined by Section 43.803 (c) 1 shall be not less than that specified. If the method for thickness determination as described in Section 43.803 (c) 2 is used, the thickness at any location shall be not less than the required thickness.

Test Methods for Density

Sec. 43.804. (a) **General.** The test to determine the density of spray-applied fireproofing shall be conducted by an approved agency.

(b) **Density Sample Groups.** There shall be density test specimens taken from a column, a beam and a deck for each 10,000 square feet of floor area or fraction thereof or from each floor if the floor area is smaller than 10,000 square feet.

(c) **Density Determination.** The density of each sample shall be determined as follows:

1. Utilizing a rectangular template as described in Section 43.803 (f), a known area of the test sample shall be marked off.
2. Utilizing the procedure described in Section 43.803 (f) and Section 43.803 (c), Method 1, at least five thickness measurements shall be taken. One measurement shall be taken at the center of the specimen and one at each of the four corners approximately 1½ inches from adjacent sides. The thickness measurement shall be determined prior to removing the sample, and the average of these five measurements shall be considered as the thickness of the specimen.
3. The specimen shall be cut along the perimeter of the template. All of the in-place material shall be carefully removed from the substrate and dried at 120°F. at a relative humidity not less than 50 percent until a constant weight is obtained. The constant weight of the dried material shall be measured.
4. The density shall be calculated in accordance with the following formula:

   Density in pounds per cubic foot:

$$\frac{W \times 1728}{l \times w \times t}$$

WHERE:

W = weight of the dried material in pounds.

l = length of the specimen in inches.

w = width of the specimen in inches.

t = thickness of the specimen in inches.

(d) **Density Acceptance Criteria.** No sample shall have a density less than 5 percent below the specified density. Where the density is less than the 5 percent tolerance allowed above, the work shall be corrected to the satisfaction of the building official.

UNIFORM BUILDING CODE STANDARD NO. 43-9

METHODS FOR CALCULATING FIRE RESISTANCE OF STEEL, CONCRETE AND WOOD CONSTRUCTION

Standard of the International Conference of Building Officials

Part I—METHOD FOR CALCULATING THE FIRE RESISTANCE OF STEEL CONSTRUCTION

See Sections 4301 (a) and 4302 (c), Uniform Building Code

Scope

Sec. 43.901. This part of this standard contains procedures by which the fire resistance of steel columns, beams, girders and trusses protected by specific materials or combinations of materials can be established by calculations. These procedures apply to the material contained in this part only.

Definition

Sec. 43.902. CERAMIC FIBER BLANKET is a mineral wool insulation material made of alumina-silica fibers and weighing 4 to 10 pcf.

Structural Steel Column Protection

Sec. 43.903. (a) **Procedures.** These procedures establish a basis for determining the fire resistance of column assemblies as a function of the thickness of fire-protection material, the weight (W) or cross-sectional area (A) of steel columns and the heated perimeter (D or P) of steel columns. As used in these sections, W is the average weight of a structural steel column in pounds per linear foot and A is the cross-sectional area of a structural steel column in square inches. The heated perimeter (D) is the inside perimeter of the fire-protection material in inches as illustrated in Figure No. 43-9-S-1.

Application of these procedures shall be limited to column assemblies in which the fire-protection material is not designed to carry any of the load acting on the column. In the absence of substantiating fire-endurance test results, ducts, conduit, piping and similar mechanical, electrical and plumbing installations shall not be embedded in any required fire-protection materials of assemblies designed in accordance with this standard. Table No. 43-9-S-A contains weight-to-heated-perimeter ratios (W/D) for both contour and box fire-protection profiles for the wide-flange shapes most often used as columns. For different fire-protection profiles or column cross sections, the weight-to-heated-perimeter ratios (W/D) and cross-sectional-area-to-heated-perimeter ratios (A/P) shall be determined in accordance with the definitions given in this section.

(b) **Gypsum Wallboard (Wide-flange, Pipe and Tubular Columns).** The fire resistance of structural steel columns with weight-to-heated-perimeter ratios (W/D) less than or equal to 3.65 and which are protected with Type X gypsum wallboard may be determined from the following expression:

$$R = 130 \left[\frac{h\ (W'/D)}{2} \right]^{0.75}$$

WHERE:

R = fire resistance (minutes).

h = total thickness of gypsum wallboard (inches).

D = heated perimeter of the structural steel column (inches).

W' = total weight of the structural steel column and gypsum wallboard protection (pounds per linear foot).

$$= W + \frac{50\ h\ D}{144}$$

The gypsum wallboard shall be supported and fastened as illustrated in either Figure No. 43-9-S-2 for fire-resistance ratings of four hours or less, or Figure No. 43-9-S-3 for fire-resistance ratings of three hours or less. The fire resistance of structural steel columns can be determined from Figure No. 43-9-S-4 for various thicknesses of gypsum wallboard as a function of the weight-to-heated-perimeter (W/D) of the column. For structural steel columns with weight-to-heated- perimeter ratios (W/D) greater than 3.65, the thickness of gypsum wallboard required for specified fire-resistance ratings shall be the same as the thickness determined for a $W14 \times 233$-wide flange shape.

(c) **Spray-applied Materials (Wide-flange Columns).** The fire resistance of wide-flange structural steel columns protected with spray-applied fire-protection materials, as illustrated in Figure No. 43-9-S-5, may be determined from the following expression:

$$R = (C_1 \frac{W}{D} + C_2)\ h$$

WHERE:

R = fire resistance (minutes).

h = thickness of spray-applied fire protection (inches).

D = heated perimeter of the structural steel column (inches).

W = average weight of steel column (pounds per linear foot).

C_1 and C_2 = material-dependent constants.

The material-dependent constants, C_1 and C_2, shall be determined for specific fire-protection materials on the basis of standard fire-endurance tests in accordance with Section 4302 (b). These constants shall be determined from results of at least four fire-endurance tests in accordance with requirements set forth in U.B.C. Standard No. 43-1. At least two tests shall be conducted on the largest and two on the smallest columns which establish the limits of applicability to the resulting equation. Test data shall be evaluated with respect to the assumption that the ratio of fire endurance to fire-protection thickness (R/h) is reasonably constant for a given column shape (W/D ratio). The tests conducted on columns of the same shape shall be designed so that the resulting fire-endurance times are approximately one and one-half hours and three and one-half hours. In evaluating the R/h ratios resulting from tests on the same column shape, differences in the range of 10 percent are typical. Differences greater than 20 percent may, however, suggest that the equation is not applicable to the specific fire-protection material under consideration and further examination of the test data is warranted.

Unless evidence is submitted to the building official substantiating a broader application, this express shall be limited to determining the fire resistance of structural steel columns with weight-to-heated-perimeter ratios (W/D) between the largest and smallest columns for which standard fire-endurance test results are available.

(d) **Spray-applied Fire-protection Materials (Pipe and Tubular Columns).** The fire resistance of pipe and tubular steel columns protected with spray-applied fire-protection materials may be determined from the following expressions:

$$R = C_3 \, (A/P) \, h + C_4$$

WHERE:

R = fire resistance (hours).

h = thickness of spray-applied fire protection (inches).

P = heated perimeter of the structural steel column (inches).

A = cross-sectional area of the structural steel column (square inches).

C_3 and
C_4 = material-dependent constants.

The material-dependent constants (C_3 and C_4) shall be determined for specific fire-protection materials on the basis of standard fire-resistance tests in accordance with Section 4302 (b). These constants shall be determined from the results of at least four fire-endurance tests in accordance with requirements set forth in U.B.C. Standard No. 43-1. At least two tests shall be conducted on each of two different column sizes as follows:

1. For the smaller of the two columns, one of the test specimens shall be protected so as to develop the minimum desired fire-resistance rating, and the second specimen shall be protected with the maximum intended thickness of fire-protection material.

2. For the larger of the two columns, one of the test specimens shall be protected with the minimum intended thickness of fire-protection material and the second specimen shall be protected so as to develop the maximum desired fire-resistance rating.

These four tests shall establish limits governing the use of the resulting equation. These limits shall define the minimum and maximum permitted thicknesses of protection and the minimum and maximum fire-resistance ratings. Additional tests may be conducted to modify any of these four limits and these additional tests may involve different column sizes. The material-dependent constants shall be determined based on all applicable test data using a linear, least-squares curve-fitting technique or similar statistical analysis.

Unless evidence is submitted to the building official substantiating a broader application, this expression shall be limited to determining the fire resistance of structural steel columns with cross-sectional-area-to-heated-perimeter ratios (A/P) between the largest and smallest columns for which standard fire-endurance test results are available.

Table No. 43-9-S-A2 contains area-to-heated-perimeter ratios (A/P) for circular, square and rectangular tubes most often used as columns.

(e) **Concrete or Concrete Masonry.** The fire resistance of structural steel columns protected with concrete, as illustrated in Figure No. 43-9-S-6, or protected with concrete masonry, as illustrated in Figure No. 43-9-S-7, may be determined from the following expression:

$$R = R_o\ (1 + 0.03m)$$

$$R_o = 10\left(\frac{W}{D}\right)^{0.7} + 17\ \frac{h^{1.6}}{k_c^{\ 0.2}}\left[1 + 26\left(\frac{H}{\rho_c c_c h(L+h)}\right)^{0.8}\right]$$

WHERE:

R = fire endurance at equilibrium moisture conditions (minutes).

R_o = fire endurance at zero moisture content (minutes).

m = equilibrium moisture content of the concrete by volume (percent).

W = average weight of the steel column (pounds per linear foot).

D = heated perimeter of the steel column (inches).

h = thickness of the cover for concrete; equivalent thickness for concrete masonry (inches).

k_c = ambient temperature thermal conductivity of the concrete (Btu/hr. ft.°F.).

H = ambient temperature thermal capacity of the steel column.
= $.11W$ (Btu/ft.°F.).

ρ_c = concrete density (pounds per cubic foot).

C_c = ambient temperature specific heat of concrete (Btu/lb.°F.).

L = interior dimension of one side of a square concrete or concrete masonry box protection (inches).

For wide-flange steel columns completely encased in concrete with all reentrant spaces filled (Figure No. 43-9-S-6, Detail C), the thermal capacity of the concrete with the reentrant spaces may be added to the thermal capacity of the steel column and the total thermal capacity may be determined by the expression:

$$H = .11W + \frac{\rho_c c_c}{144}\ (b_f\, d - A_s)$$

WHERE:

b_f = flange width of the steel column (inches).

d = depth of the steel column (inches).

A_s = cross-sectional area of the steel column (square inches).

If specific data on the properties of concrete or concrete masonry are not available, the values given in Table No. 43-9-S-B may be used.

For structural steel columns encased in concrete with all reentrant spaces filled (Figure No. 43-9-S-6, Detail C), Tables Nos. 43-98-S-C and 43-9-S-D given the thickness of concrete cover required for various fire-resistance ratings for typical wide-flange sections. The thicknesses of concrete given in these tables also apply to structural steel columns larger than those listed.

For structural steel columns protected with precast concrete column covers (Figure No. 43-9-S-6, Detail A), Tables Nos. 43-9-S-E and 43-9-S-F give the thickness of the column covers required for various fire-resistance ratings for typical wide-flange shapes. The thicknesses of concrete given in these tables also apply to structural steel columns larger than those listed.

For structural steel columns protected with concrete masonry (Figure No. 43-9-S-7), Tables Nos. 43-89-S-G and 43-9-S-H give the equivalent thickness of concrete masonry required for various fire-resistance ratings for typical wide-flange shapes. The equivalent thicknesses given in these tables also apply to structural steel columns larger than those listed.

Head and bed joints shall be fully mortared. Design and anchorage of concrete masonry shall be in accordance with Chapter 24. The thickness of column units (Figure No. 43-9-S-7) shall not be less than $1^1/_2$ inch. The nominal thickness of hollow or solid units (Figure No. 43-9-S-7) shall not be less than 4 inches.

Protected Steel Beams, Girders and Trusses

Sec. 43.904. (a) **Beams and Girders.** 1. **General.** These procedures establish a basis for determining the fire resistance of structural steel beams and girders which differ in size from that specified in approved fire-resistant assemblies as a function of the thickness of fire-protection material and the weight *W* and heated perimeter *D* of the beam or girder. The use of the methodology in this section is limited to unrestrained conditions. As used in these sections, *W* is the average weight of a structural steel member in pounds per linear foot. The heated perimeter *D* is the inside perimeter of the fire-protection material in inches as illustrated in Figure No. 43-9-S-8. The weight-to-heated-perimeter ratios (*W*/*D*) for both contour and box fire-protection profiles for the wide-flange shapes most often used as beams or girders are given in Table No. 43-9-S-I. For different shapes, the weight-to-heated-perimeter ratios (*W*/*D*) shall be determined in accordance with the definitions given in this section. Except as provided for in Section 43.904 (a) 2, structural steel beams in approved fire-resistant assemblies shall be considered the minimum permissible size. Other beam or girder shapes may be substituted, provided that the weight-to-heated-perimeter ratio (*W*/*D*) of the substitute beam is equal to or greater than that of the beam specified in the approved assembly.

2. **Spray-applied fire-protection materials.** The provisions in this section apply to structural steel beams and girders protected with spray-applied cementitious or mineral fiber materials. Larger or smaller beam and girder shapes may be substituted for beams specified in approved fire-resistant assemblies, provided that the thickness of fire-protection material is adjusted in accordance with the following expression:

$$h_2 = \left[\frac{W_1/D_1 + 0.60}{W_2/D_2 + 0.60}\right] h_1$$

WHERE:

h = thickness of spray-applied fire protection, in inches.

W = weight of the structural steel beam or girder in pounds per linear foot.

D = heated perimeter of the structural steel beam or girder, in inches.

Subscript 1 refers to the beam and fire-protection thickness in the approved assembly.

Subscript 2 refers to the substitute beam or girder and the required thickness of fire-protection materials.

This equation is limited to beams with a weight-to-heated-perimeter ratio (W/D) of 0.37 or greater. The thickness of protection shall not be less than $^3/_8$ inch.

(b) **Structural Steel Trusses.** The fire resistance of structural steel trusses protected with cementitious or mineral fiber materials spray applied to each of the individual truss elements may be determined in accordance with this section. The thickness of protection shall be determined in accordance with Sections 43.903 (c). The weight-to-heated-perimeter ratio (W/D) of truss elements which can be simultaneously exposed to fire on all sides shall be determined on the same basis as columns, as specified in Section 43.903 (a). The weight-to-heated-perimeter ratio (W/D) of truss elements which directly support floor or roof construction shall be determined on the same basis as beams and girders, as specified in Section 43.904 (a) 1.

TABLE NO. 43-9-S-A
WEIGHT-TO-HEATED-PERIMETER RATIOS (*W/D*) FOR TYPICAL STRUCTURAL STEEL WIDE FLANGE COLUMNS

STRUCTURAL SHAPE	CONTOUR PROFILE (*W/D*)	BOX PROFILE[1] (*W/D*)	STRUCTURAL SHAPE	CONTOUR PROFILE (*W/D*)	BOX PROFILE[1] (*W/D*)
W14x730	6.62	9.05	W12x87	1.20	1.76
W14x665	6.14	8.46	W12x79	1.10	1.61
W14x605	5.69	7.89	W12x72	1.00	1.48
W14x550	5.26	7.35	W12x65	0.91	1.35
W14x500	4.86	6.83	W12x58	0.91	1.31
W14x455	4.49	6.35	W12x53	0.84	1.20
W14x426	4.24	6.02	W12x50	0.89	1.23
W14x398	4.00	5.71	W12x45	0.81	1.12
W14x370	3.76	5.38	W12x40	0.72	1.00
W14x342	3.51	5.04			
W14x311	3.23	4.66	W10x112	1.78	2.57
W14x283	2.97	4.31	W10x100	1.61	2.33
W14x257	2.72	3.97	W10x88	1.43	2.08
W14x233	2.49	3.65	W10x77	1.26	1.85
W14x211	2.28	3.35	W10x68	1.13	1.66
W14x193	2.10	3.09	W10x60	1.00	1.48
W14x176	1.93	2.85	W10x54	0.91	1.34
W14x159	1.75	2.60	W10x49	0.83	1.23
W14x145	1.61	2.39	W10x45	0.87	1.24
W14x132	1.52	2.25	W10x39	0.76	1.09
W14x120	1.39	2.06	W10x33	0.65	0.93
W14x109	1.27	1.88			
W14x99	1.16	1.72	W8x67	1.34	1.94
W14x90	1.06	1.58	W8x58	1.18	1.71
W14x82	1.20	1.68	W8x48	0.99	1.44
W14x74	1.09	1.53	W8x40	0.83	1.23
W14x68	1.01	1.41	W8x35	0.73	1.08
W14x61	0.91	1.28	W8x31	0.65	0.97
W14x53	0.89	1.21	W8x28	0.67	0.96
W14x48	0.81	1.10	W8x24	0.58	0.83
W14x43	0.73	0.99	W8x21	0.57	0.77
			W8x18	0.49	0.67
W12x336	4.02	5.56			
W12x305	3.70	5.16	W6x25	0.69	1.00
W12x279	3.44	4.81	W6x20	0.56	0.82
W12x252	3.15	4.43	W6x16	0.57	0.78
W12x230	2.91	4.12	W6x15	0.42	0.63
W12x210	2.68	3.82	W6x12	0.43	0.60
W12x190	2.46	3.51	W6x9	0.33	0.46
W12x170	2.22	3.20			
W12x152	2.01	2.90	W5x19	0.64	0.93
W12x136	1.82	2.63	W6x16	0.54	0.80
W12x120	1.62	2.36			
W12x106	1.44	2.11	W4x13	0.54	0.79
W12x96	1.32	1.93			

[1]See Section 43.903 (b) for *W/D* limitations for gypsum wallboard protected assemblies.

TABLE NO. 43-9-S-A2—AREA-TO-HEATED-PERIMETER RATIOS *(A/P)* FOR TYPICAL ROUND AND SQUARE STRUCTURAL TUBING

ROUND PIPE COLUMNS STANDARD STEEL PIPE

Nominal Diameter (inches)	Thickness (inches)	A/P Ratio
12	0.375	0.39
10	0.365	0.38
8	0.322	0.33
6	0.280	0.30
5	0.258	0.27
4	0.237	0.25
3.5	0.226	0.24
3	0.216	0.24

EXTRA-STRONG STEEL PIPE COLUMNS

Nominal Diameter (inches)	Thickness (inches)	A/P Ratio
12	0.500	0.51
10	0.500	0.51
8	0.500	0.51
6	0.432	0.45
5	0.375	0.39
4	0.337	0.35
3.5	0.318	0.33
3	0.300	0.32

DOUBLE EXTRA-STRONG STEEL PIPE COLUMNS

Nominal Diameter (inches)	Thickness (inches)	A/P Ratio
8	0.875	0.85
6	0.864	0.83
5	0.750	0.72
4	0.647	0.64
3	0.600	0.58

SQUARE STRUCTURAL TUBING

Nominal Size Each Side (inches)	Thickness (inches)	A/P Ratio
16	5/8	0.15
16	1/2	0.12
14	5/8	0.17
14	1/2	0.13
14	3/8	0.10
12	5/8	0.19
12	1/2	0.16
12	3/8	0.12

SQUARE STRUCTURAL TUBING—(Continued)

Nominal Size Each Side (inches)	Thickness (inches)	A/P Ratio
10	5/8	0.22
10	9/16	0.20
10	1/2	0.18
10	3/8	0.14
10	5/16	0.12
9	5/8	0.25
9	9/16	0.22
9	1/2	0.20
9	3/8	0.16
9	5/16	0.13
8	5/8	0.27
8	9/16	0.25
8	1/2	0.23
8	3/8	0.17
8	5/16	0.15
8	1/4	0.12
7	9/16	0.28
7	1/2	0.25
7	3/8	0.20
7	5/16	0.17
7	1/4	0.13
6	9/16	0.32
6	1/2	0.29
6	3/8	0.22
6	5/16	0.19
6	1/4	0.16
6	3/16	0.12
5	1/2	0.33
5	3/8	0.26
5	5/16	0.22
5	1/4	0.18
5	3/16	0.14
4	1/2	0.40
4	3/8	0.32
4	5/16	0.27
4	1/4	0.22
4	3/16	0.17
3	5/16	0.35
3	1/4	0.29
3	3/16	0.22

(Continued)

TABLE NO. 43-9-S-A2—AREA-TO-HEATED-PERIMETER RATIOS (*A/P*) FOR TYPICAL ROUND AND SQUARE STRUCTURAL TUBING—(Continued)

RECTANGULAR STRUCTURAL TUBING		
Nominal Size (inches)	Thickness (inches)	*A/P* Ratio
16 x 12	5/8	0.17
16 x 12	1/2	0.14
16 x 8	1/2	0.18
14 x 10	5/8	0.20
14 x 10	1/2	0.16
14 x 10	3/8	0.12
12 x 8	5/8	0.23
12 x 8	9/16	0.21
12 x 8	1/2	0.19
12 x 8	3/8	0.15
12 x 6	5/8	0.28
12 x 6	9/16	0.25
12 x 6	1/2	0.23
12 x 6	3/8	0.18
10 x 8	5/8	0.25
10 x 8	9/16	0.23
10 x 8	1/2	0.21
10 x 8	3/8	0.16
10 x 8	5/16	0.13
10 x 8	1/4	0.11
10 x 6	5/8	0.29
10 x 6	9/16	0.27
10 x 6	1/2	0.24
10 x 6	3/8	0.19
10 x 6	5/16	0.16
10 x 5	5/8	0.32
10 x 5	9/16	0.30
10 x 5	1/2	0.27
10 x 5	3/8	0.21
10 x 5	5/16	0.17
9 x 7	5/8	0.25
9 x 7	9/16	0.23
9 x 7	1/2	0.18
9 x 7	3/8	0.15
9 x 7	5/16	0.12
9 x 6	5/8	0.30
9 x 6	9/16	0.27
9 x 6	1/2	0.25
9 x 6	3/8	0.19
9 x 6	5/16	0.16
9 x 5	9/16	0.30
9 x 5	1/2	0.28
9 x 5	3/8	0.21
9 x 5	5/16	0.18
8 x 6	9/16	0.29
8 x 6	1/2	0.26
8 x 6	3/8	0.20
8 x 6	5/16	0.17
8 x 6	1/4	0.14
8 x 4	9/16	0.36
8 x 4	1/2	0.33
8 x 4	3/8	0.25
8 x 4	5/16	0.21
8 x 4	1/4	0.17
7 x 5	1/2	0.30
7 x 5	3/8	0.23
7 x 5	5/16	0.20
7 x 5	1/4	0.16
6 x 5	1/2	0.31
6 x 5	3/8	0.24
6 x 5	5/16	0.21
6 x 5	1/4	0.17
6 x 5	3/16	0.13
6 x 4	1/2	0.35
6 x 4	3/8	0.27
6 x 4	5/16	0.23
6 x 4	1/4	0.19
6 x 4	3/16	0.15
6 x 3	3/8	0.32
6 x 3	5/16	0.28
6 x 3	1/4	0.23
6 x 3	3/16	0.17
5 x 3	1/2	0.42
5 x 3	3/8	0.34
5 x 3	5/16	0.29
5 x 3	1/4	0.24
5 x 3	3/16	0.18
4 x 3	5/16	0.31
4 x 3	1/4	0.26
4 x 3	3/16	0.20
4 x 2	5/16	0.39
4 x 2	1/4	0.32
4 x 2	3/16	0.25
3.5 x 2.5	1/4	0.30
3.5 x 2.5	3/16	0.23
3 x 2	1/4	0.35
3 x 2	3/16	0.27

TABLE NO. 43-9-S-B—PROPERTIES OF CONCRETE

PROPERTIES OF CONCRETE AND CONCRETE MASONRY				
	Concrete		Concrete Masonry	
	Normal-Weight	Structural Lightweight	Normal-Weight	Light-Weight
Thermal Conductivity, k_c (Btu/h ft. °F.)	0.95	0.35	0.51	0.33
Specific Heat, C_c (Btu/h/lb. °F.)	0.20	0.20	0.20	0.20
Density, p_c (pcf)	145	110	125	105
Equilibrium (free) moisture content, m, percent by volume	4	5	4	5

TABLE NO. 43-9-S-C—THICKNESS (INCHES) OF NORMAL-WEIGHT CONCRETE[1] FOR VARIOUS FIRE-RESISTANCE RATINGS FOR TYPICAL WIDE-FLANGE STRUCTURAL STEEL COLUMNS ENCASED IN CONCRETE (FIGURE NO. 43-9-S-6, DETAIL C)

<table>
<tr><th rowspan="3">FIRE-RESISTANCE RATING (Hours)</th><th colspan="28">STEEL COLUMN STRUCTURAL SHAPES</th></tr>
<tr><th colspan="7">W14X</th><th colspan="5">W12X</th><th colspan="5">W10X</th><th colspan="6">W8X</th><th colspan="5">W6X</th></tr>
<tr><th>233</th><th>176</th><th>132</th><th>90</th><th>61</th><th>48</th><th>43</th><th>152</th><th>96</th><th>65</th><th>50</th><th>40</th><th>88</th><th>49</th><th>45</th><th>39</th><th>33</th><th>67</th><th>58</th><th>48</th><th>31</th><th>21</th><th>18</th><th>25</th><th>20</th><th>16</th><th>15</th><th>9</th></tr>
<tr><td>1</td><td colspan="7">1</td><td colspan="5">1</td><td colspan="5">1</td><td colspan="6">1</td><td colspan="4">1</td><td>1½</td></tr>
<tr><td>2</td><td colspan="3">1</td><td colspan="4">1½</td><td>1</td><td colspan="4">1½</td><td colspan="4">1½</td><td>2</td><td colspan="3">1½</td><td colspan="3">2</td><td colspan="2">2</td><td colspan="3">2½</td></tr>
<tr><td>3</td><td colspan="2">1½</td><td colspan="3">2</td><td colspan="2">2½</td><td colspan="3">2</td><td colspan="2">2½</td><td>2</td><td colspan="4">2½</td><td colspan="4">2½</td><td colspan="2">3</td><td colspan="4">3</td><td>3½</td></tr>
<tr><td>4</td><td>2</td><td colspan="3">2½</td><td colspan="3">3</td><td colspan="2">2½</td><td colspan="3">3</td><td colspan="3">3</td><td colspan="2">3½</td><td colspan="2">3</td><td colspan="3">3½</td><td>4</td><td>3½</td><td colspan="4">4</td></tr>
</table>

[1]The tabulated thicknesses are based upon the assumed properties of normal-weight concrete given in Table No. 43-9-S-B.

TABLE NO. 43-9-S-D—THICKNESS (INCHES) OF STRUCTURAL LIGHTWEIGHT CONCRETE[1] FOR VARIOUS FIRE-RESISTANCE RATINGS FOR TYPICAL WIDE-FLANGE STRUCTURAL STEEL COLUMNS ENCASED IN CONCRETE (FIGURE NO. 43-9-S-6, DETAIL C)

<table>
<tr><th rowspan="3">FIRE-RESISTANCE RATING (Hours)</th><th colspan="16">STEEL COLUMN STRUCTURAL SHAPES</th></tr>
<tr><th colspan="5">W14X</th><th colspan="3">W12X</th><th colspan="4">W10X</th><th colspan="4">W8X</th></tr>
<tr><th>233</th><th>193</th><th>74</th><th>61</th><th>43</th><th>65</th><th>53</th><th>40</th><th>112</th><th>88</th><th>60</th><th>33</th><th>35</th><th>28</th><th>24</th><th>18</th></tr>
<tr><td>1</td><td colspan="5">1</td><td colspan="3">1</td><td colspan="4">1</td><td colspan="4">1</td></tr>
<tr><td>2</td><td colspan="4">1</td><td>1½</td><td colspan="2">1</td><td>1½</td><td colspan="3">1</td><td>1½</td><td colspan="4">1½</td></tr>
<tr><td>3</td><td>1</td><td colspan="3">1½</td><td>2</td><td>1½</td><td colspan="2">2</td><td colspan="2">1½</td><td colspan="2">2</td><td colspan="2">2</td><td colspan="2">2½</td></tr>
<tr><td>4</td><td colspan="2">1½</td><td>2</td><td colspan="2">2½</td><td>2</td><td colspan="2">2½</td><td colspan="2">2</td><td colspan="2">2½</td><td>2½</td><td colspan="3">3</td></tr>
</table>

[1]The tabulated thicknesses are based upon the assumed properties of structural lightweight concrete given in Table No. 43-9-S-B.

TABLE NO. 43-9-S-E—THICKNESS (INCHES) OF NORMAL-WEIGHT CONCRETE[1] PRECAST CONCRETE COVERS FOR VARIOUS FIRE-RESISTANCE RATINGS FOR TYPICAL WIDE-FLANGE STRUCTURAL STEEL COLUMNS (FIGURE NO. 43-9-S-6, DETAIL A)

<table>
<tr><th rowspan="3">FIRE-RESISTANCE RATING (Hours)</th><th colspan="31">STEEL COLUMN STRUCTURAL SHAPES</th></tr>
<tr><th colspan="8">W14X</th><th colspan="7">W12X</th><th colspan="5">W10X</th><th colspan="6">W8X</th><th colspan="5">W6X</th></tr>
<tr><th>233</th><th>211</th><th>176</th><th>145</th><th>109</th><th>99</th><th>61</th><th>43</th><th>190</th><th>152</th><th>120</th><th>96</th><th>87</th><th>58</th><th>40</th><th>112</th><th>88</th><th>77</th><th>54</th><th>33</th><th>67</th><th>58</th><th>48</th><th>28</th><th>21</th><th>18</th><th>25</th><th>20</th><th>16</th><th>12</th><th>9</th></tr>
<tr><td>1</td><td colspan="8">1½</td><td colspan="7">1½</td><td colspan="5">1½</td><td colspan="6">1½</td><td colspan="3">1½</td><td colspan="2">2</td></tr>
<tr><td>2</td><td colspan="2">1½</td><td colspan="3">2</td><td colspan="3">2½</td><td>1½</td><td colspan="3">2</td><td colspan="3">2½</td><td colspan="2">2</td><td colspan="3">2½</td><td>2</td><td colspan="3">2½</td><td colspan="2">3</td><td>2½</td><td colspan="4">3</td></tr>
<tr><td>3</td><td colspan="3">2½</td><td colspan="3">3</td><td colspan="2">3½</td><td colspan="2">2½</td><td colspan="3">3</td><td colspan="2">3½</td><td colspan="3">3</td><td colspan="2">3½</td><td>3</td><td colspan="4">3½</td><td>4</td><td colspan="2">3½</td><td colspan="3">4</td></tr>
<tr><td>4</td><td>3</td><td colspan="3">3½</td><td colspan="3">4</td><td>4½</td><td colspan="3">3½</td><td colspan="3">4</td><td>4½</td><td>3½</td><td colspan="3">4</td><td>4½</td><td colspan="3">4</td><td colspan="3">4½</td><td colspan="4">4½</td><td>5</td></tr>
</table>

[1]The tabulated thicknesses are based upon the assumed properties of normal-weight concrete given in Table No. 43-9-S-B.

TABLE NO. 43-9-S-F—THICKNESS (INCHES) OF STRUCTURAL LIGHTWEIGHT[1] PRECAST CONCRETE COVERS FOR VARIOUS FIRE-RESISTANCE RATINGS FOR TYPICAL WIDE-FLANGE STRUCTURAL STEEL COLUMNS (FIGURE NO. 43-9-S-6, DETAIL A)

<table>
<tr><th rowspan="3">FIRE-RESISTANCE RATING (Hours)</th><th colspan="31">STEEL COLUMN STRUCTURAL SHAPES</th></tr>
<tr><th colspan="8">W14X</th><th colspan="8">W12X</th><th colspan="7">W10X</th><th colspan="5">W8X</th><th colspan="3">W6X</th></tr>
<tr><th>233</th><th>176</th><th>145</th><th>132</th><th>109</th><th>99</th><th>68</th><th>43</th><th>190</th><th>152</th><th>136</th><th>106</th><th>96</th><th>87</th><th>65</th><th>40</th><th>112</th><th>100</th><th>88</th><th>77</th><th>60</th><th>39</th><th>33</th><th>67</th><th>48</th><th>35</th><th>28</th><th>18</th><th>25</th><th>15</th><th>9</th></tr>
<tr><td>1</td><td colspan="8">1½</td><td colspan="8">1½</td><td colspan="7">1½</td><td colspan="5">1½</td><td colspan="3">1½</td></tr>
<tr><td>2</td><td>1½</td><td colspan="4">1½</td><td colspan="3">2</td><td>1½</td><td colspan="4">1½</td><td colspan="3">2</td><td colspan="3">1½</td><td colspan="4">2</td><td>1½</td><td colspan="3">2</td><td>2½</td><td>2</td><td colspan="2">2½</td></tr>
<tr><td>3</td><td colspan="3">2</td><td colspan="4">2½</td><td>3</td><td colspan="3">2</td><td colspan="4">2½</td><td>3</td><td>2</td><td colspan="4">2½</td><td colspan="2">3</td><td colspan="2">2½</td><td colspan="3">3</td><td colspan="2">3</td><td>3½</td></tr>
<tr><td>4</td><td colspan="2">2½</td><td colspan="4">3</td><td colspan="2">3½</td><td colspan="2">2½</td><td colspan="4">3</td><td colspan="2">3½</td><td colspan="4">3</td><td colspan="3">3½</td><td>3</td><td colspan="3">3½</td><td>4</td><td>3½</td><td colspan="2">4</td></tr>
</table>

[1]The tabulated thicknesses are based upon the assumed properties of structural lightweight concrete given in Table No. 43-9-S-B.

TABLE NO. 43-9-S-G—EQUIVALENT THICKNESS (INCHES) OF NORMALWEIGHT CONCRETE MASONRY FIRE PROTECTION FOR TYPICAL WIDE-FLANGE STRUCTURAL STEEL COLUMNS[1] [2] (SEE FIGURE NO. 43-9-S-7)

FIRE-RESISTANCE RATING (Hours)	STRUCTURAL STEEL COLUMN SHAPES W 14 x								W 12 x								W 10 x							W 8 x					W 6 x		
	233	176	145	132	109	99	68	43	190	152	136	106	96	87	65	40	112	100	88	77	60	39	33	67	48	35	28	18	25	15	9
1	0.4	0.6	0.7	0.7	0.8	0.9	1.0	1.2	0.4	0.6	0.6	0.8	0.8	0.9	1.0	1.0	0.6	0.7	0.8	0.8	1.0	1.2	1.2	0.8	1.0	1.1	1.2	1.4	1.2	1.4	1.5
2	1.1	1.4	1.5	1.6	1.7	1.8	2.0	2.3	1.2	1.4	1.5	1.7	1.7	1.8	2.0	2.2	1.5	1.6	1.7	1.8	1.9	2.2	2.3	1.7	2.0	2.2	2.3	2.4	2.2	2.4	2.6
3	1.8	2.1	2.3	2.4	2.5	2.6	2.9	3.1	1.9	2.1	2.2	2.5	2.5	2.6	2.8	3.1	2.3	2.4	2.5	2.6	2.8	3.0	3.1	2.6	2.8	3.0	3.1	3.3	3.1	3.3	3.4
4	2.5	2.8	3.0	3.1	3.3	3.4	3.6	3.9	2.6	2.8	2.9	3.2	3.3	3.4	3.6	3.8	3.0	3.1	3.2	3.3	3.5	3.8	3.9	3.3	3.6	3.8	3.9	4.0	3.8	4.0	4.2

[1]The tabulated thicknesses are based upon the assumed properties of normal-weight concrete masonry given in Table No. 43-9-S-B.

[2]The thickness of concrete masonry units shall not be less than set forth in Section 43.903 (d).

TABLE NO. 43-9-S-H—EQUIVALENT THICKNESS (INCHES) OF LIGHTWEIGHT CONCRETE MASONRY FIRE PROTECTION FOR TYPICAL WIDE-FLANGE STRUCTURAL STEEL COLUMNS[1] [2] (SEE FIGURE NO. 43-9-S-7)

FIRE-RESISTANCE RATING (Hours)	STRUCTURAL STEEL COLUMN SHAPES W 14 x								W 12 x								W 10 x							W 8 x					W 6 x		
	233	176	145	132	109	99	68	43	190	152	136	106	96	87	65	40	112	100	88	77	60	39	33	67	48	35	28	18	25	15	9
1	0.3	0.4	0.5	0.6	0.7	0.7	0.9	1.1	0.3	0.4	0.5	0.6	0.7	0.7	0.8	1.1	0.5	0.5	0.6	0.7	0.8	1.0	1.1	0.6	0.8	1.0	1.1	1.2	1.0	1.2	1.4
2	0.9	1.1	1.3	1.3	1.5	1.5	1.8	2.0	0.9	1.1	1.2	1.4	1.5	1.5	1.7	2.0	1.2	1.3	1.4	1.5	1.7	1.9	2.0	1.5	1.7	1.9	2.0	2.2	2.0	2.2	2.3
3	1.5	1.8	1.9	2.0	2.2	2.3	2.5	2.8	1.5	1.8	1.9	2.1	2.2	2.3	2.5	2.8	1.9	2.0	2.1	2.2	2.4	2.7	2.8	2.2	2.5	2.7	2.8	3.0	2.7	3.0	3.1
4	2.1	2.4	2.6	2.7	2.9	2.9	3.2	3.5	2.1	2.4	2.5	2.8	2.8	2.9	3.2	3.5	2.5	2.7	2.8	2.9	3.1	3.4	3.5	2.9	3.2	3.4	3.5	3.7	3.4	3.7	3.8

[1]The tabulated thicknesses are based upon the assumed properties of normal-weight concrete masonry given in Table No. 43-9-S-B.

[2]The thickness of concrete masonry units shall not be less than set forth in Section 43.903 (d).

TABLE NO. 43-9-S-I
WEIGHT-TO-HEATED-PERIMETER RATIOS *W/D*
FOR TYPICAL WIDE-FLANGE BEAM AND GIRDER SHAPES

STRUCTURAL SHAPE	CONTOUR PROFILE	BOX PROFILE
W36 x 300	2.47	3.33
x 280	2.31	3.12
x 260	2.16	2.92
x 245	2.04	2.76
x 230	1.92	2.61
x 210	1.94	2.45
x 194	1.80	2.28
x 182	1.69	2.15
x 170	1.59	2.01
x 160	1.50	1.90
x 150	1.41	1.79
x 135	1.28	1.63
W33 x 241	2.11	2.86
x 221	1.94	2.64
x 201	1.78	2.42
x 152	1.51	1.94
x 141	1.41	1.80
x 130	1.31	1.67
x 118	1.19	1.53
W30 x 211	2.00	2.74
x 191	1.82	2.50
x 173	1.66	2.28
x 132	1.45	1.85
x 124	1.37	1.75
x 116	1.28	1.65
x 108	1.20	1.54
x 99	1.10	1.42
W27 x 178	1.85	2.55
x 161	1.68	2.33
x 146	1.53	2.12
x 114	1.36	1.76
x 102	1.23	1.59
x 94	1.13	1.47
x 84	1.02	1.33

(Continued)

TABLE NO. 43-9-S-I
WEIGHT-TO-HEATED-PERIMETER RATIOS *W/D* FOR TYPICAL WIDE-FLANGE BEAM AND GIRDER SHAPES—(Continued)

STRUCTURAL SHAPE	CONTOUR PROFILE	BOX PROFILE
W24 x 162	1.85	2.57
x 146	1.68	2.34
x 131	1.52	2.12
x 117	1.36	1.91
x 104	1.22	1.71
x 94	1.26	1.63
x 84	1.13	1.47
x 76	1.03	1.34
x 68	0.92	1.21
x 62	0.92	1.14
x 55	0.82	1.02
W21 x 147	1.83	2.60
x 132	1.66	2.35
x 122	1.54	2.19
x 111	1.41	2.01
x 101	1.29	1.84
x 93	1.38	1.80
x 83	1.24	1.62
x 68	1.03	1.35
x 62	0.94	1.23
x 57	0.93	1.17
x 50	0.83	1.04
x 44	0.73	0.92
W18 x 119	1.69	2.42
x 106	1.52	2.18
x 97	1.39	2.01
x 86	1.24	1.80
x 76	1.11	1.60
x 71	1.21	1.59
x 65	1.11	1.47
x 60	1.03	1.36
x 55	0.95	1.26
x 50	0.87	1.15
x 46	0.86	1.09
x 40	0.75	0.96
x 35	0.66	0.85

(Continued)

STRUCTURAL SHAPE	CONTOUR PROFILE	BOX PROFILE
W16 x 100	1.56	2.25
x 89	1.40	2.03
x 77	1.22	1.78
x 67	1.07	1.56
x 57	1.07	1.43
x 50	0.94	1.26
x 45	0.85	1.15
x 40	0.76	1.03
x 36	0.69	0.93
x 31	0.65	0.83
x 26	0.55	0.70
W14 x 132	1.83	3.00
x 120	1.67	2.75
x 109	1.53	2.52
x 99	1.39	2.31
x 90	1.27	2.11
x 82	1.41	2.12
x 74	1.28	1.93
x 68	1.19	1.78
x 61	1.07	1.61
x 53	1.03	1.48
x 48	0.94	1.35
x 43	0.85	1.22
x 38	0.79	1.09
x 34	0.71	0.98
x 30	0.63	0.87
x 26	0.61	0.79
x 22	0.52	0.68
W12 x 87	1.44	2.34
x 79	1.32	2.14
x 72	1.20	1.97
x 65	1.09	1.79
x 58	1.08	1.69
x 53	0.99	1.55
x 50	1.04	1.54
x 45	0.95	1.40
x 40	0.85	1.25
x 35	0.79	1.11
x 30	0.69	0.96
x 26	0.60	0.84
x 22	0.61	0.77
x 19	0.53	0.67
x 16	0.45	0.57
x 14	0.40	0.50

(Continued)

TABLE NO. 43-9-S-I
WEIGHT-TO-HEATED-PERIMETER RATIOS *W/D*
FOR TYPICAL WIDE-FLANGE BEAM AND GIRDER SHAPES—(Continued)

STRUCTURAL SHAPE	CONTOUR PROFILE	BOX PROFILE
W10 x 112	2.14	3.38
x 100	1.93	3.07
x 88	1.72	2.75
x 77	1.52	2.45
x 68	1.35	2.20
x 60	1.20	1.97
x 54	1.09	1.79
x 49	0.99	1.64
x 45	1.03	1.59
x 39	0.90	1.40
x 33	0.77	1.20
x 30	0.79	1.12
x 26	0.69	0.98
x 22	0.59	0.84
x 19	0.59	0.78
x 17	0.54	0.70
x 15	0.48	0.63
x 12	0.38	0.51
W8 x 67	1.61	2.55
x 58	1.41	2.26
x 48	1.18	1.91
x 40	1.00	1.63
x 35	0.88	1.44
x 31	0.79	1.29
x 28	0.80	1.24
x 24	0.69	1.07
x 21	0.66	0.96
x 18	0.57	0.84
x 15	0.54	0.74
x 13	0.47	0.65
x 10	0.37	0.51
W6 x 25	0.82	1.33
x 20	0.67	1.09
x 16	0.66	0.96
x 15	0.51	0.83
x 12	0.51	0.75
x 9	0.39	0.57
W5 x 19	0.76	1.24
x 16	0.65	1.07
W4 x 13	0.65	1.05

FIGURE NO. 43-9-S-1
DETERMINATION OF THE HEATED PERIMETER OF STRUCTURAL STEEL COLUMNS

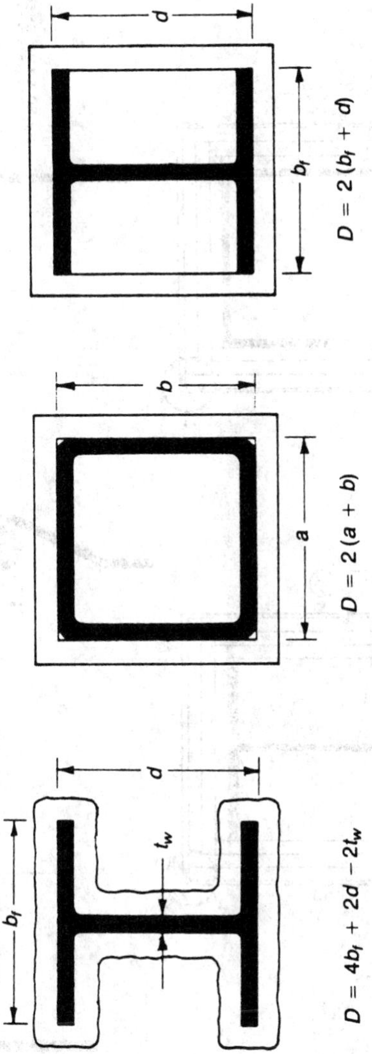
d
b_f
t_w
$D = 4b_f + 2d - 2t_w$
b
a
$D = 2(a + b)$
d
b_f
$D = 2(b_f + d)$

FIGURE NO. 43-9-S-2
GYPSUM WALLBOARD PROTECTED STRUCTURAL STEEL COLUMNS WITH SHEET STEEL COLUMN COVERS
(FOUR HOURS OR LESS)

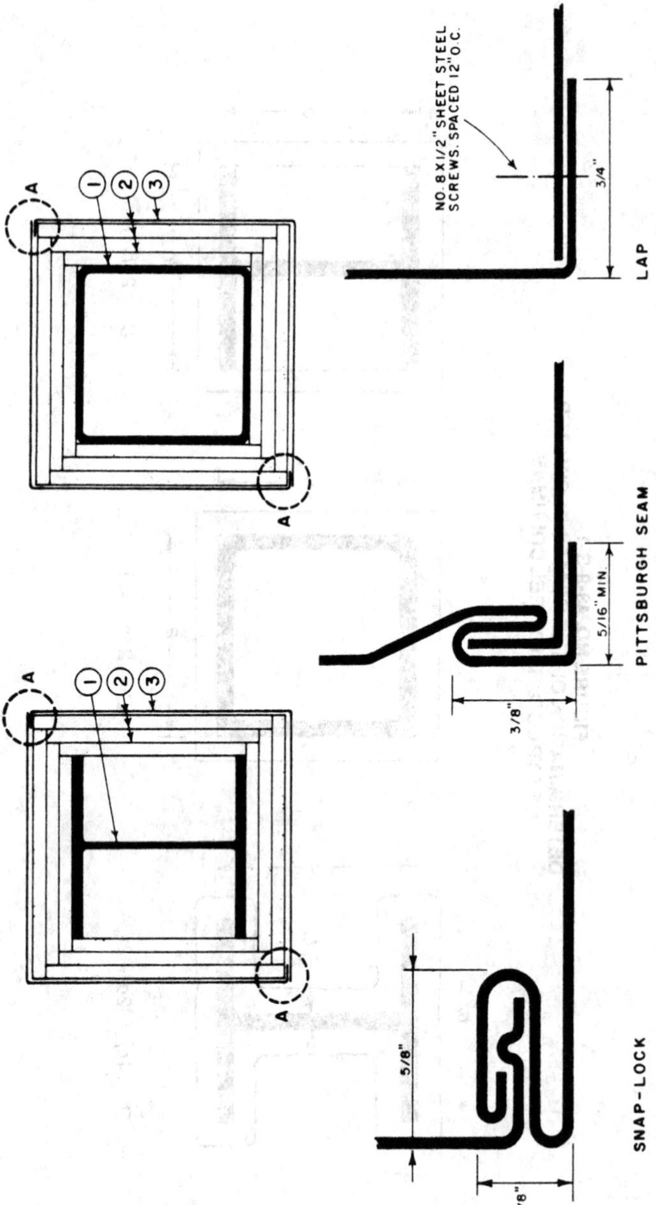
A
1
2
3
A
NO. 8 X 1/2" SHEET STEEL SCREWS. SPACED 12" O.C.
3/4"
LAP
5/16" MIN.
3/8"
PITTSBURGH SEAM
5/8"
3/8"
SNAP-LOCK

Notes:

1. Structural steel column, either wide-flange or tubular shapes.
2. Type X gypsum wallboard. For single-layer applications, the wallboard shall be applied vertically with no horizontal joints. For multiple-layer applications, horizontal joints are permitted at a minimum spacing of 8 feet, provided that the joints in successive layers are staggered at least 12 inches. The total required thickness of wallboard shall be determined on the basis of the specified fire-resistance rating and the weight and heated perimeter of the column. For fire-resistance ratings of two hours or less, one of the required layers of gypsum wallboard may be applied to the exterior of the sheet steel column covers with 1-inch-long Type S screws spaced 1 inch from the wallboard edge and 8 inches on center. For such installations, 0.016-inch-minimum-thickness galvanized steel corner beads with 1½-inch legs shall be attached to the wallboard with Type S screws spaced 12 inches on center.
3. For fire-resistance ratings of three hours or less, the column covers shall be fabricated from 0.024-inch-minimum-thickness galvanized or stainless steel. For four-hour fire-resistance ratings, the column covers shall be fabricated from 0.024-inch-minimum-thickness stainless steel. The column covers shall be erected with the snap lock or Pittsburgh joint details.

   For fire-resistance ratings of two hours or less, column covers fabricated from 0.027-inch-minimum-thickness galvanized or stainless steel may be erected with lap joints. The lap joints may be located anywhere around the perimeter of the column cover. The lap joints shall be secure with ½-inch-long No. 8 sheet metal screws spaced 12 inches on center.

   The column covers shall be provided with a minimum expansion clearance of ⅛ inch per linear foot between the ends of the cover and any restraining construction.

FIGURE NO. 43-9-S-3
GYPSUM WALLBOARD PROTECTED STRUCTURAL STEEL COLUMNS WITH STEEL STUD/SCREW ATTACHMENT SYSTEM (THREE HOURS OR LESS)

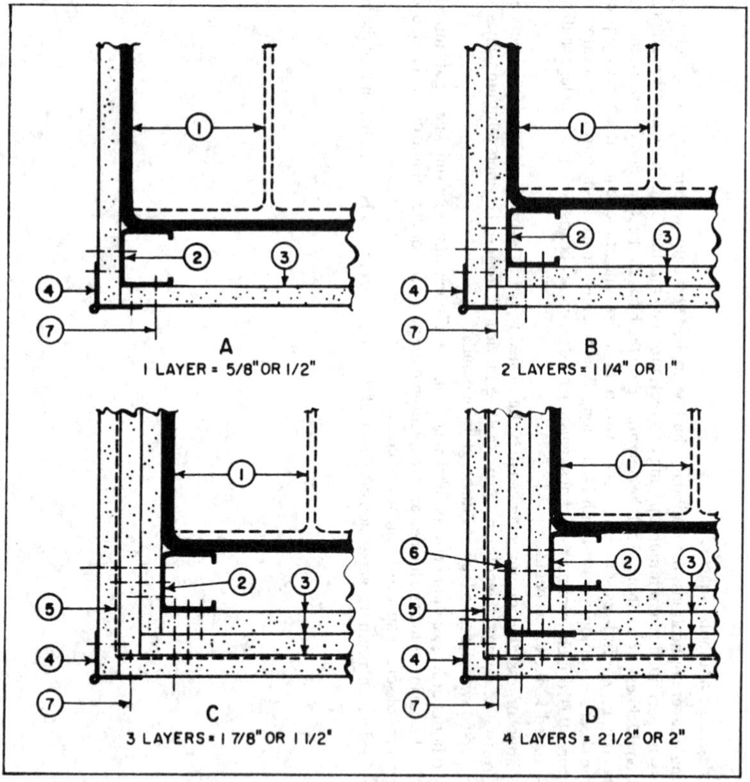
A
1 LAYER = 5/8" OR 1/2"
B
2 LAYERS = 1 1/4" OR 1"
C
3 LAYERS = 1 7/8" OR 1 1/2"
D
4 LAYERS = 2 1/2" OR 2"

Notes:

1. Structural steel column, either wide-flange or tubular shapes.
2. One and five-eighths-inch-deep studs fabricated from 0.021-inch-minimum-thickness galvanized steel with 1⁵⁄₁₆- or 1⁷⁄₁₆-inch legs and ¼-inch stiffening flanges. The length of the steel studs shall be ½ inch less than the height of the assembly.
3. Type X gypsum wallboard. For single-layer applications, the wallboard shall be applied vertically with no horizontal joints. For multiple-layer applications, horizontal joints are permitted at a minimum spacing of 8 feet, provided that the joints in successive layers are staggered at least 12 inches. The total required thickness of wallboard shall be determined on the basis of the specified fire-resistance rating and the weight and heated perimeter of the column.
4. Galvanized steel corner beads (0.016-inch minimum thickness) with 1½-inch legs attached to the wallboard with 1-inch-long Type S screws spaced 12 inches on center.

5. No. 18 SWG steel tie wires spaced 24 inches on center.
6. Sheet metal angles with 2-inch legs fabricated from 0.021-inch-minimum-thickness galvanized steel.
7. Type S screws 1-inch long shall be used for attaching the first layer of wallboard to the steel studs and the third layer to the sheet metal angles at 24 inches on center. Type S screws 1¾ inches long shall be used for attaching the second layer of wallboard to the steel studs and the fourth layer to the sheet metal angles at 12 inches on center. Type S screws 2¼ inches long shall be used for attaching the third layer of wallboard to the steel studs at 12 inches on center.

FIGURE NO. 43-9-S-4
FIRE RESISTANCE OF STRUCTURAL STEEL COLUMNS PROTECTED WITH VARIOUS THICKNESSES OF TYPE X GYPSUM WALLBOARD

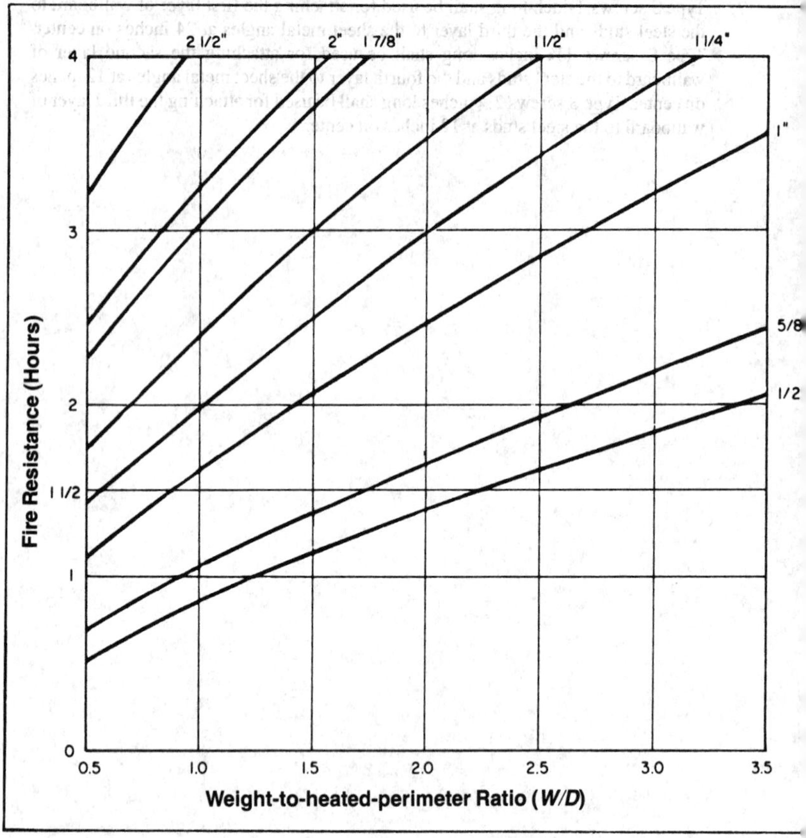

2 1/2"
2"
1 7/8"
1 1/2"
1 1/4"
1"
5/8
1/2
Fire Resistance (Hours)
0
1
1 1/2
2
3
4
0.5
1.0
1.5
2.0
2.5
3.0
3.5
Weight-to-heated-perimeter Ratio (W/D)

Note: The *W/D* ratios for typical wide-flange columns are listed in Table No. 43-9-S-A. For other column shapes, the *W/D* ratios shall be determined in accordance with Section 43.903.

FIGURE NO. 43-9-S-5
WIDE-FLANGE STRUCTURAL STEEL COLUMN
WITH SPRAY-APPLIED FIRE PROTECTION

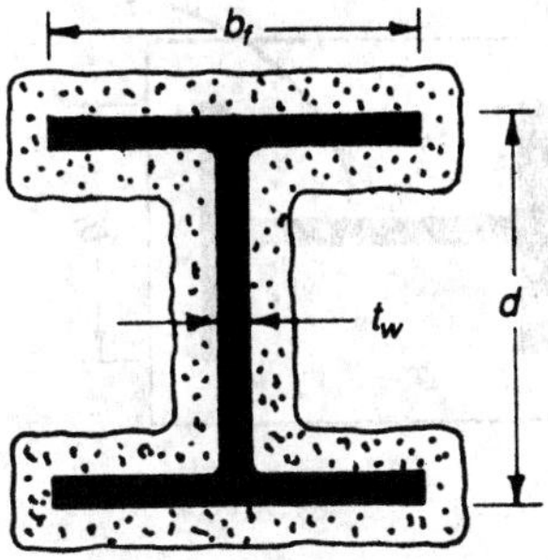

b_f
t_w
d

FIGURE NO. 43-9-S-6
CONCRETE-PROTECTED STRUCTURAL STEEL COLUMNS

DETAIL A PRECAST CONCRETE COLUMN COVERS

DETAIL B CONCRETE-ENCASED STRUCTURAL TUBE

DETAIL C CONCRETE-ENCASED WIDE FLANGE SHAPE

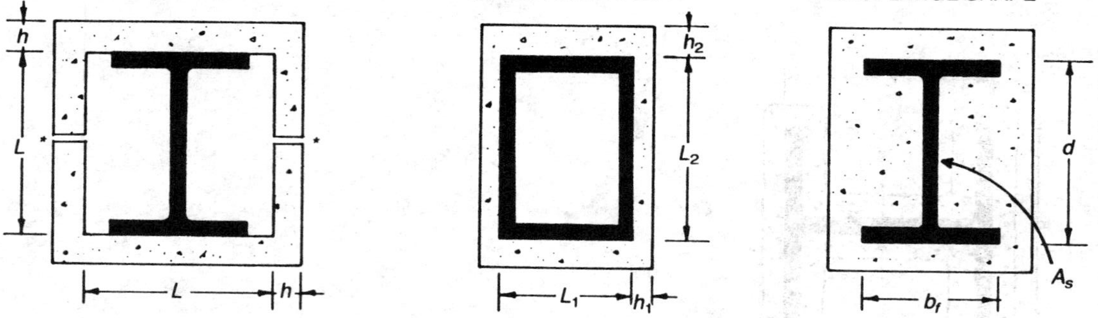
h
L
*
*
L
h
h2
L2
L1
h1
d
As
bf

Note: When the inside perimeter of the concrete protection is not square, L shall be taken as the average of L_1 and L_2. When the thickness of concrete cover is not constant, h shall be taken as the average of h_1 and h_2.

*Joints shall be protected with a minimum 1-inch thickness of ceramic fiber blanket, but in no case less than one half the thickness of the column cover. The joint width shall not exceed 1 inch maximum.

FIGURE NO. 43-9-S-7
CONCRETE MASONRY PROTECTED STRUCTURAL STEEL COLUMNS

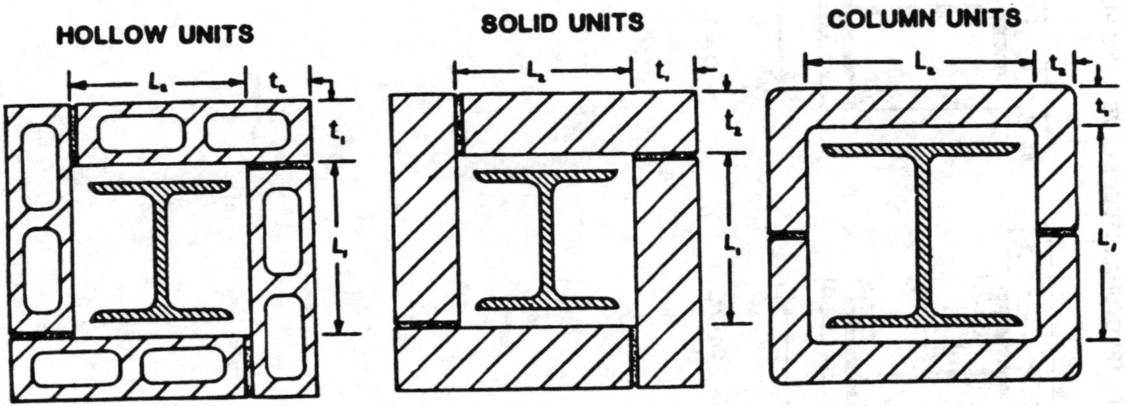
HOLLOW UNITS
SOLID UNITS
COLUMN UNITS
L2
t2
t1
L1

Note: The dimension L in the fire-resistance equation shall be the average of L_1 and L_2. The dimension h in the fire-resistance equation shall be based on the equivalent thickness of the concrete masonry unit. For solid concrete masonry, h equals the lesser of t_1 or t_2. For hollow concrete masonry, h equals the lesser of t_1 or t_2, times the percent solid of the unit expressed as a decimal.

FIGURE NO. 43-9-S-8
DETERMINATION OF THE HEATED PERIMETER OF STRUCTURAL STEEL BEAMS AND GIRDERS

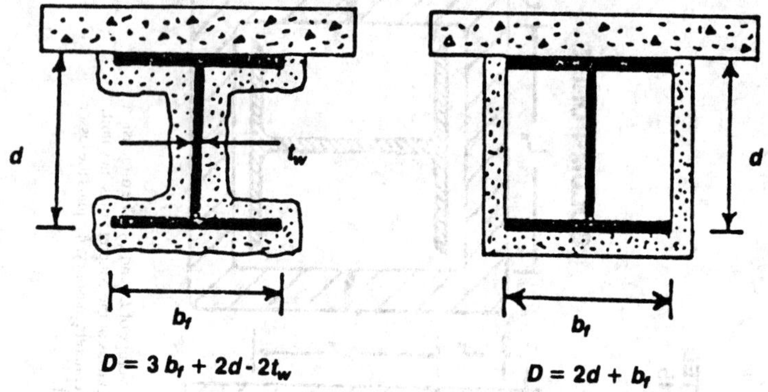
d
t_w
b_f
$D = 3b_f + 2d - 2t_w$
d
b_f
$D = 2d + b_f$

Part II—METHOD FOR CALCULATING THE FIRE RESISTANCE OF CONCRETE CONSTRUCTION
See Section 4302 (c), Uniform Building Code

Scope

Sec. 43.921. This part of this standard contains procedures by which the fire resistance of concrete of specific materials or combinations of materials can be established by calculations. These procedures apply to the material contained in this part only. Procedures shown in this standard for calculating the fire resistance of concrete construction shall apply to all cast-in-place and precast concrete, conventionally reinforced or prestressed. The procedures shall not apply to single or double "T" precast, prestressed (pretensioned) units in wall or floor-roof assemblies.

Definitions

Sec. 43.922. CARBONATE AGGREGATE CONCRETE is concrete made with aggregates consisting mainly of calcium or magnesium carbonate, e.g., limestone or dolomite.

CELLULAR CONCRETE is a lightweight insulating concrete made by mixing a preformed foam with portland cement slurry and having a dry unit weight of approximately 30 pcf.

CERAMIC FIBER BLANKET is a mineral wool insulation material made of alumina-silica fibers and weighing 4 to 10 pcf.

GLASS FIBER BOARD is fibrous glass roof insulation consisting of inorganic glass fibers formed into rigid boards using a binder. The board has a top surface faced with asphalt and kraft paper reinforced with glass fibers.

LIGHTWEIGHT AGGREGATE CONCRETE is concrete made with aggregates of expanded clay, shale, slag or slate or sintered fly ash and weighing 85 to 115 pcf.

MINERAL BOARD is a rigid felted thermal insulation board consisting of either felted mineral fiber or cellular beads of expanded aggregate formed into flat rectangular units.

PERLITE CONCRETE is a lightweight insulating concrete having a dry unit weight of appoximately 30 pcf made with perlite concrete aggregate. Perlite aggregate is produced from a volcanic rock which when heated expands to form a glass-like material of cellular structure.

SAND-LIGHTWEIGHT CONCRETE is concrete made with a combination of expanded clay, shale, slag or slate or sintered fly ash and natural sand. Its unit weight is generally between 105 and 120 pcf.

SILICEOUS AGGREGATE CONCRETE is concrete made with normal-weight aggregates consisting mainly of silica or compounds other than calcium or magnesium carbonate.

VERMICULITE CONCRETE is a lightweight insulating concrete made with vermiculite concrete aggregate which is laminated micaceous material produced by expanding the ore at high temperatures. When added to a portland cement slurry, the resulting concrete has a dry unit weight of approximately 30 pcf.

Concrete Walls

Sec. 43.923. (a) **Walls, Cast-in-place or Precast.** 1. The minimum equivalent thicknesses of cast-in-place or precast concrete walls for fire-resistance ratings of one hour to four hours are shown in Table No. 43-9-C-A. For solid walls with flat vertical surfaces, the equivalent thickness is the same as the thickness. The values in Table No. 43-9-C-A apply to plain, reinforced or prestressed concrete walls.

2. For hollow-core precast concrete wall panels in which the cores are of constant cross-section throughout the length, the equivalent thickness may be calculated by dividing the net cross-sectional area (the gross cross section minus the area of the cores) of the panel by its width.

3. Where all of the core spaces of hollow-core wall panels are filled with loose-fill material, such as expanded shale, clay or slag, or vermiculite or perlite, the fire-resistance rating of the wall is the same as that of a solid wall of the same concrete type and of the same overall thickness.

4. The thickness of panels with tapered cross sections shall be that determined at a distance $2t$ or 6 inches, whichever is less, from the point of minimum thickness, where t is the minimum thickness.

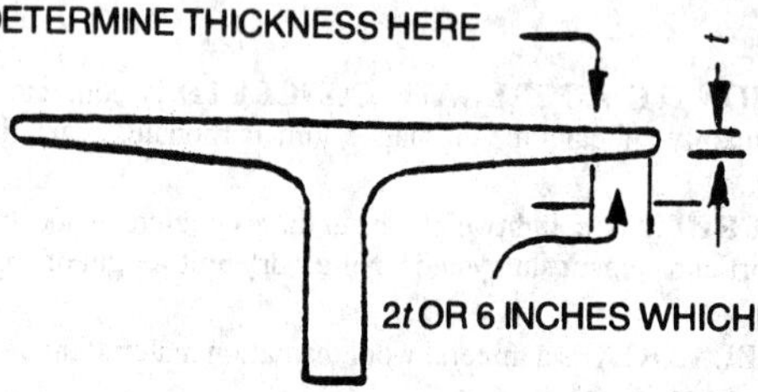
DETERMINE THICKNESS HERE
t
2t OR 6 INCHES WHICHEVER IS LESS

5. The equivalent thickness of panels with ribbed or undulating surfaces shall be determined by one of the following expressions, whichever is applicable:

for $s \geqslant 4t$, the thickness to be used shall be t

for $s \leqslant 2t$, the thickness to be used shall be t_e

for $4t > s > 2t$, the thickness to be used shall be

$$t + \left(\frac{4t}{s} - 1\right)(t_e - t)$$

WHERE:

s = Spacing of ribs or undulations.

t = Minimum thickness.

t_e = Equivalent thickness of the panel calculated as the net cross-sectional area of the panel divided by the width in which the maximum thickness used in the calculation shall not exceed $2t$.

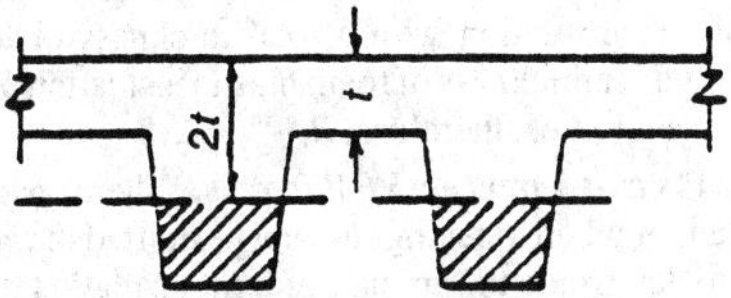
2t
t

NEGLECT SHADED AREA
IN CALCULATION OF
EQUIVALENT THICKNESS

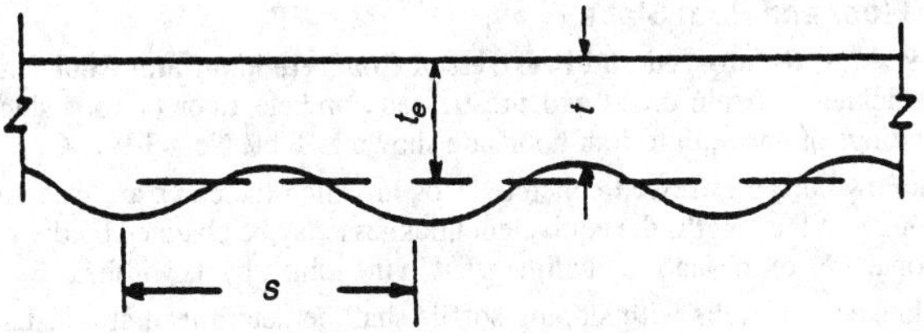
t_e
t
s

(b) **Multiwythe Walls.** 1. For walls which consist of two wythes of different types of concrete, the fire-resistance ratings may be determined from Figure No. 43-9-C-1.

2. The fire-resistance rating for wall panels consisting of two or more wythes may be determined by the formula:

$$R = (R_1^{0.59} + R_2^{0.59} + \ldots R_n^{0.59})^{1.7} \quad \text{(Equation 1)}$$

Equation 1 can also be expressed as:

$$R^{0.59} = R_1^{0.59} + R_2^{0.59} + \ldots R_n^{0.59}$$

WHERE:

R = The fire endurance of the assembly, minutes.

R_1,
R_2
and
R_n = The fire endurances of the individual wythes, minutes.

Values of $R_n^{0.59}$ for use in Equation 1 are given in Table No. 43-9-C-B.

R_1 MINUTES	$R^{0.59}$
60	11.20
90	14.22
120	16.85
180	21.41
240	25.37

3. The fire-resistance ratings of precast concrete wall panels consisting of a layer of foam plastic insulation sandwiched between two wythes of concrete may be determined by use of Equation 1. Foam plastic insulation with a total thickness of less than 1 inch shall be disregarded. The R_n value for thickness of foam plastic insulation of 1 inch or greater, for use in the calculation, is five minutes; therefore, $R_n^{0.59} = 2.5$.

(c) **Joints Between Precast Concrete Wall Panels.** Where openings in exterior walls are required to be protected, or where openings are not permitted in walls, the provisions of this section shall be used to determine the amount of joint insulation required.

Figure No. 43-9-C-2 shows thicknesses of ceramic fiber blankets to be used to protect joints between precast concrete wall panels for various panel thicknesses and for joint widths of 3/8 inch and 1 inch for fire-resistance ratings of one hour to four hours for joint widths between 3/8 inch and 1 inch, the thickness of ceramic fiber blanket may be determined by direct interpolation. Other approved tested and labeled materials may be used in place of ceramic fiber blankets.

Concrete Floor and Roof Slabs

Sec. 43.924. (a) **Reinforced and Prestressed Concrete Floor and Roof Slabs.** 1. The minimum thickness of reinforced and prestressed concrete floor or roof slabs for fire-resistance ratings of one hour to four hours are shown in Table No. 43-9-C-C.

2. For hollow-core prestressed concrete slabs in which the cores are of constant cross section throughout the length, the equivalent thickness may be obtained by dividing the net cross-sectional area of the slab, including grout in the joints, by its width.

3. The thickness of slabs with sloping soffits shall be determined at a distance $2t$ or 6 inches, whichever is less, from the point of minimum thickness, where t is the minimum thickness.

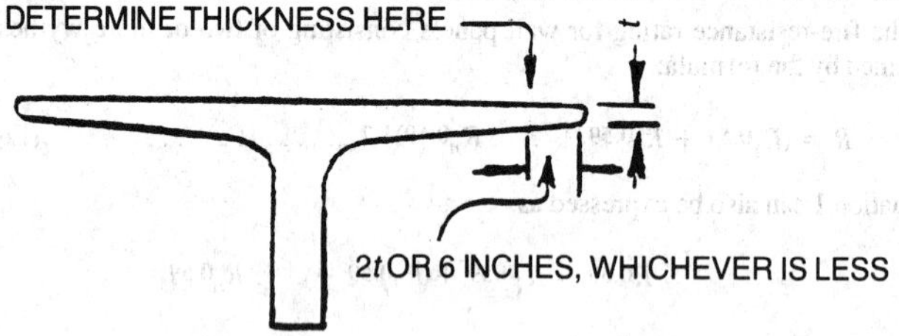
DETERMINE THICKNESS HERE
t
2t OR 6 INCHES, WHICHEVER IS LESS

4. The thickness of slabs with ribbed or undulating soffits shall be determined by one of the following expressions, whichever is applicable:

for $s \geqslant 4t$, the thickness to be used shall be t

for $s \leqslant 2t$, the thickness to be used shall be t_e

for $4t > s > 2t$, the thickness to be used shall be

$$t + \left(\frac{4t}{s} - 1\right)(t_e - t)$$

WHERE:

s = Spacing of ribs or undulations.

t = Minimum thickness.

t_e = Equivalent thickness of the panel calculated as the net cross-sectional area of the panel divided by the width in which the maximum thickness used in the calculation shall not exceed $2t$.

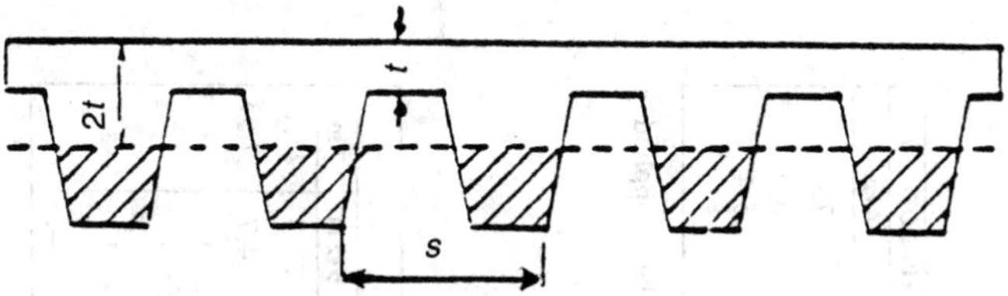
t
2t
s

NEGLECT SHADED AREA IN CALCULATION OF EQUIVALENT THICKNESS

(b) **Multicourse Floors and Roofs.** 1. Figure No. 43-9-C-3A gives information on the fire-resistance ratings of floors which consist of a base slab of concrete with a topping (overlay) of a different type of concrete.

2. Figure No. 43-9-C-3B gives information on the fire-resistance ratings of roofs which consist of a base slab of concrete with a topping (overlay) of an insulating concrete or with an insulating board and built-up roofing. Three-ply built-up roofing contributes 10 minutes to the fire-resistance rating; therefore, 10 minutes can be added to the assemblies shown in Figure No. 43-9-C-3B, Details (a), (b) and (c), but not to those shown in Figure No. 43-9-C-3B, Details (d) and (e).

(c) **Joints in Precast Slabs.** Joints between adjacent precast concrete slabs may be ignored in calculating the slab thickness, provided that a concrete topping at least 1 inch thick is used. Where no concrete topping is used, joints must be grouted to a depth of at least one third the slab thickness at the joint, but not less than 1 inch, or the joints must be made fire resistive by other approved methods.

Minimum Concrete Cover Requirements

Sec. 43.925. (a) **Slabs.** The minimum thickness of concrete cover to the positive moment reinforcement is given in Table No. 43-9-C-D for reinforced concrete and Table No. 43-9-C-E for prestressed concrete. Tables Nos. 43-9-C-D and 43-9-C-E are applicable for solid- or hollow-core one-way or two-way slabs with flat undersurfaces. Slabs may be cast-in-place or precast.

(b) **Beams.** 1. The minimum thickness of concrete cover to the positive moment reinforcement (bottom steel) for reinforced concrete beams is shown in Table No. 43-9-C-F for fire-resistance ratings of one hour to four hours.

2. The minimum thickness of concrete cover to the positive moment prestressing tendon (bottom steel) for prestressed concrete beams is shown in Table No. 43-9-C-G for fire-resistance ratings of one hour to four hours.

Concrete Columns

Sec. 43.926. (a) **Minimum Size.** Table No. 43-9-C-H shows the minimum overall dimensions of reinforced concrete columns for fire-resistance ratings of one hour to four hours.

(b) **Minimum Cover for Reinforced Concrete Columns.** The minimum cover to the main reinforcement in columns for fire-resistance ratings of one hour, one and one-half hours, two hours and three hours shall be $1^1/_2$ inches; for four-hour rating, the minimum cover to the main reinforcement shall be 2 inches for siliceous aggregate concrete and $1^1/_2$ inches for carbonate aggregate concrete or sand-lightweight concrete.

TABLE NO. 43-9-C-A
MINIMUM EQUIVALENT THICKNESS, INCHES, OF CAST-IN-PLACE OR PRECAST CONCRETE WALLS, LOAD BEARING OR NONLOAD BEARING

CONCRETE TYPE	MINIMUM WALL THICKNESS (INCHES) FOR FIRE-RESISTANCE RATING OF				
	1 Hr.	1 1/2 Hr.	2 Hr.	3 Hr.	4 Hr.
Siliceous[1]	3.5	4.3	5.0	6.2	7.0
Carbonate	3.2	4.0	4.6	5.7	6.6
Sand-lightweight	2.7	3.3	3.8	4.6	5.4
Lightweight	2.5	3.1	3.6	4.4	5.1

[1]The equivalent thickness may include the thickness of portland cement plaster or 1.5 times the thickness of gypsum plaster applied in accordance with the requirements of Chapter 47.

TABLE NO. 43-9-C-B
VALUES OF $R_n^{0.59}$ FOR USE IN EQUATION 1

TYPE OF MATERIAL	VALUES OF $R_n^{0.59}$ FOR USE IN EQUATION 1 FOR THICKNESS OF:											
	1 1/2 In.	2 In.	2 1/2 In.	3 In.	3 1/2 In.	4 In.	4 1/2 In.	5 In.	5 1/2 In.	6 In.	6 1/2 In.	7 In.
Siliceous aggregate concrete	5.3	6.5	8.1	9.5	11.3	13.0	14.9	16.9	18.8	20.7	22.8	25.1
Carbonate aggregate concrete	5.5	7.1	8.9	10.4	12.0	14.0	16.2	18.1	20.3	21.9	24.7	27.2[3]
Sand-lightweight concrete	6.5	8.2	10.5	12.8	15.5	18.1	20.7	23.3	26.0[3]	[3]	[3]	[3]
Lightweight concrete	6.6	8.8	11.2	13.7	16.5	19.1	21.9	24.7	27.8[3]	[3]	[3]	[3]
Insulating concrete[1]	9.3	13.3	16.6	18.3	23.1	26.5[3]	[3]	[3]	[3]	[3]	[3]	[3]
Air space[2]	—	—	—	—	—	—	—	—	—	—	—	—

[1]Dry unit weight of 35 pcf or less and consisting of cellular, perlite or vermiculite concrete.

[2]The $R_n^{0.59}$ value for 1/2 inch to 3 1/2 inches air space is 3.3. The $R_n^{0.59}$ value for 2 1/2 inches to 3 1/2 inches air space is 6.7.

[3]The fire-resistance rating for this thickness exceeds four hours.

TABLE NO. 43-9-C-C
MINIMUM SLAB THICKNESS FOR CONCRETE FLOORS OR ROOFS

CONCRETE TYPE	MINIMUM WALL THICKNESS (INCHES) FOR FIRE-RESISTANCE RATING OF				
	1 Hr.	1 1/2 Hr.	2 Hr.	3 Hr.	4 Hr.
Siliceous[1]	3.5	4.3	5.0	6.2	7.0
Carbonate	3.2	4.0	4.6	5.7	6.6
Sand-lightweight	2.7	3.3	3.8	4.6	5.4
Lightweight	2.5	3.1	3.6	4.4	5.1

[1]The equivalent thickness may include the thickness of portland cement plaster or 1.5 times the thickness of gypsum plaster applied in accordance with the requirements of Chapter 47.

TABLE NO. 43-9-C-D—COVER THICKNESS FOR REINFORCED CONCRETE FLOOR OR ROOF SLABS

CONCRETE AGGREGATE TYPE	THICKNESS OF COVER (INCHES) FOR FIRE-RESISTANCE RATING OF									
	Restrained[1]					Unrestrained[1]				
	1 Hr.	1 1/2 Hr.	2 Hr.	3 Hr.	4 Hr.	1 Hr.	1 1/2 Hr.	2 Hr.	3 Hr.	4 Hr.
Siliceous	3/4	3/4	3/4	3/4	3/4	3/4	3/4	1	1 1/4	1 5/8
Carbonate	3/4	3/4	3/4	3/4	3/4	3/4	3/4	3/4	1 1/4	1 1/4
Sand-lightweight	3/4	3/4	3/4	3/4	3/4	3/4	3/4	3/4	1 1/4	1 1/4
Lightweight concrete	3/4	3/4	3/4	3/4	3/4	3/4	3/4	3/4	1 1/4	1 1/4

[1]See Section 43.141 of U.B.C. Standard No. 43-1 for guidance on restrained and unrestrained assemblies.

TABLE NO. 43-9-C-E—COVER THICKNESS FOR PRESTRESSED CONCRETE FLOOR OR ROOF SLABS

CONCRETE AGGREGATE TYPE	THICKNESS OF COVER (INCHES) FOR FIRE-RESISTANCE RATING OF									
	Restrained[1]					Unrestrained[1]				
	1 Hr.	1 1/2 Hr.	2 Hr.	3 Hr.	4 Hr.	1 Hr.	1 1/2 Hr.	2 Hr.	3 Hr.	4 Hr.
Siliceous	3/4	3/4	3/4	3/4	3/4	1 1/8	1 1/2	1 3/4	2 3/8	2 3/4
Carbonate	3/4	3/4	3/4	3/4	3/4	1	1 3/8	1 5/8	2 1/8	2 1/4
Sand-lightweight	3/4	3/4	3/4	3/4	3/4	1	1 3/8	1 1/2	2	2 1/4
Lightweight concrete	3/4	3/4	3/4	3/4	3/4	1	1 3/8	1 1/2	2	2 1/4

[1]See Section 43.141 of U.B.C. Standard No. 43-1 for guidance on restrained and unrestrained assemblies.

TABLE NO. 43-9-C-F
MINIMUM COVER TO MAIN REINFORCING BARS FOR REINFORCED CONCRETE BEAMS (APPLICABLE TO ALL TYPES OF STRUCTURAL CONCRETE)

RESTRAINED OR UNRESTRAINED[1]	BEAM WIDTH[2] (Inches)	COVER THICKNESS (INCHES) FOR FIRE RESISTANCE RATING OF				
		1 Hr.	1 1/2 Hr.	2 Hr.	3 Hr.	4 Hr.
Restrained	5	3/4	3/4	3/4	1[1]	1 1/4[1]
Restrained	7	3/4	3/4	3/4	3/4	3/4
Restrained	≥ 10	3/4	3/4	3/4	3/4	3/4
Unrestrained	5	3/4	1	1 1/4	—	—
Unrestrained	7	3/4	3/4	3/4	1 3/4	3
Unrestrained	≥ 10	3/4	3/4	3/4	1	1 3/4

[1]See Section 43.141 of U.B.C. Standard No. 43-1 for guidance on restrained and unrestrained assemblies. Tabulated values for restrained assemblies apply to beams spaced more than 4 feet on centers; for restrained beams spaced 4 feet or less on centers, minimum cover of 3/4 inch is adequate for ratings of 4 hours or less.

[2]For beam widths between the tabulated values, the minimum cover thickness can be determined by direct interpolation.

TABLE NO. 43-9-C-G
MINIMUM COVER FOR PRESTRESSED CONCRETE BEAMS

RESTRAINED OR UNRESTRAINED[1]	CONCRETE AGGREGATE TYPE[2]	BEAM WIDTH[3] (Inches)	COVER THICKNESS[4] (INCHES) FOR FIRE RESISTANCE RATING OF				
			1 Hr.	1½ Hr.	2 Hr.	3 Hr.	4 Hr.
Restrained	Carb or Sil	8	1½	1½	1½	1¾[1]	2½[1]
Restrained	Carb or Sil	⩾12	1½	1½	1½	1½	1⅞[1]
Restrained	Sand LW	8	1½	1½	1½	1½	2[1]
Restrained	Sand LW	⩾12	1½	1½	1½	1½	1⅝[1]
Unrestrained	Carb or Sil	8	1½	1¾	2½	5[5]	—
Unrestrained	Carb or Sil	⩾12	1½	1½	1⅞	2½	3
Unrestrained	Sand LW	8	1½	1½	2	3¼	—
Unrestrained	Sand LW	⩾12	1½	1½	1⅝	2	2½

[1]See Section 43.141 of U.B.C. Standard No. 43-1 for guidance on restrained and unrestrained assemblies. Tabulated values for restrained assemblies apply to beams more than 4 feet on center.

[2]Carb = carbonate aggregate concrete; Sil = siliceous aggregate concrete; Sand LW = Sand lightweight concrete.

[3]For beam widths between 8 and 12 inches, minimum cover thickness can be determined by direct interpolation.

[4]The cover for an individual tendon is the minimum thickness of concrete between the surface of the tendon and the fire-exposed surface of the beam, except that for ungrouted ducts the assumed cover thickness is the minimum thickness of concrete between the surface of the duct and the surface of the beam. For beams in which several tendous are used, the cover is assumed to be the average of the minimum cover of the individual tendons. The cover for any individual tendon must be not less than one half of the value given in this table nor less than 1 inch.

[5]Not practical for 8-inch-wide beam, but shown for purposes of interpolation.

[6]This table shall not apply to I-shaped beams.

TABLE NO. 43-9-C-H
MINIMUM SIZES OF CONCRETE COLUMNS

TYPE OF CONCRETE	MINIMUM COLUMN DIMENSION (INCHES) FOR FIRE-RESISTANCE RATING OF				
	1 Hr.	1½ Hr.	2 Hr.	3 Hr.	4 Hr.
Siliceous	8	8	10	12	14
Carbonate	8	8	10	12	14
Sand-lightweight	8	8	9	10.5	12

FIGURE NO. 43-9-C-1
FIRE-RESISTANCE RATINGS OF TWO-WYTHE CONCRETE WALLS CONSISTING OF WYTHES OF DIFFERENT TYPES OF CONCRETE

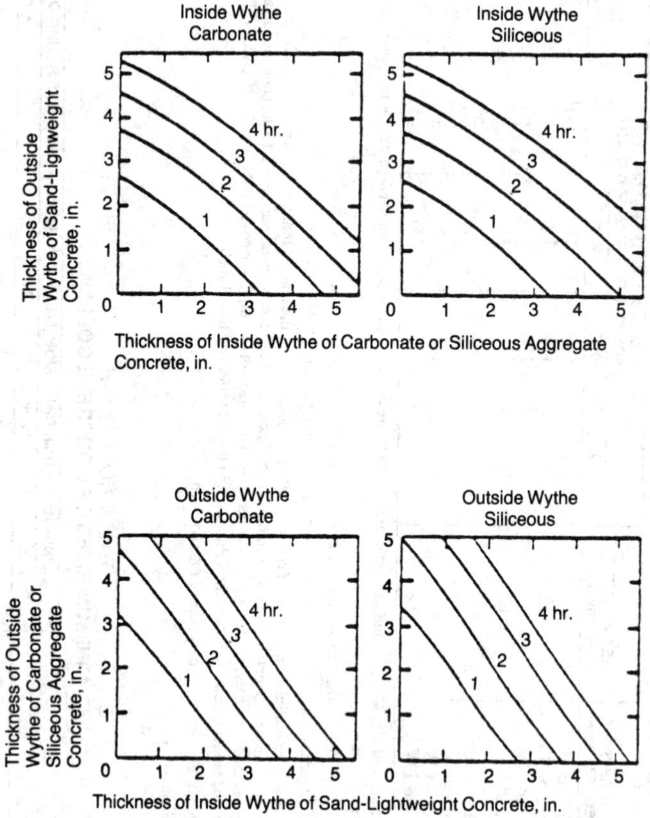
Inside Wythe
Carbonate
Inside Wythe
Siliceous
Thickness of Outside Wythe of Sand-Lighweight Concrete, in.
4 hr.
3
2
1
0
1
2
3
4
5
Thickness of Inside Wythe of Carbonate or Siliceous Aggregate Concrete, in.
Outside Wythe
Carbonate
Outside Wythe
Siliceous
Thickness of Outside Wythe of Carbonate or Siliceous Aggregate Concrete, in.
Thickness of Inside Wythe of Sand-Lightweight Concrete, in.

FIGURE NO. 43-9-C-2
MINIMUM THICKNESS OF CERAMIC FIBER BLANKET REQUIRED BETWEEN PRECAST CONCRETE WALL PANELS TO PROVIDE FIRE-RESISTANCE RATINGS OF 1 HOUR TO 4 HOURS

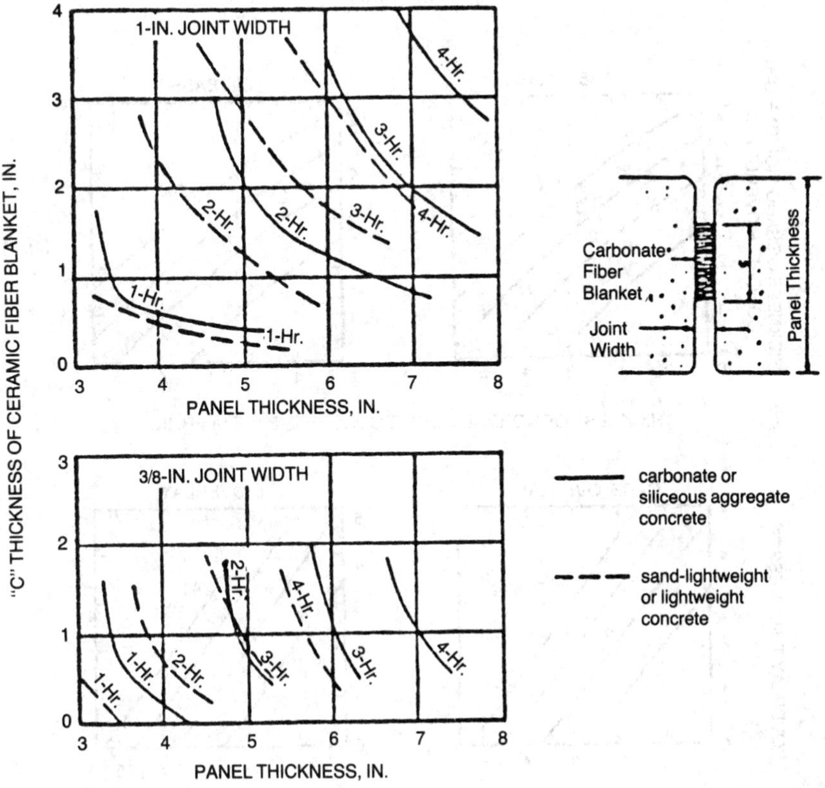
"C" THICKNESS OF CERAMIC FIBER BLANKET, IN.
1-IN. JOINT WIDTH
1-Hr.
2-Hr.
3-Hr.
4-Hr.
PANEL THICKNESS, IN.
3/8-IN. JOINT WIDTH
Carbonate Fiber Blanket
Joint Width
Panel Thickness
carbonate or siliceous aggregate concrete
sand-lightweight or lightweight concrete

FIGURE NO. 43-9-C-3A
FIRE-RESISTANCE RATINGS FOR TWO-COURSE CONCRETE FLOORS

Symbols: Carb = carbonate aggregate concrete; Sil = siliceous aggregate concrete

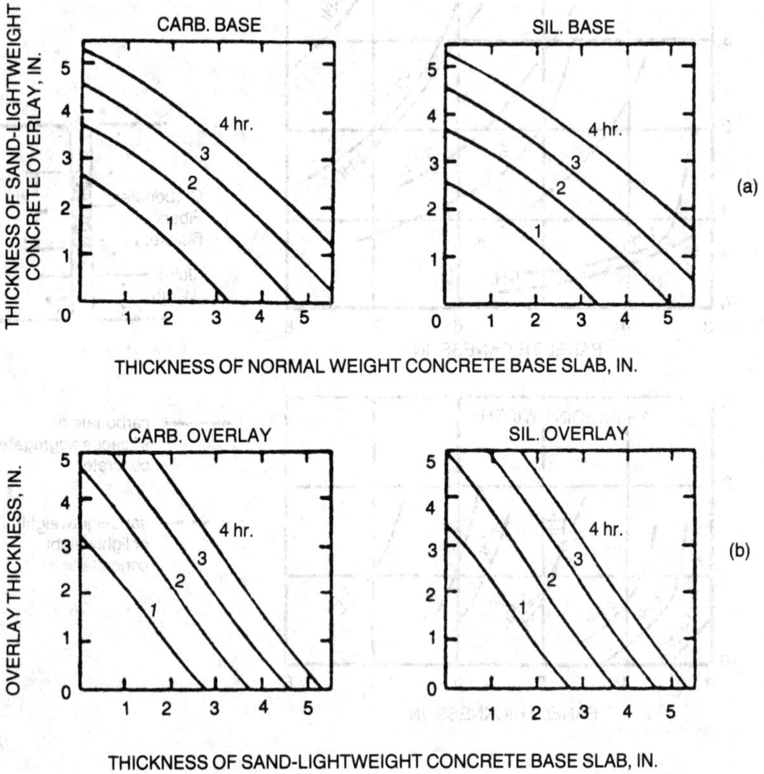
CARB. BASE
SIL. BASE
THICKNESS OF SAND-LIGHTWEIGHT CONCRETE OVERLAY, IN.
4 hr.
3
2
1
(a)
THICKNESS OF NORMAL WEIGHT CONCRETE BASE SLAB, IN.
CARB. OVERLAY
SIL. OVERLAY
OVERLAY THICKNESS, IN.
(b)
THICKNESS OF SAND-LIGHTWEIGHT CONCRETE BASE SLAB, IN.

FIGURE NO. 43-9-C-3B
FIRE-RESISTANCE RATINGS FOR CONCRETE ROOF ASSEMBLIES

Symbols: Carb = carbonate aggregate concrete; Sil = siliceous aggregate concrete; SLW = sand-lightweight concrete

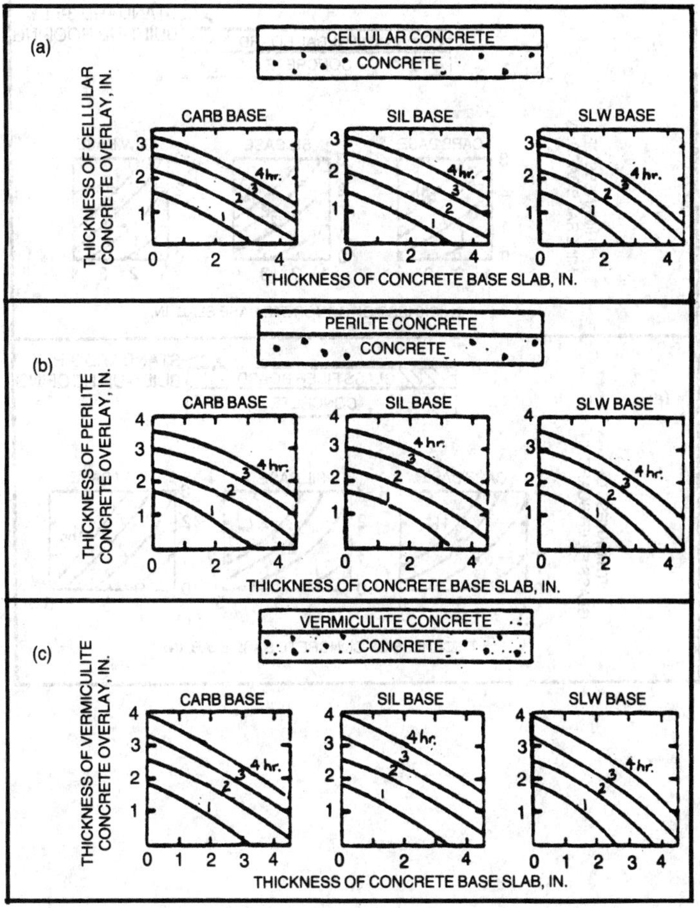

(a)
CELLULAR CONCRETE
CONCRETE
THICKNESS OF CELLULAR CONCRETE OVERLAY, IN.
CARB BASE
SIL BASE
SLW BASE
4 hr.
3
2
1
THICKNESS OF CONCRETE BASE SLAB, IN.
(b)
PERILTE CONCRETE
CONCRETE
THICKNESS OF PERLITE CONCRETE OVERLAY, IN.
CARB BASE
SIL BASE
SLW BASE
THICKNESS OF CONCRETE BASE SLAB, IN.
(c)
VERMICULITE CONCRETE
CONCRETE
THICKNESS OF VERMICULITE CONCRETE OVERLAY, IN.
CARB BASE
SIL BASE
SLW BASE
THICKNESS OF CONCRETE BASE SLAB, IN.

(Continued)

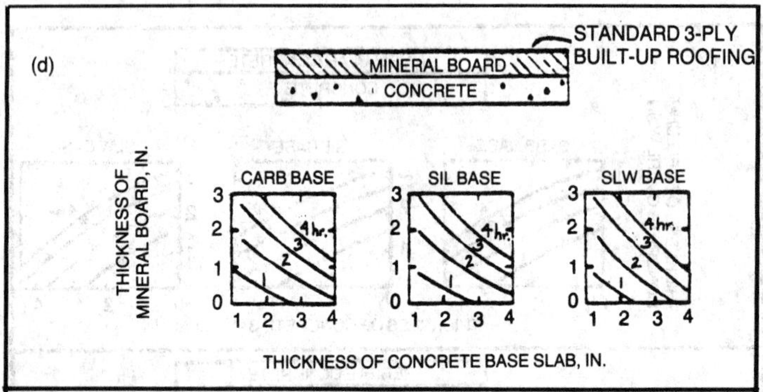
(d)
STANDARD 3-PLY BUILT-UP ROOFING
MINERAL BOARD
CONCRETE
THICKNESS OF MINERAL BOARD, IN.
CARB BASE
SIL BASE
SLW BASE
4 hr.
3
2
1
THICKNESS OF CONCRETE BASE SLAB, IN.

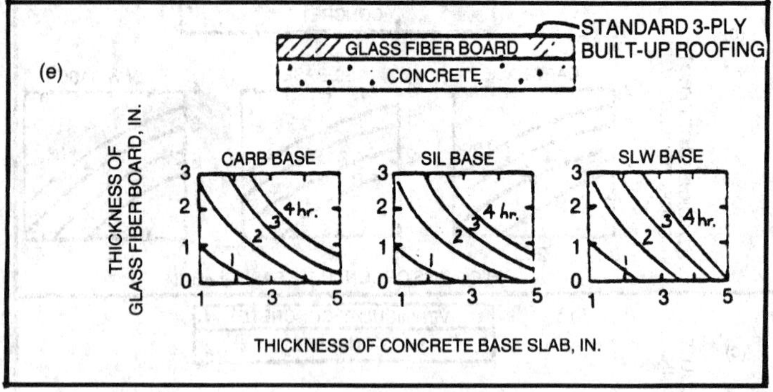
(e)
STANDARD 3-PLY BUILT-UP ROOFING
GLASS FIBER BOARD
CONCRETE
THICKNESS OF GLASS FIBER BOARD, IN.
CARB BASE
SIL BASE
SLW BASE
4 hr.
3
2
1
THICKNESS OF CONCRETE BASE SLAB, IN.

Part III
METHODS FOR CALCULATING FIRE RESISTANCE OF WOOD-FRAMED WALLS, FLOORS AND ROOFS
See Section 4302 (c), Uniform Building Code

Scope

Sec. 43.931. This part establishes acceptable calculation methods for determining the fire-resistive classification of structural parts, walls and partitions and floor-ceiling or roof-ceiling assemblies. It is intended for use in cases where fire test results specified in U.B.C. Standard No. 43-1 are not available and the specific assembly of materials is not among those listed Tables Nos. 43-A, 43-B and 43-C.

Wood-framed Walls, Floors and Roofs

General

Sec. 43.932. These procedures apply to both load-bearing and nonbearing construction. The calculated fire-resistive ratings shall only apply to one-hour construction. When the wall construction is nonsymmetrical, the provisions of Section 4304 (d) of the Building Code apply.

Procedures

Sec. 43.933. The fire-resistive rating of wood-framed construction is equal to the sum of the time assigned to the membrane on the fire-exposed side (Table No. 43-9-W-A), the time assigned to the framing members (Table No. 43-9-W-C), and the time assigned for other protective measures, such as insulation (Table No. 43-9-W-D). The membrane on the unexposed side shall not be included in determining the fire resistance of the assembly. When more than one membrane is installed on the wall surface exposed to fire, ratings of each membrane may be added.

Walls and Partitions

Sec. 43.934. Table No. 43-9-W-A lists the time of fire resistance accredited to the materials used on the fire-exposed side of walls and partitions.

Roof-Ceiling and Floor-Ceiling Assemblies

Sec. 43.935. Table No. 43-9-W-B specifies the various acceptable membranes and limits the structural frame to wood joists installed on no more than 16-inch spacings. Ratings for roof-ceiling and floor-ceiling assemblies are based on the membranes listed in Table No. 43-9-W-A being installed on the fire-exposed side in combination with membranes listed in Table No. 43-9-W-B being installed on the side not exposed to furnace temperatures.

Membrane Fastening

Sec. 43.936. Fastening the membrane to the supporting construction shall be as specified in Tables Nos. 43-B, 43-C and 25-Q of the code for corresponding membrane materials.

TABLE NO. 43-9-W-A
TIME ASSIGNED TO WALLBOARD MEMBRANES[1, 2, 4]

DESCRIPTION OF FINISH	TIME, MIN.
$^3/_8$-inch Exterior-glue plywood	5
$^1/_2$-inch Exterior-glue plywood	10
$^5/_8$-inch Exterior-glue plywood	15
$^3/_8$-inch gypsum wallboard	10[3]
$^1/_2$-inch gypsum wallboard	15
$^5/_8$-inch gypsum wallboard	30
$^1/_2$-inch Type X gypsum wallboard	25
$^5/_8$-inch Type X gypsum wallboard	40
Double $^3/_8$-inch gypsum wallboard	25
$^1/_2$ + $^3/_8$-inch gypsum wallboard	35
Double $^1/_2$-inch gypsum wallboard	40

[1]All wall panels shall be installed with the long dimension parallel to framing members or shall be backed with at least 2-inch-thick framing and gypsum panels.

[2]These values apply only when framing members are spaced a maximum of 16 inches on center.

[3]Membrane rating combined with stud rating is 25.

[4]Plywood membranes shall be limited to nonbearing applications. Other membranes shall be limited to the design stress for studs shown by Footnote 14 to Table No. 43-B

TABLE NO. 43-9-W-B
FLOORING OR ROOFING OVER WOOD FRAMING

ASSEMBLY	STRUCTURAL MEMBERS	SUBFLOOR OR ROOF DECK	FINISH FLOORING OF ROOFING
Floor	Wood joists	$^1/_2$-inch plywood or $^{11}/_{16}$-inch tongue-and-groove softwood	Hard or softwood flooring on building paper. Resilient flooring, parquet floor, felted-synthetic-fiber floor coverings, carpeting or ceramic tile on $^5/_8$-inch-thick panel-type underlay. Ceramic tile on $1^1/_4$-inch mortar bed.
Roof	Wood joists	$^1/_2$-inch plywood or $^{11}/_{16}$-inch tongue-and-groove softwood	Finish roofing material with or without insulation. See Section 4305 (a) for the addition of insulation.

TABLE NO. 43-9-W-C
TIME ASSIGNED FOR CONTRIBUTION OF WOOD FRAME[1 2]

DESCRIPTION OF FRAME	TIME ASSIGNED TO FRAME, MIN.
Wood studs 16 inches o.c.	20
Wood floor and roof joists 16 inches o.c.	10

[1]This table does not apply to studs or joists spaced more than 16 inches o.c.

[2]All studs shall be nominal 2 inches by 4 inches and all joists shall have a nominal thickness of at least 2 inches.

TABLE NO. 43-9-W-D
TIME ASSIGNED FOR ADDITIONAL PROTECTION

DESCRIPTION OF ADDITIONAL PROTECTION	FIRE RESISTANCE, MINUTES
Add to the fire-resistance rating of wood stud walls if the spaces between the studs are filled with rock-wool batts weighing not less than 1.0 lb./ft.^{2} (3.3 lb./ft.^{3}) or glass-wool batts at 0.6 lb./ft.^{2} (2.0 lb./ft.^{3}) wall surface.	15

PART IV
METHOD FOR DESIGN OF ONE-HOUR FIRE-RESISTIVE EXPOSED WOOD MEMBER (6-INCH NOMINAL OR GREATER)
See Section 4302 (c), Uniform Building Code

Scope

Sec. 43.941. Part IV of this standard applies to the design of one-hour fire-resistive exposed solid-sawn and glued-laminated timbers described in Chapter 25. The timbers shall have a minimum nominal thickness of 6 inches.

This design method for one-hour fire-resistive exposed wood members is an accepted method of determining fire-resistive construction as specified in Section 4302 (c) of the Building Code.

Design Procedures

Sec. 43.942. Design procedures, loads and allowable design stresses shall be as specified in Chapter 23 and Chapter 25. In addition, the column or beam shall be analyzed to determine the size required to sustain the design load at the end of a one-hour fire. This design procedure is specified in Section 43.943.

Calculation of Timber Size

Sec. 43.943. The following procedure shall be used to establish the fire rating of columns or beams and to determine the size required to be treated as one hour.

The fire-resistance rating, in minutes, of timber beams and columns with a minimum nominal dimension of 6 inches is equal to:

Beams—

1. $2.54\,Zb\,[4-2(b/d)]$ for beams which may be exposed to fire on four sides.
2. $2.54\,Zb\,[4-(b/d)]$ for beams which may be exposed on three sides.

Columns—

3. $2.54\,Zd\,[3-(d/b)]$ for columns which may be exposed to fire on four sides.
4. $2.54\,Zd\,[3-(d/2b)]$ for columns which may be exposed to fire on three sides. (Applies only when the smaller side of the column is the exposed face.)

WHERE:

b = the breadth (width) of a beam or larger side of a column before exposure to fire, inches.

d = the depth of a beam or smaller side of a column before exposure to fire, inches.

Z = load factor (Figure No. 43-9-1).

K_e = the effective length factor (Figure No. 43-9-2).

ℓ = the unsupported length of column, inches (Figure No. 43-9-1).

If a column is recessed into a wall and protected, its minimum dimension need not be calculated using this procedure.

Acceptance Criteria of Construction

Sec. 43.944. In addition to sizing the timber, the following conditions shall be met:

1. The minimum nominal width or thickness is 6 inches.
2. Connectors and fasteners relating to the support of the member shall be protected for equivalent fire resistance. When the minimum one-hour fire endurance is required, connectors and fasteners shall be protected from fire exposure by not less than

1 1/2 inches of wood, fire-rated gypsum board or any coating approved for one-hour rating.

3. For structural integrity of glued-laminated timbers, one additional lamination of 2-inch thickness shall be placed on the tension face of the beam and shall be equivalent in quality to that required by the design for the outer tensile lamination. The additional lamination on the tension face shall replace a core lamination to maintain the same design depth required in Section 43.943.
4. Glued-laminated timber shall be marked "Fire-rated One-hour" by the manufacturer to indicate compliance with Item 3.

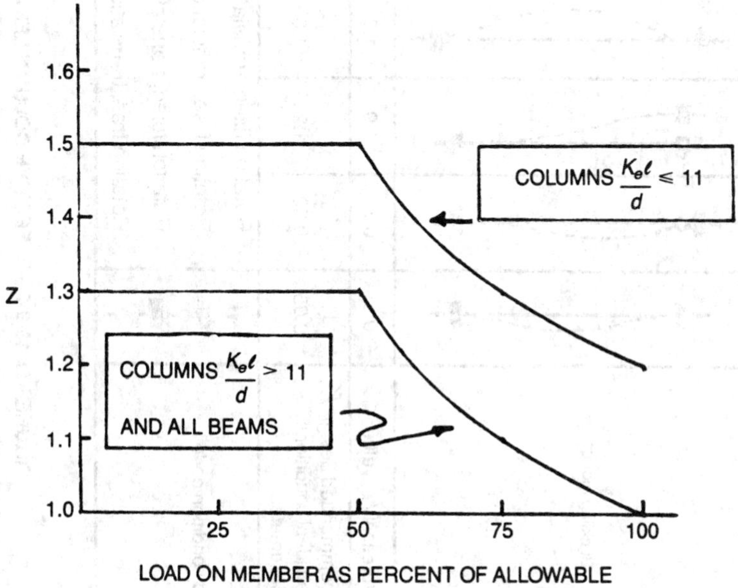
1.6
1.5
1.4
Z 1.3
1.2
1.1
1.0
COLUMNS $\frac{K_e \ell}{d} \leq 11$
COLUMNS $\frac{K_e \ell}{d} > 11$
AND ALL BEAMS
25
50
75
100
LOAD ON MEMBER AS PERCENT OF ALLOWABLE

FIGURE NO. 43-9-1—LOAD FACTOR

Buckling modes	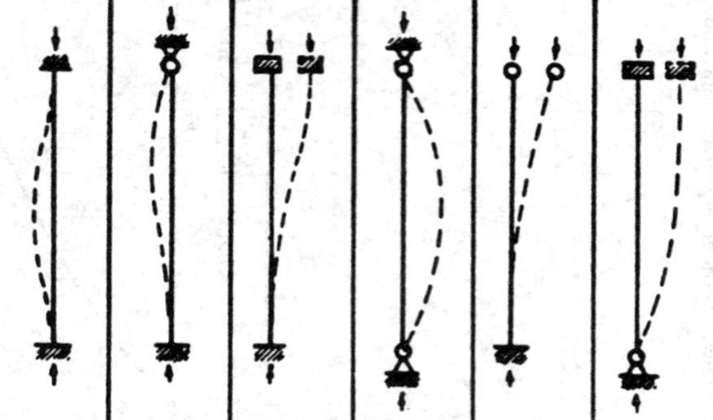					
Theoretical K_e value	0.5	0.7	1.0	1.0	2.0	2.0
Recommended design K_e when ideal conditions approximated	0.65	0.80	1.2	1.0	2.10	2.4
End condition code		Rotation fixed, translation fixed Rotation free, translation fixed Rotation fixed, translation free Rotation free, translation free				

FIGURE NO. 43-9-2—EFFECTIVE COLUMN LENGTH

UNIFORM BUILDING CODE STANDARD NO. 43-12

SMOKE DAMPERS

Based on Standard for Leakage-rated Damper for Use in Smoke-control Systems 555S, September 14, 1983, of Underwriters Laboratories Inc.

See Sections 4306 (j) and 4309, Uniform Building Code

General

Sec. 43.1201. (a) **Scope.** These requirements cover leakage-rated dampers intended for use in heating, ventilating and air-conditioning (HVAC) systems. Leakage-rated dampers are intended (1) to restrict the spread of smoke in HVAC systems that are designed to be automatically shut down in the event of a fire or (2) to control the movement of smoke within a building when the HVAC system is operational in engineered smoke-control systems.

(b) **General.** A component of a product covered by this standard shall comply with the requirements for that component and shall be used in accordance with its recognized rating and other limitations of use.

Installation and Operating Instructions

Sec. 43.1202. Installation and operating instructions shall be shipped with each damper by the manufacturer. Instructions shall be illustrated and shall include detailed directions and information adequate for the intended installation and operation of the product. Instructions shall cover mounting, sealing, wiring, opening and closing torque requirements, and duct-joining methods, if applicable, and shall be in accordance with the Mechanical Code.

The instructions are to be used as a guide in the examination and test of the product. A printed edition is required upon successful completion of the test program.

The instructions shall include recommended means of sealing the damper to ductwork or damper frame, or both.

Materials

Sec. 43.1203. (a) **General.** All electrical components, damper operators/actuators, fusible links and temperature-responsive devices shall be examined and tested as required for their intended function. Test methods shall be approved methods.

(b) **Corrosion Protection.** A ferrous metal part used in the damper assembly shall be one of the 300 Series of stainless steel or shall be provided with one of the following corrosion-protection systems:

1. A coating of hot-dipped mill-galvanized sheet steel complying with the coating designation G60 or A60 by the hot-dip process, with not less than 40 percent of the zinc on any side, based on the minimum single-spot test requirement.

2. A zinc coating, other than that provided on hot-dipped mill-galvanized sheet steel, uniformly applied to an average thickness of not less than 0.00041 inch on each surface with a minimum thickness of 0.00034 inch.
3. A cadmium coating not less than 0.0005 inch thick on both surfaces.
4. Two coats of an organic finish of the epoxy or alkyd-resin type or other outdoor paint on each surface. The acceptability of the paint may be determined by its composition or by corrosion tests.

Coated or uncoated metals used in the assembly of dampers shall be galvanically compatible.

Component springs and bearings used in the assembly of dampers shall be of material having resistance to atmospheric corrosion equivalent to brass or bronze.

A hot-dipped mill-galvanized A60 (alloyed) coating or an annealed zinc coating that is bent or similarly formed after annealing, including extruded and rolled edges and holes, and that is not otherwise required to be painted, shall be painted in the bent or formed area if the bending or forming process damages the zinc coating. If flaking or cracking of the zinc coating at the outside radius of the bent or formed section is visible at 25 power magnification, the zinc coating is to be considered damaged. Simple sheared or cut edges and punched holes are not considered to be formed.

Performance

Sec. 43.1204. (a) **General.** Three samples representative of each design or design variation, including all operational components, are to be subjected to the tests set forth in this section. The representative samples, which are intended to cover a range of damper sizes for one specific design, are to consist of (1) minimum width and maximum height, (2) maximum width and minimum height, and (3) maximum width and maximum height. In addition, two dampers, consisting of the largest and smallest sizes, are to be subjected first to the dust-loading test and then to the salt-spray test. As an option, two dampers may be subjected to the dust loading test and two additional dampers subjected independently to the salt-spray exposure test. Any component variations within the design size range may require additional samples and tests.

Both the dust-loading exposure test, Section 43.1204 (f), and the salt-spray exposure test, Section 43.1204 (g), are intended to simulate the dust and other debris that may accumulate on a damper mounted in a duct within a building, and investigate the performance of the damper while subjected to such accumulations.

(b) **Cycling Test.** A damper intended for use with an operator/actuator (that is, the electric, pneumatic or hydraulic device used to operate the damper) shall function as intended after being mechanically operated for 5,000 full-stroke (that is, close and reopen) operations, while using the recommended damper operator/actuator and while operating without duct-system pressure. For a damper intended for use without an operator/actuator, the number of full-stroke operations is to be 250 and the damper is to be cycled manually. All dampers are to be cycled while mounted in the position intended for installation.

(c) **Temperature Degradation/Cycling Test.** A damper (including any operator/actuator) that is recommended for temperatures other than ambient is to be subjected to this test prior to the leakage test. The selected elevated temperatures are to be in increments of 100°F., and the minimum temperature is to be 250°F.

A test damper (including any operator/actuator) previously subjected to the cycling test, Section 43.1204 (b), is to be exposed to the selected elevated temperature, ±5 percent for 30 minutes in the closed position.

After the 30-minute period and while at the selected elevated temperature, the damper shall function as intended while being operated through three complete operation cycles. A damper is to be operated mechanically, or if it is intended for use with an operator/actuator, cycled by using the operator/actuator that has also been subjected to the test temperature.

(d) **Leakage Test.** The amount of leakage measured during this test shall determine the leakage class of the damper, in accordance with the limitations in Table No. 43-12-A.

The dampers used for this test are to be those previously subjected to the cycling test, Section 43.1204 (b), and, if applicable, to the temperature degradation/cycling test, Section 43.1204 (c). Each damper is to be sealed against one face of an airflow measurement apparatus and cycled open and closed three times with its operator/actuator, or manually cycled if the damper is not intended for use with an operator/actuator. Prior to the test the manufacturer's recommended torque (plus 5, minus 0 percent) is to be applied to a damper intended for use with an operator/actuator. Ambient air then is to be supplied within the chamber at a rate required to maintain the specified test pressure differential (±5 percent) across the dampers. The resultant air leakage through the damper, corrected to standard temperature and pressure conditions, is to be determined using approved instrumentation and procedures. A damper intended for use without restriction as to the direction of airflow is to be tested on both sides.

The test pressures are to be 1.0 and 4.0 inches of water for all dampers. Extended range tests may be performed and reported at 8 inches, 12 inches, or both, of water at the request of the damper manufacturer.

There shall be no extrapolations above the maximum test pressures or beyond the minimum and maximum test sizes.

The damper area is to be determined from the nominal outside frame dimensions of the damper for an internal mounted damper and from the nominal inside frame dimensions for a flange-mounted damper.

The damper under test is to be mounted in the plane in which it is intended to be used and in accordance with the manufacturer's installation guidelines. A flange-mounted damper may be flange-mounted directly to the test chamber wall. For an internal-mounting damper, the test chamber wall is to be fitted with a short section of ductwork for mounting the damper. Ductwork is not to extend more than 9 inches beyond damper frame and is not to interfere with the test. A sealing means is to be used to avoid air leakage around ductwork or damper frame. Any mounting holes provided on the damper but not used are to be plugged if they provide a path for air leakage around the damper.

(e) **Operation Test.** Following completion of the leakage test, Section 43.1204 (d), and under conditions of maximum recommended airflow, the dampers shall function as intended without damage to the dampers or their components and shall completely close during each of three opening and closing cycles. The test pressure differential created in the closed position is to be recorded and shall be not less than the leakage classification rating (that is, 4, 8 or 12 inches of water). See Table No. 43-12-A. The instrumentation and procedures for all types of dampers are to be in accordance with approved standards.

The device under test is to be mounted as intended. The airflow direction is to be in the direction of normal flow through the device. If normal flow can be in either direction, and if the device reacts differently when flow is in one direction than it does when flow is in the opposite direction, the device is to be tested with the flow first in one direction, then in the other direction.

A damper intended for use with an operator/actuator is to be opened and closed by using the recommended operator/actuator. A damper not intended for use with an operator/actuator shall be manually closed using the intended releasing device and manually reopened.

(f) **Dust-loading Exposure Test.** A damper assembly shall close and latch automatically (if a latch is provided) following exposure for seven hours to an air-blown circulating grain dust-air mixture. The grain dust shall pass through a 100-mesh screen. A sample of the largest size (up to 46 inches wide by 42 inches high for vertical dampers and up to 28 inches wide by 46 inches long for horizontal dampers) and the smallest size damper are to be tested.

The test chamber is to be provided with observation windows and with auxiliary equipment to produce a circulating grain dust-air mixture. Nozzles are to be provided to direct the dust-air mixture toward the sample, and the dust particles are to be allowed to accumulate on the various parts of the damper assembly.

At the conclusion of the dust-loading exposure, the test sample is to be removed from the chamber, placed in its intended mounting position and tested for closing and latching (if a latch is provided).

(g) **Salt-spray Exposure Test.** A damper assembly shall close and latch automatically (if a latch is provided) following exposure for a period of five days to salt spray when tested as described in this section. Both the largest size (up to 46 inches wide by 42 inches high for vertical dampers and up to 28 inches wide by 46 inches long for horizontal dampers) and smallest size dampers are to be tested.

Prior to test, all dust grease or oil is to be removed from the test sample using organic solvents.

The test sample is to be installed in the test chamber with the damper open and supported in the position of intended use and exposed to the salt spray for 120 hours in accordance with approved methods, except that the salt solution is to consist of 20 percent by weight of common salt (sodium chloride) and distilled water. The pH value of this solution as collected after spraying in the test apparatus is to be between 6.5 and 7.2 and the specific gravity between 1.126 and 1.157 at 95°F. The temperature of the sample and the test chamber is to be maintained at 95 plus 2, minus 3°F. throughout the test period.

At the conclusion of the salt-spray exposure, the test sample is to be removed from the chamber and allowed to dry for 24 hours at room temperature. It then is to be placed in its intended mounting position and tested for closing and latching (if a latch is provided).

In cases where excessive buildup of zinc chloride has occurred due to reaction of the salt with galvanized steel coatings, such parts may be painted and a second sample subjected to test.

Classification

Sec. 43.1205. (a) **General.** The highest leakage obtained on the three representative samples tested in accordance with Section 43.1204 (d) shall be considered as the leakage classification for the overall design, as specified in Table No. 43-12-A.

Leakage at the prescribed pressure differentials shall be no greater than the values shown in Table No. 43-12-A within each classification.

Published ratings of performance shall be an accurate statement of the actual leakage flow of air (corrected to standard temperature and pressure conditions) at the specified pressure differential. The maximum degradation test temperature shall also be specified in the classification.

Classifications at pressure differentials of 8 or 12 inches of water shall be identified as "extended static range" classifications.

**TABLE NO. 43-12-A
LEAKAGE CLASSIFICATIONS**

	LEAKAGE, foot^3/minimum/foot^2	
Classification	**At 1.0 Inch Water**	**At 4.0 Inches Water**
0	0	0
I	4	8
II	10	20
III	40	80
IV	60	120
Extended Static Range	**At 8 Inches Water**	**At 12 Inches Water**
0	0	0
I	11	14
II	28	35
III	112	140
IV	168	210

Marking

Sec. 43.1206. Each damper (or each damper unit in a multiple assembly) shall be marked at a location that will be visible after installation with the following:

1. The manufacturer's or private labeler's name.

2. Model number or identifying symbol.
3. Date of manufacture which may be in code.
4. Arrow showing direction of airflow.
5. Installation mode—vertical and/or horizontal.
6. Leakage classification in accordance with Table No. 43-12-A.
7. Statement as to degradation test temperature—"Degradation Test Temperature __*__."
8. Maximum rated airflow rate and static pressure differential across the closed damper (4, 8 or 12 inches of water).
9. Required opening and closing torque (to be consistent with the torque required in Sections 43.1204 (d) and (e) and the intended operator/ actuator).

Damper operators/actuators shall be marked with their electrical ratings if electrical, or the maximum pressure rating if pneumatic or hydraulic.

If a manufacturer produces dampers at more than one factory, each damper shall have a distinctive marking to identify it as the product of a particular factory.

*Temperature indicated shall be ambient or the tested exposure temperature as specified in Section 43.1204 (c).

UNIFORM BUILDING CODE STANDARD NO. 43-13

HORIZONTAL SLIDING FIRE DOORS USED IN AN EXIT

Test Standard of the International Conference of Building Officials

See Sections 1002 (b) and 3304 (h), Uniform Building Code

Scope

Sec. 43.1301. This standard covers performance criteria and conditions for horizontal sliding fire doors in exits.

Application

Sec. 43.1302. Compliance with these conditions permits use of horizontal fire doors in areas specifically authorized by the code.

General

Sec. 43.1303. Installation shall be in accordance with manufacturer's instructions and nationally recognized standards.

Construction

Sec. 43.1304. Door assemblies shall be fire rated in accordance with U.B.C. Standard No. 43-2, and shall have a Class I interior finish rating. The door's power operating system shall be approved and listed. The power operating system shall be housed in a fire-resistive enclosure of the same rating as the door.

Operation

Sec. 43.1305. The door shall be power operated, be capable of manual operation in the event of power failure and be self-closing or smoke-detector-activated automatic closing. The door's power supply shall be capable of being electrically supervised at a constantly attended location and the door shall have an emergency power supply. Actuating devices shall be installed on both sides of the door and shall be inhibited from opening the door if the temperature on either side exceeds 500°F. The door shall be equipped with sensors capable of detecting obstructions in its closing path and of signaling such detection at the door location or at a constantly attended location. Automatic closing of the door or trouble conditions shall cause an audible alarm to be sounded at the door location. The alarm shall also be capable of being sounded at a constantly attended location. Operation of the activating device while the door is opening shall cause it to return to the closed position.

Performance

Sec. 43.1306. (a) **Power Operation.** The power operating system shall be examined in accordance with nationally recognized standards and shall be listed. The test report shall contain engineering data relative to tests for normal operation, electrical supervision, input and output, jarring, temperature, charging current, battery charger, undervoltage and overvoltage, standby operating power, variable ambient temperature, humidity, leakage current, transient, overload, endurance, dielectric withstand and abnormal operation. The report shall describe the mechanical operation of the power operating system in sequence as the door opens and closes under normal and emergency conditions. It shall set forth the tests performed in accordance with nationally recognized standards and the results thereof. The report shall additionally contain an analysis comparing each feature of the design against the performance test procedures.

(b) **Automatic-closing Test.** Upon receipt of the initiating device signal, the power operating system shall move the door to the closed position. The door shall begin closing within 10 seconds of receiving the signal. Closing speed shall not be less than 6 inches or more than 24 inches per second.

(c) **Ease of Operation Test.** Manufacturers shall provide a test report from an approved independent authority that the door is easily recognized and operable for its intended usage without a key, special knowledge or effort.

The actuating device shall be subjected to a measurable force load. The force shall be applied to the actuating device in the direction of egress travel (perpendicular to the door). The force to cause the actuating device to signal the power operating system to open the door shall not be more than 15 pounds.

(d) **Self-contained Power Test.** Doors equipped with a self-contained power supply shall be subjected to cycle testing. One cycle shall be defined as the time to completely close the door from the open position and return it to the open position. The self-contained power supply shall have sufficient capacity to operate the door 50 cycles without the aid of outside power.

(e) **Manual Operation Test.** With all power disconnected, and with the door in the closed position, 30 pounds of force or less shall be applied in the direction of door travel to initiate the door opening. With a sustained force of 15 pounds or less, the door shall open to the specified open distance but not less than 44 inches.

(f) **Temperature Override Test.** The door shall include temperature-sensing devices installed at the leading edge approximately 12 inches from the top of the door. These devices shall be subjected to a measurable temperature. When the temperature exceeds 500°F., the actuating devices shall be deactivated and shall not cause the door to open.

(g) **Lateral Load Test.** A lateral load shall be applied to the door in the direction of egress travel. The total load shall be equivalent to 250 pounds of force distributed over a minimum of 5 points over the total area of the closed door at locations at least 3 feet but not more than 6 feet from the floor. Under this condition, the door must meet the conditions of the ease of operation test outlined in Section 43.1306 (c).

(h) **Opening Speed.** The door shall open to a distance of 88 inches within 10 seconds after activation of the actuating device.

Conditions of Acceptance

Sec. 43.1307. A door shall be considered as meeting the requirements for acceptable performance when it conforms to the tests under Section 43.1306.

Marking

Sec. 43.1308. (a) **Label.** Doors shall bear fire-rating labels issued by a listing agency showing compliance with U.B.C. Standards Nos. 43-2 and 43-13. The label shall be of metal attached to the assembly by welding, brazing, riveting or contact adhesive.

(b) **Label Markings.** The markings on the label shall include the following:

1. Name and address of the listee.
2. Model number or type.
3. Symbol, serial or issue number issued by the listing agency.

UNIFORM BUILDING CODE STANDARD NO. 52-2

CHAMBER METHOD OF TEST FOR MEASURING THE DENSITY OF SMOKE FROM THE BURNING OR DECOMPOSITION OF PLASTIC MATERIALS

Based on Standard Test Method D 2843-70 of the American Society for Testing and Materials. Extracted, with permission, from the Annual Book of ASTM Standards, copyright American Society for Testing and Materials, 1916 Race Street, Philadelphia, PA 19103.

See Sections 417 and 520 (f), Uniform Building Code; and Section 212, Uniform Sign Code

Scope

Sec. 52.201. This method of test covers a procedure for measuring and observing the relative amounts of smoke produced by the burning or decomposition of plastics. It is intended to be used for measuring the smoke producing characteristics of plastics under controlled conditions of combustion or decomposition. The measurements are made in terms of the loss of light transmission through a collected volume of smoke produced under controlled, standardized conditions. The apparatus is constructed so that the flame and smoke can be observed during the test.

Summary of Method

Sec. 52.202. A 1-inch by 1-inch specimen of the thickness intended for use is placed on a supporting metal screen and it is burned in a laboratory test chamber (see Figure No. 52-2-1) under active flame conditions using a propane burner operating at a pressure of 40 psi. The 12-inch by 12-inch by 31-inch test chamber is instrumented with a light source, a photoelectric cell, and a meter to measure light absorption horizontally across the 12-inch light beam path. The chamber is closed during the four-minute test period except for the 1-inch-high ventilation openings around the bottom.

The light absorption data are plotted versus time. A typical plot is shown in Figure No. 52-2-2.

Significance

Sec. 52.203. This test method is designed to permit the measurement of smoke generation and of its visibility-obscuring effects (density). Results of tests made on a plastic material under conditions herein prescribed can be used to evaluate the smoke production characteristics by determining the smoke density rating of the material. The smoke density rating shall represent the total amount of smoke present in the chamber for the four-minute time interval. It is the area under the curve of light absorption versus time divided by the total area of the graph times 100.

The visual and instrumental observations from this test compare well with the visual observations of the smoke generated by plastic materials when added to a freely burning, large outdoor fire, burning conditions that are favorable to minimum smoke production. Hence, this method serves as a reliable method of identifying materials which could be expected to smoke excessively under almost all conditions of burning and decomposition.

The basic assumption underlying this procedure is that the hazard associated with smoke in human occupancies will be significant only if a material is burning or decomposing in the presence of flame. Therefore, the test specimen is exposed to flame for the duration of the test and the smoke is substantially trapped in the chamber in which combustion occurs. The usefulness of this test procedure is in its ability to measure the amount of smoke produced in a simple, direct and meaningful manner.

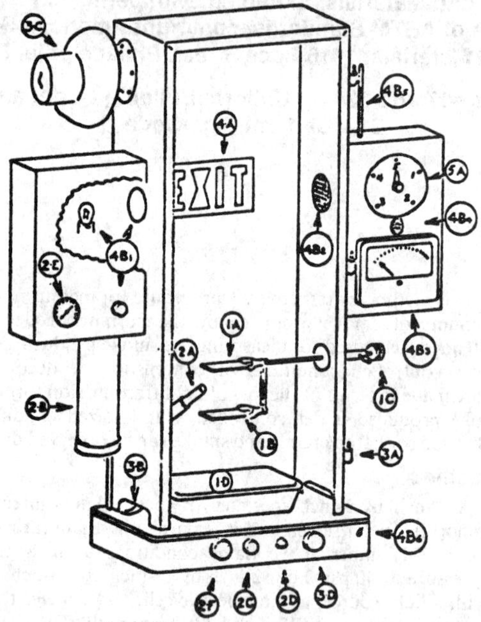
EXIT
4A
5A
1A
2A
1C
2B
1B
3A
3B
1D
2F
2C
2D
3D

FIGURE NO. 52-2-1—SCHEMATIC DIAGRAM OF SMOKE CHAMBER

1. Specimen Holder
   - A. Stainless Steel Screen
   - B. Asbestos Sheet
   - C. Adjusting Knob
   - D. Quench Pan
2. Ignition
   - A. Burner
   - B. Propane Tank
   - C. Gas Shutoff Valve
   - D. Pressure Regulator Adjustment
   - E. Pressure Indicator
   - F. Burner Positioning Knob
3. Cabinet (shown without door)
   - A. Hinges (Door gasketed three sides)
   - B. Vents (1-inch High Opening four sides)
   - C. Blower (Damper on mounting side)
   - D. Control (Blower on when damper is open)
4. Photometer
   - A. Visual System (Exit sign)
   - B. Measuring System
     1. Light Source and Adjusting Transformer
     2. Photronic Cell and Grid (To block stray light)
     3. Meter (Indicating percent to light absorbed)
     4. Temperature Compensation
     5. Photocell Temperature Monitor
     6. Range Change
5. Timer
   - A. Indicator, 0 to 5 minutes (Friction reset)

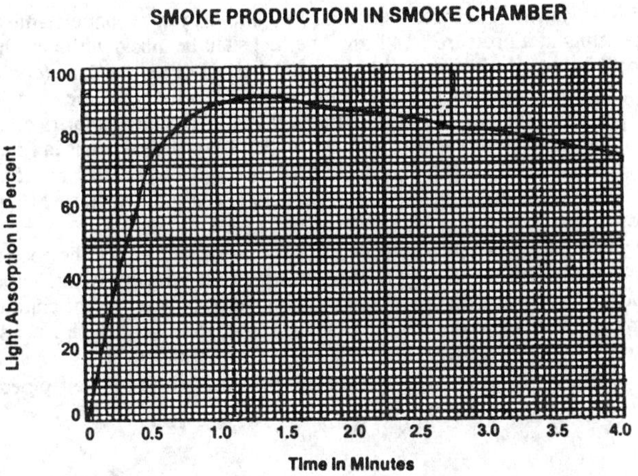
SMOKE PRODUCTION IN SMOKE CHAMBER
Light Absorption in Percent
100
80
60
40
20
0
0
0.5
1.0
1.5
2.0
2.5
3.0
3.5
4.0
Time in Minutes

FIGURE NO. 52-2-2—LIGHT ABSORPTION VERSUS TIME

Apparatus

Sec. 52.204. (a) **The Chamber.** The chamber shall consist of a No. 14 gage (B. & S.) 12-inch by 12-inch by 31-inch aluminum box to which is hinged a heat-resistant glazed glass door. This box shall be mounted on a 14-inch by 16-inch by 2¼-inch base which houses the controls. Dependent upon the materials tested, the metal may require protection from corrosion.

The chamber shall be sealed except for 1-inch by 9-inch openings on the four sides of the bottom of the chamber. A 60 CFM blower shall be mounted on one side of the chamber. The inlet duct to the blower shall be equipped with a close-fitting damper. The outlet of the blower shall be connected through a duct to the laboratory exhaust system.

The two sides adjacent to the door shall be fitted with 2¾-inch-diameter smoke tight glazed areas centered 19¾ inches above the base. At these locations and outside the chamber, boxes containing the optical equipment and additional controls shall be attached.

A removable white plastic plate shall be attached to the back of the chamber. There shall be a 3½-inch by 6-inch clear area centered about 19¾ inches above the bottom of the chamber through which is seen an illuminated white-on-red exit sign. The white background permits observation of the flame, smoke and the burning characteristics of the material. The viewing of the exit sign helps to correlate visibility and measured values.

(b) **The Specimen Holder.** The specimen shall be supported on a 2½-inch square of 4-by-4 mesh, 0.035-inch-gage stainless steel wire cloth 8 inches above the base and equidistant from all sides of the chamber. This screen shall lie in stainless steel bezel supported by a rod through the right side of the chamber. From the same rod, a similar bezel shall be located 3 inches below and it shall support a square of asbestos paper which catches any particles that may drip from the specimen during the test. By rotating the specimen holder rod, the burning specimen can be quenched in a shallow pan of water positioned below the specimen holder.

(c) **Ignition System.** The specimen shall be ignited by a propane flame from a burner operating at a pressure of 40 psi. The fuel shall be mixed with air which has been propelled through the burner by the venturi effect of the propane (commercial grade 85.0 percent minimum, gross heating value 2590 Btu per cubic foot propane meets the requirements) as it passes from a 0.006-inch-diameter orifice, and the burner shall be assembled as shown in the exploded view of the burner in Figure No. 52-2-3. The burner must be designed to provide adequate outside air. Since the orifice provides the metering effect proportionate to the supply pressure, care must be taken that the orifice is the only means of fuel egress.

The burner shall be capable of being quickly positioned under the specimen so that the axis of the burner falls on a line passing through a point $\frac{3}{10}$ inch above the base at one back corner of the chamber extending diagonally across the chamber and sloping upward at 45 degrees with the base. The exit opening of the burner shall be $10\frac{7}{32}$ inches from the reference point at the rear of the chamber.

A duct at least 6 inches outside of the chamber shall provide the air piped to the burner.

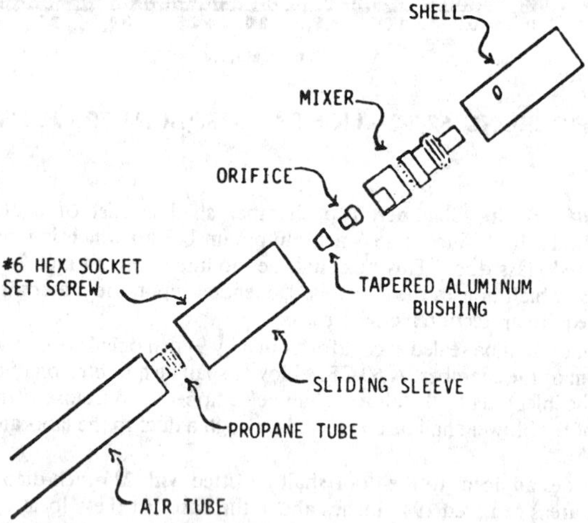
SHELL
MIXER
ORIFICE
#6 HEX SOCKET
SET SCREW
TAPERED ALUMINUM
BUSHING
SLIDING SLEEVE
PROPANE TUBE
AIR TUBE

FIGURE NO. 52-2-3—EXPLODED VIEW OF THE BURNER

Propane pressure shall be adjustable and preferably automatically regulated. Propane pressure shall be indicated by means of a Bourdon tube gage.

(d) **Photometric System.** A light source, a barrier-layer photoelectric cell and a temperature compensated meter shall be used to measure the proportion of a light beam which penetrates a 12-inch path through the smoke. The light path shall be arranged horizontally as shown in Figure No. 52-2-4.

A light source shall be mounted in a box (4 B1 Figure No. 52-2-1) extending from the left side of the chamber at the mean height of 19¾ inches above the base. The light source shall be a compact filament microscope lamp No. 1493 operated at 5.8 volts and a spherical reflector, with power supplied by a voltage regulating transformer. (The microscope lamps No. 1493 are manufactured by General Electric Company, Westinghouse and others.) A 63.5 (2½-inch) focal length lens shall focus a spot of light on the photocell in the right instrument panel.

Another box containing the photometer (4 B2 in Figure No. 52-2-1) shall be attached to the right side of the chamber. The barrier-layer photoelectric cell shall have standard observer spectral response. An egg-crate grid in front of the photocell shall be used to protect the cell from stray light. The grid shall be finished in dull black and have openings at least twice as deep as they are wide. The current produced by the photocell is indicated in terms of percent light absorption on a meter. The photocell linearity decreases as the temperature increases; compensations shall therefore be made.

The meter may have two ranges. The range change shall be accomplished by shunting the meter to one-tenth its sensitivity. When smoke accumulates to absorb 90 percent of the light beam, a momentary switch shall be depressed returning the meter to its basic sensitivity. By doing this the meter scale now reads 90 to 100 percent instead of 0 to 100 percent.

(e) **Timing Device.** A clock to indicate 15-second intervals shall be used. If the time intervals are audible it will be convenient for the operator to record his observations.

(f) **Planimeter.** A planimeter or other suitable means shall be used for measuring the area under the light absorption curve.

Test Specimens

Sec. 52.205. The specimen shall be 1 inch by 1 inch by the thickness intended for use. Thicknesses other than those intended for use may be tested and the thickness should be reported with the smoke density values.

The specimens shall be sanded, machined or die cut in a manner that produces a cut surface that is free from projecting fibers, chips and ridges.

The test sample shall consist of three specimens.

Conditioning

Sec. 52.206. Specimens shall be preconditioned and tested in accordance with Procedure A of the ASTM Method D618-61 for Method of Conditioning Plastics and Electrical Insulating Materials for Testing, unless otherwise specified.

Tests shall be conducted in a hood which has a window for observing the test.

Procedure

Sec. 52.207. Turn on photometer lamp, exit sign, and exhaust blower.

Turn on propane, ignite burner and adjust the propane pressure to 40 psi. Caution: Do not fail to light burner immediately.

Set temperature compensation.

Adjust lamp control to zero percent light absorption.

Lay the test specimen flat on the screen in such a position that the burner flame will be directly under the specimen when the burner is swung into position.

Set the timer to zero.

Shut off the exhaust blower, close the smoke chamber door and immediately position the burner under the specimen and start the timer.

Close the hood door to within 2 inches of the bottom of the hood.

Record the percent light absorbed at 15-second intervals for four minutes.

Record observations during the conduct of the test. Include the time it takes for the sample to burst into flame, time for flame extinguishment or specimen consumption, the obscuration of the exit sign by smoke accumulation and any general or usual burning characteristics noted such as melting, dripping, foaming or charring.

FIGURE NO. 52-2-4—SMOKE DENSITY TEST CHAMBER PHOTOMETER

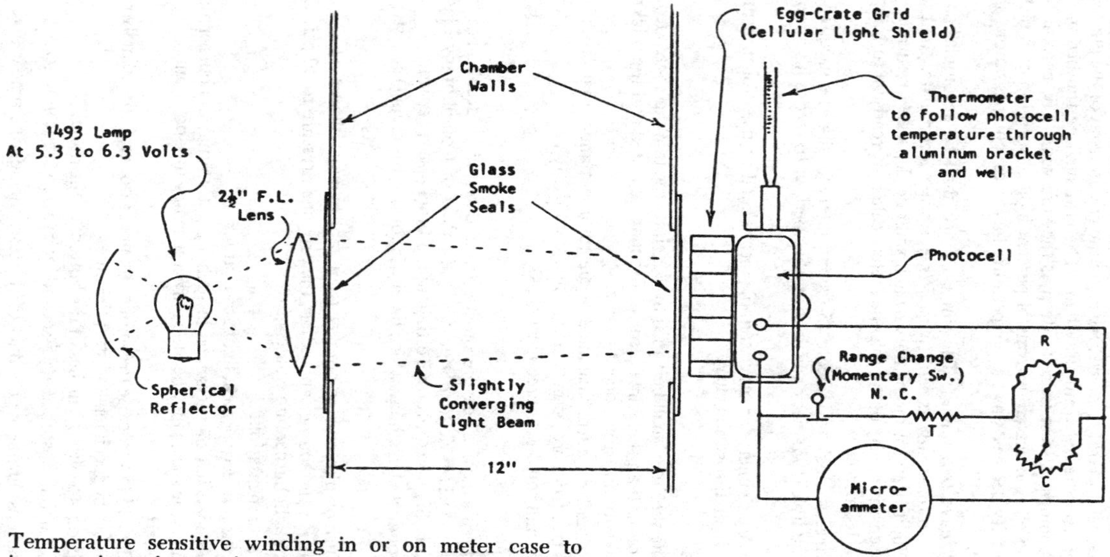
Egg-Crate Grid
(Cellular Light Shield)
Chamber
Walls
Thermometer
to follow photocell
temperature through
aluminum bracket
and well
1493 Lamp
At 5.3 to 6.3 Volts
Glass
Smoke
Seals
2½" F.L.
Lens
Photocell
R
Range Change
(Momentary Sw.)
N. C.
T
C
Spherical
Reflector
Slightly
Converging
Light Beam
12"
Micro-
ammeter

T = Temperature sensitive winding in or on meter case to increase in resistance in proportion to increase in meter resistance with temperature.

R = Potentiometer with calibrated scale to reduce resistance in proportion to decrease in photocell output with rise in temperature.

C = Potentiometer to calibrate total resistance of shunt to change meter sensitivity exactly by 10:1 ratio.

Upon completion of the test, turn on exhaust blower to ventilate the combustion products from the chamber. (It should be noted that for some materials the product of burning may be toxic, and care should be taken to guard the operator from the effects of these gases. The ventilating fan in the hood should be turned on and the damper opened immediately after the test is completed before opening the hood door in order to remove any irritating products of the test. The exhaust fan is turned off and the hood damper closed during the test to prevent back draft.)

Open the door and clean the combustion deposits from the photometer, exit sign and door glass with detergent and water. Burn off any material remaining on the screen or replace the screen and asbestos square for the next test.

Run all tests in triplicate.

Optional Procedures

Sec. 52.208. The output of the photocell may be recorded versus time on an appropriate graphic recorder.

With a suitably sensitive meter, more than one decade change may be used to separate readings in the very dense smoke range.

Treatment of Data

Sec. 52.209. The readings of 15-second intervals of light absorption for the three specimens per group shall be averaged. The average light absorption shall be plotted against time on linear paper. Figure No. 52-2-2 is a sample curve.

The total smoke produced shall be determined by measuring the area under the curve. The smoke density rating shall represent the total amount of smoke present in the chamber for the four-minute time interval. It is the area under the curve of light absorption versus time divided by the total area of the graph times 100.

Report

Sec. 52.210. The report shall include the following:

Identification of the material.

Thickness of the specimen.

Readings of light absorption at 15-second intervals for each test and average.

Plots of average light absorption versus time.

Area in percent under the light absorption-time curve (smoke density rating).

Observations on behavior of material.

Observations on obscurement of exit sign.

The details of any departure from the specifications of the method of testing.

EXAMPLE: In the light absorption-time plot in Figure No. 52-2-2, the plot has been made using 1 inch equal to 30 percent as the ordinate and 1 inch equal to 0.75 minute as the abscissa. The graph area for four minutes is found to be 17.78 square inches. The area under the curve is found to be 14.02 square inches. The smoke density rating is then computed as follows:

$$\text{Smoke Density Rating} = \frac{14.02}{17.78} \times 100$$

$$\text{in percent} = 78.8$$

UNIFORM BUILDING CODE STANDARD NO. 54-1

FLAT GLASS

Based on ASTM Standard C 1036-85

Standard Specification for Flat Glass. Extracted, with permission, from the Annual Book of ASTM Standards, copyright American Society for Testing and Materials, 1916 Race Street, Philadelphia, PA 19103.

See Sections 5401 (b) and (d), and 5406 (c), and Graphs 54-1 and 54-2, Uniform Building Code

Scope

Sec. 54.101. This standard provides general material requirements for glass regulated by the Building Code.

Definitions

Sec. 54.102. FLOAT GLASS is glass formed in a continuous ribbon by floating molten glass on a bath of molten tin in a controlled atmosphere; the glass is smooth with parallel surfaces and requires no further treatment.

FULLY TEMPERED GLASS is regular glass that has been heated and quenched in a controlled operation to provide a high level of surface compression; its strength is roughly four times that of regular glass for most types of loads; when fractured it breaks into small relatively harmless particles; it is a safety glazing material.

HEAT-STRENGTHENED GLASS is regular glass that has been heated and quenched in a controlled operation to provide a degree of surface compression; its strength is roughly two times that of regular glass; when fractured this glass breaks into large fragments, much like regular glass; it is not a safety glazing material.

INSULATING GLASS is factory-fabricated double glazing with the periphery of the air space sealed to minimize infiltration of water vapor.

LAMINATED GLASS is a sandwich of two or more glass plies bonded together with a resilient plastic interlayer, normally polyvinyl butyral; when this glass breaks, the fragments are held together by the plastic interlayer.

PATTERNED GLASS is a rolled glass with a pattern or texture impressed on one or both surfaces; some glasses with shallow patterns can be tempered or heat strengthened.

REGULAR (ANNEALED) GLASS is sheet (window) glass and plate glass with smooth surfaces that have not been modified after manufacture; it breaks into large pieces; although the terms "sheet" and "plate glass" are commonly used, they are misnomers since virtually all glass is made by the float process; this glass may be clear or tinted.

SAFETY GLASS is glass designed to minimize cutting and piercing injuries when impacted by people; fully tempered glass, laminated glass and wired glass are recognized safety glazing materials.

TEMPERED GLASS see **FULLY TEMPERED GLASS.**

WIRED GLASS is a single sheet of glass which has had a wire mesh embedded in roughly the thickness center during production; this glass, coupled with a suitable framing system is fire rated; for low levels of impact, the wire in the glass will retain the broken fragments.

Design Criteria

Sec. 54.103. The maximum allowable areas of glass subjected to wind loads, snow loads and dead loads shall not be greater than those determined from Tables Nos. 54-A and 54-B.

Table No. 54-1-A lists the coefficients of variation for various glass types. These values are used as part of the basis for Tables Nos. 54-A through 54-D. Each value applies for all glass products using each glass type. For example, the value for annealed glass would apply for laminated annealed glass and insulating glass units using annealed glass panes, as well as for single annealed glass.

Table No. 54-1-B lists the relative strengths of various glass for short term (wind) loads and long term (snow, dead) loads. These are used as part of the basis for Tables Nos. 54-A through 54-D. As with the coefficients of variation in Table No. 54-1-A, these values apply for all products using each glass type.

In cases where more than one glass type is used in a fabricated glass product (e.g., laminated glass, insulating glass) the more conservative values from Tables Nos. 54-1-A and 54-1-B apply.

Float Glass

Sec. 54.104. (a) **Thickness.** For each nominal thickness, the furnished glass thickness shall not be less than listed in Table No. 54-1-C.

(b) **Allowable Imperfections.** Imperfections shall not exceed those allowed in Table No. 54-1-D.

Wired Glass

Sec. 54.105. (a) **Wire.** The diameter of wires shall be from 0.017 to 0.025. Discoloration and slight distortion of wire is permissible.

(b) **Mesh Diamond.** Diamond mesh shall be welded, opening in mesh shall not exceed 1 1/4 inches measured across diagonals of diamond; square shall be welded, openings in mesh shall not exceed 5/8 inch measured along a side of the square; parallel stand—spacing as specified.

(c) **Thickness.** The minimum thickness shall not be less than listed in Table No. 54-1-E.

Patterned Glass

Sec. 54.106. (a) **Thickness.** The thickness shall not be less than listed in Table No. 54-1-F for each nominal thickness.

(b) **Fire Cracks and Stones.** Glass shall not have continuous fire cracks and stones that can cause spontaneous breakage in annealed glass.

A Glossary of Terms for Glass Imperfections

Sec. 54.107. CRUSH is a lightly pitted area resulting in a dull gray appearance over the region.

DIGS are deep, short scratches.

DIRT is a small particle of foreign matter imbedded in the glass surface.

GASEOUS INCLUSIONS are round or elongated bubbles in the glass.

KNOT is a transparent area of incompletely assimilated glass having an irregular knotty or tangled appearance.

LINES are fine cords or strings, usually on the surface of sheet glass.

OPEN GASEOUS INCLUSIONS are bubbles at the surface of glass which are open leaving a cavity in the finished surface.

PROCESS SURFACE DEFECTS. The surfaces of plate glass have very fine surface defects remaining from the grinding and polishing process consisting of fine pits and cracks which are denoted as "finish." When this condition is visible it is called "short finish." Float glass can also have some slight surface defects which originate in the process. These can be small particles of foreign materials on either surface or slight defects in the bottom (float) surface.

REAM is inclusions within the glass or layers or strings of glass which are not homogeneous with the main body of the glass.

RUBS are abrasions of the glass surfaces producing a frosted appearance. A rub differs from a scratch in having appreciable width.

SCRATCHES are any marking or tearing of the surface produced in manufacturing or handling which appear as though they were done by a sharp or rough instrument.

SMOKE is streaked areas appearing as slight discoloration.

STONES are any crystalline inclusions embedded in the glass.

STRINGS are transparent lines appearing as though a thread of glass had been incorporated into the sheets.

WAVES are defects resulting from irregularities of the surface of glass making objects viewed at varying angles appear wavy or bent.

TABLE NO. 54-1-A
COEFFICIENTS OF VARIATION FOR GLASS STRENGTH

GLASS TYPE	COEFFICIENT OF VARIATION
Regular (annealed)	0.25
Heat-strengthened	0.15
Fully tempered	0.10

TABLE NO. 54-1-B

GLASS TYPE	SHORT-TERM STRENGTH / LONG-TERM STRENGTH
Regular (annealed)	2.0
Heat-strengthened	1.5
Fully tempered	1.2

TABLE NO. 54-1-C
MINIMUM ALLOWABLE THICKNESSES FOR FLOAT GLASS

NOMINAL THICKNESS OR DESIGNATION (Inches)	MINIMUM ALLOWABLE THICKNESS (Inches)
Single	0.085
Lami	0.102
Double-$^1/_8$ in.	0.115
$^5/_{32}$ in.	0.149
$^3/_{16}$ in.	0.180
$^7/_{32}$ in.	0.200
$^1/_4$ in.	0.219
$^5/_{16}$ in.	0.292
$^3/_8$ in.	0.355
$^1/_2$ in.	0.469
$^5/_8$ in.	0.595
$^3/_4$ in.	0.719
$^7/_8$ in.	0.844

TABLE NO. 54-1-D
MAXIMUM ALLOWABLE IMPERFECTIONS FOR THICKNESSES OF 1/4 INCH OR LESS[1]

IMPERFECTIONS	UP TO 2.5 m^2		2.5 TO 7.0 m^2		OVER 7.0 m^2	
	Central[2]	Outer[2]	Central[2]	Outer[2]	Central[2]	Outer[2]
Gaseous inclusions, maximum size[3]	1.6 mm[4,5]	2.4 mm[4,5]	3.2 mm[4,5]	4.8 mm[4,5]	6.4 mm[4,5]	6.4 mm[4,5]
Open or translucent gaseous inclusions, maximum size[3]	1.2 mm[4,5]	1.6 mm[4,5]	1.2 mm[4,5]	1.6 mm[4,5]	6.4 mm[4,5]	6.4 mm[4,5]
Knots, dirt and stones, maximum size[3]	0.4 mm[4]	0.8 mm[4]	1.6 mm[4]	1.6 mm[4]	3.2 mm[4]	3.2 mm[4]
Scratches and rubs (intensity)	medium[7]	medium[7]	medium[7]	heavy[7]	heavy[7]	heavy[7]
Crush (intensity, maximum length)	medium[7] <1.6 mm	medium[7] <2.4 mm	medium[7] <3.2 mm	heavy[7] <4.8 mm	heavy[7] <6.4 mm	heavy[7] <6.4 mm
Digs, maximum length	1.6 mm[6]	2.4 mm[6]	3.2 mm[4]	4.8 mm[4]	6.4 mm[4]	6.4 mm[4]
Ream, strings, lines and other linear distortion (maximum angle or intensity)	45°[8] or medium[9]		90°[8] or heavy		90°[8] or heavy	
Wave (intensity)	medium[10]	medium[10]	medium[10]	heavy[10]	heavy[10]	heavy[10]
Process surface imperfections (intensity)	medium[11]	medium[11]	medium[11]	heavy[11]	heavy[11]	heavy[11]

[1]Glass greater than 6.0 mm (1/4 in.) in thickness may contain proportionally more and larger imperfections.

[2]The central area is considered to form an oval or circle centered on the light whose axes or diameters do not exceed 80 percent of the overall dimension. The remaining area is considered the outer area.

[3]Gaseous inclusions, knots, dirt and stones may be round or elongated. For elongated imperfections of this type(s) the maximum size specified shall be determined by adding the length and width of the imperfection and dividing by two, for example $(l + 11)/2$.

[4]Separated by at least 305 mm (12 in.).

[5]For imperfections of a smaller size or of less intensity, the minimum separation shall be proportionately less. The larger of the two imperfections shall govern the separation. Imperfections not specifically mentioned shall be compared to the imperfection they most closely resemble.

[6]Separated by at least 610 mm (24 in.).

[7]*Intensity (scratches, rubs and crush)*—When looking through the glass and perpendicular to it using daylight without direct sunlight or with background light suitable for observing each type of imperfection, the imperfection shall not be detectable at distances greater than the following, except for heavy intensity (see Note 3).

Intensity	**Distance**
Faint	203 mm
Light	914 mm
Medium	3.3 m
Heavy	detected at distances greater than 3.3 m

[8]Vision interference angle (see Note 1).

[9]*Intensity (ream, strings, lines and other linear distortion)*—When evaluated using the shadowgraph, the intensities of these imperfections are defined as having a shadowgraph readout at distances greater than or equal to the following (see Note 2).

Intensity	**Minimum Distance, mm**
Light	76
Medium	51
Heavy	25

[10]*Intensity (wave)*—When evaluated using the shadowgraph, the intensities of wave are defined as having shadowgraph readouts at distances greater than or equal to the following (see Note 2).

Intensity	**Minimum Distance, mm**
Medium	254
Heavy	152

[11]*Intensity (process surface imperfections)*—When viewed in normal reflected light, the imperfections are classified as follows: faint—visible only to the trained eye; light—just noticeable; medium—visible as a slight grayish haze; and heavy—readily visible as a cloudy surface.

(Continued)

(Continued)

Note 1—*Ream, Strings and Distortion (Method A)*—Place specimen in a vertical position at a distance of approximately 914 mm from a brick wall or similar background showing straight lines. The viewer shall look through the sample at a distance of 914 mm from the sample using daylight without direct sunlight or with background light suitable for observing each type of imperfection. View the sample at an angle to the surface of not less than vision interference angle in Table No. 54-1-D, for the applicable glass. The line of vision shall be perpendicular to the wall.

Note 2—*Ream, Strings, Lines and Wave (Method B, Shadowgraph)*—Focus a light projector with a 500-W lamp, or equivalent, and an objective lens with an approximate 51-mm aperture and an approximate 305-mm focal length on a flat white projection screen positioned 8 m from the light source in a dark room. Place the glass in a vertical position parallel to the screen between the light and the screen. Move the glass slowly toward the screen with a circulating motion in the plane perpendicular to the light beam. The shadowgraph readout is the distance at which the distortion just blends with the general shadow of the glass on the screen.

Note 3—*Scratches, Rubs, Stones and Gaseous Inclusions*—Place samples in a vertical position approximately 914 mm from the viewer's position. The viewer shall look through the sample using daylight without direct sunlight or with background light suitable for observing each type of imperfection.

TABLE NO. 54-1-E
MINIMUM ALLOWABLE THICKNESSES FOR WIRED GLASS

NOMINAL THICKNESS (Inches)	MINIMUM ALLOWABLE THICKNESS (Inches)
7/32	0.203
1/4	0.250
3/8	0.328

TABLE NO. 54-1-F
MINIMUM ALLOWABLE THICKNESSES FOR PATTERNED GLASS

NOMINAL THICKNESS OR DESIGNATION (Inches)	MINIMUM ALLOWABLE THICKNESS (Inches)
SS	0.085
DS	0.110
1/8	0.110
5/32	0.142
3/16	0.172
7/32	0.203
1/4	0.234
5/16	0.281
3/8	0.344

UNIFORM BUILDING CODE STANDARD NO. 54-2

SAFETY GLAZING

Part I

Based on Safety Standard for Architectural Glazing Materials (16 C.F.R., Part 1201) of the United States Consumer Product Safety Commission

See Sections 5401 (b) and (d); 5406 (b), (c) and (e); and 5408 (a), Uniform Building Code

Scope

Sec. 54.201. Part I of this standard covers safety glazing materials for use in areas subject to human impact as specified in the Uniform Building Code. Part I is applicable to safety glazing material other than polished wired glass or glazing in wardrobe doors.

Definitions

Sec. 54.202. For the purpose of this part, the definitions in Section 54.102 of U.B.C. Standard No. 54-1 are applicable.

Identification

Sec. 54.203. Each light of safety glazing material shall be identified in accordance with Sections 5402 and 5406 (b) of the Uniform Building Code and in addition with the following:

1. The category class as noted in Table No. 54-2-A shall be specified as part of a permanent label.
2. Safety plastic that only meets the requirements of Section 54.206 (d) entitled "Aging Tests (for plastics used in indoor applications only)" shall bear a statement INDOOR USE ONLY as part of a permanent label.
3. Organic-coated glass that meets the requirements of Section 54.206 (c) 2, entitled "Specimen weathering and test—organic-coated glass" and tested for exposure from one side only shall bear a permanent label on the coating stating GLAZE THIS SIDE IN and shall bear in the central 50 percent of the surface area the following message in letters at least ¼ inch high: SEE PERMANENT LABEL FOR IMPORTANT MOUNTING INSTRUCTION. The latter message shall be attached to either side of the glazing by any means which shall ensure the message will remain in place until installation.

Category Classification

Sec. 54.204. Glazing required to conform with Part I of this standard shall be classified as Category I or II glazing in accordance with the impact test requirements in Section 54.206 (a). Glass classified as Category I glazing shall not be used where Category II glass is required by Table No. 54-2-A. The categories noted in the table are based on the maximum size in square feet of the largest single glazing in the unit and the intended use of the unit.

TABLE NO. 54-2-A—MINIMUM CATEGORY CLASSIFICATION OF GLAZING

SURFACE AREA OF ONE SIDE OF SINGLE GLAZING IN THE UNIT	GLAZING IN STORM OR COMBINATION DOORS (Category Class)	GLAZING IN DOORS (Category Class)	FIXED GLAZED PANELS (Category Class)	GLAZING IN DOORS AND ENCLOSURES FOR BATHTUBS AND SHOWERS (Category Class)	SLIDING GLASS DOORS (PATIO TYPE) (Category Class)
9 square feet or less of surface area	I	I	I	II	II
More than 9 square feet of surface area	II	II	II		

Specimens to be Tested

Sec. 54.205. (a) **Thickness.** The thickness of the samples to be tested shall be recorded as a nominal thickness for glass as set forth in U.B.C. Standard No. 54-1.

(b) **Specimens.** 1. **Classification.** Safety glazing panels shall be classed in accordance with their size as "limited" or "unlimited" as set forth in Table No. 54-2-B.

TABLE NO. 54-2-B—DESCRIPTION OF SPECIMENS

CLASSIFICATION	DIMENSIONS OF SPECIMEN
Limited (for all sizes up to and including dimensions of specimens tested)	Largest size commercially produced by the manufacturer up to 34 inches by 76 inches
Unlimited (for all sizes)	34 inches by 76 inches

2. **Condition of specimens.** All specimens shall be tested as supplied by the manufacturer following removal of any temporary protective masking materials. Tests shall not commence before the specimens have been stored in the laboratory for four hours. Specimens shall be arranged to permit free circulation of air to all surfaces during this period.

3. **Number of specimens.** For impact test of any safety glazing material, four specimens of the thickness and size described in Subsection (b) 1 shall be provided.

For impact test after aging of plastic used in indoor applications, four specimens of the thickness and size described in Subsection (b) 1 shall be provided.

For boil test, three specimens 12 inches by 12 inches manufactured in a manner identical to the impact specimens and of like thickness, shall be provided.

For weathering test, the number of test specimens shall comply with the following and be of identical manufacture as the impact specimens and of like thickness: For plastic, ten specimens, ½ inch by 5 inches; for orientation specified, six organic-coated glass specimens, 2 inches by 6 inches; for orientation unspecified, nine organic-coated glass specimens, 2 inches by 6 inches, except that when the glazing material is symmetric across its thickness, 6 specimens may be used.

Samples for boil and weathering tests shall be cut from production samples of the size and thickness submitted for impact testing.

Test Specifications

Sec. 54.206. (a) **Impact Test.** 1. **General.** Unless it has been established that specimens have modulus of elasticity less than 750,000 psi and a Rockwell hardness less than 140 M or R scale, four specimens shall be impact tested in accordance with this subsection.

2. **Apparatus.** The test apparatus consists of two basic parts: (1) the test frame, and (2) the impactor.

A. **Test frame.** The test frame shall be designed to minimize movement and deflection of its members during testing. For this purpose, the structural framing and bracing members shall be steel angles (L5 x 3 x ¼ or channels (C4 x 7.25), or other sections and materials of equal or greater rigidity, as shown in Figure No. 54-2-1.

This structural framing shall be welded or securely bolted at the corners to minimize racking or twisting during testing. Also, it shall be securely bolted to the floor and braced by one of the alternate methods shown in Figure No. 54-2-1.

The clamping frame for securing the test specimen on all four edges shall be reinforced at the corners. See Detail A of Figure No. 54-2-1. Other materials may be used, provided there is positive assurance that the test specimen will contact only the neoprene strips.

Pressures on the test specimen shall be controlled, and the compression of the neoprene strips shall be between 10 and 15 percent of the original thickness of the neoprene. Securing methods such as wing bolts as shown in Detail A of Figure No. 54-2-1 and clamps shall be uniformly spaced no greater than 18 inches apart with no fewer than two on any edge. To limit the compression of the neoprene and prevent distortion of the clamping frame, metal shims of an appropriate thickness shall be used as shown in Detail A of Figure No. 54-2-1.

Any reasonable means may be used to secure the clamping frame to the test frame so long as the mounting is secure and the pressure on the glazing in the clamping frame is not significantly altered when the clamping frame is removed.

B. **Impactor.** The impactor shall be a standard leather punching bag modified as shown in Figure No. 54-2-3. The bag shall be filled with No. 7½ chilled lead shot to a total weight of completed assembly of 100 pounds ± 4 ounces. The rubber bladder shall be left in place and filled through a hole cut into the upper part. After filling the rubber bladder, the top shall either be twisted around the threaded metal rod below the metal sleeve or pulled over the metal sleeve and tied with a cord or leather thong. Note that the hanging strap shall be removed. The bag shall be laced in the normal manner. The exterior of the bag shall be completely covered with ½-inch tape as indicated in Figure No. 54-2-3.

3. **Procedure.** The impacting object (shot bag), constructed in accordance with Figure No. 54-2-3, shall be suspended from an overhead support so located that the impacting object when at rest will, at its maximum diameter, be no more than ½ inch from the surface of the specimen and no more than 2 inches from the center of the specimen (see Figure No. 54-2-1).

Each specimen shall be centered within the neoprene mounting strips before impacting, such that approximately ⅜-inch grip is provided on each edge of the specimen.

Specimens for Category I shall be impacted one time from a drop height of 18 to 18½ inches. Specimens for Category II shall be impacted one time from drop height of 48 to 48½ inches. For all specimens that are not symmetric from surface to surface, an equal number of specimens shall be impacted on each side. The drop height is to be measured from the maximum diameter of the impacting object to the horizontal center line of the specimen (see Figure No. 54-2-1). The impacting object shall be stabilized before release.

4. **Interpretation of results.** A glazing material shall be judged to pass the impact test if each of the four specimens tested meets any one of the following criteria:

A. When breakage occurs (numerous cracks and fissures may occur) no opening shall develop in the test sample through which a 3-inch-diameter solid steel sphere, weighing 4 pounds ±3 ounces, passes when placed (not dropped) in the opening and permitted to remain for a period of one second. For this criterion, the sample after being impacted shall be placed, while remaining in the clamping frame, in a horizontal, impact side-up position with a minimum of 1 foot of free space immediately beneath the specimen.

B. When breakage occurs, what appear to be the 10 largest particles shall be selected within 5 minutes subsequent to the test and shall weigh no more than the equivalent weight of 10 square inches of the original specimen. For the purposes of this section, "particle" means a portion of a broken test specimen which is determined by identifying the smallest possible perimeter around all points in the portion of the broken test specimen, always passing along cracks or exposed surfaces.

C. The specimen remains intact after the drop test, though not necessarily remaining within the clamping frame.

(b) **Boil Test (for laminated glass only).** 1. **General.** The test is made to determine the probable effect of exposure to high temperature and humidity conditions for a long period of time.

2. **Procedure.** Three 12- by 12-inch flat specimens, as submitted, shall be immersed vertically on edge in water at 150 ± 5°F. for three minutes and then quickly transferred to and similarly immersed in boiling water. The rack shall be positioned so that each specimen is surrounded by at least 1 inch of water. The specimen shall be kept in the boiling water for two hours and then removed.

3. **Interpretation of results.** The glass itself may crack in this test, but bubbles or other defects shall not develop more than ½ inch from the outer edge of the specimen or from any cracks that may develop. Any specimen in which the glass cracks to an extent confusing the results shall be discarded without prejudice and another specimen shall be tested in its stead.

(c) **Weathering Tests (for organic-coated glass used in exterior exposure applications only).** 1. **Purpose.** The purpose of these tests is to determine whether these safety glazing materials will successfully retain their safety characteristics after exposure to weathering conditions for an extended period of time. Specimens shall be exposed to weathering and then tested in accordance with this subsection.

2. **Specimen weathering and tests—organic-coated glass.** A. **Weathering.** (i) **Apparatus.** The specimens shall be subject to exposure in a xenon arc (water-cooled) Weather-Ometer employing a lamp rated at 6500 watts and automatic light-monitoring and control systems. Borosilicate inner and outer filters shall be used. An appropriate water-spray cycle shall be used. Operating procedures shall be in accordance with ASTM Recommended Practice for Operating Light- and Water-exposure Apparatus (Xenon-arc Type) for Exposure of Nonmetallic Materials.

(ii). **Procedure.** The specimens shall be retained in the Weather-Ometer for a period of 1200 ± 1 hours, and exposed to a radiant flux of 50 microwatts per square centimeter (12 calories per second per square centimeter) while monitoring at a wavelength of 340 nanometers.

For organic-coated glass having orientation specified, three specimens shall be mounted with the surface that is intended to be oriented indoors faced away from the radiation source; the other three specimens shall be kept in darkness at 73°F. for use as controls.

For organic-coated glass having orientation unspecified, three specimens shall be mounted with one of the surfaces toward the radiation, three specimens shall be mounted with the other surface toward the radiation, and three specimens shall be kept in darkness at 73°F. for use as controls. When the glazing material is symmetric across its thickness, three specimens shall be irradiated.

B. **Interpretation of results.** Specimens shall be judged satisfactory if they pass the adhesion test and the tensile strength test.

(i) **Adhesion test.** The specimens for this test are the six 2-inch by 6-inch specimens prepared for the weathering test. The specimens shall be conditioned just prior to the performance of the adhesion test at 73.5 ± 3.5°F. and 50 percent ± 2 percent relative humidity for 24 hours.

The test apparatus shall consist of a constant rate of extension (CRE) type tensile tester with the moving crosshead set to move at 12 inches per minute and load range such that the average peel force will fall at 30 percent to 50 percent of full scale, and a cutter containing new razor blades for cutting 1-inch-wide specimens (use blades one time only).

Using the 1-inch razor cutter, cut a straight strip of the organic coating in the lengthwise direction of the glass sample. Peel back about 2 inches of one end of the 1-inch-wide organic strip. Attach a strip of pressure-sensitive tape to the side of the organic strip opposite the adhesive to extend this free end to about 8 inches in length. Place the end of the glass panel from which the organic strip was removed in the lower clamp of the tensile tester and the free end of the tape in the upper clamp. Peel the remainder of the organic strip from the glass mechanically and obtain a record of the peel value. Determine the average pull for each specimen from the chart record.

The organic-coated glass adhesion shall be judged satisfactory if the average adhesion value of the three exposed specimens is no less than 90 percent of the average of the adhesion value of the three control specimens.

(ii) **Tensile strength test.** The samples for this test are the same six 2-inch by 6-inch specimens used in the adhesion test and conditioned as in Item No. 2 A.

The CRE tensile tester shall be set as follows: gage length—2 inches; crosshead speed—2 inches per minute; load range—set full-scale load so that specimens will break at 30 percent to 60 percent of full scale.

Using a ½-inch razor cutter (use blade one time only), cut a straight strip of the organic coating in the lengthwise direction of the glass sample for the full 6-inch length. Carefully peel this strip from the glass panel and test it for breaking strength in the tensile tester.

The organic coating tensile shall be judged satisfactory if the average tensile value of the three exposed specimens is no less than 75 percent of the average of the three control specimens.

(d) **Aging Tests (for plastics used in indoor applications only).** 1. **Purpose.** The purpose of this test is to determine whether plastic for indoor use only will successfully retain its safety characteristics after exposure to simulated aging conditions for an extended period of time.

2. **Apparatus.** The safety glazing materials shall be subjected to exposure to warm, humid and dry cycles, using the following apparatus:

A. **Balance.** A balance capable of weighing accurately to 0.05 percent for a test specimen weighing 0.250 pound or less, and to 0.1 percent for a test specimen weighing over 0.250 pound.

B. **Oven.** A circulating-air oven capable of maintaining the required temperature of test within ± 1.8°F.

C. **Containers.** Noncorroding containers with a shelf to support the test specimen above the solution used for maintaining the required humidity. The container shall be tightly sealed except for a small capillary which permits release of vapor pressure that might otherwise lift the top off the container. Each test specimen shall be tested preferably in a separate container.

D. **Desiccator.** A clean, dry, uncharged desiccator or equivalent closed container in which to bring test specimens to room temperature.

E. **Absorbent cloth.** Clean, nonlinting absorbent cloth for use in wiping exudation or condensed moisture from test specimens.

F. **Micrometer.** A micrometer capable of measuring dimensions of test specimens to 0.001 inch.

G. **Cold box.** A cold box capable of maintaining the required temperature of test within ± 5.4°F.

3. **Procedure.** The four plastic specimens shall be subjected to ten complete humid/dry test cycles (480 hours) in accordance with the following:

A. The test cycle shall be as follows: 24 hours at 140°F. and 95 percent humidity, followed by 24 hours at 140°F. in the oven.

B. Condition the specimen, weigh and measure dimensions as follows. One additional specimen shall be retained unexposed as a control for the effects of the exposure cycling.

(i) **Conditioning.** Condition the test specimens at 73.4 ± 3.6°F. and 50 ± 5 percent relative humidity for not less than 40 hours prior to test.

Test conditions. Conduct tests in the Standard Laboratory Atmosphere of 73.4 ± 3.6°F. and 50 ± 5 percent relative humidity, unless otherwise specified in the test methods or in this specification. In cases of disagreement, the tolerances shall be 1.8°F. and ± 2 percent relative humidity.

(ii) **Measurements of test specimens.** The following measurements shall be made on conditioned test specimens prior to testing, after reconditioning at the end of a test procedure, and at any intermediate stage as prescribed in the test procedures:

> **Weight**—The weight within 0.05 percent if the specimen weighs 0.250 pound or less, and within 0.1 percent if the specimen exceeds 0.250 pound in weight.
>
> **Dimensions**—The thickness to 0.001 inch, the plane dimension in the direction of injection or transfer to 0.001 inch, and the plane dimension across the direction of injection or transfer to 0.001 inch.
>
> **Dimensions of compression molded specimen**—The thickness to 0.001 inch, and the perpendicular dimensions in the plane at right angles to the direction of molding to 0.001 inch.

C. Expose the specimen for 24 hours on the shelf of a container maintained at 140 ± 1.8°F. in the oven, and containing a saturated solution of sodium sulfate to maintain a relative humidity of 95 percent.

D. Remove the specimen from the container, place it in the uncharged desiccator and bring to room temperature.

E. Wipe the specimen with the absorbent cloth, then weigh, measure dimensions and examine visually. Noticeable qualitative changes in surfaces, outline and general appearance of the test specimen shall be recorded after each stage of the testing procedure. These changes include color, surface irregularities, odor and splits. Changes shall also be noted as they occur, especially those which alter the shape so that intended dimensions are no longer significant.

F. Within two hours after completion of the operation described in Item C above, expose the specimen for 24 hours in the oven at 140 ± 1.8°F.

G. Place the specimen in the uncharged desiccator and bring to room temperature.

4. **Interpretation of results.** Specimens shall be judged satisfactory if, after the indoor aging test, they again pass the impact test in Subsection (a).

Part II

Based on Performance Specifications and Methods of Test for Transparent Safety Glazing Material Used in Buildings, ANSI Z97.1-1975 of the American National Standards Institute, Inc.

See Sections 5401 (b) and (d), and 5406 (c) and (e), Uniform Building Code

Scope

Sec. 54.207. Part II of this standard covers safety glazing materials for use in areas subject to human impact as specified in the Uniform Building Code. Part II is applicable to polished wired glass and glazing in wardrobe doors.

Definitions

Sec. 54.208. For the purpose of this part, the definitions in Section 54.102 of U.B.C. Standard No. 54-1 are applicable.

Identification

Sec. 54.209. Each light of safety glazing material shall be identified in accordance with Sections 5402 and 5406 (b) of the Uniform Building Code and in addition safety plastic that only meets the requirements of Section 54.211 (d) entitled "Aging Tests (for plastics used in indoor applications only)" shall bear a statement INDOOR USE ONLY as part of a permanent label.

Specimens to be Tested

Sec. 54.210. The specimens, size and number shall be in accordance with the requirements of Section 54.205.

Test Specifications

Sec. 54.211. (a) **Impact Test.** 1. **General.** The specimens tested shall be in accordance with the requirements of Section 54.206 (a) 1.

2. **Apparatus.** The test apparatus requirements for the impact test shall be in accordance with Section 54.206 (a) 2.

3. **Procedure.** The test procedure requirements for the impact test shall be in accordance with Section 54.206 (a) 3, except the specimen shall be struck with the impactor object swinging in a pendulum arc from a drop height of 12 inches. When no breakage occurs, the same specimen shall again be impacted at a drop of 18 inches, and if no breakage occurs, again at 48 inches.

4. **Interpretation of results.** The impact test shall be judged to have been satisfactorily completed if any one of the following safety criteria shall be met by each of the four specimens tested:

A. When breakage occurs at 12 inches, 18 inches or 48 inches, numerous cracks and fissures may occur but a 3-inch-diameter sphere shall not be freely passed.

B. When disintegration occurs at 12 inches, 18 inch or 48 inches, the ten largest crack-free particles selected five minutes subsequent to the test shall weigh no more than the equivalent weight of 10 square inches of the original test specimen.

NOTE: Breakage by other means could produce particles exceeding this weight.

C. When breakage occurs at 12 inches, 18 inches or 48 inches, the stiffness and hardness of the specimen shall be determined. A modulus of elasticity less than 750,000 psi and a Rockwell hardness less than M or R 140 shall indicate satisfactory compliance.

D. The specimen remains intact after one 48-inch drop test, though not necessarily remaining within the clamping frame.

(b) **Boil Test (for laminated glass only).** The boil test shall be in accordance with the requirements of Section 54.206 (b).

(c) **Weathering Tests (for plastic and organic-coated glass used in exterior exposure applications only).** 1. **General.** The purpose of these tests is to determine whether these safety glazing materials will successfully retain their safety characteristics after exposure to weathering conditions for an extended period of time. Specimens shall be exposed to simulated weathering and then tested in accordance with this subsection.

2. **Specimen weathering and tests—organic-coated glass.** A. **Weathering.** (i) **Apparatus.** The specimens shall be subjected to exposure in a twin enclosed carbon-arc lamp apparatus, such as specified as Type D or DH in ASTM Recommended Practice for Operating Light- and Water-exposure Apparatus (Carbon-arc Type) for exposure of nonmetallic materials, or equivalent.

(ii) **Procedure.** The specimens shall be exposed 2000 hours in accordance with ASTM Recommended Practice for Operating Light- and Water-exposure Apparatus (Carbon-arc Type). For the organic-coated glass, three specimens with the side marked for exterior exposure shall be exposed to the energy source. The other three specimens of organic-coated glass are controls and shall be held in darkness at 73.5 ± 3.5°F. until needed.

B. **Interpretation of results.** The specimen test after weathering shall be in accordance with the requirements of Section 54.206 (c) 2 B.

3. **Specimen weathering and test—plastic material.** A. **Weathering.** (i) **Apparatus.** The specimen shall be subjected to exposure by any one of the following methods:

(1) Twin enclosed carbon-arc such as specified as Type D or DH in ASTM G23-69 (1975).

(2) 6000 or 6500 watt xenon-arc light exposure apparatus as specified as Type B or BH in ASTM G26-77.

(3) Fixed-rack outdoor exposure in south Florida.

(ii) **Procedure.** Depending upon the exposure method chosen in (i), the appropriate procedure from the following shall apply:

(1) **Twin-carbon arc.** The panel shall be exposed for 2000 hours in accordance with ASTM D1499-64.

(2) **Xenon-arc apparatus.** The panel shall be exposed for 2900 hours in accordance with ASTM G26-77 using method A with 102 minutes of light-only exposure and 18 minutes of water spray and light exposure.

(3) **Outdoor exposure.** The unbacked panel shall be exposed for one year on a fixed rack at station latitude in south Florida.

B. **Tests after weathering.** Specimens shall be evaluated before and after exposure in accordance with the Charpy unnotched impact test. The exposed specimen shall be tested with the exposed surface subjected to tension. In the case of thin materials, the span of the specimen shall be reduced to 2 inches to avoid having the specimen bend enough to slip between the supports without breaking. The average of five specimens shall be reported. Plastic material shall be acceptable for safety glazing if the impact strength is not reduced by more than 25 percent after exposure. Some discoloration may develop, but defects other than this discoloration shall not develop. Bubbles or other noticable decompostion shall not develop in the irradiated portion.

(d) **Aging Tests (for plastic used in indoor applications only).** The aging tests shall be in accordance with the requirements of Section 54.206 (d), except that the humidity shall be 88 percent in Item No. 3 A and 85 to 95 percent in Item No. 3 C.

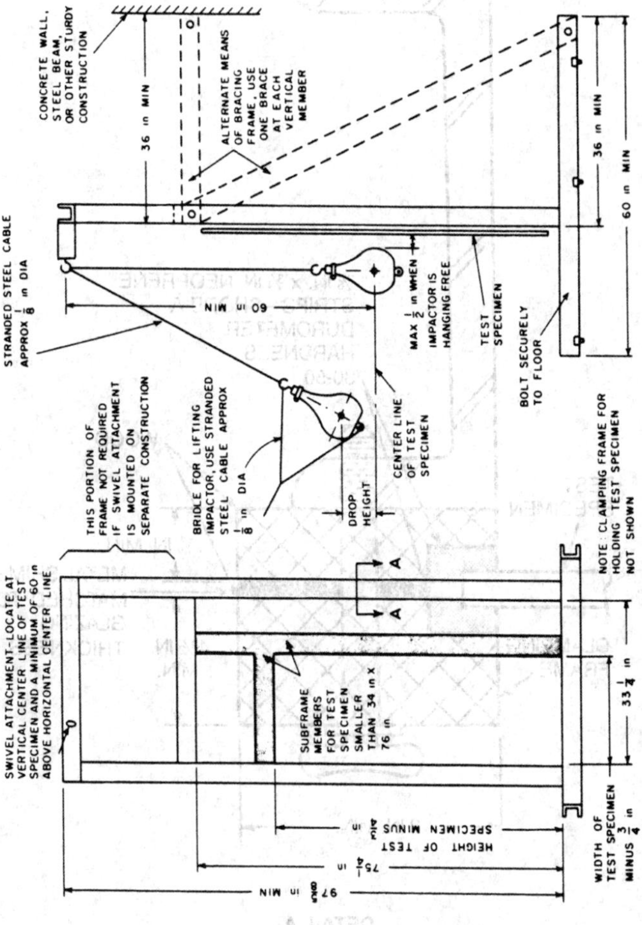
CONCRETE WALL, STEEL BEAM, OR OTHER STURDY CONSTRUCTION
36 in MIN
ALTERNATE MEANS OF BRACING FRAME, USE ONE BRACE AT EACH VERTICAL MEMBER
STRANDED STEEL CABLE APPROX 1/8 in DIA
60 in MIN
MAX 1/2 in WHEN IMPACTOR IS HANGING FREE
TEST SPECIMEN
36 in MIN
60 in MIN
BOLT SECURELY TO FLOOR
THIS PORTION OF FRAME NOT REQUIRED IF SWIVEL ATTACHMENT IS MOUNTED ON SEPARATE CONSTRUCTION
BRIDLE FOR LIFTING IMPACTOR, USE STRANDED STEEL CABLE APPROX 1/8 in DIA
CENTER LINE OF TEST SPECIMEN
DROP HEIGHT
NOTE: CLAMPING FRAME FOR HOLDING TEST SPECIMEN NOT SHOWN
A
A
SWIVEL ATTACHMENT-LOCATE AT VERTICAL CENTER LINE OF TEST SPECIMEN AND A MINIMUM OF 60 in ABOVE HORIZONTAL CENTER LINE
SUBFRAME MEMBERS FOR TEST SPECIMEN SMALLER THAN 34 in X 76 in
33 1/4 in
HEIGHT OF TEST SPECIMEN MINUS 3/4 in
75 1/4 in
97 in MIN
WIDTH OF TEST SPECIMEN MINUS 3/4 in

FIGURE NO. 54-2-1—TEST FRAME

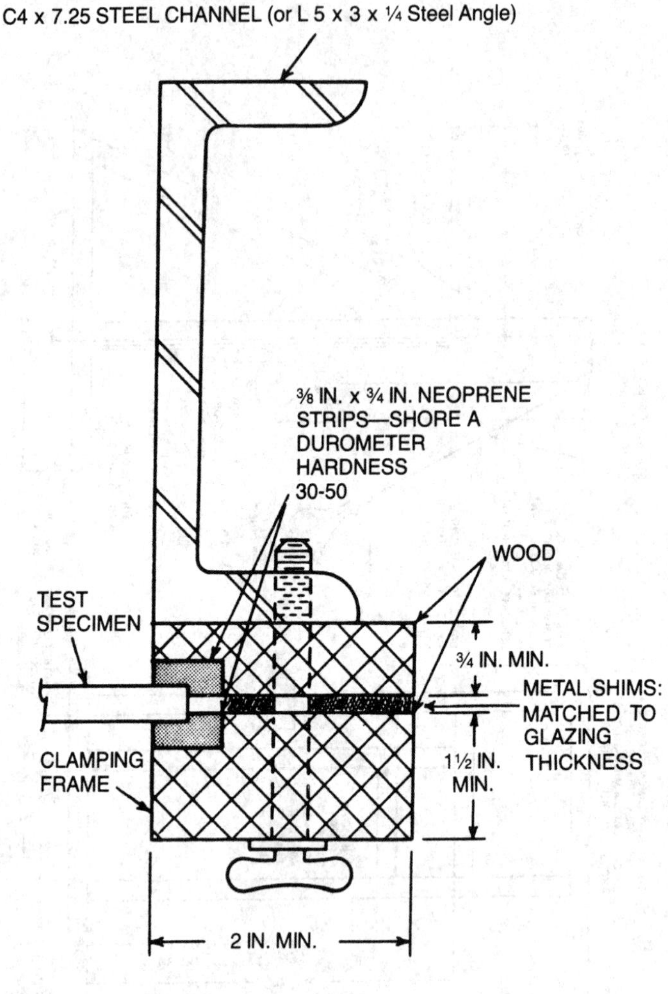
C4 x 7.25 STEEL CHANNEL (or L 5 x 3 x 1/4 Steel Angle)
3/8 IN. x 3/4 IN. NEOPRENE STRIPS—SHORE A DUROMETER HARDNESS 30-50
WOOD
TEST SPECIMEN
3/4 IN. MIN.
METAL SHIMS: MATCHED TO GLAZING THICKNESS
CLAMPING FRAME
1 1/2 IN. MIN.
2 IN. MIN.

DETAIL A
Section A-A of Figure No. 54-2-1

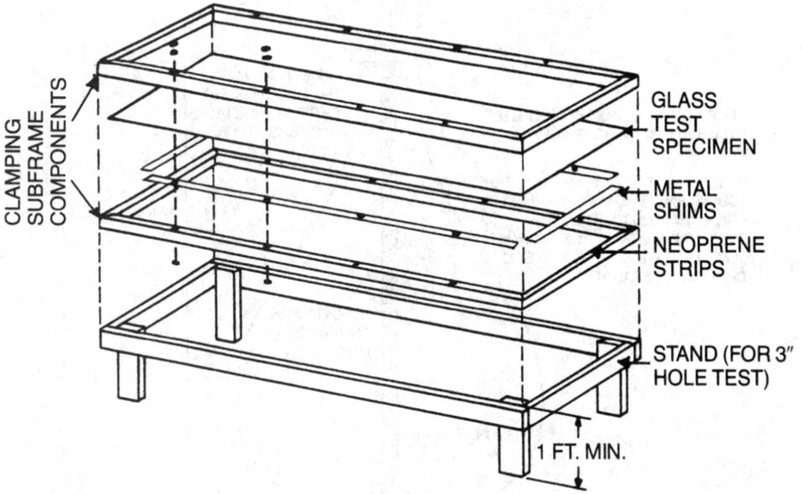
CLAMPING SUBFRAME COMPONENTS
GLASS TEST SPECIMEN
METAL SHIMS
NEOPRENE STRIPS
STAND (FOR 3″ HOLE TEST)
1 FT. MIN.

FIGURE NO. 54-2-2—GLASS TEST SPECIMEN CLAMPING FRAME (EXPLODED) AND STAND

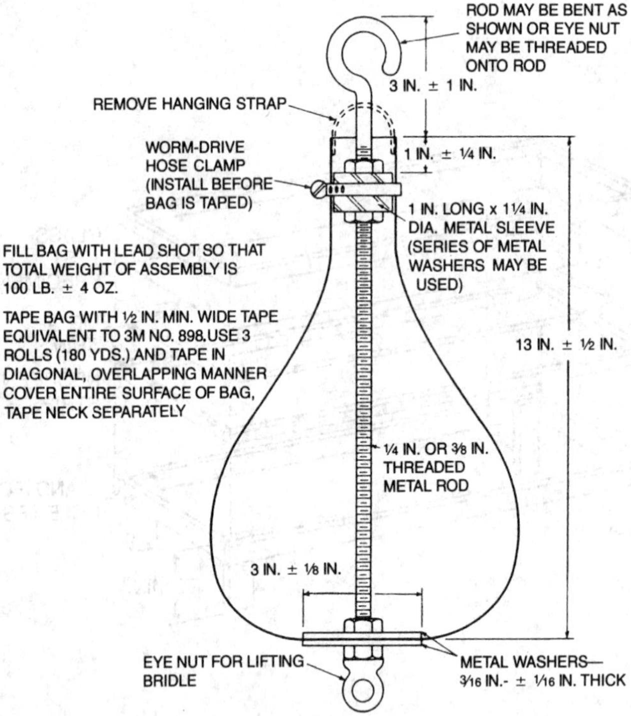
ROD MAY BE BENT AS SHOWN OR EYE NUT MAY BE THREADED ONTO ROD
3 IN. ± 1 IN.
REMOVE HANGING STRAP
WORM-DRIVE HOSE CLAMP (INSTALL BEFORE BAG IS TAPED)
1 IN. ± 1/4 IN.
1 IN. LONG x 1 1/4 IN. DIA. METAL SLEEVE (SERIES OF METAL WASHERS MAY BE USED)
FILL BAG WITH LEAD SHOT SO THAT TOTAL WEIGHT OF ASSEMBLY IS 100 LB. ± 4 OZ.
TAPE BAG WITH 1/2 IN. MIN. WIDE TAPE EQUIVALENT TO 3M NO. 898.USE 3 ROLLS (180 YDS.) AND TAPE IN DIAGONAL, OVERLAPPING MANNER COVER ENTIRE SURFACE OF BAG, TAPE NECK SEPARATELY
13 IN. ± 1/2 IN.
1/4 IN. OR 3/8 IN. THREADED METAL ROD
3 IN. ± 1/8 IN.
EYE NUT FOR LIFTING BRIDLE
METAL WASHERS— 3/16 IN.- ± 1/16 IN. THICK

FIGURE NO. 54-2-3—IMPACTOR

UNIFORM BUILDING CODE STANDARD NO. 55-1
FLAME-RETARDANT MEMBRANES
Test Standard of the International Conference of Building Officials
See Appendix Section 5502 (b), Uniform Building Code

Scope

Sec. 55.101. This standard covers requirements for flame-retardant membranes which are not noncombustible, intended for use in membrane structures as defined in the Uniform Building Code.

Test Apparatus

Sec. 55.102. The apparatus for conducting the flame test shall consist of a sheet-iron stack 12 inches square transversely, 7 feet high and supported 1 foot above the floor on legs. The stack shall be open only at top and bottom and shall be provided with an observation window of wired glass extending the full length of the front.

The stack is to be arranged so that the specimen can be suspended vertically in the stack with its full width facing the observer with the bottom of the specimen 4 inches above the top of a Bunsen burner having ⅜-inch-diameter tube and placed on the floor below the stack. The gas supply to the burner is to be natural gas or a mixture of natural and manufactured gases having a heat value of approximately 800-1000 Btu per cubic foot. With a gas pressure of 4¼ inches of water, the burner is to be adjusted to produce an 11-inch oxidizing flame having an indistinct inner cone. Guide wire and clamps are to be provided to lightly restrain the edges of the specimen.

Specimens

Sec. 55.103. At least ten specimens 5 inches by 7 feet shall be tested. Specimens shall be taken from as widely separated and symmetrically located sections as possible over the entire area of representative sample of the membrane. Where there is a grain to the sample, one-half of the specimen for each conditioning shall be taken parallel to the grain and the other one-half perpendicular to the grain. At least six of the specimens shall be conditioned as specified in Section 55.104 (a) and at least four of the specimens shall be conditioned as specified in Section 55.104 (b).

Conditioning

Sec. 55.104. (a) **Accelerated Weathering.** One of the two procedures described below shall be followed for at least six of the test specimens:

1. The apparatus shall consist of a vertical carbon arc with solid electrodes 0.5 inch in diameter (one cored electrode is used if the arc operates on alternating current) and uniform in composition throughout, mounted at the center of a vertical metal cylinder. The arc shall be surrounded by a clear globe of optical heat-resistant glass with a cutoff at 2750A, with an increase in transmission of 91 percent at 3700A, or other enclosure having equivalent absorbing and transmitting properties. The electrodes shall be renewed at intervals sufficiently frequent to insure full operative conditions of the lamp. The globe shall be cleaned when carbons are removed or at least once in each 36 hours of operation. The arc shall be operated on 13 amperes direct current or 17 amperes, 60 cycles alternating current with the voltage at the arc of 140 volts. The specimens for test shall be mounted on the inside of the cylinder facing the arc. The diameter of the cylinder shall be such that the distance of the face of the specimen holder from the center of the arc is 14¾ inches. The cylinder shall rotate about the arc at a uniform speed of approximately three

revolutions per hour. A water spray discharging about 0.7 gallon per minute shall strike each specimen in turn for about one minute during each revolution of the cylinder. Specimens shall be subjected to this exposure for 360 hours. They shall then be allowed to dry thoroughly at a temperature between 70 and 100°F.

2. The apparatus shall consist of a vertical carbon arc mounted at the center of a vertical cylinder. The arc is designed to accommodate two pairs of carbons, No. 22, upper carbons, and No. 13, lower carbons; however, the arc burns between only one pair of carbons at a time. The arc shall be operated on 60 amperes and 50 volts across the arc for alternating current or 50 amperes and 60 volts across the arc for direct current. The specimens for test shall be mounted on a rotating rack inside the cylinder and facing the arc. The diameter of the rotating rack shall be such that the distance from the center of the arc to the face of the specimen is 18¾ inches. The rack shall rotate about the arc at a uniform speed of about one revolution in two hours. No filters or enclosures shall be used between the arc and the specimens. Spray nozzles shall be mounted in the cylinder so that the specimens shall be exposed to wetting once during each revolution of the rack. Specimens shall be subjected to this exposure for 100 hours. They shall then be allowed to dry thoroughly at a temperature between 70 and 100°F.

(b) **Unweathered Samples.** At least four of the test specimens shall be conditioned in an oven having forced air circulation with free air flow around each specimen at temperatures of 140 to 145°F. for durations of not less than one hour nor more than one and one-half hours before testing. Materials which distort or melt at the above indicated oven exposure are to be conditioned at 60 to 80°F. and 25-50 percent relative humidity for not less than 24 hours. Specimens shall be removed from the oven one at a time and immediately subjected to the flame test described in Section 55.105.

Testing

Sec. 55.105. Suspend the specimen in the apparatus attaching clamps to the edges to retain the specimen in position. Position the burner so that the flame will be applied near the middle of the lower end of the specimen and fix the barrel of the burner at an angle of 25 degrees.

The test flame shall be applied to the specimen for two minutes, then withdrawn, and the duration of flaming combustion on the specimen recorded. After all flaming and afterglow on the specimen has ceased the length of char shall be determined. For purposes of this test the length of char is defined as the vertical distance on the specimen from the tip of the test flame to the top of the charred area resulting from spread of flame and afterglow. For synthetic membranes the length of char is defined as the vertical distance from the tip of the test flame to a horizontal line, above which all material is sound and in essentially original condition.

Condition of Acceptance

Sec. 55.106. When subjected to the test described in Section 55.105 material shall not continue flaming for more than two seconds after the test flame is removed from contact with the specimen. The vertical spread of burning on the material shall not exceed 10 inches above the tip of the test flame. This vertical spread shall be measured as the distance from the tip of the test flame to a horizontal line above which all material is sound and in original condition, except for possible smoke deposits.

Portions or residues of textiles or films which break or drip from the test specimens shall not continue to flame after they reach the floor of the tester.